SOLUTIONS
MANUAL

PRECALCULUS
GRAPHICAL, NUMERICAL, ALGEBRAIC
SEVENTH EDITION

Franklin D. Demana
The Ohio State University

Bert K. Waits
The Ohio State University

Gregory D. Foley
The Liberal Arts and Science Academy of Austin

Daniel Kennedy
Baylor School

PEARSON
Addison
Wesley

Boston San Francisco New York
London Toronto Sydney Tokyo Singapore Madrid
Mexico City Munich Paris Cape Town Hong Kong Montreal

Reproduced by Pearson Addison-Wesley from electronic files supplied by the author.

Copyright © 2007 Pearson Education, Inc.
Publishing as Pearson Addison-Wesley, 75 Arlington Street, Boston, MA 02116.

ISBN   0-321-36993-9

4 5 6 BB 09 08

Contents

Chapter P
Prerequisites

■ Section P.1 Real Numbers

Quick Review P.1

1. $\{1, 2, 3, 4, 5, 6\}$
2. $\{-2, -1, 0, 1, 2, 3, 4, 5, 6\}$
3. $\{-3, -2, -1\}$
4. $\{1, 2, 3, 4\}$
5. (a) 1187.75 (b) -4.72
6. (a) 20.65 (b) 0.10
7. $(-2)^3 - 2(-2) + 1 = -3$; $(1.5)^3 - 2(1.5) + 1 = 1.375$
8. $(-3)^2 + (-3)(2) + 2^2 = 7$
9. $0, 1, 2, 3, 4, 5, 6$
10. $0, 1, 2, 3, 4, 5, 6, 7, 8, 9, 10, 11, 12$

Section P.1 Exercises

1. -4.625 (terminating)
2. $0.\overline{15}$ (repeating)
3. $-2.1\overline{6}$ (repeating)
4. $0.\overline{135}$ (repeating)
5.

   all real numbers less than or equal to 2 (to the left of and including 2)
6.

   all real numbers between -2 and 5, including -2 and excluding 5
7.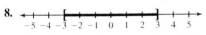

   all real numbers less than 7 (to the left of 7)
8.

   all real numbers between -3 and 3, including both -3 and 3
9.

   all real numbers less than 0 (to the left of 0)
10.

    all real numbers between 2 and 6, including both 2 and 6
11. $-1 \le x < 1$; all numbers between -1 and 1 including -1 and excluding 1
12. $-\infty < x \le 4$, or $x \le 4$; all numbers less than or equal to 4
13. $-\infty < x < 5$, or $x < 5$; all numbers less then 5
14. $-2 \le x < 2$; all numbers between -2 and 2, including -2 and excluding 2

15. $-1 < x < 2$; all numbers between -1 and 2, excluding both -1 and 2
16. $5 \le x < \infty$, or $x \ge 5$; all numbers greater than or equal to 5
17. $(-3, \infty)$; all numbers greater than -3
18. $(-7, -2)$; all numbers between -7 and -2, excluding both -7 and -2
19. $(-2, 1)$; all numbers between -2 and 1, excluding both -2 and 1
20. $[-1, \infty)$; all numbers greater than or equal to -1
21. $(-3, 4]$; all numbers between -3 and 4, excluding -3 and including 4
22. $(0, \infty)$; all numbers greater than 0
23. The real numbers greater than 4 and less than or equal to 9.
24. The real numbers greater than or equal to -1, or the real numbers which are at least -1.
25. The real numbers greater than or equal to -3, or the real numbers which are at least -3.
26. The real numbers between -5 and 7, or the real numbers greater than -5 and less than 7.
27. The real numbers greater than -1.
28. The real numbers between -3 and 0 (inclusive), or greater than or equal to -3 and less than or equal to 0.
29. $-3 < x \le 4$; endpoints -3 and 4; bounded; half-open
30. $-3 < x < -1$; endpoints -3 and -1; bounded; open
31. $x < 5$; endpoint 5; unbounded; open
32. $x \ge -6$; endpoint -6; unbounded; closed
33. His age must be greater than or equal to 29: $x \ge 29$ or $[29, \infty)$; $x = $ Bill's age
34. The costs are between 0 and 2 (inclusive): $0 \le x \le 2$ or $[0, 2]$; $x = $ cost of an item
35. The prices are between \$1.099 and \$1.399 (inclusive): $1.099 \le x \le 1.399$ or $[1.099, 1.399]$; $x = \$$ per gallon of gasoline
36. The raises are between 0.02 and 0.065: $0.02 < x < 0.065$ or $(0.02, 0.065)$; $x = $ average percent of all salary raises
37. $a(x^2 + b) = a \cdot x^2 + a \cdot b = ax^2 + ab$
38. $(y - z^3)c = y \cdot c - z^3 \cdot c = yc - z^3c$
39. $ax^2 + dx^2 = a \cdot x^2 + d \cdot x^2 = (a + d)x^2$
40. $a^3z + a^3w = a^3 \cdot z + a^3 \cdot w = a^3(z + w)$
41. The opposite of $6 - \pi$, or $-(6 - \pi) = -6 + \pi = \pi - 6$
42. The opposite of -7, or $-(-7) = 7$
43. In -5^2, the base is 5.
44. In $(-2)^7$, the base is -2.

45. (a) Associative property of multiplication

(b) Commutative property of multiplication

(c) Addition inverse property

(d) Addition identity property

(e) Distributive property of multiplication over addition

46. (a) Multiplication inverse property

(b) Multiplication identity property, or distributive property of multiplication over addition, followed by the multiplication identity property. Note that we also use the multiplicative commutative property to say that $1 \cdot u = u \cdot 1 = u$.

(c) Distributive property of multiplication over subtraction

(d) Definition of subtraction; associative property of addition; definition of subtraction

(e) Associative property of multiplication; multiplicative inverse; multiplicative identity

47. $\dfrac{x^2}{y^2}$

48. $\dfrac{(3x^2)^2 y^4}{3y^2} = \dfrac{3^2(x^2)^2 y^4}{3y^2} = \dfrac{9x^4 y^4}{3y^2} = 3x^4 y^2$

49. $\left(\dfrac{4}{x^2}\right)^2 = \dfrac{4^2}{(x^2)^2} = \dfrac{16}{x^4}$

50. $\left(\dfrac{2}{xy}\right)^{-3} = \left(\dfrac{xy}{2}\right)^3 = \dfrac{x^3 y^3}{2^3} = \dfrac{x^3 y^3}{8}$

51. $\dfrac{(x^{-3}y^2)^{-4}}{(y^6 x^{-4})^{-2}} = \dfrac{x^{12}y^{-8}}{y^{-12}x^8} = \dfrac{x^4}{y^{-4}} = x^4 y^4$

52. $\left(\dfrac{4a^3 b}{a^2 b^3}\right)\left(\dfrac{3b^2}{2a^2 b^4}\right) = \left(\dfrac{4a}{b^2}\right)\left(\dfrac{3}{2a^2 b^2}\right) = \dfrac{12a}{2a^2 b^4} = \dfrac{6}{ab^4}$

53. 3.6930338×10^{10}

54. $2.21802107 \times 10^{11}$

55. $1.93175805 \times 10^{11}$

56. $4.51908251 \times 10^{11}$

57. 4.839×10^8

58. -1.6×10^{-19}

59. $0.000\ 000\ 033\ 3$

60. $673,000,000,000$

61. $5,870,000,000,000$

62. $0.000\ 000\ 000\ 000\ 000\ 000\ 000\ 001\ 674\ 7$ (23 zeros between the decimal point and the 1)

63. $\dfrac{(1.35)(2.41) \times 10^{-7+8}}{1.25 \times 10^9} = \dfrac{3.2535 \times 10^1}{1.25 \times 10^9}$

$= \dfrac{3.2535}{1.25} \times 10^{1-9} = 2.6028 \times 10^{-8}$

64. $\dfrac{(3.7)(4.3) \times 10^{-7+6}}{2.5 \times 10^7} = \dfrac{15.91 \times 10^{-1}}{2.5 \times 10^7}$

$= \dfrac{15.91}{2.5} \times 10^{-1-7} = 6.364 \times 10^{-8}$

65. (a) When $n = 0$, the equation $a^m a^n = a^{m+n}$ becomes $a^m a^0 = a^{m+0}$. That is, $a^m a^0 = a^m$. Since $a \neq 0$, we can divide both sides of the equation by a^m. Hence $a^0 = 1$.

(b) When $n = -m$, the equation $a^m a^n = a^{m+n}$ becomes $a^m a^{-m} = a^{m+(-m)}$. That is $a^m a^{-m} = a^0$. We know from part (a) that $a^0 = 1$. Since $a \neq 0$, we can divide both sides of the equation $a^m a^{-m} = 1$ by a^m. Hence

$a^{-m} = \dfrac{1}{a^m}$.

66. (a)

Step	Quotient	Remainder
1	0	1
2	0	10
3	5	15
4	8	14
5	8	4
6	2	6
7	3	9
8	5	5
9	2	16
10	9	7
11	4	2
12	1	3
13	1	13
14	7	11
15	6	8
16	4	12
17	7	1

(b) When the remainder is repeated, the quotients generated in the long division process will also repeat.

(c) When any remainder is first repeated, the next quotient will be the same number as the quotient resulting after the first occurrence of the remainder, since the decimal representation does not terminate.

67. False. If the real number is negative, the additive inverse is positive. For example, the additive inverse of -5 is 5.

68. False. If the positive real number is less than 1, the reciprocal is greater than 1. For example, the reciprocal of $\dfrac{1}{2}$ is 2.

69. $[-2, 1)$ corresponds to $-2 \leq x < 1$. The answer is E.

70. $(-2)^4 = (-2)(-2)(-2)(-2) = 16$. The answer is A.

71. In $-7^2 = -(7^2)$, the base is 7. The answer is B.

72. $\dfrac{x^6}{x^2} = \dfrac{x^2 \cdot x^4}{x^2} = x^4$. The answer is D.

73. The whole numbers are $0, 1, 2, 3, \ldots$, so the whole numbers with magnitude less than 7 are $0, 1, 2, 3, 4, 5, 6$.

74. The natural numbers are $1, 2, 3, 4, \ldots$, so the natural numbers with magnitude less than 7 are $1, 2, 3, 4, 5, 6$.

75. The integers are $\ldots, -2, -1, 0, 1, 2, \ldots$, so the integers with magnitude less than 7 are $-6, -5, -4, -3, -2, -1, 0, 1, 2, 3, 4, 5, 6$.

■ Section P.2 Cartesian Coordinate System

Quick Review P.2

1.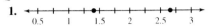

Distance: $|\sqrt{7} - \sqrt{2}| = \sqrt{7} - \sqrt{2} \approx 1.232$

2.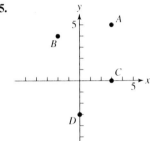

Distance: $\left|-\dfrac{5}{3} - \left(-\dfrac{9}{5}\right)\right| = \left|-\dfrac{25}{15} + \dfrac{27}{15}\right| = \left|\dfrac{2}{15}\right| = \dfrac{2}{15}$

or $0.1\overline{3}$

3.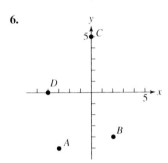

4.

5.

6.

7. 5.5

8. 21.40

9. 10

10. 18.44

Section P.2 Exercises

1. $A(1, 0); B(2, 4); C(-3, -2); D(0, -2)$

2. $A(0, 3); B(-3, 1); C(-2, 0); D(4, -1)$

3. **(a)** First quadrant

(b) On the y-axis, between quadrants I and II

(c) Second quadrant

(d) Third quadrant

4. **(a)** First quadrant

(b) On the x-axis, between quadrants II and III

(c) Third quadrant

(d) Third quadrant

5. $3 + |-3| = 3 + 3 = 6$

6. $2 - |-2| = 2 - 2 = 0$

7. $|(-2)3| = |-6| = 6$

8. $\dfrac{-2}{|-2|} = \dfrac{-2}{2} = -1$

9. Since $\pi \approx 3.14 < 4$, $|\pi - 4| = 4 - \pi$.

10. Since $\sqrt{5} \approx 2.236$ and $\dfrac{5}{2} = 2.5$, $\left|\sqrt{5} - \dfrac{5}{2}\right| = \dfrac{5}{2} - \sqrt{5}$ or

$2.5 - \sqrt{5}$.

11. $|10.6 - (-9.3)| = |10.6 + 9.3| = 19.9$

12. $|-17 - (-5)| = |-17 + 5| = |-12| = 12$

13. $\sqrt{(-3 - 5)^2 + [-1 - (-1)]^2} = \sqrt{(-8)^2 + 0^2} = \sqrt{64}$
$= 8$

14. $\sqrt{(-4 - 1)^2 + (-3 - 1)^2} = \sqrt{(-5)^2 + (-4)^2}$
$= \sqrt{25 + 16} = \sqrt{41} \approx 6.403$

15. $\sqrt{(0 - 3)^2 + (0 - 4)^2} = \sqrt{3^2 + 4^2} = \sqrt{9 + 16}$
$= \sqrt{25} = 5$

16. $\sqrt{(-1 - 2)^2 + [2 - (-3)]^2} = \sqrt{(-3)^2 + 5^2}$
$= \sqrt{9 + 25} = \sqrt{34} \approx 5.830$

17. $\sqrt{(-2 - 5)^2 + (0 - 0)^2} = \sqrt{(-7)^2 + 0^2} = \sqrt{49} = 7$

18. $\sqrt{(0 - 0)^2 + [-8 - (-1)]^2} = \sqrt{0^2 + (-7)^2} = \sqrt{49}$
$= 7$

19. An isosceles triangle

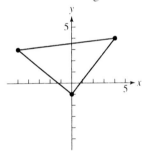

$\sqrt{(0 - (-5))^2 + (-1 - 3)^2} = \sqrt{5^2 + (-4)^2} = \sqrt{41}$

$\sqrt{(0 - (-4))^2 + (-1 - 4)^2} = \sqrt{(-4)^2 + (-5)^2}$
$= \sqrt{41}$

$\sqrt{(-5 - 4)^2 + (3 - 4)^2} = \sqrt{(-9)^2 + (-1)^2} = \sqrt{82}$

Perimeter $= 2\sqrt{41} + \sqrt{82} \approx 21.86$

Since $(\sqrt{41})^2 + (\sqrt{41})^2 = (\sqrt{82})^2$, this is a right triangle.

Area $= \dfrac{1}{2}(\sqrt{41})(\sqrt{41}) = 20.5$

20. A square

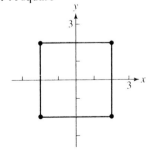

This is a square with sides of length 4. Perimeter $= 16$;
Area $= 16$

21. A parallelogram

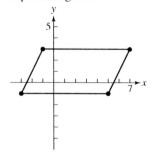

$$\sqrt{[3-(-1)]^2 + [-1-(-3)]^2} = \sqrt{4^2 + 2^2} = \sqrt{20}$$

This is a parallelogram with base 8 units and height 4 units. Perimeter $= 2\sqrt{20} + 16 \approx 24.94$; Area $= 8 \cdot 4 = 32$

22. A rectangle

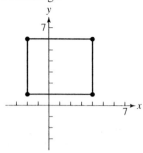

This is a rectangle with length 6 units and height 5 units. Perimeter $= 22$; Area $= 30$

23. $\dfrac{10.6 + (-9.3)}{2} = \dfrac{1.3}{2} = 0.65$

24. $\dfrac{-17 + (-5)}{2} = \dfrac{-22}{2} = -11$

25. $\left(\dfrac{-1 + 5}{2}, \dfrac{3 + 9}{2}\right) = \left(\dfrac{4}{2}, \dfrac{12}{2}\right) = (2, 6)$

26. $\left(\dfrac{3 + 6}{2}, \dfrac{\sqrt{2} + 2}{2}\right) = \left(\dfrac{9}{2}, \dfrac{2 + \sqrt{2}}{2}\right)$

27. $\left(\dfrac{-\dfrac{7}{3} + \dfrac{5}{3}}{2}, \dfrac{\dfrac{3}{4} + \left(-\dfrac{9}{4}\right)}{2}\right) = \left(\dfrac{-\dfrac{2}{3}}{2}, \dfrac{-\dfrac{6}{4}}{2}\right) = \left(-\dfrac{1}{3}, -\dfrac{3}{4}\right)$

28. $\left(\dfrac{5 + (-1)}{2}, \dfrac{-2 + (-4)}{2}\right) = \left(\dfrac{4}{2}, \dfrac{-6}{2}\right) = (2, -3)$

29.

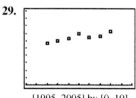

[1995, 2005] by [0, 10]

30.

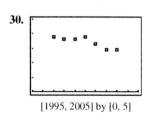

[1995, 2005] by [0, 5]

31.

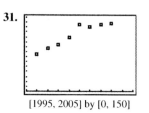

[1995, 2005] by [0, 150]

32.

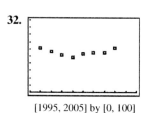

[1995, 2005] by [0, 100]

33.

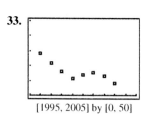

[1995, 2005] by [0, 50]

34.

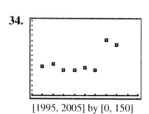

[1995, 2005] by [0, 150]

35. (a) about \$183,000   **(b)** about \$277,000

36. (a) 1996: about \$144,000; 1997: about \$183,000

$$\dfrac{183 - 144}{144} \approx 0.27$$

An increase of about 27%

(b) 2000: about \$277,000; 2001: about \$251,000

$$\dfrac{251 - 277}{277} \approx -0.09$$

A decrease of about 9%

(c) 1995: about \$120,000; 2004: about \$311,000

$$\dfrac{311 - 120}{120} \approx 1.59$$

An increase of about 159%

37. The three side lengths (distances between pairs of points) are

$$\sqrt{(4-1)^2 + (7-3)^2} = \sqrt{3^2 + 4^2} = \sqrt{9 + 16}$$
$$= \sqrt{25} = 5$$

$$\sqrt{(8-4)^2 + (4-7)^2} = \sqrt{4^2 + (-3)^2} = \sqrt{16 + 9}$$
$$= \sqrt{25} = 5$$

$$\sqrt{(8-1)^2 + (4-3)^2} = \sqrt{7^2 + 1^2} = \sqrt{49 + 1}$$
$$= \sqrt{50} = 5\sqrt{2}.$$

Since two sides of the triangle formed have the same length, the triangle is isosceles.

38. (a) Midpoint of diagonal from $(-7, -1)$ to $(3, -1)$ is
$$\left(\frac{-7 + 3}{2}, \frac{-1 + (-1)}{2}\right) = (-2, -1)$$

Midpoint of diagonal from $(-2, 4)$ to $(-2, -6)$ is
$$\left(\frac{-2 + (-2)}{2}, \frac{4 + (-6)}{2}\right) = (-2, -1)$$
Both diagonals have midpoint $(-2, -1)$, so they bisect each other.

(b) Midpoint of diagonal from $(-2, -3)$ to $(6, 7)$ is
$$\left(\frac{-2 + 6}{2}, \frac{-3 + 7}{2}\right) = (2, 2)$$
Midpoint of diagonal from $(0, 1)$ to $(4, 3)$ is
$$\left(\frac{0 + 4}{2}, \frac{1 + 3}{2}\right) = (2, 2)$$
Both diagonals have midpoint $(2, 2)$, so they bisect each other.

39. (a) Vertical side: length $= 6 - (-2) = 8$; horizontal side: length $= 3 - (-2) = 5$; diagonal side:
$$\text{length} = \sqrt{[6 - (-2)]^2 + [3 - (-2)]^2}$$
$$= \sqrt{8^2 + 5^2} = \sqrt{89}$$

(b) $8^2 + 5^2 = 64 + 25 = 89 = (\sqrt{89})^2$, so the Pythagorean Theorem implies the triangle is a right triangle.

40. (a) $\sqrt{(4 - 0)^2 + (-4 - 0)^2} = \sqrt{4^2 + (-4)^2} = \sqrt{32}$

$\sqrt{(4 - 3)^2 + (-4 - 3)^2} = \sqrt{1^2 + (-7)^2} = \sqrt{50}$

$\sqrt{(3 - 0)^2 + (3 - 0)^2} = \sqrt{3^2 + 3^2} = \sqrt{18}$

(b) Since $(\sqrt{32})^2 + (\sqrt{18})^2 = (\sqrt{50})^2$, the triangle is a right triangle.

41. $(x - 1)^2 + (y - 2)^2 = 5^2$, or $(x - 1)^2 + (y - 2)^2 = 25$

42. $[x - (-3)]^2 + (y - 2)^2 = 1^2$, or $(x + 3)^2 + (y - 2)^2 = 1$

43. $[x - (-1)]^2 + [y - (-4)]^2 = 3^2$, or $(x + 1)^2 + (y + 4)^2 = 9$

44. $(x - 0)^2 + (y - 0)^2 = (\sqrt{3})^2$, or $x^2 + y^2 = 3$

45. $(x - 3)^2 + (y - 1)^2 = 6^2$, so the center is $(3, 1)$ and the radius is 6.

46. $[x - (-4)]^2 + (y - 2)^2 = 11^2$, so the center is $(-4, 2)$ and the radius is 11.

47. $(x - 0)^2 + (y - 0)^2 = (\sqrt{5})^2$, so the center is $(0, 0)$ and the radius is $\sqrt{5}$.

48. $(x - 2)^2 + [(y - (-6)]^2 = 5^2$, so the center is $(2, -6)$ and the radius is 5.

49. $|x - 4| = 3$

50. $|y - (-2)| \geq 4$, or $|y + 2| \geq 4$

51. $|x - c| < d$

52. The distance between y and c is greater than d, so $|y - c| > d$.

53. $\dfrac{1 + a}{2} = 4$ and $\dfrac{2 + b}{2} = 4$
$1 + a = 8$ $2 + b = 8$
$a = 7$ $b = 6$

54. Show that two sides have the same length, but not all three sides have the same length:
$$\sqrt{[3 - (-1)]^2 + (2 - 0)^2} = \sqrt{4^2 + 2^2} = \sqrt{16 + 4}$$
$$= \sqrt{20} = 2\sqrt{5}$$
$$\sqrt{[5 - (-1)]^2 + (4 - 2)^2} = \sqrt{6^2 + 2^2} = \sqrt{36 + 4}$$
$$= \sqrt{40} = 2\sqrt{10}$$
$$\sqrt{(5 - 3)^2 + (4 - 0)^2} = \sqrt{2^2 + 4^2} = \sqrt{4 + 16}$$
$$= \sqrt{20} = 2\sqrt{5}.$$

55. The midpoint of the hypotenuse is $\left(\dfrac{5 + 0}{2}, \dfrac{0 + 7}{2}\right)$
$= \left(\dfrac{5}{2}, \dfrac{7}{2}\right) = (2.5, 3.5)$. The distances from this point to the vertices are:
$$\sqrt{(2.5 - 0)^2 + (3.5 - 0)^2} = \sqrt{2.5^2 + 3.5^2}$$
$$= \sqrt{6.25 + 12.25} = \sqrt{18.5}$$
$$\sqrt{(2.5 - 5)^2 + (3.5 - 0)^2} = \sqrt{(-2.5)^2 + 3.5^2}$$
$$= \sqrt{6.25 + 12.25} = \sqrt{18.5}$$
$$\sqrt{(2.5 - 0)^2 + (3.5 - 7)^2} = \sqrt{2.5^2 + (-3.5)^2}$$
$$= \sqrt{6.25 + 12.25} = \sqrt{18.5}.$$

56. $|x - 2| < 3$ means the distance from x to 2 must be less than 3. So x must be between -1 and 5. That is, $-1 < x < 5$.

57. $|x + 3| \geq 5$ means the distance from x to -3 must be 5 or more. So x can be 2 or more, or x can be -8 or less. That is, $x \leq -8$ or $x \geq 2$.

58. True. An absolute value is always greater than or equal to zero. If $a > 0$, then $|a| = a > 0$. If $a < 0$, then $|a| = -a > 0$. If $a = 0$, then $|a| = 0$.

59. True. $\dfrac{\text{length of } AM}{\text{length of } AB} = \dfrac{1}{2}$ because M is the midpoint of AB.

By similar triangles, $\dfrac{\text{length of } AM'}{\text{length of } AC} = \dfrac{\text{length of } AM}{\text{length of } AB} = \dfrac{1}{2}$,

so M' is the midpoint of AC.

60. $1 < \sqrt{3}$, so $1 - \sqrt{3} < 0$ and
$|1 - \sqrt{3}| = -(1 - \sqrt{3}) = \sqrt{3} - 1$. The answer is B.

61. For a segment with endpoints at $a = -3$ and $b = 2$, the midpoint lies at $\dfrac{a + b}{2} = \dfrac{-3 + 2}{2} = \dfrac{-1}{2} = -\dfrac{1}{2}$.
The answer is C.

62. $(x - 3)^2 + (y + 4)^2 = 2$ corresponds to $(x - h)^2 + (y - k)^2 = (\sqrt{2})^2$, with $h = 3$ and $k = -4$. So the center, (h, k), is $(3, -4)$. The answer is A.

63. In the third quadrant, both coordinates are negative. The answer is E.

64. (a) $2 + \dfrac{1}{3}(8 - 2) = 2 + \dfrac{1}{3}(6) = 2 + 2 = 4$;

$2 + \dfrac{2}{3}(6) = 2 + 4 = 6$

(b) $-3 + \dfrac{1}{3}(7 - (-3)) = -3 + \dfrac{1}{3}(10) = -3 + \dfrac{10}{3}$

$= \dfrac{1}{3}$; $-3 + \dfrac{2}{3}(7 - (-3)) = -3 + \dfrac{2}{3}(10)$

$= -3 + \dfrac{20}{3} = \dfrac{11}{3}$

(c) $a + \dfrac{1}{3}(b - a) = a + \dfrac{1}{3}b - \dfrac{1}{3}a = \dfrac{2}{3}a + \dfrac{1}{3}b$

$\qquad = \dfrac{1}{3}(2a + b) = \dfrac{2a + b}{3};$

$a + \dfrac{2}{3}(b - a) = a + \dfrac{2}{3}b - \dfrac{2}{3}a = \dfrac{1}{3}a + \dfrac{2}{3}b$

$\qquad = \dfrac{1}{3}(a + 2b) = \dfrac{a + 2b}{3}$

(d) $\left(\dfrac{2(1) + 7}{3}, \dfrac{2(2) + 11}{3}\right) = \left(\dfrac{9}{3}, \dfrac{15}{3}\right) = (3, 5);$

$\left(\dfrac{1 + 2(7)}{3}, \dfrac{2 + 2(11)}{3}\right) = \left(\dfrac{15}{3}, \dfrac{24}{3}\right) = (5, 8)$

(e) $\left(\dfrac{2a + c}{3}, \dfrac{2b + d}{3}\right); \left(\dfrac{a + 2c}{3}, \dfrac{b + 2d}{3}\right)$

65. If the legs have lengths a and b, and the hypotenuse is c units long, then without loss of generality, we can assume the vertices are $(0, 0)$, $(a, 0)$, and $(0, b)$. Then the midpoint

of the hypotenuse is $\left(\dfrac{a + 0}{2}, \dfrac{b + 0}{2}\right) = \left(\dfrac{a}{2}, \dfrac{b}{2}\right)$. The

distance to the other vertices is

$\sqrt{\left(\dfrac{a}{2}\right)^2 + \left(\dfrac{b}{2}\right)^2} = \sqrt{\dfrac{a^2}{4} + \dfrac{b^2}{4}} = \dfrac{c}{2} = \dfrac{1}{2}c.$

66.

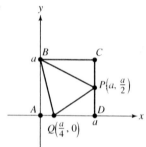

(a) Area of $\triangle BPQ$ = area of $\square ABCD$ − area of $\triangle BCP$ − area of $\triangle BAQ$ − area of $\triangle DPQ$

$= a^2 - \dfrac{1}{2}(a)\left(\dfrac{a}{2}\right) - \dfrac{1}{2}(a)\left(\dfrac{a}{4}\right) - \dfrac{1}{2}\left(\dfrac{a}{2}\right)\left(\dfrac{3}{4}a\right)$

$= a^2 - \dfrac{a^2}{4} - \dfrac{a^2}{8} - \dfrac{3a^2}{16}$

$= \dfrac{7a^2}{16}$

(b) Area of $\triangle BPQ = \dfrac{7}{16} \cdot$ (area of $\square ABCD$), which is just under half the area of the square $ABCD$.

Note that the result is the same if $a < 0$, but the location of the points in the plane is different.

For #67–69, note that since $P(a, b)$ is in the first quadrant, then a and b are positive. Hence, $-a$ and $-b$ are negative.

67. $Q(a, -b)$ is in the fourth quadrant and, since P and Q both have first coordinate a, PQ is perpendicular to the x-axis.

68. $Q(-a, b)$ is in the second quadrant and, since P and Q both have second coordinate b, PQ is perpendicular to the y-axis.

69. $Q(-a, -b)$ is in the third quadrant, and the midpoint of

PQ is $\left(\dfrac{a + (-a)}{2}, \dfrac{b + (-b)}{2}\right) = (0, 0).$

70. Let the points on the number line be $(a, 0)$ and $(b, 0)$. The distance between them is

$\sqrt{(a - b)^2 + (0 - 0)^2} = \sqrt{(a - b)^2} = |a - b|.$

■ Section P.3 Linear Equations and Inequalities

Quick Review P.3

1. $2x + 5x + 7 + y - 3x + 4y + 2$
$= (2x + 5x - 3x) + (y + 4y) + (7 + 2)$
$= 4x + 5y + 9$

2. $4 + 2x - 3z + 5y - x + 2y - z - 2$
$= (2x - x) + (5y + 2y) + (-3z - z) + (4 - 2)$
$= x + 7y - 4z + 2$

3. $3(2x - y) + 4(y - x) + x + y$
$= 6x - 3y + 4y - 4x + x + y = 3x + 2y$

4. $5(2x + y - 1) + 4(y - 3x + 2) + 1$
$= 10x + 5y - 5 + 4y - 12x + 8 + 1$
$= -2x + 9y + 4$

5. $\dfrac{2}{y} + \dfrac{3}{y} = \dfrac{5}{y}$

6. $\dfrac{1}{y - 1} + \dfrac{3}{y - 2} = \dfrac{y - 2}{(y - 1)(y - 2)} + \dfrac{3(y - 1)}{(y - 1)(y - 2)}$

$= \dfrac{y - 2 + 3y - 3}{(y - 1)(y - 2)} = \dfrac{4y - 5}{(y - 1)(y - 2)}$

7. $2 + \dfrac{1}{x} = \dfrac{2x}{x} + \dfrac{1}{x} = \dfrac{2x + 1}{x}$

8. $\dfrac{1}{x} + \dfrac{1}{y} - x = \dfrac{y}{xy} + \dfrac{x}{xy} - \dfrac{x^2 y}{xy} = \dfrac{y + x - x^2 y}{xy}$

9. $\dfrac{x + 4}{2} + \dfrac{3x - 1}{5} = \dfrac{5(x + 4)}{10} + \dfrac{2(3x - 1)}{10}$

$= \dfrac{5x + 20 + 6x - 2}{10} = \dfrac{11x + 18}{10}$

10. $\dfrac{x}{3} + \dfrac{x}{4} = \dfrac{4x}{12} + \dfrac{3x}{12} = \dfrac{7x}{12}$

Section P.3 Exercises

1. (a) and **(c):** $2(-3)^2 + 5(-3) = 2(9) - 15$

$= 18 - 15 = 3$, and $2\left(\dfrac{1}{2}\right)^2 + 5\left(\dfrac{1}{2}\right) = 2\left(\dfrac{1}{4}\right) + \dfrac{5}{2}$

$= \dfrac{1}{2} + \dfrac{5}{2} = \dfrac{6}{2} = 3.$ Meanwhile, substituting $x = -\dfrac{1}{2}$

gives -2 rather than 3.

2. (a): $\dfrac{-1}{2} + \dfrac{1}{6} = -\dfrac{3}{6} + \dfrac{1}{6} = -\dfrac{2}{6} = -\dfrac{1}{3}$ and $\dfrac{-1}{3} = -\dfrac{1}{3}.$

Or: Multiply both sides by 6: $6\left(\dfrac{x}{2}\right) + 6\left(\dfrac{1}{6}\right) = 6\left(\dfrac{x}{3}\right),$

so $3x + 1 = 2x$. Subtract $2x$ from both sides: $x + 1 = 0$. Subtract 1 from both sides: $x = -1$.

3. (b): $\sqrt{1 - 0^2} + 2 = \sqrt{1} + 2 = 1 + 2 = 3.$

Meanwhile, substituting $x = -2$ or $x = 2$ gives $\sqrt{1 - 4} + 2 = \sqrt{-3} + 2$, which is undefined.

4. (c): $(10 - 2)^{1/3} = 8^{1/3} = 2$. Meanwhile, substituting $x = -6$ gives -2 rather than 2; substituting $x = 8$ gives $6^{1/3} \approx 1.82$ rather than 2.

5. Yes: $-3x + 5 = 0$.

6. No: There is no variable x in the equation.

7. No: Subtracting x from both sides gives $3 = -5$, which is false and does not contain the variable x.

8. No: The highest power of x is 2, so the equation is quadratic and not linear.

9. No: The equation has a root in it, so it is not linear.

10. No. The equation has $\dfrac{1}{x} = x^{-1}$ in it, so it is not linear.

11. $3x = 24$
$x = 8$

12. $4x = -16$
$x = -4$

13. $3t = 12$
$t = 4$

14. $2t = 12$
$t = 6$

15. $2x - 3 = 4x - 5$
$2x = 4x - 2$
$-2x = -2$
$x = 1$

16. $4 - 2x = 3x - 6$
$-2x = 3x - 10$
$-5x = -10$
$x = 2$

17. $4 - 3y = 2y + 8$
$-3y = 2y + 4$
$-5y = 4$
$y = -\dfrac{4}{5} = -0.8$

18. $4y = 5y + 8$
$-y = 8$
$y = -8$

19. $2\left(\dfrac{1}{2}x\right) = 2\left(\dfrac{7}{8}\right)$
$x = \dfrac{7}{4} = 1.75$

20. $3\left(\dfrac{2}{3}x\right) = 3\left(\dfrac{4}{5}\right)$
$2x = \dfrac{12}{5}$
$x = \dfrac{12}{10}$
$x = \dfrac{6}{5} = 1.2$

21. $2\left(\dfrac{1}{2}x + \dfrac{1}{3}\right) = 2(1)$
$x + \dfrac{2}{3} = 2$
$x = \dfrac{4}{3}$

22. $3\left(\dfrac{1}{3}x + \dfrac{1}{4}\right) = 3(1)$
$x + \dfrac{3}{4} = 3$
$x = \dfrac{9}{4} = 2.25$

23. $6 - 8z - 10z - 15 = z - 17$
$-18z - 9 = z - 17$
$-18z = z - 8$
$-19z = -8$
$z = \dfrac{8}{19}$

24. $15z - 9 - 8z - 4 = 5z - 2$
$7z - 13 = 5z - 2$
$7z = 5z + 11$
$2z = 11$
$z = \dfrac{11}{2} = 5.5$

25. $4\left(\dfrac{2x - 3}{4} + 5\right) = 4(3x)$
$2x - 3 + 20 = 12x$
$2x + 17 = 12x$
$17 = 10x$
$x = \dfrac{17}{10} = 1.7$

26. $3(2x - 4) = 3\left(\dfrac{4x - 5}{3}\right)$
$6x - 12 = 4x - 5$
$6x = 4x + 7$
$2x = 7$
$x = \dfrac{7}{2} = 3.5$

27. $24\left(\dfrac{t + 5}{8} - \dfrac{t - 2}{2}\right) = 24\left(\dfrac{1}{3}\right)$
$3(t + 5) - 12(t - 2) = 8$
$3t + 15 - 12t + 24 = 8$
$-9t + 39 = 8$
$-9t = -31$
$t = \dfrac{31}{9}$

28. $12\left(\dfrac{t - 1}{3} + \dfrac{t + 5}{4}\right) = 12\left(\dfrac{1}{2}\right)$
$4(t - 1) + 3(t + 5) = 6$
$4t - 4 + 3t + 15 = 6$
$7t + 11 = 6$
$7t = -5$
$t = -\dfrac{5}{7}$

29. (a) The figure shows that $x = -2$ is a solution of the equation $2x^2 + x - 6 = 0$.

(b) The figure shows that $x = \dfrac{3}{2}$ is a solution of the equation $2x^2 + x - 6 = 0$.

30. (a) The figure shows that $x = 2$ is not a solution of the equation $7x + 5 = 4x - 7$.

(b) The figure shows that $x = -4$ is a solution of the equation $7x + 5 = 4x - 7$.

31. (a): $2(0) - 3 = 0 - 3 = -3 < 7$. Meanwhile, substituting $x = 5$ gives 7 (which is not less than 7); substituting $x = 6$ gives 9.

32. (b) and (c): $3(3) - 4 = 9 - 4 = 5 \geq 5$, and $3(4) - 4 = 12 - 4 = 8 \geq 5$.

33. **(b)** and **(c):** $4(2) - 1 = 8 - 1 = 7$ and $-1 < 7 \le 11$, and also $4(3) - 1 = 12 - 1 = 11$ and $-1 < 11 \le 11$. Meanwhile, substituting $x = 0$ gives -1 (which is not greater than -1).

34. **(a)**, **(b)**, and **(c):** $1 - 2(-1) = 1 + 2 = 3$ and $-3 \le 3 \le 3$; $1 - 2(0) = 1 - 0 = 1$ and $-3 \le 1 \le 3$; $1 - 2(2) = 1 - 4 = -3$ and $-3 \le -3 \le 3$.

35.

36.

37.

$$2x - 1 \le 4x + 3$$
$$2x \le 4x + 4$$
$$-2x \le 4$$
$$x \ge -2$$

38.

$$3x - 1 \ge 6x + 8$$
$$3x \ge 6x + 9$$
$$-3x \ge 9$$
$$x \le -3$$

39.

$$2 \le x + 6 < 9$$
$$-4 \le x < 3$$

40.

$$-1 \le 3x - 2 < 7$$
$$1 \le 3x < 9$$
$$\frac{1}{3} \le x < 3$$

41.

$$10 - 6x + 6x - 3 \le 2x + 1$$
$$7 \le 2x + 1$$
$$6 \le 2x$$
$$3 \le x$$
$$x \ge 3$$

42.

$$4 - 4x + 5 + 5x > 3x - 1$$
$$9 + x > 3x - 1$$
$$10 + x > 3x$$
$$10 > 2x$$
$$5 > x$$
$$x < 5$$

43. $4\left(\dfrac{5x + 7}{4}\right) \le 4(-3)$

$$5x + 7 \le -12$$
$$5x \le -19$$
$$x \le -\frac{19}{5}$$

44. $5\left(\dfrac{3x - 2}{5}\right) > 5(-1)$

$$3x - 2 > -5$$
$$3x > -3$$
$$x > -1$$

45. $3(4) \ge 3\left(\dfrac{2y - 5}{3}\right) \ge 3(-2)$

$$12 \ge 2y - 5 \ge -6$$
$$17 \ge 2y \ge -1$$
$$\frac{17}{2} \ge y \ge -\frac{1}{2}$$
$$-\frac{1}{2} \le y \le \frac{17}{2}$$

46. $4(1) > 4\left(\dfrac{3y - 1}{4}\right) > 4(-1)$

$$4 > 3y - 1 > -4$$
$$5 > 3y > -3$$
$$\frac{5}{3} > y > -1$$
$$-1 < y < \frac{5}{3}$$

47. $0 \le 2z + 5 < 8$

$$-5 \le 2z < 3$$
$$-\frac{5}{2} \le z < \frac{3}{2}$$

48. $-6 < 5t - 1 < 0$

$$-5 < 5t < 1$$
$$-1 < t < \frac{1}{5}$$

49. $12\left(\dfrac{x - 5}{4} + \dfrac{3 - 2x}{3}\right) < 12(-2)$

$$3(x - 5) + 4(3 - 2x) < -24$$
$$3x - 15 + 12 - 8x < -24$$
$$-5x - 3 < -24$$
$$-5x < -21$$
$$x > \frac{21}{5}$$

50. $6\left(\dfrac{3 - x}{2} + \dfrac{5x - 2}{3}\right) < 6(-1)$

$$3(3 - x) + 2(5x - 2) < -6$$
$$9 - 3x + 10x - 4 < -6$$
$$7x + 5 < -6$$
$$7x < -11$$
$$x < -\frac{11}{7}$$

51. $10\left(\dfrac{2y - 3}{2} + \dfrac{3y - 1}{5}\right) < 10(y - 1)$

$$5(2y - 3) + 2(3y - 1) < 10y - 10$$
$$10y - 15 + 6y - 2 < 10y - 10$$
$$16y - 17 < 10y - 10$$
$$16y < 10y + 7$$
$$6y < 7$$
$$y < \frac{7}{6}$$

52. $24\left(\dfrac{3-4y}{6}-\dfrac{2y-3}{8}\right)\ge 24(2-y)$

$4(3-4y)-3(2y-3)\ge 48-24y$

$12-16y-6y+9\ge 48-24y$

$-22y+21\ge 48-24y$

$-22y\ge 27-24y$

$2y\ge 27$

$y\ge\dfrac{27}{2}$

53. $2\left[\dfrac{1}{2}(x-4)-2x\right]\le 2[5(3-x)]$

$x-4-4x\le 10(3-x)$

$-3x-4\le 30-10x$

$-3x\le 34-10x$

$7x\le 34$

$x\le\dfrac{34}{7}$

54. $6\left[\dfrac{1}{2}(x+3)+2(x-4)\right]<6\left[\dfrac{1}{3}(x-3)\right]$

$3(x+3)+12(x-4)<2(x-3)$

$3x+9+12x-48<2x-6$

$15x-39<2x-6$

$15x<2x+33$

$13x<33$

$x<\dfrac{33}{13}$

55. $x^2-2x<0$ for $x=1$

56. $x^2-2x=0$ for $x=0,2$

57. $x^2-2x>0$ for $x=3,4,5,6$

58. $x^2-2x\le 0$ for $x=0,1,2$

59. Multiply both sides of the first equation by 2.

60. Divide both sides of the first equation by 2.

61. (a) No: they have different solutions.

$3x=6x+9\qquad x=2x+9$

$-3x=9\qquad\ \ -x=9$

$x=-3\qquad\ \ \ x=-9$

(b) Yes: the solution to both equations is $x=4$.

$6x+2=4x+10\quad 3x+1=2x+5$

$6x=4x+8\qquad\ \ \ 3x=2x+4$

$2x=8\qquad\qquad\quad x=4$

$x=4$

62. (a) Yes: the solution to both equations is $x=\dfrac{9}{2}$.

$3x+2=5x-7\quad -2x+2=-7$

$3x=5x-9\qquad\quad -2x=-9$

$-2x=-9\qquad\qquad\ \ x=\dfrac{9}{2}$

$x=\dfrac{9}{2}$

(b) No: they have different solutions.

$2x+5=x-7\quad 2x=x-7$

$2x=x-12\qquad\ x=-7$

$x=-12$

63. False. $6>2$, but $-6<-2$ because -6 lies to the left of -2 on the number line.

64. True. $2\le\dfrac{6}{3}$ includes the possibility that $2=\dfrac{6}{3}$, and this is the case.

65. $3x+5=2x+1$

Subtracting 5 from each side gives $3x=2x-4$.

The answer is E.

66. $-3x<6$

Dividing each side by -3 and reversing the $<$ gives $x>-2$.

The answer is C.

67. $x(x+1)=0$

$x=0$ or $x+1=0$

$x=-1$

The answer is A.

68. $\dfrac{2x}{3}+\dfrac{1}{2}=\dfrac{x}{4}-\dfrac{1}{3}$

Multiplying each side by 12 gives $8x+6=3x-4$.

The answer is B.

69. (c) $\dfrac{800}{801}>\dfrac{799}{800}$

(d) $-\dfrac{103}{102}>-\dfrac{102}{101}$

(e) If your calculator returns 0 when you enter $2x+1<4$, you can conclude that the value stored in x is not a solution of the inequality $2x+1<4$.

70. $P=2(L+W)$

$\dfrac{1}{2}P=L+W$

$\dfrac{1}{2}P-L=W$

$W=\dfrac{1}{2}P-L=\dfrac{P-2L}{2}$

71. $A=\dfrac{1}{2}h(b_1+b_2)$

$h(b_1+b_2)=2A$

$b_1+b_2=\dfrac{2A}{h}$

$b_1=\dfrac{2A}{h}-b_2$

72. $V=\dfrac{4}{3}\pi r^3$

$\dfrac{3}{4\pi}V=r^3$

$\sqrt[3]{\dfrac{3V}{4\pi}}=r$

$r=\sqrt[3]{\dfrac{3V}{4\pi}}$

73. $C=\dfrac{5}{9}(F-32)$

$\dfrac{9}{5}C=F-32$

$\dfrac{9}{5}C+32=F$

$F=\dfrac{9}{5}C+32$

■ Section P.4 Lines in the Plane

Exploration 1

1. The graphs of $y = mx + b$ and $y = mx + c$ have the same slope but different y-intercepts.

2.
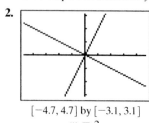

$$[-4.7, 4.7] \text{ by } [-3.1, 3.1]$$
$$m = 2$$

The angle between the two lines appears to be $90°$.

3.
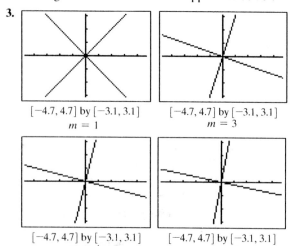

$$[-4.7, 4.7] \text{ by } [-3.1, 3.1] \qquad [-4.7, 4.7] \text{ by } [-3.1, 3.1]$$
$$m = 1 \qquad\qquad m = 3$$

$$[-4.7, 4.7] \text{ by } [-3.1, 3.1] \qquad [-4.7, 4.7] \text{ by } [-3.1, 3.1]$$
$$m = 4 \qquad\qquad m = 5$$

In each case, the two lines appear to be at right angles to one another.

Quick Review P.4

1.
$$-75x + 25 = 200$$
$$-75x = 175$$
$$x = -\frac{7}{3}$$

2.
$$400 - 50x = 150$$
$$-50x = -250$$
$$x = 5$$

3.
$$3(1 - 2x) + 4(2x - 5) = 7$$
$$3 - 6x + 8x - 20 = 7$$
$$2x - 17 = 7$$
$$2x = 24$$
$$x = 12$$

4.
$$2(7x + 1) = 5(1 - 3x)$$
$$14x + 2 = 5 - 15x$$
$$29x + 2 = 5$$
$$29x = 3$$
$$x = \frac{3}{29}$$

5.
$$2x - 5y = 21$$
$$-5y = -2x + 21$$
$$y = \frac{2}{5}x - \frac{21}{5}$$

6.
$$\frac{1}{3}x + \frac{1}{4}y = 2$$
$$12\left(\frac{1}{3}x + \frac{1}{4}y\right) = 12(2)$$
$$4x + 3y = 24$$
$$3y = -4x + 24$$
$$y = -\frac{4}{3}x + 8$$

7.
$$2x + y = 17 + 2(x - 2y)$$
$$2x + y = 17 + 2x - 4y$$
$$y = 17 - 4y$$
$$5y = 17$$
$$y = \frac{17}{5}$$

8.
$$x^2 + y = 3x - 2y$$
$$y = 3x - 2y - x^2$$
$$3y = 3x - x^2$$
$$y = x - \frac{1}{3}x^2$$

9. $\dfrac{9 - 5}{-2 - (-8)} = \dfrac{4}{6} = \dfrac{2}{3}$

10. $\dfrac{-4 - 6}{-14 - (-2)} = \dfrac{-10}{-12} = \dfrac{5}{6}$

Section P.4 Exercises

1. $m = -2$ **2.** $m = \dfrac{2}{3}$

3. $m = \dfrac{9 - 5}{4 + 3} = \dfrac{4}{7}$

4. $m = \dfrac{-3 - 1}{5 + 2} = -\dfrac{4}{7}$

5. $m = \dfrac{3 + 5}{-1 + 2} = 8$

6. $m = \dfrac{12 + 3}{-4 - 5} = -\dfrac{5}{3}$

7. $2 = \dfrac{9 - 3}{5 - x} = \dfrac{6}{5 - x}$, so $x = 2$

8. $-3 = \dfrac{y - 3}{4 + 2} = \dfrac{y - 3}{6}$, so $y = -15$

9. $3 = \dfrac{y + 5}{4 + 3} = \dfrac{y + 5}{7}$, so $y = 16$

10. $\dfrac{1}{2} = \dfrac{2 + 2}{x + 8} = \dfrac{4}{x + 8}$, so $x = 0$

11. $y - 4 = 2(x - 1)$

12. $y - 3 = -\dfrac{2}{3}(x + 4)$

13. $y + 4 = -2(x - 5)$

14. $y - 4 = 3(x + 3)$

15. Since $m = 1$, we can choose $A = 1$ and $B = -1$. Since $x = -7$, $y = -2$ solves $x - y + C = 0$, C must equal 5: $x - y + 5 = 0$. Note that the coefficients can be multiplied by any non-zero number, e.g., another answer would be $2x - 2y + 10 = 0$. This comment also applies to the following problems.

16. Since $m = 1$, we can choose $A = 1$ and $B = -1$. Since $x = -3$, $y = -8$ solves $x - y + C = 0$, C must equal -5: $x - y - 5 = 0$. See comment in #15.

17. Since $m = 0$, we can choose $A = 0$ and $B = 1$. Since $x = 1$, $y = -3$ solves $0x + y + C = 0$. C must equal 3: $0x + y + 3 = 0$, or $y + 3 = 0$. See comment in #15.

18. Since $m = -1$, we can choose $A = 1$ and $B = 1$. Since $x = -1$, $y = -5$ solves $x + y + C = 0$, C must equal 6: $x + y + 6 = 0$. See comment in #15.

19. The slope is $m = 1 = -A/B$, so we can choose $A = 1$ and $B = -1$. Since $x = -1$, $y = 2$ solves $x - y + C = 0$, C must equal 3: $x - y + 3 = 0$. See comment in #15.

20. Since m is undefined we must have $B = 0$, and we can choose $A = 1$. Since $x = 4$, $y = 5$ solves $x + 0y + C = 0$, C must equal -4: $x - 4 = 0$. See comment in #15.

21. Begin with point-slope form: $y - 5 = -3(x - 0)$, so $y = -3x + 5$.

22. Begin with point-slope form: $y - 2 = \dfrac{1}{2}(x - 1)$, so $y = \dfrac{1}{2}x + \dfrac{3}{2}$.

23. $m = -\dfrac{1}{4}$, so in point-slope form, $y - 5 = -\dfrac{1}{4}(x + 4)$, and therefore $y = -\dfrac{1}{4}x + 4$.

24. $m = \dfrac{1}{7}$, so in point-slope form, $y - 2 = \dfrac{1}{7}(x - 4)$, and therefore $y = \dfrac{1}{7}x + \dfrac{10}{7}$.

25. Solve for y: $y = -\dfrac{2}{5}x + \dfrac{12}{5}$.

26. Solve for y: $y = \dfrac{7}{12}x - 8$.

27. Graph $y = 49 - 8x$; window should include $(6.125, 0)$ and $(0, 49)$, for example, $[-5, 10] \times [-10, 60]$.

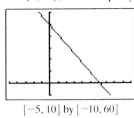
$[-5, 10]$ by $[-10, 60]$

28. Graph $y = 35 - 2x$; window should include $(17.5, 0)$ and $(0, 35)$, for example , $[-5, 20] \times [-10, 40]$.

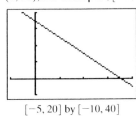
$[-5, 20]$ by $[-10, 40]$

29. Graph $y = (429 - 123x)/7$; window should include $(3.488, 0)$ and $(0, 61.29)$, for example, $[-1, 5] \times [-10, 80]$.

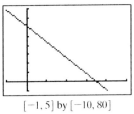
$[-1, 5]$ by $[-10, 80]$

30. Graph $y = (3540 - 2100x)/12 = 295 - 175x$; window should include $(1.686, 0)$ and $(0, 295)$, for example, $[-1, 3] \times (-50, 350]$.

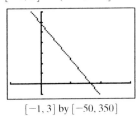
$[-1, 3]$ by $[-50, 350]$

31. (a): The slope is 1.5, compared to 1 in (b).

32. (b): The slopes are $\dfrac{7}{4}$ and 4, respectively.

33. Substitute and solve: replacing y with 14 gives $x = 4$, and replacing x with 18 gives $y = 21$.

34. Substitute and solve: replacing y with 14 gives $x = 2$, and replacing x with 18 gives $y = -18$.

35. Substitute and solve: replacing y with 14 gives $x = -10$, and replacing x with 18 gives $y = -7$.

36. Substitute and solve: replacing y with 14 gives $x = 14$, and replacing x with 18 gives $y = 20$.

37. Ymin $= -30$, Ymax $= 30$, Yscl $= 3$

38. Ymin $= -50$, Ymax $= 50$, Yscl $= 5$

39. Ymin $= -20/3$, Ymax $= 20/3$, Yscl $= 2/3$

40. Ymin $= -12.5$, Ymax $= 12.5$, Yscl $= 1.25$

In #41–44, use the fact that parallel lines have the same slope; while the slopes of perpendicular lines multiply to give -1.

41. **(a)** Parallel: $y - 2 = 3(x - 1)$, or $y = 3x - 1$.

  (b) Perpendicular: $y - 2 = -\dfrac{1}{3}(x - 1)$, or $y = -\dfrac{1}{3}x + \dfrac{7}{3}$.

42. **(a)** Parallel: $y - 3 = -2(x + 2)$, or $y = -2x - 1$.

  (b) Perpendicular: $y - 3 = \dfrac{1}{2}(x + 2)$, or $y = \dfrac{1}{2}x + 4$.

43. **(a)** Parallel: $2x + 3y = 9$, or $y = -\dfrac{2}{3}x + 3$.

  (b) Perpendicular: $3x - 2y = 7$, or $y = \dfrac{3}{2}x - \dfrac{7}{2}$.

44. **(a)** Parallel: $3x - 5y = 13$, or $y = \dfrac{3}{5}x - \dfrac{13}{5}$.

  (b) Perpendicular: $5x + 3y = 33$, or $y = -\dfrac{5}{3}x + 11$.

45. (a) $m = (67{,}500 - 42{,}000)/8 = 3187.5$, the y-intercept is $b = 42{,}000$ so $V = 3187.5t + 42{,}000$.

(b) The house is worth about $72,500 after 9.57 years.

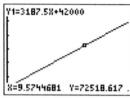

[0, 15] by [40,000, 100,000]

(c) $3187.5t + 42{,}000 = 74{,}000$: $t = 10.04$.

(d) $t = 12$ years.

46. (a) $0 \le x \le 18000$

(b) $I = 0.05x + 0.08(18{,}000 - x)$

(c) $x = 14{,}000$ dollars.

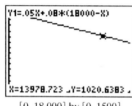

[0, 18,000] by [0, 1500]

(d) $x = 8500$ dollars.

47. $y = \dfrac{3}{8}x$, where y is altitude and x is horizontal distance.

The plane must travel $x = 32{,}000$ ft horizontally–just over 6 miles.

48. (a) $m = \dfrac{6 \text{ ft}}{100 \text{ ft}} = 0.06$.

(b) $4166.\overline{6}$ ft, or about 0.79 mile.

(c) 2217.6 ft.

49. $m = \dfrac{3}{8} = 0.375 > \dfrac{4}{12} = 0.3\overline{3}$, so asphalt shingles are acceptable.

50. We need to find the value of y when $x = 2000$, 2002, and 2003 using the equation $y = 0.4x - 791.8$.

$y = 0.4(2000) - 791.8 = 800 - 791.8 = 8.2$

$y = 0.4(2002) - 791.8 = 800.8 - 791.8 = 9$

$y = 0.4(2003) - 791.8 = 801.2 - 791.8 = 9.4$

Americans' income in the years 2000, 2002, and 2003 was, respectively, 8.2, 9, and 9.4 trillion dollars.

51. (a) Slope of the line between the points (1998, 5.9) and (1999, 6.3) is $m = \dfrac{6.3 - 5.9}{1999 - 1998} = \dfrac{0.4}{1} = 0.4$.

Using the *point-slope form* equation for the line, we have $y - 5.9 = 0.4(x - 1998)$, so $y = 0.4x - 793.3$.

(b) Using $y = 0.4x - 793.3$ and $x = 2002$, the model estimates Americans' expenditures in 2002 were $7.5 trillion.

(c) Using $y = 0.4x - 793.3$ and $x = 2006$, the model predicts Americans' expenditures in 2006 will be $9.1 trillion.

(d)

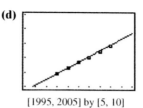

[1995, 2005] by [5, 10]

52. (a) Slope of the line between the points (1997, 85.9) and (2001, 131.3) is $m = \dfrac{131.3 - 85.9}{2001 - 1997} = \dfrac{45.4}{4} = 11.35$.

Using the *point-slope form* equation for the line, we have $y - 85.9 = 11.35(x - 1997)$, so $y = 11.35x - 22580.05$.

(b)

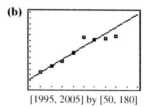

[1995, 2005] by [50, 180]

(c) Using $y = 11.35x - 22580.05$ and $x = 2006$, the model predicts U.S. imports from Mexico in 2006 will be approximately $188.1 billion.

53. (a)

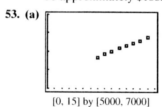

[0, 15] by [5000, 7000]

(b) Slope of the line between the points (7, 5852) and (14, 6377) is $m = \dfrac{6377 - 5852}{14 - 7} = \dfrac{525}{7} = 75$.

Using the *point-slope form* equation for the line, we have $y - 5852 = 75(x - 7)$, so $y = 75x + 5327$.

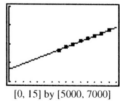

[0, 15] by [5000, 7000]

(c) The year 2006 is represented by $x = 16$. Using $y = 75x + 5327$ and $x = 16$, the model predicts the midyear world population in 2006 will be approximately 6527 million, which is a little larger than the Census Bureau estimate of 6525 million.

54. (a)

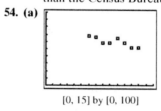

[0, 15] by [0, 100]

(b) Slope of the line between the points $(6, 67.6)$ and $(13, 52.1)$ is $m = \dfrac{52.1 - 67.6}{13 - 6} = \dfrac{-15.5}{7} = -2.2143$.
Using the *point-slope form* equation for the line, we have $y - 67.6 = -2.2143(x - 6)$, so $y = -2.2143x + 80.8857$.

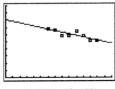

[0, 15] by [0, 100]

(c) The year 2006 is represented by $x = 16$. Using $y = -2.2143x + 80.8857$ and $x = 16$, the model predicts U.S. exports to Japan in 2006 will be approximately \$45.5 billion.

55. $\dfrac{8 - 0}{a - 3} = \dfrac{4 - 0}{3 - 0}$

$\dfrac{8}{a - 3} = \dfrac{4}{3}$

$24 = 4(a - 3)$

$6 = a - 3$

$9 = a$

56. $\dfrac{a - 0}{5 - 3} = \dfrac{2 - 0}{1 - 0}$

$\dfrac{a}{2} = 2$

$a = 4$

57. $\overline{AD} \parallel \overline{BC} \Rightarrow b = 5$;

$\overline{AB} \parallel \overline{DC} \Rightarrow \dfrac{5}{a - 4} = \dfrac{5}{2} \Rightarrow a = 6$

58. $\overline{BC} \parallel \overline{AD} \Rightarrow b = 4$;

$\overline{AB} \parallel \overline{CD} \Rightarrow \dfrac{4}{a} = \dfrac{4 - 0}{8 - 5} \Rightarrow a = 3$

59. (a) No, it is not possible for two lines with positive slopes to be perpendicular, because if both slopes are positive, they cannot multiply to -1.

(b) No, it is not possible for two lines with negative slopes to be perpendicular, because if both slopes are negative, they cannot multiply to -1.

60. (a) If $b = 0$, both lines are vertical; otherwise, both have slope $m = -a/b$, and are, therefore, parallel. If $c = d$, the lines are coincident.

(b) If either a or b equals 0, then one line is horizontal and the other is vertical. Otherwise, their slopes are $-a/b$ and b/a, respectively. In either case, they are perpendicular.

61. False. The slope of a vertical line is undefined. For example, the vertical line through $(3, 1)$ and $(3, 6)$ would have a slope of $\dfrac{6 - 1}{3 - 3} = \dfrac{5}{0}$, which is undefined.

62. True. If $b = 0$, then $a \neq 0$ and the graph of $x = \dfrac{c}{a}$ is a vertical line. If $b \neq 0$, then the graph of $y = -\dfrac{a}{b}x + \dfrac{c}{b}$ is a line with slope $-\dfrac{a}{b}$ and y-intercept $\dfrac{c}{b}$. If $b \neq 0$ and $a = 0$, $y = \dfrac{c}{b}$, which is a horizontal line. An equation of the form $ax + by = c$ is called linear for this reason.

63. With $(x_1, y_1) = (-2, 3)$ and $m = 4$, the point-slope form equation $y - y_1 = m(x - x_1)$ becomes $y - 3 = 4[x - (-2)]$ or $y - 3 = 4(x + 2)$. The answer is A.

64. With $m = 3$ and $b = -2$, the slope-intercept form equation $y = mx + b$ becomes $y = 3x + (-2)$ or $y = 3x - 2$. The answer is B.

65. When a line has a slope of $m_1 = -2$, a perpendicular line must have a slope of $m_2 = -\dfrac{1}{m_1} = \dfrac{1}{2}$. The answer is E.

66. The line through $(x_1, y_1) = (-2, 1)$ and $(x_2, y_2) = (1, -4)$ has a slope of $m = \dfrac{y_2 - y_1}{x_2 - x_1} = \dfrac{-4 - 1}{1 - (-2)} = \dfrac{-5}{3} = -\dfrac{5}{3}$. The answer is C.

67. (a)

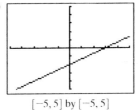

[-5, 5] by [-5, 5]

(b)

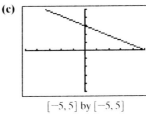

[-5, 5] by [-5, 5]

(c)

[-5, 5] by [-5, 5]

(d) From the graphs, it appears that a is the x-intercept and b is the y-intercept when $c = 1$.
Proof: The x-intercept is found by setting $y = 0$.
When $c = 1$, we have $\dfrac{x}{a} + \dfrac{0}{b} = 1$. Hence $\dfrac{x}{a} = 1$ so $x = a$. The y-intercept is found by setting $x = 0$.
When $c = 1$, we have $\dfrac{0}{a} + \dfrac{y}{b} = 1$. Hence $\dfrac{y}{b} = 1$, so $y = b$.

(e)

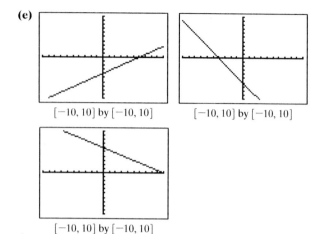

$[-10, 10]$ by $[-10, 10]$ $[-10, 10]$ by $[-10, 10]$

$[-10, 10]$ by $[-10, 10]$

From the graphs, it appears that a is half the x-intercept and b is half the y-intercept when $c = 2$. Proof: When $c = 2$, we can divide both sides by 2 and we have $\dfrac{x}{2a} + \dfrac{y}{2b} = 1$. By part (d) the x-intercept is $2a$ and the y-intercept is $2b$.

(f) By a similar argument, when $c = -1$, a is the opposite of the x-intercept and b is the opposite of the y-intercept.

68. (a)

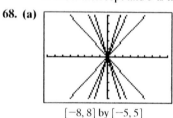

$[-8, 8]$ by $[-5, 5]$

These graphs all pass through the origin. They have different slopes.

(b) If $m > 0$, then the graphs of $y = mx$ and $y = -mx$ have the same steepness, but one increases from left to right, and the other decreases from left to right.

(c)

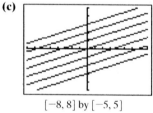

$[-8, 8]$ by $[-5, 5]$

These graphs have the same slope, but different y-intercepts.

69. As in the diagram, we can choose one point to be the origin, and another to be on the x-axis. The midpoints of the sides, starting from the origin and working around counterclockwise in the diagram, are then
$$A\left(\frac{a}{2}, 0\right), B\left(\frac{a+b}{2}, \frac{c}{2}\right), C\left(\frac{b+d}{2}, \frac{c+e}{2}\right), \text{and}$$
$$D\left(\frac{d}{2}, \frac{e}{2}\right).$$ The opposite sides are therefore parallel, since the slopes of the four lines connecting those points are:
$$m_{AB} = \frac{c}{b}; \ m_{BC} = \frac{e}{d-a}; \ m_{CD} = \frac{c}{b}; \ m_{DA} = \frac{e}{d-a}.$$

70. The line from the origin to $(3, 4)$ has slope $\dfrac{4}{3}$, so the tangent line has slope $-\dfrac{3}{4}$, and in *point-slope form*, the equation is $y - 4 = -\dfrac{3}{4}(x - 3)$.

71. A has coordinates $\left(\dfrac{b}{2}, \dfrac{c}{2}\right)$, while B is $\left(\dfrac{a+b}{2}, \dfrac{c}{2}\right)$, so the line containing A and B is the horizontal line $y = c/2$, and the distance from A to B is $\left|\dfrac{a+b}{2} - \dfrac{b}{2}\right| = \dfrac{a}{2}.$

■ Section P.5 Solving Equations Graphically, Numerically, and Algebraically

Exploration 1

1.

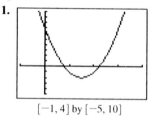

$[-1, 4]$ by $[-5, 10]$

2. Using the numerical zoom, we find the zeros to be 0.79 and 2.21.

3.

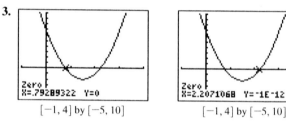

$[-1, 4]$ by $[-5, 10]$ $[-1, 4]$ by $[-5, 10]$

By this method we have zeros at 0.79 and 2.21.

4.

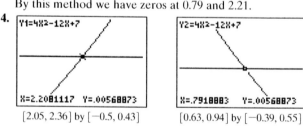

$[2.05, 2.36]$ by $[-0.5, 0.43]$ $[0.63, 0.94]$ by $[-0.39, 0.55]$

Zooming in and tracing reveals the same zeros, correct to two decimal places.

5. The answers in parts 2, 3, and 4 are the same.

6. On a calculator, evaluating $4x^2 - 12x + 7$ when $x = 0.79$ gives $y = 0.0164$ and when $x = 2.21$ gives $y = 0.0164$, so the numbers 0.79 and 2.21 are approximate zeros.

7.

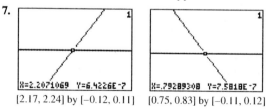

$[2.17, 2.24]$ by $[-0.12, 0.11]$ $[0.75, 0.83]$ by $[-0.11, 0.12]$

Zooming in and tracing reveals zeros of 0.792893 and 2.207107 accurate to six decimal places. If rounded to two decimal places, these would be the same as the answers found in part 3.

Quick Review P.5

1. $(3x - 4)^2 = 9x^2 - 12x - 12x + 16 = 9x^2 - 24x + 16$

2. $(2x + 3)^2 = 4x^2 + 6x + 6x + 9 = 4x^2 + 12x + 9$

3. $(2x + 1)(3x - 5) = 6x^2 - 10x + 3x - 5$
$$= 6x^2 - 7x - 5$$

4. $(3y - 1)(5y + 4) = 15y^2 + 12y - 5y - 4$
$$= 15y^2 + 7y - 4$$

5. $25x^2 - 20x + 4 = (5x - 2)(5x - 2) = (5x - 2)^2$

6. $15x^3 - 22x^2 + 8x = x(15x^2 - 22x + 8)$
$$= x(5x - 4)(3x - 2)$$

7. $3x^3 + x^2 - 15x - 5 = x^2(3x + 1) - 5(3x + 1)$
$$= (3x + 1)(x^2 - 5)$$

8. $y^4 - 13y^2 + 36 = (y^2 - 4)(y^2 - 9)$
$$= (y - 2)(y + 2)(y - 3)(y + 3)$$

9. $\dfrac{x}{2x + 1} - \dfrac{2}{x + 3}$

$$= \dfrac{x(x + 3)}{(2x + 1)(x + 3)} - \dfrac{2(2x + 1)}{(2x + 1)(x + 3)}$$

$$= \dfrac{x^2 + 3x - 4x - 2}{(2x + 1)(x + 3)} = \dfrac{x^2 - x - 2}{(2x + 1)(x + 3)}$$

$$= \dfrac{(x - 2)(x + 1)}{(2x + 1)(x + 3)}$$

10. $\dfrac{x + 1}{x^2 - 5x + 6} - \dfrac{3x + 11}{x^2 - x - 6}$

$$= \dfrac{x + 1}{(x - 3)(x - 2)} - \dfrac{3x + 11}{(x - 3)(x + 2)}$$

$$= \dfrac{(x + 1)(x + 2)}{(x - 3)(x - 2)(x + 2)} - \dfrac{(3x + 11)(x - 2)}{(x - 3)(x - 2)(x + 2)}$$

$$= \dfrac{(x^2 + 3x + 2) - (3x^2 + 5x - 22)}{(x - 3)(x - 2)(x + 2)}$$

$$= \dfrac{-2x^2 - 2x + 24}{(x - 3)(x - 2)(x + 2)}$$

$$= \dfrac{-2(x^2 + x - 12)}{(x - 3)(x - 2)(x + 2)}$$

$$= \dfrac{-2(x + 4)(x - 3)}{(x - 3)(x - 2)(x + 2)}$$

$$= \dfrac{-2(x + 4)}{(x - 2)(x + 2)} \text{ if } x \neq 3$$

Section P.5 Exercises

1.

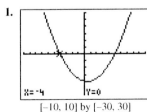

[-10, 10] by [-30, 30]

$x = -4$ or $x = 5$
The left side factors to $(x + 4)(x - 5) = 0$:
$x + 4 = 0$ or $x - 5 = 0$
  $x = -4$ $x = 5$

2.

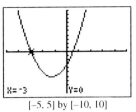

[-5, 5] by [-10, 10]

$x = -3$ or $x = 0.5$
The left side factors to $(x + 3)(2x - 1) = 0$:
$x + 3 = 0$ or $2x - 1 = 0$
  $x = -3$ $2x = 1$
                            $x = 0.5$

3.

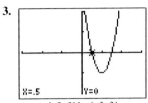

[-3, 3] by [-2, 2]

$x = 0.5$ or $x = 1.5$
The left side factors to $(2x - 1)(2x - 3) = 0$:
$2x - 1 = 0$ or $2x - 3 = 0$
  $2x = 1$ $2x = 3$
  $x = 0.5$ $x = 1.5$

4.

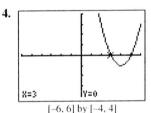

[-6, 6] by [-4, 4]

$x = 3$ or $x = 5$
Rewrite as $x^2 - 8x + 15 = 0$; the left side factors to
$(x - 3)(x - 5) = 0$:
$x - 3 = 0$ or $x - 5 = 0$
  $x = 3$ $x = 5$

5.

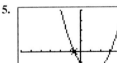

[-6, 6] by [-20, 20]

$x = -\dfrac{2}{3}$ or $x = 3$
Rewrite as $3x^2 - 7x - 6 = 0$; the left side factors to
$(3x + 2)(x - 3) = 0$:
$3x + 2 = 0$ or $x - 3 = 0$
  $x = -\dfrac{2}{3}$ $x = 3$

6.

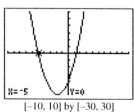

[-10, 10] by [-30, 30]

$x = -5$ or $x = \dfrac{4}{3}$

Rewrite as $3x^2 + 11x - 20 = 0$; the left side factors to $(3x - 4)(x + 5) = 0$:

$3x - 4 = 0$ or $x + 5 = 0$

$\quad x = \dfrac{4}{3}\qquad\qquad x = -5$

7. Rewrite as $(2x)^2 = 5^2$; then $2x = \pm 5$, or $x = \pm\dfrac{5}{2}$.

8. Divide both sides by 2 to get $(x - 5)^2 = 8.5$. Then $x - 5 = \pm\sqrt{8.5}$ and $x = 5 \pm \sqrt{8.5}$.

$5 \pm \sqrt{\tfrac{17}{2}}$

9. Divide both sides by 3 to get $(x + 4)^2 = \dfrac{8}{3}$. Then

$x + 4 = \pm\sqrt{\dfrac{8}{3}}$ and $x = -4 \pm \sqrt{\dfrac{8}{3}}$.

10. Divide both sides by 4 to get $(u + 1)^2 = 4.5$. Then $u + 1 = \pm\sqrt{4.5}$ and $u = -1 \pm \sqrt{4.5}$.

11. Adding $2y^2 + 8$ to both sides gives $4y^2 = 14$. Divide both sides by 4 to get $y^2 = \dfrac{7}{2}$, so $y = \pm\sqrt{\dfrac{7}{2}}$.

12. $2x + 3 = \pm 13$ so $x = \dfrac{1}{2}(-3 \pm 13)$, which gives $x = -8$ or $x = 5$.

13. $x^2 + 6x + 3^2 = 7 + 3^2$

$\quad (x + 3)^2 = 16$

$\quad\quad x + 3 = \pm\sqrt{16}$

$\quad\quad\quad x = -3 \pm 4$

$x = -7$ or $x = 1$

14. $\qquad\qquad x^2 + 5x = 9$

$x^2 + 5x + \left(\dfrac{5}{2}\right)^2 = 9 + \left(\dfrac{5}{2}\right)^2$

$\qquad (x + 2.5)^2 = 9 + 6.25$

$\qquad\quad x + 2.5 = \pm\sqrt{15.25}$

$x = -2.5 - \sqrt{15.25} \approx -6.41$ or
$x = -2.5 + \sqrt{15.25} \approx 1.41$

15. $\qquad\qquad x^2 - 7x = -\dfrac{5}{4}$

$x^2 - 7x + \left(-\dfrac{7}{2}\right)^2 = -\dfrac{5}{4} + \left(-\dfrac{7}{2}\right)^2$

$\qquad \left(x - \dfrac{7}{2}\right)^2 = 11$

$\qquad\qquad x - \dfrac{7}{2} = \pm\sqrt{11}$

$\qquad\qquad\quad x = \dfrac{7}{2} \pm \sqrt{11}$

$x = \dfrac{7}{2} - \sqrt{11} \approx 0.18$ or $x = \dfrac{7}{2} + \sqrt{11} \approx 6.82$

16. $\qquad\qquad x^2 + 6x = 4$

$x^2 + 6x + \left(\dfrac{6}{2}\right)^2 = 4 + \left(\dfrac{6}{2}\right)^2$

$\qquad (x + 3)^2 = 4 + 9$

$\qquad\quad x + 3 = \pm\sqrt{13}$

$\qquad\qquad x = -3 \pm \sqrt{13}$

$x = -3 - \sqrt{13} \approx -6.61$ or $x = -3 + \sqrt{13} \approx 0.61$

17. $\quad 2x^2 - 7x + 9 = x^2 - 2x - 3 + 3x$

$\quad 2x^2 - 7x + 9 = x^2 + x - 3$

$\qquad\quad x^2 - 8x = -12$

$x^2 - 8x + (-4)^2 = -12 + (-4)^2$

$\qquad (x - 4)^2 = 4$

$\qquad\quad x - 4 = \pm 2$

$\qquad\qquad x = 4 \pm 2$

$x = 2$ or $x = 6$

18. $\quad 3x^2 - 6x - 7 = x^2 + 3x - x^2 - x + 3$

$\qquad\quad 3x^2 - 8x = 10$

$\qquad\quad x^2 - \dfrac{8}{3}x = \dfrac{10}{3}$

$x^2 - \dfrac{8}{3}x + \left(-\dfrac{4}{3}\right)^2 = \dfrac{10}{3} + \left(-\dfrac{4}{3}\right)^2$

$\qquad \left(x - \dfrac{4}{3}\right)^2 = \dfrac{10}{3} + \dfrac{16}{9}$

$\qquad\quad x - \dfrac{4}{3} = \pm\sqrt{\dfrac{46}{9}}$

$\qquad\qquad x = \dfrac{4}{3} \pm \dfrac{1}{3}\sqrt{46}$

$x = \dfrac{4}{3} - \dfrac{1}{3}\sqrt{46} \approx -0.93$ or $x = \dfrac{4}{3} + \dfrac{1}{3}\sqrt{46} \approx 3.59$

19. $a = 1$, $b = 8$, and $c = -2$:

$x = \dfrac{-8 \pm \sqrt{8^2 - 4(1)(-2)}}{2(1)} = \dfrac{-8 \pm \sqrt{72}}{2}$

$\quad = \dfrac{-8 \pm 6\sqrt{2}}{2} = -4 \pm 3\sqrt{2}$

$x \approx -8.24$ or $x \approx 0.24$

20. $a = 2$, $b = -3$, and $c = 1$:

$x = \dfrac{3 \pm \sqrt{(-3)^2 - 4(2)(1)}}{2(2)} = \dfrac{3 \pm \sqrt{1}}{4} = \dfrac{3}{4} \pm \dfrac{1}{4}$

$x = \dfrac{1}{2}$ or $x = 1$

21. $x^2 - 3x - 4 = 0$, so
$a = 1$, $b = -3$, and $c = -4$:

$x = \dfrac{3 \pm \sqrt{(-3)^2 - 4(1)(-4)}}{2(1)} = \dfrac{3 \pm \sqrt{25}}{2} = \dfrac{3}{2} \pm \dfrac{5}{2}$

$x = -1$ or $x = 4$

22. $x^2 - \sqrt{3}x - 5 = 0$, so
$a = 1$, $b = -\sqrt{3}$, and $c = -5$:

$x = \dfrac{\sqrt{3} \pm \sqrt{(-\sqrt{3})^2 - 4(1)(-5)}}{2(1)}$

$\quad = \dfrac{\sqrt{3} \pm \sqrt{23}}{2} = \dfrac{1}{2}\sqrt{3} \pm \dfrac{1}{2}\sqrt{23}$

$x \approx -1.53$ or $x \approx 3.26$

23. $x^2 + 5x - 12 = 0$, so
$a = 1, b = 5, c = -12$

$$x = \frac{-5 \pm \sqrt{(5)^2 - 4(1)(-12)}}{2(1)}$$

$$= \frac{-5 \pm \sqrt{73}}{2} = -\frac{5}{2} \pm \frac{\sqrt{73}}{2}$$

$x \approx -6.77$ or $x \approx 1.77$

24. $x^2 - 4x - 32 = 0$, so
$a = 1, b = -4, c = -32$:

$$x = \frac{-(-4) \pm \sqrt{(-4)^2 - 4(1)(-32)}}{2(1)}$$

$$= \frac{4 \pm \sqrt{144}}{2} = 2 \pm 6$$

$x = -4$ or $x = 8$

25. x-intercept: 3; y-intercept: -2

26. x-intercepts: 1, 3; y-intercept: 3

27. x-intercepts: $-2, 0, 2$; y-intercept: 0

28. no x-intercepts; no y-intercepts

29.
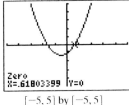
$[-5, 5]$ by $[-5, 5]$ $[-5, 5]$ by $[-5, 5]$

30.
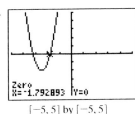
$[-5, 5]$ by $[-5, 5]$ $[-5, 5]$ by $[-5, 5]$

31.
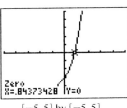
$[-5, 5]$ by $[-5, 5]$

32.
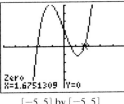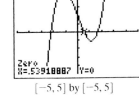
$[-5, 5]$ by $[-5, 5]$ $[-5, 5]$ by $[-5, 5]$

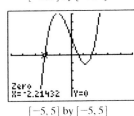
$[-5, 5]$ by $[-5, 5]$

33.
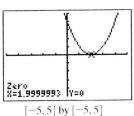
$[-5, 5]$ by $[-5, 5]$

34.
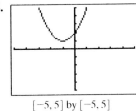
$[-5, 5]$ by $[-5, 5]$

35. $x^2 + 2x - 1 = 0$; $x \approx 0.4$

36. $x^3 - 3x = 0$; $x \approx -1.73$

37. Using TblStart $= 1.61$ and ΔTbl $= 0.001$ gives a zero at 1.62.
Using TblStart $= -0.62$ and ΔTbl $= 0.001$ gives a zero at -0.62.

38. Using TblStart $= 1.32$ and ΔTbl $= 0.001$ gives a zero at 1.32.

39. Graph $y = |x - 8|$ and $y = 2$: $t = 6$ or $t = 10$

40. Graph $y = |x + 1|$ and $y = 4$: $x = -5$ or $x = 3$

41. Graph $y = |2x + 5|$ and $y = 7$: $x = 1$ or $x = -6$

42. Graph $y = |3 - 5x|$ and $y = 4$: $x = -\frac{1}{5}$ or $x = \frac{7}{5}$

43. Graph $y = |2x - 3|$ and $y = x^2$: $x = -3$ or $x = 1$

44. Graph $y = |x + 1|$ and $y = 2x - 3$: $x = 4$

45. **(a)** The two functions are $y_1 = 3\sqrt{x + 4}$ (the one that begins on the x-axis) and $y_2 = x^2 - 1$.

(b) This is the graph of $y = 3\sqrt{x + 4} - x^2 + 1$.

(c) The x-coordinates of the intersections in the first picture are the same as the x-coordinates where the second graph crosses the x-axis.

46. Any number between 1.324 and 1.325 must have the digit 4 in its thousandths position. Such a number would round to 1.32.

47. The left side factors to $(x + 2)(x - 1) = 0$:
$x + 2 = 0$ or $x - 1 = 0$
  $x = -2$ $x = 1$

48. Graphing $y = x^2 - 18$ in (e.g.) $[-10, 10] \times [-20, 10]$ and looking for x-intercepts gives $x \approx -4.24$ or $x \approx 4.24$.
$x^2 - 3x = 12 - 3x + 6$
$x^2 - 18 = 0$

49. $2x - 1 = 5$ or $2x - 1 = -5$
   $2x = 6$ $2x = -4$
    $x = 3$ $x = -2$

50. $x + 2 = 2\sqrt{x + 3}$
$x^2 + 4x + 4 = 4(x + 3)$
          $x^2 = 8$
$x = -\sqrt{8}$ or $x = \sqrt{8}$
$-\sqrt{8}$ is an extraneous solution, $x = \sqrt{8} \approx 2.83$

51. From the graph of $y = x^3 + 4x^2 - 3x - 2$ on $[-10, 10] \times [-10, 10]$, the solutions of the equation (x-intercepts of the graph) are $x \approx -4.56$, $x \approx -0.44$, $x = 1$.

52. From the graph of $y = x^3 - 4x + 2$ on $[-10, 10] \times [-10, 10]$, the solutions of the equation (x-intercepts of the graph) are $x \approx -2.21$, $x \approx 0.54$, and $x \approx 1.68$.

53.
$$x^2 + 4x - 1 = 7 \qquad \text{or} \quad x^2 + 4x - 1 = -7$$
$$x^2 + 4x - 8 = 0 \qquad\qquad x^2 + 4x + 6 = 0$$
$$x = \frac{-4 \pm \sqrt{16 + 32}}{2} \qquad x = \frac{-4 \pm \sqrt{16 - 24}}{2}$$
$$x = -2 \pm 2\sqrt{3} \qquad \text{— no real solutions to}$$
this equation.

54. Graph $y = |x + 5| - |x - 3|$: $x = -1$

55. Graph $y = |0.5x + 3|$ and $y = x^2 - 4$: $x \approx -2.41$ or $x \approx 2.91$

56. Graph $y = \sqrt{x + 7}$ and $y = -x^2 + 5$: $x \approx -1.64$ or $x \approx 1.45$

57. **(a)** There must be 2 distinct real zeros, because $b^2 - 4ac > 0$ implies that $\pm\sqrt{b^2 - 4ac}$ are 2 distinct real numbers.

(b) There must be 1 real zero, because $b^2 - 4ac = 0$ implies that $\pm\sqrt{b^2 - 4ac} = 0$, so the root must be $x = -\dfrac{b}{a}$.

(c) There must be no real zeros, because $b^2 - 4ac < 0$ implies that $\pm\sqrt{b^2 - 4ac}$ are not real numbers.

58. For (a)–(c), answers may vary.

(a) $x^2 + 2x - 3$ has discriminant $(2)^2 - 4(1)(-3) = 16$, so it has 2 distinct real zeros. The graph (or factoring) shows the zeros are at $x = -3$ and $x = 1$.

(b) $x^2 + 2x + 1$ has discriminant $(2)^2 - 4(1)(1) = 0$, so it has 1 real zero. The graph (or factoring) shows the zero is at $x = -1$.

(c) $x^2 + 2x + 2$ has discriminant $(2)^2 - 4(1)(2) = -4$, so it has no real zeros. The graph lies entirely above the x-axis.

59. Let x be the width of the field (in yd); the length is $x + 30$. Then the field is 80 yd wide and $80 + 30 = 110$ yd long.
$$8800 = x(x + 30)$$
$$0 = x^2 + 30x - 8800$$
$$0 = (x + 110)(x - 80)$$
$$0 = x + 110 \text{ or } 0 = x - 80$$
$$x = -110 \text{ or } x = 80$$

60. Solving $x^2 + (x + 5)^2 = 18^2$, or $2x^2 + 10x - 299 = 0$, gives $x \approx 9.98$ or $x \approx -14.98$. The ladder is about $x + 5 \approx 14.98$ ft up the wall.

61. The area of the square is x^2. The area of the semicircle is $\frac{1}{2}\pi r^2 = \frac{1}{2}\pi\left(\frac{1}{2}x\right)^2$ since the radius of the semicircle is $\frac{1}{2}x$.

Then $200 = x^2 + \frac{1}{2}\pi\left(\frac{1}{2}x\right)^2$. Solving this (graphically is easiest) gives $x \approx 11.98$ ft (since x must be positive).

62. True. If 2 is an x-intercept of the graph of $y = ax^2 + bx + c$, then $y = 0$ when $x = 2$. That is, $ax^2 + bx + c = 0$ when $x = 2$.

63. False. Notice that for $x = -3$, $2x^2 = 2(-3)^2 = 18$. So x could also be -3.

64. $x(x - 3) = 0$ when $x = 0$ and when $x - 3 = 0$ or $x = 3$. The answer is D.

65. For $x^2 - 5x + ?$ to be a perfect square, ? must be replaced by the square of half of -5, which is $\left(-\dfrac{5}{2}\right)^2$. The answer is B.

66. By the quadratic formula, the solutions are
$$x = \frac{-(-3) \pm \sqrt{(-3)^2 - 4(2)(-1)}}{2(2)} = \frac{3 \pm \sqrt{17}}{4}$$
The answer is B.

67. Since an absolute value cannot be negative, there are no solutions. The answer is E.

68. **(a)**
$$ax^2 + bx + c = 0$$
$$ax^2 + bx = -c$$
$$x^2 + \frac{b}{a}x = -\frac{c}{a}$$

(b)
$$x^2 + \frac{b}{a}x + \left(\frac{1}{2}\cdot\frac{b}{a}\right)^2 = -\frac{c}{a} + \left(\frac{1}{2}\cdot\frac{b}{a}\right)^2$$
$$x^2 + \frac{b}{a}x + \left(\frac{b}{2a}\right)^2 = -\frac{c}{a} + \frac{b^2}{4a^2}$$
$$\left(x + \frac{b}{2a}\right)\left(x + \frac{b}{2a}\right) = -\frac{4ac}{4a^2} + \frac{b^2}{4a^2}$$
$$\left(x + \frac{b}{2a}\right)^2 = \frac{b^2 - 4ac}{4a^2}$$

(c)
$$x + \frac{b}{2a} = \pm\sqrt{\frac{b^2 - 4ac}{4a^2}}$$
$$x + \frac{b}{2a} = \frac{\pm\sqrt{b^2 - 4ac}}{2a}$$
$$x = -\frac{b}{2a} \pm \frac{\sqrt{b^2 - 4ac}}{2a}$$
$$x = \frac{-b \pm \sqrt{b^2 - 4ac}}{2a}$$

69. Graph $y = |x^2 - 4|$ and $y = c$ for several values of c.

(a) Let $c = 2$. The graph suggests $y = 2$ intersects $y = |x^2 - 4|$ four times.
$$|x^2 - 4| = 2 \Rightarrow x^2 - 4 = 2 \text{ or } x^2 - 4 = -2$$
$$x^2 = 6 \qquad\qquad x^2 = 2$$
$$x = \pm\sqrt{6} \qquad x = \pm\sqrt{2}$$
$|x^2 - 4| = 2$ has four solutions: $\{\pm\sqrt{2}, \pm\sqrt{6}\}$.

(b) Let $c = 4$. The graph suggests $y = 4$ intersects $y = |x^2 - 4|$ three times.
$$|x^2 - 4| = 4 \Rightarrow x^2 - 4 = 4 \text{ or } x^2 - 4 = -4$$
$$x^2 = 8 \qquad\qquad x^2 = 0$$
$$x = \pm\sqrt{8} \qquad x = 0$$

(c) Let $c = 5$. The graph suggest $y = 5$ intersects $y = |x^2 - 4|$ twice.
$$|x^2 - 4| = 5 \Rightarrow x^2 - 4 = 5 \text{ or } x^2 - 4 = -5$$
$$x^2 = 9 \qquad\qquad x^2 = -1$$
$$x = \pm 3 \qquad \text{no solution}$$
$|x^2 - 4| = 5$ has two solutions: $\{\pm 3\}$.

(d) Let $c = -1$. The graph suggests $y = -1$ does not intersect $y = |x^2 - 4|$. Since absolute value is never negative, $|x^2 - 4| = -1$ has no solutions.

(e) There is no other possible number of solutions of this equation. For any c, the solution involves solving two quadratic equations, each of which can have 0, 1, or 2 solutions.

70. (a) Let $D = b^2 - 4ac$. The two solutions are $\dfrac{-b \pm \sqrt{D}}{2a}$;

adding them gives
$$\frac{-b + \sqrt{D}}{2a} + \frac{-b - \sqrt{D}}{2a} = \frac{-2b + \sqrt{D} - \sqrt{D}}{2a}$$
$$= \frac{-2b}{2a} = -\frac{b}{a}$$

(b) Let $D = b^2 - 4ac$. The two solutions are $\dfrac{-b \pm \sqrt{D}}{2a}$;

multiplying them gives
$$\frac{-b + \sqrt{D}}{2a} \cdot \frac{-b - \sqrt{D}}{2a} = \frac{(-b)^2 - (\sqrt{D})^2}{4a^2}$$
$$= \frac{b^2 - (b^2 - 4ac)}{4a^2} = \frac{c}{a}$$

71. From #70(a), $x_1 + x_2 = -\dfrac{b}{a} = 5$. Since $a = 2$, this means $b = -10$. From #70(b), $x_1 \cdot x_2 = \dfrac{c}{a} = 3$; since $a = 2$, this means $c = 6$. The solutions are $\dfrac{10 \pm \sqrt{100 - 48}}{4}$; this reduces to $2.5 \pm \dfrac{1}{2}\sqrt{13}$, or approximately 0.697 and 4.303.

■ Section P.6 Complex Numbers

Quick Review P.6

1. $x + 9$
2. $x + 2y$
3. $a + 2d$
4. $5z - 4$
5. $x^2 - x - 6$
6. $2x^2 + 5x - 3$
7. $x^2 - 2$
8. $x^2 - 12$
9. $x^2 - 2x - 1$
10. $x^2 - 4x + 1$

Section P.6 Exercises

In #1–8, add or subtract the real and imaginary parts separately.

1. $(2 - 3i) + (6 + 5i) = (2 + 6) + (-3 + 5)i = 8 + 2i$
2. $(2 - 3i) + (3 - 4i) = (2 + 3) + (-3 - 4)i = 5 - 7i$
3. $(7 - 3i) + (6 - i) = (7 + 6) + (-3 - 1)i = 13 - 4i$
4. $(2 + i) - (9i - 3) = (2 + 3) + (1 - 9)i = 5 - 8i$
5. $(2 - i) + (3 - \sqrt{-3}) = (2 + 3) + (-1 - \sqrt{3})i$
   $= 5 - (1 + \sqrt{3})i$
6. $(\sqrt{5} - 3i) + (-2 + \sqrt{-9}) = (\sqrt{5} - 2) + (-3 + 3)i$
   $= \sqrt{5} - 2$

7. $(i^2 + 3) - (7 + i^3) = (-1 + 3) - (7 - i)$
   $= (2 - 7) + i = -5 + i$
8. $(\sqrt{7} + i^2) - (6 - \sqrt{-81}) = (\sqrt{7} - 1)$
   $- (6 - 9i) = (\sqrt{7} - 1 - 6) + 9i = (\sqrt{7} - 7) + 9i$

In #9–16, multiply out and simplify, recalling that $i^2 = -1$.

9. $(2 + 3i)(2 - i) = 4 - 2i + 6i - 3i^2$
   $= 4 + 4i + 3 = 7 + 4i$
10. $(2 - i)(1 + 3i) = 2 + 6i - i - 3i^2$
    $= 2 + 5i + 3 = 5 + 5i$
11. $(1 - 4i)(3 - 2i) = 3 - 2i - 12i + 8i^2$
    $= 3 - 14i - 8 = -5 - 14i$
12. $(5i - 3)(2i + 1) = 10i^2 + 5i - 6i - 3$
    $= -10 - i - 3 = -13 - i$
13. $(7i - 3)(2 + 6i) = 14i + 42i^2 - 6 - 18i$
    $= -42 - 6 - 4i = -48 - 4i$
14. $(\sqrt{-4} + i)(6 - 5i) = (3i)(6 - 5i) = 18i - 15i^2$
    $= 15 + 18i$
15. $(-3 - 4i)(1 + 2i) = -3 - 6i - 4i - 8i^2$
    $= -3 - 10i + 8 = 5 - 10i$
16. $(\sqrt{-2} + 2i)(6 + 5i) = (\sqrt{2} + 2)i(6 + 5i)$
    $= 6(2 + \sqrt{2})i + 5(2 + \sqrt{2})i^2$
    $= -(10 + 5\sqrt{2}) + (12 + 6\sqrt{2})i$
17. $\sqrt{-16} = 4i$
18. $\sqrt{-25} = 5i$
19. $\sqrt{-3} = \sqrt{3}i$
20. $\sqrt{-5} = \sqrt{5}i$

In #21–24, equate the real and imaginary parts.

21. $x = 2, y = 3$
22. $x = 3, y = -7$
23. $x = 1, y = 2$
24. $x = 7, y = -7/2$

In #25–28, multiply out and simplify, recalling that $i^2 = -1$.

25. $(3 + 2i)^2 = 9 + 12i + 4i^2 = 5 + 12i$
26. $(1 - i)^3 = (1 - 2i + i^2)(1 - i) = (-2i)(1 - i)$
    $= -2i + 2i^2 = -2 - 2i$
27. $\left(\dfrac{\sqrt{2}}{2} + \dfrac{\sqrt{2}}{2}i\right)^4 = \left(\dfrac{\sqrt{2}}{2}\right)^4(1 + i)^4$
    $= \dfrac{1}{4}(1 + 2i + i^2)^2 = \dfrac{1}{4}(2i)^2 = \dfrac{1}{4}(-4) = -1$
28. $\left(\dfrac{\sqrt{3}}{2} + \dfrac{1}{2}i\right)^3 = \left(\dfrac{1}{2}\right)^3(\sqrt{3} + i)^3$
    $= \dfrac{1}{8}(3 + 2\sqrt{3}i + i^2)(\sqrt{3} + i)$
    $= \dfrac{1}{4}(1 + \sqrt{3}i)(\sqrt{3} + i)$
    $= \dfrac{1}{4}(\sqrt{3} + i + 3i + \sqrt{3}i^2) = \dfrac{1}{4}(4i) = i$

In #29–32, recall that $(a + bi)(a - bi) = a^2 + b^2$.

29. $2^2 + 3^2 = 13$
30. $5^2 + 6^2 = 61$
31. $3^2 + 4^2 = 25$
32. $1^2 + (\sqrt{2})^2 = 3$

In #33–40, multiply both the numerator and denominator by the complex conjugate of the denominator, recalling that $(a + bi)(a - bi) = a^2 + b^2$.

33. $\dfrac{1}{2+i} \cdot \dfrac{2-i}{2-i} = \dfrac{2-i}{5} = \dfrac{2}{5} - \dfrac{1}{5}i$

34. $\dfrac{i}{2-i} \cdot \dfrac{2+i}{2+i} = \dfrac{2i+i^2}{5} = -\dfrac{1}{5} + \dfrac{2}{5}i$

35. $\dfrac{2+i}{2-i} \cdot \dfrac{2+i}{2+i} = \dfrac{4+4i+i^2}{5} = \dfrac{3}{5} + \dfrac{4}{5}i$

36. $\dfrac{2+i}{3i} \cdot \dfrac{-3i}{-3i} = \dfrac{-6i-3i^2}{9} = \dfrac{1}{3} - \dfrac{2}{3}i$

37. $\dfrac{(2+i)^2(-i)}{1+i} \cdot \dfrac{1-i}{1-i} = \dfrac{(4+4i+i^2)(-i+i^2)}{2}$

$= \dfrac{(3+4i)(-1-i)}{2} = \dfrac{-3-3i-4i-4i^2}{2} = \dfrac{1}{2} - \dfrac{7}{2}i$

38. $\dfrac{(2-i)(1+2i)}{5+2i} \cdot \dfrac{5-2i}{5-2i} = \dfrac{(2+4i-i-2i^2)(5-2i)}{29}$

$= \dfrac{(4+3i)(5-2i)}{29} = \dfrac{20-8i+15i-6i^2}{29}$

$= \dfrac{26}{29} + \dfrac{7}{29}i$

39. $\dfrac{(1-i)(2-i)}{1-2i} \cdot \dfrac{1+2i}{1+2i} = \dfrac{(2-i-2i+i^2)(1+2i)}{5}$

$= \dfrac{(1-3i)(1+2i)}{5} = \dfrac{1+2i-3i-6i^2}{5} = \dfrac{7}{5} - \dfrac{1}{5}i$

40. $\dfrac{(1-\sqrt{2}i)(1+i)}{1+\sqrt{2}i} \cdot \dfrac{1-\sqrt{2}i}{1-\sqrt{2}i}$

$= \dfrac{(1+i-\sqrt{2}i-\sqrt{2}i^2)(1-\sqrt{2}i)}{3}$

$= \dfrac{[1+\sqrt{2}+(1-\sqrt{2})i](1-\sqrt{2}i)}{3}$

$= \dfrac{1+\sqrt{2}-(\sqrt{2}+2)i+(1-\sqrt{2})i-(\sqrt{2}-2)i^2}{3}$

$= \dfrac{1+\sqrt{2}+\sqrt{2}-2+(-2\sqrt{2}-1)i}{3}$

$= \dfrac{2\sqrt{2}-1}{3} - \dfrac{2\sqrt{2}+1}{3}i$

In #41–44, use the quadratic formula.

41. $x = -1 \pm 2i$

42. $x = -\dfrac{1}{6} \pm \dfrac{\sqrt{23}}{6}i$

43. $x = \dfrac{7}{8} \pm \dfrac{\sqrt{15}}{8}i$

44. $x = 2 \pm \sqrt{15}i$

45. False. When $a = 0$, $z = a + bi$ becomes $z = bi$, and then $-\bar{z} = -(-bi) = bi = z$.

46. True. Because $i^2 = -1$, $i^3 = i(i^2) = -i$, and $i^4 = (i^2)^2 = 1$, we obtain $i + i^2 + i^3 + i^4 = i + (-1) + (-i) + 1 = 0$.

47. $(2 + 3i)(2 - 3i)$ is a product of conjugates and equals $2^2 + 3^2 = 13$. The answer is E.

48. $\dfrac{1}{i} = \dfrac{1}{i} \cdot \dfrac{-i}{-i} = \dfrac{-i}{1} = -i$. The answer is D.

49. Complex, nonreal solutions of polynomials with real coefficients always come in conjugate pairs. So another solution is $2 + 3i$, and the answer is A.

50. $(1 - i)^3 = (-2i)(1 - i) = -2i + 2i^2 = -2 - 2i$. The answer is C.

51. (a) $i = i$ $i^5 = i \cdot i^4 = i$

$i^2 = -1$ $i^6 = i^2 \cdot i^4 = -1$

$i^3 = (-1)i = -i$ $i^7 = i^3 \cdot i^4 = -i$

$i^4 = (-1)^2 = 1$ $i^8 = i^4 \cdot i^4 = 1 \cdot 1 = 1$

(b) $i^{-1} = \dfrac{1}{i} = \dfrac{1}{i} \dfrac{i}{i} = -i$ $i^{-5} = \dfrac{1}{i} \dfrac{1}{i^4} = \dfrac{1}{i} = -i$

$i^{-2} = \dfrac{1}{i^2} = -1$ $i^{-6} = \dfrac{1}{i^2} \cdot \dfrac{1}{i^4} = -1$

$i^{-3} = \dfrac{1}{i} \cdot \dfrac{1}{i^2} = -\dfrac{1}{i} = i$ $i^{-7} = \dfrac{1}{i^3} \cdot \dfrac{1}{i^4} = -\dfrac{1}{i} = i$

$i^{-4} = \dfrac{1}{i^2} \cdot \dfrac{1}{i^2} = (-1)(-1) = 1$ $i^{-8} = \dfrac{1}{i^4} \cdot \dfrac{1}{i^4} = 1 \cdot 1 = 1$

(c) $i^0 = 1$

(d) Answers will vary.

52. Answers will vary. One possibility: the graph has the shape of a parabola, but does not cross the x-axis when plotted in the real plane, beacause it does not have any real zeros. As a result, the function will *always* be positive or *always* be negative.

53. Let a and b be any two real numbers. Then $(a + bi) - (a - bi) = (a - a) + (b + b)i = 0 + 2bi = 2bi$.

54. $(a + bi) \cdot \overline{(a + bi)} = (a + bi) \cdot (a - bi) = a^2 + b^2$, imaginary part is zero.

55. $\overline{(a + bi) \cdot (c + di)} = \overline{(ac - bd) + (ad + bc)i} = (ac - bd) - (ad + bc)i$ and $\overline{(a + bi)} \cdot \overline{(c + di)} = (a - bi) \cdot (c - di) = (ac - bd) - (ad + bc)i$ are equal.

56. $\overline{(a + bi) + (c + di)} = \overline{(a + c) + (b + d)i} = (a + c) - (b + d)i$ and $\overline{(a + bi)} + \overline{(c + di)} = (a - bi) + (c - di) = (a + c) - (b + d)i$ are equal.

57. $(-i)^2 - i(-i) + 2 = 0$ but $(i)^2 - i(i) + 2 \neq 0$. Because the coefficient of x in $x^2 - ix + 2 = 0$ is not a real number, the complex conjugate, i, of $-i$, need not be a solution.

■ Section P.7 Solving Inequalities Algebraically and Graphically

Quick Review P.7

1. $-7 < 2x - 3 < 7$

$-4 < 2x < 10$

$-2 < x < 5$

2. $5x - 2 \geq 7x + 4$

$-2x \geq 6$

$x \leq -3$

3. $|x + 2| = 3$

$x + 2 = 3$ or $x + 2 = -3$

$x = 1$ or $x = -5$

4. $4x^2 - 9 = (2x - 3)(2x + 3)$

5. $x^3 - 4x = x(x^2 - 4) = x(x - 2)(x + 2)$

6. $9x^2 - 16y^2 = (3x - 4y)(3x + 4y)$

7. $\dfrac{z^2 - 25}{z^2 - 5z} = \dfrac{(z-5)(z+5)}{z(z-5)} = \dfrac{z+5}{z}$

8. $\dfrac{x^2 + 2x - 35}{x^2 - 10x + 25} = \dfrac{(x+7)(x-5)}{(x-5)(x-5)} = \dfrac{x+7}{x-5}$

9. $\dfrac{x}{x-1} + \dfrac{x+1}{3x-4}$

$= \dfrac{x(3x-4)}{(x-1)(3x-4)} + \dfrac{(x+1)(x-1)}{(x-1)(3x-4)}$

$= \dfrac{4x^2 - 4x - 1}{(x-1)(3x-4)}$

10. $\dfrac{2x-1}{(x-2)(x+1)} + \dfrac{x-3}{(x-2)(x-1)}$

$= \dfrac{(2x-1)(x-1) + (x-3)(x+1)}{(x-2)(x+1)(x-1)}$

$= \dfrac{(2x^2 - 3x + 1) + (x^2 - 2x - 3)}{(x-2)(x+1)(x-1)}$

$= \dfrac{3x^2 - 5x - 2}{(x-2)(x+1)(x-1)} = \dfrac{(3x+1)(x-2)}{(x-2)(x+1)(x-1)}$

if $x \neq 2$ $= \dfrac{(3x+1)}{(x+1)(x-1)}$

Section P.7 Exercises

1. $(-\infty, -9] \cup [1, \infty)$:

$x + 4 \geq 5$ or $x + 4 \leq -5$

$ x \geq 1 x \leq -9$

2. $(-\infty, -1.3) \cup (2.3, \infty)$:

$2x - 1 > 3.6$ or $2x - 1 < -3.6$

$ 2x > 4.6 2x < -2.6$

$ x > 2.3 x < -1.3$

3. $(1, 5)$: $-2 < x - 3 < 2$

$ 1 < x < 5$

4. $[-8, 2]$: $-5 \leq x + 3 \leq 5$

$ -8 \leq x \leq 2$

5. $\left(-\dfrac{2}{3}, \dfrac{10}{3}\right)$: $|4 - 3x| < 6$

$-6 < 4 - 3x < 6$

$-10 < -3x < 2$

$\dfrac{10}{3} > x > -\dfrac{2}{3}$

6. $(-\infty, 0) \cup (3, \infty)$: $|3 - 2x| > 3$

$3 - 2x > 3$ or $3 - 2x < -3$

$ -2x > 0 -2x < -6$

$ x < 0 x > 3$

7. $(-\infty, -11] \cup [7, \infty)$:

$\dfrac{x+2}{3} \leq -3$ or $\dfrac{x+2}{3} \geq 3$

$x + 2 \leq -9 x + 2 \geq 9$

$ x \leq -11 x \geq 7$

8. $[-19, 29]$: $\left|\dfrac{x-5}{4}\right| \leq 6$

$-6 \leq \dfrac{x-5}{4} \leq 6$

$-24 \leq x - 5 \leq 24$

$-19 \leq x \leq 29$

9. $2x^2 + 17x + 21 = 0$

$(2x + 3)(x + 7) = 0$

$2x + 3 = 0$ or $x + 7 = 0$

$ x = -\dfrac{3}{2}$ or $ x = -7$

The graph of $y = 2x^2 + 17x + 21$ lies below the x-axis for $-7 < x < -\dfrac{3}{2}$. Hence $\left[-7, -\dfrac{3}{2}\right]$ is the solution since the endpoints are included.

10. $6x^2 - 13x + 6 = 0$

$(2x - 3)(3x - 2) = 0$

$2x - 3 = 0$ or $3x - 2 = 0$

$ x = \dfrac{3}{2}$ or $ x = \dfrac{2}{3}$

The graph of $y = 6x^2 - 13x + 6$ lies above the x-axis for $x < \dfrac{2}{3}$ and for $x > \dfrac{3}{2}$. Hence $\left(-\infty, \dfrac{2}{3}\right] \cup \left[\dfrac{3}{2}, \infty\right)$ is the solution since the endpoints are included.

11. $2x^2 + 7x - 15 = 0$

$(2x - 3)(x + 5) = 0$

$2x - 3 = 0$ or $x + 5 = 0$

$ x = \dfrac{3}{2}$ or $ x = -5$

The graph of $y = 2x^2 + 7x - 15$ lies above the x-axis for $x < -5$ and for $x > \dfrac{3}{2}$. Hence $(-\infty, -5) \cup \left(\dfrac{3}{2}, \infty\right)$ is the solution.

12. $4x^2 - 9x + 2 = 0$

$(4x - 1)(x - 2) = 0$

$4x - 1 = 0$ or $x - 2 = 0$

$ x = \dfrac{1}{4}$ or $ x = 2$

The graph of $y = 4x^2 - 9x + 2$ lies below the x-axis for $\dfrac{1}{4} < x < 2$. Hence $\left(\dfrac{1}{4}, 2\right)$ is the solution.

13. $2 - 5x - 3x^2 = 0$

$(2 + x)(1 - 3x) = 0$

$2 + x = 0$ or $1 - 3x = 0$

$ x = -2$ or $ x = \dfrac{1}{3}$

The graph of $y = 2 - 5x - 3x^2$ lies below the x-axis for $x < -2$ and for $x > \dfrac{1}{3}$. Hence $(-\infty, -2) \cup \left(\dfrac{1}{3}, \infty\right)$ is the solution.

14.
$$21 + 4x - x^2 = 0$$
$$(7 - x)(3 + x) = 0$$
$$7 - x = 0 \quad \text{or} \quad 3 + x = 0$$
$$x = 7 \quad \text{or} \quad x = -3$$
The graph of $y = 21 + 4x - x^2$ lies above the x-axis for $-3 < x < 7$. Hence $(-3, 7)$ is the solution.

15.
$$x^3 - x = 0$$
$$x(x^2 - 1) = 0$$
$$x(x + 1)(x - 1) = 0$$
$$x = 0 \quad \text{or} \quad x + 1 = 0 \quad \text{or} \quad x - 1 = 0$$
$$x = 0 \quad \text{or} \quad x = -1 \quad \text{or} \quad x = 1$$
The graph of $y = x^3 - x$ lies above the x-axis for $x > 1$ and for $-1 < x < 0$. Hence $[-1, 0] \cup [1, \infty)$ is the solution.

16.
$$x^3 - x^2 - 30x = 0$$
$$x(x^2 - x - 30) = 0$$
$$x(x - 6)(x + 5) = 0$$
$$x = 0 \quad \text{or} \quad x - 6 = 0 \quad \text{or} \quad x + 5 = 0$$
$$x = 0 \quad \text{or} \quad x = 6 \quad \text{or} \quad x = -5$$
The graph of $y = x^3 - x^2 - 30x$ lies below the x-axis for $x < -5$ and for $0 < x < 6$. Hence $(-\infty, -5] \cup [0, 6]$ is the solution.

17. The graph of $y = x^2 - 4x - 1$ is zero for $x \approx -0.24$ and $x \approx 4.24$, and lies below the x-axis for $-0.24 < x < 4.24$. Hence $(-0.24, 4.24)$ is the approximate solution.

18. The graph of $y = 12x^2 - 25x + 12$ is zero for $x = \dfrac{4}{3}$ and $x = \dfrac{3}{4}$ and lies above the x-axis for $x < \dfrac{3}{4}$ and for $x > \dfrac{4}{3}$. Hence $\left(-\infty, \dfrac{3}{4}\right] \cup \left[\dfrac{4}{3}, \infty\right)$ is the solution.

19.
$$6x^2 - 5x - 4 = 0$$
$$(3x - 4)(2x + 1) = 0$$
$$3x - 4 = 0 \quad \text{or} \quad 2x + 1 = 0$$
$$x = \frac{4}{3} \quad \text{or} \quad x = -\frac{1}{2}$$
The graph of $y = 6x^2 - 5x - 4$ lies above the x-axis for $x < -\dfrac{1}{2}$ and for $x > \dfrac{4}{3}$. Hence $\left(-\infty, -\dfrac{1}{2}\right) \cup \left(\dfrac{4}{3}, \infty\right)$ is the solution.

20.
$$4x^2 - 1 = 0$$
$$(2x + 1)(2x - 1) = 0$$
$$2x + 1 = 0 \quad \text{or} \quad 2x - 1 = 0$$
$$x = -\frac{1}{2} \quad \text{or} \quad x = \frac{1}{2}$$
The graph of $y = 4x^2 - 1$ lies below the x-axis for $-\dfrac{1}{2} < x < \dfrac{1}{2}$. Hence $\left[-\dfrac{1}{2}, \dfrac{1}{2}\right]$ is the solution.

21. The graph of $y = 9x^2 + 12x - 1$ appears to be zero for $x \approx -1.41$ and $x \approx 0.08$. and lies above the x-axis for $x < -1.41$ and $x > 0.08$. Hence $(-\infty, -1.41] \cup [0.08, \infty)$ is the approximate solution.

22. The graph of $y = 4x^2 - 12x + 7$ appears to be zero for $x \approx 0.79$ and $x \approx 2.21$. and lies below the x-axis for $0.79 < x < 2.21$. Hence $(0.79, 2.21)$ is the approximate solution.

23.
$$4x^2 - 4x + 1 = 0$$
$$(2x - 1)(2x - 1) = 0$$
$$(2x - 1)^2 = 0$$
$$2x - 1 = 0$$
$$x = \frac{1}{2}$$
The graph of $y = 4x^2 - 4x + 1$ lies entirely above the x-axis, except at $x = \dfrac{1}{2}$. Hence $\left(-\infty, \dfrac{1}{2}\right) \cup \left(\dfrac{1}{2}, \infty\right)$ is the solution set.

24.
$$x^2 - 6x + 9 = 0$$
$$(x - 3)(x - 3) = 0$$
$$(x - 3)^2 = 0$$
$$x - 3 = 0$$
$$x = 3$$
The graph of $y = x^2 - 6x + 9$ lies entirely above the x-axis, except at $x = 3$. Hence $x = 3$ is the only solution.

25.
$$x^2 - 8x + 16 = 0$$
$$(x - 4)(x - 4) = 0$$
$$(x - 4)^2 = 0$$
$$x - 4 = 0$$
$$x = 4$$
The graph of $y = x^2 - 8x + 16$ lies entirely above the x-axis, except at $x = 4$. Hence there is no solution.

26.
$$9x^2 + 12x + 4 = 0$$
$$(3x + 2)(3x + 2) = 0$$
$$(3x + 2)^2 = 0$$
$$3x + 2 = 0$$
$$x = -\frac{2}{3}$$
The graph of $y = 9x^2 + 12x + 4$ lies entirely above the x-axis, except at $x = -\dfrac{2}{3}$. Hence every real number satisfies the inequality. The solution is $(-\infty, \infty)$.

27. The graph of $y = 3x^3 - 12x + 2$ is zero for $x \approx -2.08$, $x \approx 0.17$, and $x \approx 1.91$ and lies above the x-axis for $-2.08 < x < 0.17$ and $x > 1.91$. Hence, $[-2.08, 0.17] \cup [1.91, \infty)$ is the approximate solution.

28. The graph of $y = 8x - 2x^3 - 1$ is zero for $x \approx -2.06$, $x \approx 0.13$, and $x \approx 1.93$ and lies below the x-axis for $-2.06 < x < 0.13$ and $x > 1.93$. Hence, $(-2.06, 0.13) \cup (1.93, \infty)$ is the approximate solution.

29. $2x^3 + 2x > 5$ is equivalent to $2x^3 + 2x - 5 > 0$. The graph of $y = 2x^3 + 2x - 5$ is zero for $x \approx 1.11$ and lies above the x-axis for $x > 1.11$. So, $(1.11, \infty)$ is the approximate solution.

30. $4 \le 2x^3 + 8x$ is equivalent to $2x^3 + 8x - 4 \ge 0$. The graph of $y = 2x^3 + 8x - 4$ is zero for $x \approx 0.47$ and lies above the x-axis for $x > 0.47$. So, $[0.47, \infty)$ is the approximate solution.

31. Answers may vary. Here are some possibilities.

(a) $x^2 + 1 > 0$

(b) $x^2 + 1 < 0$

(c) $x^2 \le 0$

(d) $(x + 2)(x - 5) \le 0$

(e) $(x + 1)(x - 4) > 0$

(f) $x(x - 4) \ge 0$

32.
$$-16t^2 + 288t - 1152 = 0$$
$$t^2 - 18t + 72 = 0$$
$$(t - 6)(t - 12) = 0$$
$$t - 6 = 0 \quad \text{or} \quad t - 12 = 0$$
$$t = 6 \quad \text{or} \qquad t = 12$$
The graph of $-16t^2 + 288t - 1{,}152$ lies above the t-axis for $6 < t < 12$. Hence $[6, 12]$ is the solution. This agrees with the result obtained in Example 10.

33. $s = -16t^2 + 256t$

   (a)
$$-16t^2 + 256t = 768$$
$$-16t^2 + 256t - 768 = 0$$
$$t^2 - 16t + 48 = 0$$
$$(t - 12)(t - 4) = 0$$
$$t - 12 = 0 \quad \text{or} \quad t - 4 = 0$$
$$t = 12 \quad \text{or} \qquad t = 4$$
   The projectile is 768 ft above ground twice: at $t = 4$ sec, on the way up, and $t = 12$ sec, on the way down.

   (b) The graph of $s = -16t^2 + 256t$ lies above the graph of $s = 768$ for $4 < t < 12$. Hence the projectile's height will be at least 768 ft when t is in the interval $[4, 12]$.

   (c) The graph of $s = -16t^2 + 256t$ lies below the graph of $s = 768$ for $0 < t < 4$ and $12 < t < 16$. Hence the projectile's height will be less than or equal to 768 ft when t is in the interval $(0, 4]$ or $[12, 16)$.

34. $s = -16t^2 + 272t$

   (a)
$$-16t^2 + 272t = 960$$
$$-16t^2 + 272t - 960 = 0$$
$$t^2 - 17t + 60 = 0$$
$$(t - 12)(t - 5) = 0$$
$$t - 12 = 0 \quad \text{or} \quad t - 5 = 0$$
$$t = 12 \quad \text{or} \qquad t = 5$$
   The projectile is 960 ft above ground twice: at $t = 5$ sec, on the way up, and $t = 12$ sec, on the way down.

   (b) The graph of $s = -16t^2 + 272t$ lies above the graph of $s = 960$ for $5 < t < 12$. Hence the projectile's height will be more than 960 ft when t is in the interval $(5, 12)$.

   (c) The graph of $s = -16t^2 + 272t$ lies below the graph of $s = 960$ for $0 < t < 5$ and $12 < t < 17$. Hence the projectile's height will be less than or equal to 960 ft when t is in the interval $(0, 5]$ or $[12, 17)$.

35. Solving the corresponding equation in the process of solving an inequality reveals the boundaries of the solution set. For example, to solve the inequality $x^2 - 4 \le 0$, we first solve the corresponding equation $x^2 - 4 = 0$ and find that $x = \pm 2$. The solution, $[-2, 2]$, of inequality has ± 2 as its boundaries.

36. Let x be her average speed; then $105 < 2x$. Solving this gives $x > 52.5$, so her least average speed is 52.5 mph.

37. (a) Let $x > 0$ be the width of a rectangle; then the length is $2x - 2$ and the perimeter is $P = 2[x + (2x - 2)]$. Solving $P < 200$ and $2x - 2 > 0$ gives 1 in. $< x < 34$ in.
$$2[x + (2x - 2)] < 200 \quad \text{and} \quad 2x - 2 > 0$$
$$2(3x - 2) < 200 \qquad\qquad\qquad 2x > 2$$
$$6x - 4 < 200 \qquad\qquad\qquad\quad x > 1$$
$$6x < 204$$
$$x < 34$$

(b) The area is $A = x(2x - 2)$. We already know $x > 1$ from part (a). Solve $A \le 1200$.
$$x(2x - 2) = 1200$$
$$2x^2 - 2x - 1200 = 0$$
$$x^2 - x - 600 = 0$$
$$(x - 25)(x + 24) = 0$$
$$x - 25 = 0 \quad \text{or} \quad x + 24 = 0$$
$$x = 25 \quad \text{or} \qquad x = -24$$
The graph of $y = 2x^2 - 2x - 1200$ lies below the x-axis for $1 < x < 25$, so $A \le 1200$ when x is in the interval $(1, 25]$.

38. Substitute 20 and 40 into the equation $P = \dfrac{400}{V}$ to find the range for P: $P = \dfrac{400}{20} = 20$ and $P = \dfrac{400}{40} = 10$. The pressure can range from 10 to 20, or $10 \le P \le 20$. Alternatively, solve graphically: graph $y = \dfrac{400}{x}$ on $[20, 40] \times [0, 30]$ and observe that all y-values are between 10 and 20.

39. Let x be the amount borrowed; then $\dfrac{200{,}000 + x}{50{,}000 + x} \ge 2$. Solving for x reveals that the company can borrow no more than \$100,000.

40. False. If b is negative, there are no solutions, because the absolute value of a number is always nonnegative and every nonnegative real number is greater than any negative real number.

41. True. The absolute value of any real number is always nonnegative, i.e., greater than or equal to zero.

42. $|x - 2| < 3$
$$-3 < x - 2 < 3$$
$$-1 < x < 5$$
$$(-1, 5)$$
The answer is E.

43. The graph of $y = x^2 - 2x + 2$ lies entirely above the x-axis so $x^2 - 2x + 2 \ge 0$ for all real numbers x. The answer is D.

44. $x^2 > x$ is true for all negative x, and for positive x when $x > 1$. So the solution is $(-\infty, 0) \cup (1, \infty)$. The answer is A.

45. $x^2 \le 1$ implies $-1 \le x \le 1$, so the solution is $[-1, 1]$. The answer is D.

46. (a) The lengths of the sides of the box are x, $12 - 2x$, and $15 - 2x$, so the volume is $x(12 - 2x)(15 - 2x)$. To solve $x(12 - 2x)(15 - 2x) = 125$, graph $y = x(12 - 2x)(15 - 2x)$ and $y = 125$ and find where the graphs intersect: Either $x \approx 0.94$ in. or $x \approx 3.78$ in.

   (b) The graph of $y = x(12 - 2x)(15 - 2x)$ lies above the graph of $y = 125$ for $0.94 < y < 3.78$ (approximately). So choosing x in the interval $(0.94, 3.78)$ will yield a box with volume greater than 125 in^3.

   (c) The graph of $y = x(12 - 2x)(15 - 2x)$ lies below the graph of $y = 125$ for $0 < y < 0.94$ and for $3.78 < x < 6$ (approximately). So choosing x in either interval $(0, 0.94)$ or interval $(3.78, 6)$ will yield a box with volume at most 125 in^3.

47. $2x^2 + 7x - 15 = 10$ or $2x^2 + 7x - 15 = -10$
$2x^2 + 7x - 25 = 0$ $\quad\quad$ $2x^2 + 7x - 5 = 0$
The graph of $\quad\quad\quad\quad$ The graph of
$y = 2x^2 + 7x - 25$ $\quad\quad$ $y = 2x^2 + 7x - 5$
appears to be zero for $\quad$ appears to be zero for
$x \approx -5.69$ and $x \approx 2.19$ $\quad$ $x \approx -4.11$ and $x \approx 0.61$
Now look at the graphs of $y = |2x^2 + 7x - 15|$ and
$y = 10$. The graph of $y = |2x^2 + 7x - 15|$ lies below the
graph of $y = 10$ when $-5.69 < x < -4.11$ and when
$0.61 < x < 2.19$. Hence $(-5.69, -4.11) \cup (0.61, 2.19)$ is
the approximate solution.

48. $2x^2 + 3x - 20 = 10$ or $2x^2 + 3x - 20 = -10$
$2x^2 + 3x - 30 = 0$ $\quad\quad$ $2x^2 + 3x - 10 = 0$
The graph of $\quad\quad\quad\quad$ The graph of
$y = 2x^2 + 3x - 30$ $\quad\quad$ $y = 2x^2 + 3x - 10$
appears to be zero for $\quad$ appears to be zero for
$x \approx -4.69$ and $x \approx 3.19$ $\quad$ $x \approx -3.11$ and $x \approx 1.61$
Now look at the graphs of $y = |2x^2 + 3x - 20|$ and
$y = 10$. The graph of $y = |2x^2 + 7x - 20|$ lies above the
graph of $y = 10$ when $x < -4.69$, $-3.11 < x < 1.61$, and
$x > 3.19$. Hence $(-\infty, -4.69] \cup [-3.11, 1.61] \cup [3.19, \infty)$
is the (approximate) solution.

■ Chapter P Review

1. Endpoints 0 and 5; bounded

2. Endpoint 2; unbounded

3. $2(x^2 - x) = 2x^2 - 2x$

4. $2x^3 + 4x^2 = 2x^2 \cdot x + 2x^2 \cdot 2 = 2x^2(x + 2)$

5. $\dfrac{(uv^2)^3}{v^2u^3} = \dfrac{u^3v^6}{u^3v^2} = v^4$

6. $(3x^2y^3)^{-2} = \dfrac{1}{(3x^2y^3)^2} = \dfrac{1}{3^2(x^2)^2(y^3)^2} = \dfrac{1}{9x^4y^6}$

7. 3.68×10^9

8. 7×10^{-6}

9. 5,000,000,000

10. 0.000 000 000 000 000 000 000 000 000 910 94
(27 zeros between the decimal point and the first 9)

11. **(a)** 5.0711×10^{10}

$\quad$ **(b)** 4.63×10^9

$\quad$ **(c)** 5.0×10^8

$\quad$ **(d)** 3.995×10^9

$\quad$ **(e)** 1.4497×10^{10}

12. $-0.\overline{45}$ (repeating)

13. **(a)** Distance: $|14 - (-5)| = |19| = 19$

$\quad$ **(b)** Midpoint: $\dfrac{-5 + 14}{2} = \dfrac{9}{2} = 4.5$

14. **(a)** Distance:
$$\sqrt{[5 - (-4)]^2 + (-1 - 3)^2} = \sqrt{9^2 + (-4)^2}$$
$$= \sqrt{81 + 16} = \sqrt{97} \approx 9.85$$

$\quad$ **(b)** Midpoint:
$$\left(\frac{-4 + 5}{2}, \frac{3 + (-1)}{2}\right) = \left(\frac{1}{2}, \frac{2}{2}\right) = \left(\frac{1}{2}, 1\right)$$

15. The three side lengths (distances between pairs of points) are
$$\sqrt{[3 - (-2)]^2 + (11 - 1)^2} = \sqrt{5^2 + 10^2}$$
$$= \sqrt{25 + 100} = \sqrt{125} = 5\sqrt{5}$$
$$\sqrt{(7 - 3)^2 + (9 - 11)^2} = \sqrt{4^2 + (-2)^2}$$
$$= \sqrt{16 + 4} = \sqrt{20} = 2\sqrt{5}$$
$$\sqrt{[7 - (-2)]^2 + (9 - 1)^2} = \sqrt{9^2 + 8^2}$$
$$= \sqrt{81 + 64} = \sqrt{145}.$$
Since $(2\sqrt{5})^2 + (5\sqrt{5})^2 = 20 + 125 = 145 = (\sqrt{145})^2$
—the sum of the squares of the two shorter side lengths
equals the square of the long side length—the points
determine a right triangle.

16. The three side lengths (distances between pairs of points) are
$$\sqrt{(4 - 0)^2 + (1 - 1)^2} = \sqrt{4^2 + 0^2} = \sqrt{16} = 4$$
$$\sqrt{(2 - 0)^2 + [(1 - 2\sqrt{3}) - 1]^2} = \sqrt{2^2 + (-2\sqrt{3})^2}$$
$$= \sqrt{4 + 12} = \sqrt{16} = 4$$
$$\sqrt{(4 - 2)^2 + [1 - (1 - 2\sqrt{3})]^2} = \sqrt{2^2 + (2\sqrt{3})^2}$$
$$= \sqrt{4 + 12} = \sqrt{16} = 4.$$
Since all three sides have the same length, the figure is an
equilateral triangle.

17. $(x - 0)^2 + (y - 0)^2 = 2^2$, or $x^2 + y^2 = 4$

18. $(x - 5)^2 + [y - (-3)]^2 = 4^2$, or
$(x - 5)^2 + (y + 3)^2 = 16$

19. $[x - (-5)]^2 + [y - (-4)]^2 = 3^2$, so the center is
$(-5, -4)$ and the radius is 3.

20. $(x - 0)^2 + (y - 0)^2 = 1^2$, so the center is $(0, 0)$ and the
radius is 1.

21. **(a)** Distance between $(-3, 2)$ and $(-1, -2)$:
$$\sqrt{(-2 - 2)^2 + [-1 - (-3)]^2} = \sqrt{(-4)^2 + (2)^2}$$
$$= \sqrt{16 + 4} = \sqrt{20} \approx 4.47$$
$\quad\quad$ Distance between $(-3, 2)$ and $(5, 6)$:
$$\sqrt{(6 - 2)^2 + [5 - (-3)]^2} = \sqrt{4^2 + 8^2}$$
$$= \sqrt{16 + 64} = \sqrt{80} \approx 8.94$$
$\quad\quad$ Distance between $(5, 6)$ and $(-1, -2)$:
$$\sqrt{(-2 - 6)^2 + (-1 - 5)^2} = \sqrt{(-8)^2 + (-6)^2}$$
$$= \sqrt{64 + 36} = \sqrt{100} = 10$$

$\quad$ **(b)** $(\sqrt{20})^2 + (\sqrt{80})^2 = 20 + 80 = 100 = 10^2$, so the
Pythagorean Theorem guarantees the triangle is a
right triangle.

22. $|z - (-3)| \leq 1$, or $|z + 3| \leq 1$

23. $\dfrac{-1 + a}{2} = 3$ and $\dfrac{1 + b}{2} = 5$
$\quad\quad -1 + a = 6 \quad\quad\quad 1 + b = 10$
$\quad\quad\quad\quad a = 7 \quad\quad\quad\quad\quad b = 9$

24. $m = \dfrac{-5 + 2}{4 + 1} = -\dfrac{3}{5}$

25. $y + 1 = -\dfrac{2}{3}(x - 2)$

26. The slope is $m = -\dfrac{9}{7} = -\dfrac{A}{B}$, so we can choose $A = 9$ and $B = 7$. Since $x = -5$, $y = 4$ solves $9x + 7y + C = 0$, C must equal 17: $9x + 7y + 17 = 0$. Note that the coefficients can be multiplied by any non-zero number, e.g., another answer would be $18x + 14y + 34 = 0$.

27. Beginning with point-slope form: $y + 2 = \dfrac{4}{5}(x - 3)$, so $y = \dfrac{4}{5}x - 4.4$.

28. $m = \dfrac{2 + 4}{3 + 1} = \dfrac{3}{2}$, so in point-slope form, $y + 4 = \dfrac{3}{2}(x + 1)$, and therefore $y = \dfrac{3}{2}x - \dfrac{5}{2}$.

29. $y = 4$

30. Solve for y: $y = \dfrac{3}{4}x - \dfrac{7}{4}$.

31. The slope of the given line is the same as the line we want: $m = -\dfrac{2}{5}$, so $y + 3 = -\dfrac{2}{5}(x - 2)$, and therefore $y = -\dfrac{2}{5}x - \dfrac{11}{5}$.

32. The slope of the given line is $-\dfrac{2}{5}$, so the slope of the line we seek is $m = \dfrac{5}{2}$. Then $y + 3 = \dfrac{5}{2}(x - 2)$, and therefore $y = \dfrac{5}{2}x - 8$.

33. (a)

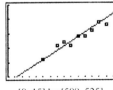

[0, 15] by [500, 525]

(b) Slope of the line between the points $(5, 506)$ and $(10, 514)$ is $m = \dfrac{514 - 506}{10 - 5} = \dfrac{8}{5} = 1.6$.

Using the *point-slope form* equation for the line, we have $y - 506 = 1.6(x - 5)$, so $y = 1.6x + 498$.

[0, 15] by [500, 525]

(c) The year 1996 is represented by $x = 6$. Using $y = 1.6x + 498$ and $x = 6$, we estimate the average SAT math score in 1996 to be 507.6, which is very close to the actual value 508.

(d) The year 2006 is represented by $x = 16$. Using $y = 1.6x + 498$ and $x = 16$, we predict the average SAT math score in 2006 will be 524.

34. (a) $4x - 3y = -33$, or $y = \dfrac{4}{3}x + 11$

(b) $3x + 4y = -6$, or $y = -\dfrac{3}{4}x - \dfrac{3}{2}$

35. $m = \dfrac{25}{10} = \dfrac{5}{2} = 2.5$

36. Both graphs look the same, but the graph on the left has slope $\dfrac{2}{3}$—less than the slope of the one on the right, which is $\dfrac{12}{15} = \dfrac{4}{5}$. The different horizontal and vertical scales for the two windows make it difficult to judge by looking at the graphs.

37. $3x - 4 = 6x + 5$
$-3x = 9$
$x = -3$

38. $\dfrac{x - 2}{3} + \dfrac{x + 5}{2} = \dfrac{1}{3}$
$2(x - 2) + 3(x + 5) = 2$
$2x - 4 + 3x + 15 = 2$
$5x + 11 = 2$
$5x = -9$
$x = -\dfrac{9}{5}$

39. $2(5 - 2y) - 3(1 - y) = y + 1$
$10 - 4y - 3 + 3y = y + 1$
$7 - y = y + 1$
$-2y = -6$
$y = 3$

40. $3(3x - 1)^2 = 21$
$(3x - 1)^2 = 7$
$3x - 1 = \pm\sqrt{7}$
$3x - 1 = -\sqrt{7}$ or $3x - 1 = \sqrt{7}$
$x = \dfrac{1}{3} - \dfrac{\sqrt{7}}{3} \approx -0.55$ $x = \dfrac{1}{3} + \dfrac{\sqrt{7}}{3} \approx 1.22$

41. $x^2 - 4x - 3 = 0$
$x^2 - 4x = 3$
$x^2 - 4x + (2)^2 = 3 + (2)^2$
$(x - 2)^2 = 7$
$x - 2 = \pm\sqrt{7}$
$x - 2 = -\sqrt{7}$ or $x - 2 = \sqrt{7}$
$x = 2 - \sqrt{7} \approx -0.65$ $x = 2 + \sqrt{7} \approx 4.65$

42. $16x^2 - 24x + 7 = 0$
Using the quadratic formula:
$x = \dfrac{24 \pm \sqrt{24^2 - 4(16)(7)}}{2(16)}$
$= \dfrac{24 \pm \sqrt{128}}{32} = \dfrac{3}{4} \pm \dfrac{\sqrt{2}}{4}$
$x = \dfrac{3}{4} - \dfrac{\sqrt{2}}{4} \approx 0.40$ or $x = \dfrac{3}{4} + \dfrac{\sqrt{2}}{4} \approx 1.10$

43. $6x^2 + 7x = 3$
$6x^2 + 7x - 3 = 0$
$(3x - 1)(2x + 3) = 0$
$3x - 1 = 0$ or $2x + 3 = 0$
$x = \dfrac{1}{3}$ or $x = -\dfrac{3}{2}$

44. $2x^2 + 8x = 0$
$2x(x + 4) = 0$
$2x = 0$ or $x + 4 = 0$
$x = 0$ or $x = -4$

45. $x(2x + 5) = 4(x + 7)$
$2x^2 + 5x = 4x + 28$
$2x^2 + x - 28 = 0$
$(2x - 7)(x + 4) = 0$
$2x - 7 = 0$ or $x + 4 = 0$
$x = \dfrac{7}{2}$ or $x = -4$

46. $4x + 1 = 3$ or $4x + 1 = -3$
$4x = 2$ or $4x = -4$
$x = \dfrac{1}{2}$ or $x = -1$

47. $4x^2 - 20x + 25 = 0$
$(2x - 5)(2x - 5) = 0$
$(2x - 5)^2 = 0$
$2x - 5 = 0$
$x = \dfrac{5}{2}$

48. $-9x^2 + 12x - 4 = 0$
$9x^2 - 12x + 4 = 0$
$(3x - 2)(3x - 2) = 0$
$(3x - 2)^2 = 0$
$3x - 2 = 0$
$x = \dfrac{2}{3}$

49. $x^2 = 3x$
$x^2 - 3x = 0$
$x(x - 3) = 0$
$x = 0$ or $x - 3 = 0$
$x = 0$ or $x = 3$

50. Solving $4x^2 - 4x + 2 = 0$ by using the quadratic formula with $a = 4$, $b = -4$, and $c = 2$ gives
$$x = \frac{4 \pm \sqrt{(-4)^2 - 4(4)(2)}}{2(4)} = \frac{4 \pm \sqrt{-16}}{8}$$
$$= \frac{4 \pm 4i}{8} = \frac{1}{2} \pm \frac{1}{2}i$$

51. Solving $x^2 - 6x + 13 = 0$ by using the quadratic formula with $a = 1$, $b = -6$, and $c = 13$ gives
$$x = \frac{6 \pm \sqrt{(-6)^2 - 4(1)(13)}}{2(1)} = \frac{6 \pm \sqrt{-16}}{2}$$
$$= \frac{6 \pm 4i}{2} = 3 \pm 2i$$

52. Solving $x^2 - 2x + 4 = 0$ by using the quadratic formula with $a = 1$, $b = -2$, and $c = 4$ gives
$$x = \frac{2 \pm \sqrt{(-2)^2 - 4(1)(4)}}{2(1)} = \frac{2 \pm \sqrt{-12}}{2}$$
$$= \frac{2 \pm 2i\sqrt{3}}{2} = 1 \pm \sqrt{3}i$$

53. $2x^2 - 3x - 1 = 0$
$$x^2 - \frac{3}{2}x - \frac{1}{2} = 0$$
$$x^2 - \frac{3}{2}x + \left(-\frac{3}{4}\right)^2 = \frac{1}{2} + \left(-\frac{3}{4}\right)^2$$
$$\left(x - \frac{3}{4}\right)^2 = \frac{17}{16}$$
$$x - \frac{3}{4} = \pm\frac{\sqrt{17}}{4}$$
$$x = \frac{3}{4} \pm \frac{\sqrt{17}}{4}$$
$$x = \frac{3}{4} - \frac{\sqrt{17}}{4} \approx -0.28 \quad \text{or} \quad x = \frac{3}{4} + \frac{\sqrt{17}}{4} \approx 1.78$$

54. $3x^2 + 4x - 1 = 0$
$$x = \frac{-4 \pm \sqrt{(4)^2 - 4(3)(-1)}}{2(3)}$$
$$= \frac{-4 \pm \sqrt{28}}{6} = -\frac{2}{3} \pm \frac{\sqrt{7}}{3}$$
$$x = -\frac{2}{3} - \frac{\sqrt{7}}{3} \approx -1.55 \quad \text{or} \quad x = -\frac{2}{3} + \frac{\sqrt{7}}{3} \approx 0.22$$

55. The graph of $y = 3x^3 - 19x^2 - 14x$ is zero for $x = 0$, $x = -\dfrac{2}{3}$, and $x = 7$.

56. The graph of $y = x^3 + 2x^2 - 4x - 8$ is zero for $x = -2$, and $x = 2$.

57. The graph of $y = x^3 - 2x^2 - 2$ is zero for $x \approx 2.36$.

58. The graph of $y = |2x - 1| - 4 + x^2$ is zero for $x = -1$ and for $x \approx 1.45$.

59. $-2 < x + 4 \le 7$
$-6 < x \le 3$
Hence $(-6, 3]$ is the solution.

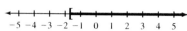

60. $5x + 1 \ge 2x - 4$
$3x \ge -5$
$x \ge -\dfrac{5}{3}$
Hence $\left[-\dfrac{5}{3}, \infty\right)$ is the solution.

61. $\dfrac{3x - 5}{4} \le -1$
$3x - 5 \le -4$
$3x \le 1$
$x \le \dfrac{1}{3}$
Hence $\left(-\infty, \dfrac{1}{3}\right]$ is the solution.

62. $-7 < 2x - 5 < 7$
$-2 < 2x < 12$
$-1 < x < 6$
Hence $(-1, 6)$ is the solution.

63. $3x + 4 \geq 2$ or $3x + 4 \leq -2$

$\qquad 3x \geq -2$ or $3x \leq -6$

$\qquad x \geq -\dfrac{2}{3}$ or $x \leq -2$

Hence $(-\infty, -2] \cup \left[-\dfrac{2}{3}, \infty\right)$ is the solution.

64. $4x^2 + 3x - 10 = 0$

$(4x - 5)(x + 2) = 0$

$4x - 5 = 0$ or $x + 2 = 0$

$\qquad x = \dfrac{5}{4}$ or $\qquad x = -2$

The graph of $y = 4x^2 + 3x - 10$ lies above the x-axis for $x < -2$ and for $x > \dfrac{5}{4}$. Hence $(-\infty, -2) \cup \left(\dfrac{5}{4}, \infty\right)$ is the solution.

65. The graph of $y = 2x^2 - 2x - 1$ is zero for $x \approx -0.37$ and $x \approx 1.37$, and lies above the x-axis for $x < -0.37$ and for $x > 1.37$. Hence $(-\infty, -0.37) \cup (1.37, \infty)$ is the approximate solution.

66. The graph of $y = 9x^2 - 12x - 1$ is zero for $x \approx -0.08$, and $x \approx 1.41$, and lies below the x-axis for $-0.08 < x < 1.41$. Hence $[-0.08, 1.41]$ is the approximate solution.

67. $x^3 - 9x \leq 3$ is equivalent to $x^3 - 9x - 3 \leq 0$. The graph of $y = x^3 - 9x - 3$ is zero for $x \approx -2.82$, $x \approx -0.34$, and $x \approx 3.15$, and lies below the x-axis for $x < -2.82$ and for $-0.34 < x < 3.15$. Hence the approximate solution is $(-\infty, -2.82] \cup [-0.34, 3.15]$.

68. The graph of $y = 4x^3 - 9x + 2$ is zero for $x \approx -1.60$, $x \approx 0.23$, and $x \approx 1.37$, and lies above the x-axis for $-1.60 < x < 0.23$ and for $x > 1.37$. Hence the approximate solution is $(-1.60, 0.23) \cup (1.37, \infty)$.

69. $\dfrac{x + 7}{5} > 2$ or $\dfrac{x + 7}{5} < -2$

$x + 7 > 10$ $\qquad$ or $\quad$ $x + 7 < -10$

$\qquad x > 3$ $\qquad\quad$ or $\qquad$ $x < -17$

Hence $(-\infty, -17) \cup (3, \infty)$ is the solution.

70. $2x^2 + 3x - 35 = 0$

$(2x - 7)(x + 5) = 0$

$2x - 7 = 0$ or $x + 5 = 0$

$\qquad x = \dfrac{7}{2}$ or $\qquad x = -5$

The graph of $y = 2x^2 + 3x - 35$ lies below the x-axis for $-5 < x < \dfrac{7}{2}$. Hence $\left(-5, \dfrac{7}{2}\right)$ is the solution.

71. $4x^2 + 12x + 9 = 0$

$(2x + 3)(2x + 3) = 0$

$\qquad (2x + 3)^2 = 0$

$\qquad\quad 2x + 3 = 0$

$\qquad\qquad x = -\dfrac{3}{2}$

The graph of $y = 4x^2 + 12x + 9$ lies entirely above the x-axis except for $x = -\dfrac{3}{2}$. Hence all real numbers satisfy the inequality. So $(-\infty, \infty)$ is the solution.

72. $x^2 - 6x + 9 = 0$

$(x - 3)(x - 3) = 0$

$\qquad (x - 3)^2 = 0$

$\qquad\quad x - 3 = 0$

$\qquad\qquad x = 3$

The graph of $y = x^2 - 6x + 9$ lies entirely above the x-axis except for $x = 3$. Hence no real number satisfies the inequality. There is no solution.

73. $(3 - 2i) + (-2 + 5i) = (3 - 2) + (-2 + 5)i$
$\qquad\qquad\qquad\qquad = 1 + 3i$

74. $(5 - 7i) - (3 - 2i) = (5 - 3) + (-7 + 2)i$
$\qquad\qquad\qquad\qquad = 2 - 5i$

75. $(1 + 2i)(3 - 2i) = 3 - 2i + 6i - 4i^2$
$\qquad\qquad\qquad\quad = 3 + 4i + 4$
$\qquad\qquad\qquad\quad = 7 + 4i$

76. $(1 + i)^3 = ((1 + i)(1 + i))(1 + i)$
$\qquad\qquad = (1 + 2i + i^2)(1 + i) = 2i(1 + i)$
$\qquad\qquad = 2i + 2i^2 = -2 + 2i$

77. $(1 + 2i)^2(1 - 2i)^2 = (1 + 4i + 4i^2)(1 - 4i + 4i^2)$
$\qquad\qquad\qquad\qquad = (-3 + 4i)(-3 - 4i)$
$\qquad\qquad\qquad\qquad = 9 - 12i + 12i - 16i^2 = 25$

78. $i^{29} = i^{28}i = (i^2)^{14}\,i = (-1)^{14}\,i = i$

79. $\sqrt{-16} = \sqrt{(16)(-1)} = 4\sqrt{-1} = 4i$

80. $\dfrac{2 + 3i}{1 - 5i} = \dfrac{2 + 3i}{1 - 5i} \cdot \dfrac{1 + 5i}{1 + 5i} = \dfrac{2 + 10i + 3i + 15i^2}{1 + 5i - 5i - 25i^2}$

$\qquad = \dfrac{-13 + 13i}{26} = -\dfrac{1}{2} + \dfrac{1}{2}i$

81. $s = -16t^2 + 320t$

(a) $-16t^2 + 320t = 1538$

$-16t^2 + 320t - 1538 = 0$

The graph of $s = -16t^2 + 320t - 1538$ is zero at

$t = \dfrac{-320 \pm \sqrt{320^2 - 4(-16)(-1538)}}{2(-16)}$

$\quad = \dfrac{-320 \pm \sqrt{3968}}{-32} = \dfrac{40 \pm \sqrt{62}}{4}$.

So $t = \dfrac{40 - \sqrt{62}}{4} \approx 8.03$ sec or

$t = \dfrac{40 + \sqrt{62}}{4} \approx 11.97$.

The projectile is 1538 ft above ground twice: at $t \approx 8$ sec, on the way up, and at $t \approx 12$ sec, on the way down.

(b) The graph of $s = -16t^2 + 320t$ lies below the graph of $s = 1538$ for $0 < t < 8$ and for $12 < t < 20$ (approximately). Hence the projectile's height will be at most 1538 ft when t is in the interval $(0, 8]$ or $[12, 20)$ (approximately).

(c) The graph of $s = -16t^2 + 320t$ lies above the graph of $s = 1538$ for $8 < t < 12$ (approximately). Hence the projectile's height will be greater than or equal to 1538 when t is in the interval $[8, 12]$ (approximately).

82. Let the take-off point be located at $(0, 0)$. We want the slope between $(0, 0)$ and $(d, 20{,}000)$ to be $\frac{4}{9}$.

$$\frac{20{,}000 - 0}{d - 0} = \frac{4}{9}$$
$$180{,}000 = 4d$$
$$45{,}000 = d$$

The airplane must fly 45,000 ft horizontally to reach an altitude of 20,000 ft.

83. (a) Let $w > 0$ be the width of a rectangle; the length is $3w + 1$ and the perimeter is $P = 2[w + (3w + 1)]$. Solve $P \le 150$.

$$2[w + (3w + 1)] \le 150$$
$$2(4w + 1) \le 150$$
$$8w + 2 \le 150$$
$$8w \le 148$$
$$w \le 18.5$$

Thus $P \le 150$ cm when w is in the interval $(0, 18.5]$.

(b) The area is $A = w(3w + 1)$. Solve $A > 1500$.

$$w(3w + 1) > 1500$$
$$3w^2 + w - 1550 > 0$$

The graph of $A = 3w^2 + w - 1500$ appears to be zero for $w \approx 22.19$ when w is positive, and lies above the w-axis for $w > 22.19$. Hence, $A > 1500$ when w is in the interval $(22.19, \infty)$ (approximately).

■ Section 1.1 Modeling and Equation Solving

Exploration 1

1. $k = \dfrac{d}{m} = \dfrac{100 - 25}{100} = \dfrac{75}{100} = 0.75$

2. $t = 6.5\% + 0.5\% = 7\%$ or 0.07

3. $m = \dfrac{d}{k}$, $s = d + td$

   $s = pm$

   $p = \dfrac{s}{m} = \dfrac{d + td}{\dfrac{d}{k}} = \dfrac{d + td}{1} \cdot \dfrac{k}{d} = \dfrac{d(1 + t)}{1} \cdot \dfrac{k}{d}$

   $= \dfrac{k(1 + t)}{1} = (0.75)(1.07) = 0.8025$

4. Yes, because $\$36.99 \times 0.8025 = \$29.68$.

5. $\$100 \div 0.8025 = \$124.61$

Exploration 2

1. Because the linear model maintains a constant positive slope, it will eventually reach the point where 100% of the prisoners are female. It will then continue to rise, giving percentages above 100%, which are impossible.

2. Yes, because 2009 is still close to the data we are modeling. We would have much less confidence in the linear model for predicting the percentage 25 years from 2000.

3. One possible answer: Males are heavily dominant in violent crime statistics, while female crimes tend to be property crimes like burglary or shoplifting. Since property crimes rates are senstive to economic conditions, a statistician might look for adverse economic factors in 1990, especially those that would affect people near or below the poverty level.

4. Yes. Table 1.1 shows that the minimum wage worker had less purchasing power in 1990 than in any other year since 1955, which gives some evidence of adverse economic conditions among lower-income Americans that year. Nonetheless, a careful sociologist would certainly want to look at other data before claiming a connection between this statistic and the female crime rate.

Quick Review 1.1

1. $(x + 4)(x - 4)$

2. $(x + 5)(x + 5)$

3. $(9y + 2)(9y - 2)$

4. $3x(x^2 - 5x + 6) = 3x(x - 2)(x - 3)$

5. $(4h^2 + 9)(4h^2 - 9) = (4h^2 + 9)(2h + 3)(2h - 3)$

6. $(x + h)(x + h)$

7. $(x + 4)(x - 1)$

8. $x^2 - 3x + 4$

9. $(2x - 1)(x - 5)$

10. $(x^2 + 5)(x^2 - 4) = (x^2 + 5)(x + 2)(x - 2)$

Section 1.1 Exercises

1. (d) (q)

2. (f) (r)

3. (a) (p)

4. (h) (o)

5. (e) (l)

6. (b) (s)

7. (g) (t)

8. (j) (k)

9. (i) (m)

10. (c) (n)

11. **(a)** The percentage increased from 1954 to 1999 and then decreased slightly from 1999 to 2004.

    (b) The greatest increase occurred between 1974 and 1979.

12. **(a)** Except for some minor fluctuations, the percentage has been decreasing overall.

    (b) The greatest decrease occurred between 1979 and 1984.

13. Women (□), Men (+)

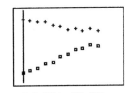

[−5, 55] by [23, 92]

14. Vice versa: The female percentages are increasing faster than the male percentages are decreasing.

15. To find the equation, first find the slope.

    Women: Slope $= \dfrac{\text{change in } y}{\text{change in } x} = \dfrac{58.5 - 32.3}{1999 - 1954} = \dfrac{26.2}{45}$
    $= 0.582$. The y-intercept is 32.3, so the equation of the line is $y = 0.582x + 32.3$.

    Men: Slope $= \dfrac{74.0 - 83.5}{1999 - 1954} = \dfrac{-9.5}{45} = -0.211$. The
    y-intercept is 83.5, so the equation of the line is
    $y = -0.211x + 83.5$.

    In both cases, x represents the number of years after 1954.

16. 2009 is 55 years since 1954, so $x = 55$.
    Women: $y = (0.582)(55) + 32.3 \approx 64.3\%$
    Men: $y = (-0.211)(55) + 83.5 \approx 71.9\%$

17. For the percentages to be the same, we need to set the two equations equal to each other.

$$0.582x + 32.3 = -0.211x + 83.5$$
$$0.793x = 51.2$$
$$x \approx 64.6$$

So, approximately 65 years after 1954 (2018), the models predict that the percentages will be about the same. To check:

Males: $y = (-0.211)(65) + 83.5 \approx 69.9\%$
Females: $y = (0.582)(65) + 32.3 \approx 69.9\%$

18. The linear equations will eventually give percentages above 100% for women and below 0% for men, neither of which is possible.

19.

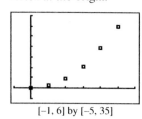

20. Let h be the height of the rectangular cake in inches. The volume of the rectangular cake is
$V_1 = 9 \cdot 13 \cdot h = 117h$ in.^{3}
The volume of the round cake is
$V_2 = \pi(4)^2(2h) \approx 3.14 \cdot 16 \cdot 2h = 100.48h$ in.^{3}
The rectangular cake gives a greater amount of cake for the same price.

21. Because all stepping stones have the same thickness, what matters is area.
The area of a square stepping stone is
$A_1 = 12 \cdot 12 = 144$ in.^{2}
The area of a round stepping stone is
$A_2 = \pi \left(\dfrac{13}{2}\right)^2 \approx 3.14(6.5)^2 = 132.665$ in.^{2}

The square stones give a greater amount of rock for the same price.

22. (a) $t = \frac{1}{4}\sqrt{180} \approx 3.35$ sec

(b) $d = 16(12.5)^2 = 2500$ ft

23. A scatter plot of the data suggests a parabola with its vertex at the origin.

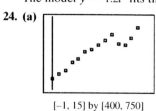

[−1, 6] by [−5, 35]

The model $y = 1.2t^2$ fits the data.

24. (a)

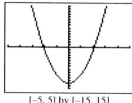

[−1, 15] by [400, 750]

(b) To find the equation, first find the slope:
$$\text{Slope} = \frac{666.1 - 452.2}{2000 - 1991} = \frac{213.9}{9} \approx 23.77.$$
The y-intercept is 452.3, so the equation of the line is
$y = 23.77x + 452.3$.

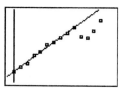

[−1, 15] by [400, 750]

(c) To find the year the number of passengers should reach 900, let $y = 900$, and solve the equation for x. $900 = 23.77x + 452.3$; $x \approx 19$, so by the model, the number of passengers should reach 900 million by 2010 (1991 + 19).

(d) The terrorist attacks on September 11, 2001, caused a major disruption in American air traffic from which the airline industry was slow to recover.

25. The lower line shows the minimum salaries, since they are lower than the average salaries.

26. The points that show the 1990 salaries are the Year 10 points. Both graphs show unprecedented increases in that year. Note: At year 10 the minimum salary jumps, but at year 11 the average salary jumps.

27. The 1995 points are third from the right, Year 15, on both graphs. There is a clear drop in the average salary right after the 1994 strike.

28. One possible answer: **(a)** The players will be happy to see the average salary continue to rise at this rate. The discrepancy between the minimum salary and the average salary will not bother baseball players like it would factory workers, because they are happy to be in the major leagues with the chance to become a star. **(b)** The team owners are not happy with this graph because it shows that their top players are being paid more and more money, forcing them to pay higher salaries to be competitive. This benefits the wealthiest owners. **(c)** Fans are unhappy with the higher ticket prices and with the emphasis on money in baseball rather than team loyalty. Fans of less wealthy teams are unhappy that rich owners are able to pay high salaries to build super-teams filled with talented free agents.

29. Adding $2v^2 + 5$ to both sides gives $3v^2 = 13$. Divide both sides by 3 to get $v^2 = \dfrac{13}{3}$, so $v = \pm\sqrt{\dfrac{13}{3}}$.

$3v^2 = 13$ is equivalent to $3v^2 - 13 = 0$. The graph of $y = 3v^2 - 13$ is zero for $v \approx -2.08$ and for $v \approx 2.08$.

[−5, 5] by [−15, 15]

30. $x + 11 = \pm 11$ so $x = -11 \pm 11$, which gives $x = -22$ or $x = 0$.

$(x + 11)^2 = 121$ is equivalent to $(x + 11)^2 - 121 = 0$. The graph of $y = (x + 11)^2 - 121$ is zero for $x = -22$ and for $x = 0$.

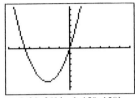

[–30, 30] by [–150, 150]

31. $2x^2 - 5x + 2 = x^2 - 5x + 6 + 3x$

$x^2 - 3x - 4 = 0$

$(x - 4)(x + 1) = 0$

$x - 4 = 0$ or $x + 1 = 0$

$x = 4$ or $x = -1$

$2x^2 - 5x + 2 = (x - 3)(x - 2) + 3x$ is equivalent to $2x^2 - 8x + 2 - (x - 3)(x - 2) = 0$. The graph of $y = 2x^2 - 8x + 2 - (x - 3)(x - 2)$ is zero for $x = -1$ and for $x = 4$.

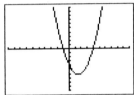

[–10, 10] by [–10, 10]

32.
$$x^2 - 7x = \frac{3}{4}$$

$$x^2 - 7x + \left(-\frac{7}{2}\right)^2 = 0.75 + \left(-\frac{7}{2}\right)^2$$

$$(x - 3.5)^2 = 0.75 + 12.25$$

$$x - 3.5 = \pm \sqrt{13}$$

$$x = 3.5 \pm \sqrt{13}$$

The graph of $y = x^2 - 7x - \dfrac{3}{4}$ is zero for $x \approx -0.11$ and for $x \approx 7.11$.

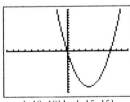

[–10, 10] by [–15, 15]

33. Rewrite as $2x^2 - 5x - 12 = 0$; the left side factors to $(2x + 3)(x - 4) = 0$:

$2x + 3 = 0$ or $x - 4 = 0$

$2x = -3$ $x = 4$

$x = -1.5$

The graph of $y = 2x^2 - 5x - 12$ is zero for $x = -1.5$ and for $x = 4$.

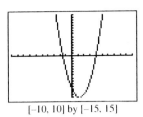

[–10, 10] by [–15, 15]

34. Rewrite as $2x^2 - x - 10 = 0$; the left side factors to $(x + 2)(2x - 5) = 0$:

$x + 2 = 0$ or $2x - 5 = 0$

$x = -2$ $2x = 5$

$x = 2.5$

The graph of $y = 2x^2 - x - 10$ is zero for $x = -2$ and for $x = 2.5$.

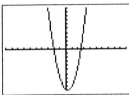

[–10, 10] by [–10, 10]

35. $x^2 + 7x - 14 = 0$, so $a = 1, b = 7$, and $c = -14$:

$$x = \frac{-7 \pm \sqrt{7^2 - 4(1)(-14)}}{2(1)} = \frac{-7 \pm \sqrt{105}}{2}$$

$$= -\frac{7}{2} \pm \frac{1}{2}\sqrt{105}$$

The graph of $y = x^2 + 7x - 14$ is zero for $x \approx -8.62$ and for $x \approx 1.62$.

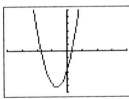

[–20, 20] by [–30, 30]

36. $x^2 - 4x - 12 = 0$, so $a = 1, b = -4$, and $c = -12$:

$$x = \frac{4 \pm \sqrt{(-4)^2 - 4(1)(-12)}}{2(1)} = \frac{4 \pm \sqrt{64}}{2}$$

$$= 2 \pm \frac{8}{2} = 2 \pm 4$$

$x = -2$ or $x = 6$

The graph of $y = x^2 - 4x - 12$ is zero for $x = -2$ and for $x = 6$.

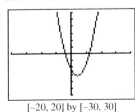

[–20, 20] by [–30, 30]

37. Change to $x^2 - 2x - 15 = 0$ (see below); this factors to $(x + 3)(x - 5) = 0$, so $x = -3$ or $x = 5$. Substituting the first of these shows that it is extraneous.

$$x + 1 = 2\sqrt{x + 4}$$
$$(x + 1)^2 = 2^2(\sqrt{x + 4})^2$$
$$x^2 + 2x + 1 = 4x + 16$$
$$x^2 - 2x - 15 = 0$$

The graph of $y = x + 1 - 2\sqrt{x + 4}$ is zero for $x = 5$.

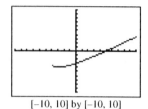

[−10, 10] by [−10, 10]

38. Change to $x^2 - 3x + 1 = 0$ (see below);

then $x = \dfrac{3 \pm \sqrt{9 - 4}}{2} = \dfrac{3}{2} \pm \dfrac{1}{2}\sqrt{5}$, so

$x = \dfrac{3}{2} - \dfrac{\sqrt{5}}{2}$. Substituting the second of these shows that it is extraneous.

$$\sqrt{x} = 1 - x$$
$$(\sqrt{x})^2 = (1 - x)^2$$
$$x = 1 - 2x + x^2$$
$$0 = x^2 - 3x + 1$$

$\sqrt{x} + x = 1$ is equivalent to $x + \sqrt{x} - 1 = 0$.

The graph of $y = x + \sqrt{x} - 1$ is zero for $x \approx 0.38$.

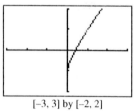

[−3, 3] by [−2, 2]

39. $x \approx 3.91$

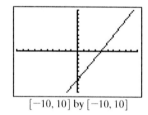

[−10, 10] by [−10, 10]

40. $x \approx -1.09$ or $x \approx 2.86$

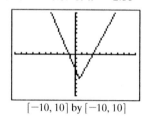

[−10, 10] by [−10, 10]

41. $x \approx 1.33$ or $x = 4$

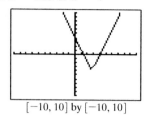

[−10, 10] by [−10, 10]

42. $x \approx 2.66$

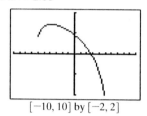

[−10, 10] by [−2, 2]

43. $x \approx 1.77$

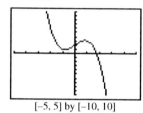

[−5, 5] by [−10, 10]

44. $x \approx 2.36$

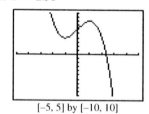

[−5, 5] by [−10, 10]

45. $x \approx -1.47$

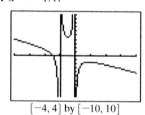

[−4, 4] by [−10, 10]

46. $\{0, 1, -1\}$

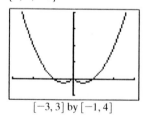

[−3, 3] by [−1, 4]

47. Model the situation using $C = 0.18x + 32$, where x is the number of miles driven and C is the cost of a day's rental.

(a) Elaine's cost is $0.18(83) + 32 = \$46.94$.

(b) If for Ramon $C = \$69.80$, then
$$x = \frac{69.80 - 32}{0.18} = 210 \text{ miles.}$$

48. (a) $4x + 5 - (x^3 + 2x^2 - x + 3) = 0$ or
$$-x^3 - 2x^2 + 5x + 2 = 0$$

(b) $-x^3 - 2x^2 + 5x + 2 = 0$

(c) A vertical line through the x-intercept of y_3 passes through the point of intersection of y_1 and y_2.

(d) At $x = 1.6813306$, $y_1 = y_2 = 11.725322$.
At $x = -0.3579264$, $y_1 = y_2 = 3.5682944$.
At $x = -3.323404$, $y_1 = y_2 = -8.293616$.

49. (a) $y = (x^{200})^{1/200} = x^{200/200} = x^1 = x$ for all $x \geq 0$.

(b) The graph looks like this:

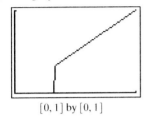

[0, 1] by [0, 1]

(c) Yes, this is different from the graph of $y = x$.

(d) For values of x close to 0, x^{200} is so small that the calculator is unable to distinguish it from zero. It returns a value of $0^{1/200} = 0$ rather than x.

50. The length of each side of the square is $x + b$, so the area of the whole square is $(x + b)^2$. The square is made up of one square with area $x \cdot x = x^2$, one square with area $b \cdot b = b^2$, and two rectangles, each with area $b \cdot x = bx$. Using these four figures, the area of the square is $x^2 + 2bx + b^2$.

51. (a) $x = -3$ or $x = 1.1$ or $x = 1.15$.

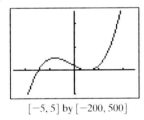

[-5, 5] by [-200, 500]

(b) $x = -3$ only.

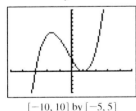

[-10, 10] by [-5, 5]

52. (a) Area: $x^2 + x\left(\dfrac{b}{2}\right) + x\left(\dfrac{b}{2}\right) = x^2 + bx$

(b) $\dfrac{b}{2} \cdot \dfrac{b}{2} = \left(\dfrac{b}{2}\right)^2$

(c) $x^2 + bx + \left(\dfrac{b}{2}\right)^2 = \left(x + \dfrac{b}{2}\right)^2$ is the algebraic formula for completing the square, just as the area $\left(\dfrac{b}{2}\right)^2$ completes the area $x^2 + bx$ to form the area $\left(x + \dfrac{b}{2}\right)^2$.

53. Let n be any integer.
$n^2 + 2n = n(n + 2)$, which is either the product of two odd integers or the product of two even integers.

The product of two odd integers is odd.

The product of two even integers is a multiple of 4, since each even integer in the product contributes a factor of 2 to the product.

Therefore, $n^2 + 2n$ is either odd or a multiple of 4.

54. One possible story: The jogger travels at an approximately constant speed throughout her workout. She jogs to the far end of the course, turns around and returns to her starting point, then goes out again for a second trip.

55. False. A product is zero if *any* factor is zero. That is, it takes only one zero factor to make the product zero.

56. False. Predictions are always fallible, and in particular an algebraic model that fits the data well for a certain range of input values may not work for other input values.

57. This is a line with a negative slope and a y-intercept of 12. The answer is C. (The graph checks.)

58. This is the graph of a square root function, but flipped left-over-right. The answer is E. (The graph checks.)

59. As x increases by ones, the y-values get farther and farther apart, which implies an increasing slope and suggests a quadratic equation. The answer is B. (The equation checks.)

60. As x increases by 2's, y increases by 4's, which implies a constant slope of 2. The answer is A. (The equation checks.)

61. (a) March

(b) $120

(c) June, after three months of poor performance

(d) Ahmad paid $(100)(\$120) = \$12{,}000$ for the stock and sold it for $(100)(\$100) = \$10{,}000$. He lost $2,000 on the stock.

(e) After reaching a low in June, the stock climbed back to a price near $140 by December. LaToya's shares had gained $2000 by that point.

(f) One possible graph:

62. (a)

[-4, 4] by [-10, 10]

(b) Factoring, we find $y = (x + 2)(x - 2)(x - 2)$. There is a double zero at $x = 2$, a zero at $x = -2$, and no other zeros (since it is a cubic).

(c) Same visually as the graph in (a).

(d) $b^2 - 4ac$ is the discriminant. In this case, $b^2 - 4ac = (-4)^2 - 4(1)(4.01) = -0.04$, which is negative. So the only real zero of the product $y = (x + 2)(x^2 - 4x + 4.01)$ is at $x = -2$.

(e) Same visually as the graph in (a).

(f) $b^2 - 4ac = (-4)^2 - 4(1)(3.99) = 0.04$, which is positive. The discriminant will provide two real zeros of the quadratic, and $(x + 2)$ provides the third. A cubic equation can have no more than three real roots.

63. (a)

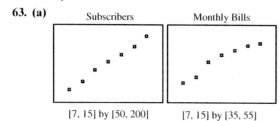

Subscribers   Monthly Bills

[7, 15] by [50, 200]   [7, 15] by [35, 55]

(b) The graph for subscribers appears to be linear. Since time t = the number of years after 1990, $t = 8$ for 1998 and $t = 14$ for 2004. The slope of the line is
$$\frac{180.4 - 69.2}{14 - 8} = \frac{111.2}{6} \approx 18.53.$$
Use the point-slope form to write the equation:
$y - 69.2 = 18.53(x - 8)$.
Solve for y: $y - 69.2 = 18.53x - 148.24$
$\ y = 18.53x - 79.04$
The linear model for subscribers as a function of years is $y = 18.53x - 79.04$.

(c) The fit is very good. The line goes through or is close to all the points.

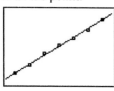

[7, 15] by [50, 200]

(d) The monthly bill scatter plot has a curved shape that could be modeled more effectively by a function with a curved graph. Some possibilities include a quadratic function (parabola), a logarithmic function, a power function (e.g., square root), a logistic function, or a sine function.

(e)

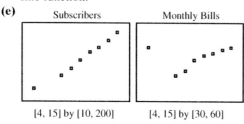

Subscribers   Monthly Bills

[4, 15] by [10, 200]   [4, 15] by [30, 60]

(f) In 1995, cellular phone technology was still emerging, so the growth rate was not as fast as it was in more recent years. Thus, the slope from 1995 ($t = 5$) to 1998 ($t = 8$) is lower than the slope from 1998 to 2004. Cellular technology was more expensive before competition brought prices down. This explains the anomaly on the monthly bill scatter plot.

64. One possible answer: The number of cell phone users is increasing steadily (as the linear model shows), and the average monthly bill is climbing more slowly as more people share the industry cost. The model shows that the number of users will continue to rise, although the linear model cannot hold up indefinitely.

■ Section 1.2 Functions and Their Properties

Exploration 1

1. From left to right, the tables are (c) constant, (b) decreasing, and (a) increasing.

2.

X moves from	ΔX	ΔY1	X moves from	ΔX	ΔY2	X moves from	ΔX	ΔY3
−2 to −1	1	0	−2 to −1	1	−2	−2 to −1	1	2
−1 to 0	1	0	−1 to 0	1	−1	−1 to 0	1	2
0 to 1	1	0	0 to 1	1	−2	0 to 1	1	2
1 to 3	2	0	1 to 3	2	−4	1 to 3	2	3
3 to 7	4	0	3 to 7	4	−6	3 to 7	4	6

3. For an increasing function, $\Delta Y/\Delta X$ is positive. For a decreasing function, $\Delta Y/\Delta X$ is negative. For a constant function, $\Delta Y/\Delta X$ is 0.

4. For lines, $\Delta Y/\Delta X$ is the slope. Lines with positive slope are increasing, lines with negative slope are decreasing, and lines with 0 slope are constant, so this supports our answers to part 3.

Quick Review 1.2

1. $x^2 - 16 = 0$
$\ x^2 = 16$
$\ x = \pm 4$

2. $9 - x^2 = 0$
$\ 9 = x^2$
$\ \pm 3 = x$

3. $x - 10 < 0$
$\ x < 10$

4. $5 - x \le 0$
$\ -x \le -5$
$\ x \ge 5$

5. As we have seen, the denominator of a function cannot be zero.
We need $\ \ x - 16 = 0$
$\ x = 16$

6. We need $\ \ x^2 - 16 = 0$
$\ x^2 = 16$
$\ x = \pm 4$

7. We need $\ \ x - 16 < 0$
$\ x < 16$

8. We need
$$x^2 - 1 = 0$$
$$x^2 = 1$$
$$x = \pm 1$$

9. We need $3 - x \le 0$ and $x + 2 < 0$
$$3 \le x \qquad\qquad x < -2$$
$$x < -2 \quad \text{and} \quad x \ge 3$$

10. We need
$$x^2 - 4 = 0$$
$$x^2 = 4$$
$$x = \pm 2$$

Section 1.2 Exercises

1. Yes, $y = \sqrt{x - 4}$ is a function of x, because when a number is substituted for x, there is at most one value produced for $\sqrt{x - 4}$.

2. No, $y = x^2 \pm 3$ is not a function of x, because when a number is substituted for x, y can be either 3 more or 3 less than x^2.

3. No, $x = 2y^2$ does not determine y as a function of x, because when a positive number is substituted for x, y can be either $\sqrt{\dfrac{x}{2}}$ or $-\sqrt{\dfrac{x}{2}}$.

4. Yes, $x = 12 - y$ determines y as a function of x, because when a number is substituted for x, there is exactly one number y which, when subtracted from 12, produces x.

5. Yes

6. No

7. No

8. Yes

9. We need $x^2 + 4 \ge 0$; this is true for all real x. Domain: $(-\infty, \infty)$.

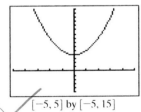

$[-5, 5]$ by $[-5, 15]$

10. We need $x - 3 \ne 0$. Domain: $(-\infty, 3) \cup (3, \infty)$.

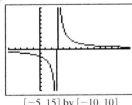

$[-5, 15]$ by $[-10, 10]$

11. We need $x + 3 \ne 0$ and $x - 1 \ne 0$. Domain: $(-\infty, -3) \cup (-3, 1) \cup (1, \infty)$.

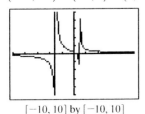

$[-10, 10]$ by $[-10, 10]$

12. We need $x \ne 0$ and $x - 3 \ne 0$. Domain: $(-\infty, 0) \cup (0, 3) \cup (3, \infty)$.

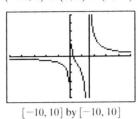

$[-10, 10]$ by $[-10, 10]$

13. We notice that $g(x) = \dfrac{x}{x^2 - 5x} = \dfrac{x}{x(x - 5)}$.

As a result, $x - 5 \ne 0$ and $x \ne 0$. Domain: $(-\infty, 0) \cup (0, 5) \cup (5, \infty)$.

$[-10, 10]$ by $[-5, 5]$

14. We need $x - 3 \ne 0$ and $4 - x^2 \ge 0$. This means $x \ne 3$ and $x^2 \le 4$; the latter implies that $-2 \le x \le 2$, so the domain is $[-2, 2]$.

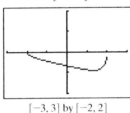

$[-3, 3]$ by $[-2, 2]$

15. We need $x + 1 \ne 0$, $x^2 + 1 \ne 0$, and $4 - x \ge 0$. The first requirement means $x \ne -1$, the second is true for all x, and the last means $x \le 4$. The domain is therefore $(-\infty, -1) \cup (-1, 4]$.

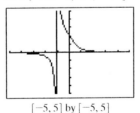

$[-5, 5]$ by $[-5, 5]$

16. We need
$$x^4 - 16x^2 \ge 0$$
$$x^2(x^2 - 16) \ge 0$$
$$x^2 = 0 \quad \text{or} \quad x^2 - 16 \ge 0$$
$$x^2 \ge 16$$
$$x = 0 \quad \text{or} \quad x \ge 4, \ x \le -4$$

Domain: $(-\infty, -4] \cup \{0\} \cup [4, \infty)$

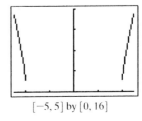

$[-5, 5]$ by $[0, 16]$

17. $f(x) = 10 - x^2$ can take on any negative value. Because x^2 is nonnegative, $f(x)$ cannot be greater than 10. The range is $(-\infty, 10]$.

18. $g(x) = 5 + \sqrt{4 - x}$ can take on any value ≥ 5, but because $\sqrt{4 - x}$ is nonnegative, $g(x)$ cannot be less than 5. The range is $[5, \infty)$.

19. The range of a function is most simply found by graphing it. As our graph shows, the range of $f(x)$ is $(-\infty, -1) \cup [0, \infty)$.

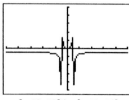

$[-10, 10]$ by $[-10, 10]$

20. As our graph illustrates, the range of $g(x)$ is $(-\infty, -1) \cup [0.75, \infty)$.

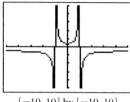

$[-10, 10]$ by $[-10, 10]$

21. Yes, non-removable

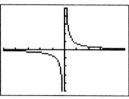

$[-10, 10]$ by $[-10, 10]$

22. Yes, removable

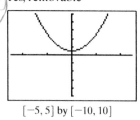

$[-5, 5]$ by $[-10, 10]$

23. Yes, non-removable

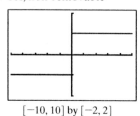

$[-10, 10]$ by $[-2, 2]$

24. Yes, non-removable

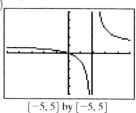

$[-5, 5]$ by $[-5, 5]$

25. Local maxima at $(-1, 4)$ and $(5, 5)$, local minimum at $(2, 2)$. The function increases on $(-\infty, -1]$, decreases on $[-1, 2]$, increases on $[2, 5]$, and decreases on $[5, \infty)$.

26. Local minimum at $(1, 2)$, $(3, 3)$ is neither, and $(5, 7)$ is a local maximum. The function decreases on $(-\infty, 1]$, increases on $[1, 5]$, and decreases on $[5, \infty)$.

27. $(-1, 3)$ and $(3, 3)$ are neither. $(1, 5)$ is a local maximum, and $(5, 1)$ is a local minimum. The function increases on $(-\infty, 1]$, decreases on $[1, 5]$, and increases on $[5, \infty)$.

28. $(-1, 1)$ and $(3, 1)$ are local minima, while $(1, 6)$ and $(5, 4)$ are local maxima. The function decreases on $(-\infty, -1]$, increases on $[-1, 1]$, decreases on $(1, 3)$, increases on $[3, 5]$, and decreases on $[5, \infty)$.

29. Decreasing on $(-\infty, -2]$; increasing on $[-2, \infty)$

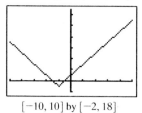

$[-10, 10]$ by $[-2, 18]$

30. Decreasing on $(-\infty, -1]$; constant on $[-1, 1]$; increasing on $[1, \infty)$

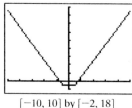

$[-10, 10]$ by $[-2, 18]$

31. Decreasing on $(-\infty, -2]$; constant on $[-2, 1]$; increasing on $[1, \infty)$

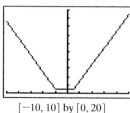

$[-10, 10]$ by $[0, 20]$

32. Decreasing on $(-\infty, -2]$; increasing on $[-2, \infty)$

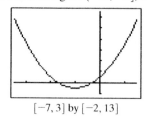

$[-7, 3]$ by $[-2, 13]$

33. Increasing on $(-\infty, 1]$; decreasing on $[1, \infty)$

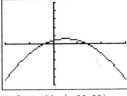

[−4, 6] by [−25, 25]

34. Increasing on $(-\infty, -0.5]$; decreasing on $[-0.5, 1.2]$, increasing on $[1.2, \infty)$. The middle values are approximate —they are actually at about −0.549 and 1.215. The values given are what might be observed on the decimal window.

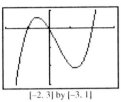

[−2, 3] by [−3, 1]

35. Constant functions are always bounded.

36.
$$x^2 > 0$$
$$-x^2 < 0$$
$$2 - x^2 < 2$$
y is bounded above by $y = 2$.

37. $2^x > 0$ for all x, so y is bounded below by $y = 0$.

38. $2^{-x} = \dfrac{1}{2^x} > 0$ for all x, so y is bounded below by $y = 0$.

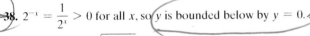

39. Since $y = \sqrt{1 - x^2}$ is always positive, we know that $y \geq 0$ for all x. We must also check for an upper bound:
$$x^2 > 0$$
$$-x^2 < 0$$
$$1 - x^2 < 1$$
$$\sqrt{1 - x^2} < \sqrt{1}$$
$$\sqrt{1 - x^2} < 1$$
Thus, y is bounded.

40. There are no restrictions on either x or x^3, so y is not bounded above or below.

41. f has a local minimum when $x = 0.5$, where $y = 3.75$. It has no maximum.

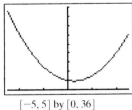

[−5, 5] by [0, 36]

42. Local maximum: $y \approx 4.08$ at $x \approx -1.15$.
Local minimum: $y \approx -2.08$ at $x \approx 1.15$.

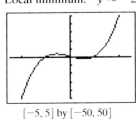

[−5, 5] by [−50, 50]

43. Local minimum: $y \approx -4.09$ at $x \approx -0.82$.
Local maximum: $y \approx -1.91$ at $x \approx 0.82$.

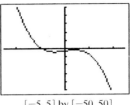

[−5, 5] by [−50, 50]

44. Local maximum: $y \approx 9.48$ at $x \approx -1.67$.
Local minimum: $y = 0$ when $x = 1$.

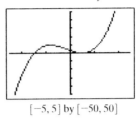

[−5, 5] by [−50, 50]

45. Local maximum: $y \approx 9.16$ at $x \approx -3.20$.
Local minima: $y = 0$ at $x = 0$ and $y = 0$ at $x = -4$.

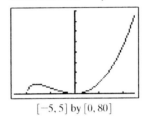

[−5, 5] by [0, 80]

46. Local maximum: $y = 0$ at $x = -2.5$.
Local minimum: $y \approx -3.13$ at $x = -1.25$.

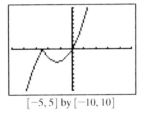

[−5, 5] by [−10, 10]

47. Even: $f(-x) = 2(-x)^4 = 2x^4 = f(x)$

48. Odd: $g(-x) = (-x)^3 = -x^3 = -g(x)$

49. Even: $f(-x) = \sqrt{(-x)^2 + 2} = \sqrt{x^2 + 2} = f(x)$

50. Even: $g(-x) = \dfrac{3}{1 + (-x)^2} = \dfrac{3}{1 + x^2} = g(x)$

51. Neither: $f(-x) = -(-x)^2 + 0.03(-x) + 5 = -x^2 - 0.03x + 5$, which is neither $f(x)$ nor $-f(x)$.

52. Neither: $f(-x) = (-x)^3 + 0.04(-x)^2 + 3 = -x^3 + 0.04x^2 + 3$, which is neither $f(x)$ nor $-f(x)$.

53. Odd: $g(-x) = 2(-x)^3 - 3(-x)$
$$= -2x^3 + 3x = -g(x)$$

54. Odd: $h(-x) = \dfrac{1}{-x} = -\dfrac{1}{x} = -h(x)$

55. The quotient $\dfrac{x}{x-1}$ is undefined at $x = 1$, indicating that $x = 1$ is a vertical asymptote. Similarly, $\lim\limits_{x \to \infty} \dfrac{x}{x-1} = 1$, indicating a horizontal asymptote at $y = 1$. The graph confirms these.

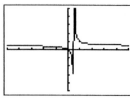

$[-10, 10]$ by $[-10, 10]$

56. The quotient $\dfrac{x-1}{x}$ is undefined at $x = 0$, indicating a possible vertical asymptote at $x = 0$. Similarly, $\lim\limits_{x \to \infty} \dfrac{x-1}{x} = 1$, indicating a possible horizontal asymptote at $y = 1$. The graph confirms those asymptotes.

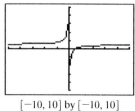

$[-10, 10]$ by $[-10, 10]$

57. The quotient $\dfrac{x+2}{3-x}$ is undefined at $x = 3$, indicating a possible vertical asymptote at $x = 3$. Similarly, $\lim\limits_{x \to \infty} \dfrac{x+2}{3-x} = -1$, indicating a possible horizontal asymptote at $y = -1$. The graph confirms these asymptotes.

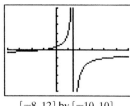

$[-8, 12]$ by $[-10, 10]$

58. Since $g(x)$ is continuous over $-\infty < x < \infty$, we do not expect a vertical asymptote. However, $\lim\limits_{x \to -\infty} 1.5^x = \lim\limits_{x \to \infty} 1.5^{-x} = \lim\limits_{x \to \infty} \dfrac{1}{1.5^x} = 0$, so we expect a horizontal asymptote $y = 0$. The graph confirms this asymptote.

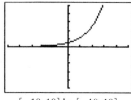

$[-10, 10]$ by $[-10, 10]$

59. The quotient $\dfrac{x^2+2}{x^2-1}$ is undefined at $x = 1$ and $x = -1$. So we expect two vertical asymptotes. Similarly, the $\lim\limits_{x \to \infty} \dfrac{x^2+2}{x^2-1} = 1$, so we expect a horizontal asymptote at $y = 1$. The graph confirms these asymptotes.

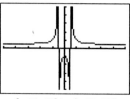

$[-10, 10]$ by $[-10, 10]$

60. We note that $x^2 + 1 > 0$ for $-\infty < x < \infty$, so we do not expect a vertical asymptote. However, $\lim\limits_{x \to \infty} \dfrac{4}{x^2+1} = 0$, so we expect a horizontal asymptote at $y = 0$. The graph confirms this.

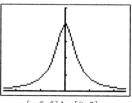

$[-5, 5]$ by $[0, 5]$

61. The quotient $\dfrac{4x-4}{x^3-8}$ does not exist at $x = 2$, so we expect a vertical asymptote there. Similarly, $\lim\limits_{x \to \infty} \dfrac{4x-4}{x^3+8} = 0$, so we expect a horizontal asymptote at $y = 0$. The graph confirms these asymptotes.

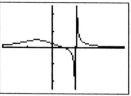

$[-4, 6]$ by $[-5, 5]$

62. The quotient $\dfrac{2x-4}{x^2-4} = \dfrac{2(x-2)}{(x-2)(x+2)} = \dfrac{2}{x+2}$. Since $x = 2$ is a removable discontinuity, we expect a vertical asymptote at only $x = -2$. Similarly, $\lim\limits_{x \to \infty} \dfrac{2}{x-2} = 0$, so we expect a horizontal asymptote at $y = 0$. The graph confirms these asymptotes.

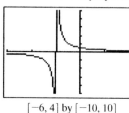

$[-6, 4]$ by $[-10, 10]$

63. The denominator is zero when $x = -\dfrac{1}{2}$, so there is a vertical asymptote at $x = -\dfrac{1}{2}$. When x is very large, $\dfrac{x+2}{2x+1}$ behaves much like $\dfrac{x}{2x} = \dfrac{1}{2}$, so there is a horizontal asymptote at $y = \dfrac{1}{2}$. The graph matching this description is (b).

64. The denominator is zero when $x = -\dfrac{1}{2}$, so there is a vertical asymptote at $x = -\dfrac{1}{2}$. When x is very large, $\dfrac{x^2+2}{2x+1}$ behaves much like $\dfrac{x^2}{2x} = \dfrac{x}{2}$, so $y = \dfrac{x}{2}$ is a slant asymptote. The graph matching this description is (c).

65. The denominator cannot equal zero, so there is no vertical asymptote. When x is very large, $\dfrac{x+2}{2x^2+1}$ behaves much like $\dfrac{x}{2x^2} = \dfrac{1}{2x}$, which for large x is close to zero. So there is a horizontal asymptote at $y = 0$. The graph matching this description is (a).

66. The denominator cannot equal zero, so there is no vertical asymptote. When x is very large, $\dfrac{x^3+2}{2x^2+1}$ behaves much like $\dfrac{x^3}{2x^2} = \dfrac{x}{2}$, so $y = \dfrac{x}{2}$ is a slant asymptote. The graph matching this description is (d).

67. (a) Since, $\displaystyle\lim_{x\to\infty} \dfrac{x}{x^2-1} = 0$, we expect a horizontal asymptote at $y = 0$. To find where our function crosses $y = 0$, we solve the equation
$$\dfrac{x}{x^2-1} = 0$$
$$x = 0 \cdot (x^2-1)$$
$$x = 0$$
The graph confirms that $f(x)$ crosses the horizontal asymptote at $(0, 0)$.

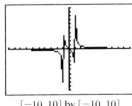

$[-10, 10]$ by $[-10, 10]$

(b) Since $\displaystyle\lim_{x\to\infty} \dfrac{x}{x^2+1} = 0$, we expect a horizontal asymptote at $y = 0$. To find where our function crosses $y = 0$, we solve the equation:
$$\dfrac{x}{x^2+1} = 0$$
$$x = 0 \cdot (x^2+1)$$
$$x = 0$$
The graph confirms that $g(x)$ crosses the horizontal asymptote at $(0, 0)$.

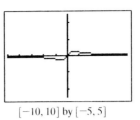

$[-10, 10]$ by $[-5, 5]$

(c) Since $\displaystyle\lim_{x\to\infty} \dfrac{x^2}{x^3+1} = 0$, we expect a horizontal asymptote at $y = 0$. To find where $h(x)$ crosses $y = 0$, we solve the equation
$$\dfrac{x^2}{x^3+1} = 0$$
$$x^2 = 0 \cdot (x^3+1)$$
$$x^2 = 0$$
$$x = 0$$
The graph confirms that $h(x)$ intersects the horizontal asymptote at $(0, 0)$.

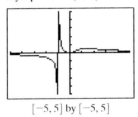

$[-5, 5]$ by $[-5, 5]$

68. We find **(a)** and **(c)** have graphs with more than one horizontal asymptote as follows:

(a) To find horizontal asymptotes, we check limits, at $x \to \infty$ and $x \to -\infty$. We also know that our numerator $|x^3+1|$, is positive for all x, and that our denominator, $8 - x^3$, is positive for $x < 2$ and negative for $x > 2$. Considering these two statements, we find
$$\lim_{x\to\infty} \dfrac{|x^3+1|}{8-x^3} = -1 \text{ and } \lim_{x\to-\infty} \dfrac{|x^3+1|}{8-x^3} = 1.$$
The graph confirms that we have horizontal asymptotes at $y = 1$ and $y = -1$.

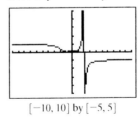

$[-10, 10]$ by $[-5, 5]$

(b) Again, we see that our numerator, $|x-1|$, is positive for all x. As a result, $g(x)$ can be negative only when $x^2 - 4 < 0$, and $g(x)$ can be positive only when $x^2 - 4 > 0$. This means that $g(x)$ can be negative only when $-2 < x < 2$; if $x < -2$ or $x > 2$, $g(x)$ will be positive. As a result, we know that
$$\lim_{x\to\infty} \dfrac{|x-1|}{x^2-4} = \lim_{x\to-\infty} \dfrac{|x-1|}{x^2-4} = 0, \text{ giving just one}$$
horizontal asymptote at $y = 0$. Our graph confirms this asymptote.

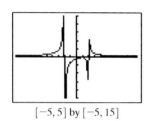

$[-5, 5]$ by $[-5, 15]$

(c) As we demonstrated earlier, we need $x^2 - 4 > 0$ otherwise our function is not defined within the real numbers. As <u>a result</u>, we know that our denominator, $\sqrt{x^2 - 4}$, is always positive [and that $h(x)$ is defined only in the domain $(-\infty, -2) \cup (2, \infty)$].

Checking limits, we find $\lim\limits_{x \to \infty} \dfrac{x}{\sqrt{x^2 - 4}} = 1$ and

$\lim\limits_{x \to -\infty} \dfrac{x}{\sqrt{x^2 - 4}} = -1$. The graph confirms that we have horizontal asymptotes at $y = 1$ and $y = -1$.

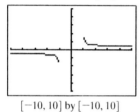

$[-10, 10]$ by $[-10, 10]$

69. (a) The vertical asymptote is $x = 0$, and this function is undefined at $x = 0$ (because a denominator can't be zero).

(b)

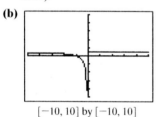

$[-10, 10]$ by $[-10, 10]$

Add the point $(0, 0)$.

(c) Yes. It passes the vertical line test.

70. The horizontal asymptotes are determined by the two limits, $\lim\limits_{x \to -\infty} f(x)$ and $\lim\limits_{x \to +\infty} f(x)$. These are at most two different numbers.

71. True. This is what it means for a set of points to be the graph of a function.

72. False. There are many function graphs that are symmetric with respect to the x-axis. One example is $f(x) = 0$.

73. Temperature is a continuous variable, whereas the other quantities all vary in steps. The answer is B.

74. "Number of balls" represents a whole number, so that the quantity changes in jumps as the ball radius is altered. The answer is C.

75. Air pressure drops with increasing height. All the other functions either steadily increase or else go both up and down. The answer is C.

76. The height of a swinging pendulum goes up and down over time as the pendulum swings back and forth. The answer is E.

77. (a)

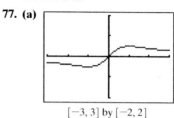

$[-3, 3]$ by $[-2, 2]$

$k = 1$

(b) $\dfrac{x}{1 + x^2} < 1 \Leftrightarrow x < 1 + x^2 \Leftrightarrow x^2 - x + 1 > 0$

But the discriminant of $x^2 - x + 1$ is negative (-3), so the graph never crosses the x-axis on the interval $(0, \infty)$.

(c) $k = -1$

(d) $\dfrac{x}{1 + x^2} > -1 \Leftrightarrow x > -1 - x^2 \Leftrightarrow x^2 + x + 1 > 0$

But the discriminant of $x^2 + x + 1$ is negative (-3), so the graph never crosses the x-axis on the interval $(-\infty, 0)$.

78. (a) Increasing

(b)

Δy
1
1.05
0.52
0.43
0.36
0.33
0.31
0.28

(c)

$\Delta\Delta y$
0.05
-0.53
-0.09
-0.07
-0.03
-0.02
-0.03

Δy is none of these since it first increases from 1 to 1.05 and then decreases.

(d) The graph rises, but bends downward as it rises.

(e) An example:

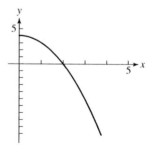

79. One possible graph:

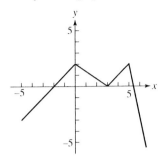

80. One possible graph:

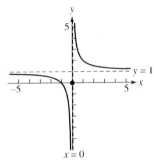

81. One possible graph:

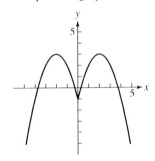

82. Answers vary.

83. (a)
$$x^2 > 0$$
$$-0.8x^2 < 0$$
$$2 - 0.8x^2 < 2$$
$f(x)$ is bounded above by $y = 2$. To determine if $y = 2$ is in the range, we must solve the equation for x: $2 = 2 - 0.8x^2$
$$0 = -0.8x^2$$
$$0 = x^2$$
$$0 = x$$
Since $f(x)$ exists at $x = 0$, $y = 2$ is in the range.

(b) $\lim\limits_{x \to \infty} \dfrac{3x^2}{3 + x^2} = \lim\limits_{x \to \infty} \dfrac{3x^2}{x^2} = \lim\limits_{x \to \infty} 3 = 3$. Thus, $g(x)$ is bounded by $y = 3$. However, when we solve for x,
we get $\quad 3 = \dfrac{3x^2}{3 + x^2}$
$$3(3 + x^2) = 3x^2$$
$$9 + 3x^2 = 3x^2$$
$$9 = 0$$
Since $9 \neq 0$, $y = 3$ is not in the range of $g(x)$.

(c) $h(x)$ is not bounded above.

(d) For all values of x, we know that $\sin(x)$ is bounded above by $y = 1$. Similarly, $2\sin(x)$ is bounded above by $y = 2 \cdot 1 = 2$. It is in the range.

(e) $\lim\limits_{x \to \infty} \dfrac{4x}{x^2 + 2x + 1} = \lim\limits_{x \to \infty} \dfrac{4x}{(x + 1)^2} =$
$\lim\limits_{x \to \infty} 4\left(\dfrac{x}{x + 1}\right)\left(\dfrac{1}{x + 1}\right) = \lim\limits_{x \to \infty} \dfrac{4}{x + 1}$
(since $x + 1 \approx x$ for very large x) $= 0$.
[Similarly, $\lim\limits_{x \to -\infty} \dfrac{4x}{x^2 + x + 1} = 0$] As a result, we
know that $g(x)$ is bounded by $y = 0$ as x goes to ∞ and $-\infty$.
However, $g(x) > 0$ for all $x > 0$ (since $(x + 1)^2 > 0$ always and $4x > 0$ when $x > 0$), so we must check points near $x = 0$ to determine where the function is at its maximum. [Since $g(x) < 0$ for all $x < 0$ (since $(x + 1)^2 > 0$ always and $4x < 0$ when $x < 0$) we can ignore those values of x since we are concerned only with the upper bound of $g(x)$.] Examining our graph, we see that $g(x)$ has an upper bound at $y = 1$, which occurs when $x = 1$. The least upper bound of $g(x) = 1$, and it is in the range of $g(x)$.

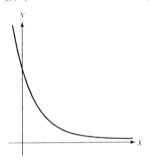

84. As the graph moves continuously from the point $(-1, 5)$ down to the point $(1, -5)$, it must cross the x-axis somewhere along the way. That x-intercept will be a zero of the function in the interval $[-1, 1]$.

85. Since f is odd, $f(-x) = -f(x)$ for all x. In particular, $f(-0) = -f(0)$. This is equivalent to saying that $f(0) = -f(0)$, and the only number which equals its opposite is 0. Therefore, $f(0) = 0$, which means the graph must pass through the origin.

86.

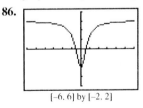

$[-6, 6]$ by $[-2, 2]$

(a) $y = 1.5$

(b) $[-1, 1.5]$

(c) $-1 \leq \dfrac{3x^2 - 1}{2x^2 + 1} \leq 1.5$
$$0 \leq 1 + \dfrac{3x^2 - 1}{2x^2 + 1} \leq 2.5$$
$$0 \leq 2x^2 + 1 + 3x^2 - 1 \leq 5x^2 + 2.5$$
$$0 \leq 5x^2 \leq 5x^2 + 2.5$$
True for all x.

■ Section 1.3 Twelve Basic Functions

Exploration 1

1. The graphs of $f(x) = \dfrac{1}{x}$ and $f(x) = \ln x$ have vertical asymptotes at $x = 0$.

2. The graph of $g(x) = \dfrac{1}{x} + \ln x$ (shown below) does have a vertical asymptote at $x = 0$.

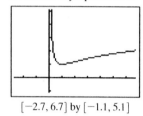

[−2.7, 6.7] by [−1.1, 5.1]

3. The graphs of $f(x) = \dfrac{1}{x}$, $f(x) = e^x$, and $f(x) = \dfrac{1}{1 + e^{-x}}$ have horizontal asymptotes at $y = 0$.

4. The graph of $g(x) = \dfrac{1}{x} + e^x$ (shown below) does have a horizontal asymptote at $y = 0$.

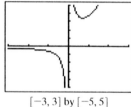

[−3, 3] by [−5, 5]

5.

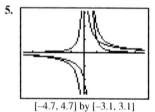

[−4.7, 4.7] by [−3.1, 3.1]

Both $f(x) = \dfrac{1}{x}$ and $g(x) = \dfrac{1}{2x^2 - x} = \dfrac{1}{x(2x - 1)}$ have vertical asymptotes at $x = 0$, but $h(x) = f(x) + g(x)$ does not; it has a removable discontinuity.

Quick Review 1.3

1. 59.34
2. $5 - \pi$
3. $7 - \pi$
4. 3
5. 0
6. 1
7. 3
8. −15
9. −4
10. $|1 - \pi| - \pi = (\pi - 1) - \pi = \pi - 1 - \pi = -1$

Section 1.3 Exercises

1. $y = x^3 + 1$; (e)
2. $y = |x| - 2$; (g)
3. $y = -\sqrt{x}$; (j)
4. $y = -\sin x$ or $y = \sin(-x)$; (a)
5. $y = -x$; (i)
6. $y = (x - 1)^2$; (f)
7. $y = \text{int}(x + 1)$; (k)
8. $y = -\dfrac{1}{x}$; (h)
9. $y = (x + 2)^3$; (d)
10. $y = e^x - 2$; (c)
11. $2 - \dfrac{4}{1 + e^{-x}}$; (l)
12. $y = \cos x + 1$; (b)
13. Exercise 8
14. Exercise 3
15. Exercises 7, 8
16. Exercise 7 (Remember that a continuous function is one that is continuous at every point *in its domain.*)
17. Exercises 2, 4, 6, 10, 11, 12
18. Exercises 3, 4, 11, 12
19. $y = x,\ y = x^3,\ y = \dfrac{1}{x},\ y = \sin x$
20. $y = x,\ y = x^3,\ y = \sqrt{x},\ y = e^x,\ y = \ln x,\ y = \dfrac{1}{1 + e^{-x}}$
21. $y = x^2,\ y = \dfrac{1}{x},\ y = |x|$
22. $y = \sin x,\ y = \cos x,\ y = \text{int}(x)$
23. $y = \dfrac{1}{x},\ y = e^x,\ y = \dfrac{1}{1 + e^{-x}}$
24. $y = x,\ y = x^3,\ y = \ln x$
25. $y = \dfrac{1}{x},\ y = \sin x,\ y = \cos x,\ y = \dfrac{1}{1 + e^{-x}}$
26. $y = x,\ y = x^3,\ y = \text{int}(x)$
27. $y = x,\ y = x^3,\ y = \dfrac{1}{x},\ y = \sin x$
28. $y = \sin x,\ y = \cos x$

29. Domain: All reals
Range: $[-5, \infty)$

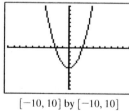

[−10, 10] by [−10, 10]

30. Domain: All reals
Range: $[0, \infty)$

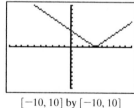

[−10, 10] by [−10, 10]

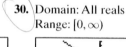

31. Domain: $(-6, \infty)$
Range: All reals

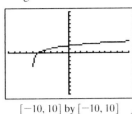

$[-10, 10]$ by $[-10, 10]$

32. Domain: $(-\infty, 0) \cup (0, \infty)$
Range: $(-\infty, 3) \cup (3, \infty)$

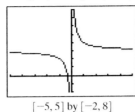

$[-5, 5]$ by $[-2, 8]$

33. Domain: All reals
Range: All integers

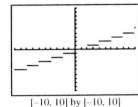

$[-10, 10]$ by $[-10, 10]$

34. Domain: All reals
Range: $[0, \infty)$

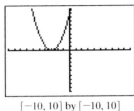

$[-10, 10]$ by $[-10, 10]$

35.

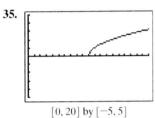

$[0, 20]$ by $[-5, 5]$

(a) $r(x)$ is increasing on $[10, \infty)$.

(b) $r(x)$ is neither odd nor even.

(c) The one extreme is a minimum value of 0 at $x = 10$.

(d) $r(x) = \sqrt{x - 10}$ is the square root function, shifted 10 units right.

36.

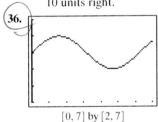

$[0, 7]$ by $[2, 7]$

(a) $f(x)$ is increasing on $\left[(2k - 1)\dfrac{\pi}{2}, (2k + 1)\dfrac{\pi}{2}\right]$ and decreasing on $\left[(2k + 1)\dfrac{\pi}{2}, (2k + 3)\dfrac{\pi}{2}\right]$, where k is an even integer.

(b) $f(x)$ is neither odd nor even.

(c) There are minimum values of 4 at $x = (2k - 1)\dfrac{\pi}{2}$ and maximum values of 6 at $x = (2k + 1)\dfrac{\pi}{2}$, where k is an even integer.

(d) $f(x) = \sin(x) + 5$ is the sine function, sin x, shifted 5 units up.

37.

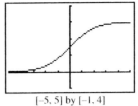

$[-5, 5]$ by $[-1, 4]$

(a) $f(x)$ is increasing on $(-\infty, \infty)$.

(b) $f(x)$ is neither odd nor even.

(c) There are no extrema.

(d) $f(x) = \dfrac{3}{1 + e^{-x}}$ is the logistic function, $\dfrac{1}{1 + e^{-x}}$, stretched vertically by a factor of 3.

38.

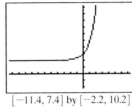

$[-11.4, 7.4]$ by $[-2.2, 10.2]$

(a) $q(x)$ is increasing on $(-\infty, \infty)$.

(b) $q(x)$ is neither odd nor even.

(c) There are no extrema.

(d) $q(x) = e^x + 2$ is the exponental function, e^x, shifted 2 units up.

39.

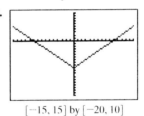

$[-15, 15]$ by $[-20, 10]$

(a) $h(x)$ is increasing on $[0, \infty)$ and decreasing on $(-\infty, 0]$.

(b) $h(x)$ is even, because it is symmetric about the y-axis.

(c) The one extremum is a minimum value of -10 at $x = 0$.

(d) $h(x) = |x| - 10$ is the absolute value function, $|x|$, shifted 10 units down.

40.

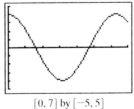

$[0, 7]$ by $[-5, 5]$

(a) $g(x)$ is increasing on $[(2k - 1)\pi, 2k\pi]$ and decreasing on $[2k\pi, (2k + 1)\pi]$, where k is an integer.

(b) $g(x)$ is even, because it is symmetric about the y-axis.

(c) There are minimum values of -4 at $x = (2k - 1)\pi$ and maximum values of 4 at $x = 2k\pi$, where k is an integer.

(d) $g(x) = 4 \cos(x)$ is the cosine function, cos x, stretched vertically by a factor of 4.

41.

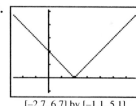

[–2.7, 6.7] by [–1.1, 5.1]

(a) $s(x)$ is increasing on $[2, \infty)$ and decreasing on $(-\infty, 2]$.

(b) $s(x)$ is neither odd nor even.

(c) The one extremum is a minimum value of 0 at $x = 2$.

(d) $s(x) = |x - 2|$ is the absolute value function, $|x|$, shifted 2 units to the right.

42.

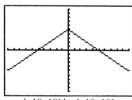

[–10, 10] by [–10, 10]

(a) $f(x)$ is increasing on $(-\infty, 0]$ and decreasing on $[0, \infty)$.

(b) $f(x)$ is even, because it is symmetric about the y-axis.

(c) The one extremum is a maximum value of 5 at $x = 0$.

(d) $f(x) = 5 - \text{abs}(x)$ is the absolute value function, $\text{abs}(x)$, reflected across the x-axis and then shifted 5 units up.

43. The end behavior approaches the horizontal asymptotes $y = 2$ and $y = -2$.

44. The end behavior approaches the horizontal asymptotes $y = 0$ and $y = 3$.

45.

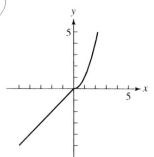

There are no points of discontinuity.

46.

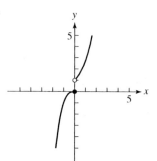

There is a point of discontinuity at $x = 0$.

47.

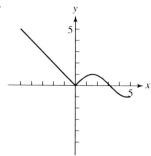

There are no points of discontinuity.

48.

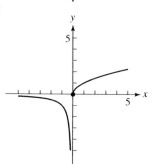

There is a point of discontinuity at $x = 0$.

49.

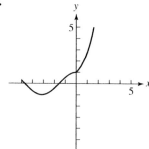

There are no points of discontinuity.

50.

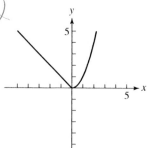

There are no points of discontinuity.

51.

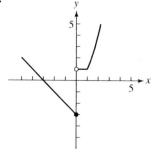

There is a point of discontinuity at $x = 0$.

52.

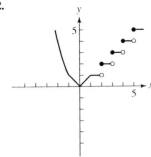

There are points of discontinuity at $x = 2, 3, 4, 5, \ldots$.

53. (a)

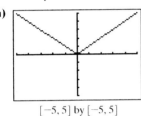

$[-5, 5]$ by $[-5, 5]$

This is $g(x) = |x|$.

(b) Squaring x and taking the (positive) square root has the same effect as the absolute value function.

$$f(x) = \sqrt{x^2} = \sqrt{|x|^2} = |x| = g(x)$$

54. (a)

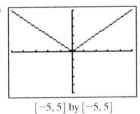

$[-5, 5]$ by $[-5, 5]$

This appears to be $f(x) = |x|$.

(b) For example, $g(1) \approx 0.99 \neq f(1) = 1$.

55. (a)

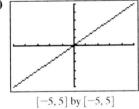

$[-5, 5]$ by $[-5, 5]$

This is the function $f(x) = x$.

(b) The fact that $\ln(e^x) = x$ shows that the natural logarithm function takes on arbitrarily large values. In particular, it takes on the value L when $x = e^L$.

56. (a)

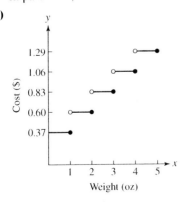

Weight (oz)

(b) One possible answer: It is similar because it has discontinuities spaced at regular intervals. It is different because its domain is the set of positive real numbers, and because it is constant on intervals of the form $(k, k + 1]$ instead of $[k, k + 1)$, where k is an integer.

57. The Greatest Integer Function $f(x) = \text{int}(x)$

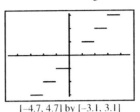

$[-4.7, 4.7]$ by $[-3.1, 3.1]$

Domain: all real numbers
Range: all integers
Continuity: There is a discontinuity at each integer value of x.
Increasing/decreasing behavior: constant on intervals of the form $[k, k + 1)$, where k is an integer
Symmetry: none
Boundedness: not bounded
Local extrema: every non-integer is both a local minimum and local maximum
Horizontal asymptotes: none
Vertical asymptotes: none
End behavior: $\text{int}(x) \to -\infty$ as $x \to -\infty$ and $\text{int}(x) \to \infty$ as $x \to \infty$.

58. False. Because the greatest integer function is not one-to-one, its inverse relation is not a function.

59. True. The asymptotes are $x = 0$ and $x = 1$.

60. Because $3 - \dfrac{1}{x} \neq 3, 0 < \dfrac{5}{1 + e^{-x}} < 5, -4 \leq 4 \cos x \leq 4$, and $\text{int}(x - 2)$ takes only integer values. The answer is A.

61. $3 < 3 + \dfrac{1}{1 + e^{-x}} < 4$. The answer is D.

62. By comparison of the graphs, the answer is C.

63. The answer is E. The others all have either a restricted domain or intervals where the function is decreasing or constant.

64. (a) Answers will vary.

(b) In this window, it appears that $\sqrt{x} < x < x^2$:

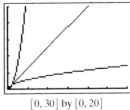

$[0, 30]$ by $[0, 20]$

(c)

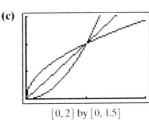

$[0, 2]$ by $[0, 1.5]$

(d) On the interval $(0, 1)$, $x^2 < x < \sqrt{x}$.
On the interval $(1, \infty)$, $\sqrt{x} < x < x^2$.
All three functions equal 1 when $x = 1$.

65. (a) A product of two odd functions is even.

(b) A product of two even functions is even.

(c) A product of an odd function and an even function is odd.

66. Answers vary.

67. (a) Pepperoni count ought to be proportional to the area of the pizza, which is proportional to the square of the radius.

(b) $12 = k(4)^2$

$$k = \frac{12}{16} = \frac{3}{4} = 0.75$$

(c) Yes, very well.

(d) The fact that the pepperoni count fits the expected quadratic model so perfectly suggests that the pizzeria uses such a chart. If repeated observations produced the same results, there would be little doubt.

68. (a) $y = e^x$ and $y = \ln x$

(b) $y = x$ and $y = \dfrac{1}{x}$

(c) With domain $[0, \infty)$, $y = x^2$ becomes the inverse of $y = \sqrt{x}$.

69. (a) At $x = 0$, $\dfrac{1}{x}$ does not exist, $e^x = 1$, $\ln x$ is not defined,

$\cos x = 1$, and $\dfrac{1}{1 + e^{-x}} = 1$.

(b) for $f(x) = x$, $f(x + y) = x + y = f(x) + f(y)$

(c) for $f(x) = e^x$, $f(xy) = e^{xy} = e^x e^y = f(x) \cdot f(y)$

(d) for $f(x) = \ln x$, $f(x + y) = \ln(xy) = \ln(x) + \ln(y)$
$= f(x) + f(y)$

(e) The odd functions: x, x^3, $\dfrac{1}{x}$, $\sin x$

■ Section 1.4 Building Functions from Functions

Exploration 1

If $f = 2x - 3$ and $g = \dfrac{x + 3}{2}$, then

$$f \circ g = 2\left(\frac{x + 3}{2}\right) - 3 = x + 3 - 3 = x.$$

If $f = |2x + 4|$ and $g = \dfrac{(x - 2)(x + 2)}{2}$,

then $f \circ g = 2\left(\dfrac{(x - 2)(x + 2)}{2}\right) + 4$

$= (x - 2)(x + 2) + 4 = x^2 - 4 + 4 = x^2$.

If $f = \sqrt{x}$ and $g = x^2$, then $f \circ g = \sqrt{x^2} = |x|$. Note, we use the absolute value of x because g is defined for $-\infty < x < +\infty$, while f is defined only for positive values of x. The absolute value function is always positive.

If $f = x^5$ and $g = x^{0.6}$, then $f \circ g = (x^{0.6})^5 = x^3$.

If $f = x - 3$ and $g = \ln(e^3 x)$, then $f \circ g = \ln(e^3 x) - 3 = \ln(e^3) + \ln x - 3 = 3 \ln e + \ln x - 3 = 3 + \ln x - 3 = \ln x$.

If $f = 2 \sin x \cos x$ and $g = \dfrac{x}{2}$, then $f \circ g = 2 \sin\dfrac{x}{2} \cos\dfrac{x}{2} = \sin\left(2\left(\dfrac{x}{2}\right)\right) = \sin x$. This is the double angle formula (*see Section 5.4*). You can see this graphically.

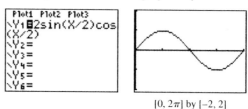

[0, 2π] by [−2, 2]

If $f = 1 - 2x^2$ and $g = \sin\left(\dfrac{x}{2}\right)$,

then $f \circ g = 1 - 2\left(\sin^2\left(\dfrac{x}{2}\right)\right) = \cos\left(2\left(\dfrac{x}{2}\right)\right) = \cos x$.

(The double angle formula for $\cos 2x$ is $\cos 2x = \cos^2 x - \sin^2 x = (1 - \sin^2 x) - \sin^2 x = 1 - 2 \sin^2 x$. *See Section 5.3*.) This can be seen graphically:

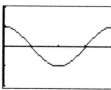

[0, 2π] by [−2, 2]

f	g	$f \circ g$
$2x - 3$	$\dfrac{x + 3}{2}$	x
$|2x + 4|$	$\dfrac{(x - 2)(x + 2)}{2}$	x^2
$\sqrt{x}$	x^2	$|x|$
x^5	$x^{0.6}$	x^3
$x - 3$	$\ln(e^3 x)$	$\ln x$
$2 \sin x \cos x$	$\dfrac{x}{2}$	$\sin x$
$1 - 2x^2$	$\sin\left(\dfrac{x}{2}\right)$	$\cos x$

Quick Review 1.4

1. $(-\infty, -3) \cup (-3, \infty)$

2. $(1, \infty)$

3. $(-\infty, 5]$

4. $(1/2, \infty)$

5. $[1, \infty)$

6. $[-1, 1]$

7. $(-\infty, \infty)$

8. $(-\infty, 0) \cup (0, \infty)$

9. $(-1, 1)$

10. $(-\infty, \infty)$

Section 1.4 Exercises

1. $(f + g)(x) = 2x - 1 + x^2; (f - g)(x) = 2x - 1 - x^2;$
$(fg)(x) = (2x - 1)(x^2) = 2x^3 - x^2.$

There are no restrictions on any of the domains, so all three domains are $(-\infty, \infty)$.

2. $(f + g)(x) = (x - 1)^2 + 3 - x =$
$\quad x^2 - 2x + 1 + 3 - x = x^2 - 3x + 4;$
$(f - g)(x) = (x - 1)^2 - 3 + x =$
$\quad x^2 - 2x + 1 - 3 + x = x^2 - x - 2;$
$(fg)(x) = (x - 1)^2(3 - x) = (x^2 - 2x + 1)(3 - x)$
$\quad = 3x^2 - x^3 - 6x + 2x^2 + 3 - x$
$\quad = -x^3 + 5x^2 - 7x + 3.$

There are no restrictions on any of the domains, so all three domains are $(-\infty, \infty)$.

3. $(f + g)(x) = \sqrt{x} + \sin x; (f - g)(x) = \sqrt{x} - \sin x;$
$(fg)(x) = \sqrt{x} \sin x.$
Domain in each case is $[0, \infty)$. For $\sqrt{x}, x \geq 0$. For $\sin x,$
$-\infty < x < \infty.$

4. $(f + g)(x) = \sqrt{x + 5} + |x + 3|;$
$(f - g)(x) = \sqrt{x + 5} - |x + 3|;$
$(fg)(x) = \sqrt{x + 5}|x + 3|.$
All three expressions contain $\sqrt{x + 5}$, so $x + 5 \geq 0$
and $x \geq -5$; all three domains are $[-5, \infty)$. For $|x + 3|,$
$-\infty < x < \infty.$

5. $(f/g)(x) = \dfrac{\sqrt{x + 3}}{x^2}; x + 3 \geq 0$ and $x \neq 0,$
so the domain is $[-3, 0) \cup (0, \infty).$
$(g/f)(x) = \dfrac{x^2}{\sqrt{x + 3}}; x + 3 > 0,$
so the domain is $(-3, \infty).$

6. $(f/g)(x) = \dfrac{\sqrt{x - 2}}{\sqrt{x + 4}} = \sqrt{\dfrac{x - 2}{x + 4}}; x - 2 \geq 0$ and
$x + 4 > 0$, so $x \geq 2$ and $x > -4$; the domain is $[2, \infty).$
$(g/f)(x) = \dfrac{\sqrt{x + 4}}{\sqrt{x - 2}} = \sqrt{\dfrac{x + 4}{x - 2}}; x + 4 \geq 0$ and
$x - 2 > 0$, so $x \geq -4$ and $x > 2$; the domain is $(2, \infty).$

7. $(f/g)(x) = \dfrac{x^2}{\sqrt{1 - x^2}}.$ The denominator cannot be zero
and the term under the square root must be positive, so
$1 - x^2 > 0.$ Therefore, $x^2 < 1$, which means that
$-1 < x < 1.$ The domain is $(-1, 1).$
$(g/f)(x) = \dfrac{\sqrt{1 - x^2}}{x^2}.$ The term under the square root
must be nonnegative, so $1 - x^2 \geq 0$ (or $x^2 \leq 1$). The
denominator cannot be zero, so $x \neq 0.$ Therefore,
$-1 \leq x < 0$ or $0 < x \leq 1.$ The domain is $[-1, 0) \cup (0, 1].$

8. $(f/g)(x) = \dfrac{x^3}{\sqrt[3]{1 - x^3}}.$ The denominator cannot be 0, so
$1 - x^3 \neq 0$ and $x^3 \neq 1.$ This means that $x \neq 1.$ There are
no restrictions on x in the numerator. The domain is
$(-\infty, 1) \cup (1, \infty).$
$(g/f)(x) = \dfrac{\sqrt[3]{1 - x^3}}{x^3}.$ The denominator cannot be 0, so
$x^3 \neq 0$ and $x \neq 0.$ There are no restrictions on x in the
numerator. The domain is $(-\infty, 0) \cup (0, \infty).$

9.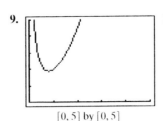
$[0, 5]$ by $[0, 5]$

10.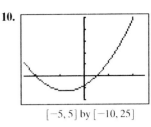
$[-5, 5]$ by $[-10, 25]$

11. $(f \circ g)(3) = f(g(3)) = f(4) = 5;$
$(g \circ f)(-2) = g(f(-2)) = g(-7) = -6$

12. $(f \circ g)(3) = f(g(3)) = f(3) = 8;$
$(g \circ f)(-2) = g(f(-2)) = g(3) = 3$

13. $(f \circ g)(3) = f(g(3)) = f(\sqrt{3 + 1}) = f(2) =$
$2^2 + 4 = 8;$
$(g \circ f)(-2) = g(f(-2)) = g((-2)^2 + 4)$
$\quad = g(8) = \sqrt{8 + 1} = 3$

14. $(f \circ g)(3) = f(g(3)) = f(9 - 3^2) = f(0) = \dfrac{0}{0 + 1} = 0;$
$(g \circ f)(-2) = g(f(-2)) = g\left(\dfrac{-2}{-2 + 1}\right)$
$\quad = g(2) = 9 - 2^2 = 5$

15. $f(g(x)) = 3(x - 1) + 2 = 3x - 3 + 2 = 3x - 1.$
Because both f and g have domain $(-\infty, \infty)$, the domain
of $f(g(x))$ is $(-\infty, \infty).$
$g(f(x)) = (3x + 2) - 1 = 3x + 1;$ again, the domain is
$(-\infty, \infty).$

16. $f(g(x)) = \left(\dfrac{1}{x - 1}\right)^2 - 1 = \dfrac{1}{(x - 1)^2} - 1.$ The domain
of g is $x \neq 1$, while the domain of f is $(-\infty, \infty)$, so the
domain of $f(g(x))$ is $x \neq 1$, or $(-\infty, 1) \cup (1, \infty).$
$g(f(x)) = \dfrac{1}{(x^2 - 1) - 1} = \dfrac{1}{x^2 - 2}.$
The domain of f is $(-\infty, \infty)$, while the domain of g is
$(-\infty, 1) \cup (1, \infty)$, so $g(f(x))$ requires that $f(x) \neq 1.$ This
means $x^2 - 1 \neq 1$, or $x^2 \neq 2$, so the domain of $g(f(x))$ is
$x \neq \pm\sqrt{2}$, or $(-\infty, -\sqrt{2}) \cup (-\sqrt{2}, \sqrt{2}) \cup (\sqrt{2}, \infty).$

17. $f(g(x)) = (\sqrt{x + 1})^2 - 2 = x + 1 - 2 = x - 1.$ The
domain of g is $x \geq -1$, while the domain of f is $(-\infty, \infty)$,
so the domain of $f(g(x))$ is $x \geq -1$, or $[-1, \infty).$
$g(f(x)) = \sqrt{(x^2 - 2) + 1} = \sqrt{x^2 - 1}.$ The domain of
f is $(-\infty, \infty)$, while the domain of g is $[-1, \infty)$, so
$g(f(x))$ requires that $f(x) \geq -1.$
This means $x^2 - 2 \geq -1$, or $x^2 \geq 1$, which means
$x \leq -1$ or $x \geq 1.$ Therefore the domain of $g(f(x))$ is
$(-\infty, -1] \cup [1, \infty).$

18. $f(g(x)) = \dfrac{1}{\sqrt{x} - 1}.$ The domain of g is $x \geq 0$, while the
domain of f is $(-\infty, 1) \cup (1, \infty)$, so $f(g(x))$ requires that
$x \geq 0$ and $g(x) \neq 1$, or $x \geq 0$, and $x \neq 1.$ The domain of
$f(g(x))$ is $[0, 1) \cup (1, \infty).$
$g(f(x)) = \sqrt{\dfrac{1}{x - 1}} = \dfrac{1}{\sqrt{x - 1}}.$ The domain of f is
$x \neq 1$, while the domain of g is $[0, \infty)$, so $g(f(x))$
requires that $x \neq 1$ and $f(x) \geq 0$, or $x \neq 1$ and
$\dfrac{1}{x - 1} \geq 0.$ The latter occurs if $x - 1 > 0$, so the
domain of $g(f(x))$ is $(1, \infty).$

19. $f(g(x)) = f(\sqrt{1 - x^2}) = (\sqrt{1 - x^2})^2 = 1 - x^2$;
the domain is $[-1, 1]$.
$g(f(x)) = g(x^2) = \sqrt{1 - (x^2)^2} = \sqrt{1 - x^4}$;
the domain is $[-1, 1]$.

20. $f(g(x)) = f(\sqrt[3]{1 - x^3}) = (\sqrt[3]{1 - x^3})^3 = 1 - x^3$;
the domain is $(-\infty, \infty)$.
$g(f(x)) = g(x^3) = \sqrt[3]{1 - (x^3)^3} = \sqrt[3]{1 - x^9}$;
the domain is $(-\infty, \infty)$.

21. $f(g(x)) = f\left(\dfrac{1}{3x}\right) = \dfrac{1}{2(1/3x)} = \dfrac{1}{2/3x} = \dfrac{3x}{2}$;
the domain is $(-\infty, 0) \cup (0, \infty)$.

$g(f(x)) = g\left(\dfrac{1}{2x}\right) = \dfrac{1}{3(1/2x)} = \dfrac{1}{3/2x} = \dfrac{2x}{3}$;
the domain is $(-\infty, 0) \cup (0, \infty)$.

22. $f(g(x)) = f\left(\dfrac{1}{x - 1}\right) = \dfrac{1}{(1/(x - 1)) + 1} = $
$\dfrac{1}{(1 + (x - 1))/(x - 1)} = \dfrac{1}{x/(x - 1)} = \dfrac{x - 1}{x}$;
the domain is all reals except 0 and 1.

$g(f(x)) = g\left(\dfrac{1}{x + 1}\right) = \dfrac{1}{(1/(x + 1)) - 1} = $
$\dfrac{1}{(1 + (x - 1))/(x + 1)} = \dfrac{1}{x/(x + 1)} = \dfrac{x + 1}{x}$;
the domain is all reals except 0 and 1.

23. One possibility: $f(x) = \sqrt{x}$ and $g(x) = x^2 - 5x$

24. One possibility: $f(x) = (x + 1)^2$ and $g(x) = x^3$

25. One possibility: $f(x) = |x|$ and $g(x) = 3x - 2$

26. One possibility: $f(x) = 1/x$ and $g(x) = x^3 - 5x + 3$

27. One possibility: $f(x) = x^5 - 2$ and $g(x) = x - 3$

28. One possibility: $f(x) = e^x$ and $g(x) = \sin x$

29. One possibility: $f(x) = \cos x$ and $g(x) = \sqrt{x}$.

30. One possibility: $f(x) = x^2 + 1$ and $g(x) = \tan x$.

31. $r = 48 + 0.03t$ in., so $V = \dfrac{4}{3}\pi r^3 = \dfrac{4}{3}\pi(48 + 0.03t)^3$;
when $t = 300$,
$V = \dfrac{4}{3}\pi(48 + 9)^3 = 246{,}924\pi \approx 775{,}734.6$ in^3.

32. The original diameter of each snowball is 4 in., so
the original radius is 2 in. and the original volume
$V = \dfrac{4}{3}\pi r^3 \approx 33.5$ in^3. The new volume is $V = 33.5 - t$,
where t is the number of 40-day periods. At the end
of 360 days, the new volume is $V = 33.5 - 9 = 24.5$.
Since $V = \dfrac{4}{3}\pi r^3$, we know that $r = \sqrt[3]{\dfrac{3V}{4\pi}} \approx 1.8$ in.
The diameter, then, is 2 times r, or ≈ 3.6 in.

33. The initial area is $(5)(7) = 35$ km^2. The new length and
width are $l = 5 + 2t$ and $w = 7 + 2t$, so $A = lw = $
$(5 + 2t)(7 + 2t)$. Solve $(7 + 2t)(5 + 2t) = 175$
(5 times its original size), either graphically or
algebraically: the positive solution is $t \approx 3.63$ seconds.

34. The initial volume is $(5)(7)(3) = 105$ cm^3. The new
length, width, and height are $l = 5 + 2t$, $w = 7 + 2t$,
and $h = 3 + 2t$, so the new volume is $V = $
$(5 + 2t)(7 + 2t)(3 + 2t)$. Solve graphically
$(5 + 2t)(7 + 2t)(3 + 2t) \geq 525$ (5 times the
original volume): $t \approx 1.62$ sec.

35. $3(1) + 4(1) = 3 + 4 = 7 \neq 5$
$3(4) + 4(-2) = 12 - 8 = 4 \neq 5$
$3(3) + 4(-1) = 9 - 4 = 5$
The answer is $(3, -1)$.

36. $(5)^2 + (1)^2 = 25 + 1 = 26 \neq 25$
$(3)^2 + (4)^2 = 9 + 16 = 25$
$(0)^2 + (-5)^2 = 0 + 25 = 25$
The answer is $(3, 4)$ and $(0, -5)$.

37. $y^2 = 25 - x^2$, $y = \sqrt{25 - x^2}$ and $y = -\sqrt{25 - x^2}$

38. $y^2 = 25 - x$, $y = \sqrt{25 - x}$ and $y = -\sqrt{25 - x}$

39. $y^2 = x^2 - 25$, $y = \sqrt{x^2 - 25}$ and $y = -\sqrt{x^2 - 25}$

40. $y^2 = 3x^2 - 25$, $y = \sqrt{3x^2 - 25}$ and $y = -\sqrt{3x^2 - 25}$

41. $x + |y| = 1 \Rightarrow |y| = -x + 1 \Rightarrow y = -x + 1$ or
$y = -(-x + 1)$. $y = 1 - x$ and $y = x - 1$

42. $x - |y| = 1 \Rightarrow |y| = x - 1 \Rightarrow y = x - 1$ or
$y = -(x - 1) = -x + 1$. $y = x - 1$ and $y = 1 - x$

43. $y^2 = x^2 \Rightarrow y = x$ and $y = -x$ or $y = |x|$ and $y = -|x|$

44. $y^2 = x \Rightarrow y = \sqrt{x}$ and $y = -\sqrt{x}$

45. False. If $g(x) = 0$, then $\left(\dfrac{f}{g}\right)(x)$ is not defined and 0 is
not in the domain of $\left(\dfrac{f}{g}\right)(x)$, even though 0 may be in
the domains of both $f(x)$ and $g(x)$.

46. False. For a number to be in the domain of $(fg)(x)$, it
must be in the domains of *both* $f(x)$ and $g(x)$, so that
$f(x)$ and $g(x)$ are both defined.

47. Composition of functions isn't necessarily commutative.
The answer is C.

48. $g(x) = \sqrt{4 - x}$ cannot equal zero and the term under
the square root must be positive, so x can be any real
number less than 4. The answer is A.

49. $(f \circ f)(x) = f(x^2 + 1) = (x^2 + 1)^2 + 1 = $
$(x^4 + 2x^2 + 1) + 1 = x^4 + 2x^2 + 2$. The answer is E.

50. $y = |x| \Rightarrow y = x$, $y = -x$; $y = -x \Rightarrow x = -y$; $x = -y$
or $x = y \Rightarrow x^2 = y^2$. The answer is B.

51. If $f(x) = e^x$ and $g(x) = 2 \ln x$, then $f(g(x)) = f(2 \ln x)$
$= e^{2 \ln x} = (e^{\ln x})^2 = x^2$. The domain is $(0, \infty)$.

If $f(x) = (x^2 + 2)^2$ and $g(x) = \sqrt{x - 2}$, then
$f(g(x)) = f(\sqrt{x - 2}) = ((\sqrt{x - 2})^2 + 2)^2 = $
$(x - 2 + 2)^2 = x^2$. The domain is $[2, \infty)$.

If $f(x) = (x^2 - 2)^2$ and $g(x) = \sqrt{2 - x}$, then
$f(g(x)) = f(\sqrt{2 - x}) = ((\sqrt{2 - x})^2 - 2)^2 = $
$(2 - x - 2)^2 = x^2$. The domain is $(-\infty, 2]$.

If $f(x) = \dfrac{1}{(x-1)^2}$ and $g(x) = \dfrac{x+1}{x}$, then

$$f(g(x)) = f\left(\dfrac{x+1}{x}\right) = \dfrac{1}{\left(\dfrac{x+1}{x} - 1\right)^2} =$$

$$\dfrac{1}{\left(\dfrac{x+1-x}{x}\right)^2} = \dfrac{1}{\dfrac{1}{x^2}} = x^2. \text{ The domain is } x \neq 0.$$

If $f(x) = x^2 - 2x + 1$ and $g(x) = x + 1$, then
$f(g(x)) = f(x+1) = (x+1)^2 - 2(x+1) + 1 = ((x+1) - 1)^2 = x^2.$ The domain is $(-\infty, \infty)$.

If $f(x) = \left(\dfrac{x+1}{x}\right)^2$ and $g(x) = \dfrac{1}{x-1}$, then

$$f(g(x)) = f\left(\dfrac{1}{x-1}\right) = \left(\dfrac{\dfrac{1}{x-1} + 1}{\dfrac{1}{x-1}}\right)^2 =$$

$$\left(\dfrac{\dfrac{1+x-1}{x-1}}{\dfrac{1}{x-1}}\right)^2 = x^2. \text{ The domain is } x \neq 1.$$

f	g	D
e^x	$2\ln x$	$(0, \infty)$
$(x^2 + 2)^2$	$\sqrt{x-2}$	$[2, \infty)$
$(x^2 - 2)^2$	$\sqrt{2-x}$	$(-\infty, 2]$
$\dfrac{1}{(x-1)^2}$	$\dfrac{x+1}{x}$	$x \neq 0$
$x^2 - 2x + 1$	$x + 1$	$(-\infty, \infty)$
$\left(\dfrac{x+1}{x}\right)^2$	$\dfrac{1}{x-1}$	$x \neq 1$

52. (a) $(fg)(x) = x^4 - 1 = (x^2 + 1)(x^2 - 1) = f(x) \cdot (x^2 - 1)$, so $g(x) = x^2 - 1$.

(b) $(f + g)(x) = 3x^2 \Rightarrow 3x^2 - (x^2 + 1) = 2x^2 - 1 = g(x)$.

(c) $(f/g)(x) = 1 \Rightarrow f(x) = g(x)$. So $g(x) = x^2 + 1$.

(d) $f(g(x)) = 9x^4 + 1$ and $f(x) = x^2 + 1$. If $g(x) = 3x^2$, then $f(g(x)) = f(3x^2) = (3x^2)^2 + 1 = 9x^4 + 1$.

(e) $g(f(x)) = 9x^4 + 1$ and $f(x) = x^2 + 1$. Then $g(x^2 + 1) = 9x^4 + 1 = 9((x^2 + 1) - 1)^2 + 1$, so $g(x) = 9(x-1)^2 + 1$.

53. (a) $(f + g)(x) = (g + f)(x) = f(x)$ if $g(x) = 0$.

(b) $(fg)(x) = (gf)(x) = f(x)$ if $g(x) = 1$.

(c) $(f \circ g)(x) = (g \circ f)(x) = f(x)$ if $g(x) = x$.

54. Yes, by definition, function composition is associative. That is, $(f \circ (g \circ h))(x) = f(g(h))(x)$ and $((f \circ g) \circ h)(x) = f(g(h))(x)$.

55. $y^2 + x^2 y - 5 = 0$. Using the quadratic formula,

$$y = \dfrac{-x^2 \pm \sqrt{(x^2)^2 - 4(1)(-5)}}{2}$$

$$= \dfrac{-x^2 \pm \sqrt{x^4 + 20}}{2}$$

so, $y_1 = \dfrac{-x^2 + \sqrt{x^4 + 20}}{2}$

and $y_2 = \dfrac{-x^2 - \sqrt{x^4 + 20}}{2}$.

$[-9.4, 9.4]$ by $[-6.2, 6.2]$

■ Section 1.5   Parametric Relations and Inverses

Exploration 1

1. T starts at -4, at the point $(8, -3)$. It stops at $T = 2$, at the point $(8, 3)$. 61 points are computed.

2. The graph is smoother because the plotted points are closer together.

3. The graph is less smooth because the plotted points are further apart. In CONNECT mode, they are connected by straight lines.

4. The smaller the Tstep, the slower the graphing proceeds. This is because the calculator has to compute more X and Y values.

5. The grapher skips directly from the point $(0, -1)$ to the point $(0, 1)$, corresponding to the T-values $T = -2$ and $T = 0$. The two points are connected by a straight line, hidden by the Y-axis.

6. With the Tmin set at -1, the grapher begins at the point $(-1, 0)$, missing the bottom of the curve entirely.

7. Leave everything else the same, but change Tmin back to -4 and Tmax to -1.

Quick Review 1.5

1. $3y = x + 6$, so $y = \dfrac{x+6}{3} = \dfrac{1}{3}x + 2$

2. $0.5y = x - 1$, so $y = \dfrac{x-1}{0.5} = 2x - 2$

3. $y^2 = x - 4$, so $y = \pm\sqrt{x-4}$

4. $y^2 = x + 6$, so $y = \pm\sqrt{x+6}$

5. $x(y + 3) = y - 2$
$xy + 3x = y - 2$
$xy - y = -3x - 2$
$y(x - 1) = -(3x + 2)$
$$y = -\dfrac{3x+2}{x-1} = \dfrac{3x+2}{1-x}$$

6. $x(y + 2) = 3y - 1$
$xy + 2x = 3y - 1$
$xy - 3y = -2x - 1$
$y(x - 3) = -(2x + 1)$
$$y = -\frac{2x + 1}{x - 3} = \frac{2x + 1}{3 - x}$$

7. $x(y - 4) = 2y + 1$
$xy - 4x = 2y + 1$
$xy - 2y = 4x + 1$
$y(x - 2) = 4x + 1$
$$y = \frac{4x + 1}{x - 2}$$

8. $x(3y - 1) = 4y + 3$
$3xy - x = 4y + 3$
$3xy - 4y = x + 3$
$y(3x - 4) = x + 3$
$$y = \frac{x + 3}{3x - 4}$$

9. $x = \sqrt{y + 3}, y \geq -3$ [and $x \geq 0$]
$x^2 = y + 3, y \geq -3$, and $x \geq 0$
$y = x^2 - 3, y \geq -3$, and $x \geq 0$

10. $x = \sqrt{y - 2}, y \geq 2$ [and $x \geq 0$]
$x^2 = y - 2, y \geq 2$, and $x \geq 0$
$y = x^2 + 2, y \geq 2$, and $x \geq 0$

Section 1.5 Exercises

1. $x = 3(2) = 6, y = 2^2 + 5 = 9$. The answer is $(6, 9)$.

2. $x = 5(-2) - 7 = -17, y = 17 - 3(-2) = 23$. The answer is $(-17, 23)$.

3. $x = 3^3 - 4(3) = 15, y = \sqrt{3 + 1} = 2$. The answer is $(15, 2)$.

4. $x = |-8 + 3| = 5, y = \dfrac{1}{-8} = -\dfrac{1}{8}$

5. (a)

t	$(x, y) = (2t, 3t - 1)$
-3	$(-6, -10)$
-2	$(-4, -7)$
-1	$(-2, -4)$
0	$(0, -1)$
1	$(2, 2)$
2	$(4, 5)$
3	$(6, 8)$

(b) $t = \dfrac{x}{2}, y = 3\left(\dfrac{x}{2}\right) - 1 = 1.5x - 1$. This is a function.

(c)
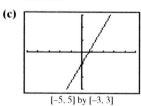
[-5, 5] by [-3, 3]

6. (a)

t	$(x, y) = (t + 1, t^2 - 2t)$
-3	$(-2, 15)$
-2	$(-1, 8)$
-1	$(0, 3)$
0	$(1, 0)$
1	$(2, -1)$
2	$(3, 0)$
3	$(4, 3)$

(b) $t = x - 1, y = (x - 1)^2 - 2(x - 1)$
$= x^2 - 2x + 1 - 2x + 2$
$= x^2 - 4x + 3$
This is a function.

(c)
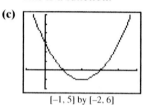
[-1, 5] by [-2, 6]

7. (a)

t	$(x, y) = (t^2, t - 2)$
-3	$(9, -5)$
-2	$(4, -4)$
-1	$(1, -3)$
0	$(0, -2)$
1	$(1, -1)$
2	$(4, 0)$
3	$(9, 1)$

(b) $t = y + 2, x = (y + 2)^2$. This is not a function.

(c)
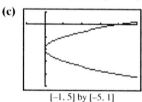
[-1, 5] by [-5, 1]

8. (a)

t	$(x, y) = (\sqrt{t}, 2t - 5)$
-3	$\sqrt{-3}$ not defined
-2	$\sqrt{-2}$ not defined
-1	$\sqrt{-1}$ not defined
0	$(0, -5)$
1	$(1, -3)$
2	$(\sqrt{2}, -1)$
3	$(\sqrt{3}, 1)$

(b) $t = x^2, y = 2x^2 - 5$. This is a function.

(c)
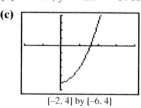
[-2, 4] by [-6, 4]

9. (a) By the vertical line test, the relation is not a function.

  (b) By the horizontal line test, the relation's inverse is a function.

10. (a) By the vertical line test, the relation is a function.

  (b) By the horizontal line test, the relation's inverse is not a function.

11. (a) By the vertical line test, the relation is a function.

  (b) By the horizontal line test, the relation's inverse is a function.

12. (a) By the vertical line test, the relation is not a function.

  (b) By the horizontal line test, the relation's inverse is a function.

13. $y = 3x - 6 \Rightarrow$
$$x = 3y - 6$$
$$3y = x + 6$$
$$f^{-1}(x) = y = \frac{x + 6}{3} = \frac{1}{3}x + 2; (-\infty, \infty)$$

14. $y = 2x + 5 \Rightarrow$
$$x = 2y + 5$$
$$2y = x - 5$$
$$f^{-1}(x) = y = \frac{x - 5}{2} = \frac{1}{2}x - \frac{5}{2};$$
$$(-\infty, \infty)$$

15. $y = \frac{2x - 3}{x + 1} \Rightarrow$
$$x = \frac{2y - 3}{y + 1}$$
$$x(y + 1) = 2y - 3$$
$$xy + x = 2y - 3$$
$$xy - 2y = -x - 3$$
$$y(x - 2) = -(x + 3)$$
$$f^{-1}(x) = y = -\frac{x + 3}{x - 2} = \frac{x + 3}{2 - x};$$
$$(-\infty, 2) \cup (2, \infty)$$

16. $y = \frac{x + 3}{x - 2} \Rightarrow$
$$x = \frac{y + 3}{y - 2}$$
$$x(y - 2) = y + 3$$
$$xy - 2x = y + 3$$
$$xy - y = 2x + 3$$
$$y(x - 1) = 2x + 3$$
$$f^{-1}(x) = y = \frac{2x + 3}{x - 1};$$
$$x \neq 1 \text{ or } (-\infty, 1) \cup (1, \infty)$$

17. $y = \sqrt{x - 3}, x \geq 3, y \geq 0 \Rightarrow$
$$x = \sqrt{y - 3}, \quad x \geq 0, y \geq 3$$
$$x^2 = y - 3, \quad x \geq 0, y \geq 3$$
$$f^{-1}(x) = y = x^2 + 3, \quad x \geq 0$$

18. $y = \sqrt{x + 2}, x \geq -2, y \geq 0 \Rightarrow$
$$x = \sqrt{y + 2}, \quad x \geq 0, y \geq -2$$
$$x^2 = y + 2, \quad x \geq 0, y \geq -2$$
$$f^{-1}(x) = y = x^2 - 2, \quad x \geq 0$$

19. $y = x^3 \Rightarrow$
$$x = y^3$$
$$f^{-1}(x) = y = \sqrt[3]{x} \; ; (-\infty, \infty)$$

20. $y = x^3 + 5 \Rightarrow$
$$x = y^3 + 5$$
$$x - 5 = y^3$$
$$f^{-1}(x) = y = \sqrt[3]{x - 5}; (-\infty, \infty)$$

21. $y = \sqrt[3]{x + 5} \Rightarrow \quad x = \sqrt[3]{y + 5}$
$$x^3 = y + 5$$
$$f^{-1}(x) = y = x^3 - 5; (-\infty, \infty)$$

22. $y = \sqrt[3]{x - 2} \Rightarrow \quad x = \sqrt[3]{y - 2}$
$$x^3 = y - 2$$
$$f^{-1}(x) = y = x^3 + 2; (-\infty, \infty)$$

23. One-to-one

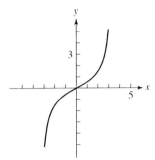

24. Not one-to-one

25. One-to-one

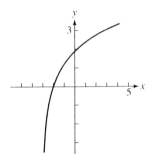

26. Not one-to-one

27. $f(g(x)) = 3\left[\frac{1}{3}(x + 2)\right] - 2 = x + 2 - 2 = x;$
$$g(f(x)) = \frac{1}{3}[(3x - 2) + 2] = \frac{1}{3}(3x) = x$$

28. $f(g(x)) = \frac{1}{4}[(4x - 3) + 3] = \frac{1}{4}(4x) = x;$
$$g(f(x)) = 4\left[\frac{1}{4}(x + 3)\right] - 3 = x + 3 - 3 = x$$

29. $f(g(x)) = [(x - 1)^{1/3}]^3 + 1 = (x - 1)^1 + 1$
$$= x - 1 + 1 = x;$$
$$g(f(x)) = [(x^3 + 1) - 1]^{1/3} = (x^3)^{1/3} = x^1 = x$$

30. $f(g(x)) = \frac{7}{\frac{7}{x}} = \frac{7}{1} \cdot \frac{x}{7} = x; g(x(x)) = \frac{7}{\frac{7}{x}} = \frac{7}{1} \cdot \frac{x}{7} = x$

31. $f(g(x)) = \dfrac{\frac{1}{x - 1} + 1}{\frac{1}{x - 1}} = (x - 1)\left(\frac{1}{x - 1} + 1\right)$
$$= 1 + x - 1 = x;$$
$$g(f(x)) = \frac{1}{\frac{1}{x + 1} - 1} = \left(\frac{1}{\frac{x + 1}{x} - 1}\right) \cdot \frac{x}{x}$$
$$= \frac{x}{x + 1 - x} = \frac{x}{1} = x$$

32. $f(g(x)) = \dfrac{\dfrac{2x+3}{x-1}+3}{\dfrac{2x+3}{x-1}-2} = \left(\dfrac{\dfrac{2x+3}{x-1}+3}{\dfrac{2x+3}{x-1}-2}\right) \cdot \left(\dfrac{x-1}{x-1}\right)$

$= \dfrac{2x+3+3(x-1)}{2x+3-2(x-1)} = \dfrac{5x}{5} = x;$

$g(f(x)) = \dfrac{2\left(\dfrac{x+3}{x-2}\right)+3}{\dfrac{x+3}{x-2}-1}$

$= \left[\dfrac{2\left(\dfrac{x+3}{x-2}\right)+3}{\dfrac{x+3}{x-2}-1}\right] \cdot \left(\dfrac{x-2}{x-2}\right)$

$= \dfrac{2(x+3)+3(x-2)}{x+3-(x-2)} = \dfrac{5x}{5} = x$

33. (a) $y = (1.08)(100) = 108$ euros

(b) $x = \dfrac{y}{1.08} = \dfrac{25}{27}y.$ This converts euros (x) to dollars (y).

(c) $x = (0.9259)(48) = \$44.44$

34. (a) $9c(x) = 5(x-32)$

$\dfrac{9}{5}c(x) = x - 32$

$\dfrac{9}{5}c(x) + 32 = x$

In this case, $c(x)$ becomes x, and x becomes $c^{-1}(x)$ for the inverse. So, $c^{-1}(x) = \dfrac{9}{5}x + 32.$ This converts Celsius temperature to Fahrenheit temperature.

(b) $(k \circ c)(x) = k(c(x)) = k\left(\dfrac{5}{9}(x-32)\right)$

$\dfrac{5}{9}(x-32) + 273.16 = \dfrac{5}{9}x + 255.38.$ This is used to convert Fahrenheit temperature to Kelvin temperature.

35. $y = e^x$ and $y = \ln x$ are inverses. If we restrict the domain of the function $y = x^2$ to the interval $[0, \infty)$, then the restricted function and $y = \sqrt{x}$ are inverses.

36. $y = x$ and $y = 1/x$ are their own inverses.

37. $y = |x|$

38. $y = x$

39. True. All the ordered pairs swap domain and range values.

40. True. This is a parametrization of the line $y = 2x + 1$.

41. The inverse of the relation given by $x^2y + 5y = 9$ is the relation given by $y^2x + 5x = 9$.

$(1)^2(2) + 5(2) = 2 + 10 = 12 \neq 9$
$(1)^2(-2) + 5(-2) = -2 - 10 = -12 \neq 9$
$(2)^2(-1) + 5(-1) = -4 - 5 = -9 \neq 9$
$(-1)^2(2) + 5(2) = 2 + 10 = 12 \neq 9$
$(-2)^2(1) + 5(1) = 4 + 5 = 9$
The answer is E.

42. The inverse of the relation given by $xy^2 - 3x = 12$ is the relation given by $yx^2 - 3y = 12$.

$(-4)(0)^2 - 3(-4) = 0 + 12 = 12$
$(1)(4)^2 - 3(1) = 16 - 3 = 13 \neq 12$
$(2)(3)^2 - 3(2) = 18 - 6 = 12$
$(12)(2)^2 - 3(12) = 48 - 36 = 12$
$(-6)(1)^2 - 3(-6) = -6 + 18 = 12$
The answer is B.

43. $f(x) = 3x - 2$
$y = 3x - 2$
The inverse relation is
$x = 3y - 2$
$x + 2 = 3y$
$\dfrac{x+2}{3} = y$
$f^{-1}(x) = \dfrac{x+2}{3}$
The answer is C.

44. $f(x) = x^3 + 1$
$y = x^3 + 1$
The inverse relation is
$x = y^3 + 1$
$x - 1 = y^3$
$\sqrt[3]{x-1} = y$
$f^{-1}(x) = \sqrt[3]{x-1}$
The answer is A.

45. (Answers may vary.)

(a) If the graph of f is unbroken, its reflection in the line $y = x$ will be also.

(b) Both f and its inverse must be one-to-one in order to be inverse functions.

(c) Since f is odd, $(-x, -y)$ is on the graph whenever (x, y) is. This implies that $(-y, -x)$ is on the graph of f^{-1} whenever (x, y) is. That implies that f^{-1} is odd.

(d) Let $y = f(x)$. Since the ratio of Δy to Δx is positive, the ratio of Δx to Δy is positive. Any ratio of Δy to Δx on the graph of f^{-1} is the same as some ratio of Δx to Δy on the graph of f, hence positive. This implies that f^{-1} is increasing.

46. (Answers may vary.)

(a) $f(x) = e^x$ has a horizontal asymptote; $f^{-1}(x) = \ln x$ does not.

(b) $f(x) = e^x$ has domain all real numbers; $f^{-1}(x) = \ln x$ does not.

(c) $f(x) = e^x$ has a graph that is bounded below; $f^{-1}(x) = \ln x$ does not.

(d) $f(x) = \dfrac{x^2 - 25}{x - 5}$ has a removable discontinuity at $x = 5$ because its graph is the line $y = x + 5$ with the point $(5, 10)$ removed. The inverse function is the line $y = x - 5$ with the point $(10, 5)$ removed. This function has a removable discontinuity, but not at $x = 5$.

47. (a) $\dfrac{\Delta y}{\Delta x} = \dfrac{97 - 70}{88 - 52} = \dfrac{27}{36} = 0.75$, which gives us the slope of the equation. To find the rest of the equation, we use one of the initial points
$$y - 70 = 0.75(x - 52)$$
$$y = 0.75x - 39 + 70$$
$$y = 0.75x + 31$$

(b) To find the inverse, we substitute y for x and x for y, and then solve for y:
$$x = 0.75y + 31$$
$$x - 31 = 0.75y$$
$$y = \frac{4}{3}(x - 31)$$

The inverse function converts scaled scores to raw scores.

48. The function must be increasing so that the *order* of the students' grades, top to bottom, will remain the same after scaling as it is before scaling. A student with a raw score of 136 gets dropped to 133, but that will still be higher than the scaled score for a student with 134.

49. (a) It does not clear the fence.

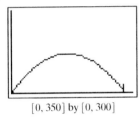

$[0, 350]$ by $[0, 300]$

(b) It still does not clear the fence.

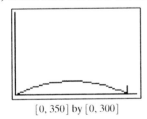

$[0, 350]$ by $[0, 300]$

(c) Optimal angle is 45°. It clears the fence.

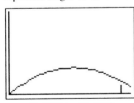

$[0, 350]$ by $[0, 300]$

50. (a)
$$x = \left(\frac{3^{1.7}}{30}(y - 65)\right)^{\frac{1}{1.7}} + 1$$
$$x - 1 = \left(\frac{3^{1.7}}{30}(y - 65)\right)^{\frac{1}{1.7}}$$
$$(x - 1)^{1.7} = \left(\frac{3^{1.7}}{30}(y - 65)\right)$$
$$\frac{30}{3^{1.7}}(x - 1)^{1.7} = y - 65$$
$$y = \frac{30}{3^{1.7}}(x - 1)^{1.7} + 65$$

This can be use to convert GPA's to percentage grades.

(b) Yes; x is restricted to the domain $[1, 4.28]$.

(c)

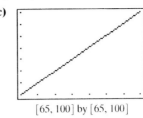

$[65, 100]$ by $[65, 100]$

The composition function of $(y \circ y^{-1})(x)$ is $y = x$, so they are inverses.

51. When $k = 1$, the scaling function is linear. Opinions will vary as to which is the best value of k.

■ Section 1.6 Graphical Transformations

Exploration 1

1.

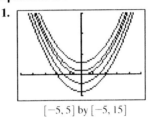

$[-5, 5]$ by $[-5, 15]$

They raise or lower the parabola along the y-axis.

2.

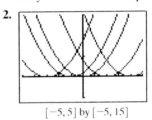

$[-5, 5]$ by $[-5, 15]$

They move the parabola left or right along the x-axis.

3.

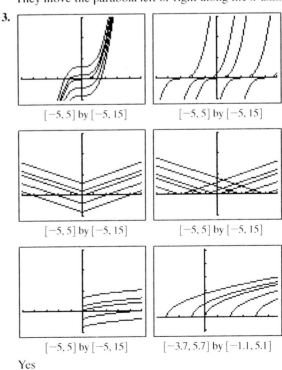

$[-5, 5]$ by $[-5, 15]$ $[-5, 5]$ by $[-5, 15]$

$[-5, 5]$ by $[-5, 15]$ $[-5, 5]$ by $[-5, 15]$

$[-5, 5]$ by $[-5, 15]$ $[-3.7, 5.7]$ by $[-1.1, 5.1]$

Yes

Exploration 2

1.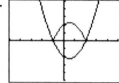

Graph C. Points with positive y-coordinates remain unchanged, while points with negative y-coordinates are reflected across the x-axis.

2.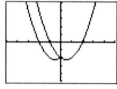

Graph A. Points with positive x-coordinates remain unchanged. Since the new function is even, the graph for negative x-values will be a reflection of the graph for positive x-values.

3.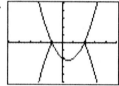

Graph F. The graph will be a reflection across the x-axis of graph C.

4.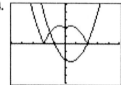

Graph D. The points with negative y-coordinates in graph A are reflected across the x-axis.

Exploration 3

1.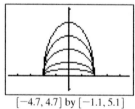

$[-4.7, 4.7]$ by $[-1.1, 5.1]$

The 1.5 and the 2 stretch the graph vertically; the 0.5 and the 0.25 shrink the graph vertically.

2.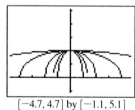

$[-4.7, 4.7]$ by $[-1.1, 5.1]$

The 1.5 and the 2 shrink the graph horizontally; the 0.5 and the 0.25 stretch the graph horizontally.

Quick Review 1.6

1. $(x + 1)^2$

2. $(x - 3)^2$

3. $(x + 6)^2$

4. $(2x + 1)^2$

5. $(x - 5/2)^2$

6. $(2x - 5)^2$

7. $x^2 - 4x + 4 + 3x - 6 + 4 = x^2 - x + 2$

8. $2(x^2 + 6x + 9) - 5x - 15 - 2 =$ $2x^2 + 12x + 18 - 5x - 17 = 2x^2 + 7x + 1$

9. $(x^3 - 3x^2 + 3x - 1) + 3(x^2 - 2x + 1) - 3x + 3$ $= x^3 - 3x^2 + 2 + 3x^2 - 6x + 3 = x^3 - 6x + 5$

10. $2(x^3 + 3x^2 + 3x + 1) - 6(x^2 + 2x + 1) +$ $6x + 6 - 2 = 2x^3 + 6x^2 + 6x + 2 - 6x^2 - 12x$ $- 6 + 6x + 6 - 2 = 2x^3$

Section 1.6 Exercises

1. Vertical translation down 3 units

2. Vertical translation up 5.2 units

3. Horizontal translation left 4 units

4. Horizontal translation right 3 units

5. Horizontal translation to the right 100 units

6. Vertical translation down 100 units

7. Horizontal translation to the right 1 unit, and vertical translation up 3 units

8. Horizontal translation to the left 50 units and vertical translation down 279 units

9. Reflection across x-axis

10. Horizontal translation right 5 units

11. Reflection across y-axis

12. This can be written as $y = \sqrt{-(x - 3)}$ or $y = \sqrt{-x + 3}$. The first of these can be interpreted as reflection across the y-axis followed by a horizontal translation to the right 3 units. The second may be viewed as a horizontal translation left 3 units followed by a reflection across the y-axis.

Note that when combining horizontal changes (horizontal translations and reflections across the y-axis), the order is "backwards" from what one may first expect: With $y = \sqrt{-(x - 3)}$, although we first subtract 3 from x then negate, the order of transformations is reflect then translate. With $y = \sqrt{-x + 3}$, although we negate x then add 3, the order of transformations is translate then reflect.

For #13–20, recognize $y = c \cdot x^3 \; (c > 0)$ as a vertical stretch (if $c > 1$) or shrink (if $0 < c < 1$) of factor c, and $y = (c \cdot x)^3$ as a horizontal shrink (if $c > 1$) or stretch (if $0 < c < 1$) of factor $1/c$. Note also that $y = (c \cdot x)^3 = c^3x^3$, so that for this function, any horizontal stretch/shrink can be interpreted as an equivalent vertical shrink/stretch (and vice versa).

13. Vertically stretch by 2

14. Horizontally shrink by 1/2, or vertically stretch by $2^3 = 8$

15. Horizontally stretch by $1/0.2 = 5$, or vertically shrink by $0.2^3 = 0.008$

16. Vertically shrink by 0.3

17. $g(x) = \sqrt{x - 6} + 2 = f(x - 6)$; starting with f, translate right 6 units to get g.

18. $g(x) = -(x + 4 - 1)^2 = -f(x + 4)$; starting with f, translate left 4 units, and reflect across the x-axis to get g.

19. $g(x) = -(x + 4 - 2)^3 = -f(x + 4)$; starting with f, translate left 4 units, and reflect across the x-axis to get g.

20. $g(x) = 2|2x| = 2f(x)$; starting with f, vertically stretch by 2 to get g.

21.

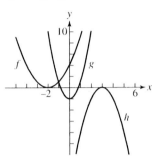

22.

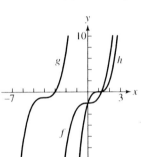

23.

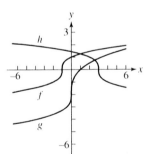

24.

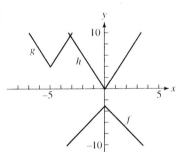

25. Since the graph is translated left 5 units, $f(x) = \sqrt{x + 5}$.

26. The graph is reflected across the y-axis and translated right 3 units. $y = \sqrt{-x}$ would be reflected across the y-axis; the horizontal translation gives
$f(x) = \sqrt{-(x - 3)} = \sqrt{3 - x}$.
See also Exercise 12 in this section, and note accompanying that solution.

27. The graph is reflected across the x-axis, translated left 2 units, and translated up 3 units. $y = -\sqrt{x}$ would be reflected across the x-axis, $y = -\sqrt{x + 2}$ adds the horizontal translation, and finally, the vertical translation gives $f(x) = -\sqrt{x + 2} + 3 = 3 - \sqrt{x + 2}$.

28. The graph is vertically stretched by 2, translated left 5 units, and translated down 3 units. $y = 2\sqrt{x}$ would be vertically stretched, $y = 2\sqrt{x + 5}$ adds the horizontal translation, and finally, the vertical translation gives $f(x) = 2\sqrt{x + 5} - 3$.

29. (a) $y = -f(x) = -(x^3 - 5x^2 - 3x + 2)$
$\qquad = -x^3 + 5x^2 + 3x - 2$

(b) $y = f(-x) = (-x)^3 - 5(-x)^2 - 3(-x) + 2$
$\qquad = -x^3 - 5x^2 + 3x + 2$

30. (a) $y = -f(x) = -(2\sqrt{x + 3} - 4) = -2\sqrt{x + 3} + 4$

(b) $y = f(-x) = 2\sqrt{-x + 3} - 4 = 2\sqrt{3 - x} - 4$

31. (a) $y = -f(x) = -(\sqrt[3]{8x}) = -2\sqrt[3]{x}$

(b) $y = f(-x) = \sqrt[3]{8(-x)} = \sqrt[3]{-8x} = -2\sqrt[3]{x}$

32. (a) $y = -f(x) = -3|x + 5|$

(b) $y = f(-x) = 3|-x + 5| = 3|5 - x|$

33. Let f be an odd function; that is, $f(-x) = -f(x)$ for all x in the domain of f. To reflect the graph of $y = f(x)$ across the y-axis, we make the transformation $y = f(-x)$. But $f(-x) = -f(x)$ for all x in the domain of f, so this transformation results in $y = -f(x)$. That is exactly the translation that reflects the graph of f across the x-axis, so the two reflections yield the same graph.

34. Let f be an odd function; that is, $f(-x) = -f(x)$ for all x in the domain of f. To reflect the graph of $y = f(x)$ across the y-axis, we make the transformation $y = f(-x)$. Then, reflecting across the x-axis yields $y = -f(-x)$. But $f(-x) = -f(x)$ for all x in the domain of f, so we have $y = -f(-x) = -[-f(x)] = f(x)$; that is, the original function.

35.

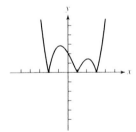

36.

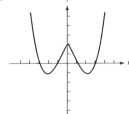

37.

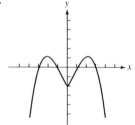

38.

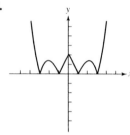

39. (a) $y_1 = 2y = 2(x^3 - 4x) = 2x^3 - 8x$

(b) $y_2 = f\left(\dfrac{x}{\frac{1}{3}}\right) = f(3x) = (3x)^3 - 4(3x) = 27x^3 - 12x$

40. (a) $y_1 = 2y = 2|x + 2|$

(b) $y_2 = f(3x) = |3x + 2|$

41. (a) $y_1 = 2y = 2(x^2 + x - 2) = 2x^2 + 2x - 4$

(b) $y_2 = f(3x) = (3x)^2 + 3x - 2 = 9x^2 + 3x - 2$

42. (a) $y_1 = 2y = 2\left(\dfrac{1}{x + 2}\right) = \dfrac{2}{x + 2}$

(b) $y_2 = f(3x) = \dfrac{1}{3x + 2}$

43. Starting with $y = x^2$, translate right 3 units, vertically stretch by 2, and translate down 4 units.

44. Starting with $y = \sqrt{x}$, translate left 1 unit, vertically stretch by 3, and reflect across x-axis.

45. Starting with $y = x^2$, ~~horizontally shrink by $\frac{1}{3}$ and~~ *vert stretch 9* translate down 4 units.

46. Starting with $y = |x|$, translate left 4 units, vertically stretch by 2, reflect across x-axis, and translate up 1 unit.

47. First stretch (multiply right side by 3): $y = 3x^2$, then translate (replace x with $x - 4$): $y = 3(x - 4)^2$.

48. First translate (replace x with $x - 4$): $y = (x - 4)^2$, then stretch (multiply right side by 3): $y = 3(x - 4)^2$.

49. First translate left (replace x with $x + 2$): $y = |x + 2|$, then stretch (multiply right side by 2): $y = 2|x + 2|$, then translate down (subtract 4 from the right side): $y = 2|x + 2| - 4$.

50. First translate left (replace x with $x + 2$): $y = |x + 2|$, then shrink (replace x with $2x$): $y = |2x + 2|$, then translate down (subtract 4 from the right side): $y = |2x + 2| - 4$. This can be simplified to $y = |2(x + 1)| - 4 = 2|x + 1| - 4$.

To make the sketches for #51–54, it is useful to apply the described transformations to several selected points on the graph. The original graph here has vertices $(-2, -4)$, $(0, 0)$, $(2, 2)$, and $(4, 0)$; in the solutions below, the images of these four points are listed.

51. Translate left 1 unit, then vertically stretch by 3, and finally translate up 2 units. The four vertices are transformed to $(-3, -10)$, $(-1, 2)$, $(1, 8)$, and $(3, 2)$.

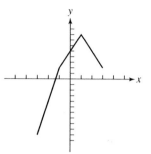

52. Translate left 1 unit, then reflect across the x-axis, and finally translate up 1 unit. The four vertices are transformed to $(-3, 5)$, $(-1, 1)$, $(1, -1)$, and $(3, 1)$.

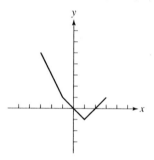

53. Horizontally shrink by $\dfrac{1}{2}$. The four vertices are transformed to $(-1, -4)$, $(0, 0)$, $(1, 2)$, $(2, 0)$.

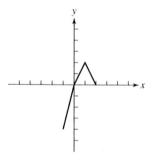

54. Translate right 1 unit, then vertically stretch by 2, and finally translate up 2 units. The four vertices are transformed to $(-1, -6)$, $(1, 2)$, $(3, 6)$, and $(5, 2)$.

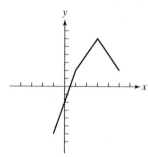

55. Reflections have more effect on points that are farther away from the line of reflection. Translations affect the distance of points from the axes, and hence change the effect of the reflections.

56. The x-intercepts are the values at which the function equals zero. The stretching (or shrinking) factors have no effect on the number zero, so those y-coordinates do not change.

57. First vertically stretch by $\dfrac{9}{5}$, then translate up 32 units.

58. Solve for C: $F = \dfrac{9}{5}C + 32$, so $C = \dfrac{5}{9}(F - 32) =$ $\dfrac{5}{9}F - \dfrac{160}{9}$. First vertically shrink by $\dfrac{5}{9}$, then translate down $\dfrac{160}{9} = 17.\overline{7}$ units.

59. False. $y = f(x + 3)$ is $y = f(x)$ translated 3 units to the *left*.

60. True. $y = f(x) - c$ represents a translation down by c units. (The translation is up when $c < 0$.)

61. To vertically stretch $y = f(x)$ by a factor of 3, multiply the $f(x)$ by 3. The answer is C.

62. To translate $y = f(x)$ 4 units to the right, subtract 4 from x inside the $f(x)$. The answer is D.

63. To translate $y = f(x)$ 2 units up, add 2 to $f(x)$: $y = f(x) + 2$. To reflect the result across the y-axis, replace x with $-x$. The answer is A.

64. To reflect $y = f(x)$ across the x-axis, multiply $f(x)$ by -1: $y = -f(x)$. To shrink the result horizontally by a factor of $\dfrac{1}{2}$, replace x with $2x$. The answer is E.

65. (a)

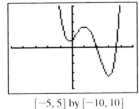

(b) Change the y-value by multiplying by the conversion rate from dollars to yen, a number that changes according to international market conditions. This results in a vertical stretch by the conversion rate.

66. Apply the same transformation to the Ymin, Ymax, and Yscl as you apply to transform the function.

67. (a) The original graph is on the left; the graph of $y = |f(x)|$ is on the right.

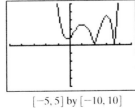

$[-5, 5]$ by $[-10, 10]$ $[-5, 5]$ by $[-10, 10]$

(b) The original graph is on the left; the graph of $y = f(|x|)$ is on the right.

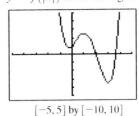 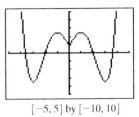

$[-5, 5]$ by $[-10, 10]$ $[-5, 5]$ by $[-10, 10]$

(c)

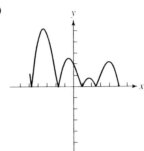

(d)

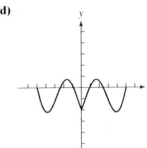

68. (a)

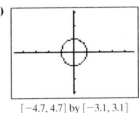

$[-4.7, 4.7]$ by $[-3.1, 3.1]$

(b)

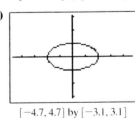

$[-4.7, 4.7]$ by $[-3.1, 3.1]$

$x = 2 \cos t$
$y = \sin t$

(c)

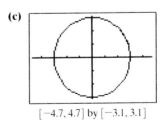

$[-4.7, 4.7]$ by $[-3.1, 3.1]$

$x = 3 \cos t$
$y = 3 \sin t$

(d)

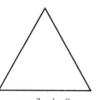

$$x = 4 \cos t$$
$$y = 2 \sin t$$

$[-4.7, 4.7]$ by $[-3.1, 3.1]$

■ Section 1.7 Modeling with Functions

Exploration 1

1.

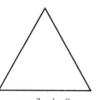

$n = 3;\ d = 0$

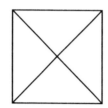

$n = 4;\ d = 2$

$n = 5;\ d = 5$

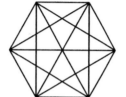

$n = 6;\ d = 9$

$n = 7;\ d = 14$

$n = 8;\ d = 20$

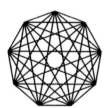

$n = 9;\ d = 27$

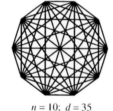

$n = 10;\ d = 35$

2.

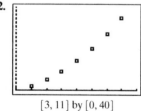

$[3, 11]$ by $[0, 40]$

3. Linear: $r^2 = 0.9758$
Power: $r^2 = 0.9903$
Quadratic: $R^2 = 1$
Cubic: $R^2 = 1$
Quartic: $R^2 = 1$

4. The best-fit curve is quadratic: $y = 0.5x^2 - 1.5x$. The cubic and quartic regressions give this same curve.

5. Since the quadratic curve fits the points perfectly, there is nothing to be gained by adding a cubic term or a quartic term. The coefficients of these terms in the regressions are zero.

6. $y = 0.5x^2 - 1.5x$. At $x = 128$,
$y = 0.5(128)^2 - 1.5(128) = 8000$

Quick Review 1.7

1. $h = 2(A/b)$

2. $h = 2A/(b_1 + b_2)$

3. $h = V/(\pi r^2)$

4. $h = 3V/(\pi r^2)$

5. $r = \sqrt[3]{\dfrac{3V}{4\pi}}$

6. $r = \sqrt{\dfrac{A}{4\pi}}$

7. $h = \dfrac{A - 2\pi r^2}{2\pi r} = \dfrac{A}{2\pi r} - r$

8. $t = I/(Pr)$

9. $P = \dfrac{A}{(1 + r/n)^{nt}} = A\left(1 + \dfrac{r}{n}\right)^{-nt}$

10. $t = \sqrt{\dfrac{2(H - s)}{g}}$

Section 1.7 Exercises

1. $3x + 5$

2. $3(x + 5)$

3. $0.17x$

4. $0.05x + 4$

5. $A = \ell w = (x + 12)(x)$

6. $A = \dfrac{1}{2}bh = \dfrac{1}{2}(x)(x + 2)$

7. $x + 0.045x = (1 + 0.045)x = 1.045x$

8. $x - 0.03x = (1 - 0.03)x = 0.97x$

9. $x - 0.40x = 0.60x$

10. $x + 0.0875x = 1.0875x$

11. Let C be the total cost and n be the number of items produced; $C = 34{,}500 + 5.75n$.

12. Let C be the total cost and n be the number of items produced; $C = (1.09)28{,}000 + 19.85n$.

13. Let R be the revenue and n be the number of items sold; $R = 3.75n$.

14. Let P be the profit, and s be the amount of sales; then $P = 200{,}000 + 0.12s$.

15. The basic formula for the volume of a right circular cylinder is $V = \pi r^2 h$, where r is the radius and h is height. Since height equals diameter ($h = d$) and the diameter is two times r ($d = 2r$), we know $h = 2r$. Then, $V = \pi r^2(2r) = 2\pi r^3$.

16. Let c = hypotenuse, a = "short" side, and b = "long" side. Then $c^2 = a^2 + b^2 = a^2 + (2a)^2 = a^2 + 4a^2 = 5a^2$, so $c = \sqrt{5a^2} = a\sqrt{5}$.

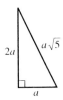

17. Let a be the length of the base. Then the other two sides of the triangle have length two times the base, or $2a$. Since the triangle is isoceles, a perpendicular dropped from the "top" vertex to the base is perpendicular. As a result,

$$h^2 + \left(\frac{a}{2}\right)^2 = (2a)^2, \text{ or } h^2 = 4a^2 - \frac{a^2}{4} = \frac{16a^2 - a^2}{4}$$

$$= \frac{15a^2}{4}, \text{ so } h = \sqrt{\frac{15a^2}{4}} = \frac{a\sqrt{15}}{2}. \text{ The triangle's area is}$$

$$A = \frac{1}{2}bh = \frac{1}{2}(a)\left(\frac{a\sqrt{15}}{2}\right) = \frac{a^2\sqrt{15}}{4}.$$

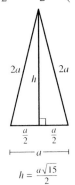

18. Since P lies at the center of the square and the circle, we know that segment $\overline{PR} = \overline{QR} = \overline{RS}$. Let ℓ be the length of these segments. Then, $\ell^2 + \ell^2 = r^2, 2\ell^2 = r^2$,

$$\ell^2 = \frac{r^2}{2}, \ell = \sqrt{\frac{r^2}{2}} = \frac{r}{\sqrt{2}} = \frac{r\sqrt{2}}{2}.$$

Since each side of the square is two times ℓ,

we know that $s = 2\ell = \left(\frac{r\sqrt{2}}{2}\right)2 = r\sqrt{2}$.

As a result, $A = s^2 = (r\sqrt{2})^2 = r^2 \cdot 2 = 2r^2$.

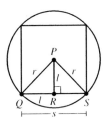

19. Let r be the radius of the sphere. Since the sphere is tangent to all six faces of the cube, we know that the height (and width, and depth) of the cube is equal to the sphere's diameter, which is two times r ($2r$). The surface area of the cube is the sum of the area of all six faces, which equals $2r \cdot 2r = 4r^2$. Thus, $A = 6 \cdot 4r^2 = 24r^2$.

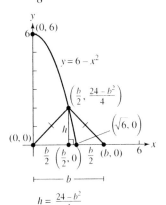

20. From our graph, we see that y provides the height of our triangle, i.e., $h = y$ when $x = \frac{b}{2}$. Since $y = 6 - x^2$

$$= 6 - \left(\frac{b}{2}\right)^2 = 6 - \frac{b^2}{4} = \frac{24 - b^2}{4}, h = \frac{24 - b^2}{4}.$$

The area of the triangle is $A = \frac{1}{2}bh = \frac{1}{2}b\left(\frac{24 - b^2}{4}\right)$

$$= \frac{24b - b^3}{8}.$$

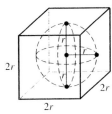

$$h = \frac{24 - b^2}{4}$$

21. Solving $x + 4x = 620$ gives $x = 124$, so $4x = 496$. The two numbers are 124 and 496.

22. $x + 2x + 3x = 714$, so $x = 119$; the second and third numbers are 238 and 357.

23. $1.035x = 36,432$, so $x = 35,200$

24. $1.023x = 184.0$, so $x = 179.9$.

25. $182 = 52t$, so $t = 3.5$ hr.

26. $560 = 45t + 55(t + 2)$, so $t = 4.5$ hours on local highways.

27. $0.60(33) = 19.8; 0.75(27) = 20.25$. The $33 shirt sells for $19.80. The $27 shirt sells for $20.25. The $33 shirt is a better bargain, because the sale price is cheaper.

28. Let x be gross sales. For the second job to be more attractive than the first, we need
$$20,000 + 0.07x > 25,000 + 0.05x, 0.02x > 5000,$$
$$x > \frac{5000}{0.02} = \$250,000.$$
Gross sales would have to exceed $250,000.

29. $71\,065\,000(1 + x) = 82\,400\,000$
$$71\,065\,000x = 82\,400\,000 - 71\,065\,000$$
$$x = \frac{82\,400\,000 - 71\,065\,000}{71\,065\,000} \approx 0.1595$$
There was a 15.95% increase in sales.

30. $26\,650\,000(1 + x) = 30\,989\,000$
$$26\,650\,000x = 30\,989\,000 - 26\,650\,000$$
$$x = \frac{30\,989\,000 - 26\,650\,000}{26\,650\,000} \approx 0.1628$$
Shipments of personal computers grew 16.28%.

31. (a) $0.10x + 0.45(100 - x) = 0.25(100)$.

(b) Graph $y_1 = 0.1x + 0.45(100 - x)$ and $y_2 = 25$. Use $x \approx 57.14$ gallons of the 10% solution and about 42.86 gal of the 45% solution.

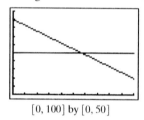

[0, 100] by [0, 50]

32. Solve $0.20x + 0.35(25 - x) = 0.26(25)$. Use $x = 15$ liters of the 20% solution and 10 liters of the 35% solution.

33. (a) The height of the box is x, and the base measures $10 - 2x$ by $18 - 2x$.
$$V(x) = x(10 - 2x)(18 - 2x)$$

(b) Because one side of the original piece of cardboard measures 10 in., $2x$ must be greater than 0 but less than 10, so that $0 < x < 5$. The domain of $V(x)$ is $(0, 5)$.

(c) Graphing $V(x)$ produces a cubic-function curve that between $x = 0$ and $x = 5$ has a maximum at approximately $(2.06, 168.1)$. The cut-out squares should measure approximately 2.06 in. by 2.06 in.

34. Solve $2x + 2(x + 16) = 136$. Two pieces that are $x = 26$ ft long are needed, along with two 42 ft pieces.

35. Equation of the parabola, to pass through $(-16, 8)$ and $(16, 8)$:
$$y = kx^2$$
$$8 = k(\pm 16)^2$$
$$k = \frac{8}{256} = \frac{1}{32}$$
$$y = \frac{1}{32}x^2$$
y-coordinate of parabola 8 in. from center:
$$y = \frac{1}{32}(8)^2 = 2$$
From that point to the top of the dish is $8 - 2 = 6$ in.

36. Solve $2x + 2(x + 3) = 54$. This gives $x = 12$; the room is 12 ft $\times$ 15 ft.

37. Original volume of water:
$$V_0 = \frac{1}{3}\pi r^2 h = \frac{1}{3}\pi(9)^2(24) \approx 2035.75 \text{ in.}^3$$
Volume lost through faucet:
$$V_1 = \text{time} \times \text{rate} = (120 \text{ sec})(5 \text{ in.}^3/\text{sec}) = 600 \text{ in.}^3$$
Find volume:
$$V_f = V_0 - V_1 = 2035.75 - 600 = 1435.75$$
Since the final cone-shaped volume of water has radius and height in a 9-to-24 ratio, or $r = \frac{3}{8}h$:
$$V_f = \frac{1}{3}\pi\left(\frac{3}{8}h\right)^2 h = \frac{3}{64}\pi h^3 = 1435.75$$
Solving, we obtain $h \approx 21.36$ in.

38. Solve $900 = 0.07x + 0.085(12,000 - x)$. $x = 8000$ dollars was invested at 7%; the other $4000 was invested at 8.5%.

39. Bicycle's speed in feet per second:
$(2 \times \pi \times 16 \text{ in./rot})(2 \text{ rot/sec}) = 64\pi \text{ in./sec}$
Unit conversion:
$$(64\pi \text{ in./sec})\left(\frac{1}{12} \text{ ft/in.}\right)\left(\frac{1}{5280} \text{ mi/ft}\right)(3600 \text{ sec/hr})$$
$$\approx 11.42 \text{ mi/hr}$$

40. Solve $1571 = 0.055x + 0.083(25,000 - x)$. $x = 18,000$ dollars was invested at 5.5%; the other $7000 was invested at 8.3%.

41. True. The correlation coefficient is close to 1 (or -1) if there is a good fit. A correlation coefficient near 0 indicates a very poor fit.

42. False. The graph over time of the height of a freely falling object is a parabola. A quadratic regression is called for.

43. The pattern of points is S-shaped, which suggests a cubic model. The answer is C.

44. The points appear to lie along a straight line. The answer is A.

45. The points appear to lie along an upward-opening parabola. The answer is B.

46. The pattern of points looks sinusoidal. The answer is E.

47. (a) $C = 100,000 + 30x$

(b) $R = 50x$

(c) $100,000 + 30x = 50x$
$$100,000 = 20x$$
$$x = 5000 \text{ pairs of shoes}$$

(d) Graph $y_1 = 100,000 + 30x$ and $y_2 = 50x$; these graphs cross when $x = 5000$ pairs of shoes. The point of intersection corresponds to the break-even point, where $C = R$.

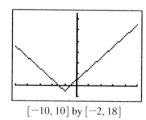

$[-10, 10]$ by $[-2, 18]$

48. Solve $48,814.20 = x + 0.12x + 0.03x + 0.004x$. Then $48,814.20 = 1.154x$, so $x = 42,300$ dollars.

49. (a) $y_1 = u(x) = 125,000 + 23x$.

    (b) $y_2 = s(x) = 125,000 + 23x + 8x = 125,000 + 31x$.

    (c) $y_3 = r_u(x) = 56x$.

    (d) $y_4 = R_s(x) = 79x$.

    (e)

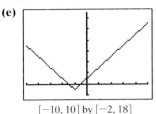

$[-10, 10]$ by $[-2, 18]$

    (f) You should recommend stringing the rackets; fewer strung rackets need to be sold to begin making a profit (since the intersection of y_2 and y_4 occurs for smaller x than the intersection of y_1 and y_3).

50. (a)

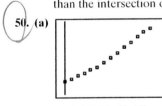

$[-1, 15]$ by $[9, 16]$

    (b) $y = 0.409x + 9.861$

    (c) $r = 0.993$, so the linear model is appropriate.

    (d) $y = 0.012x^2 + 0.247x + 10.184$

    (e) $r^2 = 0.998$, so a quadratic model is appropriate.

    (f) The linear prediction is 18.04 and the quadratic prediction is 19.92. Despite the fact that both models look good for the data, the predictions differ by 1.88. One or both of them must be ineffective, as they both cannot be right.

    (g) The linear regression and the quadratic regression are very close from $x = 0$ to $x = 13$. The quadratic regression begins to veer away from the linear regression at $x = 13$. Since there are no data points beyond $x = 13$, it is difficult to know which is accurate.

51. (a)

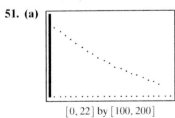

$[0, 22]$ by $[100, 200]$

    (b) List L3 $= \{112.3, 106.5, 101.5, 96.6, 92.0, 87.2, 83.1, 79.8, 75.0, 71.7, 68, 64.1, 61.5, 58.5, 55.9, 53.0, 50.8, 47.9, 45.2, 43.2\}$

(c) The regression equation is $y = 118.07 \times 0.951^x$. It fits the data extremely well.

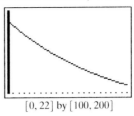

$[0, 22]$ by $[100, 200]$

52. Answers will vary in **(a)–(e)**, depending on the conditions of the experiment.

    (f) Some possible answers: the thickness of the liquid, the darkness of the liquid, the type of cup it is in, the amount of surface exposed to the air, the specific heat of the substance (a technical term that may have been learned in physics), etc.

■ Chapter 1 Review

1. (d)

2. (f)

3. (i)

4. (h)

5. (b)

6. (j)

7. (g)

8. (c)

9. (a)

10. (e)

11. (a) All reals   **(b)** All reals

12. (a) All reals   **(b)** All reals

13. (a) All reals

    (b) $g(x) = x^2 + 2x + 1 = (x + 1)^2$. At $x = -1$, $g(x) = 0$, the function's minimum. The range is $[0, \infty)$.

14. (a) All reals

    (b) $(x - 2)^2 \geq 0$ for all x, so $(x - 2)^2 + 5 \geq 5$ for all x. The range is $[5, \infty)$.

15. (a) All reals

    (b) $|x| \geq 0$ for all x, so $3|x| \geq 0$ and $3|x| + 8 \geq 8$ for all x. The range is $[8, \infty)$.

16. (a) We need $\sqrt{4 - x^2} \geq 0$ for all x, so $4 - x^2 \geq 0$, $4 \geq x^2$, $-2 \leq x \leq 2$. The domain is $[-2, 2]$.

    (b) $0 \leq \sqrt{4 - x^2} \leq 2$ for all x, so $-2 \leq \sqrt{4 - x^2} - 2 \leq 0$ for all x. The range is $[-2, 0]$.

17. (a) $f(x) = \dfrac{x}{x^2 - 2x} = \dfrac{x}{x(x - 2)}$, $x \neq 0$ and $x - 2 \neq 0$, $x \neq 2$. The domain is all reals except 0 and 2.

    (b) For $x > 2$, $f(x) > 0$ and for $x < 2$, $f(x) < 0$. $f(x)$ does not cross $y = 0$, so the range is all reals except $f(x) = 0$.

18. (a) We need
$$\sqrt{9 - x^2} > 0, 9 - x^2 > 0, 9 > x^2, -3 < x < 3.$$
The domain is $(-3, 3)$.

(b) Since $\sqrt{9 - x^2} > 0, \dfrac{1}{\sqrt{9 - x^2}} > 0.$ On the domain $(-3, 3)$, $k(0) = \dfrac{1}{3}$, a minimum, while $k(x)$ approaches ∞ when x approaches both -3 and 3, maximums for $k(x)$. The range is $\left[\dfrac{1}{3}, \infty\right)$.

19. Continuous

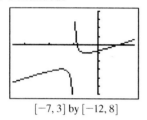

$[-7, 3]$ by $[-12, 8]$

20. Continuous

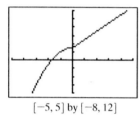

$[-5, 5]$ by $[-8, 12]$

21. (a) $x^2 - 5x \neq 0, x(x - 5) \neq 0$, so $x \neq 0$ and $x \neq 5$. We expect vertical asymptotes at $x = 0$ and $x = 5$.

(b) $y = 0$

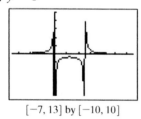

$[-7, 13]$ by $[-10, 10]$

22. (a) $x - 4 \neq 0, x \neq 4$, so we expect a vertical asymptote at $x = 4$.

(b) Since $\lim\limits_{x \to \infty} \dfrac{3x}{x - 4} = 3$ and $\lim\limits_{x \to -\infty} \dfrac{3x}{x - 4} = 3$, we also expect a horizontal asymptote at $y = 3$.

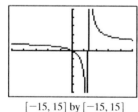

$[-15, 15]$ by $[-15, 15]$

23. (a) None

(b) Since $\lim\limits_{x \to \infty} \dfrac{7x}{\sqrt{x^2 + 10}} = 7$ and $\lim\limits_{x \to -\infty} \dfrac{7x}{\sqrt{x^2 + 10}} = -7$, we expect horizontal asymptotes at $y = 7$ and $y = -7$.

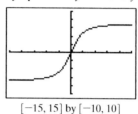

$[-15, 15]$ by $[-10, 10]$

24. (a) $x + 1 \neq 0, x \neq -1$, so we expect a vertical asymptote at $x = -1$.

(b) $\lim\limits_{x \to \infty} \dfrac{|x|}{x + 1} = 1$ and $\lim\limits_{x \to -\infty} \dfrac{|x|}{x + 1} = -1$, so we can expect horizontal asymptotes at $y = 1$ and $y = -1$.

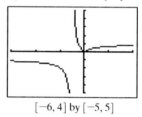

$[-6, 4]$ by $[-5, 5]$

25. $(-\infty, \infty)$

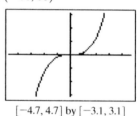

$[-4.7, 4.7]$ by $[-3.1, 3.1]$

26. $|x - 1| = 0$ when $x = 1$, which is where the function's minimum occurs. y increases over the interval $[1, \infty)$. (Over the interval $(-\infty, 1]$, it is decreasing.)

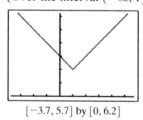

$[-3.7, 5.7]$ by $[0, 6.2]$

27. As the graph illustrates, y is increasing over the intervals $(-\infty, -1), (-1, 1),$ and $(1, \infty)$.

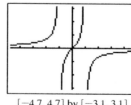

$[-4.7, 4.7]$ by $[-3.1, 3.1]$

28. As the graph illustrates, y is increasing over the intervals $(-\infty, -2)$ and $(-2, 0]$.

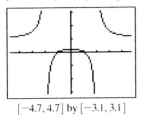

$[-4.7, 4.7]$ by $[-3.1, 3.1]$

29. $-1 \leq \sin x \leq 1$, but $-\infty < x < \infty$, so $f(x)$ is not bounded.

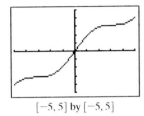

$[-5, 5]$ by $[-5, 5]$

30. $g(x) = 3$ at $x = 1$, a maximum and $g(x) = -3$, a minimum, at $x = -1$. It is bounded.

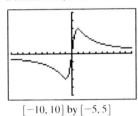

$[-10, 10]$ by $[-5, 5]$

31. $e^x > 0$ for all x, so $-e^x < 0$ and $5 - e^x < 5$ for all x. $h(x)$ is bounded above.

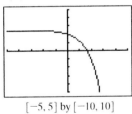

$[-5, 5]$ by $[-10, 10]$

32. The function is linear with slope $\dfrac{1}{1000}$ and y-intercept 1000. Thus $k(x)$ is not bounded.

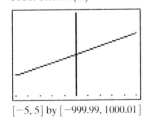

$[-5, 5]$ by $[-999.99, 1000.01]$

33. **(a)** None   **(b)** -7, at $x = -1$

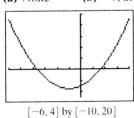

$[-6, 4]$ by $[-10, 20]$

34. **(a)** 2, at $x = -1$ **(b)** -2, at $x = 1$

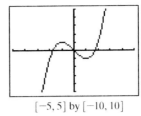

$[-5, 5]$ by $[-10, 10]$

35. **(a)** -1, at $x = 0$ **(b)** None

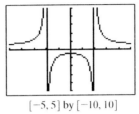

$[-5, 5]$ by $[-10, 10]$

36. **(a)** 1, at $x = 2$ **(b)** -1, at $x = -2$

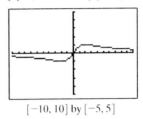

$[-10, 10]$ by $[-5, 5]$

37. The function is even since it is symmetrical about the y-axis.

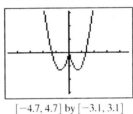

$[-4.7, 4.7]$ by $[-3.1, 3.1]$

38. Since the function is symmetrical about the origin, it is odd.

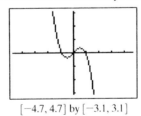

$[-4.7, 4.7]$ by $[-3.1, 3.1]$

39. Since no symmetry is exhibited, the function is neither.

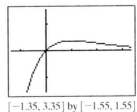

$[-1.35, 3.35]$ by $[-1.55, 1.55]$

40. Since the function is symmetrical about the origin, it is odd.

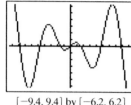

$[-9.4, 9.4]$ by $[-6.2, 6.2]$

41. $x = 2y + 3$, $2y = x - 3$, $y = \dfrac{x - 3}{2}$, so

$f^{-1}(x) = \dfrac{x - 3}{2}$.

42. $x = \sqrt[3]{y - 8}$, $x^3 = y - 8$, $y = x^3 + 8$, so

$f^{-1}(x) = x^3 + 8$.

43. $x = \dfrac{2}{y}$, $xy = 2$, $y = \dfrac{2}{x}$, so $f^{-1}(x) = \dfrac{2}{x}$.

44. $x = \dfrac{6}{y + 4}$, $(y + 4)x = 6$, $xy + 4x = 6$, $xy = 6 - 4x$,

$y = \dfrac{6 - 4x}{x}$, so $f^{-1}(x) = \dfrac{6}{x} - 4$.

45.

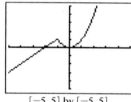

$[-5, 5]$ by $[-5, 5]$

46.

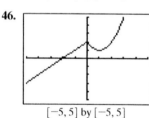

$[-5, 5]$ by $[-5, 5]$

47.

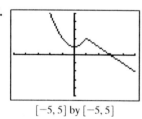

$[-5, 5]$ by $[-5, 5]$

48.

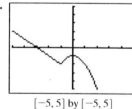

$[-5, 5]$ by $[-5, 5]$

49.

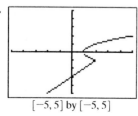

$[-5, 5]$ by $[-5, 5]$

50. No

51.

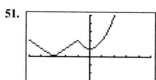

$[-5, 5]$ by $[-5, 5]$

52. $f(x) = \begin{cases} x + 3 \text{ if } x \le -1 \\ x^2 + 1 \text{ if } x > -1 \end{cases}$

53. $(f \circ g)(x) = f(g(x)) = f(x^2 - 4) = \sqrt{x^2 - 4}$.

Since $x^2 - 4 \ge 0$, $x^2 \ge 4$, $x \le -2$ or $x \ge 2$.

The domain is $(-\infty, -2] \cup [2, \infty)$.

54. $(g \circ f)(x) = g(f(x)) = g(\sqrt{x}) = (\sqrt{x})^2 - 4 = x - 4$. Since $\sqrt{x} \ge 0$, $x \ge 0$. The domain is $[0, \infty)$.

55. $(f \cdot g)(x) = f(x) \cdot g(x) = \sqrt{x} \cdot (x^2 - 4)$.

Since $\sqrt{x} \ge 0$, the domain is $[0, \infty)$.

56. $\left(\dfrac{f}{g}\right)(x) = \dfrac{f(x)}{g(x)} = \dfrac{\sqrt{x}}{x^2 - 4}$ Since $x^2 - 4 \ne 0$,

$(x + 2)(x - 2) \ne 0$, $x \ne -2$, $x \ne 2$. Also since $\sqrt{x} \ge 0$, $x \ge 0$. The domain is $[0, 2) \cup (2, \infty)$.

57. $\lim\limits_{x \to \infty} \sqrt{x} = \infty$. (Large negative values are not in the domain.)

58. $\lim\limits_{x \to \pm\infty} \sqrt{x^2 - 4} = \infty$. (The graph resembles the line $y = x$.)

59. $r^2 = \left(\dfrac{s}{2}\right)^2 + \left(\dfrac{s}{2}\right)^2 = \dfrac{2s^2}{4}$, $r = \sqrt{\dfrac{2s^2}{4}} = \dfrac{s\sqrt{2}}{2}$.

The area of the circle is

$$A = \pi r^2 = \pi \left(\dfrac{s\sqrt{2}}{2}\right)^2 = \dfrac{2\pi s^2}{4} = \dfrac{\pi s^2}{2}$$

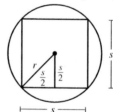

$r = \dfrac{s\sqrt{2}}{2}$

60. $A = \pi r^2 = \pi \left(\dfrac{s}{2}\right)^2 = \dfrac{\pi s^2}{4}$

61. $d = 2r$, $r = \dfrac{d}{2}$, so the radius of the tank is 10 feet.

Volume is $V = \pi r^2 \cdot h = \pi(10)^2 \cdot h = 100\pi h$

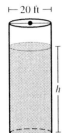

62. The volume of oil in the tank is the amount of original oil ($\pi r^2 h$) minus the amount of oil drained.
$V = \pi r^2 h - 2t = \pi(10)^2(40) - 2t = 4000\pi - 2t$

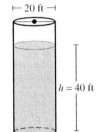

63. Since $V = 4000\pi - 2t$, we know that
$\pi r^2 h = 4000\pi - 2t$. In this case, $r = 10'$, so
$$100\pi h = 4000\pi - 2t, h = \frac{4000\pi - 2t}{100\pi} = 40 - \frac{t}{50\pi}$$

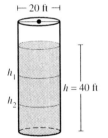

64. Since the depth of the tank is decreasing by 2 feet per hour, we know that the tank is losing a total volume of $V = \pi r^2 h = \pi(10)^2(2) = 200\pi$ cubic feet per hour. The volume of remaining oil in the tank is the amount of original oil subtracting the amount which has been drained, or $V = 4000\pi - 200\pi t$. This is a significantly higher loss than our solution in #68!

65. (a)

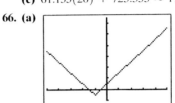

[4, 15] by [940, 1700]

(b) The regression line is $y = 61.133x + 725.333$.

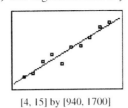

[4, 15] by [940, 1700]

(c) $61.133(20) + 725.333 \approx 1948$ (thousands of barrels)

66. (a)

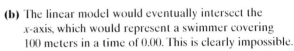

[−10, 10] by [−2, 18]

(b) The linear model would eventually intersect the *x*-axis, which would represent a swimmer covering 100 meters in a time of 0.00. This is clearly impossible.

(c) Based on the data, 52 seconds represents the limit of women's capability in this race. The addition of future data could determine a different model.

(d) The regression curve is $y = (97.100)(0.9614^x)$.

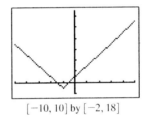

[−10, 10] by [−2, 18]

(e) $(97.100)(0.9614^{108}) \approx 1.38$. Add 52 to find the projected winning time in 2008: $1.38 + 52 = 53.38$ seconds.

67. (a) $r^2 + \left(\dfrac{h}{2}\right)^2 = (\sqrt{3})^2$,
$$\frac{h^2}{4} = 3 - r^2, h^2 = 12 - 4r^2, h = \sqrt{12 - 4r^2},$$
$$h = 2\sqrt{3 - r^2}$$

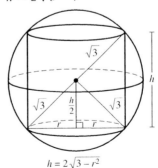

$h = 2\sqrt{3 - r^2}$

(b) $V = \pi r^2 h = (\pi r^2)(2\sqrt{3 - r^2}) = 2\pi r^2\sqrt{3 - r^2}$

(c) Since $\sqrt{3 - r^2} \geq 0$, $3 - r^2 \geq 0$
$3 \geq r^2$, $-\sqrt{3} \leq r \leq \sqrt{3}$.
However, $r < 0$ are invalid values, so the domain is $[0, \sqrt{3}]$.

(d)

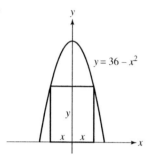

$[0, \sqrt{3}]$ by $[0, 20]$

(e) 12.57 in^3

68.

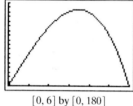

$y = 36 - x^2$

(a) $A = 2xy = 2x(36 - x^2) = 72x - 2x^3$

(b) $36 - x^2 \geq 0$, $(6 - x)(6 + x) \geq 0$, $-6 \leq x \leq 6$. However, $x < 0$ are invalid values, so the domain is $[0, 6]$.

(c)

$[0, 6]$ by $[0, 180]$

(d) The maximum area occurs when $x \approx 3.46$, or an area of approximately 166.28 square units.

Chapter 1 Project

1.

$[-1, 13]$ by $[-100, 2600]$

2. The exponential regression produces
$y \approx 21.956(1.511)^x$.

3. 2000: For $x = 13$, $y \approx 4690$
2001: For $x = 14$, $y \approx 7085$

4. The model, which is based on data from the early, high-growth period of Starbucks Coffee's company history, does not account for the effects of gradual market saturation by Starbucks and its competitors. The actual growth in the number of locations is slowing while the model increases more rapidly.

5. The logistic regression produces

$$y \approx \frac{4914.198}{1 + 269.459 \, e^{-0.486x}}.$$

6. 2000: For $x = 13$, $y \approx 3048$
2001: For $x = 14$, $y \approx 3553$

These predictions are less than the actual numbers, but are not off by as much as the numbers derived from the exponential model were. For the year 2020 ($x = 33$), the logistic model predicts about 4914 locations. (This prediction is probably too conservative.)

Chapter 2
Polynomial, Power, and Rational Functions

■ Section 2.1 Linear and Quadratic Functions and Modeling

Exploration 1

1. −$2000 per year

2. The equation will have the form $v(t) = mt + b$. The value of the building after 0 year is
$v(0) = m(0) + b = b = 50,000$.

The slope m is the rate of change, which is −2000 (dollars per year). So an equation for the value of the building (in dollars) as a function of the time (in years) is
$v(t) = -2000t + 50,000$.

3. $v(0) = 50,000$ and
$v(16) = -2000(16) + 50,000 = 18,000$ dollars

4. The equation $v(t) = 39,000$ becomes
$$-2000t + 50,000 = 39,000$$
$$-2000t = -11,000$$
$$t = 5.5 \text{ years}$$

Quick Review 2.1

1. $y = 8x + 3.6$

2. $y = -1.8x - 2$

3. $y - 4 = -\dfrac{3}{5}(x + 2)$, or $y = -0.6x + 2.8$

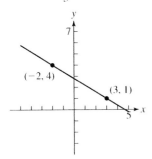

4. $y - 5 = \dfrac{8}{3}(x - 1)$, or $y = \dfrac{8}{3}x + \dfrac{7}{3}$

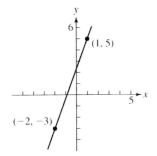

5. $(x + 3)^2 = (x + 3)(x + 3) = x^2 + 3x + 3x + 9$
$= x^2 + 6x + 9$

6. $(x - 4)^2 = (x - 4)(x - 4) = x^2 - 4x - 4x + 16$
$= x^2 - 8x + 16$

7. $3(x - 6)^2 = 3(x - 6)(x - 6) = (3x - 18)(x - 6)$
$= 3x^2 - 18x - 18x + 108 = 3x^2 - 36x + 108$

8. $-3(x + 7)^2 = -3(x + 7)(x + 7)$
$= (-3x - 21)(x + 7) = -3x^2 - 21x - 21x - 147$
$= -3x^2 - 42x - 147$

9. $2x^2 - 4x + 2 = 2(x^2 - 2x + 1) = 2(x - 1)(x - 1)$
$= 2(x - 1)^2$

10. $3x^2 + 12x + 12 = 3(x^2 + 4x + 4) = 3(x + 2)(x + 2)$
$= 3(x + 2)^2$

Section 2.1 Exercises

1. Not a polynomial function because of the exponent −5

2. Polynomial of degree 1 with leading coefficient 2

3. Polynomial of degree 5 with leading coefficient 2

4. Polynomial of degree 0 with leading coefficient 13

5. Not a polynomial function because of cube root

6. Polynomial of degree 2 with leading coefficient −5

7. $m = \dfrac{5}{7}$ so $y - 4 = \dfrac{5}{7}(x - 2) \Rightarrow f(x) = \dfrac{5}{7}x + \dfrac{18}{7}$

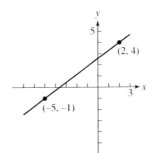

8. $m = -\dfrac{7}{9}$ so $y - 5 = -\dfrac{7}{9}(x + 3) \Rightarrow f(x) = -\dfrac{7}{9}x + \dfrac{8}{3}$

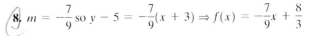

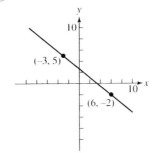

9. $m = -\dfrac{4}{3}$ so $y - 6 = -\dfrac{4}{3}(x + 4) \Rightarrow f(x) = -\dfrac{4}{3}x + \dfrac{2}{3}$

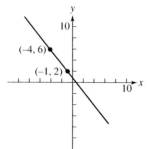

10. $m = \dfrac{5}{4}$ so $y - 2 = \dfrac{5}{4}(x - 1) \Rightarrow f(x) = \dfrac{5}{4}x + \dfrac{3}{4}$

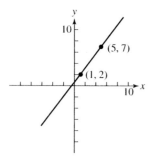

11. $m = -1$ so $y - 3 = -1(x - 0) \Rightarrow f(x) = -x + 3$

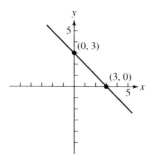

12. $m = \dfrac{1}{2}$ so $y - 2 = \dfrac{1}{2}(x - 0) \Rightarrow f(x) = \dfrac{1}{2}x + 2$

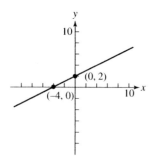

13. (a)—the vertex is at $(-1, -3)$, in Quadrant III, eliminating all but (a) and (d). Since $f(0) = -1$, it must be (a).

14. (d)—the vertex is at $(-2, -7)$, in Quadrant III, eliminating all but (a) and (d). Since $f(0) = 5$, it must be (d).

15. (b)—the vertex is in Quadrant I, at $(1, 4)$, meaning it must be either (b) or (f). Since $f(0) = 1$, it cannot be (f): if the vertex in (f) is $(1, 4)$, then the intersection with the y-axis would be about $(0, 3)$. It must be (b).

16. (f)—the vertex is in Quadrant I, at $(1, 12)$, meaning it must be either (b) or (f). Since $f(0) = 10$, it cannot be (b): if the vertex in (b) is $(1, 12)$, then the intersection with the y-axis occurs considerably lower than $(0, 10)$. It must be (f).

17. (e)—the vertex is at $(1, -3)$ in Quadrant IV, so it must be (e).

18. (c)—the vertex is at $(-1, 12)$ in Quadrant II and the parabola opens down, so it must be (c).

19. Translate the graph of $f(x) = x^2$ 3 units right to obtain the graph of $h(x) = (x - 3)^2$, and translate this graph 2 units down to obtain the graph of $g(x) = (x - 3)^2 - 2$.

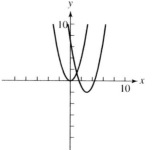

20. Vertically shrink the graph of $f(x) = x^2$ by a factor of $\dfrac{1}{4}$ to obtain the graph of $g(x) = \dfrac{1}{4}x^2$, and translate this graph 1 unit down to obtain the graph of $h(x) = \dfrac{1}{4}x^2 - 1$.

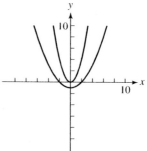

21. Translate the graph of $f(x) = x^2$ 2 units left to obtain the graph of $h(x) = (x + 2)^2$, vertically shrink this graph by a factor of $\dfrac{1}{2}$ to obtain the graph of $k(x) = \dfrac{1}{2}(x + 2)^2$, and translate this graph 3 units down to obtain the graph of $g(x) = \dfrac{1}{2}(x + 2)^2 - 3$.

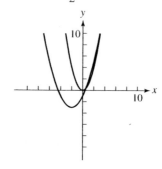

22. Vertically stretch the graph of $f(x) = x^2$ by a factor of 3 to obtain the graph of $g(x) = 3x^2$, reflect this graph across the x-axis to obtain the graph of $k(x) = -3x^2$, and translate this graph up 2 units to obtain the graph of $h(x) = -3x^2 + 2.1$

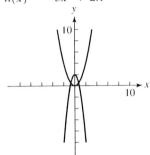

For #23–32, with an equation of the form $f(x) = a(x - h)^2 + k$, the vertex is (h, k) and the axis is $x = h$.

23. Vertex: $(1, 5)$; axis: $x = 1$

24. Vertex: $(-2, -1)$; axis: $x = -2$

25. Vertex: $(1, -7)$; axis: $x = 1$

26. Vertex: $(\sqrt{3}, 4)$; axis: $x = \sqrt{3}$

27. $f(x) = 3\left(x^2 + \dfrac{5}{3}x\right) - 4$

$$= 3\left(x^2 + 2\cdot\dfrac{5}{6}x + \dfrac{25}{36}\right) - 4 - \dfrac{25}{12} = 3\left(x + \dfrac{5}{6}\right)^2 - \dfrac{73}{12}$$

Vertex: $\left(-\dfrac{5}{6}, -\dfrac{73}{12}\right)$; axis: $x = -\dfrac{5}{6}$

28. $f(x) = -2\left(x^2 - \dfrac{7}{2}x\right) - 3$

$$= -2\left(x^2 - 2\cdot\dfrac{7}{4}x + \dfrac{49}{16}\right) - 3 + \dfrac{49}{8}$$

$$= -2\left(x - \dfrac{7}{4}\right)^2 + \dfrac{25}{8}$$

Vertex: $\left(\dfrac{7}{4}, \dfrac{25}{8}\right)$; axis: $x = \dfrac{7}{4}$

29. $f(x) = -(x^2 - 8x) + 3$

$$= -(x^2 - 2\cdot4x + 16) + 3 + 16 = -(x - 4)^2 + 19$$

Vertex: $(4, 19)$; axis: $x = 4$

30. $f(x) = 4\left(x^2 - \dfrac{1}{2}x\right) + 6$

$$= 4\left(x^2 - 2\cdot\dfrac{1}{4}x + \dfrac{1}{16}\right) + 6 - \dfrac{1}{4} = 4\left(x - \dfrac{1}{4}\right)^2 + \dfrac{23}{4}$$

Vertex: $\left(\dfrac{1}{4}, \dfrac{23}{4}\right)$; axis: $x = \dfrac{1}{4}$

31. $g(x) = 5\left(x^2 - \dfrac{6}{5}x\right) + 4$

$$= 5\left(x^2 - 2\cdot\dfrac{3}{5}x + \dfrac{9}{25}\right) + 4 - \dfrac{9}{5} = 5\left(x - \dfrac{3}{5}\right)^2 + \dfrac{11}{5}$$

Vertex: $\left(\dfrac{3}{5}, \dfrac{11}{5}\right)$; axis: $x = \dfrac{3}{5}$

32. $h(x) = -2\left(x^2 + \dfrac{7}{2}x\right) - 4$

$$= -2\left(x^2 + 2\cdot\dfrac{7}{4}x + \dfrac{49}{16}\right) - 4 + \dfrac{49}{8}$$

$$= -2\left(x + \dfrac{7}{4}\right)^2 + \dfrac{17}{8}$$

Vertex: $\left(-\dfrac{7}{4}, \dfrac{17}{8}\right)$; axis: $x = -\dfrac{7}{4}$

33. $f(x) = (x^2 - 4x + 4) + 6 - 4 = (x - 2)^2 + 2.$
Vertex: $(2, 2)$; axis: $x = 2$; opens upward; does not intersect x–axis.

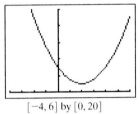

$[-4, 6]$ by $[0, 20]$

34. $g(x) = (x^2 - 6x + 9) + 12 - 9 = (x - 3)^2 + 3.$
Vertex: $(3, 3)$; axis: $x = 3$; opens upward; does not intersect x–axis.

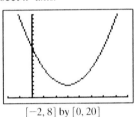

$[-2, 8]$ by $[0, 20]$

35. $f(x) = -(x^2 + 16x) + 10$
$$= -(x^2 + 16x + 64) + 10 + 64 = -(x + 8)^2 + 74.$$
Vertex: $(-8, 74)$; axis: $x = -8$; opens downward; intersects x-axis at about -16.602 and $0.602(-8 \pm \sqrt{74})$.

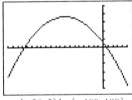

$[-20, 5]$ by $[-100, 100]$

36. $h(x) = -(x^2 - 2x) + 8 = -(x^2 - 2x + 1) + 8 + 1$
$$= -(x - 1)^2 + 9$$
Vertex: $(1, 9)$; axis: $x = 1$; opens downward; intersects x-axis at -2 and 4.

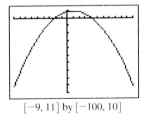

$[-9, 11]$ by $[-100, 10]$

37. $f(x) = 2(x^2 + 3x) + 7$

$= 2\left(x^2 + 3x + \dfrac{9}{4}\right) + 7 - \dfrac{9}{2} = 2\left(x + \dfrac{3}{2}\right)^2 + \dfrac{5}{2}$

Vertex: $\left(-\dfrac{3}{2}, \dfrac{5}{2}\right)$; axis: $x = -\dfrac{3}{2}$; opens upward; does not intersect the x-axis; vertically stretched by 2.

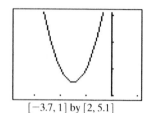

$[-3.7, 1]$ by $[2, 5.1]$

38. $g(x) = 5(x^2 - 5x) + 12$

$= 5\left(x^2 - 5x + \dfrac{25}{4}\right) + 12 - \dfrac{125}{4}$

$= 5\left(x - \dfrac{5}{2}\right)^2 - \dfrac{77}{4}$

Vertex: $\left(\dfrac{5}{2}, -\dfrac{77}{4}\right)$; axis: $x = \dfrac{5}{2}$; opens upward; intersects x-axis at about 0.538 and

$4.462 \left(\text{or } \dfrac{5}{2} \pm \dfrac{1}{10}\sqrt{385}\right)$; vertically stretched by 5.

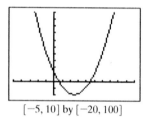

$[-5, 10]$ by $[-20, 100]$

For #39–44, use the form $y = a(x - h)^2 + k$, taking the vertex (h, k) from the graph or other given information.

39. $h = -1$ and $k = -3$, so $y = a(x + 1)^2 - 3$. Now substitute $x = 1$, $y = 5$ to obtain $5 = 4a - 3$, so $a = 2$: $y = 2(x + 1)^2 - 3$.

40. $h = 2$ and $k = -7$, so $y = a(x - 2)^2 - 7$. Now substitute $x = 0$, $y = 5$ to obtain $5 = 4a - 7$, so $a = 3$: $y = 3(x - 2)^2 - 7$.

41. $h = 1$ and $k = 11$, so $y = a(x - 1)^2 + 11$. Now substitute $x = 4$, $y = -7$ to obtain $-7 = 9a + 11$, so $a = -2$: $y = -2(x - 1)^2 + 11$.

42. $h = -1$ and $k = 5$, so $y = a(x + 1)^2 + 5$. Now substitute $x = 2$, $y = -13$ to obtain $-13 = 9a + 5$, so $a = -2$: $y = -2(x + 1)^2 + 5$.

43. $h = 1$ and $k = 3$, so $y = a(x - 1)^2 + 3$. Now substitute $x = 0$, $y = 5$ to obtain $5 = a + 3$, so $a = 2$: $y = 2(x - 1)^2 + 3$.

44. $h = -2$ and $k = -5$, so $y = a(x + 2)^2 - 5$. Now substitute $x = -4$, $y = -27$ to obtain $-27 = 4a - 5$, so $a = -\dfrac{11}{2}$: $y = -\dfrac{11}{2}(x + 2)^2 - 5$.

45. Strong positive

46. Strong negative

47. Weak positive

48. No correlation

49. (a)

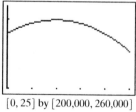

$[15, 45]$ by $[20, 50]$

(b) Strong positive

50. (a)

$[0, 90]$ by $[0, 70]$

(b) Strong negative

51. $m = -\dfrac{2350}{5} = -470$ and $b = 2350$,

so $v(t) = -470t + 2350$.

At $t = 3$, $v(3) = (-470)(3) + 2350 = \$940$.

52. Let x be the number of dolls produced each week and y be the average weekly costs. Then $m = 4.70$, and $b = 350$, so $y = 4.70x + 350$, or $500 = 4.70x + 350$: $x = 32$; 32 dolls are produced each week.

53. (a) $y \approx 0.541x + 4.072$. The slope, $m \approx 0.541$, represents the average annual increase in hourly compensation for production workers, about $0.54 per year.

(b) Setting $x = 40$ in the regression equation leads to $y \approx \$25.71$.

54. If the length is x, then the width is $50 - x$, so $A(x) = x(50 - x)$; maximum of 625 ft^2 when $x = 25$ (the dimensions are 25 ft $\times$ 25 ft).

55. (a) $[0, 100]$ by $[0, 1000]$ is one possibility.

(b) When $x \approx 107.335$ or $x \approx 372.665$ — either 107, 335 units or 372, 665 units.

56. The area of the picture and the frame, if the width of the picture is x ft, is $A(x) = (x + 2)(x + 5)$ ft^2. This equals 208 when $x = 11$, so the painting is 11 ft $\times$ 14 ft.

57. If the strip is x feet wide, the area of the strip is $A(x) = (25 + 2x)(40 + 2x) - 1000$ ft^2. This equals 504 ft^2 when $x = 3.5$ ft.

58. (a) $R(x) = (800 + 20x)(300 - 5x)$.

(b) $[0, 25]$ by $[200,000, 260,000]$ is one possibility (shown).

$[0, 25]$ by $[200,000, 260,000]$

(c) The maximum income — $250,000 — is achieved when $x = 10$, corresponding to rent of $250 per month.

59. (a) $R(x) = (26,000 - 1000x)(0.50 + 0.05x)$.

(b) Many choices of Xmax and Ymin are reasonable. Shown is $[0, 15]$ by $[10,000, 17,000]$.

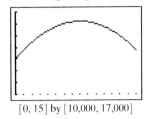

$[0, 15]$ by $[10,000, 17,000]$

(c) The maximum revenue — \$16,200 — is achieved when $x = 8$; that is, charging 90 cents per can.

60. Total sales would be $S(x) = (30 + x)(50 - x)$ thousand dollars, when x additional salespeople are hired. The maximum occurs when $x = 10$ (halfway between the two zeros, at -30 and 50).

61. (a) $g \approx 32$ ft/sec^2. $s_0 = 83$ ft and $v_0 = 92$ ft/sec. So the models are height $= s(t) = -16t^2 + 92t + 83$ and vertical velocity $= v(t) = -32t + 92$. The maximum height occurs at the vertex of $s(t)$.

$$h = -\frac{b}{2a} = -\frac{92}{2(-16)} = 2.875, \text{ and}$$

$k = s(2.875) = 215.25$. The maximum height of the baseball is about 215 ft above the field.

(b) The amount of time the ball is in the air is a zero of $s(t)$. Using the quadratic formula, we obtain

$$t = \frac{-92 \pm \sqrt{92^2 - 4(-16)(83)}}{2(-16)}$$
$$= \frac{-92 \pm \sqrt{13,776}}{-32} \approx -0.79 \text{ or } 6.54. \text{ Time is not}$$

negative, so the ball is in the air about 6.54 seconds.

(c) To determine the ball's vertical velocity when it hits the ground, use $v(t) = -32t + 92$, and solve for $t = 6.54$. $v(6.54) = -32(6.54) + 92 \approx -117$ ft/sec when it hits the ground.

62. (a) $h = -16t^2 + 48t + 3.5$.

(b) The graph is shown in the window $[0, 3.5]$ by $[0, 45]$. The maximum height is 39.5 ft, 1.5 sec after it is thrown.

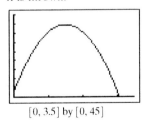

$[0, 3.5]$ by $[0, 45]$

63. (a) $h = -16t^2 + 80t - 10$. The graph is shown in the window $[0, 5]$ by $[-10, 100]$.

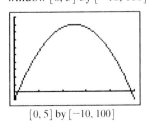

$[0, 5]$ by $[-10, 100]$

(b) The maximum height is 90 ft, 2.5 sec after it is shot.

64. The exact answer is $32\sqrt{3}$, or about 55.426 ft/sec. In addition to the guess-and-check strategy suggested, this can be found algebraically by noting that the vertex of the parabola $y = ax^2 + bx + c$ has y coordinate

$$c - \frac{b^2}{4a} = \frac{b^2}{64} \text{ (note } a = -16 \text{ and } c = 0\text{), and setting}$$

this equal to 48.

65. The quadratic regression is $y \approx 0.449x^2 + 0.934x + 114.658$. Plot this curve together with the curve $y = 450$, and then find the intersection to find when the number of patent applications will reach 450,000. Note that we use $y = 450$ because the data were given as a number of thousands. The intersection occurs at $x \approx 26.3$, so the number of applications will reach 450,000 approximately 26 years after 1980—in 2006.

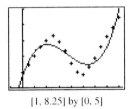

$[1, 8.25]$ by $[0, 5]$

66. (a) $m = \dfrac{6 \text{ ft}}{100 \text{ ft}} = 0.06$

(b) $r \approx 4167$ ft, or about 0.79 mile.

(c) 2217.6 ft

67. (a)

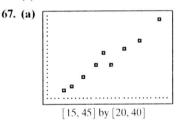

$[15, 45]$ by $[20, 40]$

(b) $y \approx 0.68x + 9.01$

(c) On average, the children gained 0.68 pound per month.

(d)

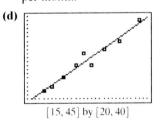

$[15, 45]$ by $[20, 40]$

(e) ≈ 29.41 lbs

68. (a) The linear regression is $y \approx 548.30x + 21,027.56$, where x represents the number of years since 1940.

(b) 2010 is 70 years after 1940, so substitute 70 into the equation to predict the median U.S. family income in 2010.

$y = 548.30(70) + 21,027.56 \approx \$59,400$.

69. The Identity Function $f(x) = x$

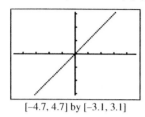

[−4.7, 4.7] by [−3.1, 3.1]

Domain: $(-\infty, \infty)$
Range: $(-\infty, \infty)$
Continuity: The function is continuous on its domain.
Increasing–decreasing behavior: Increasing for all x
Symmetry: Symmetric about the origin
Boundedness: Not bounded
Local extrema: None
Horizontal asymptotes: None
Vertical asymptotes: None
End behavior: $\lim\limits_{x \to -\infty} f(x) = -\infty$ and $\lim\limits_{x \to \infty} f(x) = \infty$

70. The Squaring Function $f(x) = x^2$

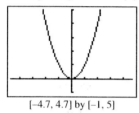

[−4.7, 4.7] by [−1, 5]

Domain: $(-\infty, \infty)$
Range: $[0, \infty)$
Continuity: The function is continuous on its domain.
Increasing–decreasing behavior: Increasing on $[0, \infty)$, decreasing on $(-\infty, 0]$.
Symmetry: Symmetric about the y-axis
Boundedness: Bounded below, but not above
Local extrema: Local minimum of 0 at $x = 0$
Horizontal asymptotes: None
Vertical asymptotes: None
End behavior: $\lim\limits_{x \to -\infty} f(x) = \lim\limits_{x \to \infty} f(x) = \infty$

71. False. For $f(x) = 3x^2 + 2x - 3$, the initial value is $f(0) = -3$.

72. True. By completing the square, we can rewrite $f(x)$ so that $f(x) = \left(x^2 - x + \dfrac{1}{4}\right) + 1 - \dfrac{1}{4}$

$= \left(x - \dfrac{1}{2}\right)^2 + \dfrac{3}{4}$. Since $f(x) \geq \dfrac{3}{4}, f(x) > 0$ for all x.

73. $m = \dfrac{1 - 3}{4 - (-2)} = \dfrac{-2}{6} = -\dfrac{1}{3}$. The answer is E.

74. $f(x) = mx + b$

$3 = -\dfrac{1}{3}(-2) + b$

$3 = \dfrac{2}{3} + b$

$b = 3 - \dfrac{2}{3} = \dfrac{7}{3}$

The answer is C.

For #75–76, $f(x) = 2(x + 3)^2 - 5$ corresponds to $f(x) = a(x - h)^2 + k$ with $a = 2$ and $(h, k) = (-3, -5)$.

75. The axis of symmetry runs vertically through the vertex: $x = -3$. The answer is B.

76. The vertex is $(h, k) = (-3, -5)$. The answer is E.

77. (a) Graphs (i), (iii), and (v) are linear functions. They can all be represented by an equation $y = ax + b$, where $a \neq 0$.

(b) In addition to graphs (i), (iii), and (v), graphs (iv) and (vi) are also functions, the difference is that (iv) and (vi) are *constant* functions, represented by $y = b, b \neq 0$.

(c) (ii) is not a function because a single value x (i.e., $x = -2$) results in a multiple number of y-values. In fact, there are infinitely many y-values that are valid for the equation $x = -2$.

78. (a) $\dfrac{f(3) - f(1)}{3 - 1} = \dfrac{9 - 1}{2} = 4$

(b) $\dfrac{f(5) - f(2)}{5 - 2} = \dfrac{25 - 4}{3} = 7$

(c) $\dfrac{f(c) - f(a)}{c - a} = \dfrac{c^2 - a^2}{c - a} = \dfrac{(c - a)(c + a)}{c - a} = c + a$

(d) $\dfrac{g(3) - g(1)}{3 - 1} = \dfrac{11 - 5}{2} = 3$

(e) $\dfrac{g(4) - g(1)}{4 - 1} = \dfrac{14 - 5}{3} = 3$

(f) $\dfrac{g(c) - g(a)}{c - a} = \dfrac{(3c + 2) - (3a + 2)}{c - a}$

$= \dfrac{3c - 3a}{c - a} = 3$

(g) $\dfrac{h(c) - h(a)}{c - a} = \dfrac{(7c - 3) - (7a - 3)}{c - a}$

$= \dfrac{7c - 7a}{c - a} = 7$

(h) $\dfrac{k(c) - k(a)}{c - a} = \dfrac{(mc + b) - (ma + b)}{c - a}$

$= \dfrac{mc - ma}{c - a} = m$

(i) $\dfrac{l(c) - l(a)}{c - a} = \dfrac{c^3 - a^3}{c - a} = \dfrac{-2b}{2a} = \dfrac{-b}{a} = -\dfrac{b}{a}$

$= \dfrac{(c - a)(c^2 + ac + a^2)}{(c - a)} = c^2 + ac + a^2$

79. Answers will vary. One possibility: When using the least-squares method, mathematicians try to minimize the residual $y_i - (ax_i + b)$, i.e., place the "predicted" y-values as close as possible to the actual y-values. If mathematicians reversed the ordered pairs, the objective would change to minimizing the residual $x_i - (cy_i + d)$, i.e., placing the "predicted" x-values as close as possible to the actual x-values. In order to obtain an exact inverse, the x- and y-values for each xy pair would have to be almost exactly the same distance from the regression line—which is statistically impossible in practice.

80. (a)

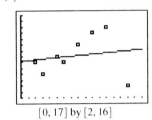

[0, 17] by [2, 16]

(b) $y \approx 0.115x + 8.245$

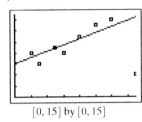

[0, 17] by [2, 16]

(c) $y \approx 0.556x + 6.093$

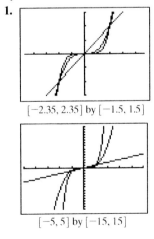

[0, 15] by [0, 15]

(d) The median–median line appears to be the better fit, because it approximates more of the data values more closely.

81. (a) If $ax^2 + bx + c = 0$, then

$$x = \frac{-b \pm \sqrt{b^2 - 4ac}}{2a}$$ by the quadratic

formula. Thus, $x_1 = \dfrac{-b + \sqrt{b^2 - 4ac}}{2a}$ and

$x_2 = \dfrac{-b - \sqrt{b^2 - 4ac}}{2a}$ and

$$x_1 + x_2 = \frac{-b + \sqrt{b^2 - 4ac} - b - \sqrt{b^2 - 4ac}}{2a}$$

$$= \frac{-2b}{2a} = \frac{-b}{a} = -\frac{b}{a}.$$

(b) Similarly,

$$x_1 \cdot x_2 = \left(\frac{-b + \sqrt{b^2 - 4ac}}{2a} \right)\left(\frac{-b - \sqrt{b^2 - 4ac}}{2a} \right)$$

$$= \frac{b^2 - (b^2 - 4ac)}{4a^2} = \frac{4ac}{4a^2} = \frac{c}{a}.$$

82. $f(x) = (x - a)(x - b) = x^2 - bx - ax + ab$

$= x^2 + (-a - b)x + ab$. If we use the vertex form of

a quadratic function, we have $h = -\left(\dfrac{-a - b}{2} \right)$

$= \dfrac{a + b}{2}$. The axis is $x = h = \dfrac{a + b}{2}$.

83. Multiply out $f(x)$ to get $x^2 - (a + b)x + ab$. Complete

the square to get $\left(x - \dfrac{a + b}{2} \right)^2 + ab - \dfrac{(a + b)^2}{4}$. The

vertex is then (h, k) where $h = \dfrac{a + b}{2}$ and

$k = ab - \dfrac{(a + b)^2}{4} = -\dfrac{(a - b)^2}{4}$.

84. x_1 and x_2 are given by the quadratic formula

$\dfrac{-b \pm \sqrt{b^2 - 4ac}}{2a}$; then $x_1 + x_2 = -\dfrac{b}{a}$, and the line of

symmetry is $x = -\dfrac{b}{2a}$, which is exactly equal to $\dfrac{x_1 + x_2}{2}$.

85. The Constant Rate of Change Theorem states that a function defined on all real numbers is a linear function if and only if it has a constant nonzero average rate of change between any two points on its graph. To prove this, suppose $f(x) = mx + b$ with m and b constants and $m \neq 0$. Let x_1 and x_2 be real numbers with $x_1 \neq x_2$. Then the average rate of change is

$$\frac{f(x_2) - f(x_1)}{x_2 - x_1} = \frac{(mx_2 + b) - (mx_1 + b)}{x_2 - x_1} =$$

$$\frac{mx_2 - mx_1}{x_2 - x_1} = \frac{m(x_2 - x_1)}{x_2 - x_1} = m, \text{ a nonzero constant.}$$

Now suppose that m and x_1 are constants, with $m \neq 0$. Let x be a real number such that $x \neq x_1$, and let f be a function defined on all real numbers such that

$$\frac{f(x) - f(x_1)}{x - x_1} = m. \text{ Then } f(x) - f(x_1) = m(x - x_1) =$$

$mx - mx_1$, and $f(x) = mx + (f(x_1) - mx_1)$.

$f(x_1) - mx_1$ is a constant; call it b. Then

$f(x_1) - mx_1 = b$; so, $f(x_1) = b + mx_1$ and

$f(x) = b + mx$ for all $x \neq x_1$. Thus, f is a linear function.

■ Section 2.2   Power Functions with Modeling

Exploration 1

1.

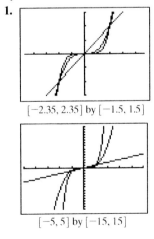

[−2.35, 2.35] by [−1.5, 1.5]

[−5, 5] by [−15, 15]

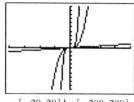

$[-20, 20]$ by $[-200, 200]$

The pairs $(0, 0)$, $(1, 1)$, and $(-1, -1)$ are common to all three graphs. The graphs are similar in that if $x < 0$, $f(x)$, $g(x)$, and $h(x) < 0$ and if $x > 0$, $f(x)$, $g(x)$, and $h(x) > 0$. They are different in that if $|x| < 1$, $f(x)$, $g(x)$, and $h(x) \to 0$ at dramatically different rates, and if $|x| > 1$, $f(x)$, $g(x)$, and $h(x) \to \infty$ at dramatically different rates.

2.

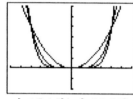

$[-1.5, 1.5]$ by $[-0.5, 1.5]$

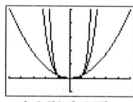

$[-5, 5]$ by $[-5, 25]$

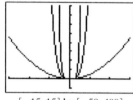

$[-15, 15]$ by $[-50, 400]$

The pairs $(0, 0)$, $(1, 1)$, and $(-1, 1)$ are common to all three graphs. The graphs are similar in that for $x \neq 0$, $f(x)$, $g(x)$, and $h(x) > 0$. They are diffferent in that if $|x| < 1$, $f(x)$, $g(x)$, and $h(x) \to 0$ at dramatically different rates, and if $|x| > 1$, $f(x)$, $g(x)$, and $h(x) \to \infty$ at dramatically different rates.

Quick Review 2.2

1. $\sqrt[3]{x^2}$

2. $\sqrt{p^5}$

3. $\dfrac{1}{d^2}$

4. $\dfrac{1}{x^7}$

5. $\dfrac{1}{\sqrt[5]{q^4}}$

6. $\dfrac{1}{\sqrt{m^3}}$

7. $3x^{3/2}$

8. $2x^{5/3}$

9. $\approx 1.71x^{-4/3}$

10. $\approx 0.71x^{-1/2}$

Section 2.2 Exercises

1. power $= 5$, constant $= -\dfrac{1}{2}$

2. power $= \dfrac{5}{3}$, constant $= 9$

3. not a power function

4. power $= 0$, constant $= 13$

5. power $= 1$, constant $= c^2$

6. power $= 5$, constant $= \dfrac{k}{2}$

7. power $= 2$, constant $= \dfrac{g}{2}$

8. power $= 3$, constant $= \dfrac{4\pi}{3}$

9. power $= -2$, constant $= k$

10. power $= 1$, constant $= m$

11. degree $= 0$, coefficient $= -4$

12. not a monomial function; negative exponent

13. degree $= 7$, coefficient $= -6$

14. not a monomial function; variable in exponent

15. degree $= 2$, coefficient $= 4\pi$

16. degree $= 1$, coefficient $= l$

17. $A = ks^2$

18. $V = kr^2$

19. $I = V/R$

20. $V = kT$

21. $E = mc^2$

22. $p = \sqrt{2gd}$

23. The weight w of an object varies directly with its mass m, with the constant of variation g.

24. The circumference C of a circle is proportional to its diameter D, with the constant of variation π.

25. The refractive index n of a medium is inversely proportional to v, the velocity of light in the medium, with constant of variation c, the constant velocity of light in free space.

26. The distance d traveled by a free-falling object dropped from rest varies directly with the square of its speed p, with the constant of variation $\dfrac{1}{2g}$.

27. power $= 4$, constant $= 2$
Domain: $(-\infty, \infty)$
Range: $[0, \infty)$
Continuous
Decreasing on $(-\infty, 0)$. Increasing on $(0, \infty)$.
Even. Symmetric with respect to y-axis.
Bounded below, but not above
Local minimum at $x = 0$.
Asymptotes: None
End Behavior: $\lim\limits_{x \to -\infty} 2x^4 = \infty$, $\lim\limits_{x \to \infty} 2x^4 = \infty$

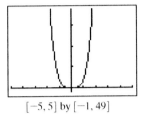
$[-5, 5]$ by $[-1, 49]$

28. power $= 3$, constant $= -3$
Domain: $(-\infty, \infty)$
Range: $(-\infty, \infty)$
Continuous
Decreasing for all x
Odd. Symmetric with respect to origin
Not bounded above or below
No local extrema
Asymptotes: None
End Behavior: $\lim\limits_{x \to -\infty} -3x^3 = \infty$, $\lim\limits_{x \to \infty} -3x^3 = -\infty$

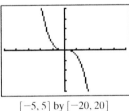
$[-5, 5]$ by $[-20, 20]$

29. power $= \dfrac{1}{4}$, constant $= \dfrac{1}{2}$

Domain: $[0, \infty)$
Range: $[0, \infty)$
Continuous
Increasing on $[0, \infty)$
Bounded below
Neither even nor odd
Local minimum at $(0, 0)$
Asymptotes: None
End Behavior: $\lim\limits_{x \to \infty} \dfrac{1}{2} \sqrt[4]{x} = \infty$

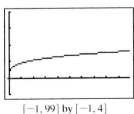
$[-1, 99]$ by $[-1, 4]$

30. power $= -3$, constant $= -2$
Domain: $(-\infty, 0) \cup (0, \infty)$
Range: $(-\infty, 0) \cup (0, \infty)$

Discontinuous at $x = 0$
Increasing on $(-\infty, 0)$. Increasing on $(0, \infty)$.
Odd. Symmetric with respect to origin
Not bounded above or below
No local extrema
Asymptotes at $x = 0$ and $y = 0$
End Behavior: $\lim\limits_{x \to -\infty} -2x^{-3} = 0$, $\lim\limits_{x \to \infty} -2x^{-3} = 0$.

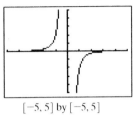
$[-5, 5]$ by $[-5, 5]$

31. Start with $y = x^4$ and shrink vertically by $\dfrac{2}{3}$. Since
$f(-x) = \dfrac{2}{3}(-x)^4 = \dfrac{2}{3}x^4$, f is even.

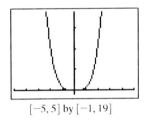
$[-5, 5]$ by $[-1, 19]$

32. Start with $y = x^3$ and stretch vertically by 5. Since
$f(-x) = 5(-x)^3 = -5x^3 = -f(x)$, f is odd.

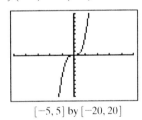
$[-5, 5]$ by $[-20, 20]$

33. Start with $y = x^5$, then stretch vertically by 1.5 and reflect over the x-axis. Since $f(-x) = -1.5(-x)^5 = 1.5x^5$ $= -f(x)$, f is odd.

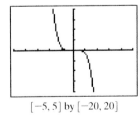
$[-5, 5]$ by $[-20, 20]$

34. Start with $y = x^6$, then stretch vertically by 2 and reflect over the x-axis. Since $f(-x) = -2(-x)^6 = -2x^6$ $= f(x)$, f is even.

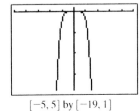
$[-5, 5]$ by $[-19, 1]$

35. Start with $y = x^8$, then shrink vertically by $\frac{1}{4}$. Since

$$f(-x) = \frac{1}{4}(-x)^8 = \frac{1}{4}x^8 = f(x), f \text{ is even.}$$

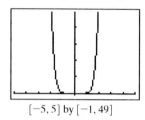

$[-5, 5]$ by $[-1, 49]$

36. Start with $y = x^7$, then shrink vertically by $\frac{1}{8}$. Since

$$f(-x) = \frac{1}{8}(-x)^7 = -\frac{1}{8}x^7 = -f(x), f \text{ is odd.}$$

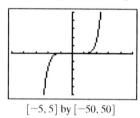

$[-5, 5]$ by $[-50, 50]$

37. (g)

38. (a)

39. (d)

40. (g)

41. (h)

42. (d)

43. $k = 3, a = \frac{1}{4}$. In the first quadrant, the function is increasing and concave down. f is undefined for $x < 0$.

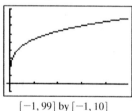

$[-1, 99]$ by $[-1, 10]$

44. $k = -4, a = \frac{2}{3}$. In the fourth quadrant, the function is decreasing and concave up. $f(-x) = -4(\sqrt[3]{(-x)^2})$
$= -4\sqrt[3]{x^2} = -4x^{2/3} = f(x), \text{ so } f \text{ is even.}$

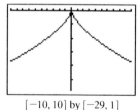

$[-10, 10]$ by $[-29, 1]$

45. $k = -2, a = \frac{4}{3}$. In the fourth quadrant, f is decreasing and concave down. $f(-x) = -2(\sqrt[3]{(-x)^4})$
$= -2(\sqrt[3]{x^4}) = -2x^{4/3} = f(x), \text{ so } f \text{ is even.}$

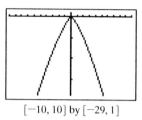

$[-10, 10]$ by $[-29, 1]$

46. $k = \frac{2}{5}, a = \frac{5}{2}$. In the first quadrant, f is increasing and concave up. f is undefined for $x < 0$.

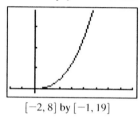

$[-2, 8]$ by $[-1, 19]$

47. $k = \frac{1}{2}, a = -3$. In the first quadrant, f is decreasing and concave up. $f(-x) = \frac{1}{2}(-x)^{-3} = \frac{1}{2(-x)^3} = -\frac{1}{2}x^{-3}$
$= -f(x), \text{ so } f \text{ is odd.}$

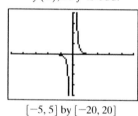

$[-5, 5]$ by $[-20, 20]$

48. $k = -1, a = -4$. In the fourth quadrant, f is increasing and concave down. $f(-x) = -(-x)^{-4} = -\frac{1}{(-x)^4}$
$= -\frac{1}{x^4} = -x^{-4} = f(x), \text{ so } f \text{ is even.}$

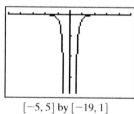

$[-5, 5]$ by $[-19, 1]$

49. $y = \frac{8}{x^2}$, power $= -2$, constant $= 8$

50. $y = -2\sqrt{x}$, power $= \frac{1}{2}$, constant $= -2$

51. $V = \dfrac{kT}{P}$, so $k = \dfrac{PV}{T} = \dfrac{(0.926 \text{ atm})(3.46 \text{ L})}{302°\text{K}}$

$= 0.0106 \dfrac{\text{atm–L}}{\text{K}}$

At $P = 1.452$ atm, $V = \dfrac{\left(0.0106 \dfrac{\text{atm–L}}{\text{K}} \right)(302°\text{K})}{1.452 \text{ atm}}$

$= 2.21$ L

52. $V = kPT$, so $k = \dfrac{V}{PT} = \dfrac{(3.46 \text{ L})}{(0.926 \text{ atm})(302°\text{K})}$

$= 0.0124 \dfrac{\text{L}}{\text{atm–K}}$

At $T = 338°$K, $V = \left(0.0124 \dfrac{\text{L}}{\text{atm–K}} \right)(0.926 \text{ atm})$

$(338°\text{K}) = 3.87$ L

53. $n = \dfrac{c}{v}$, so $v = \dfrac{c}{n} = \dfrac{\left(\dfrac{3.00 \times 10^8 \text{ m}}{\text{sec}} \right)}{2.42} = 1.24 \times 10^8 \dfrac{\text{m}}{\text{sec}}$

54. $P = kv^3$, so $k = \dfrac{P}{v^3} = \dfrac{15 \text{ w}}{(10 \text{ mph})^3} = 1.5 \times 10^{-2}$

Wind Speed (mph)	Power (W)
10	15
20	120
40	960
80	7680

Since $P = kv^3$ is a cubic, power will increase significantly with only a small increase in wind speed.

55. (a)

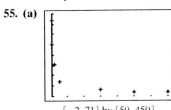

[−2, 71] by [50, 450]

(b) $r \approx 231.204 \cdot w^{-0.297}$

(c)

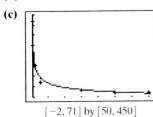

[−2, 71] by [50, 450]

(d) Approximately 37.67 beats/min, which is very close to Clark's observed value.

56. Given that n is an integer, $n \geq 1$:
If n is odd, then $f(-x) = (-x)^n = -(x^n) = -f(x)$ and so $f(x)$ is odd.
If n is even, then $f(-x) = (-x)^n = x^n = f(x)$ and so $f(x)$ is even.

57. (a)

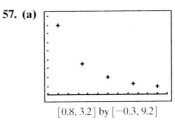

[0.8, 3.2] by [−0.3, 9.2]

(b) $y \approx 7.932 \cdot x^{-1.987}$; yes

(c)

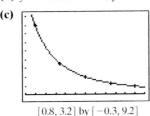

[0.8, 3.2] by [−0.3, 9.2]

(d) Approximately 2.76 $\dfrac{\text{W}}{\text{m}^2}$ and 0.697 $\dfrac{\text{W}}{\text{m}^2}$, respectively.

58. True, because $f(-x) = (-x)^{-2/3} = [(-x)^2]^{-1/3}$
$= (x^2)^{-1/3} = x^{-2/3} = f(x)$.

59. False. $f(-x) = (-x)^{1/3} = -(x^{1/3}) = -f(x)$ and so the function is odd. It is symmetric about the origin, not the y-axis.

60. $f(4) = 2(4)^{-1/2} = \dfrac{2}{4^{1/2}} = \dfrac{2}{\sqrt{4}} = \dfrac{2}{2} = 1$.
The answer is A.

61. $f(0) = -3(0)^{-1/3} = -3 \cdot \dfrac{1}{0^{1/3}} = -3 \cdot \dfrac{1}{0}$ is undefined.

Also, $f(-1) = -3(-1)^{-1/3} = -3(-1) = 3$,
$f(1) = -3(1)^{-1/3} = -3(1) = -3$, and
$f(3) = -3(3)^{-1/3} \approx -2.08$. The answer is E.

62. $f(-x) = (-x)^{2/3} = [(-x)^2]^{1/3} = (x^2)^{1/3} = x^{2/3} = f(x)$
The function is even. The answer is B.

63. $f(x) = x^{3/2} = (x^{1/2})^3 = (\sqrt{x})^3$ is defined for $x \geq 0$.
The answer is B.

64. Answers will vary. In general, however, students will find
n even: $f(x) = k \cdot x^{m/n} = k \cdot \sqrt[n]{x^m}$, so f is
undefined for $x < 0$.

m even, n odd: $f(x) = k \cdot x^{m/n} = k \cdot \sqrt[n]{x^m}$; $f(-x)$
$= k \cdot \sqrt[n]{(-x)^m} = k \cdot \sqrt[n]{x^m} = f(x)$,
so f is even.

m odd, n odd: $f(x) = k \cdot x^{m/n} = k \cdot \sqrt[n]{x^m}$; $f(-x)$
$= k \cdot \sqrt[n]{(-x)^m} = -k \cdot \sqrt[n]{x^m}$
$= -k \cdot x^{m/n} = -f(x)$, so f is odd.

65. (a)

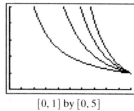
[0, 1] by [0, 5]

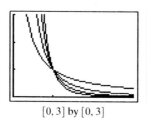
[0, 3] by [0, 3]

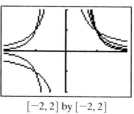
[−2, 2] by [−2, 2]

The graphs of $f(x) = x^{-1}$ and $h(x) = x^{-3}$ are similar and appear in the 1st and 3rd quadrants only. The graphs of $g(x) = x^{-2}$ and $k(x) = x^{-4}$ are similar and appear in the 1st and 2nd quadrants only. The pair (1, 1) is common to all four functions.

	f	g	h	k
Domain	$x \neq 0$	$x \neq 0$	$x \neq 0$	$x \neq 0$
Range	$y \neq 0$	$y > 0$	$y \neq 0$	$y > 0$
Continuous	yes	yes	yes	yes
Increasing		$(-\infty, 0)$		$(-\infty, 0)$
Decreasing	$(-\infty, 0), (0, \infty)$	$(0, \infty)$	$(-\infty, 0), (0, \infty)$	$(0, \infty)$
Symmetry	w.r.t. origin	w.r.t. y-axis	w.r.t. origin	w.r.t. y-axis
Bounded	not	below	not	below
Extrema	none	none	none	none
Asymptotes	x-axis, y-axis	x-axis, y-axis	x-axis, y-axis	x-axis, y-axis
End Behavior	$\lim\limits_{x \to \pm\infty} f(x) = 0$	$\lim\limits_{x \to \pm\infty} g(x) = 0$	$\lim\limits_{x \to \pm\infty} h(x) = 0$	$\lim\limits_{x \to \pm\infty} k(x) = 0$

(b)

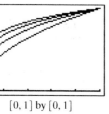
[0, 1] by [0, 1]

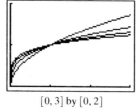
[0, 3] by [0, 2]

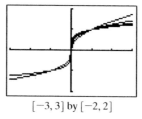
[−3, 3] by [−2, 2]

The graphs of $f(x) = x^{1/2}$ and $h(x) = x^{1/4}$ are similar and appear in the 1st quadrant only. The graphs of $g(x) = x^{1/3}$ and $k(x) = x^{1/5}$ are similar and appear in the 1st and 3rd quadrants only. The pairs (0, 0), (1, 1) are common to all four functions.

	f	g	h	k
Domain	$[0, \infty)$	$(-\infty, \infty)$	$[0, \infty)$	$(-\infty, \infty)$
Range	$y \geq 0$	$(-\infty, \infty)$	$y \geq 0$	$(-\infty, \infty)$
Continuous	yes	yes	yes	yes
Increasing	$[0, \infty)$	$(-\infty, \infty)$	$[0, \infty)$	$(-\infty, \infty)$
Decreasing				
Symmetry	none	w.r.t. origin	none	w.r.t. origin
Bounded	below	not	below	not
Extrema	min at (0, 0)	none	min at (0, 0)	none
Asymptotes	none	none	none	none
End behavior	$\lim\limits_{x \to \infty} f(x) = \infty$	$\lim\limits_{x \to \infty} g(x) = \infty$ $\lim\limits_{x \to -\infty} g(x) = -\infty$	$\lim\limits_{x \to \infty} h(x) = \infty$	$\lim\limits_{x \to \infty} k(x) = \infty$ $\lim\limits_{x \to -\infty} k(x) = -\infty$

66.

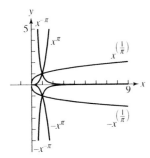

The graphs look like those shown in Figure 2.14 on page 192.

$f(x) = x^\pi$ looks like the red graph in Figure 2.14(a) because $k = 1 > 0$ and $a = \pi > 1$.

$f(x) = x^{1/\pi}$ looks like the blue graph in Figure 2.14(a) because $k = 1 > 0$ and $0 < a = 1/\pi < 1$.

$f(x) = x^{-\pi}$ looks like the green graph in Figure 2.14(a) because $k = 1 < 0$ and $a = -\pi < 0$.

$f(x) = -x^\pi$ looks like the red graph in Figure 2.14(b) because $k = -1 < 0$ and $a = \pi > 1$.

$f(x) = -x^{1/\pi}$ looks like the blue graph in Figure 2.14(b) because $k = -1 < 0$ and $a = -\pi < 0$.

$f(x) = -x^{-\pi}$ looks like the green graph in Figure 2.14(b) because $k = -1 < 0$ and $a = -\pi < 0$.

67. Our new table looks like:

Table 2.10 (revised) Average Distances and Orbit Periods for the Six Innermost Planets

Planet	Average Distance from Sun (Au)	Period of Orbit (yrs)
Mercury	0.39	0.24
Venus	0.72	0.62
Earth	1	1
Mars	1.52	1.88
Jupiter	5.20	11.86
Saturn	9.54	29.46

Source: Shupe, Dorr, Payne, Hunsiker, et al., National Geographic Atlas of the World (rev. 6th ed.). Washington, DC: National Geographic Society, 1992, plate 116.

Using these new data, we find a power function model of: $y \approx 0.99995 \cdot x^{1.50115} \approx x^{1.5}$. Since y represents years, we set $y = T$ and since x represents distance, we set $x = a$ then, $y = x^{1.5} \Rightarrow T = a^{3/2} \Rightarrow (T)^2 = (a^{3/2})^2 \Rightarrow T^2 = a^3$.

68. Using the free-fall equations in Section 2.1, we know that $s(t) = -\frac{1}{2}gt^2 + v_0 t + s_0$ and that $v(t) = -gt + v_0$. If $t = 0$ is the time at which the object is dropped, then $v_0 = 0$. So $d = s_0 - s = s_0 - \left(-\frac{1}{2}gt^2 + s_0\right) = \frac{1}{2}gt^2$ and $p = |v| = |-gt|$. Solving $d = \frac{1}{2}gt^2$ for t, we have $t = \sqrt{\frac{2d}{g}}$. Then $p = \left|-g\sqrt{\frac{2d}{g}}\right| = \sqrt{\frac{2dg^2}{g}} = \sqrt{2dg}$.
The results of Example 6 approximate this formula.

69. If f is even,
$$f(x) = f(-x), \text{ so } \frac{1}{f(x)} = \frac{1}{f(-x)}, (f(x) \neq 0).$$
Since $g(x) = \frac{1}{f(x)} = \frac{1}{f(-x)} = g(-x)$, g is also even.

If g is even,
$$g(x) = g(-x), \text{ so } g(-x) = \frac{1}{f(-x)} = g(x) = \frac{1}{f(x)}.$$
Since $\frac{1}{f(-x)} = \frac{1}{f(x)}, f(-x) = f(x)$, and f is even.

If f is odd,
$$f(x) = -f(x), \text{ so } \frac{1}{f(x)} = -\frac{1}{f(x)}, f(x) \neq 0.$$
Since $g(x) = \frac{1}{f(x)} = -\frac{1}{f(x)} = -g(x)$, g is also odd.

If g is odd,
$$g(x) = g(-x), \text{ so } g(-x) = \frac{1}{f(-x)} = -g(x) = -\frac{1}{f(x)}.$$
Since $\frac{1}{f(-x)} = -\frac{1}{f(x)}, f(-x) = -f(x)$, and f is odd.

70. Let $g(x) = x^{-a}$ and $f(x) = x^a$. Then $g(x) = 1/x^a = 1/f(x)$. Exercise 69 shows that $g(x) = 1/f(x)$ is even if and only if $f(x)$ is even, and $g(x) = 1/f(x)$ is odd if and only if $f(x)$ is odd. Therefore, $g(x) = x^{-a}$ is even if and only if $f(x) = x^a$ is even, and that $g(x) = x^{-a}$ is odd if and only if $f(x) = x^a$ is odd.

71. (a) The force F acting on an object varies jointly as the mass m of the object and the acceleration a of the object.

(b) The kinetic energy KE of an object varies jointly as the mass m of the object and the square of the velocity v of the object.

(c) The force of gravity F acting on two objects varies jointly as their masses m_1 and m_2 and inversely as the square of the distance r between their centers, with the constant of variation G, the universal gravitational constant.

■ Section 2.3 Polynomial Functions of Higher Degree with Modeling

Exploration 1

1. (a) $\lim\limits_{x \to \infty} 2x^3 = \infty$, $\lim\limits_{x \to -\infty} 2x^3 = -\infty$

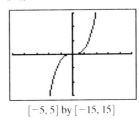

$[-5, 5]$ by $[-15, 15]$

(b) $\lim\limits_{x\to\infty}(-x^3) = -\infty$, $\lim\limits_{x\to-\infty}(-x^3) = \infty$

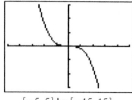

$[-5, 5]$ by $[-15, 15]$

(c) $\lim\limits_{x\to\infty}x^5 = \infty$, $\lim\limits_{x\to-\infty}x^5 = -\infty$

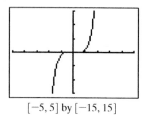

$[-5, 5]$ by $[-15, 15]$

(d) $\lim\limits_{x\to\infty}(-0.5x^7) = -\infty$, $\lim\limits_{x\to-\infty}(-0.5x^7) = \infty$

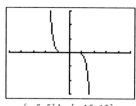

$[-5, 5]$ by $[-15, 15]$

2. (a) $\lim\limits_{x\to\infty}(-3x^4) = -\infty$, $\lim\limits_{x\to-\infty}(-3x^4) = -\infty$

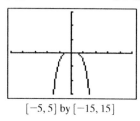

$[-5, 5]$ by $[-15, 15]$

(b) $\lim\limits_{x\to\infty}0.6x^4 = \infty$, $\lim\limits_{x\to-\infty}0.6x^4 = \infty$

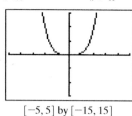

$[-5, 5]$ by $[-15, 15]$

(c) $\lim\limits_{x\to\infty}2x^6 = \infty$, $\lim\limits_{x\to-\infty}2x^6 = \infty$

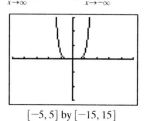

$[-5, 5]$ by $[-15, 15]$

(d) $\lim\limits_{x\to\infty}(-0.5x^2) = -\infty$, $\lim\limits_{x\to-\infty}(-0.5x^2) = -\infty$

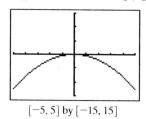

$[-5, 5]$ by $[-15, 15]$

3. (a) $\lim\limits_{x\to\infty}(-0.3x^5) = -\infty$, $\lim\limits_{x\to-\infty}(-0.3x^5) = \infty$

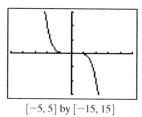

$[-5, 5]$ by $[-15, 15]$

(b) $\lim\limits_{x\to\infty}(-2x^2) = -\infty$, $\lim\limits_{x\to-\infty}(-2x^2) = -\infty$

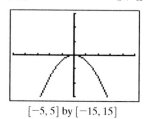

$[-5, 5]$ by $[-15, 15]$

(c) $\lim\limits_{x\to\infty}3x^4 = \infty$, $\lim\limits_{x\to-\infty}3x^4 = \infty$

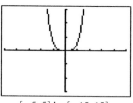

$[-5, 5]$ by $[-15, 15]$

(d) $\lim\limits_{x\to\infty}2.5x^3 = \infty$, $\lim\limits_{x\to-\infty}2.5x^3 = -\infty$

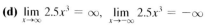

$[-5, 5]$ by $[-15, 15]$

If $a_n > 0$ and $n > 0$, $\lim\limits_{x\to\infty}f(x) = \infty$ and $\lim\limits_{x\to-\infty}f(x) = -\infty$. If $a_n < 0$ and $n > 0$, $\lim\limits_{x\to\infty}f(x) = -\infty$ and $\lim\limits_{x\to-\infty}f(x) = \infty$.

Exploration 2

1. $y = 0.0061x^3 + 0.0177x^2 - 0.5007x + 0.9769$ It is an exact fit, which we expect with only 4 data points!

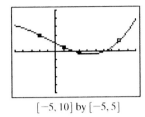

[−5, 10] by [−5, 5]

2. $y = -0.375x^4 + 6.917x^3 - 44.125x^2 + 116.583x - 111$ It is an exact fit, exactly what we expect with only 5 data points!

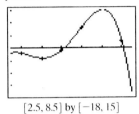

[2.5, 8.5] by [−18, 15]

Quick Review 2.3

1. $(x - 4)(x + 3)$
2. $(x - 7)(x - 4)$
3. $(3x - 2)(x - 3)$
4. $(2x - 1)(3x - 1)$
5. $x(3x - 2)(x - 1)$
6. $2x(3x - 2)(x - 3)$
7. $x = 0, x = 1$
8. $x = 0, x = -2, x = 5$
9. $x = -6, x = -3, x = 1.5$
10. $x = -6, x = -4, x = 5$

Section 2.3 Exercises

1. Start with $y = x^3$, shift to the right by 3 units, and then stretch vertically by 2. y-intercept: $(0, -54)$

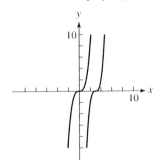

2. Start with $y = x^3$, shift to the left by 5 units, and then reflect over the x-axis. y-intercept: $(0, -125)$

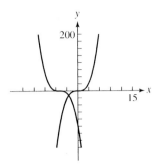

3. Start with $y = x^3$, shift to the left by 1 unit, vertically shrink by $\frac{1}{2}$, reflect over the x-axis, and then vertically shift up 2 units. y-intercept: $\left(0, \frac{3}{2}\right)$

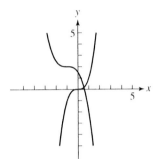

4. Start with $y = x^3$, shift to the right by 3 units, vertically shrink by $\frac{2}{3}$, and vertically shift up 1 unit. y-intercept: $(0, -17)$

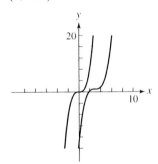

5. Start with $y = x^4$, shift to the left 2 units, vertically stretch by 2, reflect over the x-axis, and vertically shift down 3 units. y-intercept: $(0, -35)$

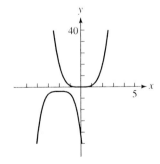

6. Start with $y = x^4$, shift to the right 1 unit, vertically stretch by 3, and vertically shift down 2 units. y-intercept: $(0, 1)$

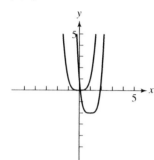

7. local maximum: $\approx (0.79, 1.19)$, zeros: $x = 0$ and $x \approx 1.26$. The general shape of f is like $y = -x^4$, but near the origin, f behaves a lot like its other term, $2x$. f is neither even nor odd.

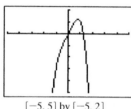

$[-5, 5]$ by $[-5, 2]$

8. local maximum at $(0, 0)$ and local minima at $(1.12, -3.13)$ and $(-1.12, -3.13)$, zeros: $x = 0$, $x \approx 1.58$, $x \approx -1.58$. f behaves a lot like $y = 2x^4$ except in the interval $[-1.58, 1.58]$, where it behaves more like its second building block term, $-5x^2$.

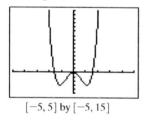

$[-5, 5]$ by $[-5, 15]$

9. Cubic function, positive leading coefficient. The answer is (c).

10. Cubic function, negative leading coefficient. The answer is (b).

11. Higher than cubic, positive leading coefficient. The answer is (a).

12. Higher than cubic, negative leading coefficient. The answer is (d).

13. One possibility:

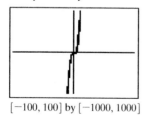

$[-100, 100]$ by $[-1000, 1000]$

14. One possibility:

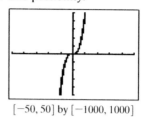

$[-50, 50]$ by $[-1000, 1000]$

15. One possibility:

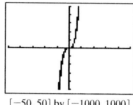

$[-50, 50]$ by $[-1000, 1000]$

16. One possibility:

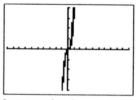

$[-100, 100]$ by $[-2000, 2000]$

For #17–24, when one end of a polynomial function's graph curves up into Quadrant I or II, this indicates a limit at ∞. And when an end curves down into Quadrant III or IV, this indicates a limit at $-\infty$.

17.

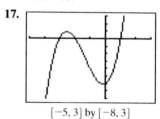

$[-5, 3]$ by $[-8, 3]$

$\lim\limits_{x \to \infty} f(x) = \infty$

$\lim\limits_{x \to -\infty} f(x) = -\infty$

18.

$[-5, 5]$ by $[-15, 15]$

$\lim\limits_{x \to \infty} f(x) = -\infty$

$\lim\limits_{x \to -\infty} f(x) = \infty$

19.

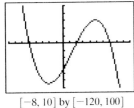

$[-8, 10]$ by $[-120, 100]$

$\lim\limits_{x \to \infty} f(x) = -\infty$

$\lim\limits_{x \to -\infty} f(x) = \infty$

20.

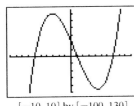

$[-10, 10]$ by $[-100, 130]$

$\lim\limits_{x \to \infty} f(x) = \infty$

$\lim\limits_{x \to -\infty} f(x) = -\infty$

21.

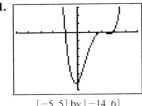

$[-5, 5]$ by $[-14, 6]$

$\lim\limits_{x \to \infty} f(x) = \infty$

$\lim\limits_{x \to -\infty} f(x) = \infty$

22.

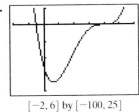

$[-2, 6]$ by $[-100, 25]$

$\lim\limits_{x \to \infty} f(x) = \infty$

$\lim\limits_{x \to -\infty} f(x) = \infty$

23.

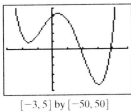

$[-3, 5]$ by $[-50, 50]$

$\lim\limits_{x \to \infty} f(x) = \infty$

$\lim\limits_{x \to -\infty} f(x) = \infty$

24.

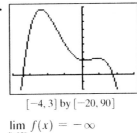

$[-4, 3]$ by $[-20, 90]$

$\lim\limits_{x \to \infty} f(x) = -\infty$

$\lim\limits_{x \to -\infty} f(x) = -\infty$

For #25–28, the end behavior of a polynomial is governed by the highest-degree term.

25. $\lim\limits_{x \to \infty} f(x) = \infty$, $\lim\limits_{x \to -\infty} f(x) = \infty$

26. $\lim\limits_{x \to \infty} f(x) = -\infty$, $\lim\limits_{x \to -\infty} f(x) = \infty$

27. $\lim\limits_{x \to \infty} f(x) = -\infty$, $\lim\limits_{x \to -\infty} f(x) = \infty$

28. $\lim\limits_{x \to \infty} f(x) = -\infty$, $\lim\limits_{x \to -\infty} f(x) = -\infty$

29. (a); There are 3 zeros: they are -2.5, 1, and 1.1.

30. (b); There are 3 zeros: they are 0.4, approximately 0.429 (actually 3/7), and 3.

31. (c); There are 3 zeros: approximately -0.273 (actually $-3/11$), -0.25, and 1.

32. (d); There are 3 zeros: -2, 0.5, and 3.

For #33–35, factor or apply the quadratic formula.

33. -4 and 2

34. -2 and 2/3

35. 2/3 and $-1/3$

For #36–38, factor out x, then factor or apply the quadratic formula.

36. 0, -5, and 5

37. 0, $-2/3$, and 1

38. 0, -1, and 2

39. Degree 3; zeros: $x = 0$ (multiplicity 1, graph crosses x-axis), $x = 3$ (multiplicity 2, graph is tangent)

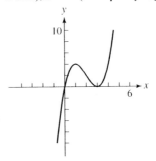

40. Degree 4; zeros: $x = 0$ (multiplicity 3, graph crosses x-axis), $x = 2$ (multiplicity 1, graph crosses x-axis)

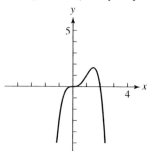

41. Degree 5; zeros: $x = 1$ (multiplicity 3, graph crosses x-axis), $x = -2$ (multiplicity 2, graph is tangent)

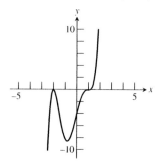

42. Degree 6; zeros: $x = 3$ (multiplicity 2, graph is tangent), $x = -5$ (multiplicity 4, graph is tangent)

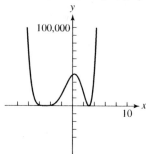

43. Zeros: -2.43, -0.74, 1.67

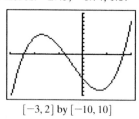

$[-3, 2]$ by $[-10, 10]$

44. Zeros: -1.73, 0.26, 4.47

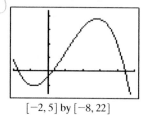

$[-2, 5]$ by $[-8, 22]$

45. Zeros: -2.47, -1.46, 1.94

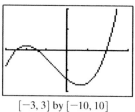

$[-3, 3]$ by $[-10, 10]$

46. Zeros: -4.53, 2

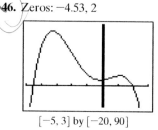

$[-5, 3]$ by $[-20, 90]$

47. Zeros: -4.90, -0.45, 1, 1.35

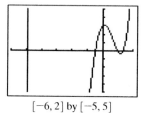

$[-6, 2]$ by $[-5, 5]$

48. Zeros: -1.98, -0.16, 1.25, 2.77, 3.62

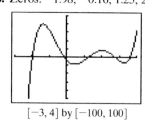

$[-3, 4]$ by $[-100, 100]$

49. 0, -6, and 6. Algebraically — factor out x first.

50. -11, -1, and 10. Graphically. Cubic equations *can* be solved algebraically, but methods of doing so are more complicated than the quadratic formula.

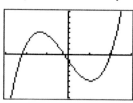

$[-15, 15]$ by $[-800, 800]$

51. -5, 1, and 11. Graphically.

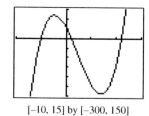

$[-10, 15]$ by $[-300, 150]$

52. -6, 2, and 8. Graphically.

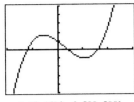

[–10, 15] by [–500, 500]

For #53–56, the "minimal" polynomials are given; any constant (or any other polynomial) can be multiplied by the answer given to give another answer.

53. $f(x) = (x - 3)(x + 4)(x - 6)$
$= x^3 - 5x^2 - 18x + 72$

54. $f(x) = (x + 2)(x - 3)(x + 5) = x^3 + 4x^2 - 11x - 30$

55. $f(x) = (x - \sqrt{3})(x + \sqrt{3})(x - 4)$
$= (x^2 - 3)(x - 4) = x^3 - 4x^2 - 3x + 12$

56. $f(x) = (x - 1)(x - 1 - \sqrt{2})(x - 1 + \sqrt{2})$
$= (x - 1)[(x - 1)^2 - 2] = x^3 - 3x^2 + x + 1$

57. $y = 0.25x^3 - 1.25x^2 - 6.75x + 19.75$

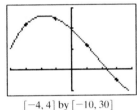

[–4, 4] by [–10, 30]

58. $y = 0.074x^3 - 0.167x^2 + 0.611x + 4.48$

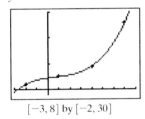

[–3, 8] by [–2, 30]

59. $y = -2.21x^4 + 45.75x^3 - 339.79x^2 + 1075.25x - 1231$

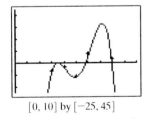

[0, 10] by [–25, 45]

60. $y = -0.017x^4 + 0.226x^3 + 0.289x^2 - 3.202x - 21$

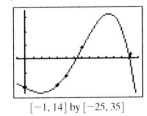

[–1, 14] by [–25, 35]

61. $f(x) = x^7 + x + 100$ has an odd-degree leading term, which means that in its end behavior it will go toward $-\infty$ at one end and toward ∞ at the other. Thus the graph must cross the x-axis at least once. That is to say, $f(x)$ takes on both positive and negative values, and thus by the Intermediate Value Theorem, $f(x) = 0$ for some x.

62. $f(x) = x^9 - x + 50$ has an odd-degree leading term, which means that in its end behavior it will go toward $-\infty$ at one end and toward ∞ at the other. Thus the graph must cross the x-axis at least once. That is to say, $f(x)$ takes on both positive and negative values, and thus by the Intermediate Value Theorem, $f(x) = 0$ for some x.

63. (a)

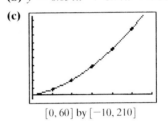

[0, 60] by [–10, 210]

(b) $y = 0.051x^2 + 0.97x + 0.26$

(c)

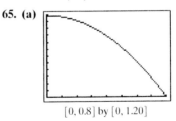

[0, 60] by [–10, 210]

(d) $y(25) \approx 56.39$ ft

(e) Using the quadratic equation to solve $0 = 0.051x^2 + 0.97x + (0.26 - 300)$, we find two answers: $x = 67.74$ mph and $x = -86.76$ mph. Clearly the negative value is extraneous.

64. (a) $P(x) = R(x) - C(x)$ is positive if $29.73 < x < 541.74$ (approx.), so they need between 30 and 541 customers.

(b) $P(x) = 60000$ when $x = 200.49$ or $x = 429.73$. Either 201 or 429 customers gives a profit slightly over \$60,000; 200 or 430 customers both yield slightly less than \$60,000.

65. (a)

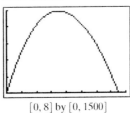

[0, 0.8] by [0, 1.20]

(b) 0.3391 cm from the center of the artery

66. (a) The height of the box will be x, the width will be $15 - 2x$, and the length $60 - 2x$.

(b) Any value of x between approximately 0.550 and 6.786 inches.

[0, 8] by [0, 1500]

67. The volume is $V(x) = x(10 - 2x)(25 - 2x)$; use any x with $0 < x \le 0.929$ or $3.644 \le x < 5$.

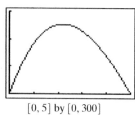

[0, 5] by [0, 300]

68. Determine where the function is positive: $0 < x < 21.5$. (The side lengths of the rectangle are 43 and 62 units.)

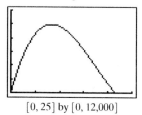

[0, 25] by [0, 12,000]

69. True. Because f is continuous and
$f(1) = (1)^3 - (1)^2 - 2 = -2 < 0$
while $f(2) = (2)^3 - (2)^2 - 2 = 2 > 0$,
the Intermediate Value Theorem assures us that the graph of f crosses the x-axis ($f(x) = 0$) somewhere between $x = 1$ and $x = 2$.

70. False. If $a > 0$, the graph of $f(x) = (x + a)^2$ is obtained by translating the graph of $f(x) = x^2$ to the left by a units. Translation to the right corresponds to $a < 0$.

71. When $x = 0$, $f(x) = 2(x - 1)^3 + 5 = 2(-1)^3 + 5 = 3$. The answer is C.

72. In $f(x) = (x - 2)^2(x + 2)^3(x + 3)^7$, the factor $x - 2$ occurs twice. So $x = 2$ is a zero of multiplicity 2, and the answer is B.

73. The graph indicates three zeros, each of multiplicity 1: $x = -2$, $x = 0$, and $x = 2$. The end behavior indicates a negative leading coefficient. So $f(x) = -x(x + 2)(x - 2)$, and the answer is B.

74. The graph indicates four zeros: $x = -2$ (multiplicity 2), $x = 0$ (multiplicity 1) and $x = 2$ (multiplicity 2). The end behavior indicates a positive leading coefficient. So $f(x) = x(x + 2)^2(x - 2)$, and the answer is A.

75. The first view shows the end behavior of the function, but obscures the fact that there are two local maxima and a local minimum (and 4 x-axis intersections) between -3 and 4. These are visible in the second view, but missing is the minimum near $x = 7$ and the x-axis intersection near $x = 9$. The second view suggests a degree 4 polynomial rather than degree 5.

76. The end behavior is visible in the first window, but not the details of the behavior near $x = 1$. The second view shows those details, but at the loss of the end behavior.

77. The exact behavior near $x = 1$ is hard to see. A zoomed–in view around the point $(1, 0)$ suggests that the graph just touches the x-axis at 0 without actually crossing it — that is, $(1, 0)$ is a local maximum. One possible window is $[0.9999, 1.0001]$ by $[-1 \times 10^{-7}, 1 \times 10^{-7}]$.

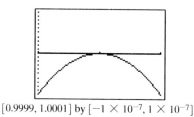

$[0.9999, 1.0001]$ by $[-1 \times 10^{-7}, 1 \times 10^{-7}]$

78. This also has a maximum near $x = 1$ — but this time a window such as $[0.6, 1.4]$ by $[-0.1, 0.1]$ reveals that the graph actually rises above the x-axis and has a maximum at $(0.999, 0.025)$.

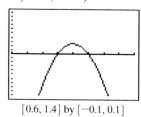

$[0.6, 1.4]$ by $[-0.1, 0.1]$

79. A maximum and minimum are not visible in the standard window, but can be seen on the window $[0.2, 0.4]$ by $[5.29, 5.3]$.

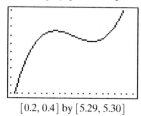

$[0.2, 0.4]$ by $[5.29, 5.30]$

80. A maximum and minimum are not visible in the standard window, but can be seen on the window $[0.95, 1.05]$ by $[-6.0005, -5.9995]$.

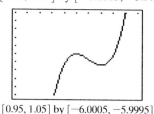

$[0.95, 1.05]$ by $[-6.0005, -5.9995]$

81. The graph of $y = 3(x^3 - x)$ (shown on the window $[-2, 2]$ by $[-5, 5]$) increases, then decreases, then increases; the graph of $y = x^3$ only increases. Therefore, this graph cannot be obtained from the graph of $y = x^3$ by the transformations studied in Chapter 1 (translations, reflections, and stretching/shrinking). Since the right side includes only these transformations, there can be no solution.

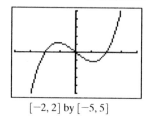

$[-2, 2]$ by $[-5, 5]$

82. The graph of $y = x^4$ has a "flat bottom," while the graph of $y = x^4 + 3x^3 - 2x - 3$ (shown on $[-4, 2]$ by $[-8, 5]$) is "bumpy." Therefore, this graph cannot be obtained from the graph of $y = x^4$ through the transformations of Chapter 1. Since the right side includes only these transformations, there can be no solution.

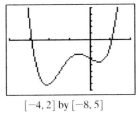

$[-4, 2]$ by $[-8, 5]$

83. (a) Substituting $x = 2$, $y = 7$, we find that
$7 = 5(2 - 2) + 7$, so Q is on line L, and also
$f(2) = -8 + 8 + 18 - 11 = 7$, so Q is on the graph of $f(x)$.

(b) Window $[1.8, 2.2]$ by $[6, 8]$. Calculator output will not show the detail seen here.

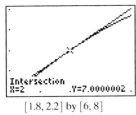

$[1.8, 2.2]$ by $[6, 8]$

(c) The line L also crosses the graph of $f(x)$ at $(-2, -13)$.

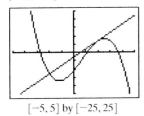

$[-5, 5]$ by $[-25, 25]$

84. (a) Note that $f(a) = a^n$ and $f(-a) = -a^n$; $m = \dfrac{y_2 - y_1}{x_2 - x_1}$
$= \dfrac{-a^n - a^n}{-a - a} = \dfrac{-2a^n}{-2a} = a^{n-1}$.

(b) First observe that $f(x_0) = (a^{1/(n-1)})^n = a^{n/(n-1)}$.
Using point–slope form:
$y - a^{n/(n-1)} = a^{n-1}(x - a^{1/(n-1)})$.

(c) With $n = 3$ and $a = 3$, this equation becomes
$y - 3^{3/2} = 3^2(x - 3^{1/2})$, or $y = 9(x - \sqrt{3}) + 3\sqrt{3}$
$= 9x - 6\sqrt{3}$. So $y = x^3$.

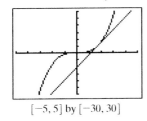

$[-5, 5]$ by $[-30, 30]$

85. (a) Label the points of the diagram as shown, adding the horizontal segment $\overline{FH}$. Therefore, ΔECB is similar

(in the geometric sense) to ΔHGB, and also ΔABC is similar to ΔAFH. Therefore:
$\dfrac{HG}{EC} = \dfrac{BG}{BC}$, or $\dfrac{8}{x} = \dfrac{D-u}{D}$, and also $\dfrac{AF}{AB} = \dfrac{FH}{BC}$,
or $\dfrac{y-8}{y} = \dfrac{D-u}{D}$. Then $\dfrac{8}{x} = \dfrac{y-8}{y}$.

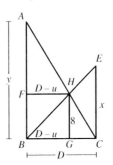

(b) Equation (a) says $\dfrac{8}{x} = 1 - \dfrac{8}{y}$. Multiply both sides by xy: $8y = xy - 8x$. Subtract xy from both sides and factor: $y(8 - x) = -8$. Divide both sides by $8 - x$:
$y = \dfrac{-8}{8 - x}$. Factor out -1 from numerator and denominator: $y = \dfrac{8}{x - 8}$.

(c) Applying the Pythagorean Theorem to ΔEBC and ΔABC, we have $x^2 + D^2 = 20^2$ and $y^2 + D^2 = 30^2$, which combine to give $D^2 = 400 - x^2 = 900 - y^2$, or $y^2 - x^2 = 500$. Substituting $y = 8x/(x - 8)$, we get $\left(\dfrac{8x}{x - 8}\right)^2 - x^2 = 500$, so that
$\dfrac{64x^2}{(x - 8)^2} - x^2 = 500$, or $64x^2 - x^2(x - 8)^2$
$= 500(x - 8)^2$. Expanding this gives $500x^2 - 8000x + 32,000 = 64x^2 - x^4 + 16x^3 - 64x^2$. This is equivalent to $x^4 - 16x^3 + 500x^2 - 8000x + 32,000 = 0$.

(d) The two solutions are $x \approx 5.9446$ and $x \approx 11.7118$. Based on the figure, x must be between 8 and 20 for this problem, so $x \approx 11.7118$. Then $D = \sqrt{20^2 - x^2}$ ≈ 16.2121 ft.

86. (a) Regardless of the value of b, $f(-b) = 1 - b$, $\lim\limits_{x \to \infty} f(x) = +\infty$, $\lim\limits_{x \to -\infty} f(x) = -\infty$, and the graph of f has a y-intercept of 1. If $|b| \le \sqrt{3}$, the graph of f is strictly increasing. If $|b| > \sqrt{3}$, f has one local maximum and one local minimum. If $|b|$ is large, the graph of f appears to have a double root at 0 and a single root at $-b$, because $f(x) = x^3 + bx^2 = x^2(x + b)$ for large x.

(b) Answers will vary.

(c)

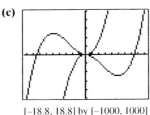

$[-18.8, 18.8]$ by $[-1000, 1000]$

■ Section 2.4 Real Zeros of Polynomial Functions

Quick Review 2.4

1. $x^2 - 4x + 7$

2. $x^2 - \dfrac{5}{2}x - 3$

3. $7x^3 + x^2 - 3$

4. $2x^2 - \dfrac{2}{3}x + \dfrac{7}{3}$

5. $x(x^2 - 4) = x(x^2 - 2^2) = x(x + 2)(x - 2)$

6. $6(x^2 - 9) = 6(x^2 - 3^2) = 6(x + 3)(x - 3)$

7. $4(x^2 + 2x - 15) = 4(x + 5)(x - 3)$

8. $x(15x^2 - 22x + 8) = x(3x - 2)(5x - 4)$

9. $(x^3 + 2x^2) - (x + 2) = x^2(x + 2) - 1(x + 2)$
   $= (x + 2)(x^2 - 1) = (x + 2)(x + 1)(x - 1)$

10. $x(x^3 + x^2 - 9x - 9) = x[(x^3 + x^2) - (9x + 9)]$
    $= x([x^2(x + 1) - 9(x + 1)]$
    $= x(x + 1)(x^2 - 9) = x(x + 1)(x^2 - 3^2)$
    $= x(x + 1)(x + 3)(x - 3)$

Section 2.4 Exercises

1.
$$
\begin{array}{r}
x - 1 \\
x - 1 \overline{\smash{)}\ x^2 - 2x + 3} \\
\underline{x^2 - x} \\
-x + 3 \\
\underline{-x + 1} \\
2
\end{array}
$$

$f(x) = (x - 1)^2 + 2;\ \dfrac{f(x)}{x - 1} = x - 1 + \dfrac{2}{x - 1}$

2.
$$
\begin{array}{r}
x^2 - x + 1 \\
x + 1 \overline{\smash{)}\ x^3 + 0x^2 + 0x - 1} \\
\underline{x^3 + x^2} \\
-x^2 + 0x \\
\underline{-x^2 - x} \\
x - 1 \\
\underline{x + 1} \\
-2
\end{array}
$$

$f(x) = (x^2 - x + 1)(x + 1) - 2;$

$\dfrac{f(x)}{x + 1} = x^2 - x + 1 - \dfrac{2}{x + 1}$

3.
$$
\begin{array}{r}
x^2 + x + 4 \\
x + 3 \overline{\smash{)}\ x^3 + 4x^2 + 7x - 9} \\
\underline{x^3 + 3x^2} \\
x^2 + 7x \\
\underline{x^2 + 3x} \\
4x - 9 \\
\underline{4x + 12} \\
-21
\end{array}
$$

$f(x) = (x^2 + x + 4)(x + 3) - 21;$

$\dfrac{f(x)}{x + 3} = x^2 + x + 4 - \dfrac{21}{x + 3}$

4.
$$
\begin{array}{r}
2x^2 - 5x + \tfrac{7}{2} \\
2x + 1 \overline{\smash{)}\ 4x^3 - 8x^2 + 2x - 1} \\
\underline{4x^3 + 2x^2} \\
-10x^2 + 2x \\
\underline{-10x^2 - 5x} \\
7x - 1 \\
\underline{7x + \tfrac{7}{2}} \\
-\tfrac{9}{2}
\end{array}
$$

$f(x) = \left(2x^2 - 5x + \dfrac{7}{2}\right)(2x + 1) - \dfrac{9}{2};$

$\dfrac{f(x)}{2x + 1} = 2x^2 - 5x + \dfrac{7}{2} - \dfrac{9/2}{2x + 1}$

5.
$$
\begin{array}{r}
x^2 - 4x + 12 \\
x^2 + 2x - 1 \overline{\smash{)}\ x^4 - 2x^3 + 3x^2 - 4x + 6} \\
\underline{x^4 + 2x^3 - x^2} \\
-4x^3 + 4x^2 - 4x \\
\underline{-4x^3 - 8x^2 + 4x} \\
12x^2 - 8x + 6 \\
\underline{12x^2 + 24x - 12} \\
-32x + 18
\end{array}
$$

$f(x) = (x^2 - 4x + 12)(x^2 + 2x - 1) - 32x + 18;$

$\dfrac{f(x)}{x^2 + 2x - 1} = x^2 - 4x + 12 + \dfrac{-32x + 18}{x^2 + 2x - 1}$

6.
$$
\begin{array}{r}
x^2 - 3x + 5 \\
x^2 + 1 \overline{\smash{)}\ x^4 - 3x^3 + 6x^2 - 3x + 5} \\
\underline{x^4 + x^2} \\
-3x^3 + 5x^2 - 3x \\
\underline{-3x^3 - 3x} \\
5x^2 + 5 \\
\underline{5x^2 + 5} \\
0
\end{array}
$$

$f(x) = (x^2 - 3x + 5)(x^2 + 1);\ \dfrac{f(x)}{x^2 + 1} = x^2 - 3x + 5$

7. $\dfrac{x^3 - 5x^2 + 3x - 2}{x + 1} = x^2 - 6x + 9 + \dfrac{-11}{x + 1}$

$$
\begin{array}{r|rrrr}
-1 & 1 & -5 & 3 & -2 \\
   &   & -1 & 6 & -9 \\
\hline
   & 1 & -6 & 9 & -11
\end{array}
$$

8. $\dfrac{2x^4 - 5x^3 + 7x^2 - 3x + 1}{x - 3}$

$= 2x^3 + x^2 + 10x + 27 + \dfrac{82}{x - 3}$

$$
\begin{array}{r|rrrrr}
3 & 2 & -5 & 7 & -3 & 1 \\
  &   & 6 & 3 & 30 & 81 \\
\hline
  & 2 & 1 & 10 & 27 & 82
\end{array}
$$

9. $\dfrac{9x^3 + 7x^2 - 3x}{x - 10} = 9x^2 + 97x + 967 + \dfrac{9670}{x - 10}$

$$\underline{10|} \quad \begin{array}{rrrr} 9 & 7 & -3 & 0 \\ & 90 & 970 & 9670 \\ \hline 9 & 97 & 967 & 9670 \end{array}$$

10. $\dfrac{3x^4 + x^3 - 4x^2 + 9x - 3}{x + 5}$

$\quad = 3x^3 - 14x^2 + 66x - 321 + \dfrac{1602}{x + 5}$

$$\underline{-5|} \quad \begin{array}{rrrrr} 3 & 1 & -4 & 9 & -3 \\ & -15 & 70 & -330 & 1605 \\ \hline 3 & -14 & 66 & -321 & 1602 \end{array}$$

11. $\dfrac{5x^4 - 3x + 1}{4 - x}$

$\quad = -5x^3 - 20x^2 - 80x - 317 + \dfrac{-1269}{4 - x}$

$$\underline{4|} \quad \begin{array}{rrrrr} -5 & 0 & 0 & 3 & -1 \\ & -20 & -80 & -320 & -1268 \\ \hline -5 & -20 & -80 & -317 & -1269 \end{array}$$

12. $\dfrac{x^8 - 1}{x + 2}$

$\quad = x^7 - 2x^6 + 4x^5 - 8x^4 + 16x^3 - 32x^2 + 64x - 128$

$\quad + \dfrac{255}{x + 2}$

$$\underline{-2|} \quad \begin{array}{rrrrrrrrr} 1 & 0 & 0 & 0 & 0 & 0 & 0 & 0 & -1 \\ & -2 & 4 & -8 & 16 & -32 & 64 & -128 & 256 \\ \hline 1 & -2 & 4 & -8 & 16 & -32 & 64 & -128 & 255 \end{array}$$

13. The remainder is $f(2) = 3$.

14. The remainder is $f(1) = -4$.

15. The remainder is $f(-3) = -43$.

16. The remainder is $f(-2) = 2$.

17. The remainder is $f(2) = 5$.

18. The remainder is $f(-1) = 23$.

19. Yes: 1 is a zero of the second polynomial.

20. Yes: 3 is a zero of the second polynomial.

21. No: when $x = 2$, the second polynomial evaluates to 10.

22. Yes: 2 is a zero of the second polynomial.

23. Yes: -2 is a zero of the second polynomial.

24. No: when $x = -1$, the second polynomial evaluates to 2.

25. From the graph it appears that $(x + 3)$ and $(x - 1)$ are factors.

$$\underline{-3|} \quad \begin{array}{rrrr} 5 & -7 & -49 & 51 \\ & -15 & 66 & -51 \\ \hline \end{array}$$
$$\underline{1|} \quad \begin{array}{rrrr} 5 & -22 & -17 & 0 \\ & 5 & -17 & \\ \hline 5 & -17 & 0 & \end{array}$$

$f(x) = (x + 3)(x - 1)(5x - 17)$

26. From the graph it appears that $(x + 2)$ and $(x - 3)$ are factors.

$$\underline{-2|} \quad \begin{array}{rrrr} 5 & -12 & -23 & 42 \\ & -10 & 44 & -42 \\ \hline \end{array}$$
$$\underline{3|} \quad \begin{array}{rrrr} 5 & -22 & 21 & 0 \\ & 15 & -21 & \\ \hline 5 & -7 & 0 & \end{array}$$

$f(x) = (x + 2)(x - 3)(5x - 7)$

27. $2(x + 2)(x - 1)(x - 4) = 2x^3 - 6x^2 - 12x + 16$

28. $2(x + 1)(x - 3)(x + 5) = 2x^3 + 6x^2 - 26x - 30$

29. $2(x - 2)\left(x - \dfrac{1}{2}\right)\left(x - \dfrac{3}{2}\right)$

$\quad = \dfrac{1}{2}(x - 2)(2x - 1)(2x - 3)$

$\quad = 2x^3 - 8x^2 + \dfrac{19}{2}x - 3$

30. $2(x + 3)(x + 1)(x)\left(x - \dfrac{5}{2}\right)$

$\quad = x(x + 3)(x + 1)(2x - 5)$

$\quad = 2x^4 + 3x^3 - 14x^2 - 15x$

31. Since $f(-4) = f(3) = f(5) = 0$, it must be that $(x + 4)$, $(x - 3)$, and $(x - 5)$ are factors of f. So $f(x) = k(x + 4)(x - 3)(x - 5)$ for some constant k.
Since $f(0) = 180$, we must have $k = 3$. So $f(x) = 3(x + 4)(x - 3)(x - 5)$

32. Since $f(-2) = f(1) = f(5) = 0$, it must be that $(x + 2)$, $(x - 1)$, and $(x - 5)$ are factors of f. So $f(x) = k(x + 2)(x - 1)(x - 5)$ for some constant k.
Since $f(-1) = 24$, we must have $k = 2$, so $f(x) = 2(x + 2)(x - 1)(x - 5)$

33. Possible rational zeros: $\dfrac{\pm 1}{\pm 1, \pm 2, \pm 3, \pm 6}$, or $\pm 1, \pm \dfrac{1}{2}, \pm \dfrac{1}{3}$, $\pm \dfrac{1}{6}$; 1 is a zero.

34. Possible rational zeros: $\dfrac{\pm 1, \pm 2, \pm 7, \pm 14}{\pm 1, \pm 3}$, or $\pm 1, \pm 2, \pm 7$, $\pm 14, \pm \dfrac{1}{3}, \pm \dfrac{2}{3}, \pm \dfrac{7}{3}, \pm \dfrac{14}{3}; \dfrac{7}{3}$ is a zero.

35. Possible rational zeros: $\dfrac{\pm 1, \pm 3, \pm 9}{\pm 1, \pm 2}$, or $\pm 1, \pm 3, \pm 9, \pm \dfrac{1}{2}$, $\pm \dfrac{3}{2}, \pm \dfrac{9}{2}; \dfrac{3}{2}$ is a zero.

36. Possible rational zeros: $\dfrac{\pm 1, \pm 2, \pm 3, \pm 4, \pm 6, \pm 12}{\pm 1, \pm 2, \pm 3, \pm 6}$, or ± 1, $\pm 2, \pm 3, \pm 4, \pm 6, \pm 12, \pm \dfrac{1}{2}, \pm \dfrac{3}{2}, \pm \dfrac{1}{3}, \pm \dfrac{2}{3}, \pm \dfrac{4}{3}, \pm \dfrac{1}{6}; -\dfrac{4}{3}$ and $\dfrac{3}{2}$ are zeros.

37.
$$\underline{3|} \quad \begin{array}{rrrr} 2 & -4 & 1 & -2 \\ & 6 & 6 & 21 \\ \hline 2 & 2 & 7 & 19 \end{array}$$

Since all numbers in the last line are ≥ 0, 3 is an upper bound for the zeros of f.

38.

$$
\begin{array}{r|rrrr}
5 & 2 & -5 & -5 & -1 \\
  &   & 10 & 25 & 100 \\
\hline
  & 2 & 5 & 20 & 99
\end{array}
$$

Since all values in the last line are ≥ 0, 5 is an upper bound for the zeros of $f(x)$.

39.

$$
\begin{array}{r|rrrrr}
2 & 1 & -1 & 1 & 1 & -12 \\
  &   & 2 & 2 & 6 & 14 \\
\hline
  & 1 & 1 & 3 & 7 & 2
\end{array}
$$

Since all values in the last line are ≥ 0, 2 is an upper bound for the zeros of $f(x)$.

40.

$$
\begin{array}{r|rrrrr}
3 & 4 & -6 & -7 & 9 & 2 \\
  &   & 12 & 18 & 33 & 126 \\
\hline
  & 4 & 6 & 11 & 42 & 128
\end{array}
$$

Since all values in the last line are ≥ 0, 3 is an upper bound for the zeros of $f(x)$.

41.

$$
\begin{array}{r|rrrr}
-1 & 3 & -4 & 1 & 3 \\
   &   & -3 & 7 & -8 \\
\hline
   & 3 & -7 & 8 & -5
\end{array}
$$

Since the values in the last line alternate signs, -1 is a lower bound for the zeros of $f(x)$.

42.

$$
\begin{array}{r|rrrr}
-3 & 1 & 2 & 2 & 5 \\
   &   & -3 & 3 & -15 \\
\hline
   & 1 & -1 & 5 & -10
\end{array}
$$

Since the values in the last line alternate signs, -3 is a lower bound for the zeros of $f(x)$.

43.

$$
\begin{array}{r|rrrr}
0 & 1 & -4 & 7 & -2 \\
  &   & 0 & 0 & 0 \\
\hline
  & 1 & -4 & 7 & -2
\end{array}
$$

Since the values in the last line alternate signs, 0 is a lower bound for the zeros of $f(x)$.

44.

$$
\begin{array}{r|rrrr}
-4 & 3 & -1 & -5 & -3 \\
   &   & -12 & 52 & -188 \\
\hline
   & 3 & -13 & 47 & -191
\end{array}
$$

Since the values in the last line alternate signs, -4 is a lower bound for the zeros of $f(x)$.

45. By the Upper and Lower Bound Tests, -5 is a lower bound and 5 is an upper bound. No zeros outside window.

$$
\begin{array}{r|rrrrr}
-5 & 6 & -11 & -7 & 8 & -34 \\
   &   & -30 & 205 & -990 & 4910 \\
\hline
   & 6 & -41 & 198 & -982 & 4876
\end{array}
$$

$$
\begin{array}{r|rrrrr}
5 & 6 & -11 & -7 & 8 & -34 \\
  &   & 30 & 95 & 440 & 2240 \\
\hline
  & 6 & 19 & 88 & 448 & 2206
\end{array}
$$

46. By the Upper and Lower Bound Tests, -5 is a lower bound and 5 is an upper bound. No zeros outside window.

$$
\begin{array}{r|rrrrrr}
-5 & 1 & -1 & 0 & 21 & 19 & -3 \\
   &   & -5 & 30 & -150 & 645 & -3320 \\
\hline
   & 1 & -6 & 30 & -129 & 664 & -3323
\end{array}
$$

$$
\begin{array}{r|rrrrrr}
5 & 1 & -1 & 0 & 21 & 19 & -3 \\
  &   & 5 & 20 & 100 & 605 & 3120 \\
\hline
  & 1 & 4 & 20 & 121 & 624 & -3117
\end{array}
$$

47. Synthetic division shows that the Upper and Lower Bound Tests were not met. There *are* zeros not shown (approx. -11.002 and 12.003), because -5 and 5 are not bounds for zeros of $f(x)$.

$$
\begin{array}{r|rrrrrr}
-5 & 1 & -4 & -129 & 396 & -8 & 3 \\
   &   & -5 & 45 & 420 & -4080 & 20{,}440 \\
\hline
   & 1 & -9 & -84 & 816 & -4088 & -20{,}443
\end{array}
$$

$$
\begin{array}{r|rrrrrr}
5 & 1 & -4 & -129 & 396 & -8 & 3 \\
  &   & 5 & 5 & -620 & -1120 & -5640 \\
\hline
  & 1 & 1 & -124 & -224 & -1128 & -5637
\end{array}
$$

48. Synthetic division shows that the lower/upper bounds tests were not met. There *are* zeros not shown (approx. -8.036 and 9.038), because -5 and 5 are not bounds for zeros of $f(x)$.

$$
\begin{array}{r|rrrrrr}
-5 & 2 & -5 & -141 & 216 & -91 & 25 \\
   &   & -10 & 75 & 330 & -2730 & 14{,}105 \\
\hline
   & 2 & -15 & -66 & 546 & -2821 & 14{,}130
\end{array}
$$

$$
\begin{array}{r|rrrrrr}
5 & 2 & -5 & -141 & 216 & -91 & 25 \\
  &   & 10 & 25 & -580 & -1820 & -9555 \\
\hline
  & 2 & 5 & -116 & -364 & -1911 & -9530
\end{array}
$$

For #49–56, determine the rational zeros using a grapher (and the Rational Zeros Test as necessary). Use synthetic division to reduce the function to a quadratic polynomial, which can be solved with the quadratic formula (or otherwise). The first two are done in detail; for the rest, we show only the synthetic division step(s).

49. Possible rational zeros: $\dfrac{\pm 1, \pm 2, \pm 3, \pm 6}{\pm 1, \pm 2}$, or

$\pm 1, \pm 2, \pm 3, \pm 6, \pm \dfrac{1}{2}, \pm \dfrac{3}{2}$. The only rational zero is $\dfrac{3}{2}$.
Synthetic division (below) leaves $2x^2 - 4$, so the irrational zeros are $\pm \sqrt{2}$.

$$
\begin{array}{r|rrrr}
3/2 & 2 & -3 & -4 & 6 \\
    &   & 3 & 0 & -6 \\
\hline
    & 2 & 0 & -4 & 0
\end{array}
$$

50. Possible rational zeros: $\pm 1, \pm 3, \pm 9$. The only rational zero is -3. Synthetic division (below) leaves $x^2 - 3$, so the irrational zeros are $\pm \sqrt{3}$.

$$
\begin{array}{r|rrrr}
-3 & 1 & 3 & -3 & -9 \\
   &   & -3 & 0 & 9 \\
\hline
   & 1 & 0 & -3 & 0
\end{array}
$$

51. Rational: -3; irrational: $1 \pm \sqrt{3}$

$$
\begin{array}{r|rrrr}
-3 & 1 & 1 & -8 & -6 \\
   &   & -3 & 6 & 6 \\
\hline
   & 1 & -2 & -2 & 0
\end{array}
$$

52. Rational: 4; irrational: $1 \pm \sqrt{2}$

$$
\begin{array}{r|rrrr}
4 & 1 & -6 & 7 & 4 \\
  &   & 4 & -8 & -4 \\
\hline
  & 1 & -2 & -1 & 0
\end{array}
$$

53. Rational: -1 and 4; irrational: $\pm\sqrt{2}$

$$
\begin{array}{r|rrrrr}
-1 & 1 & -3 & -6 & 6 & 8 \\
 & & -1 & 4 & 2 & -8 \\
\hline
 & 1 & -4 & -2 & 8 & 0
\end{array}
$$

$$
\begin{array}{r|rrrr}
4 & 1 & -4 & -2 & 8 \\
 & & 4 & 0 & -8 \\
\hline
 & 1 & 0 & -2 & 0
\end{array}
$$

54. Rational: -1 and 2; irrational: $\pm\sqrt{5}$

$$
\begin{array}{r|rrrrr}
-1 & 1 & -1 & -7 & 5 & 10 \\
 & & -1 & 2 & 5 & -10 \\
\hline
 & 1 & -2 & -5 & 10 & 0
\end{array}
$$

$$
\begin{array}{r|rrrr}
2 & 1 & -2 & -5 & 10 \\
 & & 2 & 0 & -10 \\
\hline
 & 1 & 0 & -5 & 0
\end{array}
$$

55. Rational: $-\dfrac{1}{2}$ and 4; irrational: none

$$
\begin{array}{r|rrrrr}
4 & 2 & -7 & -2 & -7 & -4 \\
 & & 8 & 4 & 8 & 4 \\
\hline
 & 2 & 1 & 2 & 1 & 0
\end{array}
$$

$$
\begin{array}{r|rrrr}
-1/2 & 2 & 1 & 2 & 1 \\
 & & -1 & 0 & -1 \\
\hline
 & 2 & 0 & 2 & 0
\end{array}
$$

56. Rational: $\dfrac{2}{3}$; irrational: about -0.6823

$$
\begin{array}{r|rrrrr}
2/3 & 3 & -2 & 3 & 1 & -2 \\
 & & 2 & 0 & 2 & 2 \\
\hline
 & 3 & 0 & 3 & 3 & 0
\end{array}
$$

57. The supply and demand graphs are shown on the window $[0, 50]$ by $[0, 100]$. They intersect when $p = \$36.27$, at which point the supply and demand equal 53.7.

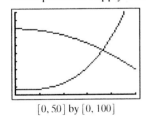

$[0, 50]$ by $[0, 100]$

58. The supply and demand graphs, shown on the window $[0, 150]$ by $[0, 1600]$, intersect when $p = \$106.99$. There $S(p) = D(p) = 1010.15$.

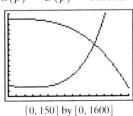

$[0, 150]$ by $[0, 1600]$

59. Using the Remainder Theorem, the remainder is $(-1)^{40} - 3 = -2$.

60. Using the Remainder Theorem, the remainder is $1^{63} - 17 = -16$.

61. (a) Lower bound:

$$
\begin{array}{r|rrrrr}
-5 & 1 & 2 & -11 & -13 & 38 \\
 & & -5 & 15 & -20 & 165 \\
\hline
 & 1 & -3 & 4 & -33 & 203
\end{array}
$$

Upper bound:

$$
\begin{array}{r|rrrrr}
4 & 1 & 2 & -11 & -13 & 38 \\
 & & 4 & 24 & 52 & 156 \\
\hline
 & 1 & 6 & 13 & 39 & 194
\end{array}
$$

The Upper and Lower Bound Tests are met, so all real zeros of f lie on the interval $[-5, 4]$.

(b) Potential rational zeros:

$$\frac{Factors\ of\ 38}{Factors\ of\ 1} : \frac{\pm1, \pm2, \pm19, \pm38}{\pm1}$$

A graph shows that 2 is most promising, so we verify with synthetic division:

$$
\begin{array}{r|rrrrr}
2 & 1 & 2 & -11 & -13 & 38 \\
 & & 2 & 8 & -6 & -38 \\
\hline
 & 1 & 4 & -3 & -19 & 0
\end{array}
$$

Use the Remainder Theorem:

$f(-2) = 20 \neq 0 \quad f(-38) = 1{,}960{,}040$

$f(-1) = 39 \neq 0 \quad f(38) = 2{,}178{,}540$

$f(1) = 17 \neq 0 \quad f(-19) = 112{,}917$

$\qquad\qquad\qquad f(19) = 139{,}859$

Since all possible rational roots besides 2 yield non-zero function values, there are no other rational roots.

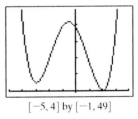

$[-5, 4]$ by $[-1, 49]$

(c) $f(x) = (x - 2)(x^3 + 4x^2 - 3x - 19)$

(d) From our graph, we find that one irrational zero of x is $x \approx 2.04$.

(e) $f(x) \approx (x - 2)(x - 2.04)(x^2 + 6.04x + 9.3216)$

62. (a) $D \approx 0.0669t^3 - 0.7420t^2 + 2.1759t + 0.8250$

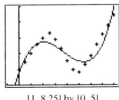

$[1, 8.25]$ by $[0, 5]$

(b) When $t = 0$, $D \approx 0.8250$ m.

(c) The graph changes direction at $t \approx 2.02$ and at $t \approx 5.38$. Lewis is approximately 2.74 m from the motion detector at $t = 2.02$ and 1.47 m from the motion detector at $t = 5.38$.

63. False. $x - a$ is a factor if and only if $f(a) = 0$. So $(x + 2)$ is a factor if and only if $f(-2) = 0$.

64. True. By the Remainder Theorem, the remainder when $f(x)$ is divided by $x - 1$ is $f(1)$, which equals 3.

65. The statement $f(3) = 0$ means that $x = 3$ is a zero of $f(x)$ and that 3 is an x-intercept of the graph of $f(x)$. And it follows that $x - 3$ is a factor of $f(x)$ and thus that the remainder when $f(x)$ is divided by $x - 3$ is zero. So the answer is A.

66. By the Rational Zeros Theorem, every rational root of $f(x)$ must be among the numbers $\pm 1, \pm 3, \pm\dfrac{1}{2}, \pm\dfrac{3}{2}$.

The answer is E.

67. $f(x) = (x + 2)(x^2 + x - 1) - 3$ yields a remainder of -3 when divided by either $x + 2$ or $x^2 + x - 1$, from which it follows that $x + 2$ is not a factor of $f(x)$ and that $f(x)$ is not evenly divisible by $x + 2$. The answer is B.

68. Answers A through D can be verified to be true. And because $f(x)$ is a polynomial function of odd degree, its graph must cross the x-axis somewhere. The answer is E.

69. (a) The volume of a sphere is $V = \dfrac{4}{3}\pi r^3$. In this case, the radius of the buoy is 1, so the buoy's volume is $\dfrac{4}{3}\pi$.

(b) Total weight $=$ volume $\cdot \dfrac{\text{weight}}{\text{unit volume}}$

$=$ volume $\cdot$ density. In this case, the density of the buoy is $\dfrac{1}{4}d$, so, the weight W_b of the buoy is

$$W_b = \dfrac{4\pi}{3} \cdot \dfrac{1}{4}d = \dfrac{d\pi}{3}.$$

(c) The weight of the displaced water is W_{H_2O} = volume $\cdot$ density. We know from geometry that the volume of a spherical cap is

$$V = \dfrac{\pi}{6}(3r^2 + h^2)\,h, \text{ so,}$$

$$W_{H_2O} = \dfrac{\pi}{6}(3r^2 + x^2)\,x \cdot d = \dfrac{\pi d}{6}x(3r^2 + x^2)$$

(d) Setting the two weights equal, we have:

$W_b = W_{H_2O}$

$\dfrac{\pi d}{3} = \dfrac{\pi d}{6}(3r^2 + x^2)x$

$2 = (3r^2 + x^2)x$

$0 = (6x - 3x^2 + x^2)x - 2$

$0 = -2x^3 + 6x^2 - 2$

$0 = x^3 - 3x^2 + 1$

Solving graphically, we find that $x \approx 0.6527$ m, the depth that the buoy will sink.

70. The weight of the buoy, W_b, with density $\dfrac{1}{5}d$, is

$$W_b = \dfrac{4\pi}{3} \cdot \dfrac{1}{5}d = \dfrac{4\pi d}{15}. \text{ So,}$$

$W_b = W_{H_2O}$

$\dfrac{4\pi d}{15} = \dfrac{\pi d}{6}(3r^2 + x^2)x$

$\dfrac{24}{15} = (3r^2 + x^2)x$

$0 = (6x - 3x^2 + x^2)x - \dfrac{8}{5}$

$0 = -2x^3 + 6x^2 - \dfrac{8}{5}$

$0 = x^3 - 3x^2 + \dfrac{4}{5}$

Solving graphically, we find that $x \approx 0.57$ m, the depth the buoy would sink.

71. (a) Shown is one possible view, on the window $[0, 600]$ by $[0, 500]$.

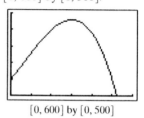

$[0, 600]$ by $[0, 500]$

(b) The maximum population, after 300 days, is 460 turkeys.

(c) $P = 0$ when $t \approx 523.22$ — about 523 days after release.

(d) Answers will vary. One possibility: After the population increases to a certain point, they begin to compete for food and eventually die of starvation.

72. (a) d is the independent variable.

(b) A good choice is $[0, 172]$ by $[0, 5]$.

(c) $s = 1.25$ when $d \approx 95.777$ ft. (found graphically)

73. (a) 2 sign changes in $f(x)$, 1 sign change in $f(-x) = -x^3 + x^2 + x + 1$; 0 or 2 positive zeros, 1 negative zero.

(b) No positive zeros, 1 or 3 negative zeros.

(c) 1 positive zero, no negative zeros.

(d) 1 positive zero, 1 negative zero.

74.

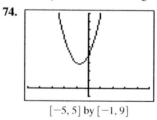

$[-5, 5]$ by $[-1, 9]$

The functions are not exactly the same, when $x \neq 3$, we have $f(x) = \dfrac{(x - 3)(2x^2 + 3x + 4)}{(x - 3)}$

$= 2x^2 + 3x + 4 = g(x)$

The domain of f is $(-\infty, 3) \cup (3, \infty)$ while the domain of g is $(-\infty, \infty)$. f is discontinuous at $x = 3$. g is continuous.

75. $\dfrac{4x^3 - 5x^2 + 3x + 1}{2x - 1}$

$= \dfrac{2x^3 - \dfrac{5}{2}x^2 + \dfrac{3}{2}x + \dfrac{1}{2}}{x - \dfrac{1}{2}}$ Divide numerator and denominator by 2.

zero of divisor $\quad \dfrac{1}{2}\Big|\ \ 2 \ -\dfrac{5}{2} \ \ \dfrac{3}{2} \ \ \dfrac{1}{2}\ $ Write coefficients of dividend.

line for products $\qquad\qquad 1\ -\dfrac{3}{4}\ \ \dfrac{3}{8}$

line for sums $\qquad\ \ 2\ -\dfrac{3}{2}\ \ \dfrac{3}{4}\ \ \dfrac{7}{8}$ Quotient, remainder

Copy 2 into the first quotient position. Multiply $2 \cdot \dfrac{1}{2} = 1$

and add this to $-\dfrac{5}{2}$. Multiply $-\dfrac{3}{2} \cdot \dfrac{1}{2} = -\dfrac{3}{4}$ and add this to

$\dfrac{3}{2}$. Multiply $\dfrac{3}{4} \cdot \dfrac{1}{2} = \dfrac{3}{8}$ and add this to $\dfrac{1}{2}$. The last line tells

us $\left(x - \dfrac{1}{2}\right)\left(2x^2 - \dfrac{3}{2}x + \dfrac{3}{4}\right) + \dfrac{7}{8}$

$= 2x^3 - \dfrac{5}{4}x^2 + \dfrac{3}{2}x + \dfrac{1}{2}.$

76. Graph both functions in the same viewing window to see if they differ significantly. If the graphs lie on top of each other, then they are approximately equal in that viewng window.

77. (a) $g(x) = 3f(x)$, so the zeros of f and the zeros of g are identical. If the coefficients of a polynomial are rational, we may multiply that polynomial by the least common multiple (LCM) of the denominators of the coefficients to obtain a polynomial, with integer coefficients, that has the same zeros as the original.

(b) The zeros of $f(x)$ are the same as the zeros of

$6f(x) = 6x^3 - 7x^2 - 40x + 21.$ Possible rational

zeros: $\dfrac{\pm 1, \pm 3, \pm 7, \pm 21}{\pm 1, \pm 2, \pm 3, \pm 6}$, or

$\pm 1, \pm 3, \pm 7, \pm 21, \pm\dfrac{1}{2}, \pm\dfrac{3}{2},$

$\pm\dfrac{7}{2}, \pm\dfrac{21}{2}, \pm\dfrac{1}{3}, \pm\dfrac{7}{3}, \pm\dfrac{1}{6}, \pm\dfrac{7}{6}.$ The actual zeros are

$-7/3, 1/2,$ and $3.$

(c) The zeros of $f(x)$ are the same as the zeros of $12f(x) = 12x^3 - 30x^2 - 37x + 30.$

Possible rational zeros:

$\dfrac{\pm 1, \pm 2, \pm 3, \pm 5, \pm 6, \pm 10, \pm 15, \pm 30}{\pm 1, \pm 2, \pm 3, \pm 4, \pm 6, \pm 12}$, or

$\pm 1, \pm 2, \pm 3, \pm 5, \pm 6, \pm 10, \pm 15, \pm 30, \pm\dfrac{1}{2}, \pm\dfrac{3}{2}, \pm\dfrac{5}{2},$

$\pm\dfrac{15}{2}, \pm\dfrac{1}{3}, \pm\dfrac{2}{3}, \pm\dfrac{5}{3}, \pm\dfrac{10}{3}, \pm\dfrac{1}{4}, \pm\dfrac{3}{4}, \pm\dfrac{5}{4}, \pm\dfrac{15}{4}, \pm\dfrac{1}{6},$

$\pm\dfrac{5}{6}, \pm\dfrac{1}{12}, \pm\dfrac{5}{12}.$

There are no rational zeros.

78. Let $f(x) = x^2 - 2 = (x + \sqrt{2})(x - \sqrt{2}).$ Notice that $\sqrt{2}$ is a zero of f. By the Rational Zeros Theorem, the only possible rational zeros of f are ± 1 and ± 2. Because $\sqrt{2}$ is none of these, it must be irrational.

79. (a) Approximate zeros: $-3.126, -1.075, 0.910, 2.291$

(b) $f(x) \approx g(x)$
$= (x + 3.126)(x + 1.075)(x - 0.910)(x - 2.291)$

(c) Graphically: Graph the original function and the approximate factorization on a variety of windows and observe their similarity. Numerically: Compute $f(c)$ and $g(c)$ for several values of c.

■ Section 2.5 Complex Zeros and the Fundamental Theorem of Algebra

Exploration 1

1. $f(2i) = (2i)^2 - i(2i) + 2 = -4 + 2 + 2 = 0;$
$f(-i) = (-i)^2 - i(-i) + 2 = -1 - 1 + 2 = 0;$ no.

2. $g(i) = i^2 - i + (1 + i) = -1 - i + 1 + i = 0;$
$g(1 - i) = (1 - i)^2 - (1 - i) + (1 + i) =$
$-2i + 2i = 0;$ no.

3. The Complex Conjugate Zeros Theorem does not necessarily hold true for a polynomial function with *complex* coefficients.

Quick Review 2.5

1. $(3 - 2i) + (-2 + 5i) = (3 - 2) + (-2 + 5)i$
$\qquad\qquad\qquad\qquad\qquad = 1 + 3i$

2. $(5 - 7i) - (3 - 2i) = (5 - 3) + (-7 - (-2))i$
$\qquad\qquad\qquad\qquad\qquad = 2 - 5i$

3. $(1 + 2i)(3 - 2i) = 1(3 - 2i) + 2i(3 - 2i)$
$\qquad\qquad\qquad\quad = 3 - 2i + 6i - 4i^2$
$\qquad\qquad\qquad\quad = 7 + 4i$

4. $\dfrac{2 + 3i}{1 - 5i} = \dfrac{2 + 3i}{1 - 5i} \cdot \dfrac{1 + 5i}{1 + 5i}$

$= \dfrac{2 + 10i + 3i + 15i^2}{1^2 + 5^2}$

$= \dfrac{-13 + 13i}{26}$

$= -\dfrac{1}{2} + \dfrac{1}{2}i$

5. $(2x - 3)(x + 1)$

6. $(3x + 1)(2x - 5)$

7. $x = \dfrac{5 \pm \sqrt{25 - 4(1)(11)}}{2} = \dfrac{5 \pm \sqrt{-19}}{2}$

$= \dfrac{5}{2} \pm \dfrac{\sqrt{19}}{2}i$

8. $x = \dfrac{-3 \pm \sqrt{9 - 4(2)(7)}}{4} = \dfrac{-3 \pm \sqrt{-47}}{4}$

$= -\dfrac{3}{4} \pm \dfrac{\sqrt{47}}{4}i$

9. $\dfrac{\pm 1, \pm 2}{\pm 1, \pm 3}$, or $\pm 1, \pm 2, \pm\dfrac{1}{3}, \pm\dfrac{2}{3}$

10. $\dfrac{\pm 1, \pm 3}{\pm 1, \pm 2, \pm 4}$, or $\pm 1, \pm 3, \pm\dfrac{1}{2}, \pm\dfrac{3}{2}, \pm\dfrac{1}{4}, \pm\dfrac{3}{4}$

Section 2.5 Exercises

1. $(x - 3i)(x + 3i) = x^2 - (3i)^2 = x^2 + 9$. The factored form shows the zeros to be $x = \pm 3i$. The absence of real zeros means that the graph has no x-intercepts.

2. $(x + 2)(x - \sqrt{3}\,i)(x + \sqrt{3}\,i) = (x + 2)(x^2 + 3)$
$= x^3 + 2x^2 + 3x + 6$. The factored form shows the zeros to be $x = -2$ and $x = \pm\sqrt{3}i$. The real zero $x = -2$ is the x-intercept of the graph.

3. $(x - 1)(x - 1)(x + 2i)(x - 2i)$
$= (x^2 - 2x + 1)(x^2 + 4)$
$= x^4 - 2x^3 + 5x^2 - 8x + 4$. The factored form shows the zeros to be $x = 1$ (multiplicity 2) and $x = \pm 2i$. The real zero $x = 1$ is the x-intercept of the graph.

4. $x(x - 1)(x - 1 - i)(x - 1 + i)$
$= (x^2 - x)[x - (1 + i)][x - (1 - i)]$
$= (x^2 - x)[x^2 - (1 - i + 1 + i)\,x + (1 + 1)]$
$= (x^2 - x)(x^2 - 2x + 2) = x^4 - 3x^3 + 4x^2 - 2x$.
The factored form shows the zeros to be $x = 0$, $x = 1$, and $x = 1 \pm i$. The real zeros $x = 0$ and $x = 1$ are the x-intercepts of the graph.

In #5–16, any constant multiple of the given polynomial is also an answer.

5. $(x - i)(x + i) = x^2 + 1$

6. $(x - 1 + 2i)(x - 1 - 2i) = x^2 - 2x + 5$

7. $(x - 1)(x - 3i)(x + 3i) = (x - 1)(x^2 + 9)$
$= x^3 - x^2 + 9x - 9$

8. $(x + 4)(x - 1 + i)(x - 1 - i)$
$= (x + 4)(x^2 - 2x + 2) = x^3 + 2x^2 - 6x + 8$

9. $(x - 2)(x - 3)(x - i)(x + i)$
$= (x - 2)(x - 3)(x^2 + 1)$
$= x^4 - 5x^3 + 7x^2 - 5x + 6$

10. $(x + 1)(x - 2)(x - 1 + i)(x - 1 - i)$
$= (x + 1)(x - 2)(x^2 - 2x + 2)$
$= x^4 - 3x^3 + 2x^2 + 2x - 4$

11. $(x - 5)(x - 3 - 2i)(x - 3 + 2i)$
$= (x - 5)(x^2 - 6x + 13) = x^3 - 11x^2 + 43x - 65$

12. $(x + 2)(x - 1 - 2i)(x - 1 + 2i)$
$= (x + 2)(x^2 - 2x + 5) = x^3 + x + 10$

13. $(x - 1)^2(x + 2)^3 = x^5 + 4x^4 + x^3 - 10x^2 - 4x + 8$

14. $(x + 1)^3(x - 3) = x^4 - 6x^2 - 8x - 3$

15. $(x - 2)^2(x - 3 - i)(x - 3 + i)$
$= (x - 2)^2(x^2 - 6x + 10)$
$= (x^2 - 4x + 4)(x^2 - 6x + 10)$
$= x^4 - 10x^3 + 38x^2 - 64x + 40$

16. $(x + 1)^2(x + 2 + i)(x + 2 - i)$
$= (x + 1)^2(x^2 + 4x + 5)$
$= (x^2 + 2x + 1)(x^2 + 4x + 5)$
$= x^4 + 6x^3 + 14x^2 + 14x + 5$

In #17–20, note that the graph crosses the x-axis at odd-multiplicity zeros, and "kisses" (touches but does not cross) the x-axis where the multiplicity is even.

17. (b)

18. (c)

19. (d)

20. (a)

In #21–26, the number of complex zeros is the same as the degree of the polynomial; the number of real zeros can be determined from a graph. The latter always differs from the former by an even number (when the coefficients of the polynomial are real).

21. 2 complex zeros; none real.

22. 3 complex zeros; all 3 real.

23. 3 complex zeros; 1 real.

24. 4 complex zeros; 2 real.

25. 4 complex zeros; 2 real.

26. 5 complex zeros; 1 real.

In #27–32, look for real zeros using a graph (and perhaps the Rational Zeros Test). Use synthetic division to factor the polynomial into one or more linear factors and a quadratic factor. Then use the quadratic formula to find complex zeros.

27. Inspection of the graph reveals that $x = 1$ is the only real zero. Dividing $f(x)$ by $x - 1$ leaves $x^2 + x + 5$ (below). The quadratic formula gives the remaining zeros of $f(x)$.

$$1\rfloor \quad \begin{array}{cccc} 1 & 0 & 4 & -5 \\ & 1 & 1 & 5 \\ \hline 1 & 1 & 5 & 0 \end{array}$$

Zeros: $x = 1$, $x = -\dfrac{1}{2} \pm \dfrac{\sqrt{19}}{2}i$

$f(x)$
$= (x - 1)\left[x - \left(-\dfrac{1}{2} - \dfrac{\sqrt{19}}{2}i\right)\right]\left[x - \left(-\dfrac{1}{2} + \dfrac{\sqrt{19}}{2}i\right)\right]$
$= \dfrac{1}{4}(x - 1)(2x + 1 + \sqrt{19}\,i)(2x + 1 - \sqrt{19}\,i)$

28. Zeros: $x = 3$ (graphically) and $x = \dfrac{7}{2} \pm \dfrac{\sqrt{43}}{2}i$ (applying the quadratic formula to $x^2 - 7x + 23$).

$$3\rfloor \quad \begin{array}{cccc} 1 & -10 & 4 & -69 \\ & 3 & -21 & 69 \\ \hline 1 & -7 & 23 & 0 \end{array}$$

$f(x)$
$= (x - 3)\left[x - \left(\dfrac{7}{2} - \dfrac{\sqrt{43}}{2}i\right)\right]\left[x - \left(\dfrac{7}{2} + \dfrac{\sqrt{43}}{2}i\right)\right]$
$= \dfrac{1}{4}(x - 3)(2x - 7 + \sqrt{43}\,i)(2x - 7 - \sqrt{43}\,i)$

29. Zeros: $x = \pm 1$ (graphically) and $x = -\dfrac{1}{2} \pm \dfrac{\sqrt{23}}{2}i$ (applying the quadratic formula to $x^2 + x + 6$).

$$1\rfloor \quad \begin{array}{ccccc} 1 & 1 & 5 & -1 & -6 \\ & 1 & 2 & 7 & 6 \\ \hline 1 & 2 & 7 & 6 & 0 \end{array}$$

$$-1\rfloor \quad \begin{array}{cccc} 1 & 2 & 7 & 6 \\ & -1 & -1 & -6 \\ \hline 1 & 1 & 6 & 0 \end{array}$$

$f(x) = (x - 1)(x + 1)\left[x - \left(-\dfrac{1}{2} - \dfrac{\sqrt{23}}{2}i\right)\right]$
$\left[x - \left(-\dfrac{1}{2} + \dfrac{\sqrt{23}}{2}i\right)\right]$
$= \dfrac{1}{4}(x - 1)(x + 1)(2x + 1 + \sqrt{23}\,i)(2x + 1 - \sqrt{23}\,i)$

30. Zeros: $x = -2$ and $x = \dfrac{1}{3}$ (graphically) and

$x = -\dfrac{1}{2} \pm \dfrac{\sqrt{3}}{2} i$ (applying the quadratic formula to

$3x^2 + 3x + 3 = 3(x^2 + x + 1)$).

$$
\begin{array}{r|rrrrr}
-2 & 3 & 8 & 6 & 3 & -2 \\
   &   & -6 & -4 & -4 & 2 \\
\hline
   & 3 & 2 & 2 & -1 & 0 \\
\end{array}
$$

$$
\begin{array}{r|rrrr}
1/3 & 3 & 2 & 2 & -1 \\
    &   & 1 & 1 & 1 \\
\hline
    & 3 & 3 & 3 & 0 \\
\end{array}
$$

$f(x) = (x + 2)(3x - 1)\left[x - \left(-\dfrac{1}{2} - \dfrac{\sqrt{3}}{2} i\right)\right]$

$\left[x - \left(-\dfrac{1}{2} + \dfrac{\sqrt{3}}{2} i\right)\right]$

$= \dfrac{1}{4}(x + 2)(3x - 1)(2x + 1 + \sqrt{3}\, i)$

$(2x + 1 - \sqrt{3}\, i)$

31. Zeros: $x = -\dfrac{7}{3}$ and $x = \dfrac{3}{2}$ (graphically) and $x = 1 \pm 2i$

(applying the quadratic formula to $6x^2 - 12x + 30$

$= 6(x^2 - 2x + 5)$).

$$
\begin{array}{r|rrrrrr}
-7/3 & 6 & -7 & -1 & 67 & -105 \\
     &   & -14 & 49 & -112 & 105 \\
\hline
     & 6 & -21 & 48 & -45 & 0 \\
\end{array}
$$

$$
\begin{array}{r|rrrr}
3/2 & 6 & -21 & 48 & -45 \\
    &   & 9 & -18 & 45 \\
\hline
    & 6 & -12 & 30 & 0 \\
\end{array}
$$

$f(x) = (3x + 7)(2x - 3)[x - (1 - 2i)]$

$[x - (1 + 2i)]$

$= (3x + 7)(2x - 3)(x - 1 + 2i)(x - 1 - 2i)$

32. Zeros: $x = -\dfrac{3}{5}$ and $x = 5$ (graphically) and $x = \dfrac{3}{2} \pm i$

$= (5x + 3)(x - 5)(2x - 3 + 2i)(2x - 3 - 2i)$

(applying the quadratic formula to $20x^2 - 60x + 65$

$= 5(4x^2 - 12x + 13)$).

$$
\begin{array}{r|rrrrr}
5 & 20 & -148 & 269 & -106 & -195 \\
  &   & 100 & -240 & 145 & 195 \\
\hline
  & 20 & -48 & 29 & 39 & 0 \\
\end{array}
$$

$$
\begin{array}{r|rrrr}
-3/5 & 20 & -48 & 29 & 39 \\
     &   & -12 & 36 & -39 \\
\hline
     & 20 & -60 & 65 & 0 \\
\end{array}
$$

$f(x) = (5x + 3)(x - 5)[2x - (3 - 2i)]$

$[2x - (3 + 2i)]$

$= (5x + 3)(x - 5)(2x - 3 + 2i)(2x - 3 - 2i)$

In #33–36, since the polynomials' coefficients are real, for the given zero $z = a + bi$, the complex conjugate $\bar{z} = a - bi$ must also be a zero. Divide $f(x)$ by $x - z$ and $x - \bar{z}$ to reduce to a quadratic.

33. First divide $f(x)$ by $x - (1 + i)$ (synthetically). Then divide the result, $x^3 + (-1 + i)x^2 - 3x + (3 - 3i)$, by $x - (1 - i)$. This leaves the polynominal $x^2 - 3$. Zeros: $x = \pm\sqrt{3}$, $x = 1 \pm i$

$$
\begin{array}{r|rrrrr}
1 + i & 1 & -2 & -1 & 6 & -6 \\
      &   & 1 + i & -2 & -3 - 3i & 6 \\
\hline
      & 1 & -1 + i & -3 & 3 - 3i & 0 \\
\end{array}
$$

$$
\begin{array}{r|rrrr}
1 - i & 1 & -1 + i & -3 & 3 - 3i \\
      &   & 1 - i & 0 & -3 + 3i \\
\hline
      & 1 & 0 & -3 & 0 \\
\end{array}
$$

$f(x) = (x - \sqrt{3})(x + \sqrt{3})[x - (1 - i)][x - (1 + i)]$

$= (x - \sqrt{3})(x + \sqrt{3})(x - 1 + i)(x - 1 - i)$

34. First divide $f(x)$ by $x - 4i$. Then divide the result, $x^3 + 4ix^2 - 3x - 12i$, by $x + 4i$. This leaves the polynomial $x^2 - 3$. Zeros: $x = \pm\sqrt{3}$, $x = \pm 4i$

$$
\begin{array}{r|rrrrr}
4i & 1 & 0 & 13 & 0 & -48 \\
   &   & 4i & -16 & -12i & 48 \\
\hline
   & 1 & 4i & -3 & -12i & 0 \\
\end{array}
$$

$$
\begin{array}{r|rrrr}
-4i & 1 & 4i & -3 & -12i \\
    &   & -4i & 0 & 12i \\
\hline
    & 1 & 0 & -3 & 0 \\
\end{array}
$$

$f(x) = (x - \sqrt{3})(x + \sqrt{3})(x - 4i)(x + 4i)$

35. First divide $f(x)$ by $x - (3 - 2i)$. Then divide the result, $x^3 + (-3 - 2i)x^2 - 2x + 6 + 4i$, by $x - (3 + 2i)$. This leaves $x^2 - 2$. Zeros: $x = \pm\sqrt{2}$, $x = 3 \pm 2i$

$$
\begin{array}{r|rrrrr}
3 - 2i & 1 & -6 & 11 & 12 & -26 \\
       &   & 3 - 2i & -13 & -6 + 4i & 26 \\
\hline
       & 1 & -3 - 2i & -2 & 6 + 4i & 0 \\
\end{array}
$$

$$
\begin{array}{r|rrrr}
3 + 2i & 1 & -3 - 2i & -2 & 6 + 4i \\
       &   & 3 + 2i & 0 & -6 - 4i \\
\hline
       & 1 & 0 & -2 & 0 \\
\end{array}
$$

$f(x) = (x - \sqrt{2})(x + \sqrt{2})[x - (3 - 2i)]$

$[x - (3 + 2i)]$

$= (x - \sqrt{2})(x + \sqrt{2})(x - 3 + 2i)(x - 3 - 2i)$

36. First divide $f(x)$ by $x - (1 + 3i)$. Then divide the result, $x^3 + (-1 + 3i)x^2 - 5x + 5 - 15i$, by $x - (1 - 3i)$. This leaves $x^2 - 5$. Zeros: $x = \pm\sqrt{5}$, $x = 1 \pm 3i$

$$
\begin{array}{r|rrrrr}
1 + 3i & 1 & -2 & 5 & 10 & -50 \\
       &   & 1 + 3i & -10 & -5 - 15i & 50 \\
\hline
       & 1 & -1 + 3i & -5 & 5 - 15i & 0 \\
\end{array}
$$

$$
\begin{array}{r|rrrr}
1 - 3i & 1 & -1 + 3i & -5 & 5 - 15i \\
       &   & 1 - 3i & 0 & -5 + 15i \\
\hline
       & 1 & 0 & -5 & 0 \\
\end{array}
$$

$f(x) = (x - \sqrt{5})(x + \sqrt{5})[x - (1 - 3i)]$

$[x - (1 + 3i)]$

$= (x - \sqrt{5})(x + \sqrt{5})(x - 1 + 3i)(x - 1 - 3i)$

For #37–42, find real zeros graphically, then use synthetic division to find the quadratic factors. Only the synthetic divison step is shown.

37. $f(x) = (x - 2)(x^2 + x + 1)$

$$\begin{array}{r|rrrr} 2 & 1 & -1 & -1 & -2 \\ & & 2 & 2 & 2 \\ \hline & 1 & 1 & 1 & 0 \end{array}$$

38. $f(x) = (x - 2)(x^2 + x + 3)$

$$\begin{array}{r|rrrr} 2 & 1 & -1 & 1 & -6 \\ & & 2 & 2 & 6 \\ \hline & 1 & 1 & 3 & 0 \end{array}$$

39. $f(x) = (x - 1)(2x^2 + x + 3)$

$$\begin{array}{r|rrrr} 1 & 2 & -1 & 2 & -3 \\ & & 2 & 1 & 3 \\ \hline & 2 & 1 & 3 & 0 \end{array}$$

40. $f(x) = (x - 1)(3x^2 + x + 2)$

$$\begin{array}{r|rrrr} 1 & 3 & -2 & 1 & -2 \\ & & 3 & 1 & 2 \\ \hline & 3 & 1 & 2 & 0 \end{array}$$

41. $f(x) = (x - 1)(x + 4)(x^2 + 1)$

$$\begin{array}{r|rrrrr} 1 & 1 & 3 & -3 & 3 & -4 \\ & & 1 & 4 & 1 & 4 \\ \hline & 1 & 4 & 1 & 4 & 0 \end{array}$$

$$\begin{array}{r|rrrr} -4 & 1 & 4 & 1 & 4 \\ & & -4 & 0 & -4 \\ \hline & 1 & 0 & 1 & 0 \end{array}$$

42. $f(x) = (x - 3)(x + 1)(x^2 + 4)$

$$\begin{array}{r|rrrrr} 3 & 1 & -2 & 1 & -8 & -12 \\ & & 3 & 3 & 12 & 12 \\ \hline & 1 & 1 & 4 & 4 & 0 \end{array}$$

$$\begin{array}{r|rrrr} -1 & 1 & 1 & 4 & 4 \\ & & -1 & 0 & -4 \\ \hline & 1 & 0 & 4 & 0 \end{array}$$

43. Solve for h: $\frac{\pi}{3}(15h^2 - h^3)(62.5) = \frac{4}{3}\pi(125)(20)$, so that $15h^2 - h^3 = 160$. Of the three solutions (found graphically), only $h \approx 3.776$ ft makes sense in this setting.

44. Solve for h: $\frac{\pi}{3}(15h^2 - h^3)(62.5) = \frac{4}{3}\pi(125)(45)$, so that $15h^2 - h^3 = 360$. Of the three solutions (found graphically), only $h \approx 6.513$ ft makes sense in this setting.

45. Yes: $(x + 2)(x^2 + 1) = x^3 + 2x^2 + x + 2$ is one such polynomial. Other examples can be obtained by multiplying any other quadratic with no real zeros by $(x + 2)$.

46. No; by the Complex Conjugate Zeros Theorem, for such a polynomial, if $2i$ is a zero, so is $-2i$.

47. No: if all coefficients are real, $1 - 2i$ and $1 + i$ must also be zeros, giving 5 zeros for a degree 4 polynomial.

48. Yes: $f(x) = (x - 1 - 3i)(x - 1 + 3i)(x - 1 - i)$ $(x - 1 + i) = x^4 - 4x^3 + 16x^2 - 24x + 20$ is one such polynomial; all other examples would be multiples of this polynomial.

49. $f(x)$ must have the form $a(x - 3)(x + 1)(x - 2 + i)(x - 2 - i)$; since $f(0) = a(-3)(1)(-2 + i)(-2 - i) = -15a = 30$, we know that $a = -2$. Multiplied out, this gives $f(x) = -2x^4 + 12x^3 - 20x^2 - 4x + 30$.

50. $f(x)$ must have the form $a(x - 1 - 2i)(x - 1 + 2i)(x - 1 - i)(x - 1 + i)$; since $f(0) = a(-1 - 2i)(-1 + 2i)(-1 - i)(-1 + i)$ $= a(5)(2) = 10a = 20$, we know that $a = 2$. Multiplied out, this gives $f(x) = 2x^4 - 8x^3 + 22x^2 - 28x + 20$.

51. (a) The model is $D \approx -0.0820t^3 + 0.9162t^2 - 2.5126t + 3.3779$.

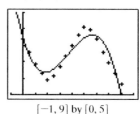

[−1, 9] by [0, 5]

(b) Sally walks toward the detector, turns and walks away (or walks backward), then walks toward the detector again.

(c) The model "changes direction" at $t \approx 1.81$ sec ($D \approx 1.35$ m) and $t \approx 5.64$ sec (when $D \approx 3.65$ m).

52. (a) $D \approx 0.2434t^2 - 1.7159t + 4.4241$

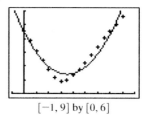

[−1, 9] by [0, 6]

(b) Jacob walks toward the detector, then turns and walks away (or walks backward).

(c) The model "changes direction" at $t \approx 3.52$ (when $D \approx 1.40$ m).

53. False. Complex, nonreal solutions always come in conjugate pairs, so that if $1 - 2i$ is a zero, then $1 + 2i$ must also be a zero.

54. False. All three zeros could be real. For instance, the polynomial $f(x) = x(x - 1)(x - 2) = x^3 - 3x^2 + 2x$ has degree 3, real coefficients, and no non-real zeros. (The zeros are 0, 1, and 2.)

55. Both the sum and the product of two complex conjugates are real numbers, and the absolute value of a complex number is always real. The square of a complex number, on the other hand, need not be real. The answer is E.

56. Allowing for multiplicities other than 1, then, the polynomial can have anywhere from 1 to 5 distinct real zeros. But it cannot have no real zeros at all. The answer is A.

57. Because the complex, non-real zeros of a real-coefficient polynomial always come in conjugate pairs, a polynomial of degree 5 can have either 0, 2, or 4 non-real zeros. The answer is C.

58. A polynomial with real coefficients can never have an odd number of non-real complex zeros. The answer is E.

59. (a)

Power	Real Part	Imaginary Part
7	8	-8
8	16	0
9	16	16
10	0	32

(b) $(1 + i)^7 = 8 - 8i$

$(1 + i)^8 = 16$

$(1 + i)^9 = 16 + 16i$

$(1 + i)^{10} = 32i$

(c) Reconcile as needed.

60. (a) $(a + bi)(a + bi) = a^2 + 2abi + bi^2$
$= a^2 + 2abi - b^2$

(b) $a^2 - b^2 = 0 \quad\quad\quad\quad\quad\quad\quad (1)$

$2abi = i$, so $2ab = 1 \quad\quad\quad\quad (2)$

(c) From (1), we have:

$a^2 - b^2 = 0$

$(a + b)(a - b) = 0$

$a = -b, a = b$

Substituting into (2), we find:

$a = b: 2ab = 1 \quad\quad\quad a = -b: 2ab = 1$

$\quad\quad\quad 2b^2 = 1 \quad\quad\quad\quad\quad -2b^2 = 1$

$\quad\quad\quad b^2 = \dfrac{1}{2} \quad\quad\quad\quad\quad b^2 = -\dfrac{1}{2}$

$\quad\quad\quad b = \pm\sqrt{\dfrac{1}{2}} \quad\quad\quad\quad b^2 = \sqrt{\dfrac{1}{2}}$

$\quad\quad\quad\quad\quad\quad\quad\quad\quad\quad\quad\quad b = \pm i\sqrt{\dfrac{1}{2}}$

Since a and b must be real, we have

$(a, b) = \left\{ \left(\dfrac{\sqrt{2}}{2}, \dfrac{\sqrt{2}}{2} \right), \left(-\dfrac{\sqrt{2}}{2}, -\dfrac{\sqrt{2}}{2} \right) \right\}.$

(d) Checking $\left(\dfrac{\sqrt{2}}{2}, \dfrac{\sqrt{2}}{2} \right)$ first.

$\left(\dfrac{\sqrt{2}}{2} + \dfrac{\sqrt{2}}{2}i \right)^2 = \left(\dfrac{\sqrt{2}}{2} \right)^2 (1 + i)^2$

$= \dfrac{1}{2}(1 + 2i + i^2) = \dfrac{1}{2}(1 - 1 + 2i) = \dfrac{2i}{2} = i$

Checking $\left(-\dfrac{\sqrt{2}}{2}, -\dfrac{\sqrt{2}}{2} \right)$

$\left(-\dfrac{\sqrt{2}}{2} - \dfrac{\sqrt{2}}{2}i \right)^2 = \left(-\dfrac{\sqrt{2}}{2} \right)^2 (1 + i)^2$

$= \dfrac{1}{2}(1 + 2i + i^2) = \dfrac{1}{2}(1 - 1 + 2i) = \dfrac{2i}{2} = i$

(e) The two square roots of i are:

$\left(\dfrac{\sqrt{2}}{2} + \dfrac{\sqrt{2}}{2}i \right)$ and $\left(-\dfrac{\sqrt{2}}{2} - \dfrac{\sqrt{2}}{2}i \right)$

61. $f(i) = i^3 - i(i)^2 + 2i(i) + 2 = -i + i - 2 + 2 = 0.$
One can also take the last number of the bottom row from synthetic division.

62. $f(-2i) = (-2i)^3 - (2 - i)(-2i)^2 + (2 - 2i)(-2i) - 4$
$= 8i + (2 - i)(4) - (2 - 2i)(2i) - 4 =$
$8i + 8 - 4i - 4i - 4 - 4 = 0.$
One can also take the last number of the bottom row from synthetic division.

63. Synthetic division shows that $f(i) = 0$ (the remainder), and at the same time gives
$f(x) \div (x - i) = x^2 + 3x - i = h(x)$, so
$f(x) = (x - i)(x^2 + 3x - i)$.

$\underline{i|} \quad 1 \quad 3 - i \quad -4i \quad -1$
$\quad\quad\quad\quad\quad\quad i \quad\quad 3i \quad\quad 1$
$\quad\quad\quad 1 \quad\quad 3 \quad\quad -i \quad\quad 0$

64. Synthetic division shows that $f(1 + i) = 0$ (the remainder), and at the same time gives
$f(x) \div (x - 1 - i) = x^2 + 1 = h(x)$, so
$f(x) = (x - 1 - i)(x^2 + 1)$.

$\underline{1 + i|} \quad 1 \quad -1 - i \quad 1 \quad -1 - i$
$\quad\quad\quad\quad\quad\quad\quad 1 + i \quad\quad 0 \quad 1 + i$
$\quad\quad\quad\quad 1 \quad\quad\quad 0 \quad\quad 1 \quad\quad 0$

65. From graphing (or the Rational Zeros Test), we expect $x = 2$ to be a zero of $f(x) = x^3 - 8$. Indeed, $f(2) = 8 - 8 = 0$. So, $x = 2$ is a zero of $f(x)$. Using synthetic division we obtain:

$\underline{2|} \quad 1 \quad 0 \quad 0 \quad -8$
$\quad\quad\quad\quad\quad 2 \quad 4 \quad\quad 8$
$\quad\quad\quad 1 \quad 2 \quad 4 \quad\quad 0$

$f(x) = (x - 2)(x^2 + 2x + 4)$. We then apply the quadratic formula to find that the cube roots of $x^3 - 8$ are $2, -1 + \sqrt{3}i$, and $-1 - \sqrt{3}i$.

66. From graphing (or the Rational Zeros Test), we expect $x = -4$ to be a zero of $f(x) = x^3 + 64$. Indeed $f(-4) = -64 + 64 = 0$, so $x = -4$ is a zero of $f(x)$. Using synthetic division, we obtain:

$\underline{-4|} \quad 1 \quad 0 \quad 0 \quad 64$
$\quad\quad\quad\quad\quad\quad -4 \quad 16 \quad -64$
$\quad\quad\quad\quad 1 \quad -4 \quad 16 \quad\quad 0$

$f(x) = (x + 4)(x^2 - 4x + 16)$. We then apply the quadratic formula to find that the cube roots of $x^3 + 64$ are $-4, 2 + 2\sqrt{3}i$, and $2 - 2\sqrt{3}i$.

■ Section 2.6 Graphs of Rational Functions

Exploration 1

1. $g(x) = \dfrac{1}{x - 2}$

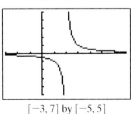

$[-3, 7]$ by $[-5, 5]$

2. $h(x) = -\dfrac{1}{x - 5}$

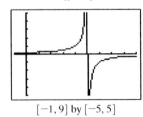

$[-1, 9]$ by $[-5, 5]$

3. $k(x) = \dfrac{3}{x + 4} - 2$

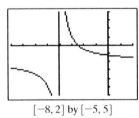

$[-8, 2]$ by $[-5, 5]$

Quick Review 2.6

1. $f(x) = (2x - 1)(x + 3) \Rightarrow x = -3$ or $x = \dfrac{1}{2}$

2. $f(x) = (3x + 4)(x - 2) \Rightarrow x = -\dfrac{4}{3}$ or $x = 2$

3. $g(x) = (x + 2)(x - 2) \Rightarrow x = \pm 2$

4. $g(x) = (x + 1)(x - 1) \Rightarrow x = \pm 1$

5. $h(x) = (x - 1)(x^2 + x + 1) \Rightarrow x = 1$

6. $h(x) = (x - i)(x + i) \Rightarrow$ no real zeros

7.
$$
\begin{array}{r}
2 \\
x - 3 \overline{) \, 2x + 1} \\
2x - 6 \\
\hline
7
\end{array}
$$
Quotient: 2, Remainder: 7

8.
$$
\begin{array}{r}
2 \\
2x - 1 \overline{) \, 4x + 3} \\
4x - 2 \\
\hline
5
\end{array}
$$
Quotient: 2, Remainder: 5

9.
$$
\begin{array}{r}
3 \\
x \overline{) \, 3x - 5} \\
3x \\
\hline
-5
\end{array}
$$
Quotient: 3, Remainder: -5

10.
$$
\begin{array}{r}
\frac{5}{2} \\
2x \overline{) \, 5x - 1} \\
5x \\
\hline
-1
\end{array}
$$
Quotient: $\dfrac{5}{2}$, Remainder: -1

Section 2.6 Exercises

1. The domain of $f(x) = 1/(x + 3)$ is all real numbers $x \neq -3$. The graph suggests that $f(x)$ has a vertical asymptote at $x = -3$.

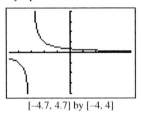

$[-4.7, 4.7]$ by $[-4, 4]$

As x approaches -3 from the left, the values of $f(x)$ decrease without bound. As x approaches -3 from the right, the values of $f(x)$ increase without bound. That is, $\lim\limits_{x \to -3^-} f(x) = -\infty$ and $\lim\limits_{x \to -3^+} f(x) = \infty$.

2. The domain of $f(x) = -3/(x - 1)$ is all real numbers $x \neq 1$. The graph suggests that $f(x)$ has a vertical asymptote at $x = 1$.

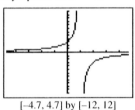

$[-4.7, 4.7]$ by $[-12, 12]$

As x approaches 1 from the left, the values of $f(x)$ increase without bound. As x approaches 1 from the right, the values of $f(x)$ decrease without bound. That is, $\lim\limits_{x \to 1^-} f(x) = \infty$ and $\lim\limits_{x \to 1^+} f(x) = -\infty$.

3. The domain of $f(x) = -1/(x^2 - 4)$ is all real numbers $x \neq -2, 2$. The graph suggests that $f(x)$ has vertical asymptotes at $x = -2$ and $x = 2$.

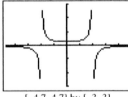

$[-4.7, 4.7]$ by $[-3, 3]$

As x approaches -2 from the left, the values of $f(x)$ decrease without bound, and as x approaches -2 from the right, the values of $f(x)$ increase without bound. As x approaches 2 from the left, the values of $f(x)$ increase without bound, and as x approaches 2 from the right, the values of $f(x)$ decrease without bound. That is, $\lim\limits_{x \to -2^-} f(x) = -\infty$, $\lim\limits_{x \to -2^+} f(x) = \infty$, $\lim\limits_{x \to 2^-} f(x) = \infty$, and $\lim\limits_{x \to 2^+} f(x) = -\infty$.

4. The domain of $f(x) = 2/(x^2 - 1)$ is all real numbers $x \neq -1, 1$. The graph suggests that $f(x)$ has vertical asymptotes at $x = -1$ and $x = 1$.

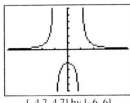

[-4.7, 4.7] by [-6, 6]

As x approaches -1 from the left, the values of $f(x)$ increase without bound, and as x approaches -1 from the right, the values of $f(x)$ decrease without bound. As x approaches 1 from the left, the values of $f(x)$ decrease without bound, and as x approaches 1 from the right, the values of $f(x)$ increase without bound. That is,

$\lim\limits_{x \to -1^-} f(x) = \infty$, $\lim\limits_{x \to -1^+} f(x) = -\infty$, $\lim\limits_{x \to 1^-} f(x) = -\infty$,

and $\lim\limits_{x \to 1^+} f(x) = \infty$.

5. Translate right 3 units. Asymptotes: $x = 3$, $y = 0$.

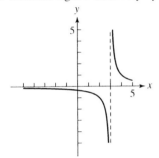

6. Translate left 5 units, reflect across x-axis, vertically stretch by 2. Asymptotes: $x = -5$, $y = 0$.

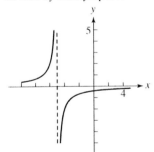

7. Translate left 3 units, reflect across x-axis, vertically stretch by 7, translate up 2 units.
Asymptotes: $x = -3$, $y = 2$.

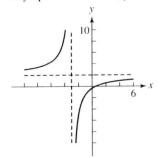

8. Translate right 1 unit, translate up 3 units.
Asymptotes: $x = 1$, $y = 3$.

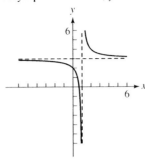

9. Translate left 4 units, vertically stretch by 13, translate down 2 units. Asymptotes: $x = -4$, $y = -2$.

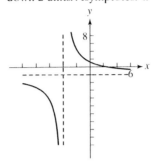

10. Translate right 5 units, vertically stretch by 11, reflect across x-axis, translate down 3 units. Asymptotes: $x = 5$, $y = -3$.

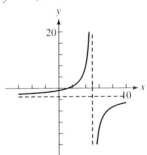

11. $\lim\limits_{x \to 3^-} f(x) = \infty$

12. $\lim\limits_{x \to 3^+} f(x) = -\infty$

13. $\lim\limits_{x \to \infty} f(x) = 0$

14. $\lim\limits_{x \to -\infty} f(x) = 0$

15. $\lim\limits_{x \to -3^+} f(x) = \infty$

16. $\lim\limits_{x \to -3^-} f(x) = -\infty$

17. $\lim\limits_{x \to -\infty} f(x) = 5$

18. $\lim\limits_{x \to \infty} f(x) = 5$

19. The graph of $f(x) = (2x^2 - 1)/(x^2 + 3)$ suggests that there are no vertical asymptotes and that the horizontal asymptote is $y = 2$.

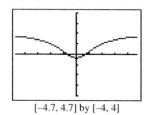

[−4.7, 4.7] by [−4, 4]

The domain of $f(x)$ is all real numbers, so there are indeed no vertical asymptotes. Using polynomial long division, we find that

$$f(x) = \frac{2x^2 - 1}{x^2 + 3} = 2 - \frac{7}{x^2 + 3}$$

When the value of $|x|$ is large, the denominator $x^2 + 3$ is a large positive number, and $7/(x^2 + 3)$ is a small positive number, getting closer to zero as $|x|$ increases. Therefore,

$$\lim_{x \to \infty} f(x) = \lim_{x \to -\infty} f(x) = 2,$$

so $y = 2$ is indeed a horizontal asymptote.

20. The graph of $f(x) = 3x^2/(x^2 + 1)$ suggests that there are no vertical asymptotes and that the horizontal asymptote is $y = 3$.

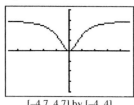

[−4.7, 4.7] by [−4, 4]

The domain of $f(x)$ is all real numbers, so there are indeed no vertical asymptotes. Using polynomial long division, we find that

$$f(x) = \frac{3x^2}{x^2 + 1} = 3 - \frac{3}{x^2 + 1}$$

When the value of $|x|$ is large, the denominator $x^2 + 1$ is a large positive number, and $3/(x^2 + 1)$ is a small positive number, getting closer to zero as $|x|$ increases. Therefore,

$$\lim_{x \to \infty} f(x) = \lim_{x \to -\infty} f(x) = 3,$$

so $y = 3$ is indeed a horizontal asymptote.

21. The graph of $f(x) = (2x + 1)/(x^2 - x)$ suggests that there are vertical asymptotes at $x = 0$ and $x = 1$, with $\lim_{x \to 0^-} f(x) = \infty$, $\lim_{x \to 0^+} f(x) = -\infty$, $\lim_{x \to 1^-} f(x) = -\infty$, and $\lim_{x \to 1^+} f(x) = \infty$, and that the horizontal asymptote is $y = 0$.

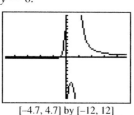

[−4.7, 4.7] by [−12, 12]

The domain of $f(x) = (2x + 1)/(x^2 - x) = (2x + 1)/[x(x - 1)]$ is all real numbers $x \neq 0, 1$, so there are indeed vertical asymptotes at $x = 0$ and $x = 1$. Rewriting one rational expression as two, we find that

$$f(x) = \frac{2x + 1}{x^2 - x} = \frac{2x}{x^2 - x} + \frac{1}{x^2 - x}$$

$$= \frac{2}{x - 1} + \frac{1}{x^2 - x}$$

When the value of $|x|$ is large, both terms get close to zero. Therefore,

$$\lim_{x \to \infty} f(x) = \lim_{x \to -\infty} f(x) = 0,$$

so $y = 0$ is indeed a horizontal asymptote.

22. The graph of $f(x) = (x - 3)/(x^2 + 3x)$ suggests that there are vertical asymptotes at $x = -3$ and $x = 0$, with $\lim_{x \to -3^-} f(x) = -\infty$, $\lim_{x \to -3^+} f(x) = \infty$, $\lim_{x \to 0^-} f(x) = \infty$, and $\lim_{x \to 0^+} f(x) = -\infty$, and that the horizontal asymptote is $y = 0$.

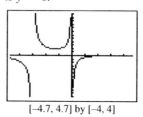

[−4.7, 4.7] by [−4, 4]

The domain of $f(x) = (x - 3)/(x^2 + 3x) = (x - 3)/[x(x + 3)]$ is all real numbers $x \neq -3, 0$, so there are indeed vertical asymptotes at $x = -3$ and $x = 0$. Rewriting one rational expression as two, we find that

$$f(x) = \frac{x - 3}{x^2 + 3x} = \frac{x}{x^2 + 3x} - \frac{3}{x^2 + 3x}$$

$$= \frac{1}{x + 3} - \frac{3}{x^2 + 3x}$$

When the value of $|x|$ is large, both terms get close to zero. Therefore,

$$\lim_{x \to \infty} f(x) = \lim_{x \to -\infty} f(x) = 0,$$

so $y = 0$ is indeed a horizontal asymptote.

23. Intercepts: $\left(0, \dfrac{2}{3}\right)$ and $(2, 0)$. Asymptotes: $x = -1$, $x = 3$, and $y = 0$.

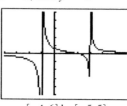

[−4, 6] by [−5, 5]

24. Intercepts: $\left(0, -\dfrac{2}{3}\right)$ and $(-2, 0)$. Asymptotes: $x = -3$, $x = 1$, and $y = 0$.

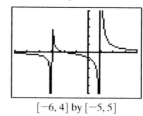

[−6, 4] by [−5, 5]

25. No intercepts. Asymptotes: $x = -1$, $x = 0$, $x = 1$, and $y = 0$.

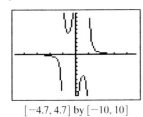

$[-4.7, 4.7]$ by $[-10, 10]$

26. No intercepts. Asymptotes: $x = -2$, $x = 0$, $x = 2$, and $y = 0$.

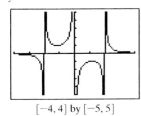

$[-4, 4]$ by $[-5, 5]$

27. Intercepts: $(0, 2)$, $(-1.28, 0)$, and $(0.78, 0)$. Asymptotes: $x = 1$, $x = -1$, and $y = 2$.

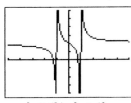

$[-5, 5]$ by $[-4, 6]$

28. Intercepts: $(0, -3)$, $(-1.84, 0)$, and $(2.17, 0)$. Asymptotes: $x = -2$, $x = 2$, and $y = -3$.

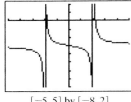

$[-5, 5]$ by $[-8, 2]$

29. Intercept: $\left(0, \dfrac{3}{2}\right)$. Asymptotes: $x = -2$, $y = x - 4$.

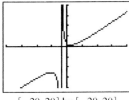

$[-20, 20]$ by $[-20, 20]$

30. Intercepts: $\left(0, -\dfrac{7}{3}\right)$, $(-1.54, 0)$, and $(4.54, 0)$.

Asymptotes: $x = -3$, $y = x - 6$.

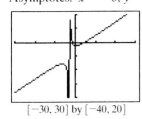

$[-30, 30]$ by $[-40, 20]$

31. (d); Xmin $= -2$, Xmax $= 8$, Xscl $= 1$, and Ymin $= -3$, Ymax $= 3$, Yscl $= 1$.

32. (b); Xmin $= -6$, Xmax $= 2$, Xscl $= 1$, and Ymin $= -3$, Ymax $= 3$, Yscl $= 1$.

33. (a); Xmin $= -3$, Xmax $= 5$, Xscl $= 1$, and Ymin $= -5$, Ymax $= 10$, Yscl $= 1$.

34. (f); Xmin $= -6$, Xmax $= 2$, Xscl $= 1$, and Ymin $= -5$, Ymax $= 5$, Yscl $= 1$.

35. (e); Xmin $= -2$, Xmax $= 8$, Xscl $= 1$, and Ymin $= -3$, Ymax $= 3$, Yscl $= 1$.

36. (c); Xmin $= -3$, Xmax $= 5$, Xscl $= 1$, and Ymin $= -3$, Ymax $= 8$, Yscl $= 1$.

37. For $f(x) = 2/(2x^2 - x - 3)$, the numerator is never zero, and so $f(x)$ never equals zero and the graph has no x-intercepts. Because $f(0) = -2/3$, the y-intercept is $-2/3$. The denominator factors as $2x^2 - x - 3 = (2x - 3)(x + 1)$, so there are vertical asymptotes at $x = -1$ and $x = 3/2$. And because the degree of the numerator is less than the degree of the denominator, the horizontal asymptote is $y = 0$. The graph supports this information and allows us to conclude that

$$\lim_{x \to -1^-} f(x) = \infty, \ \lim_{x \to -1^+} f(x) = -\infty, \ \lim_{x \to (3/2)^-} f(x) = -\infty,$$
and $\lim_{x \to (3/2)^+} f(x) = \infty$.

The graph also shows a local maximum of $-16/25$ at $x = 1/4$.

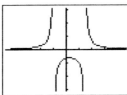

$[-4.7, 4.7]$ by $[-3.1, 3.1]$

Intercept: $\left(0, -\dfrac{2}{3}\right)$

Domain: $(-\infty, -1) \cup \left(-1, \dfrac{3}{2}\right) \cup \left(\dfrac{3}{2}, \infty\right)$

Range: $\left(-\infty, -\dfrac{16}{25}\right) \cup (0, \infty)$

Continuity: All $x \neq -1, \dfrac{3}{2}$

Increasing on $(-\infty, -1)$ and $\left(-1, \dfrac{1}{4}\right)$

Decreasing on $\left[\dfrac{1}{4}, \dfrac{3}{2}\right)$ and $\left(\dfrac{3}{2}, \infty\right)$

Not symmetric.
Unbounded.

Local maximum at $\left(\dfrac{1}{4}, -\dfrac{16}{25}\right)$

Horizontal asymptote: $y = 0$
Vertical asymptotes: $x = -1$ and $x = 3/2$
End behavior: $\lim_{x \to -\infty} f(x) = \lim_{x \to \infty} f(x) = 0$

38. For $g(x) = 2/(x^2 + 4x + 3)$, the numerator is never zero, and so $g(x)$ never equals zero and the graph has no x-intercepts. Because $g(0) = 2/3$, the y-intercept is 2/3. The denominator factors as
$$x^2 + 4x + 3 = (x + 1)(x + 3),$$
so there are vertical asymptotes at $x = -3$ and $x = -1$. And because the degree of the numerator is less than the degree of the denominator, the horizontal asymptote is $y = 0$. The graph supports this information and allows us to conclude that
$$\lim_{x \to -3^-} g(x) = \infty, \lim_{x \to -3^+} g(x) = -\infty, \lim_{x \to -1^-} g(x) = -\infty,$$
and $\lim_{x \to -1^+} g(x) = \infty$.
The graph also shows a local maximum of -2 at $x = -2$.

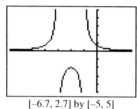

[-6.7, 2.7] by [-5, 5]

Intercept: $\left(0, \dfrac{2}{3}\right)$

Domain: $(-\infty, -3) \cup (-3, -1) \cup (-1, \infty)$
Range: $(-\infty, -2] \cup (0, \infty)$
Continuity: All $x \neq -3, -1$
Increasing on $(-\infty, -3)$ and $(-3, -2]$
Decreasing on $[-2, -1)$ and $(-1, \infty)$
Not symmetric.
Unbounded.
Local maximum at $(-2, -2)$
Horizontal asymptote: $y = 0$
Vertical asymptotes: $x = -3$ and $x = -1$
End behavior: $\lim_{x \to -\infty} g(x) = \lim_{x \to \infty} g(x) = 0$

39. For $h(x) = (x - 1)/(x^2 - x - 12)$, the numerator is zero when $x = 1$, so the x-intercept of the graph is 1. Because $h(0) = 1/12$, the y-intercept is 1/12. The denominator factors as
$$x^2 - x - 12 = (x + 3)(x - 4),$$
so there are vertical asymptotes at $x = -3$ and $x = 4$. And because the degree of the numerator is less than the degree of the denominator, the horizontal asymptote is $y = 0$. The graph supports this information and allows us to conclude that
$$\lim_{x \to -3^-} h(x) = -\infty, \lim_{x \to -3^+} h(x) = \infty, \lim_{x \to 4^-} h(x) = -\infty,$$
and $\lim_{x \to 4^+} h(x) = \infty$.

The graph shows no local extrema.

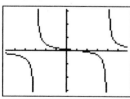

[-5.875, 5.875] by [-3.1, 3.1]

Intercepts: $\left(0, \dfrac{1}{12}\right)$, $(1, 0)$

Domain: $(-\infty, -3) \cup (-3, 4) \cup (4, \infty)$
Range: $(-\infty, \infty)$
Continuity: All $x \neq -3, 4$
Decreasing on $(-\infty, -3)$, $(-3, 4)$, and $(4, \infty)$
Not symmetric.
Unbounded.
No local extrema.
Horizontal asymptote: $y = 0$
Vertical asymptotes: $x = -3$ and $x = 4$
End behavior: $\lim_{x \to -\infty} h(x) = \lim_{x \to \infty} h(x) = 0$

40. For $k(x) = (x + 1)/(x^2 - 3x - 10)$, the numerator is zero when $x = -1$, so the x-intercept of the graph is -1. Because $k(0) = -1/10$, the y-intercept is $-1/10$. The denominator factors as
$$x^2 - 3x - 10 = (x + 2)(x - 5),$$
so there are vertical asymptotes at $x = -2$ and $x = 5$.

And because the degree of the numerator is less than the degree of the denominator, the horizontal asymptote is $y = 0$. The graph supports this information and allows us to conclude that
$$\lim_{x \to -2^-} k(x) = -\infty, \lim_{x \to -2^+} k(x) = \infty,$$
$$\lim_{x \to 5^-} k(x) = -\infty, \text{ and } \lim_{x \to 5^+} k(x) = \infty.$$
The graph shows no local extrema.

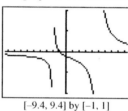

[-9.4, 9.4] by [-1, 1]

Intercepts: $(-1, 0)$, $(0, -0.1)$
Domain: $(-\infty, -2) \cup (-2, 5) \cup (5, \infty)$
Range: $(-\infty, \infty)$
Continuity: All $x \neq -2, 5$
Decreasing on $(-\infty, -2)$, $(-2, 5)$, and $(5, \infty)$
Not symmetric.
Unbounded.
No local extrema.
Horizontal asymptote: $y = 0$
Vertical asymptotes: $x = -2$ and $x = 5$
End behavior: $\lim_{x \to -\infty} k(x) = \lim_{x \to \infty} k(x) = 0$

41. For $f(x) = (x^2 + x - 2)/(x^2 - 9)$, the numerator factors as
$$x^2 + x - 2 = (x + 2)(x - 1),$$
so the x-intercepts of the graph are -2 and 1. Because $f(0) = 2/9$, the y-intercept is 2/9. The denominator factors as
$$x^2 - 9 = (x + 3)(x - 3),$$
so there are vertical asymptotes at $x = -3$ and $x = 3$. And because the degree of the numerator equals the degree of the denominator with a ratio of leading terms that equals 1, the horizontal asymptote is $y = 1$. The graph supports this information and allows us to conclude that
$$\lim_{x \to -3^-} f(x) = \infty, \lim_{x \to -3^+} f(x) = -\infty, \lim_{x \to 3^-} f(x) = -\infty,$$
and $\lim_{x \to 3^+} f(x) = \infty$.

The graph also shows a local maximum of about 0.260 at about $x = -0.675$.

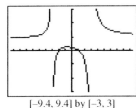

[-9.4, 9.4] by [-3, 3]

Intercepts: $(-2, 0)$, $(1, 0)$, $\left(0, \dfrac{2}{9}\right)$

Domain: $(-\infty, -3) \cup (-3, 3) \cup (3, \infty)$
Range: $(-\infty, 0.260] \cup (1, \infty)$
Continuity: All $x \neq -3, 3$
Increasing on $(-\infty, -3)$ and $(-3, -0.675]$
Decreasing on $[-0.675, 3)$ and $(3, \infty)$
Not symmetric.
Unbounded.
Local maximum at about $(-0.675, 0.260)$
Horizontal asymptote: $y = 1$
Vertical asymptotes: $x = -3$ and $x = 3$
End behavior: $\lim\limits_{x \to -\infty} f(x) = \lim\limits_{x \to \infty} f(x) = 1$.

42. For $g(x) = (x^2 - x - 2)/(x^2 - 2x - 8)$, the numerator factors as
$x^2 - x - 2 = (x + 1)(x - 2)$,
so the x-intercepts of the graph are -1 and 2. Because $g(0) = 1/4$, the y-intercept is $1/4$. The denominator factors as
$x^2 - 2x - 8 = (x + 2)(x - 4)$,
so there are vertical asymptotes at $x = -2$ and $x = 4$. And because the degree of the numerator equals the degree of the denominator with a ratio of leading terms that equals 1, the horizontal asymptote is $y = 1$. The graph supports this information and allows us to conclude that
$\lim\limits_{x \to -2^-} g(x) = \infty$, $\lim\limits_{x \to -2^+} g(x) = -\infty$, $\lim\limits_{x \to 4^-} g(x) = -\infty$,
and $\lim\limits_{x \to 4^+} g(x) = \infty$.

The graph also shows a local maximum of about 0.260 at about $x = 0.324$.

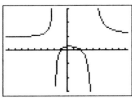

[-9.4, 9.4] by [-3, 3]

Intercepts: $(-1, 0)$, $(2, 0)$, $\left(0, \dfrac{1}{4}\right)$

Domain: $(-\infty, -2) \cup (-2, 4) \cup (4, \infty)$
Range: $(-\infty, 0.260] \cup (1, \infty)$
Continuity: All $x \neq -2, 4$
Increasing on $(-\infty, -2)$ and $(-2, 0.324]$
Decreasing on $[0.324, 4)$ and $(4, \infty)$
Not symmetric.
Unbounded.
Local maximum at about $(0.324, 0.260)$
Horizontal asymptote: $y = 1$
Vertical asymptotes: $x = -2$ and $x = 4$
End behavior: $\lim\limits_{x \to -\infty} g(x) = \lim\limits_{x \to \infty} g(x) = 1$

43. For $h(x) = (x^2 + 2x - 3)/(x + 2)$, the numerator factors as
$x^2 + 2x - 3 = (x + 3)(x - 1)$,
so the x-intercepts of the graph are -3 and 1. Because $h(0) = -3/2$, the y-intercept is $-3/2$. The denominator is zero when $x = -2$, so there is a vertical asymptote at $x = -2$. Using long division, we rewrite $h(x)$ as

$$h(x) = \frac{x^2 + 2x - 2}{x + 2} = x - \frac{2}{x + 2},$$

so the end-behavior asymptote of $h(x)$ is $y = x$. The graph supports this information and allows us to conclude that
$\lim\limits_{x \to -2^-} h(x) = \infty$ and $\lim\limits_{x \to -2^+} h(x) = -\infty$.
The graph shows no local extrema.

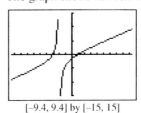

[-9.4, 9.4] by [-15, 15]

Intercepts: $(-3, 0)$, $(1, 0)$, $\left(0, -\dfrac{3}{2}\right)$

Domain: $(-\infty, -2) \cup (-2, \infty)$
Range: $(-\infty, \infty)$
Continuity: All $x \neq -2$
Increasing on $(-\infty, -2)$ and $(-2, \infty)$
Not symmetric.
Unbounded.
No local extrema.
Horizontal asymptote: None
Vertical asymptote: $x = -2$
Slant asymptote: $y = x$
End behavior: $\lim\limits_{x \to -\infty} h(x) = -\infty$ and $\lim\limits_{x \to \infty} h(x) = \infty$.

44. For $k(x) = (x^2 - x - 2)/(x - 3)$, the numerator factors as
$x^2 - x - 2 = (x + 1)(x - 2)$,
so the x-intercepts of the graph are -1 and 2. Because $k(0) = 2/3$, the y-intercept is $2/3$. The denominator is zero when $x = 3$, so there is a vertical asymptote at $x = 3$. Using long division, we rewrite $k(x)$ as

$$h(x) = \frac{x^2 - x - 2}{x - 3} = x + 2 + \frac{4}{x - 3},$$

so the end-behavior asymptote of $k(x)$ is $y = x + 2$. The graph supports this information and allows us to conclude that $\lim\limits_{x \to 3^-} k(x) = -\infty$ and $\lim\limits_{x \to 3^+} k(x) = \infty$.
The graph shows a local maximum of 1 at $x = 1$ and a local minimum of 9 at $x = 5$.

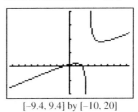

[-9.4, 9.4] by [-10, 20]

Intercepts: $(-1, 0)$, $(2, 0)$, $\left(0, \dfrac{2}{3}\right)$

Domain: $(-\infty, 3) \cup (3, \infty)$

Range: $(-\infty, 1] \cup [9, \infty)$

Continuity: All $x \neq 3$

Increasing on $(-\infty, 1]$ and $[5, \infty)$

Decreasing on $[1, 3)$ and $(3, 5]$

Not symmetric.

Unbounded.

Local maximum at $(1, 1)$; local minimum at $(5, 9)$

Horizontal asymptote: None

Vertical asymptote: $x = 3$

Slant asymptote: $y = x + 2$

End behavior: $\displaystyle\lim_{x \to -\infty} k(x) = -\infty$ and $\displaystyle\lim_{x \to \infty} k(x) = \infty$.

45. Divide $x^2 - 2x - 3$ by $x - 5$ to show that
$$f(x) = \frac{x^2 - 2x + 3}{x - 5} = x + 3 + \frac{18}{x - 5}.$$
The end-behavior asymptote of $f(x)$ is $y = x + 3$.

(a)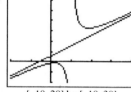

[-10, 20] by [-10, 30]

(b)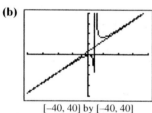

[-40, 40] by [-40, 40]

46. Divide $2x^2 + 2x - 3$ by $x + 3$ to show that
$$f(x) = \frac{2x^2 + 2x - 3}{x + 3} = 2x - 4 + \frac{9}{x + 3}.$$
The end-behavior asymptote of $f(x)$ is $y = 2x - 4$.

(a)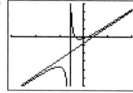

[-15, 10] by [-30, 20]

(b)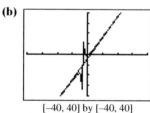

[-40, 40] by [-40, 40]

47. Divide $x^3 - x^2 + 1$ by $x + 2$ to show that
$$f(x) = \frac{x^3 - x^2 + 1}{x + 2} = x^2 - 3x + 6 - \frac{11}{x + 2}.$$
The end-behavior asymptote of $f(x)$ is $y = x^2 - 3x + 6$.

(a)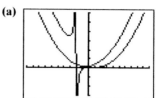

[-10, 10] by [-30, 60]

(b)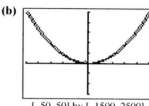

[-50, 50] by [-1500, 2500]

48. Divide $x^3 + 1$ by $x - 1$ to show that
$$f(x) = \frac{x^3 + 1}{x - 1} = x^2 + x + 1 + \frac{2}{x - 1}.$$
The end-behavior asymptote of $f(x)$ is $y = x^2 + x + 1$.

(a)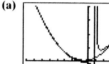

[-8, 8] by [-20, 40]

(b)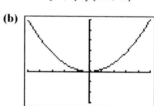

[-50, 50] by [-1500, 2500]

49. Divide $x^4 - 2x + 1$ by $x - 2$ to show that
$$f(x) = \frac{x^4 - 2x + 1}{x - 2} = x^3 + 2x^2 + 4x + 6 + \frac{13}{x - 2}.$$

The end-behavior asymptote of $f(x)$ is
$$y = x^3 + 2x^2 + 4x + 6.$$

(a)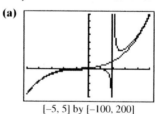

[-5, 5] by [-100, 200]

(b)

[-20, 20] by [-5000, 5000]

50. Divide $x^5 + 1$ by $x^2 + 1$ to show that
$$f(x) = \frac{x^5 + 1}{x^2 + 1} = x^3 - x + \frac{x + 1}{x^2 + 1}.$$
The end-behavior asymptote of $f(x)$ is $y = x^3 - x$.

(a) There are no vertical asymptotes, since the denominator $x^2 + 1$ is never zero.

(b)

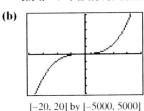

[–20, 20] by [–5000, 5000]

51. For $f(x) = (3x^2 - 2x + 4)/(x^2 - 4x + 5)$, the numerator is never zero, and so $f(x)$ never equals zero and the graph has no x-intercepts. Because $f(0) = 4/5$, the y-intercept is $4/5$. The denominator is never zero, and so there are no vertical asymptotes. And because the degree of the numerator equals the degree of the denominator with a ratio of leading terms that equals 3, the horizontal asymptote is $y = 3$. The graph supports this information. The graph also shows a local maximum of about 14.227 at about $x = 2.445$ and a local minimum of about 0.773 at about $x = -0.245$.

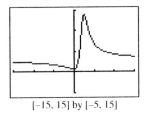

[–15, 15] by [–5, 15]

Intercept: $\left(0, \dfrac{4}{5}\right)$

Domain: $(-\infty, \infty)$
Range: $[0.773, 14.227]$
Continuity: $(-\infty, \infty)$
Increasing on $[-0.245, 2.445]$
Decreasing on $(-\infty, -0.245], [2.445, \infty)$
Not symmetric.
Bounded.
Local maximum at (2.445, 14.227); local minimum at $(-0.245, 0.773)$
Horizontal asymptote: $y = 3$
No vertical asymptotes.
End behavior: $\displaystyle\lim_{x \to -\infty} f(x) = \lim_{x \to \infty} f(x) = 3$

52. For $g(x) = (4x^2 + 2x)/(x^2 - 4x + 8)$, the numerator factors as
$4x^2 + 2x = 2x(2x + 1)$,
so the x-intercepts of the graph are $-1/2$ and 0. Because $g(0) = 0$, the y-intercept is 0. The denominator is never zero, and so there are no vertical asymptotes. And because the degree of the numerator equals the degree of the denominator with a ratio of leading terms that equals 4, the horizontal asymptote is $y = 4$. The graph supports this information. The graph also shows a local maximum of about 9.028 at about $x = 3.790$ and a local minimum of about -0.028 at about $x = -0.235$.

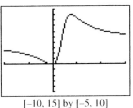

[–10, 15] by [–5, 10]

Intercepts: $\left(-\dfrac{1}{2}, 0\right)$, $(0, 0)$

Domain: $(-\infty, \infty)$
Range: $[-0.028, 9.028]$
Continuity: $(-\infty, \infty)$
Increasing on $[-0.235, 3.790]$
Decreasing on $(-\infty, -0.235], [3.790, \infty)$.
Not symmetric.
Bounded.
Local maximum at (3.790, 9.028); local minimum at $(-0.235, -0.028)$
Horizontal asymptote: $y = 4$
No vertical asymptotes.
End behavior: $\displaystyle\lim_{x \to -\infty} g(x) = \lim_{x \to \infty} g(x) = 4$

53. For $h(x) = (x^3 - 1)/(x - 2)$, the numerator factors as
$x^3 - 1 = (x - 1)(x^2 + x + 1)$,
so the x-intercept of the graph is 1. The y-intercept is $h(0) = 1/2$. The denominator is zero when $x = 2$, so the vertical asymptote is $x = 2$. Because we can rewrite $h(x)$ as
$$h(x) = \frac{x^3 - 1}{x - 2} = x^2 + 2x + 4 + \frac{7}{x - 2},$$
we know that the end-behavior asymptote is $y = x^2 + 2x + 4$. The graph supports this information and allows us to conclude that
$\displaystyle\lim_{x \to 2^-} h(x) = -\infty,\ \lim_{x \to 2^+} h(x) = \infty.$
The graph also shows a local maximum of about 0.586 at about $x = 0.442$, a local minimum of about 0.443 at about $x = -0.384$, and another local minimum of about 25.970 at about $x = 2.942$.

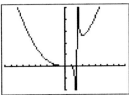

[–10, 10] by [–20, 50]

Intercepts: $(1, 0)$, $\left(0, \dfrac{1}{2}\right)$

Domain: $(-\infty, 2) \cup (2, \infty)$
Range: $(-\infty, \infty)$
Continuity: All real $x \neq 2$
Increasing on $[-0.384, 0.442], [2.942, \infty)$
Decreasing on $(-\infty, -0.384], [0.442, 2), (2, 2.942]$
Not symmetric.
Unbounded.
Local maximum at (0.442, 0.586); local minimum at $(-0.384, 0.443)$ and (2.942, 25.970)
No horizontal asymptote. End-behavior asymptote:
$y = x^2 + 2x + 4$
Vertical asymptote: $x = 2$
End behavior: $\displaystyle\lim_{x \to -\infty} h(x) = \lim_{x \to \infty} h(x) = \infty$

54. For $k(x) = (x^3 - 2)/(x + 2)$, the numerator is zero when $x = \sqrt[3]{2}$, so the x-intercept of the graph is $\sqrt[3]{2}$. The y-intercept is $k(0) = -1$. The denominator is zero when $x = -2$, so the vertical asymptote is $x = -2$. Because we can rewrite $k(x)$ as

$$k(x) = \frac{x^3 - 2}{x + 2} = x^2 - 2x + 4 - \frac{10}{x - 2},$$

we know that the end-behavior asymptote is $y = x^2 - 2x + 4$. The graph supports this information and allows us to conclude that $\lim_{x \to -2^-} k(x) = \infty$, $\lim_{x \to -2^+} k(x) = -\infty$.

The graph also shows a local minimum of about 28.901 at about $x = -3.104$.

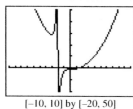

[–10, 10] by [–20, 50]

Intercepts: $(\sqrt[3]{2}, 0)$, $(0, -1)$
Domain: $(-\infty, -2) \cup (-2, \infty)$
Range: $(-\infty, \infty)$
Continuity: All real $x \neq -2$
Increasing on $[-3.104, -2)$, $(-2, \infty)$
Decreasing on $(-\infty, -3.104]$
Not symmetric.
Unbounded.
Local minimum at $(-3.104, 28.901)$
No horizontal asymptote. End-behavior asymptote:
    $y = x^2 - 2x + 4$
Vertical asymptote: $x = -2$
End behavior: $\lim_{x \to -\infty} k(x) = \lim_{x \to \infty} k(x) = \infty$

55. $f(x) = (x^3 - 2x^2 + x - 1)/(2x - 1)$ has only one x-intercept, and we can use the graph to show that it is about 1.755. The y-intercept is $f(0) = 1$. The denominator is zero when $x = 1/2$, so the vertical asymptote is $x = 1/2$. Because we can rewrite $f(x)$ as

$$f(x) = \frac{x^3 - 2x^2 + x - 1}{2x - 1}$$
$$= \frac{1}{2}x^2 - \frac{3}{4}x + \frac{1}{8} - \frac{7}{16(2x - 1)},$$

we know that the end-behavior asymptote is

$y = \frac{1}{2}x^2 - \frac{3}{4}x + \frac{1}{8}$. The graph supports this information and allows us to conclude that $\lim_{x \to 1/2^-} f(x) = \infty$, $\lim_{x \to 1/2^+} f(x) = -\infty$.

The graph also shows a local minimum of about 0.920 at about $x = -0.184$.

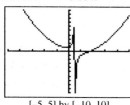

[–5, 5] by [–10, 10]

Intercepts: $(1.755, 0)$, $(0, 1)$

Domain: All $x \neq \frac{1}{2}$

Range: $(-\infty, \infty)$

Continuity: All $x \neq \frac{1}{2}$

Increasing on $[-0.184, 0.5)$, $(0.5, \infty)$
Decreasing on $(-\infty, -0.184]$
Not symmetric.
Unbounded.
Local minimum at $(-0.184, 0.920)$
No horizontal asymptote. End-behavior

asymptote: $y = \frac{1}{2}x^2 - \frac{3}{4}x + \frac{1}{8}$

Vertical asymptote: $x = \frac{1}{2}$

End behavior: $\lim_{x \to -\infty} f(x) = \lim_{x \to \infty} f(x) = \infty$

56. $g(x) = (2x^3 - 2x^2 - x + 5)/(x - 2)$ has only one x-intercept, and we can use the graph to show that it is about -1.189. The y-intercept is $g(0) = -5/2$. The denominator is zero when $x = 2$, so the vertical asymptote is $x = 2$. Because we can rewrite $g(x)$ as

$$g(x) = \frac{2x^3 - 2x^2 - x + 5}{x - 2} = 2x^2 + 2x + 3 + \frac{11}{x - 2},$$

we know that the end-behavior asymptote is $y = 2x^2 + 2x + 3$. The graph supports this information and allows us to conclude that $\lim_{x \to 2^-} g(x) = -\infty$, $\lim_{x \to 2^+} g(x) = \infty$.

The graph also shows a local minimum of about 37.842 at about $x = 2.899$.

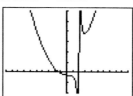

[–10, 10] by [–20, 60]

Intercepts: $(-1.189, 0)$, $(0, -2.5)$
Domain: All $x \neq 2$
Range: $(-\infty, \infty)$
Continuity: All $x \neq 2$
Increasing on $[2.899, \infty)$
Decreasing on $(-\infty, 2)$, $(2, 2.899]$
Not symmetric.
Unbounded.
Local minimum at $(2.899, 37.842)$
No horizontal asymptote. End-behavior asymptote:
    $y = 2x^2 + 2x + 3$
Vertical asymptote: $x = 2$
End behavior: $\lim_{x \to -\infty} g(x) = \lim_{x \to \infty} g(x) = \infty$

57. For $h(x) = (x^4 + 1)/(x + 1)$, the numerator is never zero, and so $h(x)$ never equals zero and the graph has no x-intercepts. Because $h(0) = 1$, the y-intercept is 1. So the one intercept is the point $(0, 1)$. The denominator is zero when $x = -1$, so $x = -1$ is a vertical asymptote. Divide $x^4 + 1$ by $x + 1$ to show that

$$h(x) = \frac{x^4 + 1}{x + 1} = x^3 - x^2 + x - 1 + \frac{2}{x + 1}.$$

The end-behavior asymptote of $h(x)$ is
$y = x^3 - x^2 + x - 1$.

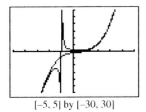

[–5, 5] by [–30, 30]

58. $k(x) = (2x^5 + x^2 - x + 1)/(x^2 - 1)$ has only one
x-intercept, and we can use the graph to show that it is
about -1.108. Because $k(0) = -1$, the y-intercept is -1.
So the intercepts are $(-1.108, 0)$ and $(0, -1)$. The denominator is zero when $x = \pm 1$, so $x = -1$ and $x = 1$ are
vertical asymptotes. Divide $2x^5 + x^2 - x + 1$ by $x^2 - 1$
to show that
$$k(x) = \frac{2x^5 + x^2 - x + 1}{x^2 - 1} = 2x^3 + 2x + 1 + \frac{x + 2}{x^2 - 1}.$$
The end-behavior asymptote of $k(x)$ is
$y = 2x^3 + 2x + 1$.

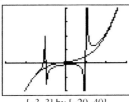

[–3, 3] by [–20, 40]

59. For $f(x) = (x^5 - 1)/(x + 2)$, the numerator factors as
$x^5 - 1 = (x - 1)(x^4 + x^3 + x^2 + x + 1)$, and since the
second factor is never zero (as can be verified by
Descartes' Rule of Signs or by graphing), the x-intercept
of the graph is 1. Because $f(0) = -1/2$, the y-intercept is
$-1/2$. So the intercepts are $(1, 0)$ and $(0, -1/2)$.
The denominator is zero when $x = -2$, so $x = -2$ is a
vertical asymptote. Divide $x^5 - 1$ by $x + 2$ to show that
$$f(x) = \frac{x^5 - 1}{x + 2} = x^4 - 2x^3 + 4x^2 - 8x + 16 - \frac{33}{x + 2}.$$
The end-behavior asymptote of $f(x)$ is
$y = x^4 - 2x^3 + 4x^2 - 8x + 16$.

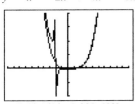

[–10, 10] by [–200, 400]

60. For $g(x) = (x^5 + 1)/(x - 1)$, the numerator factors as
$x^5 + 1 = (x + 1)(x^4 - x^3 + x^2 - x + 1)$, and since the
second factor is never zero (as can be verified by graphing), the x-intercept of the graph is -1. Because
$g(0) = -1$, the y-intercept is -1. So the intercepts are
$(-1, 0)$ and $(0, -1)$. The denominator is zero when $x = 1$,
so $x = 1$ is a vertical asymptote. Divide $x^5 + 1$ by $x - 1$
to show that
$$g(x) = \frac{x^5 + 1}{x - 1} = x^4 + x^3 + x^2 + x + 1 + \frac{2}{x - 1}.$$
The end-behavior asymptote of $g(x)$ is
$y = x^4 + x^3 + x^2 + x + 1$.

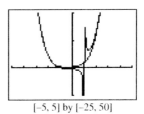

[–5, 5] by [–25, 50]

61. $h(x) = (2x^3 - 3x + 2)/(x^3 - 1)$ has only one
x-intercept, and we can use the graph to show that it is
about -1.476. Because $h(0) = -2$, the y-intercept is -2.
So the intercepts are $(-1.476, 0)$ and $(0, -2)$. The denominator is zero when $x = 1$, so $x = 1$ is a vertical asymptote. Divide $2x^3 - 3x + 2$ by $x^3 - 1$ to show that
$$h(x) = \frac{2x^3 - 3x + 2}{x^3 - 1} = 2 - \frac{3x - 4}{x^3 - 1}.$$
The end-behavior asymptote of $h(x)$ is $y = 2$, a horizontal
line.

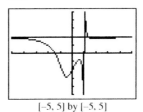

[–5, 5] by [–5, 5]

62. For $k(x) = (3x^3 + x - 4)/(x^3 + 1)$, the numerator
factors as $3x^3 + x - 4 = (x - 1)(3x^2 + 3x + 4)$,
and since the second factor is never zero (as can be verified
by Descartes' Rule of Signs or by graphing), the x-intercept
of the graph is 1. Because $k(0) = -4$, the y-intercept is -4.
So the intercepts are $(1, 0)$ and $(0, -4)$. The denominator is
zero when $x = -1$, so $x = -1$ is a vertical asymptote. Divide
$3x^3 + x - 4$ by $x^3 + 1$ to show that
$$k(x) = \frac{3x^3 + x - 4}{x^3 + 1} = 3 + \frac{x - 7}{x^3 + 1}.$$
The end-behavior asymptote of $k(x)$ is $y = 3$, a horizontal
line.

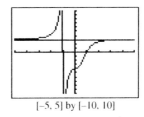

[–5, 5] by [–10, 10]

63. False. If the denominator is never zero, there will be no
vertical asymptote. For example, $f(x) = 1/(x^2 + 1)$ is a
rational function and has no vertical asymptotes.

64. False. A rational function is the quotient of two polynomials, and $\sqrt{x^2 + 4}$ is not a polynomial.

65. The excluded values are those for which $x^3 + 3x = 0$,
namely 0 and -3. The answer is E.

66. $g(x)$ results from $f(x)$ by replacing x with $x + 3$, which
represents a shift of 3 units to the left. The answer is A.

67. Since $x + 5 = 0$ when $x = -5$, there is a vertical asymptote. And because $x^2/(x + 5) = x - 5 + 25/(x + 5)$,
the end behavior is characterized by the slant asymptote
$y = x - 5$. The answer is D.

68. The quotient of the leading terms is x^4, so the answer is E.

69. (a) No: the domain of f is $(-\infty, 3) \cup (3, \infty)$; the domain of g is all real numbers.

(b) No: while it is not defined at 3, it does not tend toward $\pm\infty$ on either side.

(c) Most grapher viewing windows do not reveal that f is undefined at 3.

(d) Almost—but not quite; they are equal for all $x \neq 3$.

70. (a) $f(x) = \dfrac{x^2 + x - 2}{x - 1} = \dfrac{(x + 2)(x - 1)}{x - 1} = x + 2$

$= g(x)$ when $x \neq 1$

	f	g
Asymptotes	$x = 1$	none
Intercepts	$(0, 2)\ (-2, 0)$	$(0, 2)\ (-2, 0)$
Domain	$(-\infty, 1) \cup (1, \infty)$	$(-\infty, \infty)$

The functions are identical at all points except $x = 1$, where f has a discontinuity.

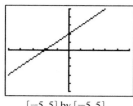

$[-5, 5]$ by $[-5, 5]$

(b) $f(x) = \dfrac{x^2 - 1}{x + 1} = \dfrac{(x + 1)(x - 1)}{x + 1} = x - 1$

$= g(x)$ when $x \neq -1$

	f	g
Asymptotes	$x = -1$	none
Intercepts	$(0, -1)\ (1, 0)$	$(0, -1)\ (1, 0)$
Domain	$(-\infty, -1) \cup (-1, \infty)$	$(-\infty, \infty)$

The functions are identical except at $x = -1$, where f has a discontinuity.

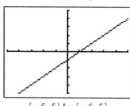

$[-5, 5]$ by $[-5, 5]$

(c) $f(x) = \dfrac{x^2 - 1}{x^3 - x^2 - x + 1} = \dfrac{x^2 - 1}{(x^2 - 1)(x - 1)}$

$= \dfrac{1}{x - 1} = g(x)$ when $x \neq -1$

	f	g
Asymptotes	$x = 1, x = -1$	$x = 1$
Intercepts	$(0, -1)$	$(0, -1)$
Domain	$(-\infty, -1) \cup (-1, 1)$ $\cup (1, \infty)$	$(-\infty, 1) \cup (1, \infty)$

The functions are identical except at $x = -1$, where $f(x)$ has a discontinuity.

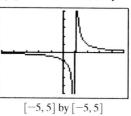

$[-5, 5]$ by $[-5, 5]$

	f	g
Asymptotes	$x = 1, x = -2$	$x = -2$
Intercepts	$\left(0, \dfrac{1}{2}\right)$	$\left(0, \dfrac{1}{2}\right)$
Domain	$(-\infty, -2) \cup$ $(-2, 1) \cup (1, \infty)$	$(-\infty, -2) \cup (-2, \infty)$

(d) $f(x) = \dfrac{x - 1}{x^2 + x - 2} = \dfrac{x - 1}{(x + 2)(x - 1)} = \dfrac{1}{x + 2}$

$= g(x)$ when, $x \neq -2$

Except at $x = 1$, where f has a discontinuity, the functions are identical.

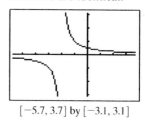

$[-5.7, 3.7]$ by $[-3.1, 3.1]$

71. (a) The volume is $f(x) = k/x$, where x is pressure and k is a constant. $f(x)$ is a quotient of polynomials and hence is rational, but $f(x) = k \cdot x^{-1}$, so is a power function with constant of variation k and pressure -1.

(b) If $f(x) = kx^a$, where a is a negative integer, then the power function f is also a rational function.

(c) $V = \dfrac{k}{P}$, so $k = (2.59)(0.866) = 2.24294$.

If $P = 0.532$, then $V = \dfrac{2.24294}{0.532} \approx 4.22$ L.

72. (a)

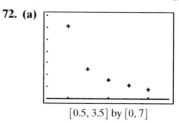

$[0.5, 3.5]$ by $[0, 7]$

(b) One method for determining k is to find the power regression for the data points using a calculator, discussed in previous sections. By this method, we find that a good approximation of the data points is given by the curve $y \approx 5.81 \cdot x^{-1.88}$. Since -1.88 is very close to -2, we graph the curve to see if $k = 5.81$ is reasonable.

(c)

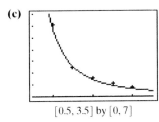

$[0.5, 3.5]$ by $[0, 7]$

(d) At 2.2 m, the light intensity is approximately 1.20 W/m². At 4.4 m, the light intensity is approximately 0.30 W/m².

73. Horizontal asymptotes: $y = -2$ and $y = 2$.

Intercepts: $\left(0, -\dfrac{3}{2}\right), \left(\dfrac{3}{2}, 0\right)$

$$h(x) = \begin{cases} \dfrac{2x - 3}{x + 2} & x \geq 0 \\[2mm] \dfrac{2x - 3}{-x + 2} & x < 0 \end{cases}$$

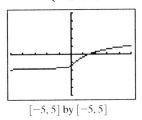

$[-5, 5]$ by $[-5, 5]$

74. Horizontal asymptotes: $y = \pm 3$.

Intercepts: $\left(0, \dfrac{5}{3}\right), \left(-\dfrac{5}{3}, 0\right)$

$$h(x) = \begin{cases} \dfrac{3x + 5}{x + 3} & x \geq 0 \\[2mm] \dfrac{3x + 5}{-x + 3} & x < 0 \end{cases}$$

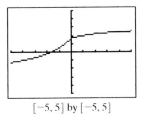

$[-5, 5]$ by $[-5, 5]$

75. Horizontal asymptotes: $y = \pm 3$.

Intercepts: $\left(0, \dfrac{5}{4}\right), \left(\dfrac{5}{3}, 0\right)$

$$f(x) = \begin{cases} \dfrac{5 - 3x}{x + 4} & x \geq 0 \\[2mm] \dfrac{5 - 3x}{-x + 4} & x < 0 \end{cases}$$

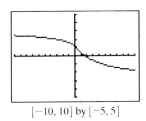

$[-10, 10]$ by $[-5, 5]$

76. Horizontal asymptotes: $y = \pm 2$. Intercepts: $(0, 2), (1, 0)$

$$f(x) = \begin{cases} \dfrac{2 - 2x}{x + 1} & x \geq 0 \\[2mm] 2 & x < 0 \end{cases}$$

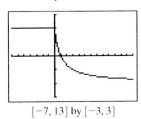

$[-7, 13]$ by $[-3, 3]$

77. The graph of f is the graph of $y = \dfrac{1}{x}$ shifted horizontally $-d/c$ units, stretched vertically by a factor of $|bc - ad|/c^2$, reflected across the x-axis if and only if $bc - ad < 0$, and then shifted vertically by a/c.

78. Yes, domain $= (-\infty, -1) \cup (-1, 0) \cup (0, 1) \cup (1, \infty)$; range $= (-\infty, 1) \cup (1, \infty)$; continuous and decreasing on each interval within their common domain; x-intercepts $= (-1 \pm \sqrt{5})/2$; no y-intercepts; hole at $(0, 1)$; horizontal asymptote of $y = 1$; vertical asymptotes of $x = \pm 1$; neither even nor odd; unbounded; no local extrema; end behavior: $\displaystyle\lim_{|x| \to \infty} f(x) = \lim_{|x| \to \infty} g(x) = 1$.

■ Section 2.7 Solving Equations in One Variable

Quick Review 2.7

1. The denominator is $x^2 + x - 12 = (x - 3)(x + 4)$, so the new numerator is $2x(x + 4) = 2x^2 + 8x$.

2. The numerator is $x^2 - 1 = (x - 1)(x + 1)$, so the new denominator is $(x + 1)(x + 1) = x^2 + 2x + 1$.

3. The LCD is the LCM of 12, 18, and 6, namely 36.

$$\frac{5}{12} + \frac{7}{18} - \frac{5}{6} = \frac{15}{36} + \frac{14}{36} - \frac{30}{36}$$
$$= -\frac{1}{36}$$

4. The LCD is $x(x - 1)$.

$$\frac{3}{x - 1} - \frac{1}{x} = \frac{3x}{x(x - 1)} - \frac{x - 1}{x(x - 1)}$$
$$= \frac{3x - x + 1}{x(x - 1)}$$
$$= \frac{2x + 1}{x^2 - x}$$

5. The LCD is $(2x + 1)(x - 3)$.

$$\frac{x}{2x + 1} - \frac{2}{x - 3} = \frac{x(x - 3)}{(2x + 1)(x - 3)} - \frac{2(2x + 1)}{(2x + 1)(x - 3)}$$
$$= \frac{x^2 - 3x - 4x - 2}{(2x + 1)(x - 3)}$$
$$= \frac{x^2 - 7x - 2}{(2x + 1)(x - 3)}$$

6. $x^2 - 5x + 6 = (x - 2)(x - 3)$ and
$x^2 - x - 6 = (x + 2)(x - 3)$, so the LCD is
$(x - 2)(x - 3)(x + 2)$.

$$\frac{x + 1}{x^2 - 5x + 6} - \frac{3x + 11}{x^2 - x - 6}$$

$$= \frac{(x + 1)(x + 2)}{(x - 2)(x - 3)(x + 2)} - \frac{(3x + 11)(x - 2)}{(x - 2)(x - 3)(x + 2)}$$

$$= \frac{x^2 + 3x + 2 - 3x^2 - 5x + 22}{(x - 2)(x - 3)(x + 2)}$$

$$= \frac{-2x^2 - 2x + 24}{(x - 2)(x - 3)(x + 2)}$$

$$= \frac{-2(x - 3)(x + 4)}{(x - 2)(x - 3)(x + 2)}$$

$$= \frac{-2x - 8}{(x - 2)(x + 2)}, x \neq 3$$

7. For $2x^2 - 3x - 1 = 0$: $a = 2, b = -3$, and $c = -1$.

$$x = \frac{-b \pm \sqrt{b^2 - 4ac}}{2a}$$

$$= \frac{-(-3) \pm \sqrt{(-3)^2 - 4(2)(-1)}}{2(2)}$$

$$= \frac{3 \pm \sqrt{9 - (-8)}}{4} = \frac{3 \pm \sqrt{17}}{4}$$

8. For $2x^2 - 5x - 1 = 0$: $a = 2, b = -5$, and $c = -1$.

$$x = \frac{-b \pm \sqrt{b^2 - 4ac}}{2a}$$

$$= \frac{-(-5) \pm \sqrt{(-5)^2 - 4(2)(-1)}}{2(2)}$$

$$= \frac{5 \pm \sqrt{25 - (-8)}}{4} = \frac{5 \pm \sqrt{33}}{4}$$

9. For $3x^2 + 2x - 2 = 0$: $a = 3, b = 2$, and $c = -2$.

$$x = \frac{-b \pm \sqrt{b^2 - 4ac}}{2a}$$

$$= \frac{-2 \pm \sqrt{(2)^2 - 4(3)(-2)}}{2(3)}$$

$$= \frac{-2 \pm \sqrt{4 - (-24)}}{6} = \frac{-2 \pm \sqrt{28}}{6}$$

$$= \frac{-2 \pm 2\sqrt{7}}{6} = \frac{-1 \pm \sqrt{7}}{3}$$

10. For $x^2 - 3x - 9 = 0$: $a = 1, b = -3$, and $c = -9$.

$$x = \frac{-b \pm \sqrt{b^2 - 4ac}}{2a}$$

$$= \frac{-(-3) \pm \sqrt{(-3)^2 - 4(1)(-9)}}{2(1)}$$

$$= \frac{3 \pm \sqrt{9 - (-36)}}{2} = \frac{3 \pm \sqrt{45}}{2}$$

$$= \frac{3 \pm 3\sqrt{5}}{2}$$

Section 2.7 Exercises

1. Algebraically: $\dfrac{x - 2}{3} + \dfrac{x + 5}{3} = \dfrac{1}{3}$

$$(x - 2) + (x + 5) = 1$$
$$2x + 3 = 1$$
$$2x = -2$$
$$x = -1$$

Numerically: For $x = -1$,
$$\frac{x - 2}{3} + \frac{x + 5}{3} = \frac{-1 - 2}{3} + \frac{-1 + 5}{3}$$
$$= \frac{-3}{3} + \frac{4}{3}$$
$$= \frac{1}{3}$$

2. Algebraically: $x + 2 = \dfrac{15}{x}$

$$x^2 + 2x = 15 \ (x \neq 0)$$
$$x^2 + 2x - 15 = 0$$
$$(x - 3)(x + 5) = 0$$
$$x - 3 = 0 \quad \text{or} \quad x + 5 = 0$$
$$x = 3 \quad \text{or} \quad x = -5$$

Numerically: For $x = 3$,
$x + 2 = 3 + 2 = 5$ and
$\dfrac{15}{x} = \dfrac{15}{3} = 5$.

For $x = -5$,
$x + 2 = -5 + 2 = -3$ and
$\dfrac{15}{x} = \dfrac{15}{-5} = -3$.

3. Algebraically: $x + 5 = \dfrac{14}{x}$

$$x^2 + 5x = 14 \quad (x \neq 0)$$
$$x^2 + 5x - 14 = 0$$
$$(x - 2)(x + 7) = 0$$
$$x - 2 = 0 \quad \text{or} \quad x + 7 = 0$$
$$x = 2 \quad \text{or} \quad x = -7$$

Numerically: For $x = 2$,
$x + 5 = 2 + 5 = 7$ and
$\dfrac{14}{x} = \dfrac{14}{2} = 7$.

For $x = -7$,
$x + 5 = -7 + 5 = -2$ and
$\dfrac{14}{x} = \dfrac{14}{-7} = -2$.

4. Algebraically: $\dfrac{1}{x} - \dfrac{2}{x - 3} = 4$

$$(x - 3) - 2x = 4x(x - 3) \ (x \neq 0, 3)$$
$$-x - 3 = 4x^2 - 12x$$
$$-4x^2 + 11x - 3 = 0$$

$$x = \frac{-11 \pm \sqrt{11^2 - 4(-4)(-3)}}{2(-4)}$$

$$= \frac{-11 \pm \sqrt{73}}{-8}$$

$$x = \frac{11 + \sqrt{73}}{8} \approx 2.443 \quad \text{or} \quad x = \frac{11 - \sqrt{73}}{8} \approx 0.307$$

Numerically: Use a graphing calculator to support your answers numerically.

5. Algebraically: $x + \dfrac{4x}{x-3} = \dfrac{12}{x-3}$

$x(x-3) + 4x = 12 \ (x \neq 3)$

$x^2 - 3x + 4x = 12$

$x^2 + x - 12 = 0$

$(x+4)(x-3) = 0$

$x + 4 = 0 \quad \text{or} \quad x - 3 = 0$

$x = -4 \quad \text{or} \qquad x = 3$ — but $x = 3$ is extraneous.

Numerically: For $x = -4$,

$x + \dfrac{4x}{x-3} = -4 + \dfrac{4(-4)}{-4-3} = -4 + \dfrac{16}{7} = -\dfrac{12}{7}$ and

$\dfrac{12}{x-3} = \dfrac{12}{-4-3} = -\dfrac{12}{7}$.

6. Algebraically: $\dfrac{3}{x-1} + \dfrac{2}{x} = 8$

$3x + 2(x-1) = 8x(x-1) \quad (x \neq 0, 1)$

$5x - 2 = 8x^2 - 8x$

$-8x^2 + 13x - 2 = 0$

$x = \dfrac{-13 \pm \sqrt{13^2 - 4(-8)(-2)}}{2(-8)}$

$= \dfrac{-13 \pm \sqrt{105}}{-16}$

$x = \dfrac{13 + \sqrt{105}}{16} \approx 1.453$ or $x = \dfrac{13 - \sqrt{105}}{16} \approx 0.172$

Numerically: Use a graphing calculator to support your answers numerically.

7. Algebraically: $x + \dfrac{10}{x} = 7$

$x^2 + 10 = 7x \quad (x \neq 0)$

$x^2 - 7x + 10 = 0$

$(x-2)(x-5) = 0$

$x - 2 = 0 \quad \text{or} \quad x - 5 = 0$

$x = 2 \quad \text{or} \qquad x = 5$

Graphically: The graph of $f(x) = x + \dfrac{10}{x} - 7$ suggests

that the x-intercepts are 2 and 5.

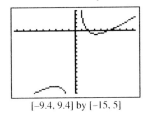

[−9.4, 9.4] by [−15, 5]

Then the solutions are $x = 2$ and $x = 5$.

8. Algebraically: $x + 2 = \dfrac{15}{x}$

$x^2 + 2x = 15 \quad (x \neq 0)$

$x^2 + 2x - 15 = 0$

$(x+5)(x-3) = 0$

$x + 5 = 0 \quad \text{or} \quad x - 3 = 0$

$x = -5 \quad \text{or} \qquad x = 3$

Graphically: The graph of $f(x) = x + 2 - \dfrac{15}{x}$ suggests

that the x-intercepts are −5 and 3.

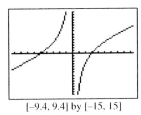

[−9.4, 9.4] by [−15, 15]

Then the solutions are $x = -5$ and $x = 3$.

9. Algebraically: $x + \dfrac{12}{x} = 7$

$x^2 + 12 = 7x \quad (x \neq 0)$

$x^2 - 7x + 12 = 0$

$(x-3)(x-4) = 0$

$x - 3 = 0 \quad \text{or} \quad x - 4 = 0$

$x = 3 \quad \text{or} \qquad x = 4$

Graphically: The graph of $f(x) = x + \dfrac{12}{x} - 7$ suggests

that the x-intercepts are 3 and 4.

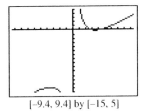

[−9.4, 9.4] by [−15, 5]

Then the solutions are $x = 3$ and $x = 4$.

10. Algebraically: $x + \dfrac{6}{x} = -7$

$x^2 + 6 = -7x \quad (x \neq 0)$

$x^2 + 7x + 6 = 0$

$(x+6)(x+1) = 0$

$x + 6 = 0 \quad \text{or} \quad x + 1 = 0$

$x = -6 \quad \text{or} \qquad x = -1$

Graphically: The graph of $f(x) = x + \dfrac{6}{x} + 7$ suggests

that the x-intercepts are −6 and −1.

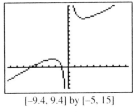

[−9.4, 9.4] by [−5, 15]

Then the solutions are $x = -6$ and $x = -1$.

11. Algebraically: $2 - \dfrac{1}{x+1} = \dfrac{1}{x^2 + x}$

$\left[\text{and } x^2 + x = x(x+1)\right]$

$2(x^2 + x) - x = 1 \quad (x \neq 0, -1)$

$2x^2 + x - 1 = 0$

$(2x-1)(x+1) = 0$

$2x - 1 = 0 \quad \text{or} \quad x + 1 = 0$

$x = \dfrac{1}{2} \quad \text{or} \qquad x = -1$

— but $x = -1$ is extraneous.

Graphically: The graph of $f(x) = 2 - \dfrac{1}{x+1} - \dfrac{1}{x^2 + x}$

suggests that the x-intercept is $\dfrac{1}{2}$. There is a hole at

$x = -1$.

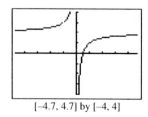

[−4.7, 4.7] by [−4, 4]

Then the solution is $x = \dfrac{1}{2}$.

12. Algebraically: $2 - \dfrac{3}{x + 4} = \dfrac{12}{x^2 + 4x}$

[and $x^2 + 4x = x(x + 4)$]

$2(x^2 + 4x) - 3x = 12 \quad (x \neq 0, -4)$

$2x^2 + 5x - 12 = 0$

$(2x - 3)(x + 4) = 0$

$2x - 3 = 0 \quad \text{or} \quad x + 4 = 0$

$x = \dfrac{3}{2} \quad \text{or} \quad x = -4$

— but $x = -4$ is extraneous.

Graphically: The graph of $f(x) = 2 - \dfrac{3}{x + 4} - \dfrac{12}{x^2 + 4x}$

suggests that the x-intercept is $\dfrac{3}{2}$. There is a hole at

$x = -4$.

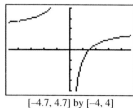

[−4.7, 4.7] by [−4, 4]

Then the solution is $x = \dfrac{3}{2}$.

13. Algebraically: $\dfrac{3x}{x + 5} + \dfrac{1}{x - 2} = \dfrac{7}{x^2 + 3x - 10}$

[and $x^2 + 3x - 10 = (x + 5)(x - 2)$]

$3x(x - 2) + (x + 5) = 7 \quad (x \neq -5, 2)$

$3x^2 - 5x - 2 = 0$

$(3x + 1)(x - 2) = 0$

$3x + 1 = 0 \quad \text{or} \quad x - 2 = 0$

$x = -\dfrac{1}{3} \quad \text{or} \quad x = 2$

— but $x = 2$ is extraneous.

Graphically: The graph of

$f(x) = \dfrac{3x}{x + 5} + \dfrac{1}{x - 2} - \dfrac{7}{x^2 + 3x - 10}$ suggests that

the x-intercept is $-\dfrac{1}{3}$. There is a hole at $x = 2$.

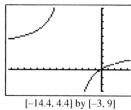

[−14.4, 4.4] by [−3, 9]

Then the solution is $x = -\dfrac{1}{3}$.

14. Algebraically: $\dfrac{4x}{x + 4} + \dfrac{3}{x - 1} = \dfrac{15}{x^2 + 3x - 4}$

[and $x^2 + 3x - 4 = (x + 4)(x - 1)$]

$4x(x - 1) + 3(x + 4) = 15 \quad (x \neq -4, 1)$

$4x^2 - x - 3 = 0$

$(4x + 3)(x - 1) = 0$

$4x + 3 = 0 \quad \text{or} \quad x - 1 = 0$

$x = -\dfrac{3}{4} \quad \text{or} \quad x = 1$

— but $x = 1$ is extraneous.

Graphically: The graph of

$f(x) = \dfrac{4x}{x + 4} + \dfrac{3}{x - 1} - \dfrac{15}{x^2 + 3x - 4}$ suggests that

the x-intercept is $-\dfrac{3}{4}$. There is a hole at $x = 1$.

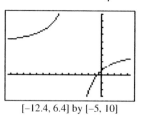

[−12.4, 6.4] by [−5, 10]

Then the solution is $x = -\dfrac{3}{4}$.

15. Algebraically: $\dfrac{x - 3}{x} - \dfrac{3}{x + 1} + \dfrac{3}{x^2 + x} = 0$

[and $x^2 + x = x(x + 1)$]

$(x - 3)(x + 1) - 3x + 3 = 0 \quad (x \neq 0, -1)$

$x^2 - 5x = 0$

$x(x - 5) = 0$

$x = 0 \quad \text{or} \quad x - 5 = 0$

$x = 0 \quad \text{or} \quad x = 5$ — but $x = 0$ is extraneous.

Graphically: The graph of

$f(x) = \dfrac{x - 3}{x} - \dfrac{3}{x + 1} + \dfrac{3}{x^2 + x}$ suggests that the

x-intercept is 5. The x-axis hides a hole at $x = 0$.

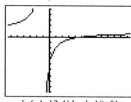

[−6.4, 12.4] by [−10, 5]

Then the solution is $x = 5$.

16. Algebraically: $\dfrac{x + 2}{x} - \dfrac{4}{x - 1} + \dfrac{2}{x^2 - x} = 0$

[and $x^2 - x = x(x - 1)$]

$(x + 2)(x - 1) - 4x + 2 = 0 \quad (x \neq 0, 1)$

$x^2 - 3x = 0$

$x(x - 3) = 0$

$x = 0 \quad \text{or} \quad x - 3 = 0$

$x = 0 \quad \text{or} \quad x = 3$ — but $x = 0$ is extraneous.

Graphically: The graph of

$$f(x) = \frac{x+2}{x} - \frac{4}{x-1} + \frac{2}{x^2 - x}$$

suggests that the x-intercept is 3. The x-axis hides a hole at $x = 0$.

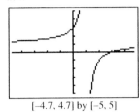

[−4.7, 4.7] by [−5, 5]

Then the solution is $x = 3$.

17. Algebraically: $\dfrac{3}{x+2} + \dfrac{6}{x^2 + 2x} = \dfrac{3-x}{x}$

[and $x^2 + 2x = x(x+2)$]

$3x + 6 = (3-x)(x+2)$ $(x \neq -2, 0)$

$3x + 6 = -x^2 + x + 6$

$x^2 + 2x = 0$

$x(x+2) = 0$

$x = 0$ or $x + 2 = 0$

$x = 0$ or $x = -2$

— but both solutions are extraneous.

No real solutions.

Graphically: The graph of

$$f(x) = \frac{3}{x+2} + \frac{6}{x^2 + 2x} - \frac{3-x}{x}$$ suggests that there

are no x-intercepts. There is a hole at $x = -2$, and the x-axis hides a "hole" at $x = 0$.

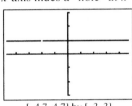

[−4.7, 4.7] by [−3, 3]

Then there are no real solutions.

18. Algebraically: $\dfrac{x+3}{x} - \dfrac{2}{x+3} = \dfrac{6}{x^2 + 3x}$

[and $x^2 + 3x = x(x+3)$]

$(x+3)^2 - 2x = 6$ $(x \neq -3, 0)$

$x^2 + 4x + 3 = 0$

$(x+1)(x+3) = 0$

$x + 1 = 0$ or $x + 3 = 0$

$x = -1$ or $x = -3$

— but $x = -3$ is extraneous.

Graphically: The graph of

$$f(x) = \frac{x+3}{x} - \frac{2}{x+3} - \frac{6}{x^2 + 3x}$$

suggests that the x-intercept is -1. There is a hole at $x = -3$.

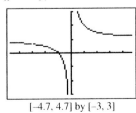

[−4.7, 4.7] by [−3, 3]

Then the solution is $x = -3$.

19. There is no x-intercept at $x = -2$. That is the extraneous solution.

20. There is no x-intercept at $x = 3$. That is the extraneous solution.

21. Neither possible solution corresponds to an x-intercept of the graph. Both are extraneous.

22. There is no x-intercept at $x = 3$. That is the extraneous solution.

23. $\dfrac{2}{x-1} + x = 5$

$2 + x(x-1) = 5(x-1)$ $(x \neq 1)$

$x^2 - x + 2 = 5x - 5$

$x^2 - 6x + 7 = 0$

$x = \dfrac{-(-6) \pm \sqrt{(-6)^2 - 4(1)(7)}}{2(1)}$

$x = \dfrac{6 \pm \sqrt{8}}{2} = 3 \pm \sqrt{2}$

$x = 3 + \sqrt{2} \approx 4.414$ or

$x = 3 - \sqrt{2} \approx 1.586$

24. $\dfrac{x^2 - 6x + 5}{x^2 - 2} = 3$

$x^2 - 6x + 5 = 3(x^2 - 2)$ $(x \neq \pm\sqrt{2})$

$-2x^2 - 6x + 11 = 0$

$x = \dfrac{-(-6) \pm \sqrt{(-6)^2 - 4(-2)(11)}}{2(-2)}$

$x = \dfrac{6 \pm \sqrt{124}}{-4} = \dfrac{-3 \pm \sqrt{31}}{2}$

$x = \dfrac{-3 + \sqrt{31}}{2} \approx 1.284$ or

$x = \dfrac{-3 - \sqrt{31}}{2} \approx -4.284$

25. $\dfrac{x^2 - 2x + 1}{x + 5} = 0$

$x^2 - 2x + 1 = 0$ $(x \neq 5)$

$(x-1)^2 = 0$

$x - 1 = 0$

$x = 1$

26. $\dfrac{3x}{x+2} + \dfrac{2}{x-1} = \dfrac{5}{x^2 + x - 2}$

[and $x^2 + x - 2 = (x+2)(x-1)$]

$3x(x-1) + 2(x+2) = 5$ $(x \neq -2, 1)$

$3x^2 - x - 1 = 0$

$x = \dfrac{-(-1) \pm \sqrt{(-1)^2 - 4(3)(-1)}}{2(3)}$

$x = \dfrac{1 \pm \sqrt{13}}{6}$

$x = \dfrac{1 + \sqrt{13}}{6} \approx 0.768$ or

$x = \dfrac{1 - \sqrt{13}}{6} \approx -0.434$

27. $\dfrac{4x}{x + 4} + \dfrac{5}{x - 1} = \dfrac{15}{x^2 + 3x - 4}$

[and $x^2 + 3x - 4 = (x + 4)(x - 1)$]

$4x(x - 1) + 5(x + 4) = 15 \quad (x \neq -4, 1)$

$\qquad 4x^2 + x + 5 = 0$

The discriminant is $b^2 - 4ac = 1^2 - 4(4)(5) = -79 < 0$.
There are no real solutions.

28. $\dfrac{3x}{x + 1} + \dfrac{5}{x - 2} = \dfrac{15}{x^2 - x - 2}$

[and $x^2 - x - 2 = (x + 1)(x - 2)$]

$3x(x - 2) + 5(x + 1) = 15 \quad (x \neq -1, 2)$

$\qquad 3x^2 - x - 10 = 0$

$\qquad (3x + 5)(x - 2) = 0$

$\qquad 3x + 5 = 0 \quad$ or $\quad x - 2 = 0$

$\qquad x = -\dfrac{5}{3} \quad$ or $\qquad x = 2$

— but $x = 2$ is extraneous.

The solution is $x = -\dfrac{5}{3}$.

29. $x^2 + \dfrac{5}{x} = 8$

$x^3 + 5 = 8x \quad (x \neq 0)$

Using a graphing calculator to find the x-intercepts of
$f(x) = x^3 - 8x + 5$ yields the solutions
$x \approx -3.100$, $x \approx 0.661$, and $x \approx 2.439$.

30. $x^2 - \dfrac{3}{x} = 7$

$x^3 - 3 = 7x \quad (x \neq 0)$

Using a graphing calculator to find the x-intercepts of
$f(x) = x^3 - 7x - 3$ yields the solutions
$x \approx -2.398$, $x \approx -0.441$, and $x \approx 2.838$.

31. (a) The total amount of solution is $(125 + x)$ mL; of this,
the amount of acid is x plus 60% of the original
amount, or $x + 0.6(125)$.

(b) $y = 0.83$

(c) $C(x) = \dfrac{x + 75}{x + 125} = 0.83$. Multiply both sides by
$x + 125$, then rearrange to get $0.17x = 28.75$, so that
$x \approx 169.12$ mL.

32. (a) $C(x) = \dfrac{x + 0.35(100)}{x + 100} = \dfrac{x + 35}{x + 100}$

(b) Graph $C(x)$ along with $y = 0.75$; observe where
the first graph intersects the second.

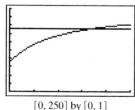

[0, 250] by [0, 1]

For $x = 160$, $C(x) = 0.75$. Use 160 mL.

(c) Starting from $\dfrac{x + 35}{x + 100} = 0.75$, multiply by $x + 100$
and rearrange to get $0.25x = 40$, so that $x = 160$ mL
That is how much pure acid must be added.

33. (a) $C(x) = \dfrac{3000 + 2.12x}{x}$

(b) A profit is realized if $C(x) < 2.75$, or
$3000 + 2.12x < 2.75x$. Then $3000 < 0.63x$,
so that $x > 4761.9$—4762 hats per week.

(c) They must have $2.75x - (3000 + 2.12x) > 1000$ or
$0.63x > 4000$: 6350 hats per week.

34. (a) $P(10) = 200$, $P(40) = 350$, $P(100) = 425$

(b) As $t \to \infty$, $P(t) \to 500$. So, yes. The horizontal asymptote is $y = 500$.

(c) $\displaystyle\lim_{t \to \infty} P(t) = \lim_{t \to \infty}\left(500 - \dfrac{9000}{t + 20}\right) = 500$, so the bear
population will never exceed 500.

35. (a) If x is the length, then $182/x$ is the width.

$$P(x) = 2x + 2\left(\dfrac{182}{x}\right) = 2x + \dfrac{364}{x}$$

(b) The graph of $P(x) = 2x + 364/x$ has a minimum
when $x \approx 13.49$, so that the rectangle is square. Then
$P(13.49) = 2(13.49) + 364/13.49 \approx 53.96$ ft.

36. (a)

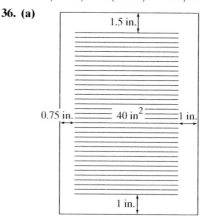

The height of the print material is $40/x$. The total
area is

$$A(x) = (x + 0.75 + 1)\left(\dfrac{40}{x} + 1.5 + 1\right)$$

$$= (x + 1.75)\left(\dfrac{40}{x} + 2.5\right)$$

(b) The graph of $A(x) = (x + 1.75)\left(\dfrac{40}{x} + 2.5\right)$
has a minimum when $x \approx 5.29$, so the dimensions
are about $5.29 + 1.75 = 7.04$ in. wide by
$40/5.29 + 2.5 \approx 10.06$ in. high. And
$A(5.29) \approx 70.8325$ in.^{2}

37. (a) Since $V = \pi r^2 h$, the height here is $V/(\pi r^2)$. And
since in general, $S = 2\pi r^2 + 2\pi r h = 2\pi r^2 + 2V/r$,
here $S(x) = 2\pi x^2 + 1000/x$
$(0.5 \, L = 500 \text{ cm}^3)$.

(b) Solving $2\pi x^2 + 1000/x = 900$ graphically by finding
the zeros of $f(x) = 2\pi x^2 + 1000/x - 900$ yields two
solutions: either $x \approx 1.12$ cm, in which case
$h \approx 126.88$ cm, or $x \approx 11.37$ cm, in which case
$h \approx 1.23$ cm.

38. (a) If x is the length, then $1000/x$ is the width. The total area is $A(x) = (x + 4)(1000/x + 4)$.

(b) The least area comes when the pool is square, so that $x = \sqrt{1000} \approx 31.62$ ft. With dimensions 35.62 ft $\times$ 35.62 ft for the plot of land, $A(31.62) \approx 1268.98$ ft^2.

39. (a)
$$\frac{1}{R} = \frac{1}{R_1} + \frac{1}{R_2}$$
$$\frac{1}{R} = \frac{1}{2.3} + \frac{1}{x}$$
$$2.3x = xR + 2.3R$$
$$R(x) = \frac{2.3x}{x + 2.3}$$

(b) $2.3x = xR + 2.3R$
$$x = \frac{2.3R}{2.3 - R}$$
For $R = 1.7$, $x \approx 6.52$ ohms.

40. (a) If x is the length, then $200/x$ is the width.
$$P(x) = 2x + 2\left(\frac{200}{x}\right) = 2x + \frac{400}{x}$$

(b) $70 = 2x + \dfrac{400}{x}$
$$70x = 2x^2 + 400$$
$$2x^2 - 70x + 400 = 0$$
The quadratic formula gives
$x \approx 7.1922$ or $x \approx 27.8078$.
When one of those values is considered as the length, the other is the width. The dimensions are 7.1922 m $\times$ 27.8078 m.

41. (a) Drain A can drain 1/4.75 of the pool per hour, while drain B can drain $1/t$ of the pool per hour. Together, they can drain a fraction
$$D(t) = \frac{1}{4.75} + \frac{1}{t} = \frac{t + 4.75}{4.75t}$$
of the pool in 1 hour.

(b) The information implies that $D(t) = 1/2.6$, so we solve
$$\frac{1}{2.6} = \frac{1}{4.75} + \frac{1}{t}.$$
Graphically: The function $f(t) = \dfrac{1}{2.6} - \dfrac{1}{4.75} - \dfrac{1}{t}$ has a zero at $t \approx 5.74$ h, so that is the solution.

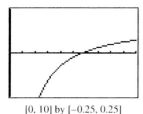

[0, 10] by [−0.25, 0.25]

Algebraically: $\dfrac{1}{2.6} = \dfrac{1}{4.75} + \dfrac{1}{t}$
$$4.75t = 2.6t + 2.6(4.75)$$
$$t = \frac{2.6\,(4.75)}{4.75 - 2.6}$$
$$\approx 5.74$$

42. (a) With x as the bike speed, $x + 43$ is the car speed. Biking time = $17/x$ and driving time = $53/(x + 43)$, so
$$T = \frac{17}{x} + \frac{53}{x + 43}.$$

(b) Graphically: The function $f(x) = \dfrac{5}{3} - \dfrac{17}{x} - \dfrac{53}{x + 43}$ has a zero at $x \approx 20.45$.

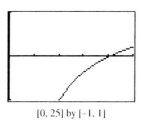

[0, 25] by [−1, 1]

Algebraically: 1 h 40 min $= 1\dfrac{2}{3}$ h $= \dfrac{5}{3}$ h
$$\frac{5}{3} = \frac{17}{x} + \frac{53}{x + 43}$$
$$5x(x + 43) = 51(x + 43) + 159x$$
$$5x^2 + 215x = 51x + 2193 + 159x$$
$$5x^2 + 5x - 2193 = 0$$
Using the quadratic formula and selecting the positive solution yields
$$x = \frac{-5 + \sqrt{43{,}885}}{10} \approx 20.45.$$
The rate of the bike was about 20.45 mph.

43. (a)

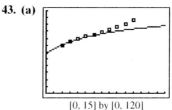

[0, 15] by [0, 120]

(b) When $x = 15$, $y = 120 - 500/(15 + 8) \approx 98.3$. In 2005, sales are estimated at about \$98.3 billion.

44. (a)

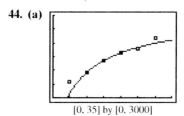

[0, 35] by [0, 3000]

(b) When $x = 35$, $y = 3000 - 39{,}500/(35 + 9) \approx 2102$. In 2005, the number of wineries is estimated to be 2102.

45. False. An extraneous solution is a value that, though generated by the solution-finding process, does not work in the original equation. In an equation containing rational expressions, an extraneous solution is typically a solution to the version of the equation that has been cleared of fractions but not to the original version.

46. True. For a fraction to equal zero, the numerator has to be zero, and 1 is not zero.

47. $x - \dfrac{3x}{x+2} = \dfrac{6}{x+2}$

$x(x+2) - 3x = 6 \quad (x \neq -2)$

$x^2 - x - 6 = 0$

$(x-3)(x+2) = 0$

$x = 3$ or $x = -2$ — but $x = -2$ is extraneous.

The answer is D.

48. $1 - \dfrac{3}{x} = \dfrac{6}{x^2 + 2x}$ [and $x^2 + 2x = x(x+2)$]

$x^2 + 2x - 3(x+2) = 6 \quad (x \neq -2, 0)$

$x^2 - x - 12 = 0$

$(x+3)(x-4) = 0$

$x = -3$ or $x = 4$

The answer is C.

49. $\dfrac{x}{x+2} + \dfrac{2}{x-5} = \dfrac{14}{x^2 - 3x - 10}$

[and $x^2 - 3x - 10 = (x+2)(x-5)$]

$x(x-5) + 2(x+2) = 14 \quad (x \neq -2, 5)$

$x^2 - 3x - 10 = 0$

$(x+2)(x-5) = 0$

$x = -2$ or $x = 5$ — but both solutions are extraneous.

The answer is E.

50. 0.2×10 or $2 =$ liters of pure acid in 20% solution

0.30×30 or $9 =$ liters of pure acid in 30% solution

$\dfrac{\text{L of pure acid}}{\text{L of mixture}} =$ concentration of acid

$\dfrac{2+9}{10+30} = \dfrac{11}{40} = 0.275 = 27.5\%$

The answer is D.

51. (a) The LCD is $x^2 + 2x = x(x+2)$.

$f(x) = \dfrac{x-3}{x} + \dfrac{3}{x+2} + \dfrac{6}{x^2 + 2x}$

$= \dfrac{(x-3)(x+2)}{x^2 + 2x} + \dfrac{3x}{x^2 + 2x} + \dfrac{6}{x^2 + 2x}$

$= \dfrac{x^2 - x - 6 + 3x + 6}{x^2 + 2x}$

$= \dfrac{x^2 + 2x}{x^2 + 2x}$

(b) All $x \neq 0, -2$

(c) $f(x) = \begin{cases} 1 & x \neq -2, 0 \\ \text{undefined} & x = -2 \text{ or } x = 0 \end{cases}$

(d) The graph appears to be the horizontal line $y = 1$ with holes at $x = -2$ and $x = 0$.

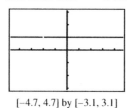

$[-4.7, 4.7]$ by $[-3.1, 3.1]$

This matches the definition in part (c).

52. $y = 1 + \dfrac{1}{1+x}$

$y(1+x) = (1+x) + 1$

$y + xy = x + 2$

$xy - x = 2 - y$

$x = \dfrac{2-y}{y-1}$

53. $y = 1 - \dfrac{1}{1-x}$

$y(1-x) = (1-x) - 1$

$y - xy = -x$

$y = xy - x$

$x = \dfrac{y}{y-1}$

54. $y = 1 + \dfrac{1}{1 + \dfrac{1}{x}}$

$y = 1 + \dfrac{x}{1+x}$

$y(1+x) = (1+x) + x$

$y + xy = 2x + 1$

$xy - 2x = 1 - y$

$x = \dfrac{1-y}{y-2}$

55. $y = 1 + \dfrac{1}{1 + \dfrac{1}{1-x}}$

$y = 1 + \dfrac{1-x}{1-x+1}$

$y = 1 + \dfrac{1-x}{2-x}$

$y(2-x) = (2-x) + (1-x)$

$2y - xy = 3 - 2x$

$2y - 3 = xy - 2x$

$x = \dfrac{2y-3}{y-2}$

■ Section 2.8 Solving Inequalities in One Variable

Exploration 1

1. (a)

$(+)(-)(+)$	$(+)(-)(+)$	$(+)(+)(+)$
Negative	Negative	Positive $\ x$

$-3 \qquad 2$

(b)

$[-5, 5]$ by $[-250, 50]$

2. (a)

$(-)(+)(-)(+)$	$(-)(+)(-)(+)$	$(-)(+)(+)(+)$
Positive	Positive	Negative $\ x$

$-2 \qquad -1$

(b)

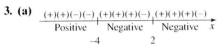

$[-3, 1]$ by $[-30, 20]$

3. (a)

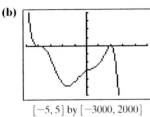

$$\underset{-4 \qquad\quad 2}{\underset{\text{Positive} \quad\; \text{Negative} \quad\; \text{Negative} \;\; x}{\overset{(+)(+)(-)(-) \;\;\; (+)(+)(+)(-) \;\;\; (+)(+)(+)(-)}{\rule{6cm}{0.4pt}}}}$$

(b)

$[-5, 5]$ by $[-3000, 2000]$

Quick Review 2.8

1. $\lim\limits_{x \to \infty} f(x) = \infty, \; \lim\limits_{x \to -\infty} f(x) = -\infty$

2. $\lim\limits_{x \to \infty} f(x) = -\infty, \; \lim\limits_{x \to -\infty} f(x) = -\infty$

3. $\lim\limits_{x \to \infty} g(x) = \infty, \; \lim\limits_{x \to -\infty} g(x) = \infty$

4. $\lim\limits_{x \to \infty} g(x) = \infty, \; \lim\limits_{x \to -\infty} g(x) = -\infty$

5. $\dfrac{x^3 + 5}{x}$

6. $\dfrac{x^3 - 3}{x}$

7. $\dfrac{x(x - 3) - 2(2x + 1)}{(2x + 1)(x - 3)} = \dfrac{x^2 - 3x - 4x - 2}{(2x + 1)(x - 3)}$

$= \dfrac{x^2 - 7x - 2}{(2x + 1)(x - 3)} = \dfrac{x^2 - 7x - 2}{2x^2 - 5x - 3}$

8. $\dfrac{x(3x - 4) + (x + 1)(x - 1)}{(x - 1)(3x - 4)} = \dfrac{3x^2 - 4x + x^2 - 1}{(x - 1)(3x - 4)}$

$= \dfrac{4x^2 - 4x - 1}{(x - 1)(3x - 4)} = \dfrac{4x^2 - 4x - 1}{3x^2 - 7x + 4}$

9. (a) $\dfrac{\pm 1, \; \pm 3}{\pm 1, \; \pm 2}$ or $\pm 1, \; \pm\dfrac{1}{2}, \; \pm 3, \; \pm\dfrac{3}{2}$

(b) A graph suggests that -1 and $\dfrac{3}{2}$ are good candidates for zeros.

$$\begin{array}{r|rrrr} \underline{-1} & 2 & 1 & -4 & -3 \\ & & -2 & 1 & 3 \\ \hline \underline{3/2} & 2 & -1 & -3 & 0 \\ & & 3 & 3 \\ \hline & 2 & 2 & 0 \end{array}$$

$2x^3 + x^2 - 4x - 3 = (x + 1)\left(x - \dfrac{3}{2}\right)(2x + 2)$

$= (x + 1)(2x - 3)(x + 1)$

10. (a) $\dfrac{\pm 1, \; \pm 2, \; \pm 4, \; \pm 8}{\pm 1, \; \pm 3}$

or $\pm 1, \; \pm\dfrac{1}{3}, \; \pm 2, \; \pm\dfrac{2}{3}, \; \pm 4, \; \pm\dfrac{4}{3}, \; \pm 8, \; \pm\dfrac{8}{3}$

(b) A graph suggests that -2 and 1 are good candidates for zeros.

$$\begin{array}{r|rrrr} \underline{-2} & 3 & -1 & -10 & 8 \\ & & -6 & 14 & -8 \\ \hline \underline{1} & 3 & -7 & 4 & 0 \\ & & 3 & -4 \\ \hline & 3 & -4 & 0 \end{array}$$

$3x^2 - x^2 - 10x + 8 = (x + 2)(x - 1)(3x - 4)$

Section 2.8 Exercises

1. (a) $f(x) = 0$ when $x = -2, -1, 5$

(b) $f(x) > 0$ when $-2 < x < -1$ or $x > 5$

(c) $f(x) < 0$ when $x < -2$ or $-1 < x < 5$

$$\underset{-2 \qquad\;\; -1 \qquad\quad\;\; 5}{\underset{\text{Negative} \; \text{Positive} \; \text{Negative} \; \text{Positive} \;\; x}{\overset{(-)(-)(-) \;\; (+)(-)(-) \;\; (+)(+)(-) \;\; (+)(+)(+)}{\rule{6cm}{0.4pt}}}}$$

2. (a) $f(x) = 0$ when $x = 7, -\dfrac{1}{3}, -4$

(b) $f(x) > 0$ when $-4 < x < -\dfrac{1}{3}$ or $x > 7$

(c) $f(x) < 0$ when $x < -4$ or $-\dfrac{1}{3} < x < 7$

$$\underset{-4 \qquad\;\; -\frac{1}{3} \qquad\quad 7}{\underset{\text{Negative} \; \text{Positive} \; \text{Negative} \; \text{Positive} \;\; x}{\overset{(-)(-)(-) \;\; (-)(-)(+) \;\; (-)(+)(+) \;\; (+)(+)(+)}{\rule{6cm}{0.4pt}}}}$$

3. (a) $f(x) = 0$ when $x = -7, -4, 6$

(b) $f(x) > 0$ when $x < -7$ or $-4 < x < 6$ or $x > 6$

(c) $f(x) < 0$ when $-7 < x < -4$

$$\underset{-7 \qquad\;\; -4 \qquad\quad 6}{\underset{\text{Positive} \; \text{Negative} \; \text{Positive} \; \text{Positive} \;\; x}{\overset{(-)(-)(-)^2 \;\; (+)(-)(-)^2 \;\; (+)(+)(-)^2 \;\; (+)(+)(+)^2}{\rule{6cm}{0.4pt}}}}$$

4. (a) $f(x) = 0$ when $x = -\dfrac{3}{5}, 1$

(b) $f(x) > 0$ when $x < -\dfrac{3}{5}$ or $x > 1$

(c) $f(x) < 0$ when $-\dfrac{3}{5} < x < 1$

$$\underset{-\frac{3}{5} \qquad\qquad 1}{\underset{\text{Positive} \qquad \text{Negative} \qquad \text{Positive} \;\; x}{\overset{(-)(+)(-) \qquad (+)(+)(-) \qquad (+)(+)(+)}{\rule{6cm}{0.4pt}}}}$$

5. (a) $f(x) = 0$ when $x = 8, -1$

(b) $f(x) > 0$ when $-1 < x < 8$ or $x > 8$

(c) $f(x) < 0$ when $x < -1$

$$\underset{-1 \qquad\qquad 8}{\underset{\text{Negative} \qquad \text{Positive} \qquad \text{Positive} \;\; x}{\overset{(+)(-)^2(-)^3 \quad (+)(-)^2(+)^3 \quad (+)(+)^2(+)^3}{\rule{6cm}{0.4pt}}}}$$

6. (a) $f(x) = 0$ when $x = -2, 9$

(b) $f(x) > 0$ when $-2 < x < 9$ or $x > 9$

(c) $f(x) < 0$ when $x < -2$

$$\begin{array}{c|c|c} \underset{\text{Negative}}{(-)^3(+)(-)^4} & \underset{\text{Positive}}{(+)^3(+)(-)^4} & \underset{\text{Positive}}{(+)^3(+)(+)^4} \\ \hline -2 & & 9 \end{array} \longrightarrow x$$

7. $(x + 1)(x - 3)^2 = 0$ when $x = -1, 3$

$$\begin{array}{c|c|c} \underset{\text{Negative}}{(-)(-)^2} & \underset{\text{Positive}}{(+)(-)^2} & \underset{\text{Positive}}{(+)(+)^2} \\ \hline -1 & & 3 \end{array} \longrightarrow x$$

By the sign chart, the solution of $(x + 1)(x - 3)^2 > 0$ is $(-1, 3) \cup (3, \infty)$.

8. $(2x + 1)(x - 2)(3x - 4) = 0$ when $x = -\dfrac{1}{2}, 2, \dfrac{4}{3}$

$$\begin{array}{c|c|c|c} \underset{\text{Negative}}{(-)(-)(-)} & \underset{\text{Positive}}{(+)(-)(-)} & \underset{\text{Negative}}{(+)(-)(+)} & \underset{\text{Positive}}{(+)(+)(+)} \\ \hline -\frac{1}{2} & \frac{4}{3} & 2 \end{array} \longrightarrow x$$

By the sign chart, the solution of

$(2x + 1)(x - 2)(3x - 4) \le 0$ is $\left(-\infty, -\dfrac{1}{2}\right] \cup \left[\dfrac{4}{3}, 2\right]$.

9. $(x + 1)(x^2 - 3x + 2) = (x + 1)(x - 1)(x - 2) = 0$ when $x = -1, 1, 2$

$$\begin{array}{c|c|c|c} \underset{\text{Negative}}{(-)(-)(-)} & \underset{\text{Positive}}{(+)(-)(-)} & \underset{\text{Negative}}{(+)(+)(-)} & \underset{\text{Positive}}{(+)(+)(+)} \\ \hline -1 & 1 & 2 \end{array} \longrightarrow x$$

By the sign chart, the solution of

$(x + 1)(x - 1)(x - 2) < 0$ is $(-\infty, -1) \cup (1, 2)$.

10. $(2x - 7)(x^2 - 4x + 4) = (2x - 7)(x - 2)^2 = 0$ when

$x = \dfrac{7}{2}, 2$

$$\begin{array}{c|c|c} \underset{\text{Negative}}{(-)(-)^2} & \underset{\text{Negative}}{(-)(+)^2} & \underset{\text{Positive}}{(+)(+)^2} \\ \hline 2 & \frac{7}{2} \end{array} \longrightarrow x$$

By the sign chart, the solution of $(2x - 7)(x - 2)^2 > 0$

is $\left(\dfrac{7}{2}, \infty\right)$.

11. By the Rational Zeros Theorem, the possible rational

zeros are $\pm 1, \pm\dfrac{1}{2}, \pm 2, \pm 3, \pm\dfrac{3}{2}, \pm 6$. A graph

suggests that $-2, \dfrac{1}{2}$, and 3 are good candidates to be zeros.

$$\begin{array}{r|rrrr} -2 & 2 & -3 & -11 & 6 \\ & & -4 & 14 & -6 \\ \hline 3 & 2 & -7 & 3 & 0 \\ & & 6 & -3 & \\ \hline & 2 & -1 & 0 & \end{array}$$

$2x^3 - 3x^2 - 11x + 6 = (x + 2)(x - 3)(2x - 1) = 0$

when $x = -2, 3, \dfrac{1}{2}$

$$\begin{array}{c|c|c|c} \underset{\text{Negative}}{(-)(-)(-)} & \underset{\text{Positive}}{(+)(-)(-)} & \underset{\text{Negative}}{(+)(-)(+)} & \underset{\text{Positive}}{(+)(+)(+)} \\ \hline -2 & \frac{1}{2} & 3 \end{array} \longrightarrow x$$

By the sign chart, the solution of

$(x + 2)(x - 3)(2x - 1) \ge 0$ is $\left[-2, \dfrac{1}{2}\right] \cup [3, \infty)$.

12. By the Rational Zeros Theorem, the possible rational zeros are $\pm 1, \pm 2, \pm 3, \pm 6$. A graph suggests that -1, 2, and 3 are good candidates to be zeros.

$$\begin{array}{r|rrrr} -1 & 1 & -4 & 1 & 6 \\ & & -1 & 5 & -6 \\ \hline 2 & 1 & -5 & 6 & 0 \\ & & 2 & -6 & \\ \hline & 1 & -3 & 0 & \end{array}$$

$x^3 - 4x^2 + x + 6 = (x + 1)(x - 2)(x - 3) = 0$

when $x = -1, 2, 3$.

$$\begin{array}{c|c|c|c} \underset{\text{Negative}}{(-)(-)(-)} & \underset{\text{Positive}}{(+)(-)(-)} & \underset{\text{Negative}}{(+)(+)(-)} & \underset{\text{Positive}}{(+)(+)(+)} \\ \hline -1 & 2 & 3 \end{array} \longrightarrow x$$

By the sign chart, the solution of

$(x + 1)(x - 2)(x - 3) \le 0$ is $(-\infty, -1] \cup [2, 3]$.

13. The zeros of $f(x) = x^3 - x^2 - 2x$ appear to be $-1, 0$, and 2. Substituting these values into f confirms this. The graph shows that the solution of $x^3 - x^2 - 2x \ge 0$ is $[-1, 0] \cup [2, \infty)$.

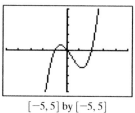

$[-5, 5]$ by $[-5, 5]$

14. The zeros of $f(x) = 2x^3 - 5x^2 + 3x$ appear to be $0, 1$,

and $\dfrac{3}{2}$. Substituting these values into f confirms this.

The graph shows that the solution of $2x^3 - 5x^2 + 3x < 0$

is $(-\infty, 0) \cup \left(1, \dfrac{3}{2}\right)$.

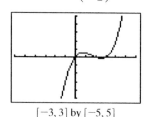

$[-3, 3]$ by $[-5, 5]$

15. The zeros of $f(x) = 2x^3 - 5x^2 - x + 6$ appear to be

$-1, \dfrac{3}{2}$ and 2. Substituting these values into f confirms this.

The graph shows that the solution of

$2x^3 - 5x^2 - x + 6 > 0$ is $\left(-1, \dfrac{3}{2}\right) \cup (2, \infty)$.

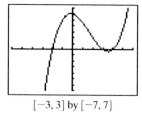

$[-3, 3]$ by $[-7, 7]$

16. The zeros of $f(x) = x^3 - 4x^2 - x + 4$ appear to be -1, 1, and 4. Substituting these values into f confirms this. The graph shows that the solution of $x^3 - 4x^2 - x + 4 \le 0$ is $(-\infty, -1] \cup [1, 4]$.

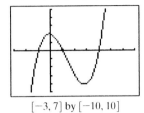

$[-3, 7]$ by $[-10, 10]$

17. The only zero of $f(x) = 3x^3 - 2x^2 - x + 6$ is found graphically to be $x \approx -1.15$. The graph shows that the solution of $3x^3 - 2x^2 - x + 6 \ge 0$ is approximately $[-1.15, \infty)$.

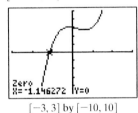

$[-3, 3]$ by $[-10, 10]$

18. The only zero of $f(x) = -x^3 - 3x^2 - 9x + 4$ is found graphically to be $x \approx 0.39$. The graph shows that the solution of $-x^3 - 3x^2 - 9x + 4 < 0$ is approximately $(0.39, \infty)$.

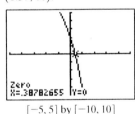

$[-5, 5]$ by $[-10, 10]$

19. The zeros of $f(x) = 2x^4 - 3x^3 - 6x^2 + 5x + 6$ appear to be -1, $\dfrac{3}{2}$, and 2. Substituting these into f confirms this. The graph shows that the solution of
$2x^4 - 3x^3 - 6x^2 + 5x + 6 < 0$ is $\left(\dfrac{3}{2}, 2\right)$.

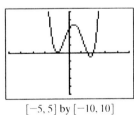

$[-5, 5]$ by $[-10, 10]$

20. The zero of $f(x) = 3x^4 - 5x^3 - 12x^2 + 12x + 16$ appear to be $-\dfrac{4}{3}$, -1, and 2. Substituting these into f confirms this. The graph shows that the solution of $3x^4 - 5x^3 - 12x^2 + 12x + 16 \ge 0$ is
$\left(-\infty, -\dfrac{4}{3}\right] \cup [-1, \infty)$.

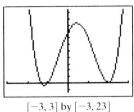

$[-3, 3]$ by $[-3, 23]$

21. $f(x) = (x^2 + 4)(2x^2 + 3)$

   (a) The solution is $(-\infty, \infty)$, because both factors of $f(x)$ are always positive.

   (b) $(-\infty, \infty)$, for the same reason as in part (a).

   (c) There are no solutions, because both factors of $f(x)$ are always positive.

   (d) There are no solutions, for the same reason as in part (c).

22. $f(x) = (x^2 + 1)(-2 - 3x^2)$

   (a) There are no solutions, because $x^2 + 1$ is always positive and $-2 - 3x^2$ is always negative.

   (b) There are no solutions, for the same reason as in part (a).

   (c) $(-\infty, \infty)$, because $x^2 + 1$ is always positive and $-2 - 3x^2$ is always negative.

   (d) $(-\infty, \infty)$, for the same reason as in part (c).

23. $f(x) = (2x^2 - 2x + 5)(3x - 4)^2$
The first factor is always positive because the leading term has a positive coefficient and the discriminant $(-2)^2 - 4(2)(5) = -36$ is negative. The only zero is $x = 4/3$, with multiplicity two, since that is the solution for $3x - 4 = 0$.

   (a) True for all $x \ne \dfrac{4}{3}$

   (b) $(-\infty, \infty)$

   (c) There are no solutions.

   (d) $x = \dfrac{4}{3}$

24. $f(x) = (x^2 + 4)(3 - 2x)^2$
The first factor is always positive. The only zero is $x = 3/2$, with multiplicity two, since that is the solution for $3 - 2x = 0$.

   (a) True for all $x \ne \dfrac{3}{2}$

   (b) $(-\infty, \infty)$

   (c) There are no solutions.

   (d) $x = \dfrac{3}{2}$

25. (a) $f(x) = 0$ when $x = 1$

   (b) $f(x)$ is undefined when $x = -\dfrac{3}{2}$, 4

   (c) $f(x) > 0$ when $-\dfrac{3}{2} < x < 1$ or $x > 4$

   (d) $f(x) < 0$ when $x < -\dfrac{3}{2}$ or $1 < x < 4$

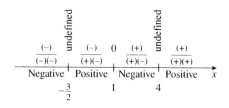

26. **(a)** $f(x) = 0$ when $x = \dfrac{7}{2}, -1$

(b) $f(x)$ is undefined when $x = -5$

(c) $f(x) > 0$ when $-5 < x < -1$ or $x > \dfrac{7}{2}$

(d) $f(x) < 0$ when $x < -5$ or $-1 < x < \dfrac{7}{2}$

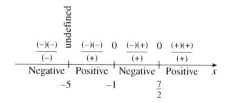

27. **(a)** $f(x) = 0$ when $x = 0, -3$

(b) $f(x)$ is undefined when $x < -3$

(c) $f(x) > 0$ when $x > 0$

(d) $f(x) < 0$ when $-3 < x < 0$

$$\begin{array}{c}
\quad\;\; 0 \qquad\quad 0 \\
\hline
\;\;\;\;\;\;\;\;\;\;\;\dfrac{(-)(+)}{} \quad \dfrac{(+)(+)}{} \\
\text{Undefined} \;\; \text{Negative} \quad \text{Positive} \quad x \\
\qquad\quad -3 \qquad\quad 0
\end{array}$$

28. **(a)** $f(x) = 0$ when $x = 0, -\dfrac{9}{2}$

(b) None. $f(x)$ is never undefined

(c) $f(x) > 0$ when $x \neq -\dfrac{9}{2}, 0$

(d) None. $f(x)$ is never negative

$$\begin{array}{c}
\dfrac{(-)^2|-|}{} \quad 0 \quad \dfrac{(-)^2|+|}{} \quad 0 \quad \dfrac{(+)^2|+|}{} \\
\text{Positive} \quad\; \text{Positive} \quad\;\; \text{Positive} \quad x \\
\quad -\dfrac{9}{2} \qquad\qquad 0
\end{array}$$

29. **(a)** $f(x) = 0$ when $x = -5$

(b) $f(x)$ is undefined when $x = -\dfrac{1}{2}, x = 1, x < -5$

(c) $f(x) > 0$ when $-5 < x < -\dfrac{1}{2}$ or $x > 1$

(d) $f(x) < 0$ when $-\dfrac{1}{2} < x < 1$

$$\begin{array}{c}
\;\;\; 0 \quad (+) \qquad (+) \qquad\quad (+) \\
\hline
\qquad\quad \dfrac{}{(-)(-)} \quad \dfrac{}{(+)(-)} \quad \dfrac{}{(+)(+)} \\
\text{Undefined} \; \text{Positive} \;\; \text{Negative} \;\; \text{Positive} \; x \\
\quad -5 \qquad -\dfrac{1}{2} \qquad\;\; 1
\end{array}$$

30. **(a)** $f(x) = 0$ when $x = 1$

(b) $f(x)$ is undefined when $x = 4, x \leq -2$

(c) $f(x) > 0$ when $-2 < x < 1$ or $x > 4$

(d) $f(x) < 0$ when $1 < x < 4$

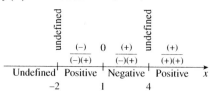

31. **(a)** $f(x) = 0$ when $x = 3$

(b) $f(x)$ is undefined when $x = 4, x < 3$

(c) $f(x) > 0$ when $3 < x < 4$ or $x > 4$

(d) None. $f(x)$ is never negative

$$\begin{array}{c}
\;\; 0 \quad \dfrac{(+)(+)}{(-)^2} \qquad \dfrac{(+)(+)}{(+)^2} \\
\text{Undefined} \;\; \text{Positive} \qquad \text{Positive} \quad x \\
\qquad\quad 3 \qquad\qquad 4
\end{array}$$

32. **(a)** None. $f(x)$ is never 0

(b) $f(x)$ is undefined when $x \leq 5$

(c) $f(x) > 0$ when $5 < x < \infty$

(d) None. $f(x)$ is never negative

$$\begin{array}{c}
\qquad\qquad\qquad \dfrac{(+)}{(+)(+)} \\
\text{Undefined} \qquad\qquad \text{Positive} \quad x \\
\qquad\quad 5
\end{array}$$

33. $f(x) = \dfrac{x-1}{x^2-4} = \dfrac{x-1}{(x+2)(x-2)}$ has points of potential sign change at $x = -2, 1, 2$.

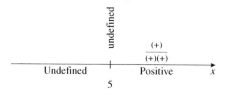

By the sign chart, the solution of $\dfrac{x-1}{x^2-4} < 0$ is $(-\infty, -2) \cup (1, 2)$.

34. $f(x) = \dfrac{x+2}{x^2-9} = \dfrac{x+2}{(x+3)(x-3)}$ has points of potential sign change at $x = -3, -2, 3$.

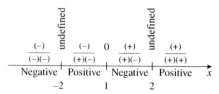

By the sign chart, the solution of $\dfrac{x+2}{x^2-9} < 0$ is $(-\infty, -3) \cup (-2, 3)$.

35. $f(x) = \dfrac{x^2 - 1}{x^2 + 1} = \dfrac{(x + 1)(x - 1)}{(x^2 + 1)}$ has points of potential sign change at $x = -1, 1$.

$\dfrac{(-)(-)}{(+)}$	0	$\dfrac{(+)(-)}{(+)}$	0	$\dfrac{(+)(+)}{(+)}$	
Positive		Negative		Positive	x
	-1		1		

By the sign chart, the solution of $\dfrac{x^2 - 1}{x^2 + 1} \le 0$ is $[-1, 1]$.

36. $f(x) = \dfrac{x^2 - 4}{x^2 + 4} = \dfrac{(x + 2)(x - 2)}{x^2 + 4}$ has points of potential sign change at $x = -2, 2$.

$\dfrac{(-)(-)}{(+)}$	0	$\dfrac{(+)(-)}{(+)}$	0	$\dfrac{(+)(+)}{(+)}$	
Positive		Negative		Positive	x
	-2		2		

By the sign chart, the solution of $\dfrac{x^2 - 4}{x^2 + 4} > 0$ is $(-\infty, -2) \cup (2, \infty)$.

37. $f(x) = \dfrac{x^2 + x - 12}{x^2 - 4x + 4} = \dfrac{(x + 4)(x - 3)}{(x - 2)^2}$ has points of potential sign change at $x = -4, 2, 3$.

$\dfrac{(-)(-)}{(-)^2}$	0	$\dfrac{(+)(-)}{(-)^2}$	undefined	$\dfrac{(+)(-)}{(+)^2}$	0	$\dfrac{(+)(+)}{(+)^2}$	
Positive		Negative		Negative		Positive	x
	-4		2		3		

By the sign chart, the solution of $\dfrac{x^2 + x - 12}{x^2 - 4x + 4} > 0$ is $(-\infty, -4) \cup (3, \infty)$.

38. $f(x) = \dfrac{x^2 + 3x - 10}{x^2 - 6x + 9} = \dfrac{(x + 5)(x - 2)}{(x - 3)^2}$ has points of potential sign change at $x = -5, 2, 3$.

$\dfrac{(-)(-)}{(-)^2}$	0	$\dfrac{(+)(-)}{(-)^2}$	0	$\dfrac{(+)(+)}{(-)^2}$	undefined	$\dfrac{(+)(+)}{(+)^2}$	
Positive		Negative		Positive		Positive	x
	-5		2		3		

By the sign chart, the solution of $\dfrac{x^2 + 3x - 10}{x^2 - 6x + 9} < 0$ is $(-5, 2)$.

39. $f(x) = \dfrac{x^3 - x}{x^2 + 1} = \dfrac{x(x + 1)(x - 1)}{x^2 + 1}$ has points of potential sign change at $x = -1, 0, 1$.

$\dfrac{(-)(-)(-)}{(+)}$	0	$\dfrac{(-)(+)(-)}{(+)}$	0	$\dfrac{(+)(+)(-)}{(+)}$	0	$\dfrac{(+)(+)(+)}{(+)}$	
Negative		Positive		Negative		Positive	x
	-1		0		1		

By the sign chart, the solution of $\dfrac{x^3 - x}{x^2 + 1} \ge 0$ is $[-1, 0] \cup [1, \infty)$.

40. $f(x) = \dfrac{x^3 - 4x}{x^2 + 2} = \dfrac{x(x + 2)(x - 2)}{x^2 + 2}$ has points of potential sign change at $x = -2, 0, 2$.

$\dfrac{(-)(-)(-)}{(+)}$	0	$\dfrac{(-)(+)(-)}{(+)}$	0	$\dfrac{(+)(+)(-)}{(+)}$	0	$\dfrac{(+)(+)(+)}{(+)}$	
Negative		Positive		Negative		Positive	x
	-2		0		2		

By the sign chart, the solution of $\dfrac{x^3 - 4x}{x^2 + 2} \le 0$ is $(-\infty, -2] \cup [0, 2]$.

41. $f(x) = x|x - 2|$ has points of potential sign change at $x = 0, 2$.

$(-)|-|$	0	$(+)|-|$	0	$(+)|+|$	
Negative		Positive		Positive	x
	0		2		

By the sign chart, the solution of $x|x - 2| > 0$ is $(0, 2) \cup (2, \infty)$.

42. $f(x) = \dfrac{x - 3}{|x + 2|}$ has points of potential sign change at $x = -2, 3$.

$\dfrac{(-)}{|-|}$	undefined	$\dfrac{(-)}{|+|}$	0	$\dfrac{(+)}{|+|}$	
Negative		Negative		Positive	x
	-2		3		

By the sign chart, the solution of $\dfrac{x - 3}{|x + 2|} < 0$ is $(-\infty, -2) \cup (-2, 3)$.

43. $f(x) = (2x - 1)\sqrt{x + 4}$ has a point of potential sign change at $x = \dfrac{1}{2}$. Note that the domain of f is $[-4, \infty)$.

		$(-)(+)$	0	$(+)(+)$	
Undefined		Negative		Positive	x
	-4		$\dfrac{1}{2}$		

By the sign chart, the solution of $(2x - 1)\sqrt{x + 4} < 0$ is $\left(-4, \dfrac{1}{2}\right)$.

44. $f(x) = (3x - 4)\sqrt{2x + 1}$ has a point of potential sign change at $x = \dfrac{4}{3}$. Note that the domain of f is $\left[-\dfrac{1}{2}, \infty\right)$.

		$(-)(+)$	0	$(+)(+)$	
Undefined		Negative		Positive	x
	$-\dfrac{1}{2}$		$\dfrac{4}{3}$		

By the sign chart, the solution of $(3x - 4)\sqrt{2x + 1} \ge 0$ is $\left[\dfrac{4}{3}, \infty\right)$.

45. $f(x) = \dfrac{x^3(x-2)}{(x+3)^2}$ has points of potential sign change at $x = -3, 0, 2$.

$$\begin{array}{c} \overset{\text{undefined}}{\Big|} \\ \dfrac{(-)^3(-)}{(-)^2} \quad \dfrac{(-)^3(-)}{(+)^2} \quad 0 \quad \dfrac{(+)^3(-)}{(+)^2} \quad 0 \quad \dfrac{(+)^3(+)}{(+)^2} \\ \underset{\text{Positive}}{\rule{0pt}{0pt}} \quad \underset{\text{Positive}}{\rule{0pt}{0pt}} \quad \underset{\text{Negative}}{\rule{0pt}{0pt}} \quad \underset{\text{Positive}}{\rule{0pt}{0pt}} \quad x \\ \qquad -3 \qquad 0 \qquad 2 \end{array}$$

By the sign chart, the solution of $\dfrac{x^3(x-2)}{(x+3)^2} < 0$ is $(0, 2)$.

46. $f(x) = \dfrac{(x-5)^4}{x(x+3)} \ge 0$ has points of potential sign change at $x = -3, 0, 5$.

$$\begin{array}{c} \overset{\text{undefined}}{\Big|} \quad \overset{\text{undefined}}{\Big|} \\ \dfrac{(-)^4}{(-)(-)} \quad \dfrac{(-)^4}{(-)(+)} \quad \dfrac{(-)^4}{(+)(+)} \quad 0 \quad \dfrac{(+)^4}{(+)(+)} \\ \underset{\text{Positive}}{\rule{0pt}{0pt}} \quad \underset{\text{Negative}}{\rule{0pt}{0pt}} \quad \underset{\text{Positive}}{\rule{0pt}{0pt}} \quad \underset{\text{Positive}}{\rule{0pt}{0pt}} \quad x \\ \qquad -3 \qquad 0 \qquad 5 \end{array}$$

By the sign chart, the solution of $\dfrac{(x-5)^4}{x(x+3)} \ge 0$ is $(-\infty, -3) \cup (0, \infty)$.

47. $f(x) = x^2 - \dfrac{2}{x} = \dfrac{x^3 - 2}{x}$ has points of potential sign change at $x = 0, \sqrt[3]{2}$.

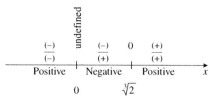

By the sign chart, the solution of $x^2 - \dfrac{2}{x} > 0$ is $(-\infty, 0) \cup (\sqrt[3]{2}, \infty)$.

48. $f(x) = x^2 + \dfrac{4}{x} = \dfrac{x^3 + 4}{x}$ has points of potential sign change at $x = 0, -\sqrt[3]{4}$.

$$\begin{array}{c} \overset{\text{undefined}}{\Big|} \\ \dfrac{(-)}{(-)} \quad 0 \quad \dfrac{(+)}{(-)} \quad \dfrac{(+)}{(+)} \\ \underset{\text{Positive}}{\rule{0pt}{0pt}} \quad \underset{\text{Negative}}{\rule{0pt}{0pt}} \quad \underset{\text{Positive}}{\rule{0pt}{0pt}} \quad x \\ \qquad -\sqrt[3]{4} \qquad 0 \end{array}$$

By the sign chart, the solution of $x^2 + \dfrac{4}{x} \ge 0$ is $(-\infty, -\sqrt[3]{4}] \cup (0, \infty)$.

49. $f(x) = \dfrac{1}{x+1} + \dfrac{1}{x-3} = \dfrac{2(x-1)}{(x+1)(x-3)}$ has points of potential sign change at $x = -1, 1, 3$.

$$\begin{array}{c} \overset{\text{undefined}}{\Big|} \quad \overset{\text{undefined}}{\Big|} \\ \dfrac{(-)}{(-)(-)} \quad \dfrac{(-)}{(+)(-)} \quad 0 \quad \dfrac{(+)}{(+)(-)} \quad \dfrac{(+)}{(+)(+)} \\ \underset{\text{Negative}}{\rule{0pt}{0pt}} \quad \underset{\text{Positive}}{\rule{0pt}{0pt}} \quad \underset{\text{Negative}}{\rule{0pt}{0pt}} \quad \underset{\text{Positive}}{\rule{0pt}{0pt}} \quad x \\ \qquad -1 \qquad 1 \qquad 3 \end{array}$$

By the sign chart, the solution of $\dfrac{1}{x+1} + \dfrac{1}{x-3} \le 0$ is $(-\infty, -1) \cup [1, 3)$.

50. $f(x) = \dfrac{1}{x+2} - \dfrac{2}{x-1} = \dfrac{-x-5}{(x+2)(x-1)}$ has points of potential sign change at $x = -5, -2, 1$.

$$\begin{array}{c} \overset{\text{undefined}}{\Big|} \quad \overset{\text{undefined}}{\Big|} \\ \dfrac{(+)}{(-)(-)} \quad 0 \quad \dfrac{(-)}{(-)(-)} \quad \dfrac{(-)}{(+)(-)} \quad \dfrac{(-)}{(+)(+)} \\ \underset{\text{Positive}}{\rule{0pt}{0pt}} \quad \underset{\text{Negative}}{\rule{0pt}{0pt}} \quad \underset{\text{Positive}}{\rule{0pt}{0pt}} \quad \underset{\text{Negative}}{\rule{0pt}{0pt}} \quad x \\ \qquad -5 \qquad -2 \qquad 1 \end{array}$$

By the sign chart, the solution of $\dfrac{1}{x+2} - \dfrac{2}{x-1} > 0$ is $(-\infty, -5) \cup (-2, 1)$.

51. $f(x) = (x+3)|x-1|$ has points of potential sign change at $x = -3, 1$.

$$\begin{array}{c} \quad 0 \qquad 0 \\ (-)|-| \quad (+)|-| \quad (+)|+| \\ \underset{\text{Negative}}{\rule{0pt}{0pt}} \quad \underset{\text{Positive}}{\rule{0pt}{0pt}} \quad \underset{\text{Positive}}{\rule{0pt}{0pt}} \quad x \\ \qquad -3 \qquad 1 \end{array}$$

By the sign chart, the solution of $(x+3)|x-1| \ge 0$ is $[-3, \infty)$.

52. $f(x) = (3x+5)^2|x-2|$ is always 0 or positive since $(3x+5)^2 \ge 0$ for all real x and $|x-2| \ge 0$ for all real x. Thus the inequality $(3x+5)^2|x-2| < 0$ has no solution.

53. $f(x) = \dfrac{(x-5)|x-2|}{\sqrt{2x-2}}$ has points of potential sign change at $x = 2, 5$. Note that the domain of f is $(1, \infty)$.

$$\begin{array}{c} \overset{\text{undefined}}{\Big|} \\ \dfrac{(-)|-|}{(+)} \quad 0 \quad \dfrac{(-)|+|}{(+)} \quad 0 \quad \dfrac{(+)|+|}{(+)} \\ \underset{\text{Undefined}}{\rule{0pt}{0pt}} \quad \underset{\text{Negative}}{\rule{0pt}{0pt}} \quad \underset{\text{Negative}}{\rule{0pt}{0pt}} \quad \underset{\text{Positive}}{\rule{0pt}{0pt}} \quad x \\ \qquad 1 \qquad 2 \qquad 5 \end{array}$$

By the sign chart, the solution of $\dfrac{(x-5)|x-2|}{\sqrt{2x-2}} \ge 0$ is $[5, \infty)$.

54. $f(x) = \dfrac{x^2(x-4)^3}{\sqrt{x+1}}$ has points of potential sign change at $x = 0, 4$. Note that the domain of f is $(-1, \infty)$.

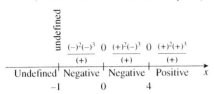

By the sign chart, the solution of $\dfrac{x^2(x-4)^3}{\sqrt{x+1}} < 0$ is $(-1, 0) \cup (0, 4)$.

55. One way to solve the inequality is to graph $y = 3(x-1) + 2$ and $y = 5x + 6$ together, then find the interval along the x-axis where the first graph is below or intersects the second graph. Another way is to solve for x algebraically.

56. Let x be the number of hours worked. The repair charge is $25 + 18x$; this must be less than \$100. Starting with $25 + 18x < 100$, we have $18x < 75$, so $x < 4.166...$ Therefore, the electrician worked no more than 4 hours 7.5 minutes (which rounds to 4 hours).

57. Let $x > 0$ be the width of a rectangle; then the length is $2x - 2$ and the perimeter is $P = 2[x + (2x - 2)]$. Solving $P < 200$ and $2x - 2 > 0$ (below) gives 1 in. $< x <$ 34 in.

$$
\begin{array}{ll}
2[x + (2x - 2)] < 200 & \text{and} \quad 2x - 2 > 0 \\
2(3x - 2) < 200 & \qquad\quad 2x > 2 \\
6x - 4 < 200 & \qquad\quad\; x > 1 \\
6x < 204 & \\
x < 34 &
\end{array}
$$

58. Let x be the number of candy bars made. Then the costs are $C = 0.13x + 2000$, and the income is $I = 0.35x$. Solving $C < I$ (below) gives $x > 9090.91$. The company will need to make and sell 9091 candy bars to make a profit.

$$
\begin{array}{r}
0.13x + 2000 < 0.35x \\
2000 < 0.22x \\
x > 9090.91
\end{array}
$$

59. The lengths of the sides of the box are x, $12 - 2x$, and $15 - 2x$, so the volume is $x(12 - 2x)(15 - 2x)$. To solve $x(12 - 2x)(15 - 2x) \le 100$, graph $f(x) = x(12 - 2x)(15 - 2x) - 100$ and find the zeros: $x \approx 0.69$ and $x \approx 4.20$.

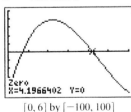

[0, 6] by [−100, 100]

From the graph, the solution of $f(x) \le 0$ is approximately $[0, 0.69] \cup [4.20, 6]$. The squares should be such that either 0 in. $\le x \le$ 0.69 in. or 4.20 in. $\le x \le$ 6 in.

60. The circumference of the base of the cone is $8\pi - x$, $r = 4 - \dfrac{x}{2\pi}$, and $h = \sqrt{16 - \left(4 - \dfrac{x}{2\pi}\right)^2}$. The volume is $v = \dfrac{1}{3}\pi\left(4 - \dfrac{x}{2\pi}\right)^2 \sqrt{16 - \left(4 - \dfrac{x}{2\pi}\right)^2}$.

To solve $v \ge 21$, graph $v - 21$ and find the zeros: $x \approx 1.68$ in. or $x \approx 9.10$.

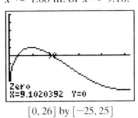

[0, 26] by [−25, 25]

From the graph, the solution of $v - 21 \ge 0$ is approximately $[1.68, 9.10]$. The arc length should be in the range of 1.68 in. $\le x \le$ 9.10 in.

61. (a) $\dfrac{1}{2}L = 500$ cm^3

$$V = \pi x^2 h = 500 \Rightarrow h = \dfrac{500}{\pi x^2}$$

$$S = 2\pi xh + 2\pi x^2 = 2\pi x\left(\dfrac{500}{\pi x^2}\right) + 2\pi x^2$$

$$= \dfrac{1000}{x} + 2\pi x^2 = \dfrac{1000 + 2\pi x^3}{x}$$

(b) Solve $S < 900$ by graphing $\dfrac{1000 + 2\pi x^3}{x} - 900$ and finding its zeros: $x \approx 1.12$ and $x \approx 11.37$

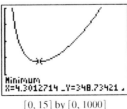

[0, 15] by [−1000, 1000]

From the graph, the solution of $S - 900 < 0$ is approximately $(1.12, 11.37)$. So the radius is between 1.12 cm and 11.37 cm. The corresponding height must be between 1.23 cm and 126.88 cm.

(c) Graph S and find the minimum graphically.

[image: graph with Minimum X=4.3012714 Y=348.73421]

[0, 15] by [0, 1000]

The minimum surface area is about 348.73 cm^2.

62. (a) $\dfrac{1}{R} = \dfrac{1}{2.3} + \dfrac{1}{x}$

$$2.3x = Rx + 2.3R = R(x + 2.3)$$

$$R = \dfrac{2.3x}{x + 2.3}$$

(b) $R \geq 1.7 \Rightarrow \dfrac{2.3x}{x + 2.3} \geq 1.7$

$$\dfrac{2.3x}{x + 2.3} - 1.7 \geq 0$$

$$\dfrac{2.3x - 1.7(x + 2.3)}{x + 2.3} \geq 0$$

$$\dfrac{0.6x - 3.91}{x + 2.3} \geq 0$$

The function $f(x) = \dfrac{0.6x - 3.91}{x + 2.3}$ has a point of

potential sign change at $x = \dfrac{391}{60} \approx 6.5$. Note that the

domain of f is $(-2.3, \infty)$.

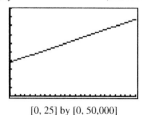

By the sign chart, the solution of $f(x) \geq 0$ is about $[6.5, \infty)$. The resistance in the second resistor is at least 6.5 ohms.

63. (a) $y \approx 993.870x + 19,025.768$

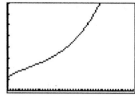

[0, 25] by [0, 50,000]

(b) From the graph of $y = 993.870x + 19,025.768$, we find that $y = 40,000$ when $x \approx 21.2$. The per capita income will exceed \$40,000 in the year 2011.

64. (a) $y \approx 7.883x^3 - 214.972x^2 + 6479.797x + 62,862.278$

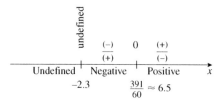

[0, 25] by [0, 400,000]

(b) From the graph of $y \approx 7.883x^3 - 214.972x^2 + 6479.797x + 62,862.278$, we find that $y = 250,000$ when $x \approx 28$. The per capita income will exceed \$250,000 in the year 2008.

65. False. Because the factor x^4 has an even power, it does not change sign at $x = 0$.

66. True. Because the denominator factor $(x + 2)$ has an odd power (namely 1), it changes sign at $x = -2$.

67. x must be positive but less than 1. The answer is C.

68. The statement is true so long as the numerator does not equal zero. The answer is B.

69. The statement is true so long as the denominator is negative and the numerator is nonzero. Thus x must be less than three but nonzero. The answer is D.

70. The expression $(x^2 - 1)^2$ cannot be negative for any real x, and it can equal zero only for $x = \pm 1$. The answer is A.

71. $f(x) = \dfrac{(x - 1)(x + 2)^2}{(x - 3)(x + 1)}$

Vertical asymptotes: $x = -1$, $x = 3$

x-intercepts: $(-2, 0)$, $(1, 0)$

y-intercept: $\left(0, \dfrac{4}{3}\right)$

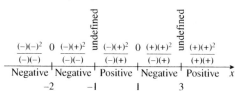

By hand:

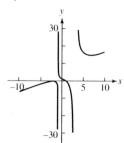

Grapher:

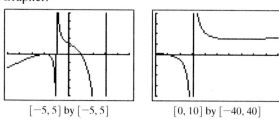

$[-5, 5]$ by $[-5, 5]$ $[0, 10]$ by $[-40, 40]$

72. $g(x) = \dfrac{(x - 3)^4}{x^2 + 4x} = \dfrac{(x - 3)^4}{x(x + 4)}$

Vertical asymptotes: $x = -4$, $x = 0$

x-intercept: $(3, 0)$

y-intercept: None

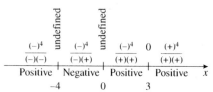

Sketch:

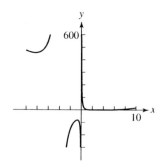

Grapher:

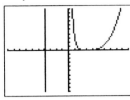 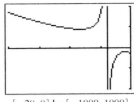

$[-10, 10]$ by $[-10, 10]$ $[-20, 0]$ by $[-1000, 1000]$

73. (a) $|x - 3| < 1/3 \Rightarrow |3x - 9| < 1 \Rightarrow$
$|3x - 5 - 4| < 1 \Rightarrow |f(x) - 4| < 1$.

For example:
$|f(x) - 4| = |(3x - 5) - 4| = |3x - 9|$

$\qquad = 3|x - 3| < 3\left(\dfrac{1}{3}\right) = 1$

(b) If x stays within the dashed vertical lines, $f(x)$ will stay within the dashed horizontal lines. For the example in part (a), the graph shows that for
$\dfrac{8}{3} < x < \dfrac{10}{3}$ (that is, $|x - 3| < \dfrac{1}{3}$), we have
$3 < f(x) < 5$ (that is, $|f(x) - 4| < 1$).

(c) $|x - 3| < 0.01 \Rightarrow |3x - 9| < 0.03 \Rightarrow$
$|3x - 5 - 4| < 0.03 \Rightarrow |f(x) - 4| < 0.03$. The dashed lines would be closer to $x = 3$ and $y = 4$.

74. When $x^2 - 4 \geq 0$, $y = 1$, and when $x^2 - 4 \not\geq 0$, $y = 0$.

75. One possible answer: Given $0 < a < b$, multiplying both sides of $a < b$ by a gives $a^2 < ab$; multiplying by b gives $ab < b^2$. Then, by the transitive property of inequality, we have $a^2 < b^2$.

76. One possible answer: Given $0 < a < b$, multiplying both sides of $a < b$ by $\dfrac{1}{ab}$ gives $\dfrac{1}{b} < \dfrac{1}{a}$, which is equivalent to $\dfrac{1}{a} > \dfrac{1}{b}$.

■ Chapter 2 Review

For #1 and 2, first find the slope of the line. Then use algebra to put into $y = mx + b$ format.

1. $m = \dfrac{-9 - (-2)}{4 - (-3)} = \dfrac{-7}{7} = -1$, $(y + 9) = -1(x - 4)$,
$y = -x - 5$

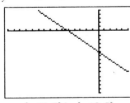

$[-15, 5]$ by $[-15, 5]$

2. $m = \dfrac{-2 - 6}{1 - (-3)} = \dfrac{-8}{4} = -2$, $(y + 2) = -2(x - 1)$,
$y = -2x$

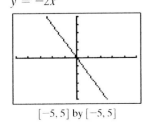

$[-5, 5]$ by $[-5, 5]$

3. Starting from $y = x^2$, translate right 2 units and vertically stretch by 3 (either order), then translate up 4 units.

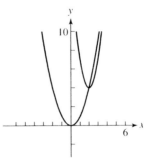

4. Starting from $y = x^2$, translate left 3 units and reflect across x-axis (either order), then translate up 1 unit.

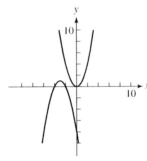

5. Vertex: $(-3, 5)$; axis: $x = -3$

6. Vertex: $(5, -7)$; axis: $x = 5$

7. $f(x) = -2(x^2 + 8x) - 31$
$\qquad = -2(x^2 + 8x + 16) + 32 - 31 = -2(x + 4)^2 + 1$;
Vertex: $(-4, 1)$; axis: $x = -4$

8. $g(x) = 3(x^2 - 2x) + 2 = 3(x^2 - 2x + 1) - 3 + 2 = 3(x - 1)^2 - 1$; Vertex: $(1, -1)$; axis: $x = 1$

For #9–12, use the form $y = a(x - h)^2 + k$, where (h, k), the vertex, is given.

9. $h = -2$ and $k = -3$ are given, so $y = a(x + 2)^2 - 3$.
Using the point $(1, 2)$, we have $2 = 9a - 3$, so $a = \dfrac{5}{9}$;
$y = \dfrac{5}{9}(x + 2)^2 - 3$.

10. $h = -1$ and $k = 1$ are given, so $y = a(x + 1)^2 + 1$.
Using the point $(3, -2)$, we have $-2 = 16a + 1$, so
$a = -\dfrac{3}{16}$; $y = -\dfrac{3}{16}(x + 1)^2 + 1$.

11. $h = 3$ and $k = -2$ are given, so $y = a(x - 3)^2 - 2$.
Using the point $(5, 0)$, we have $0 = 4a - 2$, so $a = \dfrac{1}{2}$:
$y = \dfrac{1}{2}(x - 3)^2 - 2$.

12. $h = -4$ and $k = 5$ are given, so $y = a(x + 4)^2 + 5$.
Using the point $(0, -3)$, we have $-3 = 16a + 5$,
so $a = -\dfrac{1}{2}$; $y = -\dfrac{1}{2}(x + 4)^{-2} + 5$.

13.

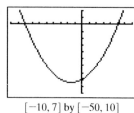

$[-10, 7]$ by $[-50, 10]$

14.

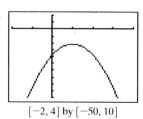

$[-2, 4]$ by $[-50, 10]$

15.

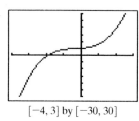

$[-4, 3]$ by $[-30, 30]$

16.

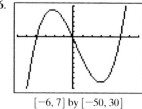

$[-6, 7]$ by $[-50, 30]$

17. $S = kr^2$ $(k = 4\pi)$

18. $F = \dfrac{k}{d^2}$ $(k = $ gravitational constant$)$

19. The force F needed varies directly with the distance x from its resting position, with constant of variation k.

20. The area of a circle A varies directly with the square of its radius.

21. $k = 4$, $a = \dfrac{1}{3}$. In Quadrant I, $f(x)$ is increasing and concave down since $0 < a < 1$.

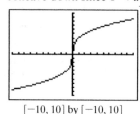

$[-10, 10]$ by $[-10, 10]$

$f(-x) = 4(-x)^{1/3} = -4x^{1/3} = -f(x)$, so f is odd.

22. $k = -2$, $a = \dfrac{3}{4}$. In Quadrant IV, $f(x)$ is decreasing and concave up since $0 < a < 1$. f is not defined for $x < 0$.

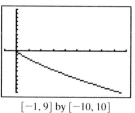

$[-1, 9]$ by $[-10, 10]$

23. $k = -2$, $a = -3$. In Quadrant IV, f is increasing and concave down. $f(-x) = -2(-x)^{-3} = \dfrac{-2}{(-x)^3} = \dfrac{-2}{-x^3}$

$= \dfrac{2}{x^3} = 2x^{-3} = -f(x)$, so f is odd.

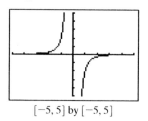

$[-5, 5]$ by $[-5, 5]$

24. $k = \dfrac{2}{3}$, $a = -4$. In Quadrant I, $f(x)$ is decreasing and concave up. $f(-x) = \dfrac{2}{3}(-x)^{-4} = \dfrac{2}{3} \cdot \dfrac{1}{(-x)^4}$

$= \dfrac{2}{3x^4} = \dfrac{2}{3}x^{-4} = f(x)$, so f is even.

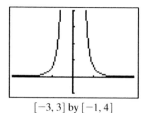

$[-3, 3]$ by $[-1, 4]$

25. $\dfrac{2x^3 - 7x^2 + 4x - 5}{x - 3} = 2x^2 - x + 1 - \dfrac{2}{x - 3}$

$$
\begin{array}{r}
2x^2 - x + 1 \\
x - 3 \overline{) 2x^3 - 7x^2 + 4x - 5} \\
\underline{2x^3 - 6x^2} \\
-x^2 + 4x \\
\underline{-x^2 + 3x} \\
x - 5 \\
\underline{x - 3} \\
-2
\end{array}
$$

26. $\dfrac{x^4 + 3x^3 + x^2 - 3x + 3}{x + 2} = x^3 + x^2 - x - 1 + \dfrac{5}{x + 2}$

$$
\begin{array}{r}
x^3 + x^2 - x - 1 \\
x + 2 \overline{)\, x^4 + 3x^3 + x^2 - 3x + 3} \\
\underline{x^4 + 2x^3} \\
x^3 + x^2 \\
\underline{x^3 + 2x^2} \\
-x^2 - 3x \\
\underline{-x^2 - 2x} \\
-x + 3 \\
\underline{-x - 2} \\
5
\end{array}
$$

27. $\dfrac{2x^4 - 3x^3 + 9x^2 - 14x + 7}{x^2 + 4}$

$= 2x^2 - 3x + 1 + \dfrac{-2x + 3}{x^2 + 4}$

$$
\begin{array}{r}
2x^2 - 3x + 1 \\
x^2 + 4 \overline{)\, 2x^4 - 3x^3 + 9x^2 - 14x + 7} \\
\underline{2x^4 \quad\;\; + 8x^2} \\
-3x^3 + x^2 - 14x + 7 \\
\underline{-3x^3 \quad\quad - 12x} \\
x^2 - 2x + 7 \\
\underline{x^2 \quad\;\; + 4} \\
-2x + 3
\end{array}
$$

28. $\dfrac{3x^4 - 5x^3 - 2x^2 + 3x - 6}{3x + 1} = x^3 - 2x^2 + 1 + \dfrac{-7}{3x + 1}$

$$
\begin{array}{r}
x^3 - 2x^2 \quad\quad + 1 \\
3x + 1 \overline{)\, 3x^4 - 5x^3 - 2x^2 + 3x - 6} \\
\underline{3x^4 + x^3} \\
-6x^3 - 2x^2 + 3x - 6 \\
\underline{-6x^3 - 2x^2} \\
3x - 6 \\
\underline{3x + 1} \\
-7
\end{array}
$$

29. Remainder: $f(-2) = -39$

30. Remainder: $f(3) = -2$

31. Yes: 2 is a zero of the second polynomial.

32. No: $x = -3$ yields 1 from the second polynomial.

33.
$$
\begin{array}{r|rrrr}
5 & 1 & -5 & 3 & 4 \\
& & 5 & 0 & 15 \\
\hline
& 1 & 0 & 3 & 19
\end{array}
$$
Yes, $x = 5$ is an upper bound for the zeros of $f(x)$ because all entries on the bottom row are nonnegative.

34.
$$
\begin{array}{r|rrrrr}
4 & 4 & -16 & 8 & 16 & -12 \\
& & 16 & 0 & 32 & 192 \\
\hline
& 4 & 0 & 8 & 48 & 180
\end{array}
$$
Yes, $x = 4$ is an upper bound for the zeros of $f(x)$ because all entries on the bottom row are nonnegative.

35.
$$
\begin{array}{r|rrrrr}
-3 & 4 & 4 & -15 & -17 & -2 \\
& & -12 & 24 & -27 & 132 \\
\hline
& 4 & -8 & 9 & -44 & 130
\end{array}
$$
Yes, $x = -3$ is a lower bound for the zeros of $f(x)$ because all entries on the bottom row alternate signs.

36.
$$
\begin{array}{r|rrrr}
-3 & 2 & 6 & 1 & -6 \\
& & -6 & 0 & -3 \\
\hline
& 2 & 0 & 1 & -9
\end{array}
$$
Yes, $x = -3$ is a lower bound for the zeros of $f(x)$ because all entries on the bottom row alternate signs (remember that $0 = -0$).

37. Possible rational zeros: $\dfrac{\pm 1, \pm 2, \pm 3, \pm 6}{\pm 1, \pm 2}$,

or $\pm 1, \pm 2, \pm 3, \pm 6, \pm\dfrac{1}{2}, \pm\dfrac{3}{2}; -\dfrac{3}{2}$ and 2 are zeros.

38. Possible rational zeros: $\dfrac{\pm 1, \pm 7}{\pm 1, \pm 2, \pm 3, \pm 6}$,

or $\pm 1, \pm 7, \pm\dfrac{1}{2}, \pm\dfrac{7}{2}, \pm\dfrac{1}{3}, \pm\dfrac{7}{3}, \pm\dfrac{1}{6}, \pm\dfrac{7}{6}; \dfrac{7}{3}$ is a zero.

39. $(1 + i)^3 = (1 + 2i + i^2)(1 + i) = (2i)(1 + i)$
$= -2 + 2i$

40. $(1 + 2i)^2(1 - 2i)^2 = [(1 + 2i)(1 - 2i)]^2 = (1 + 2^2)^2$
$= 25$

41. $i^{29} = i$

42. $\sqrt{-16} = 4i$

For #43–44, use the quadratic formula.

43. $x = \dfrac{6 \pm \sqrt{36 - 52}}{2} = \dfrac{6 \pm 4i}{2} = 3 \pm 2i$

44. $x = \dfrac{2 \pm \sqrt{4 - 16}}{2} = \dfrac{2 \pm 2\sqrt{3}i}{2} = 1 \pm \sqrt{3}i$

45. (c) $f(x) = (x - 2)^2$ is a quadratic polynomial that has vertex $(2, 0)$ and y-intercept $(0, 4)$, so its graph must be graph (c).

46. (d) $f(x) = (x - 2)^3$ is a cubic polynomial that passes through $(2, 0)$ and $(0, -8)$, so its graph must be graph (d).

47. (b) $f(x) = (x - 2)^4$ is a quartic polynomial that passes through $(2, 0)$ and $(0, 16)$, so its graph must be graph (b).

48. (a) $f(x) = (x - 2)^5$ is a quintic polynomial that passes through $(2, 0)$ and $(0, -32)$, so its graph must be graph (a).

In #49–52, use a graph and the Rational Zeros Test to determine zeros.

49. Rational: 0 (multiplicity 2) — easily seen by inspection. Irrational: $5 \pm \sqrt{2}$ (using the quadratic formula, after taking out a factor of x^2). No non-real zeros.

50. Rational: ± 2. Irrational: $\pm\sqrt{3}$. No nonreal zeros. These zeros may be estimated from a graph, or by dividing $k(t)$ by $t - 2$ and $t + 2$ then applying the quadratic formula, or by using the quadratic formula on $k(t)$ to determine that $t^2 = \dfrac{7 \pm \sqrt{49 - 48}}{2}$, i.e., t^2 is 3 or 4.

51. Rational: none. Irrational: approximately $-2.34, 0.57, 3.77$. No non-real zeros.

52. Rational: none. Irrational: approximately -3.97, -0.19. Two non-real zeros.

53. The only rational zero is $-\dfrac{3}{2}$. Dividing by $x + \dfrac{3}{2}$ (below) leaves $2x^2 - 12x + 20$, which has zeros

$$\frac{12 \pm \sqrt{144 - 160}}{4} = 3 \pm i. \text{ Therefore}$$

$$f(x) = (2x + 3)[x - (3 - i)][x - (3 + i)]$$
$$= (2x + 3)(x - 3 + i)(x - 3 - i).$$

$$
\begin{array}{r|rrrr}
-3/2 & 2 & -9 & 2 & 30 \\
     &   & -3 & 18 & -30 \\
\hline
     & 2 & -12 & 20 & 0
\end{array}
$$

54. The only rational zero is $\dfrac{4}{5}$. Dividing by $x - \dfrac{4}{5}$ (below) leaves $5x^2 - 20x - 15$, which has zeros

$$\frac{20 \pm \sqrt{400 + 300}}{10} = 2 \pm \sqrt{7}. \text{ Therefore}$$

$$f(x) = (5x - 4)\left[x - \left(2 + \sqrt{7}\right)\right]\left[x - \left(2 - \sqrt{7}\right)\right]$$
$$= (5x - 4)\left(x - 2 - \sqrt{7}\right)\left(x - 2 + \sqrt{7}\right).$$

$$
\begin{array}{r|rrrr}
4/5 & 5 & -24 & 1 & 12 \\
    &   & 4 & -16 & -12 \\
\hline
    & 5 & -20 & -15 & 0
\end{array}
$$

55. All zeros are rational: 1, -1, $\dfrac{2}{3}$, and $-\dfrac{5}{2}$. Therefore

$f(x) = (3x - 2)(2x + 5)(x - 1)(x + 1)$; this can be confirmed by multiplying out the terms or graphing the original function and the factored form of the function.

56. Since all coefficients are real, $1 - 2i$ is also a zero. Dividing synthetically twice leaves the quadratic $x^2 - 6x + 10$, which has zeros $3 \pm i$.

$f(x) = [x - (1 + 2i)][x - (1 - 2i)][x - (3 + i)]$
$[x - (3 - i)] = (x - 1 - 2i)(x - 1 + 2i)$
$(x - 3 - i)(x - 3 + i)$

$$
\begin{array}{r|rrrrr}
1 + 2i & 1 & -8 & 27 & -50 & 50 \\
       &   & 1 + 2i & -11 - 12i & 40 + 20i & -50 \\
\hline
       & 1 & -7 + 2i & 16 - 12i & -10 + 20i & 0
\end{array}
$$

$$
\begin{array}{r|rrrr}
1 - 2i & 1 & -7 + 2i & 16 - 12i & -10 + 20i \\
       &   & 1 - 2i & -6 + 12i & 10 - 20i \\
\hline
       & 1 & -6 & 10 & 0
\end{array}
$$

In #57–60, determine rational zeros (graphically or otherwise) and divide synthetically until a quadratic remains. If more real zeros remain, use the quadratic formula.

57. The only real zero is 2; dividing by $x - 2$ leaves the quadratic factor $x^2 + x + 1$, so

$f(x) = (x - 2)(x^2 + x + 1)$.

$$
\begin{array}{r|rrrr}
2 & 1 & -1 & -1 & -2 \\
  &   & 2 & 2 & 2 \\
\hline
  & 1 & 1 & 1 & 0
\end{array}
$$

58. The only rational zero is -1; dividing by $x + 1$ leaves the quadratic factor $9x^2 - 12x - 1$, which has zeros

$$\frac{12 \pm \sqrt{144 + 36}}{18} = \frac{2}{3} \pm \frac{1}{3}\sqrt{5}. \text{ Then}$$

$f(x) = (x + 1)(9x^2 - 12x - 1)$.

$$
\begin{array}{r|rrrr}
-1 & 9 & -3 & -13 & -1 \\
   &   & -9 & 12 & 1 \\
\hline
   & 9 & -12 & -1 & 0
\end{array}
$$

59. The two real zeros are 1 and $\dfrac{3}{2}$; dividing by $x - 1$ and $x - \dfrac{3}{2}$ leaves the quadratic factor $2x^2 - 4x + 10$, so

$f(x) = (2x - 3)(x - 1)(x^2 - 2x + 5)$.

$$
\begin{array}{r|rrrrr}
1 & 2 & -9 & 23 & -31 & 15 \\
  &   & 2 & -7 & 16 & -15 \\
\hline
  & 2 & -7 & 16 & -15 & 0
\end{array}
\qquad
\begin{array}{r|rrrr}
3/2 & 2 & -7 & 16 & -15 \\
    &   & 3 & -6 & 15 \\
\hline
    & 2 & -4 & 10 & 0
\end{array}
$$

60. The two real zeros are -1 and $-\dfrac{2}{3}$; dividing by $x + 1$ and $x + \dfrac{2}{3}$ leaves the quadratic factor $3x^2 - 12x + 15$, so

$f(x) = (3x + 2)(x + 1)(x^2 - 4x + 5)$.

$$
\begin{array}{r|rrrrr}
-1 & 3 & -7 & -3 & 17 & 10 \\
   &   & -3 & 10 & -7 & -10 \\
\hline
   & 3 & -10 & 7 & 10 & 0
\end{array}
\qquad
\begin{array}{r|rrrr}
-2/3 & 3 & -10 & 7 & 10 \\
     &   & -2 & 8 & -10 \\
\hline
     & 3 & -12 & 15 & 0
\end{array}
$$

61. $(x - \sqrt{5})(x + \sqrt{5})(x - 3) = x^3 - 3x^2 - 5x + 15$. Other answers may be found by multiplying this polynomial by any real number.

62. $(x + 3)^2 = x^2 + 6x + 9$ (This may be multiplied by any real number.)

63. $(x - 3)(x + 2)(3x - 1)(2x + 1)$
$= 6x^4 - 5x^3 - 38x^2 - 5x + 6$ (This may be multiplied by any real number.)

64. The third zero must be $1 - i$:
$(x - 2)(x - 1 - i)(x - 1 + i) = x^3 - 4x^2 + 6x - 4$
(This may be multiplied by any real number.)

65. $(x + 2)^2(x - 4)^2 = x^4 - 4x^3 - 12x^2 + 32x + 64$
(This may be multiplied by any real number.)

66. The third zero must be $2 + i$, so
$f(x) = a(x + 1)(x - 2 - i)(x - 2 + i)$.
Since $f(2) = 6$, $a = 2$:
$f(x) = 2(x + 1)(x - 2 - i)(x - 2 + i)$
$= 2x^3 - 6x^2 + 2x + 10$.

67. $f(x) = -1 + \dfrac{2}{x - 5}$; translate right 5 units and vertically stretch by 2 (either order), then translate down 1 unit. Horizontal asymptote: $y = -1$; vertical asymptote: $x = 5$.

68. $f(x) = 3 - \dfrac{1}{x - 2}$; translate left 2 units and reflect across x-axis (either order), then translate up 3 units. Horizontal asymptote: $y = 3$; vertical asymptote: $x = -2$.

69. Asymptotes: $y = 1$, $x = -1$, and $x = 1$.
Intercept: $(0, -1)$.

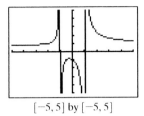

$[-5, 5]$ by $[-5, 5]$

70. Asymptotes: $y = 2$, $x = -3$, and $x = 2$.
Intercept: $\left(0, -\dfrac{7}{6}\right)$.

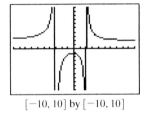

$[-10, 10]$ by $[-10, 10]$

71. End-behavior asymptote: $y = x - 7$.
Vertical asymptote: $x = -3$. Intercept: $\left(0, \dfrac{5}{3}\right)$.

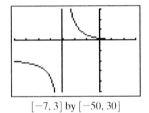

$[-7, 3]$ by $[-50, 30]$

72. End-behavior asymptote: $y = x - 6$.
Vertical asymptote: $x = -3$. Intercepts: approx.
$(-1.54, 0)$, $(4.54, 0)$, and $\left(0, -\dfrac{7}{3}\right)$.

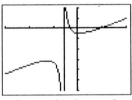

$[-15, 10]$ by $[-30, 10]$

73. $f(x) = \dfrac{x^3 + x^2 - 2x + 5}{x + 2}$ has only one x-intercept,
and we can use the graph to show that it is about -2.552.
The y-intercept is $f(0) = 5/2$. The denominator is zero
when $x = -2$, so the vertical asymptote is $x = -2$.
Because we can rewrite $f(x)$ as
$$f(x) = \dfrac{x^3 + x^2 - 2x + 5}{x + 2} = x^2 - x + \dfrac{5}{x + 2},$$
we know that the end-behavior asymptote is $y = x^2 - x$.
The graph supports this information and allows us to
conclude that
$$\lim_{x \to -2^-} = -\infty, \quad \lim_{x \to -2^+} = \infty.$$
The graph also shows a local minimum of about 1.63 at
about $x = 0.82$.

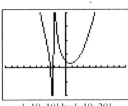

$[-10, 10]$ by $[-10, 20]$

y-intercept: $\left(0, \dfrac{5}{2}\right)$

x-intercept: $(-2.55, 0)$

Domain: All $x \neq -2$
Range: $(-\infty, \infty)$
Continuity: All $x \neq -2$
Increasing on $[0.82, \infty)$
Decreasing on $(-\infty, -2)$, $(-2, 0.82]$
Not symmetric.
Unbounded.
Local minimum: $(0.82, 1.63)$
No horizontal asymptote. End-behavior
asymptote: $y = x^2 - x$
Vertical asymptote: $x = -2$.
End behavior: $\lim_{x \to -\infty} f(x) = \lim_{x \to \infty} f(x) = \infty$

74. $f(x) = \dfrac{-x^4 + x^2 + 1}{x - 1}$ has two x-intercepts, and we
can use the graph to show that they are about -1.27 and
1.27. The y-intercept is $f(0) = -1$. The denominator is
zero when $x = 1$, so the vertical asymptote is $x = 1$.
Because we can rewrite $f(x)$ as
$$f(x) = \dfrac{-x^4 + x^2 + 1}{x - 1} = -x^3 - x^2 + \dfrac{1}{x - 1},$$
we know that the end-behavior asymptote is
$y = -x^3 - x^2$. The graph supports this information and
allows us to conclude that $\lim_{x \to 1^-} = -\infty$ and $\lim_{x \to 1^+} = \infty$.
The graph shows no local extrema.

$[-4.7, 4.7]$ by $[-10, 10]$

y-intercept: $(0, 1)$
x-intercepts: $(-1.27, 0)$, $(1.27, 0)$

Domain: All $x \neq 1$
Range: $(-\infty, \infty)$
Continuity: All $x \neq 1$
Never increasing
Decreasing on $(-\infty, 1)$, $(1, \infty)$
No symmetry.
Unbounded.
No local extrema.
No horizontal asymptote. End-behavior asymptote:
$y = -x^3 - x^2$
Vertical asymptote: $x = 1$
End behavior: $\lim_{x \to -\infty} f(x) = \infty$; $\lim_{x \to \infty} f(x) = -\infty$

75. Multiply by x: $2x^2 - 11x + 12 = 0$, so $x = \dfrac{3}{2}$ or $x = 4$.

76. Multiply by $(x + 2)(x - 3) = x^2 - x - 6$:
$x(x - 3) + 5(x + 2) = 25$, or $x^2 + 2x - 15 = 0$,
so $x = -5$ or $x = 3$. The latter is extraneous; the only
solution is $x = -5$.

For #77–78, find the zeros of $f(x)$ and then determine where
the function is positive or negative by creating a sign chart.

77. $f(x) = (x - 3)(2x + 5)(x + 2)$, so the zeros of $f(x)$
are $x = \left\{ -\dfrac{5}{2}, -2, 3 \right\}$.

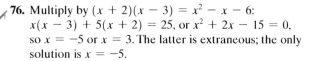

As our sign chart indicates, $f(x) < 0$ on the interval
$\left(-\infty, -\dfrac{5}{2} \right) \cup (-2, 3)$.

78. $f(x) = (x - 2)^2(x + 4)(3x + 1)$, so the zeros of $f(x)$
are $x = \left\{ -4, -\dfrac{1}{3}, 2 \right\}$.

$$\underset{\text{Positive}}{\overset{(+)(-)(-)}{\rule{0pt}{0pt}}} \mid \underset{\text{Negative}}{\overset{(+)(+)(-)}{\rule{0pt}{0pt}}} \mid \underset{\text{Positive}}{\overset{(+)(+)(+)}{\rule{0pt}{0pt}}} \mid \underset{\text{Positive}}{\overset{(+)(+)(+)}{\rule{0pt}{0pt}}}$$

As our sign chart indicates, $f(x) \geq 0$ on the interval
$(-\infty, -4] \cup \left[-\dfrac{1}{3}, \infty \right)$.

79. Zeros of numerator and denominator: -3, -2, and 2.
Choose -4, -2.5, 0, and 3; $\dfrac{x + 3}{x^2 - 4}$ is positive at -2.5 and
3, and equals 0 at -3, so the solution is $[-3, -2) \cup (2, \infty)$.

80. $\dfrac{x^2 - 7}{x^2 - x - 6} - 1 = \dfrac{x - 1}{x^2 - x - 6}$. Zeros of numerator and
denominator: -2, 1, and 3. Choose -3, 0, 2, and 4;
$\dfrac{x - 1}{x^2 - x - 6}$ is negative at -3 and 2, so the solution
is $(-\infty, -2) \cup (1, 3)$.

81. Since the function is always positive, we need only worry
about the equality $(2x - 1)^2|x + 3| = 0$. By inspection,
we see this holds true only when $x = \left\{ -3, \dfrac{1}{2} \right\}$.

82. $\sqrt{x + 3}$ exists only when $x \geq -3$, so we are concerned
only with the interval $(-3, \infty)$. Further $|x - 4|$ is always 0
or positive, so the only possible value for a sign change is
$x = 1$. For $-3 < x < 1$, $\dfrac{(x - 1)|x - 4|}{\sqrt{x + 3}}$ is negative, and
for $1 < x < 4$ or $4 < x < \infty$, $\dfrac{(x - 1)|x + 4|}{\sqrt{x + 3}}$ is positive.
So the solution is $(1, 4) \cup (4, \infty)$.

83. Synthetic division reveals that we *cannot* conclude that
5 is an upper bound (since there are both positive and
negative numbers on the bottom row), while -5 *is* a

lower bound (because all numbers on the bottom row
alternate signs). Yes, there is another zero (at $x \approx 10.0002$).

5	1	−10	−3	28	20	−2
		5	−25	−140	−560	−2700
	1	−5	−28	−112	−540	−2702
−5	1	−10	−3	28	20	−2
		−5	75	−360	1660	−8400
	1	−15	72	−332	1680	−8402

84. **(a)** $h = -16t^2 + 170t + 6$

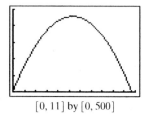

[0, 11] by [0, 500]

(b) When $t \approx 5.3125$, $h \approx 457.5625$.

(c) The rock will hit the ground after about 10.66 sec.

85. **(a)** $V = (\text{height})(\text{width})(\text{length})$
$= x(30 - 2x)(70 - 2x)$ in.^{3}

(b) Either $x \approx 4.57$ or $x \approx 8.63$ in.

86. **(a)** & **(b)**

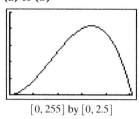

[0, 255] by [0, 2.5]

(c) When $d \approx 170$ ft, $s \approx 2.088$ ft.

(d) One possibility: The beam may taper off (become thin-
ner) from west to east — e.g., perhaps it measures 8 in.
by 8 in. at the west end, but only 7 in. by 7 in. on the
east end. Then we would expect the beam to bend more
easily closer to the east end (though not at the extreme
east end, since it is anchored to the piling there).
Another possibility: The two pilings are made of
different materials.

87. **(a)** The tank is made up of a cylinder, with volume
$\pi x^2(140 - 2x)$, and a sphere, with volume $\dfrac{4}{3}\pi x^3$.
Thus, $V = \dfrac{4}{3}\pi x^3 + \pi x^2(140 - 2x)$.

(b)

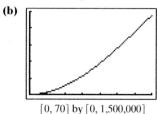

[0, 70] by [0, 1,500,000]

(c) The largest volume occurs when $x = 70$ (so it is actually a sphere). This volume is $\frac{4}{3}\pi(70)^3 \approx 1{,}436{,}755$ ft^3.

88. (a) $y = 18.694x^2 - 88.144x + 2393.022$

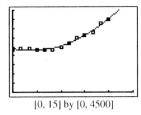

[0, 15] by [0, 4500]

(b) $y = -0.291x^4 + 7.100x^3 - 35.865x^2 + 48.971x + 2336.634$

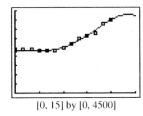

[0, 15] by [0, 4500]

(c) For $x = 16$, the quadratic model yields $y \approx \$5768$ and the quartic model yields $y \approx \$3949$.

(d) The quadratic model, which has a positive leading coefficient, predicts that the amount of the Pell Grant will always increase. The quartic model, which has a negative leading coefficient, predicts that eventually the amount of the Pell Grant will decrease over time.

89. (a) $y = 1.401x + 4.331$

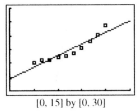

[0, 15] by [0, 30]

(b) $y = 0.188x^2 - 1.411x + 13.331$

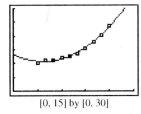

[0, 15] by [0, 30]

(c) **Linear:** Solving $1.401x + 4.331 = 30$ graphically, we find that $y = 30$ when $x \approx 18.32$. The spending will exceed \$30 million in the year 2008.

Quadratic: Solving $0.188x^2 - 1.411x + 13.331 = 30$ graphically, we find that $y = 30$ when $x \approx 13.89$. The spending will exceed \$30 million in the year 2003.

90. (a) Each shinguard costs \$4.32 plus a fraction of the overhead: $C = 4.32 + 4000/x$.

(b) Solve $x(5.25 - 4.32 - 4000/x) = 8000$: $0.93x = 12{,}000$, so $x \approx 12{,}903.23$ — round up to 12,904.

91. (a) $P(15) = 325$, $P(70) = 600$, $P(100) = 648$

(b) $y = \dfrac{640}{0.8} = 800$

(c) The deer population approaches (but never equals) 800.

92. (a) $\dfrac{1}{1.2} = \dfrac{1}{x} + \dfrac{1}{R_2}$, so $\dfrac{1}{R_2} = \dfrac{1}{1.2} - \dfrac{1}{x} = \dfrac{x - 1.2}{1.2x}$.

Then, $R_2 = \dfrac{1.2x}{x - 1.2}$.

(b) When $x = 3$, $R_2 = \dfrac{3.6}{3 - 1.2} = \dfrac{3.6}{1.8} = 2$ ohms.

93. (a) $C(x) = \dfrac{50}{50 + x}$

(b) Shown is the window $[0, 50]$ by $[0, 1]$, with the graphs of $y = C(x)$ and $y = 0.6$. The two graphs cross when $x \approx 33.33$ ounces of distilled water.

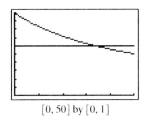

[0, 50] by [0, 1]

(c) Algebraic solution of $\dfrac{50}{50 + x} = 0.6$ leads to $50 = 0.6(50 + x)$, so that $0.6x = 20$, or $x = \dfrac{100}{3} \approx 33.33$.

94. (a) Let h be the height (in cm) of the can; we know the volume is 1 L $= 1000$ cm$^3 = \pi x^2 h$, so $h = \dfrac{1000}{\pi x^2}$. Then $S = 2\pi x^2 + 2\pi xh = 2\pi x^2 + 2000/x$.

(b) Solve $2\pi x^2 + 2000/x = 900$, or equivalently, $2\pi x^3 - 900x + 2000 = 0$. Graphically we find that either $x \approx 2.31$ cm and $h \approx 59.75$ cm, or $x \approx 10.65$ and $h \approx 2.81$ cm.

(c) Approximately $2.31 < x < 10.65$ (graphically) and $2.81 < h < 59.75$.

95. (a) Let y be the height of the tank; $1000 = x^2y$, so $y = 1000/x^2$. The surface area equals the area of the base plus 4 times the area of one side. Each side is a rectangle with dimensions $x \times y$, so $S = x^2 + 4xy = x^2 + 4000/x$.

(b) Solve $x^2 + 4000/x = 600$, or $x^3 - 600x + 4000 = 0$ (a graphical solution is easiest): Either $x = 20$, giving dimensions 20 ft by 20 ft by 2.5 ft or $x \approx 7.32$, giving approximate dimensions 7.32 by 7.32 by 18.66.

(c) $7.32 < x < 20$ (lower bound approximate), so y must be between 2.5 ft and about 18.66 ft.

Chapter 2 Project

Answers are based on the sample data shown in the table.

1.

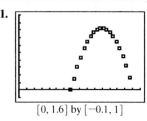

$[0, 1.6]$ by $[-0.1, 1]$

2. We estimate the vertex to lie halfway between the two data points with the greatest height, so that h is the average of 1.075 and 1.118, or about 1.097. We estimate k to be 0.830, which is slightly greater than the greatest height in the data, 0.828.

Noting that $y = 0$ when $x = 0.688$, we solve $0 = a(0.688 - 1.097)^2 + 0.830$ to find $a \approx -4.962$. So the estimated quadratic model is $y = -4.962(x - 1.097)^2 + 0.830$.

3. The sign of a affects the direction the parabola opens. The magnitude of a affects the vertical stretch of the graph. Changes to h cause horizontal shifts to the graph, while changes to k cause vertical shifts.

4. $y \approx -4.962x^2 - 10.887x - 5.141$

5. $y \approx -4.968x^2 + 10.913x - 5.160$

6. $y \approx -4.968x^2 + 10.913x - 5.160$

$\approx -4.968 \, (x^2 - 2.1967x + 1.0386)$

$$= -4.968 \left[x^2 - 2.1967x + \left(\frac{2.1967}{2} \right)^2 - \left(\frac{2.1967}{2} \right)^2 + 1.0386 \right]$$

$$= -4.968 \left[\left(x - \frac{2.1967}{2} \right)^2 - 0.1678 \right]$$

$$\approx -4.968 \, (x - 1.098)^2 + 0.833$$

Chapter 3
Exponential, Logistic, and Logarithmic Functions

■ Section 3.1 Exponential and Logistic Functions

Exploration 1

1. The point (0, 1) is common to all four graphs, and all four functions can be described as follows:

   Domain: $(-\infty, \infty)$
   Range: $(0, \infty)$
   Continuous
   Always increasing
   Not symmetric
   No local extrema
   Bounded below by $y = 0$, which is also the only
      asymptote
   $\lim\limits_{x\to\infty} f(x) = \infty$, $\lim\limits_{x\to-\infty} f(x) = 0$

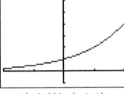

$y_1 = 2^x$

$[-2, 2]$ by $[-1, 6]$

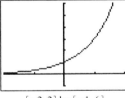

$y_2 = 3^x$

$[-2, 2]$ by $[-1, 6]$

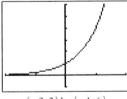

$y_3 = 4^x$

$[-2, 2]$ by $[-1, 6]$

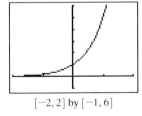

$y_4 = 5^x$

$[-2, 2]$ by $[-1, 6]$

2. The point (0, 1) is common to all four graphs, and all four functions can be described as follows:

   Domain: $(-\infty, \infty)$
   Range: $(0, \infty)$
   Continuous
   Always decreasing
   Not symmetric
   No local extrema
   Bounded below by $y = 0$, which is also the only
      asymptote
   $\lim\limits_{x\to\infty} g(x) = 0$, $\lim\limits_{x\to-\infty} g(x) = \infty$

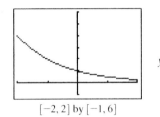

$y_1 = \left(\dfrac{1}{2}\right)^x$

$[-2, 2]$ by $[-1, 6]$

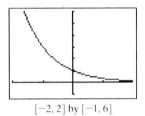

$y_2 = \left(\dfrac{1}{3}\right)^x$

$[-2, 2]$ by $[-1, 6]$

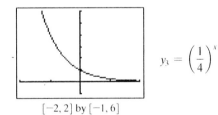

$y_3 = \left(\dfrac{1}{4}\right)^x$

$[-2, 2]$ by $[-1, 6]$

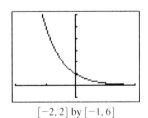

$y_4 = \left(\dfrac{1}{5}\right)^x$

$[-2, 2]$ by $[-1, 6]$

Exploration 2

1.

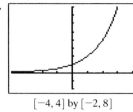

$f(x) = 2^x$

$[-4, 4]$ by $[-2, 8]$

2.

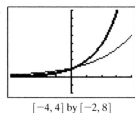

$f(x) = 2^x$
$g(x) = e^{0.4x}$

$[-4, 4]$ by $[-2, 8]$

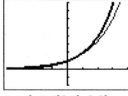

$f(x) = 2^x$
$g(x) = e^{0.5x}$

$[-4, 4]$ by $[-2, 8]$

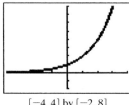

$f(x) = 2^x$
$g(x) = e^{0.6x}$

$[-4, 4]$ by $[-2, 8]$

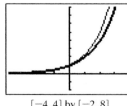

$f(x) = 2^x$
$g(x) = e^{0.7x}$

$[-4, 4]$ by $[-2, 8]$

$f(x) = 2^x$
$g(x) = e^{0.8x}$

$[-4, 4]$ by $[-2, 8]$

$k = 0.7$ most closely matches the graph of $f(x)$.

3. $k \approx 0.693$

Quick Review 3.1

1. $\sqrt[3]{-216} = -6$ since $(-6)^3 = -216$

2. $\sqrt[3]{\dfrac{125}{8}} = \dfrac{5}{2}$ since $5^3 = 125$ and $2^3 = 8$

3. $27^{2/3} = (3^3)^{2/3} = 3^2 = 9$

4. $4^{5/2} = (2^2)^{5/2} = 2^5 = 32$

5. $\dfrac{1}{2^{12}}$

6. $\dfrac{1}{3^8}$

7. $\dfrac{1}{a^6}$

8. b^{15}

9. -1.4 since $(-1.4)^5 = -5.37824$

10. 3.1, since $(3.1)^4 = 92.3521$

Section 3.1 Exercises

1. Not an exponential function because the base is variable and the exponent is constant. It is a power function.

2. Exponential function, with an initial value of 1 and base of 3.

3. Exponential function, with an initial value of 1 and base of 5.

4. Not an exponential function because the exponent is constant. It is a constant function.

5. Not an exponential function because the base is variable.

6. Not an exponential function because the base is variable. It is a power function.

7. $f(0) = 3 \cdot 5^0 = 3 \cdot 1 = 3$

8. $f(-2) = 6 \cdot 3^{-2} = \dfrac{6}{9} = \dfrac{2}{3}$

9. $f\left(\dfrac{1}{3}\right) = -2 \cdot 3^{1/3} = -2\sqrt[3]{3}$

10. $f\left(-\dfrac{3}{2}\right) = 8 \cdot 4^{-3/2} = \dfrac{8}{(2^2)^{3/2}} = \dfrac{8}{2^3} = \dfrac{8}{8} = 1$

11. $f(x) = \dfrac{3}{2} \cdot \left(\dfrac{1}{2}\right)^x$

12. $g(x) = 12 \cdot \left(\dfrac{1}{3}\right)^x$

13. $f(x) = 3 \cdot (\sqrt{2})^x = 3 \cdot 2^{x/2}$

14. $g(x) = 2 \cdot \left(\dfrac{1}{e}\right)^x = 2e^{-x}$

15. Translate $f(x) = 2^x$ by 3 units to the right. Alternatively,

$g(x) = 2^{x-3} = 2^{-3} \cdot 2^x = \dfrac{1}{8} \cdot 2^x = \dfrac{1}{8} \cdot f(x)$, so it can be

obtained from $f(x)$ using a vertical shrink by a factor of $\dfrac{1}{8}$.

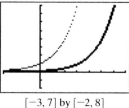

$[-3, 7]$ by $[-2, 8]$

16. Translate $f(x) = 3^x$ by 4 units to the left. Alternatively, $g(x) = 3^{x+4} = 3^4 \cdot 3^x = 81 \cdot 3^x = 81 \cdot f(x)$, so it can be obtained by vertically stretching $f(x)$ by a factor of 81.

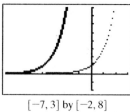

$[-7, 3]$ by $[-2, 8]$

17. Reflect $f(x) = 4^x$ over the y-axis.

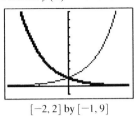

$[-2, 2]$ by $[-1, 9]$

18. Reflect $f(x) = 2^x$ over the y-axis and then shift by 5 units to the right.

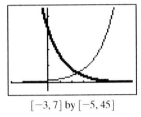

$[-3, 7]$ by $[-5, 45]$

19. Vertically stretch $f(x) = 0.5^x$ by a factor of 3 and then shift 4 units up.

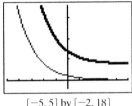

$[-5, 5]$ by $[-2, 18]$

20. Vertically stretch $f(x) = 0.6^x$ by a factor of 2 and then horizontally shrink by a factor of 3.

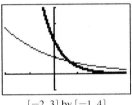

$[-2, 3]$ by $[-1, 4]$

21. Reflect $f(x) = e^x$ across the y-axis and horizontally shrink by a factor of 2.

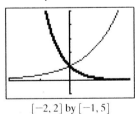

$[-2, 2]$ by $[-1, 5]$

22. Reflect $f(x) = e^x$ across the x-axis and y-axis. Then, horizontally shrink by a factor of 3.

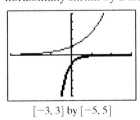

$[-3, 3]$ by $[-5, 5]$

23. Reflect $f(x) = e^x$ across the y-axis, horizontally shrink by a factor of 3, translate 1 unit to the right, and vertically stretch by a factor of 2.

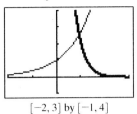

$[-2, 3]$ by $[-1, 4]$

24. Horizontally shrink $f(x) = e^x$ by a factor of 2, vertically stretch by a factor of 3 and shift down one unit.

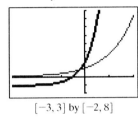

$[-3, 3]$ by $[-2, 8]$

25. Graph (a) is the only graph shaped and positioned like the graph of $y = b^x, b > 1$.

26. Graph (d) is the reflection of $y = 2^x$ across the y-axis.

27. Graph (c) is the reflection of $y = 2^x$ across the x-axis.

28. Graph (e) is the reflection of $y = 0.5^x$ across the x-axis.

29. Graph (b) is the graph of $y = 3^{-x}$ translated down 2 units.

30. Graph (f) is the graph of $y = 1.5^x$ translated down 2 units.

31. Exponential decay; $\lim_{x \to \infty} f(x) = 0$; $\lim_{x \to -\infty} f(x) = \infty$

32. Exponential decay; $\lim_{x \to \infty} f(x) = 0$; $\lim_{x \to -\infty} f(x) = \infty$

33. Exponential decay: $\lim_{x \to \infty} f(x) = 0$; $\lim_{x \to -\infty} f(x) = \infty$

34. Exponential growth: $\lim_{x \to \infty} f(x) = \infty$; $\lim_{x \to -\infty} f(x) = 0$

35. $x < 0$

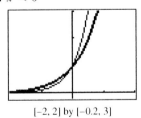

$[-2, 2]$ by $[-0.2, 3]$

36. $x > 0$

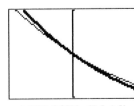

$[-0.25, 0.25]$ by $[0.5, 1.5]$

37. $x < 0$

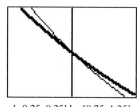

[−0.25, 0.25] by [0.75, 1.25]

38. $x > 0$

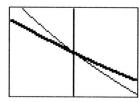

[−0.25, 0.25] by [0.75, 1.25]

39. $y_1 = y_3$, since $3^{2x+4} = 3^{2(x+2)} = (3^2)^{x+2} = 9^{x+2}$.

40. $y_2 = y_3$, since $2 \cdot 2^{3x-2} = 2^1 \, 2^{3x-2} = 2^{1+3x-2} = 2^{3x-1}$.

41. y-intercept: $(0, 4)$. Horizontal asymptotes: $y = 0$, $y = 12$.

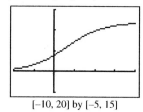

[−10, 20] by [−5, 15]

42. y-intercept: $(0, 3)$. Horizontal asymptotes: $y = 0$, $y = 18$.

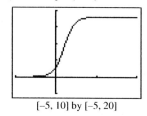

[−5, 10] by [−5, 20]

43. y-intercept: $(0, 4)$. Horizontal asymptotes: $y = 0$, $y = 16$.

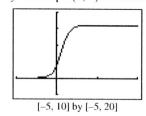

[−5, 10] by [−5, 20]

44. y-intercept: $(0, 3)$. Horizontal asymptotes: $y = 0$, $y = 9$.

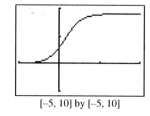

[−5, 10] by [−5, 10]

45.

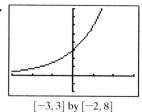

[−3, 3] by [−2, 8]

Domain: $(-\infty, \infty)$
Range: $(0, \infty)$
Continuous
Always increasing
Not symmetric
Bounded below by $y = 0$, which is also the only asymptote
No local extrema
$\lim\limits_{x \to \infty} f(x) = \infty$, $\lim\limits_{x \to -\infty} f(x) = 0$

46.

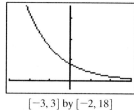

[−3, 3] by [−2, 18]

Domain: $(-\infty, \infty)$
Range: $(0, \infty)$
Continuous
Always decreasing
Not symmetric
Bounded below by $y = 0$, which is the only asymptote
No local extrema
$\lim\limits_{x \to \infty} f(x) = 0$, $\lim\limits_{x \to -\infty} f(x) = \infty$

47.

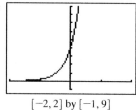

[−2, 2] by [−1, 9]

Domain: $(-\infty, \infty)$
Range: $(0, \infty)$
Continuous
Always increasing
Not symmetric
Bounded below by $y = 0$, which is the only asymptote
No local extrema
$\lim\limits_{x \to \infty} f(x) = \infty$, $\lim\limits_{x \to -\infty} f(x) = 0$

48.

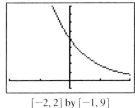

$[-2, 2]$ by $[-1, 9]$

Domain: $(-\infty, \infty)$
Range: $(0, \infty)$
Continuous
Always decreasing
Not symmetric
Bounded below by $y = 0$, which is also the only asymptote
No local extrema
$\lim\limits_{x \to \infty} f(x) = 0$, $\lim\limits_{x \to -\infty} f(x) = \infty$

49.

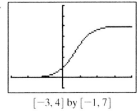

$[-3, 4]$ by $[-1, 7]$

Domain: $(-\infty, \infty)$
Range: $(0, 5)$
Continuous
Always increasing
Symmetric about $(0.69, 2.5)$
Bounded below by $y = 0$ and above by $y = 5$; both are asymptotes
No local extrema
$\lim\limits_{x \to \infty} f(x) = 5$, $\lim\limits_{x \to -\infty} f(x) = 0$

50.

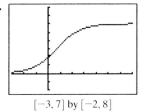

$[-3, 7]$ by $[-2, 8]$

Domain: $(-\infty, \infty)$
Range: $(0, 6)$
Continuous
Always increasing
Symmetric about $(0.69, 3)$
Bounded below by $y = 0$ and above by $y = 6$; both are asymptotes
No local extrema
$\lim\limits_{x \to \infty} f(x) = 6$, $\lim\limits_{x \to -\infty} f(x) = 0$

For #51–52, refer to Example 7 on page 285 in the text.

51. Let $P(t)$ be Austin's population t years after 1990. Then with exponential growth, $P(t) = P_0 b^t$ where $P_0 = 465,622$. From Table 3.7, $P(10) = 465,622 b^{10} = 656,562$. So,

$$b = \sqrt[10]{\frac{656,562}{465,622}} \approx 1.0350.$$

Solving graphically, we find that the curve $y = 465,622(1.0350)^t$ intersects the line $y = 800,000$ at $t \approx 15.75$. Austin's population will pass 800,000 in 2006.

52. Let $P(t)$ be the Columbus's population t years after 1990. Then with exponential growth, $P(t) = P_0 b^t$ where $P_0 = 632,910$. From Table 3.7, $P(10) = 632,910 b^{10} = 711,470$. So,

$$b = \sqrt[10]{\frac{711,470}{632,910}} \approx 1.0118.$$

Solving graphically, we find that the curve $y = 632,910(1.0118)^t$ intersects the line $y = 800,000$ at $t \approx 20.02$. Columbus's population will pass 800,000 in 2010.

53. Using the results from Exercises 51 and 52, we represent Austin's population as $y = 465,622(1.0350)^t$ and Columbus's population as $y = 632,910(1.0118)^t$. Solving graphically, we find that the curves intersect at $t \approx 13.54$. The two populations will be equal, at 741,862, in 2003.

54. From the results in Exercise 53, the populations are equal at 741,862. Austin has the faster growth after that, because b is bigger ($1.0350 > 1.0118$). So Austin will reach 1 million first. Solving graphically, we find that the curve $y = 465,622(1.0350)^t$ intersects the line $y = 1,000,000$ at $t \approx 22.22$. Austin's population will reach 1 million in 2012.

55. Solving graphically, we find that the curve

$$y = \frac{12.79}{(1 + 2.402e^{-0.0309x})}$$ intersects the line $y = 10$ when

$t \approx 69.67$. Ohio's population stood at 10 million in 1969.

56. (a) $P(50) = \dfrac{19.875}{1 + 57.993e^{-0.035005(50)}} \approx 1.794558$
or 1,794,558 people

(b) $P(210) = \dfrac{19.875}{1 + 57.993e^{-0.035005(210)}} \approx 19.161673$ or 19,161,673 people

(c) $\lim\limits_{x \to \infty} P(t) = 19.875$ or 19,875,000 people.

57. (a) When $t = 0$, $B = 100$.

(b) When $t = 6$, $B \approx 6394$.

58. (a) When $t = 0$, $C = 20$ grams.

(b) When $t = 10,400$, $C \approx 5.647$. After about 5700.22 years, 10 grams remain.

59. False. If $a > 0$ and $0 < b < 1$, or if $a < 0$ and $b > 1$, then $f(x) = a \cdot b^x$ is decreasing.

60. True. For $f(x) = \dfrac{c}{1 + a \cdot b^x}$ the horizontal asymptotes are $y = 0$ and $y = c$, where c is the limit of growth.

61. Only 8^x has the form $a \cdot b^x$ with a nonzero and b positive but not equal to 1. The answer is E.

62. For $b > 0$, $f(0) = b^0 = 1$. The answer is C.

63. The growth factor of $f(x) = a \cdot b^x$ is the base b. The answer is A.

64. With $x > 0$, $a^x > b^x$ requires $a > b$ (regardless of whether $x < 1$ or $x > 1$). The answer is B.

65. (a)

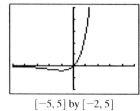

$[-5, 5]$ by $[-2, 5]$

Domain: $(-\infty, \infty)$

Range: $\left[-\dfrac{1}{e}, \infty \right)$

Intercept: $(0, 0)$

Decreasing on $(-\infty, -1]$: Increasing on $[-1, \infty)$

Bounded below by $y = -\dfrac{1}{e}$

Local minimum at $\left(-1, -\dfrac{1}{e} \right)$

Asymptote $y = 0$.

$\lim\limits_{x \to \infty} f(x) = \infty$, $\lim\limits_{x \to -\infty} f(x) = 0$

(b)

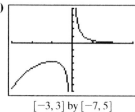

$[-3, 3]$ by $[-7, 5]$

Domain: $(-\infty, 0) \cup (0, \infty)$
Range: $(-\infty, -e] \cup (0, \infty)$
No intercepts
Increasing on $(-\infty, -1]$;
Decreasing on $[-1, 0) \cup (0, \infty)$
Not bounded
Local maxima at $(-1, -e)$
Asymptotes: $x = 0$, $y = 0$.
$\lim\limits_{x \to \infty} g(x) = 0$, $\lim\limits_{x \to -\infty} g(x) = -\infty$

66. (a) $2^x = (2^2)^2 = 2^4$, so $x = 4$

(b) $3^x = 3^3$, so $x = 3$

(c) $8^{x/2} = 4^{x+1}, (2^2)^{x/2} = (2^2)^{x+1} \cdot \dfrac{3x}{2} = 2x + 2,$

$3x = 4x + 4, x = -4$

(d) $9^x = 3^{x+1}, (3^2)^x = 3^{x+1}, 2x = x + 1, x = 1$

67. (a) y_1—$f(x)$ decreases less rapidly as x decreases.

(b) y_3—as x increases, $g(x)$ decreases ever more rapidly.

68. $c = 2^a$: to the graph of $(2^a)^x$ apply a vertical stretch by 2^b, since $f(ax + b) = 2^{ax+b} = 2^{ax}2^b = (2^b)(2^a)^x$.

69. $a \neq 0, c = 2$.

70. $a < 0, c = 1$.

71. $a > 0$ and $b > 1$, or $a < 0$ and $0 < b < 1$.

72. $a > 0$ and $0 < b < 1$, or $a < 0$ and $b > 1$.

73. Since $0 < b < 1$, $\lim\limits_{x \to -\infty} (1 + a \cdot b^x) = \infty$ and

$\lim\limits_{x \to \infty} (1 + a \cdot b^x) = 1$. Thus, $\lim\limits_{x \to -\infty} \dfrac{c}{1 + a \cdot b^x} = 0$ and

$\lim\limits_{x \to \infty} \dfrac{c}{1 + a \cdot b^x} = c$.

■ Section 3.2 Exponential and Logistic Modeling

Quick Review 3.2

1. 0.15

2. 4%

3. $(1.07)(23)$

4. $(0.96)(52)$

5. $b^2 = \dfrac{160}{40} = 4$, so $b = \pm\sqrt{4} = \pm 2$.

6. $b^3 = \dfrac{9}{243}$, so $b = \sqrt[3]{\dfrac{9}{243}} = \sqrt[3]{\dfrac{1}{27}} = \dfrac{1}{3}$.

7. $b = \sqrt[6]{\dfrac{838}{782}} \approx 1.01$

8. $b = \sqrt[5]{\dfrac{521}{93}} \approx 1.41$

9. $b = \sqrt[4]{\dfrac{91}{672}} \approx 0.61$

10. $b = \sqrt[7]{\dfrac{56}{127}} \approx 0.89$

Section 3.2 Exercises

For #1–20, use the model $P(t) = P_0(1 + r)^t$.

1. $r = 0.09$, so $P(t)$ is an exponential growth function of 9%.

2. $r = 0.018$, so $P(t)$ is an exponential growth function of 1.8%.

3. $r = -0.032$, so $f(x)$ is an exponential decay function of 3.2%.

4. $r = -0.0032$, so $f(x)$ is an exponential decay function of 0.32%.

5. $r = 1$, so $g(t)$ is an exponential growth function of 100%.

6. $r = -0.95$, so $g(t)$ is an exponential decay function of 95%.

7. $f(x) = 5 \cdot (1 + 0.17)^x = 5 \cdot 1.17^x$ (x = years)

8. $f(x) = 52 \cdot (1 + 0.023)^x = 52 \cdot 1.023^x$ (x = days)

9. $f(x) = 16 \cdot (1 - 0.5)^x = 16 \cdot 0.5^x$ (x = months)

10. $f(x) = 5 \cdot (1 - 0.0059) = 5 \cdot 0.9941^x$ (x = weeks)

11. $f(x) = 28{,}900 \cdot (1 - 0.026)^x = 28{,}900 \cdot 0.974^x$ (x = years)

12. $f(x) = 502{,}000 \cdot (1 + 0.017)^x = 502{,}000 \cdot 1.017^x$ (x = years)

13. $f(x) = 18 \cdot (1 + 0.052)^x = 18 \cdot 1.052^x$ (x = weeks)

14. $f(x) = 15 \cdot (1 - 0.046)^x = 15 \cdot 0.954^x$ (x = days)

15. $f(x) = 0.6 \cdot 2^{x/3}$ (x = days)

16. $f(x) = 250 \cdot 2^{x/7.5} = 250 \cdot 2^{2x/15}$ (x = hours)

17. $f(x) = 592 \cdot 2^{-x/6}$ (x = years)

18. $f(x) = 17 \cdot 2^{-x/32}$ (x = hours)

19. $f_0 = 2.3, \dfrac{2.875}{2.3} = 1.25 = r + 1$, so

$f(x) = 2.3 \cdot 1.25^x$ (Growth Model)

20. $g_0 = -5.8, \dfrac{-4.64}{-5.8} = 0.8 = r + 1$, so

$g(x) = -5.8 \cdot (0.8)^x$ (Decay Model)

For #21–22, use $f(x) = f_0 \cdot b^x$

21. $f_0 = 4$, so $f(x) = 4 \cdot b^x$. Since $f(5) = 4 \cdot b^5 = 8.05$,

$b^5 = \dfrac{8.05}{4}, b = \sqrt[5]{\dfrac{8.05}{4}} \approx 1.15. f(x) \approx 4 \cdot 1.15^x$

22. $f_0 = 3$, so $f(x) = 3 \cdot b^x$. Since $f(4) = 3 \cdot b^4 = 1.49$

$b^4 = \dfrac{1.49}{3}, b = \sqrt[4]{\dfrac{1.49}{3}} \approx 0.84. f(x) \approx 3 \cdot 0.84^x$

For #23–28, use the model $f(x) = \dfrac{c}{1 + a \cdot b^x}$.

23. $c = 40, a = 3$, so $f(1) = \dfrac{40}{1 + 3b} = 20, 20 + 60b = 40$,

$60b = 20, b = \dfrac{1}{3}$, thus $f(x) = \dfrac{40}{1 + 3 \cdot \left(\dfrac{1}{3}\right)^x}$.

24. $c = 60, a = 4$, so $f(1) = \dfrac{60}{1 + 4b} = 24, 60 = 24 + 96b$,

$96b = 36, b = \dfrac{3}{8}$, thus $f(x) = \dfrac{60}{1 + 4\left(\dfrac{3}{8}\right)^x}$.

25. $c = 128, a = 7$, so $f(5) = \dfrac{128}{1 + 7b^5} = 32$,

$128 = 32 + 224b^5, 224b^5 = 96, b^5 = \dfrac{96}{224}$,

$b = \sqrt[5]{\dfrac{96}{224}} \approx 0.844$, thus $f(x) \approx \dfrac{128}{1 + 7 \cdot 0.844^x}$.

26. $c = 30, a = 5$, so $f(3) = \dfrac{30}{1 + 5b^3} = 15, 30 = 15 + 75b^3$,

$75b^3 = 15, b^3 = \dfrac{15}{75} = \dfrac{1}{5}, b = \sqrt[3]{\dfrac{1}{5}} \approx 0.585$,

thus $f(x) \approx \dfrac{30}{1 + 5 \cdot 0.585^x}$.

27. $c = 20, a = 3$, so $f(2) = \dfrac{20}{1 + 3b^2} = 10, 20 = 10 + 30b^2$,

$30b^2 = 10, b^2 = \dfrac{1}{3}, b = \sqrt{\dfrac{1}{3}} \approx 0.58$,

thus $f(x) = \dfrac{20}{1 + 3 \cdot 0.58^x}$.

28. $c = 60, a = 3$, so $f(8) = \dfrac{60}{1 + 3b^8} = 30, 60 = 30 + 90b^8$,

$90b^8 = 30, b^8 = \dfrac{1}{3}, b = \sqrt[8]{\dfrac{1}{3}} \approx 0.87$,

thus $f(x) = \dfrac{60}{1 + 3 \cdot 0.87^x}$.

29. $P(t) = 736,000(1.0149)^t; P(t) = 1,000,000$ when $t \approx 20.73$ years, or the year 2020.

30. $P(t) = 478,000(1.0628)^t; P(t) = 1,000,000$ when $t \approx 12.12$ years, or the year 2012.

31. The model is $P(t) = 6250(1.0275)^t$.

  (a) In 1915: about $P(25) \approx 12,315$. In 1940: about $P(50) \approx 24,265$.

  (b) $P(t) = 50,000$ when $t \approx 76.65$ years after 1890 — in 1966.

32. The model is $P(t) = 4200(1.0225)^t$.

  (a) In 1930: about $P(20) \approx 6554$. In 1945: about $P(35) \approx 9151$.

  (b) $P(t) = 20,000$ when $t \approx 70.14$ years after 1910 — about 1980.

33. (a) $y = 6.6\left(\dfrac{1}{2}\right)^{t/14}$, where t is time in days.

  (b) After 38.11 days.

34. (a) $y = 3.5\left(\dfrac{1}{2}\right)^{t/65}$, where t is time in days.

  (b) After 117.48 days.

35. One possible answer: Exponential and linear functions are similar in that they are always increasing or always decreasing. However, the two functions vary in how *quickly* they increase or decrease. While a linear function will increase or decrease at a steady rate over a given interval, the rate at which exponential functions increase or decrease over a given interval will vary.

36. One possible answer: Exponential functions and logistic functions are similar in the sense that they are always increasing or always decreasing. They differ, however, in the sense that logistic functions have both an upper and lower limit to their growth (or decay), while exponential functions generally have only a lower limit. (Exponential functions just keep growing.)

37. One possible answer: From the graph we see that the doubling time for this model is 4 years. This is the time required to double from 50,000 to 100,000, from 100,000 to 200,000, or from any population size to twice that size. Regardless of the population size, it takes 4 years for it to double.

38. One possible answer: The number of atoms of a radioactive substance that change to a nonradioactive state in a given time is a fixed percentage of the number of radioactive atoms initially present. So the time it takes for half of the atoms to change state (the half-life) does not depend on the initial amount.

39. When $t = 1, B \approx 200$—the population doubles every hour.

40. The half-life is about 5700 years.

For #41–42, use the formula $P(h) = 14.7 \cdot 0.5^{h/3.6}$, where h is miles above sea level.

41. $P(10) = 14.7 \cdot 0.5^{10/3.6} = 2.14$ lb/in^2

42. $P(h) = 14.7 \cdot 0.5^{h/3.6}$ intersects $y = 2.5$ when $h \approx 9.20$ miles above sea level.

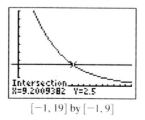

[−1, 19] by [−1, 9]

43. The exponential regression model is
$P(t) = 1149.61904(1.012133)^t$, where $P(t)$ is measured in thousands of people and t is years since 1900. The predicted population for Los Angeles for 2003 is $P(103) \approx 3981$, or 3,981,000 people. This is an overestimate of 161,000 people, an error of $\dfrac{161,000}{3,820,000} \approx 0.04 = 4\%$.

44. The exponential regression model using 1950–2000 data is
$P(t) = 20.84002(1.04465)^t$, where $P(t)$ is measured in thousands of people and t is years since 1900. The predicted population for Phoenix for 2003 is $P(103) \approx 1874$, or 1,874,000 people. This is an overestimate of 486,000 people, an error of $\dfrac{486,000}{1,388,000} \approx 0.35 = 35\%$.

The exponential regression model using 1960–2000 data is $P(t) = 86.70393(1.02760)^t$, where $P(t)$ is measured in thousands of people and t is years since 1900. The predicted population for Phoenix for 2003 is $P(103) \approx 1432$, or 1,432,000 people. This is an overestimate of 44,000 people, an error of $\dfrac{44,000}{1,388,000} \approx 0.03 = 3\%$.

The equations in #45–46 can be solved either algebraically or graphically; the latter approach is generally faster.

45. (a) $P(0) = 16$ students.

(b) $P(t) = 200$ when $t \approx 13.97$ — about 14 days.

(c) $P(t) = 300$ when $t \approx 16.90$ — about 17 days.

46. (a) $P(0) = 11$.

(b) $P(t) = 600$ when $t \approx 24.51$ — after 24 or 25 years.

(c) As $t \to \infty$, $P(t) \to 1001$—the population never rises above this level.

47. The logistic regression model is
$P(x) = \dfrac{837.7707752}{1 + 9.668309563e^{-.015855579x}}$, where x is the number of years since 1900 and $P(x)$ is measured in millions of people. In the year 2010, $x = 110$, so the model predicts a population of

$P(110) = \dfrac{837.7707752}{1 + 9.668309563e^{(-.015855579)(110)}} = $
$\dfrac{837.7707752}{1 + 9.668309563e^{(-1.74411369)}} = \dfrac{837.7707752}{2.690019034} \approx 311.4$
$\approx 311,400,000$ people.

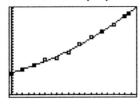

[–1, 109] by [0, 310]

48. $P(t) \approx \dfrac{1,301,614}{1 + 21.603 \cdot e^{-0.05055t}}$, which is the same model as the solution in Example 8 of Section 3.1. Note that t represents the number of years since 1900.

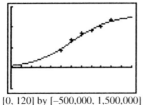

[0, 120] by [–500,000, 1,500,000]

49. $P(x) \approx \dfrac{19.875}{1 + 57.993e^{-0.035005x}}$ where x is the number of years after 1800 and P is measured in millions. Our model is the same as the model in Exercise 56 of Section 3.1.

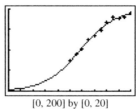

[0, 200] by [0, 20]

50. $P(x) \approx \dfrac{15.64}{1 + 11799.36e^{-0.043241x}}$, where x is the number of years since 1800 and P is measured in millions.

As $x \to \infty$, $P(x) \to 15.64$, or nearly 16 million, which is significantly less than New York's population limit of 20 million. The population of Arizona, according to our models, will not surpass the population of New York. Our graph confirms this.

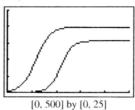

[0, 500] by [0, 25]

51. False. This is true for *logistic* growth, not for exponential growth.

52. False. When $r < 0$, the base of the function, $1 + r$, is merely less than 1.

53. The base is $1.049 = 1 + 0.049$, so the constant percentage growth rate is $0.049 = 4.9\%$. The answer is C.

54. The base is $0.834 = 1 - 0.166$, so the constant percentage decay rate is $0.166 = 16.6\%$. The answer is B.

55. The growth can be modeled as $P(t) = 1 \cdot 2^{t/4}$. Solve $P(t) = 1000$ to find $t \approx 39.86$. The answer is D.

56. Check $S(0), S(2), S(4), S(6),$ and $S(8)$. The answer is E.

57. (a) $P(x) \approx \dfrac{694.27}{1 + 7.90e^{-0.017x}}$, where x is the number of years since 1900 and P is measured in millions. $P(100) \approx 277.9$, or 277,900,000 people.

(b) The logistic model underestimates the 2000 population by about 3.5 million, an error of around 1.2%.

(c) The logistic model predicted a value closer to the actual value than the exponential model, perhaps indicating a better fit.

58. (a) Using the exponential growth model and the data from 1900–2050, Mexico's population can be represented by $M(x) \approx 13.62 \cdot 1.018^x$ where x is the number of years since 1900 and M is measured in millions. Using 1900–2000 data for the U.S., and the exponential growth model, the population of the United States can be represented by $P(x) \approx 80.55 \cdot 1.013^x$, where x is the number of years since 1900 and P is measured in millions. Since Mexico's rate of growth outpaces the United States' rate of growth, the model predicts that

Mexico will eventually have a larger population. Our graph indicates this will occur at $x \approx 349$, or 2249.

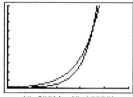

[0, 500] by [0, 10000]

(b) Using logistic growth models and the same data,

$$M(x) \approx \frac{165.38}{1 + 39.65e^{-0.041x}} \text{ while}$$

$$P(x) \approx \frac{798.80}{1 + 9.19e^{-0.016x}}$$

Using this model, Mexico's population will not exceed that of the United States, confirmed by our graph.

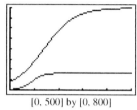

[0, 500] by [0, 800]

(c) According to the logistic growth models, the maximum sustainable populations are:
Mexico—165 million people.
U.S.—799 million people.

(d) Answers will vary. However, a logistic model acknowledges that there is a limit to how much a country's population can grow.

59. $\sinh(-x) = \dfrac{e^{-x} - e^{-(-x)}}{2} = \dfrac{e^{-x} - e^{x}}{2}$

$= -\left(\dfrac{e^{x} - e^{-x}}{2}\right) = -\sinh(x)$, so the function is odd.

60. $\cosh(-x) = \dfrac{e^{-x} + e^{-(-x)}}{2} = \dfrac{e^{-x} + e^{x}}{2} = \dfrac{e^{x} + e^{-x}}{2}$

$= \cosh(x)$, so the function is even.

61. (a) $\dfrac{\sinh(x)}{\cosh(x)} = \dfrac{\dfrac{e^{x} - e^{-x}}{2}}{\dfrac{e^{x} + e^{-x}}{2}}$

$= \dfrac{e^{x} - e^{-x}}{2} \cdot \dfrac{2}{e^{x} + e^{-x}} = \dfrac{e^{x} - e^{-x}}{e^{x} + e^{-x}} = \tanh(x)$.

(b) $\tanh(-x) = \dfrac{e^{-x} - e^{-(-x)}}{e^{-x} + e^{-(-x)}} = \dfrac{e^{-x} - e^{x}}{e^{-x} + e^{x}}$

$= -\dfrac{e^{x} - e^{-x}}{e^{x} + e^{-x}} = -\tanh(x)$, so the function is odd.

(c) $f(x) = 1 + \tanh(x) = 1 + \dfrac{e^{x} - e^{-x}}{e^{x} + e^{-x}}$

$= \dfrac{e^{x} + e^{-x} + e^{x} - e^{-x}}{e^{x} + e^{-x}} = \dfrac{2e^{x}}{e^{x} + e^{-x}}$

$= \dfrac{e^{x}}{e^{x}}\left(\dfrac{2}{1 + e^{-x}e^{-x}}\right) = \dfrac{2}{1 + e^{-2x}}$,

which is a logistic function of $c = 2$, $a = 1$, and $k = 2$.

■ Section 3.3 Logarithmic Functions and Their Graphs

Exploration 1

1.

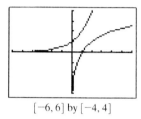

$[-6, 6]$ by $[-4, 4]$

2. Same graph as part 1.

Quick Review 3.3

1. $\dfrac{1}{25} = 0.04$

2. $\dfrac{1}{1000} = 0.001$

3. $\dfrac{1}{5} = 0.2$

4. $\dfrac{1}{2} = 0.5$

5. $\dfrac{2^{33}}{2^{28}} = 2^{5} = 32$

6. $\dfrac{3^{26}}{3^{24}} = 3^{2} = 9$

7. $5^{1/2}$

8. $10^{1/3}$

9. $\left(\dfrac{1}{e}\right)^{1/2} = e^{-1/2}$

10. $\left(\dfrac{1}{e^{2}}\right)^{1/3} = e^{-2/3}$

Section 3.3 Exercises

1. $\log_4 4 = 1$ because $4^1 = 4$

2. $\log_6 1 = 0$ because $6^0 = 1$

3. $\log_2 32 = 5$ because $2^5 = 32$

4. $\log_3 81 = 4$ because $3^4 = 81$

5. $\log_5 \sqrt[3]{25} = \dfrac{2}{3}$ because $5^{2/3} = \sqrt[3]{25}$

6. $\log_6 \dfrac{1}{\sqrt[5]{36}} = -\dfrac{2}{5}$ because $6^{-2/5} = \dfrac{1}{6^{2/5}} = \dfrac{1}{\sqrt[5]{36}}$

7. $\log 10^3 = 3$

8. $\log 10,000 = \log 10^4 = 4$

9. $\log 100,000 = \log 10^5 = 5$

10. $\log 10^{-4} = -4$

11. $\log \sqrt[3]{10} = \log 10^{1/3} = \dfrac{1}{3}$

12. $\log \dfrac{1}{\sqrt{1000}} = \log 10^{-3/2} = \dfrac{-3}{2}$

13. $\ln e^3 = 3$

14. $\ln e^{-4} = -4$

15. $\ln \dfrac{1}{e} = \ln e^{-1} = -1$

16. $\ln 1 = \ln e^0 = 0$

17. $\ln \sqrt[4]{e} = \ln e^{1/4} = \dfrac{1}{4}$

18. $\ln \dfrac{1}{\sqrt{e^7}} = \ln e^{-7/2} = \dfrac{-7}{2}$

19. 3, because $b^{\log_b 3} = 3$ for any $b > 0$.

20. 8, because $b^{\log_b 8} = 8$ for any $b > 0$.

21. $10^{\log (0.5)} = 10^{\log_{10} (0.5)} = 0.5$

22. $10^{\log 14} = 10^{\log_{10} 14} = 14$

23. $e^{\ln 6} = e^{\log_e 6} = 6$

24. $e^{\ln (1/5)} = e^{\log_e (1/5)} = 1/5$

25. $\log 9.43 \approx 0.9745 \approx 0.975$ and $10^{0.9745} \approx 9.43$

26. $\log 0.908 \approx -0.042$ and $10^{-0.042} \approx 0.908$

27. $\log (-14)$ is undefined because $-14 < 0$.

28. $\log (-5.14)$ is undefined because $-5.14 < 0$.

29. $\ln 4.05 \approx 1.399$ and $e^{1.399} \approx 4.05$

30. $\ln 0.733 \approx -0.311$ and $e^{-0.311} \approx 0.733$

31. $\ln (-0.49)$ is undefined because $-0.49 < 0$.

32. $\ln (-3.3)$ is undefined because $-3.3 < 0$.

33. $x = 10^2 = 100$

34. $x = 10^4 = 10,000$

35. $x = 10^{-1} = \dfrac{1}{10} = 0.1$

36. $x = 10^{-3} = \dfrac{1}{1000} = 0.001$

37. $f(x)$ is undefined for $x > 1$. The answer is (d).

38. $f(x)$ is undefined for $x < -1$. The answer is (b).

39. $f(x)$ is undefined for $x < 3$. The answer is (a).

40. $f(x)$ is undefined for $x > 4$. The answer is (c).

41. Starting from $y = \ln x$: translate left 3 units.

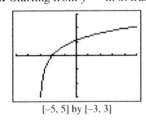

$[-5, 5]$ by $[-3, 3]$

42. Starting from $y = \ln x$: translate up 2 units.

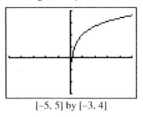

$[-5, 5]$ by $[-3, 4]$

43. Starting from $y = \ln x$: reflect across the y-axis and translate up 3 units.

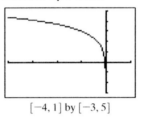

$[-4, 1]$ by $[-3, 5]$

44. Starting from $y = \ln x$: reflect across the y-axis and translate down 2 units.

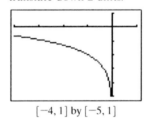

$[-4, 1]$ by $[-5, 1]$

45. Starting from $y = \ln x$: reflect across the y-axis and translate right 2 units.

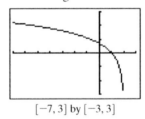

$[-7, 3]$ by $[-3, 3]$

46. Starting from $y = \ln x$: reflect across the y-axis and translate right 5 units.

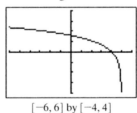

$[-6, 6]$ by $[-4, 4]$

47. Starting from $y = \log x$: translate down 1 unit.

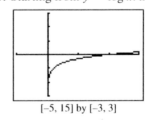

$[-5, 15]$ by $[-3, 3]$

48. Starting from $y = \log x$: translate right 3 units.

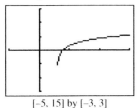

[-5, 15] by [-3, 3]

49. Starting from $y = \log x$: reflect across both axes and vertically stretch by 2.

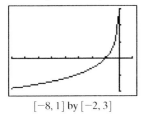

[-8, 1] by [-2, 3]

50. Starting from $y = \log x$: reflect across both axes and vertically stretch by 3.

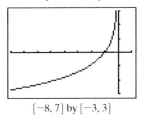

[-8, 7] by [-3, 3]

51. Starting from $y = \log x$: reflect across the y-axis, translate right 3 units, vertically stretch by 2, translate down 1 unit.

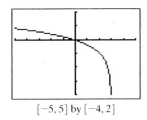

[-5, 5] by [-4, 2]

52. Starting from $y = \log x$: reflect across both axes, translate right 1 unit, vertically stretch by 3, translate up 1 unit.

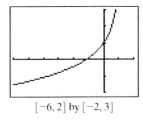

[-6, 2] by [-2, 3]

53.

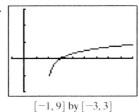

[-1, 9] by [-3, 3]

Domain: $(2, \infty)$
Range: $(-\infty, \infty)$
Continuous
Always increasing
Not symmetric
Not bounded
No local extrema
Asymptote at $x = 2$
$\lim\limits_{x \to \infty} f(x) = \infty$

54.

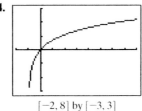

[-2, 8] by [-3, 3]

Domain: $(-1, \infty)$
Range: $(-\infty, \infty)$
Continuous
Always increasing
Not symmetric
Not bounded
No local extrema
Asymptote: $x = -1$
$\lim\limits_{x \to \infty} f(x) = \infty$

55.

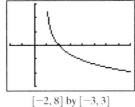

[-2, 8] by [-3, 3]

Domain: $(1, \infty)$
Range: $(-\infty, \infty)$
Continuous
Always decreasing
Not symmetric
Not bounded
No local extrema
Asymptotes: $x = 1$
$\lim\limits_{x \to \infty} f(x) = -\infty$

56.

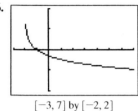

[−3, 7] by [−2, 2]

Domain: $(-2, \infty)$
Range: $(-\infty, \infty)$
Continuous
Always decreasing
Not symmetric
Not bounded
No local extrema
Asymptotes: $x = -2$
$\lim\limits_{x \to \infty} f(x) = -\infty$

57.

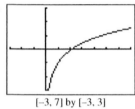

[−3, 7] by [−3, 3]

Domain: $(0, \infty)$
Range: $(-\infty, \infty)$
Continuous
Increasing on its domain
No symmetry
Not bounded
No local extrema
Asymptote at $x = 0$
$\lim\limits_{x \to \infty} f(x) = \infty$

58.

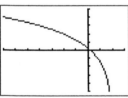

[−7, 3, 1] by [−10, 10, 2]

Domain: $(-\infty, 2)$
Range: $(-\infty, \infty)$
Continuous
Decreasing on its domain
No symmetry
Not bounded
No local extrema
Asymptote at $x = 2$.
$\lim\limits_{x \to -\infty} f(x) = \infty$

59. (a) $\beta = 10 \log \left(\dfrac{10^{-11}}{10^{-12}} \right) = 10 \log 10 = 10(1) = 10 \text{ dB}$

(b) $\beta = 10 \log \left(\dfrac{10^{-5}}{10^{-12}} \right) = 10 \log 10^7 = 10(7) = 70 \text{ dB}$

(c) $\beta = 10 \log \left(\dfrac{10^{3}}{10^{-12}} \right) = 10 \log 10^{15} = 10(15) = 150 \text{ dB}$

60. $I = 12 \cdot 10^{-0.0705} \approx 10.2019$ lumens.

61. The logarithmic regression model is
$y = -246461780.3 + 32573678.51 \ln x$, where x is the
year and y is the population. Graph the function and use
TRACE to find that $x \approx 2023$ when $y \approx 150,000,000$.
The population of San Antonio will reach 1,500,000 people in the year 2023.

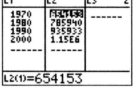

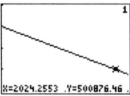

[1970, 2030] by [600,000, 1,700,000]

62. The logarithmic regression model is
$y = 56360880.18 - 7337490.871 \ln x$, where x is the year
and y is the population. Graph the function and use
TRACE to find that $x \approx 2024$ when $y \approx 500,000$. The
population of Milwaukee will reach 500,000 people in the
year 2024.

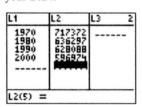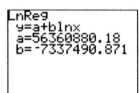

[1970, 2030] by [400,000, 800,000]

63. True, by the definition of a logarithmic function.

64. True, by the definition of common logarithm.

65. $\log 2 \approx 0.30103$. The answer is C.

66. $\log 5 \approx 0.699$ but $2.5 \log 2 \approx 0.753$. The answer is A.

67. The graph of $f(x) = \ln x$ lies entirely to the right of the
origin. The answer is B.

68. For $f(x) = 2 \cdot 3^x$, $f^{-1}(x) = \log_3(x/2)$
because $f^{-1}(f(x)) = \log_3(2 \cdot 3^x/2)$
$\qquad\qquad\qquad = \log_3 3^x$
$\qquad\qquad\qquad = x$

The answer is A.

69.

$f(x)$	3^x	$\log_3 x$
Domain	$(-\infty, \infty)$	$(0, \infty)$
Range	$(0, \infty)$	$(-\infty, \infty)$
Intercepts	$(0, 1)$	$(1, 0)$
Asymptotes	$y = 0$	$x = 0$

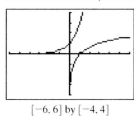

$[-6, 6]$ by $[-4, 4]$

70.

$f(x)$	5^x	$\log_5 x$
Domain	$(-\infty, \infty)$	$(0, \infty)$
Range	$(0, \infty)$	$(-\infty, \infty)$
Intercepts	$(0, 1)$	$(1, 0)$
Asymptotes	$y = 0$	$x = 0$

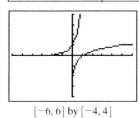

$[-6, 6]$ by $[-4, 4]$

71. $b = \sqrt[e]{e}$. The point that is common to both graphs is (e, e).

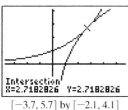

Intersection
X=2.7182826   Y=2.7182826

$[-3.7, 5.7]$ by $[-2.1, 4.1]$

72. 0 is not in the domain of the logarithm functions because 0 is not in the range of exponential functions; that is, a^x is never equal to 0.

73. Reflect across the x-axis.

74. Reflect across the x-axis.

■ Section 3.4 Properties of Logarithmic Functions

Exploration 1

1. $\log (2 \cdot 4) \approx 0.90309$,
$\log 2 + \log 4 \approx 0.30103 + 0.60206 \approx 0.90309$

2. $\log \left(\dfrac{8}{2}\right) \approx 0.60206$, $\log 8 - \log 2 \approx 0.90309 - 0.30103$
≈ 0.60206

3. $\log 2^3 \approx 0.90309$, $3 \log 2 \approx 3(0.30103) \approx 0.90309$

4. $\log 5 = \log \left(\dfrac{10}{2}\right) = \log 10 - \log 2 \approx 1 - 0.30103$
$= 0.69897$

5. $\log 16 = \log 2^4 = 4 \log 2 \approx 1.20412$
$\log 32 = \log 2^5 = 5 \log 2 \approx 1.50515$
$\log 64 = \log 2^6 = 6 \log 2 \approx 1.80618$

6. $\log 25 = \log 5^2 = 2 \log 5 = 2 \log \left(\dfrac{10}{2}\right)$
$= 2(\log 10 - \log 2) \approx 1.39794$
$\log 40 = \log (4 \cdot 10) = \log 4 + \log 10 \approx 1.60206$
$\log 50 = \log \left(\dfrac{100}{2}\right) = \log 100 - \log 2 \approx 1.69897$

The list consists of 1, 2, 4, 5, 8, 16, 20, 25, 32, 40, 50, 64, and 80.

Exploration 2

1. False

2. False; $\log_3 (7x) = \log_3 7 + \log_3 x$

3. True

4. True

5. False; $\log \dfrac{x}{4} = \log x - \log 4$

6. True

7. False; $\log_5 x^2 = \log_5 x + \log_5 x = 2 \log_5 x$

8. True

Quick Review 3.4

1. $\log 10^2 = 2$

2. $\ln e^3 = 3$

3. $\ln e^{-2} = -2$

4. $\log 10^{-3} = -3$

5. $\dfrac{x^5 y^{-2}}{x^2 y^{-4}} = x^{5-2} y^{-2-(-4)} = x^3 y^2$

6. $\dfrac{u^{-3} v^7}{u^{-2} v^2} = \dfrac{v^{7-2}}{u^{-2-(-3)}} = \dfrac{v^5}{u}$

7. $(x^6 y^{-2})^{1/2} = (x^6)^{1/2} (y^{-2})^{1/2} = \dfrac{|x|^3}{|y|}$

8. $(x^{-8} y^{12})^{3/4} = (x^{-8})^{3/4} (y^{12})^{3/4} = \dfrac{|y|^9}{x^6}$

9. $\dfrac{(u^2 v^{-4})^{1/2}}{(27 u^6 v^{-6})^{1/3}} = \dfrac{|u| |v|^{-2}}{3u^2 v^{-2}} = \dfrac{1}{3|u|}$

10. $\dfrac{(x^{-2} y^3)^{-2}}{(x^3 y^{-2})^{-3}} = \dfrac{x^4 y^{-6}}{x^{-9} y^6} = \dfrac{x^{13}}{y^{12}}$

Section 3.4 Exercises

1. $\ln 8x = \ln 8 + \ln x = 3 \ln 2 + \ln x$

2. $\ln 9y = \ln 9 + \ln y = 2 \ln 3 + \ln y$

3. $\log \dfrac{3}{x} = \log 3 - \log x$

4. $\log \dfrac{2}{y} = \log 2 - \log y$

5. $\log_2 y^5 = 5 \log_2 y$

6. $\log_2 x^{-2} = -2 \log_2 x$

7. $\log x^3 y^2 = \log x^3 + \log y^2 = 3 \log x + 2 \log y$

8. $\log xy^3 = \log x + \log y^3 = \log x + 3 \log y$

9. $\ln \dfrac{x^2}{y^3} = \ln x^2 - \ln y^3 = 2 \ln x - 3 \ln y$

10. $\log 1000x^4 = \log 1000 + \log x^4 = 3 + 4 \log x$

11. $\log \sqrt[4]{\dfrac{x}{y}} = \dfrac{1}{4}(\log x - \log y) = \dfrac{1}{4} \log x - \dfrac{1}{4} \log y$

12. $\ln \dfrac{\sqrt[3]{x}}{\sqrt[3]{y}} = \dfrac{1}{3}(\ln x - \ln y) = \dfrac{1}{3} \ln x - \dfrac{1}{3} \ln y$

13. $\log x + \log y = \log xy$

14. $\log x + \log 5 = \log 5x$

15. $\ln y - \ln 3 = \ln(y/3)$

16. $\ln x - \ln y = \ln(x/y)$

17. $\dfrac{1}{3} \log x = \log x^{1/3} = \log \sqrt[3]{x}$

18. $\dfrac{1}{5} \log z = \log z^{1/5} = \log \sqrt[5]{z}$

19. $2 \ln x + 3 \ln y = \ln x^2 + \ln y^3 = \ln (x^2 y^3)$

20. $4 \log y - \log z = \log y^4 - \log z = \log \left(\dfrac{y^4}{z} \right)$

21. $4 \log (xy) - 3 \log (yz) = \log (x^4 y^4) - \log (y^3 z^3)$

$= \log \left(\dfrac{x^4 y^4}{y^3 z^3} \right) = \log \left(\dfrac{x^4 y}{z^3} \right)$

22. $3 \ln (x^3 y) + 2 \ln (yz^2) = \ln (x^9 y^3) + \ln (y^2 z^4)$

$= \ln (x^9 y^5 z^4)$

In #23–28, natural logarithms are shown, but common (base-10) logarithms would produce the same results.

23. $\dfrac{\ln 7}{\ln 2} \approx 2.8074$

24. $\dfrac{\ln 19}{\ln 5} \approx 1.8295$

25. $\dfrac{\ln 175}{\ln 8} \approx 2.4837$

26. $\dfrac{\ln 259}{\ln 12} \approx 2.2362$

27. $\dfrac{\ln 12}{\ln 0.5} = -\dfrac{\ln 12}{\ln 2} \approx -3.5850$

28. $\dfrac{\ln 29}{\ln 0.2} = -\dfrac{\ln 29}{\ln 5} \approx -2.0922$

29. $\log_3 x = \dfrac{\ln x}{\ln 3}$

30. $\log_7 x = \dfrac{\ln x}{\ln 7}$

31. $\log_2(a + b) = \dfrac{\ln(a + b)}{\ln 2}$

32. $\log_5(c - d) = \dfrac{\ln(c - d)}{\ln 5}$

33. $\log_2 x = \dfrac{\log x}{\log 2}$

34. $\log_4 x = \dfrac{\log x}{\log 4}$

35. $\log_{1/2}(x + y) = \dfrac{\log(x + y)}{\log (1/2)} = -\dfrac{\log(x + y)}{\log 2}$

36. $\log_{1/3}(x - y) = \dfrac{\log(x - y)}{\log(1/3)} = -\dfrac{\log(x - y)}{\log 3}$

37. Let $x = \log_b R$ and $y = \log_b S$.
Then $b^x = R$ and $b^y = S$, so that
$$\dfrac{R}{S} = \dfrac{b^x}{b^y} = b^{x-y}$$
$$\log_b \left(\dfrac{R}{S} \right) = \log_b b^{x-y} = x - y = \log_b R - \log_b S$$

38. Let $x = \log_b R$. Then $b^x = R$, so that
$$R^c = (b^x)^c = b^{c \cdot x}$$
$$\log_b R^c = \log_b b^{c \cdot x} = c \cdot x = c \log_b R$$

39. Starting from $g(x) = \ln x$: vertically shrink by a factor $1/\ln 4 \approx 0.72$.

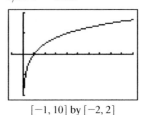

$[-1, 10]$ by $[-2, 2]$

40. Starting from $g(x) = \ln x$: vertically shrink by a factor $1/\ln 7 \approx 0.51$.

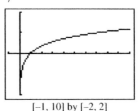

$[-1, 10]$ by $[-2, 2]$

41. Starting from $g(x) = \ln x$: reflect across the x-axis, then vertically shrink by a factor $1/\ln 3 \approx 0.91$.

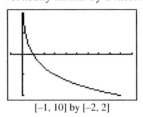

$[-1, 10]$ by $[-2, 2]$

42. Starting from $g(x) = \ln x$: reflect across the x-axis, then shrink vertically by a factor of $1/\ln 5 \approx 0.62$.

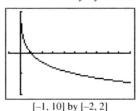

$[-1, 10]$ by $[-2, 2]$

43. (b): $[-5, 5]$ by $[-3, 3]$, with Xscl $= 1$ and Yscl $= 1$ (graph $y = \ln(2 - x)/\ln 4$).

44. (c): $[-2, 8]$ by $[-3, 3]$, with Xscl $= 1$ and Yscl $= 1$ (graph $y = \ln(x - 3)/\ln 6$).

45. (d): $[-2, 8]$ by $[-3, 3]$, with Xscl $= 1$ and Yscl $= 1$
(graph $y = \ln(x - 2)/\ln 0.5$).

46. (a): $[-8, 4]$ by $[-8, 8]$, with Xscl $= 1$ and Yscl $= 1$
(graph $y = \ln(3 - x)/\ln 0.7$).

47.

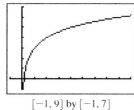

$[-1, 9]$ by $[-1, 7]$

Domain: $(0, \infty)$
Range: $(-\infty, \infty)$
Continuous
Always increasing
Asymptote: $x = 0$
$\lim\limits_{x \to \infty} f(x) = \infty$

$$f(x) = \log_2 (8x) = \frac{\ln (8x)}{\ln (2)}$$

48.

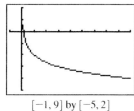

$[-1, 9]$ by $[-5, 2]$

Domain: $(0, \infty)$
Range: $(-\infty, \infty)$
Continuous
Always decreasing
Asymptote: $x = 0$
$\lim\limits_{x \to \infty} f(x) = -\infty$

$$f(x) = \log_{1/3} (9x) = \frac{\ln (9x)}{\ln \left(\dfrac{1}{3}\right)}$$

49.

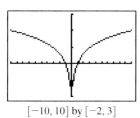

$[-10, 10]$ by $[-2, 3]$

Domain: $(-\infty, 0) \cup (0, \infty)$
Range: $(-\infty, \infty)$
Discontinuous at $x = 0$
Decreasing on interval $(-\infty, 0)$; increasing on
 interval $(0, \infty)$
Asymptote: $x = 0$
$\lim\limits_{x \to \infty} f(x) = \infty$, $\lim\limits_{x \to -\infty} f(x) = \infty$,

50.

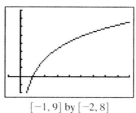

$[-1, 9]$ by $[-2, 8]$

Domain: $(0, \infty)$
Range: $(-\infty, \infty)$
Continuous
Always increasing
Asymptote: $x = 0$
$\lim\limits_{x \to \infty} f(x) = \infty$

51. In each case, take the exponent of 10, add 12, and
multiply the result by 10.

(a) 0

(b) 10

(c) 60

(d) 80

(e) 100

(f) 120 $(1 = 10^0)$

52. (a) $R = \log \dfrac{250}{2} + 4.25 = \log 125 + 4.25 \approx 6.3469.$

(b) $R = \log \dfrac{300}{4} + 3.5 = \log 75 + 3.5 \approx 5.3751$

53. $\log \dfrac{I}{12} = -0.00235(40) = -0.094,$ so
$I = 12 \cdot 10^{-0.094} \approx 9.6645$ lumens.

54. $\log \dfrac{I}{12} = -0.0125(10) = -0.125,$ so
$I = 12 \cdot 10^{-0.125} \approx 8.9987$ lumens.

55. From the change-of-base formula, we know that
$$f(x) = \log_3 x = \frac{\ln x}{\ln 3} = \frac{1}{\ln 3} \cdot \ln x \approx 0.9102 \ln x.$$
$f(x)$ can be obtained from $g(x) = \ln x$ by vertically
stretching by a factor of approximately 0.9102.

56. From the change-of-base formula, we know that
$$f(x) = \log_{0.8} x = \frac{\log x}{\log 0.8} = \frac{1}{\log 0.8} \cdot \log x \approx -10.32 \log x.$$
$f(x)$ can be obtained from $g(x) = \log x$ by reflecting
across the x-axis and vertically stretching by a factor of
approximately 10.32.

57. True. This is the product rule for logarithms.

58. False. The logarithm of a positive number less than 1 is
negative. For example, $\log 0.01 = -2$.

59. $\log 12 = \log (3 \cdot 4) = \log 3 + \log 4$ by the product rule.
The answer is B.

60. $\log_9 64 = (\ln 64)/(\ln 9)$ by the change-of-base formula.
The answer is C.

61. $\ln x^5 = 5 \ln x$ by the power rule. The answer is A.

62. $\log_{1/2} x^2 = 2 \log_{1/2} |x|$

$$= 2 \frac{\ln|x|}{\ln(1/2)}$$

$$= 2 \frac{\ln|x|}{\ln 1 - \ln 2}$$

$$= -2 \frac{\ln|x|}{\ln 2}$$

$$= -2 \log_2 |x|$$

The answer is E.

63. (a) $f(x) = 2.75 \cdot x^{5.0}$

(b) $f(7.1) \approx 49{,}616$

(c)

$\ln(x)$	1.39	1.87	2.14	2.30
$\ln(y)$	7.94	10.37	11.71	12.53

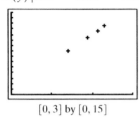

[0, 3] by [0, 15]

(d) $\ln(y) = 5.00 \ln x + 1.01$

(e) $a \approx 5, b \approx 1$ so $f(x) = e^1 x^5 = ex^5 \approx 2.72x^5$. The two equations are the same.

64. (a) $f(x) = 8.095 \cdot x^{-0.113}$

(b) $f(9.2) = 8.095 \cdot (9.2)^{-0.113} \approx 6.30$

(c)

$\ln(x)$	0.69	1.10	1.57	2.04
$\ln(y)$	2.01	1.97	1.92	1.86

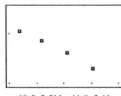

[0.5, 2.5] by [1.8, 2.1]

(d) $\ln(y) = -0.113 \ln(x) + 2.09$

(e) $a \approx -0.113, b \approx 2.1$ so $f(x) = e^{2.1} \cdot x^{-0.113}$ $\approx 8.09x^{-0.113}$.

65. (a)

$\log(w)$	−0.70	−0.52	0.30	0.70	1.48	1.70	1.85
$\log(r)$	2.62	2.48	2.31	2.08	1.93	1.85	1.86

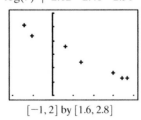

[−1, 2] by [1.6, 2.8]

(b) $\log r = (-0.30) \log w + 2.36$

(c)

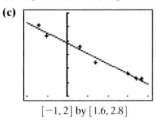

[−1, 2] by [1.6, 2.8]

(d) $\log r = (-0.30) \log (450) + 2.36 \approx 1.58, r \approx 37.69$, very close

(e) One possible answer: Consider the power function
$$y = a \cdot x^b \text{ then:}$$
$$\log y = \log (a \cdot x^b)$$
$$= \log a + \log x^b$$
$$= \log a + b \log x$$
$$= b(\log x) + \log a$$
which is clearly a linear function of the form $f(t) = mt + c$ where $m = b, c = \log a, f(t) = \log y$ and $t = \log x$. As a result, there is a linear relationship between $\log y$ and $\log x$.

66. $\log 4 = \log 2^2 = 2 \log 2$
$\log 6 = \log 2 + \log 3$
$\log 8 = \log 2^3 = 3 \log 2$
$\log 9 = \log 3^2 = 2 \log 3$
$\log 12 = \log 3 + \log 4 = \log 3 + 2 \log 2$
$\log 16 = \log 2^4 = 4 \log 2$
$\log 18 = \log 2 + \log 9 = \log 2 + 2 \log 3$
$\log 24 = \log 2 + \log 12 = 3 \log 2 + \log 3$
$\log 27 = \log 3^3 = 3 \log 3$
$\log 32 = \log 2^5 = 5 \log 2$
$\log 36 = \log 6 + \log 6 = 2 \log 2 + 2 \log 3$
$\log 48 = \log 4 + \log 12 = 4 \log 2 + \log 3$
$\log 54 = \log 2 + \log 27 = \log 2 + 3 \log 3$
$\log 72 = \log 8 + \log 9 = 3 \log 2 + 2 \log 3$
$\log 81 = \log 3^4 = 4 \log 3$
$\log 96 = \log (3 \cdot 32) = \log 3 + \log 32 = \log 3 + 5 \log 2$

For #67–68, solve graphically.

67. $\approx 6.41 < x < 93.35$

68. $\approx 1.26 \le x \le 14.77$

69. (a)

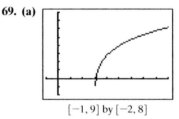

[−1, 9] by [−2, 8]

Domain of f and g: $(3, \infty)$

(b)

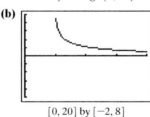

[0, 20] by [−2, 8]

Domain of f and g: $(5, \infty)$

(c)

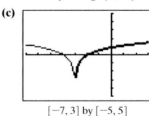

[−7, 3] by [−5, 5]

Domain of f: $(-\infty, -3) \cup (-3, \infty)$
Domain of g: $(-3, \infty)$
Answers will vary.

70. Recall that $y = \log_a x$ can be written as $x = a^y$.

Let $y = \log_a b$

$$a^y = b$$
$$\log a^y = \log b$$
$$y \log a = \log b$$
$$y = \frac{\log b}{\log a} = \log_a b$$

71. Let $y = \dfrac{\log x}{\ln x}$. By the change-of-base formula,

$$y = \frac{\log x}{\dfrac{\log x}{\log e}} = \log x \cdot \frac{\log e}{\log x} = \log e \approx 0.43$$

Thus, y is a constant function.

72.

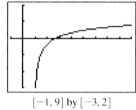

$[-1, 9]$ by $[-3, 2]$

Domain: $(1, \infty)$
Range: $(-\infty, \infty)$
Continuous
Increasing
Not symmetric
Vertical asymptote: $x = 1$
$\lim\limits_{x \to \infty} f(x) = \infty$
One-to one, hence invertible $(f^{-1}(x) = e^{e^x})$

■ Section 3.5 Equation Solving and Modeling

Exploration 1

1. $\log(4 \cdot 10) \approx 1.60206$
$\log(4 \cdot 10^2) \approx 2.60206$
$\log(4 \cdot 10^3) \approx 3.60206$
$\log(4 \cdot 10^4) \approx 4.60206$
$\log(4 \cdot 10^5) \approx 5.60206$
$\log(4 \cdot 10^6) \approx 6.60206$
$\log(4 \cdot 10^7) \approx 7.60206$
$\log(4 \cdot 10^8) \approx 8.60206$
$\log(4 \cdot 10^9) \approx 9.60206$
$\log(4 \cdot 10^{10}) \approx 10.60206$

2. The integers increase by 1 for every increase in a power of 10.

3. The decimal parts are exactly equal.

4. $4 \cdot 10^{10}$ is nine orders of magnitude greater than $4 \cdot 10$.

Quick Review 3.5

In #1–4, graphical support (i.e., graphing both functions on a square window) is also useful.

1. $f(g(x)) = e^{2\ln(x^{1/2})} = e^{\ln x} = x$ and $g(f(x)) = \ln(e^{2x})^{1/2}$
$= \ln(e^x) = x.$

2. $f(g(x)) = 10^{(\log x^2)/2} = 10^{\log x} = x$ and
$g(f(x)) = \log(10^{x/2})^2 = \log(10^x) = x.$

3. $f(g(x)) = \dfrac{1}{3}\ln(e^{3x}) = \dfrac{1}{3}(3x) = x$ and
$g(f(x)) = e^{3(1/3\ln x)} = e^{\ln x} = x.$

4. $f(g(x)) = 3\log(10^{x/6})^2 = 6\log(10^{x/6}) = 6(x/6) = x$
and $g(f(x)) = 10^{(3\log x^2)/6} = 10^{(6\log x)/6} = 10^{\log x} = x.$

5. 7.783×10^8 km

6. 1×10^{-15} m

7. 602,000,000,000,000,000,000,000

8. 0.000 000 000 000 000 000 000 000 001 66 (26 zeros between the decimal point and the 1)

9. $(1.86 \times 10^5)(3.1 \times 10^7) = (1.86)(3.1) \times 10^{5+7}$
$= 5.766 \times 10^{12}$

10. $\dfrac{8 \times 10^{-7}}{5 \times 10^{-6}} = \dfrac{8}{5} \times 10^{-7-(-6)} = 1.6 \times 10^{-1}$

Section 3.5 Exercises

For #1–18, take a logarithm of both sides of the equation, when appropriate.

1. $36\left(\dfrac{1}{3}\right)^{x/5} = 4$
$$\left(\frac{1}{3}\right)^{x/5} = \frac{1}{9}$$
$$\left(\frac{1}{3}\right)^{x/5} = \left(\frac{1}{3}\right)^2$$
$$\frac{x}{5} = 2$$
$$x = 10$$

2. $32\left(\dfrac{1}{4}\right)^{x/3} = 2$
$$\left(\frac{1}{4}\right)^{x/3} = \frac{1}{16}$$
$$\left(\frac{1}{4}\right)^{x/3} = \left(\frac{1}{4}\right)^2$$
$$\frac{x}{3} = 2$$
$$x = 6$$

3. $2 \cdot 5^{x/4} = 250$
$$5^{x/4} = 125$$
$$5^{x/4} = 5^3$$
$$\frac{x}{4} = 3$$
$$x = 12$$

4. $3 \cdot 4^{x/2} = 96$
$$4^{x/2} = 32$$
$$4^{x/2} = 4^{5/2}$$
$$\frac{x}{2} = \frac{5}{2}$$
$$x = 5$$

5. $10^{-x/3} = 10$, so $-x/3 = 1$, and therefore $x = -3$.

6. $5^{-x/4} = 5$, so $-x/4 = 1$, and therefore $x = -4$.

7. $x = 10^4 = 10,000$

8. $x = 2^5 = 32$

9. $x - 5 = 4^{-1}$, so $x = 5 + 4^{-1} = 5.25$.

10. $1 - x = 4^1$, so $x = -3$.

11. $x = \dfrac{\ln 4.1}{\ln 1.06} = \log_{1.06} 4.1 \approx 24.2151$

12. $x = \dfrac{\ln 1.6}{\ln 0.98} = \log_{0.98} 1.6 \approx -23.2644$

13. $e^{0.035x} = 4$, so $0.035x = \ln 4$, and therefore

$$x = \frac{1}{0.035} \ln 4 \approx 39.6084.$$

14. $e^{0.045x} = 3$, so $0.045x = \ln 3$, and therefore

$$x = \frac{1}{0.045} \ln 3 \approx 24.4136.$$

15. $e^{-x} = \dfrac{3}{2}$, so $-x = \ln \dfrac{3}{2}$, and therefore

$$x = -\ln \frac{3}{2} \approx -0.4055.$$

16. $e^{-x} = \dfrac{5}{3}$, so $-x = \ln \dfrac{5}{3}$, and therefore

$$x = -\ln \frac{5}{3} \approx -0.5108.$$

17. $\ln(x - 3) = \dfrac{1}{3}$, so $x - 3 = e^{1/3}$, and therefore

$$x = 3 + e^{1/3} \approx 4.3956.$$

18. $\log(x + 2) = -2$, so $x + 2 = 10^{-2}$, and therefore $x = -2 + 10^{-2} = -1.99$.

19. We must have $x(x + 1) > 0$, so $x < -1$ or $x > 0$. Domain: $(-\infty, -1) \cup (0, \infty)$; graph (e).

20. We must have $x > 0$ and $x + 1 > 0$, so $x > 0$. Domain: $(0, \infty)$; graph (f).

21. We must have $\dfrac{x}{x + 1} > 0$, so $x < -1$ or $x > 0$. Domain: $(-\infty, -1) \cup (0, \infty)$; graph (d).

22. We must have $x > 0$ and $x + 1 > 0$, so $x > 0$. Domain: $(0, \infty)$; graph (c).

23. We must have $x > 0$. Domain: $(0, \infty)$; graph (a).

24. We must have $x^2 > 0$, so $x \neq 0$. Domain: $(-\infty, 0) \cup (0, \infty)$; graph (b).

For #25–38, algebraic solutions are shown (and are generally the only way to get *exact* answers). In many cases solving graphically would be faster; graphical support is also useful.

25. Write both sides as powers of 10, leaving $10^{\log x^2} = 10^6$, or $x^2 = 1{,}000{,}000$. Then $x = 1000$ or $x = -1000$.

26. Write both sides as powers of e, leaving $e^{\ln x^2} = e^4$, or $x^2 = e^4$. Then $x = e^2 \approx 7.389$ or $x = -e^2 \approx -7.389$.

27. Write both sides as powers of 10, leaving $10^{\log x^4} = 10^2$, or $x^4 = 100$. Then $x^2 = 10$, and $x = \pm\sqrt{10}$.

28. Write both sides as powers of e, leaving $e^{\ln x^6} = e^{12}$, or $x^6 = e^{12}$. Then $x^2 = e^4$, and $x = \pm e^2$.

29. Multiply both sides by $3 \cdot 2^x$, leaving $(2^x)^2 - 1 = 12 \cdot 2^x$, or $(2^x)^2 - 12 \cdot 2^x - 1 = 0$. This is quadratic in 2^x,

leading to $2^x = \dfrac{12 \pm \sqrt{144 + 4}}{2} = 6 \pm \sqrt{37}$. Only

$6 + \sqrt{37}$ is positive, so the only answer is

$$x = \frac{\ln(6 + \sqrt{37})}{\ln 2} = \log_2(6 + \sqrt{37}) \approx 3.5949.$$

30. Multiply both sides by $2 \cdot 2^x$, leaving $(2^x)^2 + 1 = 6 \cdot 2^x$, or $(2^x)^2 - 6 \cdot 2^x + 1 = 0$. This is quadratic in 2^x, leading to

$$2^x = \frac{6 \pm \sqrt{36 - 4}}{2} = 3 \pm 2\sqrt{2}. \text{ Then}$$

$$x = \frac{\ln(3 \pm 2\sqrt{2})}{\ln 2} = \log_2 (3 \pm 2\sqrt{2}) \approx \pm 2.5431.$$

31. Multiply both sides by $2e^x$, leaving $(e^x)^2 + 1 = 8e^x$, or $(e^x)^2 - 8e^x + 1 = 0$. This is quadratic in e^x, leading to

$$e^x = \frac{8 \pm \sqrt{64 - 4}}{2} = 4 \pm \sqrt{15}. \text{ Then}$$

$$x = \ln(4 \pm \sqrt{15}) \approx \pm 2.0634.$$

32. This is quadratic in e^x, leading to

$$e^x = \frac{-5 \pm \sqrt{25 + 24}}{4} = \frac{-5 \pm 7}{4}. \text{ Of these two}$$

numbers, only $\dfrac{-5 + 7}{4} = \dfrac{1}{2}$ is positive, so $x = \ln \dfrac{1}{2}$

$\approx -0.6931.$

33. $\dfrac{500}{200} = 1 + 25e^{0.3x}$, so $e^{0.3x} = \dfrac{3}{50} = 0.06$, and therefore

$$x = \frac{1}{0.3} \ln 0.06 \approx -9.3780.$$

34. $\dfrac{400}{150} = 1 + 95e^{-0.6x}$, so $e^{-0.6x} = \dfrac{1}{57}$, and therefore

$$x = \frac{1}{-0.6} \ln \frac{1}{57} \approx 6.7384.$$

35. Multiply by 2, then combine the logarithms to obtain $\ln \dfrac{x + 3}{x^2} = 0$. Then $\dfrac{x + 3}{x^2} = e^0 = 1$, so $x + 3 = x^2$.

The solutions to this quadratic equation are

$$x = \frac{1 \pm \sqrt{1 + 12}}{2} = \frac{1}{2} \pm \frac{1}{2}\sqrt{13} \approx 2.3028.$$

36. Multiply by 2, then combine the logarithms to obtain $\log \dfrac{x^2}{x + 4} = 2$. Then $\dfrac{x^2}{x + 4} = 10^2 = 100$, so $x^2 = 100(x + 4)$. The solutions to this quadratic equation

are $x = \dfrac{100 \pm \sqrt{10000 + 1600}}{2} = 50 \pm 10\sqrt{29}$. The

original equation requires that $x > 0$, so $50 - 10\sqrt{29}$ is extraneous; the only actual solution is $x = 50 + 10\sqrt{29} \approx 103.852.$

37. $\ln[(x - 3)(x + 4)] = 3 \ln 2$, so $(x - 3)(x + 4) = 8$, or $x^2 + x - 20 = 0$. This factors to $(x - 4)(x + 5) = 0$, so $x = 4$ (an actual solution) or $x = -5$ (extraneous, since $x - 3$ and $x + 4$ must be positive).

38. $\log[(x - 2)(x + 5)] = 2 \log 3$, so $(x - 2)(x + 5) = 9$, or $x^2 + 3x - 19 = 0$.

Then $x = \dfrac{-3 \pm \sqrt{9 + 76}}{2} = -\dfrac{3}{2} \pm \dfrac{1}{2}\sqrt{85}$. The actual

solution is $x = -\dfrac{3}{2} + \dfrac{1}{2}\sqrt{85} \approx 3.1098$; since $x - 2$ must

be positive, the other algebraic solution,

$$x = -\frac{3}{2} - \frac{1}{2}\sqrt{85}, \text{ is extraneous.}$$

39. A \$100 bill has the value of 1000, or 10^3, dimes so they differ by an order of magnitude of 3.

40. A 2 kg hen weighs 2000, or $2 \cdot 10^3$, grams while a 20 g canary weighs $2 \cdot 10$ grams. They differ by an order of magnitude of 2.

41. $7 - 5.5 = 1.5$. They differ by an order of magnitude of 1.5.

42. $4.1 - 2.3 = 1.8$. They differ by an order of magnitude of 1.8.

43. Given

$$\beta_1 = 10 \log \frac{I_1}{I_0} = 95$$

$$\beta_2 = 10 \log \frac{I_2}{I_0} = 65,$$

we seek the logarithm of the ratio I_1/I_2.

$$10 \log \frac{I_1}{I_0} - 10 \log \frac{I_2}{I_0} = \beta_1 - \beta_2$$

$$10 \left(\log \frac{I_1}{I_0} - \log \frac{I_2}{I_0} \right) = 95 - 65$$

$$10 \log \frac{I_1}{I_2} = 30$$

$$\log \frac{I_1}{I_2} = 3$$

The two intensities differ by 3 orders of magnitude.

44. Given

$$\beta_1 = 10 \log \frac{I_1}{I_0} = 70$$

$$\beta_2 = 10 \log \frac{I_2}{I_0} = 10,$$

we seek the logarithm of the ratio I_1/I_2.

$$10 \log \frac{I_1}{I_0} - 10 \log \frac{I_2}{I_0} = \beta_1 - \beta_2$$

$$10 \left(\log \frac{I_1}{I_0} - \log \frac{I_2}{I_0} \right) = 70 - 10$$

$$10 \log \frac{I_1}{I_2} = 60$$

$$\log \frac{I_1}{I_2} = 6$$

The two intensities differ by 6 orders of magnitude.

45. Assuming that T and B are the same for the two quakes, we have $7.9 = \log a_1 - \log T + B$ and $6.6 = \log a_2 - \log T + B$, so $7.9 - 6.6 = 1.3 = \log(a_1/a_2)$. Then $a_1/a_2 = 10^{1.3}$, so $a_1 \approx 19.95 a_2$—the Mexico City amplitude was about 20 times greater.

46. If T and B were the same, we have $7.2 = \log a_1 - \log T + B$ and $6.6 = \log a_2 - \log T + B$, so $7.2 - 6.6 = 0.6 = \log(a_1/a_2)$. Then $a_1/a_2 = 10^{0.6}$, so $a_1 \approx 3.98 a_2$—Kobe's amplitude was about 4 times greater.

47. (a) Carbonated water: $-\log [H^+] = 3.9$
$$\log [H^+] = -3.9$$
$$[H^+] = 10^{-3.9} \approx 1.26 \times 10^{-4}$$
Household ammonia: $-\log [H^+] = 11.9$
$$\log [H^+] = -11.9$$
$$[H^+] = 10^{-11.9} \approx 1.26 \times 10^{-12}$$

(b) $\dfrac{[H^+] \text{ of carbonated water}}{[H^+] \text{ of household ammonia}} = \dfrac{10^{-3.9}}{10^{-11.9}} = 10^8$

(c) They differ by an order of magnitude of 8.

48. (a) Stomach acid: $-\log [H^+] = 2.0$
$$\log [H^+] = -2.0$$
$$[H^+] = 10^{-2.0} = 1 \times 10^{-2}$$
Blood: $-\log [H^+] = 7.4$
$$\log [H^+] = -7.4$$
$$[H^+] = 10^{-7.4} \approx 3.98 \times 10^{-8}$$

(b) $\dfrac{[H^+] \text{ of stomach acid}}{[H^+] \text{ of blood}} = \dfrac{10^{-2}}{10^{-7.4}} \approx 2.51 \times 10^5$

(c) They differ by an order of magnitude of 5.4.

The equations in #49–50 can be solved either algebraically or graphically; the latter approach is generally faster.

49. Substituting known information into $T(t) = T_m + (T_0 - T_m)e^{-kt}$ leaves $T(t) = 22 + 70e^{-kt}$.

Using $T(12) = 50 = 22 + 70e^{-12k}$, we have $e^{-12k} = \dfrac{2}{5}$, so

$k = -\dfrac{1}{12} \ln \dfrac{2}{5} \approx 0.0764$. Solving $T(t) = 30$ yields

$t \approx 28.41$ minutes.

50. Substituting known information into $T(t) = T_m + (T_0 - T_m)e^{-kt}$ leaves $T(t) = 65 + 285e^{-kt}$.
Using $T(20) = 120 = 65 + 285e^{-20k}$, we have

$e^{-20k} = \dfrac{11}{57}$, so $k = -\dfrac{1}{20} \ln \dfrac{11}{57} \approx 0.0823$. Solving

$T(t) = 90$ yields $t \approx 29.59$ minutes.

51. (a)

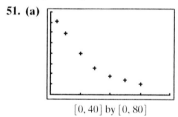

[0, 40] by [0, 80]

(b)

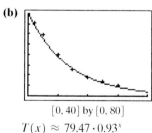

[0, 40] by [0, 80]

$T(x) \approx 79.47 \cdot 0.93^x$

(c) $T(0) + 10 = 79.47 + 10 \approx 89.47°C$

52. (a)

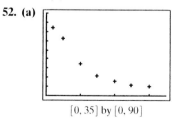

[0, 35] by [0, 90]

(b)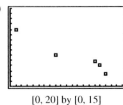

[0, 35] by [0, 90]

$T(x) \approx 79.96 \cdot 0.93^x$

(c) $T(0) + 0 \approx 79.96 = 79.96°C$.

53. (a)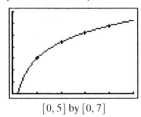

[0, 20] by [0, 15]

(b) The scatter plot is better because it accurately represents the times between the measurements. The equal spacing on the bar graph suggests that the measurements were taken at equally spaced intervals, which distorts our perceptions of how the consumption has changed over time.

54. Answers will vary.

55. Logarithmic seems best — the scatterplot of (x, y) looks most logarithmic. (The data can be modeled by $y = 3 + 2 \ln x$.)

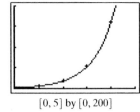

[0, 5] by [0, 7]

56. Exponential — the scatterplot of (x, y) is *exactly* exponential. (The data can be modeled by $y = 2 \cdot 3^x$.)

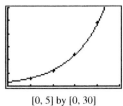

[0, 5] by [0, 200]

57. Exponential — the scatterplot of (x, y) is *exactly* exponential. (The data can be modeled by $y = \dfrac{3}{2} \cdot 2^x$.)

[0, 5] by [0, 30]

58. Linear — the scatterplot of (x, y) is *exactly* linear ($y = 2x + 3$.)

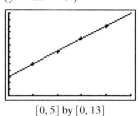

[0, 5] by [0, 13]

59. False. The order of magnitude of a positive number is its *common* logarithm.

60. True. In the formula $T(t) = T_m + (T_0 - T_m)e^{-kt}$, the term $(T_0 - T_m)e^{-kt}$ goes to zero at t gets large, so that $T(t)$ approaches T_m.

61. $2^{3x-1} = 32$
$2^{3x-1} = 2^5$
$3x - 1 = 5$
$x = 2$
The answer is B.

62. $\ln x = -1$
$e^{\ln x} = e^{-1}$
$x = \dfrac{1}{e}$
The answer is B.

63. Given

$$R_1 = \log \frac{a_1}{T} + B = 8.1$$

$$R_2 = \log \frac{a_2}{T} + B = 6.1,$$

we seek the ratio of amplitudes (severities) a_1/a_2.

$$\left(\log \frac{a_1}{T} + B \right) - \left(\log \frac{a_2}{T} + B \right) = R_1 - R_2$$

$$\log \frac{a_1}{T} - \log \frac{a_2}{T} = 8.1 - 6.1$$

$$\log \frac{a_1}{a_2} = 2$$

$$\frac{a_1}{a_2} = 10^2 = 100$$

The answer is E.

64. As the second term on the right side of the formula $T(t) = T_m + (T_0 - T_m)e^{-kt}$ indicates, and as the graph confirms, the model is exponential.

The answer is A.

65. A logistic regression $\left(f(x) = \dfrac{4443}{1 + 169.96e^{-0.0354x}} \right)$ most closely matches the data, and would provide a natural "cap" to the population growth at approx. 4.4 million people. (Note: $x =$ number of years since 1900.)

66. The logistic regression model $\left(f(x) = \dfrac{2930}{1 + 17.29e^{-0.0263x}} \right)$ matches the data well and provides a natural cap of 2.9 million people. (Note: x = number of years since 1900.)

67. (a)

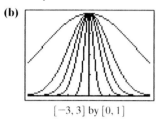

$[-3, 3]$ by $[0, 10]$

As k increases, the bell curve stretches vertically. Its height increases and the slope of the curve seems to steepen.

(b)

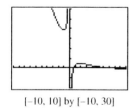

$[-3, 3]$ by $[0, 1]$

As c increases, the bell curve compresses horizontally. Its slope seems to steepen, increasing more rapidly to $(0, 1)$ and decreasing more rapidly from $(0, 1)$.

68. Let $\dfrac{u}{v} = 10^n, u, v > 0$

$$\log \frac{u}{v} = \log 10^n$$

$\log u - \log v = n \log 10$

$\log u - \log v = n(1) = n$

For the initial expression to be true, either u and v are both powers of ten, or they are the same constant k multiplied by powers of 10 (i.e., either $u = 10^k$ and $v = 10^m$ or $u = a \cdot 10^k$ and $v = a \cdot 10^m$, where a, k, and m are constants). As a result, u and v vary by an order of magnitude n. That is, u is n orders of magnitude greater than v.

69. (a) r cannot be negative since it is a distance.

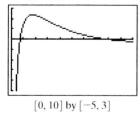

$[-10, 10]$ by $[-10, 30]$

(b) $[0, 10]$ by $[-5, 3]$ is a good choice. The maximum energy, approximately 2.3807, occurs when $r \approx 1.729$.

$[0, 10]$ by $[-5, 3]$

70. Since $T_0 \approx 66.156$ and $T_m = 4.5$, we have

$(66.156 - 4.5)e^{-kt} = 61.656 \times (0.92770)^t$

$61.656e^{-kt} = 61.656 \times (0.92770)^t$

$e^{-kt} = \dfrac{61.656}{61.656} \times (0.92770)^t$

$e^{-kt} = 1 \times (0.92770)^t$

$\ln e^{-kt} = \ln (1 \cdot (0.92770)^t)$

$-kt = \ln (1) + \ln (0.92770)^t$

$-kt = 0 + t \ln (0.92770)$

$k = -\ln (0.92770)$

≈ 0.075

71. One possible answer: We "map" our data so that all points (x, y) are plotted as $(\ln x, y)$. If these "new" points are linear—and thus can be represented by some standard linear regression $y = ax + b$—we make the same substitution $(x \rightarrow \ln x)$ and find $y = a \ln x + b$, a logarithmic regression.

72. One possible answer: We "map" our data so that all points (x, y) are plotted as $(\ln x, \ln y)$. If these "new" points are linear—and thus can be represented by some standard linear regression $y = ax + b$—we make the same "mapping" $(x \rightarrow \ln x, y \rightarrow \ln y)$ and find $\ln y = a \ln x + b$. Using algebra and the properties of algorithms, we have:

$\ln y = a \ln x + b$

$e^{\ln y} = e^{a \ln x + b}$

$y = e^{a \ln x} \cdot e^b$

$= e^{\ln x^a} \cdot e^b$

$= e^b \cdot x^a$

$= c x^a$, where $c = e^b$, exactly the power regression

The equations and inequalities in #73–76 must be solved graphically—they cannot be solved algebraically. For #77–78, algebraic solution is possible, although a graphical approach may be easier.

73. $x \approx 1.3066$

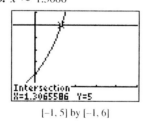

Intersection
X=1.3065586   Y=5

$[-1, 5]$ by $[-1, 6]$

74. $x \approx 0.4073$ or $x \approx 0.9333$

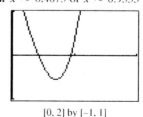

$[0, 2]$ by $[-1, 1]$

75. $0 < x < 1.7115$ (approx.)

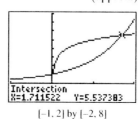

Intersection
X=1.711522   Y=5.537383

$[-1, 2]$ by $[-2, 8]$

76. $x \le -20.0855$ (approx.)

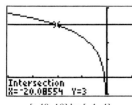

Intersection
X=-20.08554 Y=3

$[-40, 10]$ by $[-1, 4]$

77. $\log x - 2 \log 3 > 0$, so $\log(x/9) > 0$. Then $\dfrac{x}{9} > 10^0 = 1$,

so $x > 9$.

78. $\log(x + 1) - \log 6 < 0$, so $\log \dfrac{x+1}{6} < 0$.

Then $\dfrac{x+1}{6} < 10^0 = 1$, so $x + 1 < 6$, or $x < 5$. The

original equation also requires that $x + 1 > 0$, so the

solution is $-1 < x < 5$.

■ Section 3.6 Mathematics of Finance

Exploration 1

1.

k	A
10	1104.6
20	1104.9
30	1105
40	1105
50	1105.1
60	1105.1
70	1105.1
80	1105.1
90	1105.1
100	1105.1

A approaches a limit of about 1105.1.

2. $y = 1000e^{0.1} \approx 1105.171$ is an upper bound (and asymptote) for $A(x)$. $A(x)$ approaches, but never equals, this bound.

Quick Review 3.6

1. $200 \cdot 0.035 = 7$

2. $150 \cdot 0.025 = 3.75$

3. $\dfrac{1}{4} \cdot 7.25\% = 1.8125\%$

4. $\dfrac{1}{12} \cdot 6.5\% \approx 0.5417\%$

5. $\dfrac{78}{120} = 0.65 = 65\%$

6. $\dfrac{28}{80} = 0.35 = 35\%$

7. $0.32x = 48$ gives $x = 150$

8. $0.84x = 176.4$ gives $x = 210$

9. $300 (1 + 0.05) = 315$ dollars

10. $500 (1 + 0.45) = 522.50$ dollars

Section 3.6 Exercises

1. $A = 1500(1 + 0.07)^6 \approx \$2251.10$

2. $A = 3200(1 + 0.08)^4 \approx \$4353.56$

3. $A = 12{,}000(1 + 0.075)^7 \approx \$19{,}908.59$

4. $A = 15{,}500(1 + 0.095)^{12} \approx \$46{,}057.58$

5. $A = 1500\left(1 + \dfrac{0.07}{4}\right)^{20} \approx \$2122.17$

6. $A = 3500\left(1 + \dfrac{0.05}{4}\right)^{40} \approx \$5752.67$

7. $A = 40{,}500\left(1 + \dfrac{0.038}{12}\right)^{240} \approx \$86{,}496.26$

8. $A = 25{,}300\left(1 + \dfrac{0.045}{12}\right)^{300} \approx \$77{,}765.69$

9. $A = 1250e^{(0.054)(6)} \approx \$1728.31$

10. $A = 3350e^{(0.062)(8)} \approx \$5501.17$

11. $A = 21{,}000e^{(0.037)(10)} \approx \$30{,}402.43$

12. $A = 8875e^{(0.044)(25)} \approx \$26{,}661.97$

13. $FV = 500 \cdot \dfrac{\left(1 + \dfrac{0.07}{4}\right)^{24} - 1}{\dfrac{0.07}{4}} \approx \$14{,}755.51$

14. $FV = 300 \cdot \dfrac{\left(1 + \dfrac{0.06}{4}\right)^{48} - 1}{\dfrac{0.06}{4}} \approx \$20{,}869.57$

15. $FV = 450 \cdot \dfrac{\left(1 + \dfrac{0.0525}{12}\right)^{120} - 1}{\dfrac{0.0525}{12}} \approx \$70{,}819.63$

16. $FV = 610 \cdot \dfrac{\left(1 + \dfrac{0.065}{12}\right)^{300} - 1}{\dfrac{0.065}{12}} \approx \$456{,}790.28$

17. $PV = 815.37 \cdot \dfrac{1 - \left(1 + \dfrac{0.047}{12}\right)^{-60}}{\dfrac{0.047}{12}} \approx \$43{,}523.31$

18. $PV = 1856.82 \cdot \dfrac{1 - \left(1 + \dfrac{0.065}{12}\right)^{-360}}{\dfrac{0.065}{12}} \approx \$293{,}769.01$

19. $R = \dfrac{PV \cdot i}{1 - (1 + i)^{-n}} = \dfrac{(18{,}000)\left(\dfrac{0.054}{12}\right)}{1 - \left(1 + \dfrac{0.054}{12}\right)^{-72}} \approx \$293.24$

20. $R = \dfrac{PV \cdot i}{1 - (1 + i)^{-n}} = \dfrac{(154{,}000)\left(\dfrac{0.072}{12}\right)}{1 - \left(1 + \dfrac{0.072}{12}\right)^{-180}} \approx \$1401.47$

In #21–24, the time must be rounded up to the end of the next compounding period.

21. Solve $2300\left(1 + \dfrac{0.09}{4}\right)^{4t} = 4150 : (1.0225)^{4t} = \dfrac{83}{46}$, so

$t = \dfrac{1}{4}\dfrac{\ln(83/46)}{\ln 1.0225} \approx 6.63$ years — round to 6 years

9 months (the next full compounding period).

22. Solve $8000\left(1 + \dfrac{0.09}{12}\right)^{12t} = 16{,}000 : (1.0075)^{12t} = 2$, so

$t = \dfrac{1}{12}\dfrac{\ln 2}{\ln 1.0075} \approx 7.73$ years — round to 7 years

9 months (the next full compounding period).

23. Solve $15{,}000\left(1 + \dfrac{0.08}{12}\right)^{12t} = 45{,}000 : (1.0067)^{12t} = 3$, so

$t = \dfrac{1}{12}\dfrac{\ln 3}{\ln 1.0067} \approx 13.71$ years — round to 13 years

9 months (the next full compounding period). Note: A graphical solution provides $t \approx 13.78$ years—round to 13 years 10 months.

24. Solve $1.5\left(1 + \dfrac{0.08}{4}\right)^{4t} = 3.75 : (1.02)^{4t} = 2.5$, so

$t = \dfrac{1}{4}\dfrac{\ln 2.5}{\ln 1.02} \approx 11.57$ years — round to 11 years

9 months (the next full compounding period).

25. Solve $22{,}000\left(1 + \dfrac{r}{365}\right)^{(365)(5)} = 36{,}500 :$

$1 + \dfrac{r}{365} = \left(\dfrac{73}{44}\right)^{1/1825}$, so $r \approx 10.13\%$

26. Solve $8500\left(1 + \dfrac{r}{12}\right)^{(12)(5)} = 3 \cdot 8500 :$

$1 + \dfrac{r}{12} = 3^{1/60}$, so $r \approx 22.17\%$

27. Solve $14.6(1 + r)^6 = 22 : \ 1 + r = \left(\dfrac{110}{73}\right)^{1/6}$, so

$r \approx 7.07\%$.

28. Solve $18(1 + r)8 = 25 : \ 1 + r = \left(\dfrac{25}{18}\right)^{1/8}$, so $r \approx 4.19\%$.

In #29–30, the time must be rounded up to the end of the next compounding period.

29. Solve $\left(1 + \dfrac{0.0575}{4}\right)^{4t} = 2 : \ t = \dfrac{1}{4}\dfrac{\ln 2}{\ln 1.014375} \approx 12.14$

— round to 12 years 3 months.

30. Solve $\left(1 + \dfrac{0.0625}{12}\right)^{12t} = 3 :$

$t = \dfrac{1}{12}\dfrac{\ln 3}{\ln(1 + 0.0625/12)} \approx 17.62$ — round to 17 years

8 months.

For #31–34, use the formula $S = Pe^{rt}$.

31. Time to double: solve $2 = e^{0.09t}$, leading to

$t = \dfrac{1}{0.09}\ln 2 \approx 7.7016$ years. After 15 years:

$S = 12{,}500e^{(0.09)(15)} \approx \$48{,}217.82$

32. Time to double: solve $2 = e^{0.08t}$, leading to

$t = \dfrac{1}{0.08}\ln 2 \approx 8.6643$ years. After 15 years:

$S = 32{,}500e^{(0.08)(15)} \approx \$107{,}903.80$.

33. APR: solve $2 = e^{4r}$, leading to $r = \dfrac{1}{4}\ln 2 \approx 17.33\%$.

After 15 years: $S = 9500e^{(0.1733)(15)} \approx \$127{,}816.26$ (using the "exact" value of r).

34. APR: solve $2 = e^{6r}$, leading to $r = \dfrac{1}{6}\ln 2 \approx 11.55\%$.

After 15 years: $S = 16{,}800e^{(0.1155)(15)} \approx \$95{,}035.15$ (using the "exact" value of r).

In #35–40, the time must be rounded up to the end of the next compounding period (except in the case of continuous compounding).

35. Solve $\left(1 + \dfrac{0.04}{4}\right)^{4t} = 2 : \ t = \dfrac{1}{4}\dfrac{\ln 2}{\ln 1.01} \approx 17.42$ — round

to 17 years 6 months.

36. Solve $\left(1 + \dfrac{0.08}{4}\right)^{4t} = 2 : \ t = \dfrac{1}{4}\dfrac{\ln 2}{\ln 1.02} \approx 8.751$ — round

to 9 years (*almost by 8 years 9 months*).

37. Solve $1.07^t = 2 : \ t = \dfrac{\ln 2}{\ln 1.07} \approx 10.24$ — round to 11 years.

38. Solve $\left(1 + \dfrac{0.07}{4}\right)^{4t} = 2 : \ t = \dfrac{1}{4}\dfrac{\ln 2}{\ln 1.0175} \approx 9.99$ —

round to 10 years.

39. Solve $\left(1 + \dfrac{0.07}{12}\right)^{12t} = 2 : \ t = \dfrac{1}{12}\dfrac{\ln 2}{\ln(1 + 0.07/12)}$

≈ 9.93 — round to 10 years.

40. Solve $e^{0.07t} = 2 : \ t = \dfrac{1}{0.07}\ln 2 \approx 9.90$ years.

For #41–44, observe that the initial balance has no effect on the APY.

41. APY $= \left(1 + \dfrac{0.06}{4}\right)^4 - 1 \approx 6.14\%$

42. APY $= \left(1 + \dfrac{0.0575}{365}\right)^{365} - 1 \approx 5.92\%$

43. APY $= e^{0.063} - 1 \approx 6.50\%$

44. APY $= \left(1 + \dfrac{0.047}{12}\right)^{12} - 1 \approx 4.80\%$

45. The APYs are $\left(1 + \dfrac{0.05}{12}\right)^{12} - 1 \approx 5.1162\%$ and

$\left(1 + \dfrac{0.051}{4}\right)^4 - 1 \approx 5.1984\%$. So, the better investment

is 5.1% compounded quarterly.

46. The APYs are $5\dfrac{1}{8}\% = 5.125\%$ and $e^{0.05} - 1 \approx 5.1271\%$.

So, the better investment is 5% compounded continuously.

For #47–50, use the formula $S = R\dfrac{(1 + i)^n - 1}{i}$.

47. $i = \dfrac{0.0726}{12} = 0.00605$ and $R = 50$, so

$S = 50\dfrac{(1.00605)^{(12)(25)} - 1}{0.00605} \approx \$42{,}211.46$.

48. $i = \dfrac{0.155}{12} = 0.0129\ldots$ and $R = 50$, so

$$S = 50\,\frac{(1.0129)^{(12)(20)} - 1}{0.0129} \approx \$80{,}367.73.$$

49. $i = \dfrac{0.124}{12} = 0.0103$; solve

$$250{,}000 = R\,\frac{(1.0103)^{(12)(20)} - 1}{0.0103} \text{ to obtain } R \approx \$239.42$$

per month (round up, since \$239.41 will not be adequate).

50. $i = \dfrac{0.045}{12} = 0.00375$; solve

$$120{,}000 = R\,\frac{(1.00375)^{(12)(30)} - 1}{0.00375} \text{ to obtain } R \approx \$158.03$$

per month (round up, since \$158.02 will not be adequate).

For #51–54, use the formula $A = R\,\dfrac{1 - (1 + i)^{-n}}{i}$.

51. $i = \dfrac{0.0795}{12} = 0.006625$; solve

$$9000 = R\,\frac{1 - (1.006625)^{-(12)(4)}}{0.006625} \text{ to obtain } R \approx \$219.51$$

per month.

52. $i = \dfrac{0.1025}{12} = 0.0085417$; solve

$$4500 = R\,\frac{1 - (1.0085417)^{-(12)(3)}}{0.0085417} \text{ to obtain } R \approx \$145.74$$

per month (roundup, since \$145.73 will not be adequate).

53. $i = \dfrac{0.0875}{12} = 0.0072917$; solve

$$86{,}000 = R\,\frac{1 - (1.0072917)^{-(12)(30)}}{0.0072917} \text{ to obtain } R \approx \$676.57$$

per month (roundup, since \$676.56 will not be adequate).

54. $i = \dfrac{0.0925}{12} = 0.0077083$; solve $100{,}000 = $

$$R\,\frac{1 - (1.0077083)^{-(12)(25)}}{0.0077083} \text{ to obtain } R \approx \$856.39 \text{ per}$$

month (roundup, since \$856.38 will not be adequate).

55. (a) With $i = \dfrac{0.12}{12} = 0.01$, solve

$$86{,}000 = 1050\,\frac{1 - (1.01)^{-n}}{0.01}; \text{ this leads to}$$

$$(1.01)^{-n} = 1 - \frac{860}{1050} = \frac{19}{105}, \text{ so } n \approx 171.81$$

months, or about 14.32 years. The mortgage will be paid off after 172 months (14 years, 4 months). The last payment will be less than \$1050. A reasonable estimate of the final payment can be found by taking the fractional part of the computed value of n above, 0.81, and multiplying by \$1050, giving about \$850.50. To figure the exact amount of the final payment,

solve $86{,}000 = 1050\,\dfrac{1 - (1.01)^{-171}}{0.01} + R\,(1.01)^{-172}$

(the present value of the first 171 payments, plus the present value of a payment of R dollars 172 months from now). This gives a final payment of $R \approx \$846.57$.

(b) The total amount of the payments under the original plan is $360 \cdot \$884.61 = \$318{,}459.60$. The total using the higher payments is $172 \cdot \$1050 = \$180{,}660$ (or $171 \cdot \$1050 + \$846.57 = \$180{,}396.57$ if we use the correct amount of the final payment)—a difference of \$137,859.60 (or \$138,063.03 using the correct final payment).

56. (a) After 10 years, the remaining loan balance is

$$86{,}000(1.01)^{120} - 884.61\,\frac{(1.01)^{120} - 1}{0.01} \approx \$80{,}338.75$$

(this is the future value of the initial loan balance, minus the future value of the loan payments). With \$1050 payments, the time required is found by solving

$$80{,}338.75 = 1050\,\frac{1 - (1.01)^{-n}}{0.01}; \text{ this leads to}$$

$(1.01)^{-n} \approx 0.23487$, so $n \approx 145.6$ months, or about 12.13 (additional) years. The mortgage will be paid off after a total of 22 years 2 months, with the final payment being less than \$1050. A reasonable estimate of the final payment is $(0.6)(\$1050) \approx \$630.00$ (see the previous problem); to figure the exact amount, solve

$$80{,}338.75 = 1050\,\frac{1 - (1.01)^{-145}}{0.01} + R(1.01)^{-146},$$

which gives a final payment of $R \approx \$626.93$.

(b) The original plan calls for a total of \$318,459.60 in payments; this plan calls for $120 \cdot \$884.61 + 146 \cdot \$1050 = \$259{,}453.20$ (or $120 \cdot \$884.61 + 145 \cdot \$1050 + \$626.93 = \$259{,}030.13$)— a savings of \$59,006.40 (or \$59,429.47).

57. One possible answer: The APY is the percentage increase from the initial balance $S(0)$ to the end-of-year balance $S(1)$; specifically, it is $S(1)/S(0) - 1$. Multiplying the initial balance by P results in the end-of-year balance being multiplied by the same amount, so that the ratio remains unchanged. Whether we start with a \$1 investment, or a \$1000 investment, $\text{APY} = \left(1 + \dfrac{r}{k}\right)^k - 1$.

58. One possible answer: The APR will be lower than the APY (except under annual compounding), so the bank's offer looks more attractive when the APR is given. Assuming monthly compounding, the APY is about 4.594%; quarterly and daily compounding give approximately 4.577% and 4.602%, respectively.

59. One possible answer: Some of these situations involve counting things (e.g., populations), so that they can only take on whole number values — exponential models which predict, e.g., 439.72 fish, have to be interpreted in light of this fact.

Technically, bacterial growth, radioactive decay, and compounding interest also are "counting problems" — for example, we cannot have fractional bacteria, or fractional atoms of radioactive material, or fractions of pennies. However, because these are generally very large numbers, it is easier to ignore the fractional parts. (This might also apply when one is talking about, e.g., the population of the whole world.)

Another distinction: while we often use an exponential model for all these situations, it generally fits better (over long periods of time) for radioactive decay than for most of the others. Rates of growth in populations (esp. human populations) tend to fluctuate more than exponential models suggest. Of course, an exponential model also fits well in compound interest situations where the interest rate is held constant, but there are many cases where interest rates change over time.

60. (a) Steve's balance will always remain $1000, since interest is not added to it. Every year he receives 6% of that $1000 in interest: 6% in the first year, then another 6% in the second year (for a total of $2 \cdot 6\% = 12\%$), then another 6% (totaling $3 \cdot 6\% = 18\%$), etc. After t years, he has earned $6t\%$ of the $1000 investment, meaning that altogether he has $1000 + 1000 \cdot 0.06t = 1000(1 + 0.06t)$.

(b) The table is shown below; the second column gives values of $1000(1.06)^t$. The effects of annual compounding show up beginning in year 2.

Years	Not Compounded	Compounded
0	1000.00	1000.00
1	1060.00	1060.00
2	1120.00	1123.60
3	1180.00	1191.02
4	1240.00	1262.48
5	1300.00	1338.23
6	1360.00	1418.52
7	1420.00	1503.63
8	1480.00	1593.85
9	1540.00	1689.48
10	1600.00	1790.85

61. False. The limit, with continuous compounding, is $A = Pe^{rt} = 100\,e^{0.05} \approx \$105.13$.

62. True. The calculation of interest paid involves compounding, and the compounding effect is greater for longer repayment periods.

63. $A = P(1 + r/k)^{kt} = 2250(1 + 0.07/4)^{4(6)} \approx \$3412.00$. The answer is B.

64. Let $x =$ APY. Then $1 + x = (1 + 0.06/12)^{12} \approx 1.0617$. So $x \approx 0.0617$. The answer is C.

65. $FV = R((1 + i)^n - 1)/i =$ $300((1 + 0.00375)^{240} - 1)/0.00375 \approx \$116{,}437.31$. The answer is E.

66. $R = PV\,i/(1 - (1 + i)^{-n})$ $= 120{,}000(0.0725/12)/(1 - (1 + 0.0725/12)^{-180})$ $\approx \$1095.44$. The answer is A.

67. The last payment will be $364.38.

68. One possible answer:

The answer is (c). This graph shows the loan balance decreasing at a fairly steady rate over time. By contrast, the early payments on a 30-year mortgage go mostly toward interest, while the late payments go mostly toward paying down the debt. So the graph of loan balance versus time for a 30-year mortgage at double the interest rate would start off nearly horizontal and more steeply decrease over time.

69. (a) Matching up with the formula $S = R\,\dfrac{(1 + i)^n - 1}{i}$, where $i = r/k$, with r being the rate and k being the number of payments per year, we find $r = 8\%$.

(b) $k = 12$ payments per year.

(c) Each payment is $R = \$100$.

70. (a) Matching up with the formula $A = R\,\dfrac{1 - (1 + i)^{-n}}{i}$, where $i = r/k$, with r being the rate and k being number of payments per year, we find $r = 8\%$.

(b) $k = 12$ payments per year.

(c) Each payment is $R = \$200$.

■ Chapter 3 Review

1. $f\left(\dfrac{1}{3}\right) = -3 \cdot 4^{1/3} = -3\sqrt[3]{4}$

2. $f\left(-\dfrac{3}{2}\right) = 6 \cdot 3^{-3/2} = \dfrac{6}{\sqrt{27}} = \dfrac{2}{\sqrt{3}}$

For #3–4, recall that exponential functions have the form $f(x) = a \cdot b^x$.

3. $a = 3$, so $f(2) = 3 \cdot b^2 = 6$, $b^2 = 2$, $b = \sqrt{2}$, $f(x) = 3 \cdot 2^{x/2}$

4. $a = 2$, so $f(3) = 2 \cdot b^3 = 1$, $b^3 = \dfrac{1}{2}$, $b = 2^{-1/3}$, $f(x) = 2 \cdot 2^{-x/3}$

5. $f(x) = 2^{-2x} + 3$ — starting from 2^x, horizontally shrink by $\dfrac{1}{2}$, reflect across y-axis, and translate up 3 units.

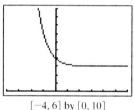

$[-4, 6]$ by $[0, 10]$

6. $f(x) = 2^{-2x}$ — starting from 2^x, horizontally shrink by $\dfrac{1}{2}$, reflect across the y-axis, reflect across x-axis.

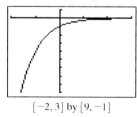

$[-2, 3]$ by $[9, -1]$

7. $f(x) = -2^{-3x} - 3$ — starting from 2^x, horizontally shrink by $\dfrac{1}{3}$, reflect across the y-axis, reflect across x-axis, translate down 3 units.

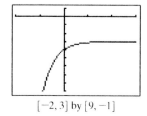

$[-2, 3]$ by $[9, -1]$

8. $f(x) = 2^{-3x} + 3$ — starting from 2^x, horizontally shrink by $\frac{1}{3}$, reflect across the y-axis, translate up 3 units.

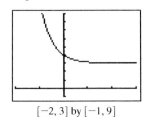

$[-2, 3]$ by $[-1, 9]$

9. Starting from e^x, horizontally shrink by $\frac{1}{2}$, then translate right $\frac{3}{2}$ units — or translate right 3 units, then horizontally shrink by $\frac{1}{2}$.

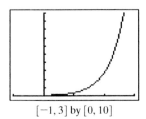

$[-1, 3]$ by $[0, 10]$

10. Starting from e^x, horizontally shrink by $\frac{1}{3}$, then translate right $\frac{4}{3}$ units — or translate right 4 units, then horizontally shrink by $\frac{1}{3}$.

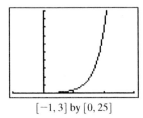

$[-1, 3]$ by $[0, 25]$

11. $f(0) = \dfrac{100}{5 + 3} = 12.5$, $\displaystyle\lim_{x \to -\infty} f(x) = 0$, $\displaystyle\lim_{x \to \infty} f(x) = 20$
y-intercept: $(0, 12.5)$; Asymptotes: $y = 0$ and $y = 20$

12. $f(0) = \dfrac{50}{5 + 2} = \dfrac{50}{7}$, $\displaystyle\lim_{x \to -\infty} f(x) = 0$, $\displaystyle\lim_{x \to \infty} f(x) = 10$
y-intercept: $\left(0, \dfrac{50}{7}\right) \approx (0, 7.14)$
Asymptotes: $y = 0$, $y = 10$

13. It is an exponential decay function.
$\displaystyle\lim_{x \to \infty} f(x) = 2$, $\displaystyle\lim_{x \to -\infty} f(x) = \infty$

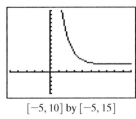

$[-5, 10]$ by $[-5, 15]$

14. Exponential growth function
$\displaystyle\lim_{x \to \infty} f(x) = \infty$, $\displaystyle\lim_{x \to -\infty} f(x) = 1$

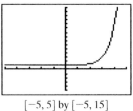

$[-5, 5]$ by $[-5, 15]$

15.

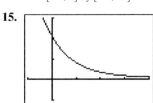

$[-1, 4]$ by $[-10, 30]$

Domain: $(-\infty, \infty)$
Range: $(1, \infty)$
Continuous
Always decreasing
Not symmetric
Bounded below by $y = 1$, which is also the only asymptote
No local extrema
$\displaystyle\lim_{x \to \infty} f(x) = 1$, $\displaystyle\lim_{x \to -\infty} f(x) = \infty$

16.

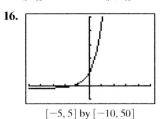

$[-5, 5]$ by $[-10, 50]$

Domain: $(-\infty, \infty)$
Range: $(-2, \infty)$
Continuous
Always increasing
Not symmetric
Bounded below by $y = -2$, which is also the only asymptote
No local extrema
$\displaystyle\lim_{x \to \infty} g(x) = \infty$, $\displaystyle\lim_{x \to -\infty} g(x) = -2$

17.

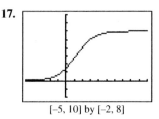

$[-5, 10]$ by $[-2, 8]$

Domain: $(-\infty, \infty)$
Range: $(0, 6)$
Continuous
Increasing
Symmetric about $(1.20, 3)$
Bounded above by $y = 6$ and below by $y = 0$, the two asymptotes
No extrema
$\displaystyle\lim_{x \to \infty} f(x) = 6$, $\displaystyle\lim_{x \to -\infty} f(x) = 0$

18.

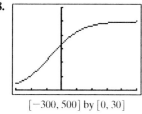

[−300, 500] by [0, 30]

Domain: $(-\infty, \infty)$
Range: $(0, 25)$
Continuous
Always increasing
Symmetric about $(-69.31, 12.5)$
Bounded above by $y = 25$ and below by $y = 0$, the two asymptotes
No local extrema
$\lim_{x \to \infty} g(x) = 25$, $\lim_{x \to -\infty} g(x) = 0$

For #19–22, recall that exponential functions are of the form $f(x) = a \cdot (1 + r)^{kx}$.

19. $a = 24$, $r = 0.053$, $k = 1$; so $f(x) = 24 \cdot 1.053^x$, where $x = $ days.

20. $a = 67{,}000$, $r = 0.0167$, $k = 1$, so $f(x) = 67{,}000 \cdot 1.0167^x$, where $x = $ years.

21. $a = 18$, $r = 1$, $k = \dfrac{1}{21}$, so $f(x) = 18 \cdot 2^{x/21}$, where $x = $ days.

22. $a = 117$, $r = -\dfrac{1}{2}$, $k = \dfrac{1}{262}$, so

$f(x) = 117 \cdot \left(\dfrac{1}{2}\right)^{x/262} = 117 \cdot 2^{-x/262}$, where $x = $ hours.

For #23–26, recall that logistic functions are expressed in $f(x) = \dfrac{c}{1 + ae^{-bx}}$.

23. $c = 30$, $a = 1.5$, so $f(2) = \dfrac{30}{1 + 1.5e^{-2b}} = 20$,

$30 = 20 + 30e^{-2b}$, $30e^{-2b} = 10$, $e^{-2b} = \dfrac{1}{3}$,

$-2b \ln e = \ln \dfrac{1}{3} \approx -1.0986$, so $b \approx 0.55$.

Thus, $f(x) = \dfrac{30}{1 + 1.5e^{-0.55x}}$

24. $c = 20$, $a \approx 2.33$, so $f(3) = \dfrac{20}{1 + 2.33e^{-3b}} = 15$,

$20 = 15 + 35e^{-3b}$, $35e^{-3b} = 5$, $e^{-3b} = \dfrac{1}{7}$,

$-3b \ln e = \ln \dfrac{1}{7} \approx -1.9459$, so $b \approx 0.65$.

Thus, $f(x) = \dfrac{20}{1 + 2.33e^{-0.65x}}$ $b = .522$

25. $c = 20$, $a = 3$, so $f(3) = \dfrac{20}{1 + 3e^{-3b}} = 10$,

$20 = 10 + 30e^{-3b}$, $30e^{-3b} = 10$, $e^{-3b} = \dfrac{10}{30} = \dfrac{1}{3}$,

$-3b \ln e = \ln \dfrac{1}{3} \approx -1.0986$, so $b \approx 0.37$.

Thus, $f(x) \approx \dfrac{20}{1 + 3e^{-0.37x}}$ $.491$

26. $c = 44$, $a = 3$, so $f(5) = \dfrac{44}{1 + 3e^{-5b}} = 22$,

$44 = 22 + 66e^{-5b}$, $66e^{-5b} = 22$, $e^{-5b} = \dfrac{22}{66} = \dfrac{1}{3}$,

$-5b \ln e = \ln \dfrac{1}{3} \approx -1.0986$, so $b \approx 0.22$.

Thus, $f(x) \approx \dfrac{44}{1 + 3e^{-0.22x}}$ $b = .803$

27. $\log_2 32 = \log_2 2^5 = 5 \log_2 2 = 5$

28. $\log_3 81 = \log_3 3^4 = 4 \log_3 3 = 4$

29. $\log \sqrt[3]{10} = \log 10^{\frac{1}{3}} = \dfrac{1}{3} \log 10 = \dfrac{1}{3}$

30. $\ln \dfrac{1}{\sqrt{e^7}} = \ln e^{-\frac{7}{2}} = -\dfrac{7}{2} \ln e = -\dfrac{7}{2}$

31. $x = 3^5 = 243$

32. $x = 2^y$

33. $\left(\dfrac{x}{y}\right) = e^{-2}$

$x = \dfrac{y}{e^2}$

34. $\left(\dfrac{a}{b}\right) = 10^{-3}$

$a = \dfrac{b}{1000}$

35. Translate left 4 units.

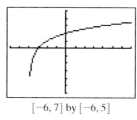

[−6, 7] by [−6, 5]

36. Reflect across y-axis and translate right 4 units — or translate left 4 units, then reflect across y-axis.

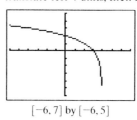

[−6, 7] by [−6, 5]

37. Translate right 1 unit, reflect across x-axis, and translate up 2 units.

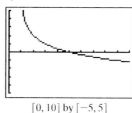

[0, 10] by [−5, 5]

38. Translate left 1 unit, reflect across x-axis, and translate up 4 units.

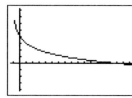

[−1.4, 17.4] by [−4.2, 8.2]

39.

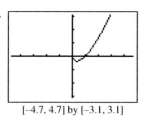

[−4.7, 4.7] by [−3.1, 3.1]

Domain: $(0, \infty)$

Range: $\left[-\dfrac{1}{e}, \infty \right) \approx [-0.37, \infty)$

Continuous

Decreasing on $(0, 0.37]$; increasing on $[0.37, \infty)$

Not symmetric

Bounded below

Local minimum at $\left(\dfrac{1}{e}, -\dfrac{1}{e} \right)$

$\lim\limits_{x \to \infty} f(x) = \infty$

40.

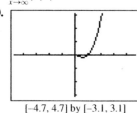

[−4.7, 4.7] by [−3.1, 3.1]

Domain: $(0, \infty)$

Range: $[-0.18, \infty)$

Continuous

Decreasing on $(0, 0.61]$; increasing on $[0.61, \infty)$

Not symmetric

Bounded below

Local minimum at $(0.61, -0.18)$

No asymptotes

$\lim\limits_{x \to \infty} f(x) = \infty$

41.

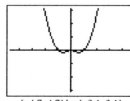

[−4.7, 4.7] by [−3.1, 3.1]

Domain: $(-\infty, 0) \cup (0, \infty)$

Range: $[-0.18, \infty)$

Discontinuous at $x = 0$

Decreasing on $(-\infty, -0.61]$, $(0, 0.61]$;

Increasing on $[-0.61, 0)$, $[0.61, \infty)$

Symmetric across y-axis

Bounded below

Local minima at $(-0.61, -0.18)$
  and $(0.61, -0.18)$

No asymptotes

$\lim\limits_{x \to \infty} f(x) = \infty$, $\lim\limits_{x \to -\infty} f(x) = \infty$

42.

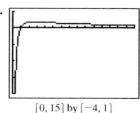

[0, 15] by [−4, 1]

Domain: $(0, \infty)$

Range: $\left(-\infty, \dfrac{1}{e} \right] \approx (-\infty, 0.37]$

Continuous

Increasing on $(0, e] \approx (0, 2.72]$,

Decreasing $[e, \infty) \approx [2.72, \infty)$

Not symmetric

Bounded above

Local maximum at $\left(e, \dfrac{1}{e} \right) \approx (2.72, 0.37)$

Asymptotes: $y = 0$ and $x = 0$

$\lim\limits_{x \to \infty} f(x) = 0$

43. $x = \log 4 \approx 0.6021$

44. $x = \ln 0.25 = -1.3863$

45. $x = \dfrac{\ln 3}{\ln 1.05} \approx 22.5171$

46. $x = e^{5.4} = 221.4064$

47. $x = 10^{-7} = 0.0000001$

48. $x = 3 + \dfrac{\ln 5}{\ln 3} \approx 4.4650$

49. $\log_2 x = 2$, so $x = 2^2 = 4$

50. $\log_3 x = \dfrac{7}{2}$, so $x = 3^{7/2} = 27\sqrt{3} \approx 46.7654$

51. Multiply both sides by $2 \cdot 3^x$, leaving $(3^x)^2 - 1 = 10 \cdot 3^x$, or $(3^x)^2 - 10 \cdot 3^x - 1 = 0$. This is quadratic in 3^x, leading to $3^x = \dfrac{10 \pm \sqrt{100 + 4}}{2} = 5 \pm \sqrt{26}$. Only $5 + \sqrt{26}$ is positive, so the only answer is $x = \log_3(5 + \sqrt{26}) \approx 2.1049$.

52. Multiply both sides by $4 + e^{2x}$, leaving $50 = 44 + 11e^{2x}$, so $11e^{2x} = 6$. Then $x = \dfrac{1}{2} \ln \dfrac{6}{11} \approx -0.3031$.

53. $\log[(x + 2)(x - 1)] = 4$, so $(x + 2)(x - 1) = 10^4$.

The solutions to this quadratic equation are

$x = \dfrac{1}{2}(-1 \pm \sqrt{40{,}009})$, but of these two numbers, only

the positive one, $x = \dfrac{1}{2}(\sqrt{40{,}009} - 1) \approx 99.5112$,

works in the original equation.

54. $\ln \dfrac{3x + 4}{2x + 1} = 5$, so $3x + 4 = e^5(2x + 1)$.

Then $x = \dfrac{4 - e^5}{2e^5 - 3} \approx -0.4915$.

55. $\log_2 x = \dfrac{\ln x}{\ln 2}$

56. $\log_{1/6}(6x^2) = \log_{1/6} 6 + \log_{1/6} x^2 = \log_{1/6} 6 + 2\log_{1/6}|x|$

$= -1 + \dfrac{2\ln|x|}{\ln 1/6} = -1 + \dfrac{2\ln|x|}{\ln 6^{-1}} = -1 - \dfrac{2\ln|x|}{\ln 6}$

57. $\log_5 x = \dfrac{\log x}{\log 5}$

58. $\log_{1/2}(4x^3) = \log_{1/2} 4 + \log_{1/2} x^3 = -2 + 3\log_{1/2} x$

$= -2 - 3\log_2 x$

$= -2 - \dfrac{3\log x}{\log 2}$

59. Increasing, intercept at $(1, 0)$. The answer is (c).

60. Decreasing, intercept at $(1, 0)$. The answer is (d).

61. Intercept at $(-1, 0)$. The answer is (b).

62. Intercept at $(0, 1)$. The answer is (a).

63. $A = 450(1 + 0.046)^3 \approx \$515.00$

64. $A = 4800\left(1 + \dfrac{0.062}{4}\right)^{(4)(17)} \approx \$13,660.81$

65. $A = Pe^{rt}$

66. $i = \dfrac{r}{k}$, $n = kt$, so $FV = R \cdot \dfrac{\left(1 + \dfrac{r}{k}\right)^{kt} - 1}{\left(\dfrac{r}{k}\right)}$

67. $PV = \dfrac{550\left(1 - \left(1 + \dfrac{0.055}{12}\right)^{(-12)(5)}\right)}{\left(\dfrac{0.055}{12}\right)} \approx \$28,794.06$

68. $PV = \dfrac{953\left(1 - \left(1 + \dfrac{0.0725}{26}\right)^{(-26)(15)}\right)}{\left(\dfrac{0.0725}{26}\right)} \approx \$226,396.22$

69. $20e^{-3k} = 50$, so $k = -\dfrac{1}{3}\ln\dfrac{5}{2} \approx -0.3054$.

70. $20e^{-k} = 30$, so $k = -\ln\dfrac{3}{2} \approx -0.4055$.

71. $P(t) = 2.0956 \cdot 1.01218^t$, where x is the number of years since 1900. In 2005, $P(105) = 2.0956 \cdot 1.01218^{105} \approx 7.5$ million.

72. $P(t) = \dfrac{14.3614}{(1 + 2.0083e^{-0.0249t})}$, where x is the number of years since 1900. In 2010, $P(110) \approx 12.7$ million.

73. (a) $f(0) = 90$ units.

(b) $f(2) \approx 32.8722$ units.

(c)

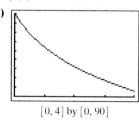

$[0, 4]$ by $[0, 90]$

74. (a) $P(t) = 123,000(1 - 0.024)^t = 123,000(0.976)^t$.

(b) $P(t) = 90,000$ when $t = \dfrac{\ln(90/123)}{\ln 0.976} \approx 12.86$ years.

75. (a) $P(t) = 89,000(1 - 0.018)^t = 89,000(0.982)^t$.

(b) $P(t) = 50,000$ when $t = \dfrac{\ln(50/89)}{\ln 0.982} \approx 31.74$ years.

76. (a) $P(0) \approx 5.3959$ — 5 or 6 students.

(b) $P(3) \approx 80.6824$ — 80 or 81 students.

(c) $P(t) = 100$ when $1 + e^{4-t} = 3$, or $t = 4 - \ln 2 \approx 3.3069$ — sometime on the fourth day.

(d) As $t \to \infty$, $P(t) \to 300$.

77. (a) $P(t) = 20 \cdot 2^t$, where t is time in months. (Other possible answers: $20 \cdot 2^{12t}$ if t is in years, or $20 \cdot 2^{t/30}$ if t is in days).

(b) $P(12) = 81,920$ rabbits after 1 year. $P(60) \approx 2.3058 \times 10^{19}$ rabbits after 5 years.

(c) Solve $20 \cdot 2^t = 10,000$ to find $t = \log_2 500 \approx 8.9658$ months — 8 months and about 29 days.

78. (a) $P(t) = 4 \cdot 2^t = 2^{t+2}$, where t is time in days.

(b) $P(4) = 64$ guppies after 4 days. $P(7) = 512$ guppies after 1 week.

(c) Solve $4 \cdot 2^t = 2000$ to find $t = \log_2 500 = 8.9658$ days — 8 days and about 23 hours.

79. (a) $S(t) = S_0 \cdot \left(\dfrac{1}{2}\right)^{t/1.5}$, where t is time in seconds.

(b) $S(1.5) = S_0/2$. $S(3) = S_0/4$.

(c) If $1\,g = S(60) = S_0 \cdot \left(\dfrac{1}{2}\right)^{60/1.5} = S_0 \cdot \left(\dfrac{1}{2}\right)^{40}$, then

$S_0 = 2^{40} \approx 1.0995 \times 10^{12}\,g = 1.0995 \times 10^9\,kg$

$= 1,099,500$ metric tons.

80. (a) $S(t) = S_0 \cdot \left(\dfrac{1}{2}\right)^{t/2.5}$, where t is time in seconds.

(b) $S(2.5) = S_0/2$. $S(7.5) = S_0/8$.

(c) If $1\,g = S(60) = S_0 \cdot \left(\dfrac{1}{2}\right)^{60/2.5} = S_0 \cdot \left(\dfrac{1}{2}\right)^{24}$, then

$S_0 = 2^{24} = 16,777,216\,g = 16,777.216\,kg$.

81. Let $a_1 = $ the amplitude of the ground motion of the Feb 4 quake, and let $a_2 = $ the amplitude of the ground motion of the May 30 quake. Then:

$$6.1 = \log \frac{a_1}{T} + B \quad \text{and} \quad 6.9 = \log \frac{a_2}{T} + B$$

$$\left(\log \frac{a_2}{T} + B\right) - \left(\log \frac{a_1}{T} + B\right) = 6.9 - 6.1$$

$$\log \frac{a_2}{T} - \log \frac{a_1}{T} = 0.8$$

$$\log \frac{a_2}{a_1} = 0.8$$

$$\frac{a_2}{a_1} = 10^{0.8}$$

$$a_2 \approx 6.31 \, a_1$$

The ground amplitude of the deadlier quake was approximately 6.31 times stronger.

82. (a) Seawater:
$$-\log [H^+] = 7.6$$
$$\log [H^+] = -7.6$$
$$[H^+] = 10^{-7.6} \approx 2.51 \times 10^{-8}$$

Milk of Magnesia:
$$-\log [H^+] = 10.5$$
$$\log [H^+] = -10.5$$
$$[H^+] = 10^{-10.5} \approx 3.16 \times 10^{-11}$$

(b) $\dfrac{[H^+] \text{ of Seawater}}{[H^+] \text{ of Milk of Magnesia}} = \dfrac{10^{-7.6}}{10^{-10.5}} \approx 794.33$

(c) They differ by an order of magnitude of 2.9.

83. Solve $1500\left(1 + \dfrac{0.08}{4}\right)^{4t} = 3750$: $(1.02)^{4t} = 2.5$,

so $t = \dfrac{1}{4} \dfrac{\ln 2.5}{\ln 1.02} \approx 11.5678$ years — round to 11 years 9 months (the next full compounding period).

84. Solve $12{,}500e^{0.09t} = 37{,}500$: $e^{0.09t} = 3$,

so $t = \dfrac{1}{0.09} \ln 3 = 12.2068$ years.

85. $t = 133.83 \ln \dfrac{700}{250} \approx 137.7940$ — about 11 years 6 months.

86. $t = 133.83 \ln \dfrac{500}{50} \approx 308.1550$ — about 25 years 9 months.

87. $r = \left(1 + \dfrac{0.0825}{12}\right)^{12} - 1 \approx 8.57\%$

88. $r = e^{0.072} - 1 \approx 7.47\%$

89. $I = 12 \cdot 10^{(-0.0125)(25)} = 5.84$ lumens

90. $\log_b x = \dfrac{\ln x}{\ln b}$. This is a vertical stretch if $e^{-1} < b < e$ (so that $|\ln b| < 1$), and a shrink if $0 < b < e^{-1}$ or $b > e$. (There is also a reflection if $0 < b < 1$.)

91. $\log_b x = \dfrac{\log x}{\log b}$. This is a vertical stretch if $\dfrac{1}{10} < b < 10$ (so that $|\log b| < 1$), and a shrink if $0 < b < \dfrac{1}{10}$ or $b > 10$. (There is also a reflection if $0 < b < 1$.)

92. $g(x) = \ln[a \cdot b^x] = \ln a + \ln b^x = \ln a + x \ln b$. This has a slope $\ln b$ and y-intercept $\ln a$.

93. (a) $P(0) = 16$ students.

(b) $P(t) = 800$ when $1 + 99e^{-0.4t} = 2$, or $e^{0.4t} = 99$,

so $t = \dfrac{1}{0.4} \ln 99 \approx 11.4878$ — about $11\frac{1}{2}$ days.

(c) $P(t) = 400$ when $1 + 99e^{-0.4t} = 4$, or $e^{0.4t} = 33$,

so $t = \dfrac{1}{0.4} \ln 33 \approx 8.7413$ — about 8 or 9 days.

94. (a) $P(0) = 12$ deer.

(b) $P(t) = 1000$ when $1 + 99e^{-0.4t} = 1.2$, so

$t = -\dfrac{1}{0.4} \ln \dfrac{0.2}{99} \approx 15.5114$ — about $15\frac{1}{2}$ years.

(c) As $t \to \infty$, $P(t) \to 1200$ (and the population never rises above that level).

95. The model is $T = 20 + 76e^{-kt}$, and $T(8) = 65$

$= 20 + 76e^{-8k}$. Then $e^{-8k} = \dfrac{45}{76}$, so $k = -\dfrac{1}{8} \ln \dfrac{45}{76}$

≈ 0.0655. Finally, $T = 25$ when $25 = 20 + 76e^{-kt}$,

so $t = -\dfrac{1}{k} \ln \dfrac{5}{76} \approx 41.54$ minutes.

96. The model is $T = 75 + 145e^{-kt}$, and $T(35) = 150$

$= 75 + 145e^{-35k}$. Then $e^{-35k} = \dfrac{75}{145}$, so $k = -\dfrac{1}{35} \ln \dfrac{15}{29}$

≈ 0.0188. Finally, $T = 95$ when $95 = 75 + 145e^{-kt}$,

so $t = -\dfrac{1}{k} \ln \dfrac{20}{145} \approx 105.17$ minutes.

97. (a) Matching up with the formula $S = R \dfrac{(1 + i)^n - 1}{i}$, where $i = r/k$, with r being the rate and k being the number of payments per year, we find $r = 9\%$.

(b) $k = 4$ payments per year.

(c) Each payment is $R = \$100$.

98. (a) Matching up with the formula $A = R \dfrac{1 - (1 + i)^{-n}}{i}$, where $i = r/k$, with r being the rate and k being the number of payments per year, we find $r = 11\%$.

(b) $k = 4$ payments per year.

(c) Each payment is $R = \$200$.

99. (a) Grace's balance will always remain $1000, since interest is not added to it. Every year she receives 5% of that $1000 in interest; after t years, she has been paid $5t\%$ of the $1000 investment, meaning that altogether she has $1000 + 1000 \cdot 0.05t = 1000(1 + 0.05t)$.

(b) The table is shown below; the second column gives values of $1000e^{0.05t}$. The effects of compounding continuously show up immediately.

Years	Not Compounded	Compounded
0	1000.00	1000.00
1	1050.00	1051.27
2	1100.00	1105.17
3	1150.00	1161.83
4	1200.00	1221.40
5	1250.00	1284.03
6	1300.00	1349.86
7	1350.00	1419.07
8	1400.00	1491.82
9	1450.00	1568.31
10	1500.00	1648.72

Chapter 3 Project

Answers are based on the sample data shown in the table.

2. Writing each maximum height as a (rounded) percentage of the previous maximum height produces the following table.

Bounce Number	Percentage Return
0	N/A
1	79%
2	77%
3	76%
4	78%
5	79%

The average is 77.8%

3.

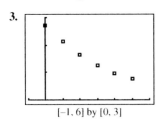

[−1, 6] by [0, 3]

4. Each successive height will be predicted by multiplying the previous height by the same percentage of rebound. The rebound height can therefore be predicted by the equation $y = HP^x$ where x is the bounce number. From the sample data, $H = 2.7188$ and $P \approx 0.778$.

5. $y = HP^x$ becomes $y \approx 2.7188 \cdot 0.778^x$.

6. The regression equation is $y \approx 2.733 \cdot 0.776^x$. Both H and P are close to, though not identical with, the values in the earlier equation.

7. A different ball could be dropped from the same original height, but subsequent maximum heights would in general change because the rebound percentage changed. So P would change in the equation.

8. H would be changed by varying the height from which the ball was dropped. P would be changed by using a different type of ball or a different bouncing surface.

9. $y = HP^x$
$\quad = H(e^{\ln P})^x$
$\quad = He^{(\ln P)x}$
$\quad = 2.7188\, e^{-0.251x}$

10. $\ln y = \ln(HP^x)$
$\qquad = \ln H + x \ln P$
This is a linear equation.

11.

Bounce Number	ln (Height)
0	1.0002
1	0.76202
2	0.50471
3	0.23428
4	−0.01705
5	−0.25125

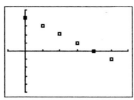

[−1, 6] by [−1.25, 1.25]

The linear regression produces
$Y = \ln y \approx -0.253x + 1.005$. Since $\ln y \approx (\ln P)x + \ln H$, the slope of the line is $\ln P$ and the Y-intercept (that is, the $\ln y$-intercept) is $\ln H$.

Chapter 4
Trigonometric Functions

■ Section 4.1 Angles and Their Measures

Exploration 1

1. $2\pi r$

2. 2π radians (2π lengths of thread)

3. No, not quite, since the distance πr would require a piece of thread π times as long, and $\pi > 3$.

4. π radians

Quick Review 4.1

1. $C = 2\pi \cdot 2.5 = 5\pi$ in.

2. $C = 2\pi \cdot 4.6 = 9.2\pi$ m

3. $r = \dfrac{1}{2\pi} \cdot 12 = \dfrac{6}{\pi}$ m

4. $r = \dfrac{1}{2\pi} \cdot 8 = \dfrac{4}{\pi}$ ft

5. (a) $s = 47.52$ ft (b) $s = 39.77$ km

6. (a) $v = 26.1$ m/sec (b) $v = 8.06$ ft/sec

7. $60\,\dfrac{\text{mi}}{\text{hr}} \cdot 5280\,\dfrac{\text{ft}}{\text{mi}} \cdot \dfrac{1}{3600}\,\dfrac{\text{hr}}{\text{sec}} = 88$ ft/sec

8. $45\,\dfrac{\text{mi}}{\text{hr}} \cdot 5280\,\dfrac{\text{ft}}{\text{mi}} \cdot \dfrac{1}{3600}\,\dfrac{\text{hr}}{\text{sec}} = 66$ ft/sec

9. $8.8\,\dfrac{\text{ft}}{\text{sec}} \cdot \dfrac{1}{5280}\,\dfrac{\text{mi}}{\text{ft}} \cdot 3600\,\dfrac{\text{sec}}{\text{hr}} = 6$ mph

10. $132\,\dfrac{\text{ft}}{\text{sec}} \cdot \dfrac{1}{5280}\,\dfrac{\text{mi}}{\text{ft}} \cdot 3600\,\dfrac{\text{sec}}{\text{hr}} = 90$ mph

Section 4.1 Exercises

1. $23°12' = \left(23 + \dfrac{12}{60}\right)^\circ = 23.2°$

2. $35°24' = \left(35 + \dfrac{24}{60}\right)^\circ = 35.4°$

3. $118°44'15'' = \left(118 + \dfrac{44}{60} + \dfrac{15}{3600}\right)^\circ = 118.7375°$

4. $48°30'36'' = \left(48 + \dfrac{30}{60} + \dfrac{36}{3600}\right)^\circ = 48.51°$

5. $21.2° = 21°(60 \cdot 0.2)' = 21°12'$

6. $49.7° = 49°(60 \cdot 0.7)' = 49°42'$

7. $118.32° = 118°(60 \cdot 0.32)' = 118°19.2'$
$= 118°19'(60 \cdot 0.2)'' = 118°19'12''$

8. $99.37° = 99°(60 \cdot 0.37)' = 99°22.2'$
$= 99°22'(60 \cdot 0.2)'' = 99°22'12''$

For #9–16, use the formula $s = r\theta$, and the equivalent forms $r = s/\theta$ and $\theta = s/r$.

9. $60° \cdot \dfrac{\pi}{180°} = \dfrac{\pi}{3}$ rad

10. $90° \cdot \dfrac{\pi}{180°} = \dfrac{\pi}{2}$ rad

11. $120° \cdot \dfrac{\pi}{180°} = \dfrac{2\pi}{3}$ rad

12. $150° \cdot \dfrac{\pi}{180°} = \dfrac{5\pi}{6}$ rad

13. $71.72° \cdot \dfrac{\pi}{180°} \approx 1.2518$ rad

14. $11.83° \cdot \dfrac{\pi}{180°} \approx 0.2065$ rad

15. $61°24' = \left(61 + \dfrac{24}{60}\right)^\circ = 61.4° \cdot \dfrac{\pi}{180°} \approx 1.0716$ rad

16. $75°30' = \left(75 + \dfrac{30}{60}\right)^\circ = 75.5° \cdot \dfrac{\pi}{180°} \approx 1.3177$ rad

17. $\dfrac{\pi}{6} \cdot \dfrac{180°}{\pi} = 30°$

18. $\dfrac{\pi}{4} \cdot \dfrac{180°}{\pi} = 45°$

19. $\dfrac{\pi}{10} \cdot \dfrac{180°}{\pi} = 18°$

20. $\dfrac{3\pi}{5} \cdot \dfrac{180°}{\pi} = 108°$

21. $\dfrac{7\pi}{9} \cdot \dfrac{180°}{\pi} = 140°$

22. $\dfrac{13\pi}{20} \cdot \dfrac{180°}{\pi} = 117°$

23. $2 \cdot \dfrac{180}{\pi} \approx 114.59°$

24. $1.3 \cdot \dfrac{180}{\pi} \approx 74.48°$

25. $s = 50$ in.

26. $s = 70$ cm

27. $r = 6/\pi$ ft

28. $r = 7.5/\pi$ cm

29. $\theta = 3$ radians

30. $\theta = \dfrac{4}{7}$ radians

31. $r = \dfrac{360}{\pi}$ cm

32. $s = (5 \text{ ft})(18°)\left(\dfrac{2\pi \cdot}{360°}\right) = \dfrac{\pi}{2}$ ft

33. $\theta = s_1/r_1 = \dfrac{9}{11}$ rad and $s_2 = r_2\theta = 36$

34. $\theta = s_1/r_1 = 4.5$ rad and $r_2 = s_2/\theta = 16$ km

35. The angle is $10° \cdot \dfrac{\pi}{180°} = \dfrac{\pi}{18}$ rad, so the curved side

measures $\dfrac{11\pi}{18}$ in. The two straight sides measures 11 in.

each, so the perimeter is $11 + 11 + \dfrac{11\pi}{18} \approx 24$ inches.

36. The angle is $100° \cdot \dfrac{\pi}{180°} = \dfrac{5\pi}{9}$ rad, so

$$7 = \frac{5\pi}{9}r.$$

Then

$$r = \frac{63}{5\pi} \approx 4 \text{ cm}.$$

37. Five pieces of track form a semicircle, so each arc has a central angle of $\pi/5$ radians. The inside arc length is $r_i(\pi/5)$ and the outside arc length is $r_o(\pi/5)$. Since $r_o(\pi/5) - r_i(\pi/5) = 3.4$ inches, we conclude that $r_o - r_i = 3.4(5/\pi) \approx 5.4$ inches.

38. Let the diameter of the inner (red) circle be d. The inner circle's perimeter is 37.7 inches, which equals πd. Then the next-largest (yellow) circle has a perimeter of $\pi(d + 6 + 6) = \pi d + 12\pi = 37.7 + 12\pi \approx 75.4$ inches.

39. (a) NE is 45°. (b) NNE is 22.5°. (c) WSW is 247.5°.

40. (a) SSW is 202.5°. (b) WNW is 292.5°. (c) NNW is 337.5°.

41. ESE is closest at 112.5°.

42. SW is closest at 225°.

43. The angle between them is $\theta = 9°42' = 9.7° \approx 0.1693$ radians, so the distance is about $s = r\theta = (25)(0.1693) \approx 4.23$ statute miles.

44. Since $C = \pi d$, a tire travels a distance πd with each revolution.

(a) Each tire travels at a speed of $800\,\pi d$ in. per minute, or

$$\left(\frac{800\pi d \text{ in.}}{1 \text{ min}}\right)\left(\frac{60 \text{ min}}{1 \text{ hr}}\right)\left(\frac{1 \text{ mi}}{63{,}360 \text{ in.}}\right) \approx 2.38d \text{ mi/hr}.$$

Vehicle	d	Speed $\approx 2.38d$
Taurus	26.16	62.26 mph
Charger	28.63	68.14 mph
Mariner	28.95	68.90 mph

(b) $\left(\dfrac{\pi d \text{ in.}}{1 \text{ rev}}\right)\left(\dfrac{1 \text{ mi}}{63{,}360 \text{ in.}}\right) = \dfrac{\pi d}{63{,}360}$ mi/rev, so each mile

requires $\dfrac{63{,}360}{\pi d} \approx \dfrac{20{,}168}{d}$ revolutions.

Taurus: $\dfrac{20{,}168}{26.16} \approx 770.95$ revolutions

Mariner: $\dfrac{20{,}168}{28.95} \approx 696.65$ revolutions

The Taurus must make just over 74 more revolutions.

(c) In each revolution, the tire would cover a distance of πd_{new} rather than πd_{old}, so that the car would travel $(\pi d_{\text{new}})/(\pi d_{\text{old}}) = d_{\text{new}}/d_{\text{old}} = 28/26.16 \approx 1.07$ miles for every mile the car's instruments would show. Both the odometer and speedometer readings would be low.

45. $v = 44$ ft/sec and $r = 13$ in., so

$$\omega = v/r = \left(44\,\frac{\text{ft}}{\text{sec}} \cdot 60\,\frac{\text{sec}}{\text{min}}\right) \div \left(13 \text{ in.} \cdot \frac{1}{12}\,\frac{\text{ft}}{\text{in.}} \cdot 2\pi\,\frac{\text{rad}}{\text{rev}}\right)$$

$$\approx 387.85 \text{ rpm}.$$

46. (a) $\dfrac{S}{W} = \dfrac{R}{100} \Rightarrow S = \dfrac{WR}{100}$ mm.

25.4 mm = 1 in., so

$$S = \frac{WR}{100} \cdot \frac{1}{25.4} = \frac{WR}{2540} \text{ in.}$$

(b) $D + 2S = D + 2\left(\dfrac{WR}{2540}\right) = D + \dfrac{WR}{1270}$ in.

(c) Taurus: $D = 16 + \dfrac{215 \cdot 60}{1270} \approx 26.16$ in.

Charger: $D = 18 + \dfrac{225 \cdot 60}{1270} \approx 28.63$ in.

Mariner: $D = 16 + \dfrac{235 \cdot 70}{1270} \approx 28.95$ in.

Ridgeline: $D = 17 + \dfrac{245 \cdot 65}{1270} \approx 29.54$ in.

47. $\omega = 2000$ rpm and $r = 5$ in., so

$$v = r\omega = \left(5 \text{ in.} \cdot 12\,\frac{\text{teeth}}{\text{in.}}\right) \cdot$$

$$\left(2000\,\frac{\text{rev}}{\text{min}} \cdot 2\pi\,\frac{\text{rad}}{\text{rev}} \cdot \frac{1}{60}\,\frac{\text{min}}{\text{sec}}\right) \approx 12{,}566.37 \text{ teeth per}$$

second.

48.

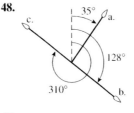

49.

50. $257 \text{ naut mi} \cdot \dfrac{3956\pi}{10{,}800}\,\dfrac{\text{stat mi}}{\text{naut mi}} \approx 296$ statute miles

51. $895 \text{ stat mi} \cdot \dfrac{10{,}800}{3956\pi}\,\dfrac{\text{naut mi}}{\text{stat mi}} \approx 778$ nautical miles

52. (a) Lane 5 has inside radius 37 m, while the inside radius of lane 6 is 38 m, so over the whole semicircle, the difference is $38\pi - 37\pi = \pi \approx 3.142$ m. (This would be the answer for any two adjacent lanes.)

(b) $38\pi - 33\pi = 5\pi \approx 15.708$ m.

53. (a) $s = r\theta = (4)(4\pi) = 16\pi \approx 50.265$ in., or $\frac{4}{3}\pi$
≈ 4.189 ft.

(b) $r\theta = 2\pi \approx 6.283$ ft.

54. $s = r\theta = (52)\left(\frac{\pi}{180}\right) = \frac{13}{45}\pi \approx 0.908$ ft

55. (a) $\omega_1 = 120\,\frac{\text{rev}}{\text{min}} \cdot 2\pi\,\frac{\text{rad}}{\text{rev}} \cdot \frac{1}{60}\,\frac{\text{min}}{\text{sec}} = 4\pi$ rad/sec

(b) $v = R\omega_1 = (7\text{ cm})\left(4\pi\,\frac{\text{rad}}{\text{sec}}\right) = 28\pi$ cm/sec

(c) $\omega_2 = v/r = \left(28\pi\,\frac{\text{cm}}{\text{sec}}\right) \div (4\text{ cm}) = 7\pi$ rad/sec

56. (a) $\omega = 135\,\frac{\text{rev}}{\text{min}} \cdot 2\pi\,\frac{\text{rad}}{\text{rev}} \cdot \frac{1}{60}\,\frac{\text{min}}{\text{sec}} = 4.5\pi$ rad/sec

(b) $v = r\omega = (1.2\text{ m})\left(4.5\pi\,\frac{\text{rad}}{\text{sec}}\right) = 5.4\pi$ m/sec

(c) The radius to this halfway point is $r^* = \frac{1}{2}r = 0.6$ m,

so $v = r^*\omega = (0.6\text{ m})\left(4.5\pi\,\frac{\text{rad}}{\text{sec}}\right) = 2.7\pi$ m/sec.

57. True. In the amount of time it takes for the merry-go-round to complete one revolution, horse B travels a distance of $2\pi r$, where r is B's distance from the center. In the same time, horse A travels a distance of $2\pi(2r) = 2(2\pi r)$ — twice as far as B.

58. False. If all three radian measures were integers, their sum would be an integer. But the sum must equal π, which is not an integer.

59. $x^\circ = x^\circ\left(\frac{\pi\text{ rad}}{180^\circ}\right) = \frac{\pi x}{180}$. The answer is C.

60. If the perimeter is 4 times the radius, the arc is two radii long, which implies an angle of 2 radians. The answer is A.

61. Let n be the number of revolutions per minute.
$\left(\frac{26\pi\text{ in.}}{1\text{ rev}}\right)\left(\frac{n\text{ rev}}{1\text{ min}}\right)\left(\frac{60\text{ min}}{1\text{ hr}}\right)\left(\frac{1\text{ mi}}{63{,}360\text{ in.}}\right)$
$\approx 0.07735\,n$ mph.
Solving $0.07735\,n = 10$ yields $n \approx 129$.
The answer is B.

62. The size of the circle does not affect the size of the angle. The radius and the subtended arc length both double, so that their ratio stays the same.
The answer is C.

In #63–66, we need to "borrow" 1° and change it to $60'$ in order to complete the subtraction.

63. $122^\circ 25' - 84^\circ 23' = 38^\circ 02'$

64. $117^\circ 09' - 74^\circ 0' = 43^\circ 09'$

65. $93^\circ 16' - 87^\circ 39' = 92^\circ 76' - 87^\circ 39' = 5^\circ 37'$

66. $122^\circ 20' - 80^\circ 12' = 42^\circ 08'$

In #67–70, find the difference in the latitude. Convert this difference to minutes; this is the distance in nautical miles. The Earth's diameter is not needed.

67. The difference in latitude is $34^\circ 03' - 32^\circ 43' = 1^\circ 20'$
$= 80$ minutes of arc, which is 80 naut mi.

68. The difference in latitude is $47^\circ 36' - 37^\circ 47' = 9^\circ 49'$
$= 589$ minutes of arc, which is 589 naut mi.

69. The difference in latitude is $44^\circ 59' - 29^\circ 57' = 15^\circ 02'$
$= 902$ minutes of arc, which is 902 naut mi.

70. The difference in latitude is $42^\circ 20' - 33^\circ 45' = 8^\circ 35'$
$= 515$ minutes of arc, which is 515 naut mi.

71. The whole circle's area is πr^2; the sector with central angle θ makes up $\theta/2\pi$ of that area, or $\frac{\theta}{2\pi} \cdot \pi r^2 = \frac{1}{2}\theta r^2$.

72. (a) $A = \frac{1}{2}(5.9)^2\left(\frac{\pi}{5}\right) \approx 3.481\pi = 10.936$ ft^2.

(b) $A = \frac{1}{2}(1.6)^2(3.7) = 4.736$ km^2.

73.

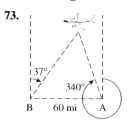

74. Bike wheels: $\omega_1 = v_1/r = (66\text{ ft/sec} \cdot 12\text{ in./ft}) \div (14\text{ in.})$
≈ 56.5714 rad/sec. The wheel sprocket must have the same angular velocity: $\omega_2 = \omega_1 \approx 56.5714$ rad/sec. For the pedal sprocket, we first need the velocity of the chain, using the wheel sprocket: $v_2 \approx (\frac{3}{2}$ in.$)(56.5714$ rad/sec$)$ ≈ 84.8571 in./sec. Then the pedal sprocket's angular velocity is $\omega_3 = (84.8571$ in./sec$) \div (4.5$ in.$) \approx 18.9$ rad/sec.

■ Section 4.2 Trigonometric Functions of Acute Angles

Exploration 1

1. sin and csc, cos and sec, and tan and cot.

2. $\tan\theta$

3. $\sec\theta$

4. 1

5. $\sin\theta$ and $\cos\theta$

Exploration 2

1. Let $\theta = 60^\circ$. Then

$$\sin\theta = \frac{\sqrt{3}}{2} \approx 0.866 \qquad\qquad \csc\theta = \frac{2}{\sqrt{3}} \approx 1.155$$

$$\cos\theta = \frac{1}{2} \qquad\qquad\qquad \sec\theta = 2$$

$$\tan\theta = \sqrt{3} \approx 1.732 \qquad \cot\theta = \frac{1}{\sqrt{3}} \approx 0.577$$

2. The values are the same, but for different functions. For example, sin 30° is the same as cos 60°, cot 30° is the same as tan 60°, etc.

3. The value of a trig function at θ is the same as the value of its co-function at $90^\circ - \theta$.

Quick Review 4.2

1. $x = \sqrt{5^2 + 5^2} = \sqrt{50} = 5\sqrt{2}$

2. $x = \sqrt{8^2 + 12^2} = \sqrt{208} = 4\sqrt{13}$

3. $x = \sqrt{10^2 - 8^2} = 6$

4. $x = \sqrt{4^2 - 2^2} = \sqrt{12} = 2\sqrt{3}$

5. $8.4 \text{ ft} \cdot 12 \dfrac{\text{in}}{\text{ft}} = 100.8 \text{ in.}$

6. $940 \text{ ft} \cdot \dfrac{1}{5280} \dfrac{\text{mi}}{\text{ft}} = \dfrac{47}{264} \approx 0.17803 \text{ mi}$

7. $a = (0.388)(20.4) = 7.9152 \text{ km}$

8. $b = \dfrac{23.9}{1.72} \approx 13.895 \text{ ft}$

9. $\alpha = 13.3 \cdot \dfrac{2.4}{31.6} \approx 1.0101$ (no units)

10. $\beta = 5.9 \cdot \dfrac{6.15}{8.66} \approx 4.18995$ (no units)

Section 4.2 Exercises

1. $\sin\theta = \dfrac{4}{5}, \cos\theta = \dfrac{3}{5}, \tan\theta = \dfrac{4}{3}, \csc\theta = \dfrac{5}{4}, \sec\theta = \dfrac{5}{3},$
$\cot\theta = \dfrac{3}{4}.$

2. $\sin\theta = \dfrac{8}{\sqrt{113}}, \cos\theta = \dfrac{7}{\sqrt{113}}, \tan\theta = \dfrac{8}{7}; \csc\theta = \dfrac{\sqrt{113}}{8},$
$\sec\theta = \dfrac{\sqrt{113}}{7}, \cot\theta = \dfrac{7}{8}.$

3. $\sin\theta = \dfrac{12}{13}, \cos\theta = \dfrac{5}{13}, \tan\theta = \dfrac{12}{5}; \csc\theta = \dfrac{13}{12},$
$\sec\theta = \dfrac{13}{5}, \cot\theta = \dfrac{5}{12}.$

4. $\sin\theta = \dfrac{8}{17}, \cos\theta = \dfrac{15}{17}, \tan\theta = \dfrac{8}{15}; \csc\theta = \dfrac{17}{8},$
$\sec\theta = \dfrac{17}{15}, \cot\theta = \dfrac{15}{8}.$

5. The hypotenuse length is $\sqrt{7^2 + 11^2} = \sqrt{170}$, so
$\sin\theta = \dfrac{7}{\sqrt{170}}, \cos\theta = \dfrac{11}{\sqrt{170}}, \tan\theta = \dfrac{7}{11}; \csc\theta = \dfrac{\sqrt{170}}{7},$
$\sec\theta = \dfrac{\sqrt{170}}{11}, \cot\theta = \dfrac{11}{7}.$

6. The adjacent side length is $\sqrt{8^2 - 6^2} = \sqrt{28} = 2\sqrt{7}$, so
$\sin\theta = \dfrac{3}{4}, \cos\theta = \dfrac{\sqrt{7}}{4}, \tan\theta = \dfrac{3}{\sqrt{7}}; \csc\theta = \dfrac{4}{3},$
$\sec\theta = \dfrac{4}{\sqrt{7}}, \cot\theta = \dfrac{\sqrt{7}}{3}.$

7. The opposite side length is $\sqrt{11^2 - 8^2} = \sqrt{57}$, so
$\sin\theta = \dfrac{\sqrt{57}}{11}, \cos\theta = \dfrac{8}{11}, \tan\theta = \dfrac{\sqrt{57}}{8}; \csc\theta = \dfrac{11}{\sqrt{57}},$
$\sec\theta = \dfrac{11}{8}, \cot\theta = \dfrac{8}{\sqrt{57}}.$

8. The adjacent side length is $\sqrt{13^2 - 9^2} = \sqrt{88} = 2\sqrt{22}$,
so $\sin\theta = \dfrac{9}{13}, \cos\theta = \dfrac{2\sqrt{22}}{13}, \tan\theta = \dfrac{9}{2\sqrt{22}}; \csc\theta = \dfrac{13}{9},$
$\sec\theta = \dfrac{13}{2\sqrt{22}}, \cot\theta = \dfrac{2\sqrt{22}}{9}.$

9. Using a right triangle with hypotenuse 7 and legs 3
(opposite) and $\sqrt{7^2 - 3^2} = \sqrt{40} = 2\sqrt{10}$ (adjacent),
we have $\sin\theta = \dfrac{3}{7}, \cos\theta = \dfrac{2\sqrt{10}}{7}, \tan\theta = \dfrac{3}{2\sqrt{10}};$
$\csc\theta = \dfrac{7}{3}, \sec\theta = \dfrac{7}{2\sqrt{10}}, \cot\theta = \dfrac{2\sqrt{10}}{3}.$

10. Using a right triangle with hypotenuse 3 and legs 2
(opposite) and $\sqrt{3^2 - 2^2} = \sqrt{5}$ (adjacent), we have
$\sin\theta = \dfrac{2}{3}, \cos\theta = \dfrac{\sqrt{5}}{3}, \tan\theta = \dfrac{2}{\sqrt{5}}; \csc\theta = \dfrac{3}{2},$
$\sec\theta = \dfrac{3}{\sqrt{5}}, \cot\theta = \dfrac{\sqrt{5}}{2}.$

11. Using a right triangle with hypotenuse 11 and legs 5
(adjacent) and $\sqrt{11^2 - 5^2} = \sqrt{96} = 4\sqrt{6}$ (opposite),
we have $\sin\theta = \dfrac{4\sqrt{6}}{11}, \cos\theta = \dfrac{5}{11}, \tan\theta = \dfrac{4\sqrt{6}}{5};$
$\csc\theta = \dfrac{11}{4\sqrt{6}}, \sec\theta = \dfrac{11}{5}, \cot\theta = \dfrac{5}{4\sqrt{6}}.$

12. Using a right triangle with hypotenuse 8 and legs 5
(adjacent) and $\sqrt{8^2 - 5^2} = \sqrt{39}$ (opposite), we have
$\sin\theta = \dfrac{\sqrt{39}}{8}, \cos\theta = \dfrac{5}{8}, \tan\theta = \dfrac{\sqrt{39}}{5}; \csc\theta = \dfrac{8}{\sqrt{39}},$
$\sec\theta = \dfrac{8}{5}, \cot\theta = \dfrac{5}{\sqrt{39}}.$

13. Using a right triangle with legs 5 (opposite) and
9 (adjacent) and hypotenuse $\sqrt{5^2 + 9^2} = \sqrt{106}$, we have
$\sin\theta = \dfrac{5}{\sqrt{106}}, \cos\theta = \dfrac{9}{\sqrt{106}}, \tan\theta = \dfrac{5}{9}; \csc\theta = \dfrac{\sqrt{106}}{5},$
$\sec\theta = \dfrac{\sqrt{106}}{9}, \cot\theta = \dfrac{9}{5}.$

14. Using a right triangle with legs 12 (opposite) and
13 (adjacent) and hypotenuse $\sqrt{12^2 + 13^2} = \sqrt{313}$,
we have $\sin\theta = \dfrac{12}{\sqrt{313}}, \cos\theta = \dfrac{13}{\sqrt{313}}, \tan\theta = \dfrac{12}{13};$
$\csc\theta = \dfrac{\sqrt{313}}{12}, \sec\theta = \dfrac{\sqrt{313}}{13}, \cot\theta = \dfrac{13}{12}.$

15. Using a right triangle with legs 3 (opposite) and
11 (adjacent) and hypotenuse $\sqrt{3^2 + 11^2} = \sqrt{130}$,
we have $\sin\theta = \dfrac{3}{\sqrt{130}}, \cos\theta = \dfrac{11}{\sqrt{130}}, \tan\theta = \dfrac{3}{11};$
$\csc\theta = \dfrac{\sqrt{130}}{3}, \sec\theta = \dfrac{\sqrt{130}}{11}, \cot\theta = \dfrac{11}{3}.$

16. Using a right triangle with hypotenuse 12 and legs 5 (opposite) and $\sqrt{12^2 - 5^2} = \sqrt{119}$ (adjacent), we have $\sin\theta = \dfrac{5}{12}$, $\cos\theta = \dfrac{\sqrt{119}}{12}$, $\tan\theta = \dfrac{5}{\sqrt{119}}$; $\csc\theta = \dfrac{12}{5}$, $\sec\theta = \dfrac{12}{\sqrt{119}}$, $\cot\theta = \dfrac{\sqrt{119}}{5}$.

17. Using a right triangle with hypotenuse 23 and legs 9 (opposite) and $\sqrt{23^2 - 9^2} = \sqrt{448} = 8\sqrt{7}$ (adjacent), we have $\sin\theta = \dfrac{9}{23}$, $\cos\theta = \dfrac{8\sqrt{7}}{23}$, $\tan\theta = \dfrac{9}{8\sqrt{7}}$; $\csc\theta = \dfrac{23}{9}$, $\sec\theta = \dfrac{23}{8\sqrt{7}}$, $\cot\theta = \dfrac{8\sqrt{7}}{9}$.

18. Using a right triangle with hypotenuse 17 and legs 5 (adjacent) and $\sqrt{17^2 - 5^2} = \sqrt{264} = 2\sqrt{66}$. (opposite), we have $\sin\theta = \dfrac{2\sqrt{66}}{17}$, $\cos\theta = \dfrac{5}{17}$, $\tan\theta = \dfrac{2\sqrt{66}}{5}$; $\csc\theta = \dfrac{17}{2\sqrt{66}}$, $\sec\theta = \dfrac{17}{5}$, $\cot\theta = \dfrac{5}{2\sqrt{66}}$.

19. $\dfrac{\sqrt{3}}{2}$

20. 1

21. $\sqrt{3}$

22. 2

23. $\dfrac{1}{\sqrt{2}} = \dfrac{\sqrt{2}}{2}$

24. $\dfrac{2}{\sqrt{3}} = \dfrac{2\sqrt{3}}{3}$

25. $\sec 45° = 1/\cos 45° \approx 1.4142$. Squaring this result yields 2.0000, so $\sec 45° = \sqrt{2}$.

26. $\sin 60° \approx 0.8660$. Squaring this result yields $0.7500 = 3/4$, so $\sin 60° = \sqrt{3/4} = \sqrt{3}/2$.

27. $\csc(\pi/3) = 1/\sin(\pi/3) \approx 1.1547$. Squaring this result yields 1.3333 or essentially 4/3, so $\csc(\pi/3) = \sqrt{4/3} = 2/\sqrt{3} = 2\sqrt{3}/3$.

28. $\tan(\pi/3) \approx 1.73205$. Squaring this result yields 3.0000, so $\tan(\pi/3) = \sqrt{3}$.

For #29–40, the answers marked with an asterisk (*) should be found in DEGREE mode; the rest should be found in RADIAN mode. Since most calculators do not have the secant, cosecant, and cotangent functions built in, the reciprocal versions of these functions are shown.

29. ≈ 0.961*

30. ≈ 0.141*

31. ≈ 0.943*

32. ≈ 0.439*

33. ≈ 0.268

34. ≈ 0.208

35. $\dfrac{1}{\cos 49°} \approx 1.524$*

36. $\dfrac{1}{\sin 19°} \approx 3.072$*

37. $\dfrac{1}{\tan 0.89} \approx 0.810$

38. $\dfrac{1}{\cos 1.24} \approx 3.079$

39. $\dfrac{1}{\tan(\pi/8)} \approx 2.414$

40. $\dfrac{1}{\sin(\pi/10)} \approx 3.236$

41. $\theta = 30° = \dfrac{\pi}{6}$

42. $\theta = 60° = \dfrac{\pi}{3}$

43. $\theta = 60° = \dfrac{\pi}{3}$

44. $\theta = 45° = \dfrac{\pi}{4}$

45. $\theta = 60° = \dfrac{\pi}{3}$

46. $\theta = 45° = \dfrac{\pi}{4}$

47. $\theta = 30° = \dfrac{\pi}{6}$

48. $\theta = 30° = \dfrac{\pi}{6}$

49. $x = \dfrac{15}{\sin 34°} \approx 26.82$

50. $z = \dfrac{23}{\cos 39°} \approx 29.60$

51. $y = \dfrac{32}{\tan 57°} \approx 20.78$

52. $x = 14\sin 43° \approx 9.55$

53. $y = 6/\sin 35° \approx 10.46$

54. $x = 50\cos 66° \approx 20.34$

For #55–58, choose whichever of the following formulas is appropriate:

$$a = \sqrt{c^2 - b^2} = c\sin\alpha = c\cos\beta = b\tan\alpha = \dfrac{b}{\tan\beta}$$

$$b = \sqrt{c^2 - a^2} = c\cos\alpha = c\sin\beta = a\tan\beta = \dfrac{a}{\tan\alpha}$$

$$c = \sqrt{a^2 + b^2} = \dfrac{a}{\cos\beta} = \dfrac{a}{\sin\alpha} = \dfrac{b}{\sin\beta} = \dfrac{b}{\cos\alpha}$$

If one angle is given, subtract from 90° to find the other angle.

55. $b = \dfrac{a}{\tan\alpha} = \dfrac{12.3}{\tan 20°} \approx 33.79$, $c = \dfrac{a}{\sin\alpha} = \dfrac{12.3}{\sin 20°} \approx 35.96$, $\beta = 90° - \alpha = 70°$

56. $a = c\sin\alpha = 10\sin 41° \approx 6.56$, $b = c\cos\alpha = 10\cos 41° \approx 7.55$, $\beta = 90° - \alpha = 49°$

57. $b = a\tan\beta = 15.58\tan 55° \approx 22.25$, $c = \dfrac{a}{\cos\beta} = \dfrac{15.58}{\cos 55°} \approx 27.16$, $\alpha = 90° - \beta = 35°$

58. $b = a\tan\beta = 5\tan 59° \approx 8.32$, $c = \dfrac{a}{\cos\beta} = \dfrac{5}{\cos 59°} \approx 9.71$, $\alpha = 90° - \beta = 31°$

59. 0. As θ gets smaller and smaller, the side opposite θ gets smaller and smaller, so its ratio to the hypotenuse approaches 0 as a limit.

60. 1. As θ gets smaller and smaller, the side adjacent to θ approaches the hypotenuse in length, so its ratio to the hypotenuse approaches 1 as a limit.

61. $h = 55\tan 75° \approx 205.26$ ft

62. $h = 5 + 120\tan 8° \approx 21.86$ ft

63. $A = 12 \cdot \dfrac{5}{\sin 54°} \approx 74.16$ ft^2

64. $h = 130\tan 82.9° \approx 1043.70$ ft

65. $AC = 100\tan 75°12'42'' \approx 378.80$ ft

66. Connect the three points on the arc to the center of the circle, forming three triangles, each with hypotenuse 10 ft. The horizontal legs of the three triangles have lengths $10\cos 67.5° \approx 3.827$, $10\cos 45° \approx 7.071$, and $10\cos 22.5° \approx 9.239$. The widths of the four strips are therefore,

$$3.827 - 0 = 3.827 \text{ (strip } A\text{)}$$
$$7.071 - 3.827 = 3.244 \text{ (strip } B\text{)}$$
$$9.239 - 7.071 = 2.168 \text{ (strip } C\text{)}$$
$$10 - 9.239 = 0.761 \text{ (strip } D\text{)}$$

Allen needs to correct his data for strips B and C.

67. False. This is only true if θ is an acute angle in a right triangle. (Then it is true by definition.)

68. False. The larger the angle of a triangle, the smaller its cosine.

69. $\sec 90° = \dfrac{1}{\cos 90°} = \dfrac{1}{0}$ is undefined. The answer is E.

70. $\sin \theta = \dfrac{\text{opp}}{\text{hyp}} = \dfrac{3}{5}$. The answer is A.

71. If the unknown slope is m, then $m \sin \theta = -1$, so $m = -\dfrac{1}{\sin \theta} = -\csc \theta$. The answer is D.

72. For all θ, $-1 \le \cos \theta \le 1$. The answer is B.

73. For angles in the first quadrant, sine values will be increasing, cosine values will be decreasing and only tangent values can be greater than 1. Therefore, the first column is tangent, the second column is sine, and the third column is cosine.

74. For angles in the first quadrant, secant values will be increasing, and cosecant and cotangent values will be decreasing. We recognize that $\csc (30°) = 2$. Therefore, the first column is secant, the second column is cotangent, and the third column is cosecant.

75. The distance d_A from A to the mirror is $5 \cos 30°$; the distance from B to the mirror is $d_B = d_A - 2$. Then

$$PB = \frac{d_B}{\cos \beta} = \frac{d_A - 2}{\cos 30°} = 5 - \frac{2}{\cos 30°}$$
$$= 5 - \frac{4}{\sqrt{3}} \approx 2.69 \text{ m}.$$

76. Let P be the point at which we should aim; let α and β be the angles as labeled in #73. Since $\alpha = \beta$, $\tan \alpha = \tan \beta$. P should be x inches to the right of C, where x is chosen so that $\tan \alpha = \dfrac{x}{15} = \tan \beta = \dfrac{30 - x}{10}$. Then $10x = 15(30 - x)$, so $25x = 450$, which gives $x = 18$. Aim 18 in. to the right of C (or 12 in. to the left of D).

77. One possible proof:

$$(\sin \theta)^2 + (\cos \theta)^2 = \left(\frac{a}{c}\right)^2 + \left(\frac{b}{c}\right)^2$$
$$= \frac{a^2}{c^2} + \frac{b^2}{c^2}$$
$$= \frac{a^2 + b^2}{c^2}$$
$$= \frac{c^2}{c^2} \qquad \text{(Pythagorean theorem: } a^2 + b^2 = c^2.\text{)}$$
$$= 1$$

78. Let h be the length of the altitude to base b and denote the area of the triangle by A. Then

$$\frac{h}{a} = \sin \theta$$
$$\therefore h = a \sin \theta$$

Since $A = \dfrac{1}{2} bh$, we can substitute $h = a \sin \theta$ to get

$$A = \frac{1}{2} ab \sin \theta.$$

■ Section 4.3   Trigonometry Extended: The Circular Functions

Exploration 1

1. The side opposite θ in the triangle has length y and the hypotenuse has length r. Therefore
$$\sin \theta = \frac{\text{opp}}{\text{hyp}} = \frac{y}{r}.$$

2. $\cos \theta = \dfrac{\text{adj}}{\text{hyp}} = \dfrac{x}{r}$

3. $\tan \theta = \dfrac{\text{opp}}{\text{adj}} = \dfrac{y}{x}$

4. $\cot \theta = \dfrac{x}{y}$; $\sec \theta = \dfrac{r}{x}$; $\csc \theta = \dfrac{r}{y}$

Exploration 2

1. The x-coordinates on the unit circle lie between -1 and 1, and $\cos t$ is always an x-coordinate on the unit circle.

2. The y-coordinates on the unit circle lie between -1 and 1, and $\sin t$ is always a y-coordinate on the unit circle.

3. The points corresponding to t and $-t$ on the number line are wrapped to points above and below the x-axis with the same x-coordinates. Therefore $\cos t$ and $\cos (-t)$ are equal.

4. The points corresponding to t and $-t$ on the number line are wrapped to points above and below the x-axis with exactly opposite y-coordinates. Therefore $\sin t$ and $\sin (-t)$ are opposites.

5. Since 2π is the distance around the unit circle, both t and $t + 2\pi$ get wrapped to the same point.

6. The points corresponding to t and $t + \pi$ get wrapped to points on either end of a diameter on the unit circle. These points are symmetric with respect to the origin and therefore have coordinates (x, y) and $(-x, -y)$. Therefore $\sin t$ and $\sin (t + \pi)$ are opposites, as are $\cos t$ and $\cos (t + \pi)$.

7. By the observation in (6), $\tan t$ and $\tan(t + \pi)$ are ratios of the form $\dfrac{y}{x}$ and $\dfrac{-y}{-x}$, which are either equal to each other or both undefined.

8. The sum is always of the form $x^2 + y^2$ for some (x, y) on the unit circle. Since the equation of the unit circle is $x^2 + y^2 = 1$, the sum is always 1.

9. Answers will vary. For example, there are similar statements that can be made about the functions cot, sec, and csc.

Quick Review 4.3

1. $-30°$

2. $-150°$

3. $45°$

4. $240°$

5. $\tan \dfrac{\pi}{6} = \dfrac{1}{\sqrt{3}} = \dfrac{\sqrt{3}}{3}$

6. $\cot \dfrac{\pi}{4} = 1$

7. $\csc \dfrac{\pi}{4} = \sqrt{2}$

8. $\sec \dfrac{\pi}{3} = 2$

9. Using a right triangle with hypotenuse 13 and legs 5 (opposite) and $\sqrt{13^2 - 5^2} = 12$ (adjacent), we have

$\sin \theta = \dfrac{5}{13}$, $\cos \theta = \dfrac{12}{13}$, $\tan \theta = \dfrac{5}{12}$; $\csc \theta = \dfrac{13}{5}$,

$\sec \theta = \dfrac{13}{12}$, $\cot \theta = \dfrac{12}{5}$.

10. Using a right triangle with hypotenuse 17 and legs 15 (adjacent) and $\sqrt{17^2 - 15^2} = 8$ (opposite), we have

$\sin \theta = \dfrac{8}{17}$, $\cos \theta = \dfrac{15}{17}$, $\tan \theta = \dfrac{8}{15}$; $\csc \theta = \dfrac{17}{8}$,

$\sec \theta = \dfrac{17}{15}$, $\cot \theta = \dfrac{15}{8}$.

Section 4.3 Exercises

1. The $450°$ angle lies on the positive-y axis $(450° - 360° = 90°)$, while the others are all coterminal in Quadrant II.

2. The $-\dfrac{5\pi}{3}$ angle lies in Quadrant I $\left(-\dfrac{5\pi}{3} + 2\pi = \dfrac{\pi}{3}\right)$, while the others are all coterminal in Quadrant IV.

In #3–12, recall that the distance from the origin is $r = \sqrt{x^2 + y^2}$.

3. $\sin \theta = \dfrac{2}{\sqrt{5}}$, $\cos \theta = -\dfrac{1}{\sqrt{5}}$, $\tan \theta = -2$; $\csc \theta = \dfrac{\sqrt{5}}{2}$,

$\sec \theta = -\sqrt{5}$, $\cot \theta = -\dfrac{1}{2}$.

4. $\sin \theta = -\dfrac{3}{5}$, $\cos \theta = \dfrac{4}{5}$, $\tan \theta = -\dfrac{3}{4}$; $\csc \theta = -\dfrac{5}{3}$,

$\sec \theta = \dfrac{5}{4}$, $\cot \theta = -\dfrac{4}{3}$.

5. $\sin \theta = -\dfrac{1}{\sqrt{2}}$, $\cos \theta = -\dfrac{1}{\sqrt{2}}$, $\tan \theta = 1$; $\csc \theta = -\sqrt{2}$,

$\sec \theta = -\sqrt{2}$, $\cot \theta = 1$.

6. $\sin \theta = -\dfrac{5}{\sqrt{34}}$, $\cos \theta = \dfrac{3}{\sqrt{34}}$, $\tan \theta = -\dfrac{5}{3}$;

$\csc \theta = -\dfrac{\sqrt{34}}{5}$, $\sec \theta = \dfrac{\sqrt{34}}{3}$, $\cot \theta = -\dfrac{3}{5}$.

7. $\sin \theta = \dfrac{4}{5}$, $\cos \theta = \dfrac{3}{5}$, $\tan \theta = \dfrac{4}{3}$; $\csc \theta = \dfrac{5}{4}$,

$\sec \theta = \dfrac{5}{3}$, $\cot \theta = \dfrac{3}{4}$.

8. $\sin \theta = -\dfrac{3}{\sqrt{13}}$, $\cos \theta = -\dfrac{2}{\sqrt{13}}$, $\tan \theta = \dfrac{3}{2}$;

$\csc \theta = -\dfrac{\sqrt{13}}{3}$, $\sec \theta = -\dfrac{\sqrt{13}}{2}$, $\cot \theta = \dfrac{2}{3}$.

9. $\sin \theta = 1$, $\cos \theta = 0$, $\tan \theta$ undefined; $\csc \theta = 1$, $\sec \theta$ undefined, $\cot \theta = 0$.

10. $\sin \theta = 0$, $\cos \theta = -1$, $\tan \theta = 0$; $\csc \theta$ undefined, $\sec \theta = -1$, $\cot \theta$ undefined.

11. $\sin \theta = -\dfrac{2}{\sqrt{29}}$, $\cos \theta = \dfrac{5}{\sqrt{29}}$, $\tan \theta = -\dfrac{2}{5}$;

$\csc \theta = -\dfrac{\sqrt{29}}{2}$, $\sec \theta = \dfrac{\sqrt{29}}{5}$, $\cot \theta = -\dfrac{5}{2}$.

12. $\sin \theta = -\dfrac{1}{\sqrt{2}}$, $\cos \theta = \dfrac{1}{\sqrt{2}}$, $\tan \theta = -1$;

$\csc \theta = -\sqrt{2}$, $\sec \theta = \sqrt{2}$, $\cot \theta = -1$.

For #13–16, determine the quadrant(s) of angles with the given measures, and then use the fact that $\sin t$ is positive when the terminal side of the angle is above the x-axis (in Quadrants I and II) and $\cos t$ is positive when the terminal side of the angle is to the right of the y-axis (in quadrants I and IV). Note that since $\tan t = \sin t / \cos t$, the sign of $\tan t$ can be determined from the signs of $\sin t$ and $\cos t$: if $\sin t$ and $\cos t$ have the same sign, the answer to (c) will be '+'; otherwise it will be '−'. Thus $\tan t$ is positive in Quadrants I and III.

13. These angles are in Quadrant I. **(a)** + (i.e., $\sin t > 0$). **(b)** + (i.e., $\cos t > 0$). **(c)** + (i.e., $\tan t > 0$).

14. These angles are in Quadrant II. **(a)** +. **(b)** −. **(c)** −.

15. These angles are in Quadrant III. **(a)** −. **(b)** −. **(c)** +.

16. These angles are in Quadrant IV. **(a)** −. **(b)** +. **(c)** −.

For #17–20, use strategies similar to those for the previous problem set.

17. $143°$ is in Quadrant II, so $\cos 143°$ is negative.

18. $192°$ is in Quadrant III, so $\tan 192°$ is positive.

19. $\dfrac{7\pi}{8}$ rad is in Quadrant II, so $\cos \dfrac{7\pi}{8}$ is negative.

20. $\dfrac{4\pi}{5}$ rad is in Quadrant II, so $\tan \dfrac{4\pi}{5}$ is negative.

21. A $(2, 2)$; $\tan 45° = \dfrac{y}{x} = 1 \Rightarrow y = x$.

22. B $(-1, \sqrt{3})$; $\tan \dfrac{2\pi}{3} = \dfrac{y}{x} = -\sqrt{3}$. $\dfrac{2\pi}{3}$ is in Quadrant II, so x is negative.

23. C $(-\sqrt{3}, -1)$; $\dfrac{7\pi}{6}$ is in Quadrant III, so x and y are both negative. $\tan \dfrac{7\pi}{6} = \dfrac{1}{\sqrt{3}}$.

24. D $(1, -\sqrt{3})$; $-60°$ is in Quadrant IV, so x is positive while y is negative. $\tan (-60°) = -\sqrt{3}$.

For #25–36, recall that the reference angle is the acute angle formed by the terminal side of the angle in standard position and the x-axis.

25. The reference angle is $60°$. A right triangle with a $60°$ angle at the origin has the point $P(-1, \sqrt{3})$ as one vertex, with hypotenuse length $r = 2$, so $\cos 120° = \dfrac{x}{r} = -\dfrac{1}{2}$.

26. The reference angle is $60°$. A right triangle with a $60°$ angle at the origin has the point $P(1, -\sqrt{3})$ as one vertex, so $\tan 300° = \dfrac{y}{x} = -\sqrt{3}$.

27. The reference angle is the given angle, $\frac{\pi}{3}$. A right triangle with a $\frac{\pi}{3}$ radian angle at the origin has the point $P(1, \sqrt{3})$ as one vertex, with hypotenuse length $r = 2$, so $\sec \frac{\pi}{3} = \frac{r}{x} = 2$.

28. The reference angle is $\frac{\pi}{4}$. A right triangle with a $\frac{\pi}{4}$ radian angle at the origin has the point $P(1, 1)$ as one vertex, with hypotenuse length $r = \sqrt{2}$, so $\csc \frac{3\pi}{4} = \frac{r}{y} = \sqrt{2}$.

29. The reference angle is $\frac{\pi}{6}$ (in fact, the given angle is coterminal with $\frac{\pi}{6}$). A right triangle with a $\frac{\pi}{6}$ radian angle at the origin has the point $P(\sqrt{3}, 1)$ as one vertex, with hypotenuse length $r = 2$, so $\sin \frac{13\pi}{6} = \frac{y}{r} = \frac{1}{2}$.

30. The reference angle is $\frac{\pi}{3}$ (in fact, the given angle is coterminal with $\frac{\pi}{3}$). A right triangle with a $\frac{\pi}{3}$ radian angle at the origin has the point $P(1, \sqrt{3})$ as one vertex, with hypotenuse length $r = 2$, so $\cos \frac{7\pi}{3} = \frac{x}{r} = \frac{1}{2}$.

31. The reference angle is $\frac{\pi}{4}$ (in fact, the given angle is coterminal with $\frac{\pi}{4}$). A right triangle with a $\frac{\pi}{4}$ radian angle at the origin has the point $P(1, 1)$ as one vertex, so $\tan \frac{-15\pi}{4} = \frac{y}{x} = 1$.

32. The reference angle is $\frac{\pi}{4}$. A right triangle with a $\frac{\pi}{4}$ radian angle at the origin has the point $P(-1, -1)$ as one vertex, so $\cot \frac{13\pi}{4} = \frac{x}{y} = 1$.

33. $\cos \frac{23\pi}{6} = \cos \frac{11\pi}{6} = \frac{\sqrt{3}}{2}$

34. $\cos \frac{17\pi}{4} = \cos \frac{\pi}{4} = \frac{\sqrt{2}}{2}$

35. $\sin \frac{11\pi}{3} = \sin \frac{5\pi}{3} = -\frac{\sqrt{3}}{2}$

36. $\cot \frac{19\pi}{6} = \cot \frac{7\pi}{6} = \sqrt{3}$

37. $-450°$ is coterminal with $270°$, on the negative y-axis. **(a)** -1 **(b)** 0 **(c)** Undefined

38. $-270°$ is coterminal with $90°$, on the positive y-axis. **(a)** 1 **(b)** 0 **(c)** Undefined

39. 7π radians is coterminal with π radians, on the negative x-axis. **(a)** 0 **(b)** -1 **(c)** 0

40. $\frac{11\pi}{2}$ radians is coterminal with $\frac{3\pi}{2}$ radians, on the negative y-axis. **(a)** -1 **(b)** 0 **(c)** Undefined

41. $\frac{-7\pi}{2}$ radians is coterminal with $\frac{\pi}{2}$ radians, on the positive y-axis. **(a)** 1 **(b)** 0 **(c)** Undefined

42. -4π radians is coterminal with 0 radians, on the positive x-axis. **(a)** 0 **(b)** 1 **(c)** 0

43. Since $\cot \theta > 0$, $\sin \theta$ and $\cos \theta$ have the same sign, so $\sin \theta = +\sqrt{1 - \cos^2 \theta} = \frac{\sqrt{5}}{3}$, and $\tan \theta = \frac{\sin \theta}{\cos \theta} = \frac{\sqrt{5}}{2}$.

44. Since $\tan \theta < 0$, $\sin \theta$ and $\cos \theta$ have opposite signs, so $\cos \theta = -\sqrt{1 - \sin^2 \theta} = -\frac{\sqrt{15}}{4}$, and $\cot \theta = \frac{\cos \theta}{\sin \theta} = -\sqrt{15}$.

45. $\cos \theta = +\sqrt{1 - \sin^2 \theta} = \frac{\sqrt{21}}{5}$, so $\tan \theta = \frac{\sin \theta}{\cos \theta} = -\frac{2}{\sqrt{21}}$ and $\sec \theta = \frac{1}{\cos \theta} = \frac{5}{\sqrt{21}}$.

46. $\sec \theta$ has the same sign as $\cos \theta$, and since $\cot \theta > 0$, $\sin \theta$ must also be negative. With $x = -3$, $y = -7$, and $r = \sqrt{3^2 + 7^2} = \sqrt{58}$, we have $\sin \theta = -\frac{7}{\sqrt{58}}$ and $\cos \theta = -\frac{3}{\sqrt{58}}$.

47. Since $\cos \theta < 0$ and $\cot \theta < 0$, $\sin \theta$ must be positive. With $x = -4$, $y = 3$, and $r = \sqrt{4^2 + 3^2} = 5$, we have $\sec \theta = -\frac{5}{4}$ and $\csc \theta = \frac{5}{3}$.

48. Since $\sin \theta > 0$ and $\tan \theta < 0$, $\cos \theta$ must be negative. With $x = -3$, $y = 4$, and $r = \sqrt{4^2 + 3^2} = 5$, we have $\csc \theta = \frac{5}{4}$ and $\cot \theta = -\frac{3}{4}$.

49. $\sin \left(\frac{\pi}{6} + 49{,}000\pi \right) = \sin \left(\frac{\pi}{6} \right) = \frac{1}{2}$

50. $\tan (1{,}234{,}567\pi) - \tan (7{,}654{,}321\pi)$ $= \tan (\pi) - \tan (\pi) = 0$

51. $\cos \left(\frac{5{,}555{,}555\pi}{2} \right) = \cos \left(\frac{\pi}{2} \right) = 0$

52. $\tan \left(\frac{3\pi - 70{,}000\pi}{2} \right) = \tan \left(\frac{3\pi}{2} \right) = $ undefined.

53. The calculator's value of the irrational number π is necessarily an approximation. When multiplied by a very large number, the slight error of the original approximation is magnified sufficiently to throw the trigonometric functions off.

54. $\sin t$ is the y-coordinate of the point on the unit circle after measuring counterclockwise t units from $(1, 0)$. This will repeat every 2π units (and not before), since the distance around the circle is 2π.

55. $\mu = \frac{\sin 83°}{\sin 36°} \approx 1.69$

56. $\sin \theta_2 = \frac{\sin 42°}{1.52} \approx 0.44$

57. **(a)** When $t = 0$, $d = 0.4$ in.

(b) When $t = 3$, $d = 0.4 e^{-0.6} \cos 12 \approx 0.1852$ in.

58. When $t = 0, \theta = 0.25$ (rad). When $t = 2.5$, $\theta = 0.25 \cos 2.5 \approx -0.2003$ rad.

59. The difference in the elevations is 600 ft, so $d = 600/\sin \theta$. Then:

(a) $d = 600\sqrt{2} \approx 848.53$ ft.

(b) $d = 600$ ft.

(c) $d \approx 933.43$ ft.

60. January ($t = 1$): $72.4 + 61.7 \sin \dfrac{\pi}{6} = 103.25$.

April ($t = 4$): $72.4 + 61.7 \sin \dfrac{2\pi}{3} \approx 125.83$.

June ($t = 6$): $72.4 + 61.7 \sin \pi = 72.4$.

October ($t = 10$): $72.4 + 61.7 \sin \dfrac{5\pi}{3} \approx 18.97$.

December ($t = 12$): $72.4 + 61.7 \sin 2\pi = 72.4$. June and December are the same; perhaps by June most people have suits for the summer, and by December they are beginning to purchase them for next summer (or as Christmas presents, or for mid-winter vacations).

61. True. Any angle in a triangle measures between $0°$ and $180°$. Acute angles ($<90°$) determine reference triangles in Quadrant I, where the cosine is positive, while obtuse angles ($>90°$) determine reference triangles in Quadrant II, where the cosine is negative.

62. True. The point determines a reference triangle in Quadrant IV, with $r = \sqrt{8^2 + (-6)^2} = 10$. Thus $\sin \theta = y/x = -6/10 = -0.6$

63. If $\sin \theta = 0.4$, then $\sin(-\theta) + \csc \theta = -\sin \theta + \dfrac{1}{\sin \theta}$

$= -0.4 + \dfrac{1}{0.4} = 2.1$. The answer is E.

64. If $\cos \theta = 0.4$, then $\cos(\theta + \pi) = -\cos \theta = -0.4$. The answer is B.

65. $(\sin t)^2 + (\cos t)^2 = 1$ for all t. The answer is A.

66. $\sin \theta = -\sqrt{1 - \cos^2 \theta}$, because $\tan \theta$

$= (\sin \theta)/(\cos \theta) > 0$. So $\sin \theta = -\sqrt{1 - \dfrac{25}{169}} = -\dfrac{12}{13}$.

The answer is A.

67. Since $\sin \theta > 0$ and $\tan \theta < 0$, the terminal side must be in Quadrant II, so $\theta = \dfrac{5\pi}{6}$.

68. Since $\cos \theta > 0$ and $\sin \theta < 0$, the terminal side must be in Quadrant IV, so $\theta = \dfrac{11\pi}{6}$.

69. Since $\tan \theta < 0$ and $\sin \theta < 0$, the terminal side must be in Quadrant IV, so $\theta = \dfrac{7\pi}{4}$.

70. Since $\sin \theta < 0$ and $\tan \theta > 0$, the terminal side must be in Quadrant III, so $\theta = \dfrac{5\pi}{4}$.

71. The two triangles are congruent: both have hypotenuse 1, and the corresponding angles are congruent—the smaller acute angle has measure t in both triangles, and the two acute angles in a right triangle add up to $\pi/2$.

72. These coordinates give the lengths of the legs of the triangles from #71, and these triangles are congruent. For example, the length of the horizontal leg of the triangle with vertex P is given by the (absolute value of the) x-coordinate of P; this must be the same as the (absolute value of the) y-coordinate of Q.

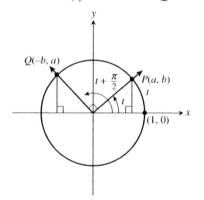

73. One possible answer: Starting from the point (a, b) on the unit circle—at an angle of t, so that $\cos t = a$—then measuring a quarter of the way around the circle (which corresponds to adding $\pi/2$ to the angle), we end at $(-b, a)$, so that $\sin(t + \pi/2) = a$. For (a, b) in Quadrant I, this is shown in the figure above; similar illustrations can be drawn for the other quadrants.

74. One possible answer: Starting from the point (a, b) on the unit circle—at an angle of t, so that $\sin t = b$—then measuring a quarter of the way around the circle (which corresponds to adding $\pi/2$ to the angle), we end at $(-b, a)$, so that $\cos(t + \pi/2) = -b = -\sin t$. For (a, b) in Quadrant I, this is shown in the figure above; similar illustrations can be drawn for the other quadrants.

75. Starting from the point (a, b) on the unit circle—at an angle of t, so that $\cos t = a$—then measuring a quarter of the way around the circle (which corresponds to adding $\pi/2$ to the angle), we end at $(-b, a)$, so that $\sin(t + \pi/2) = a$. This holds true when (a, b) is in Quadrant II, just as it did for Quadrant I.

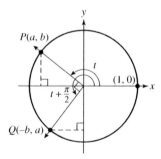

76. (a) Both triangles are right triangles with hypotenuse 1, and the angles at the origin are both t (for the triangle on the left, the angle is the supplement of $\pi - t$). Therefore the vertical legs are also congruent; their lengths correspond to the sines of t and $\pi - t$.

(b) The points P and Q are reflections of each other across the y-axis, so they are the same distance (but opposite directions) from the y-axis. Alternatively, use the congruent triangles argument from part (a).

77. Seven decimal places are shown so that the slight differences can be seen. The magnitude of the relative error is less than 1% when $|\theta| < 0.2441$ (approximately). This can be seen by extending the table to larger values of θ, or by graphing $\left| \dfrac{\sin \theta - \theta}{\sin \theta} \right| - 0.01$.

78. Let (x, y) be the coordinates of the point that corresponds to t under the wrapping. Then
$$1 + (\tan t)^2 = 1 + \left(\frac{y}{x} \right)^2 = \frac{x^2 + y^2}{x^2} = \frac{1}{x^2} = (\sec t)^2.$$
(Note that $x^2 + y^2 = 1$ because (x, y) is on the unit circle.)

79. This Taylor polynomial is generally a very good approximation for $\sin \theta$—in fact, the relative error (see #77) is less than 1% for $|\theta| < 1$ (approx.). It is better for θ close to 0; it is slightly larger than $\sin \theta$ when $\theta < 0$ and slightly smaller when $\theta > 0$.

77.

θ	$\sin \theta$	$\sin \theta - \theta$	$\left\| \dfrac{\sin \theta - \theta}{\sin \theta} \right\|$
−0.03	−0.0299955	0.0000045	0.0001500
−0.02	−0.0199987	0.0000013	0.0000667
−0.01	−0.0099998	0.0000002	0.0000167
0	0	0	—
0.01	0.0099998	−0.0000002	0.0000167
0.02	0.0199987	−0.0000013	0.0000667
0.03	0.0299955	−0.0000045	0.0001500

79.

θ	$\sin \theta$	$\theta - \dfrac{1}{6}\theta^3$	$\sin \theta - \left(\theta - \dfrac{1}{6}\theta^3 \right)$
−0.3	−0.2955202	−0.2955000	−0.0000202
−0.2	−0.1986693	−0.1986667	−0.0000027
−0.1	−0.0998334	−0.0998333	−0.0000001
0	0	0	0
0.1	0.0998334	0.0998333	0.0000001
0.2	0.1986693	0.1986667	0.0000027
0.3	0.2955202	0.2955000	0.0000202

80. This Taylor polynomial is generally a very good approximation for $\cos \theta$ —in fact, the relative error (see #77) is less than 1% for $|\theta| < 1.2$ (approx.). It is better for θ close to 0; it is slightly larger than $\cos \theta$ when $\theta \neq 0$.

θ	$\cos \theta$	$1 - \dfrac{1}{2}\theta^2 + \dfrac{1}{24}\theta^4$	$\cos \theta - \left(1 - \dfrac{1}{2}\theta^2 + \dfrac{1}{24}\theta^4 \right)$
−0.3	0.9553365	0.9553375	−0.0000010
−0.2	0.9800666	0.9800667	−0.0000001
−0.1	0.9950042	0.9950042	−0.0000000
0	1	1	0
0.1	0.9950042	0.9950042	−0.0000000
0.2	0.9800666	0.9800667	−0.0000001
0.3	0.9553365	0.9553375	−0.0000010

■ Section 4.4 Graphs of Sine and Cosine: Sinusoids

Exploration 1

1. $\pi/2$ (at the point $(0, 1)$)

2. $3\pi/2$ (at the point $(0, -1)$)

3. Both graphs cross the x-axis when the y-coordinate on the unit circle is 0.

4. (Calculator exploration)

5. The sine function tracks the y-coordinate of the point as it moves around the unit circle. After the point has gone completely around the unit circle (a distance of 2π), the same pattern of y-coordinates starts over again.

6. Leave all the settings as they are shown at the start of the Exploration, except change Y_{2T} to cos(T).

Quick Review 4.4

1. In order: $+$, $+$, $-$, $-$

2. In order: $+$, $-$, $-$, $+$

3. In order: $+$, $-$, $+$, $-$

4. $135° \cdot \dfrac{\pi}{180°} = \dfrac{3\pi}{4}$

5. $-150° \cdot \dfrac{\pi}{180°} = -\dfrac{5\pi}{6}$

6. $450° \cdot \dfrac{\pi}{180°} = \dfrac{5\pi}{2}$

7. Starting with the graph of y_1, vertically stretch by 3 to obtain the graph of y_2.

8. Starting with the graph of y_1, reflect across y-axis to obtain the graph of y_2.

9. Starting with the graph of y_1, vertically shrink by 0.5 to obtain the graph of y_2.

10. Starting with the graph of y_1, translate down 2 units to obtain the graph of y_2.

Section 4.4 Exercises

In #1–6, for $y = a \sin x$, the amplitude is $|a|$. If $|a| > 1$, there is a vertical stretch by a factor of $|a|$, and if $|a| < 1$, there is a vertical shrink by a factor of $|a|$. When $a < 0$, there is also a reflection across the x-axis.

1. Amplitude 2; vertical stretch by a factor of 2.

2. Amplitude 2/3; vertical shrink by a factor of 2/3.

3. Amplitude 4; vertical stretch by a factor of 4, reflection across the x-axis.

4. Amplitude 7/4; vertical stretch by a factor of 7/4, reflection across the x-axis.

5. Amplitude 0.73; vertical shrink by a factor of 0.73.

6. Amplitude 2.34; vertical stretch by a factor of 2.34, reflection across the x-axis.

In #7–12, for $y = \cos bx$, the period is $2\pi/|b|$. If $|b| > 1$, there is a horizontal shrink by a factor of $1/|b|$, and if $|b| < 1$, there is a horizontal stretch by a factor of $1/|b|$. When $b < 0$, there is also a reflection across the y-axis. For $y = a \cos bx$, a has the same effects as in #1–6.

7. Period $2\pi/3$; horizontal shrink by a factor of $1/3$.

8. Period $2\pi/(1/5) = 10\pi$; horizontal stretch by a factor of $1/(1/5) = 5$.

9. Period $2\pi/7$; horizontal shrink by a factor of $1/7$, reflection across the y-axis.

10. Period $2\pi/0.4 = 5\pi$; horizontal stretch by a factor of $1/0.4 = 2.5$, reflection across the y-axis.

11. Period $2\pi/2 = \pi$; horizontal shrink by a factor of $1/2$. Also a vertical stretch by a factor of 3.

12. Period $2\pi/(2/3) = 3\pi$; horizontal stretch by a factor of $1/(2/3) = 3/2$. Also a vertical shrink by a factor of $1/4$.

In #13–16, the amplitudes of the graphs for $y = a \sin bx$ and $y = a \cos bx$ are governed by a, while the period is governed by b, just as in #1–12. The frequency is 1/period.

13. For $y = 3 \sin (x/2)$, the amplitude is 3, the period is $2\pi/(1/2) = 4\pi$, and the frequency is $1/(4\pi)$.

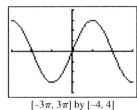
[−3π, 3π] by [−4, 4]

14. For $y = 2 \cos (x/3)$, the amplitude is 2, the period is $2\pi/(1/3) = 6\pi$, and the frequency is $1/(6\pi)$.

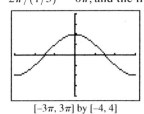
[−3π, 3π] by [−4, 4]

15. For $y = -(3/2) \sin 2x$, the amplitude is 3/2, the period is $2\pi/2 = \pi$, and the frequency is $1/\pi$.

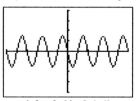
[−3π, 3π] by [−4, 4]

16. For $y = -4 \sin (2x/3)$, the amplitude is 4, the period is $2\pi/(2/3) = 3\pi$, and the frequency is $1/(3\pi)$.

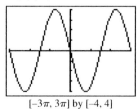
[−3π, 3π] by [−4, 4]

Note: the frequency for each graph in #17–22 is $1/(2\pi)$.

17. Period 2π, amplitude $= 2$

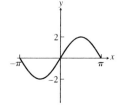

18. Period 2π, amplitude $= 2.5$

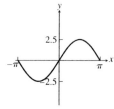

19. Period 2π, amplitude $= 3$

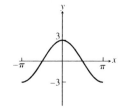

20. Period 2π, amplitude $= 2$

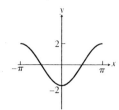

21. Period 2π, amplitude $= 0.5$

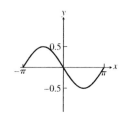

22. Period 2π, amplitude $= 4$

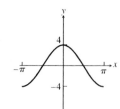

23. Period π, amplitude = 5, frequency = $1/\pi$

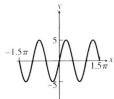

24. Period 4π, amplitude = 3, frequency = $1/(4\pi)$

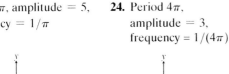

25. Period $2\pi/3$, amplitude = 0.5, frequency = $3/2\pi$

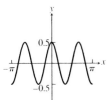

26. Period $\pi/2$, amplitude = 20, frequency = $2/\pi$

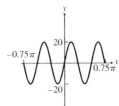
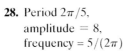

27. Period 8π, amplitude = 4, frequency = $1/(8\pi)$

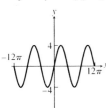

28. Period $2\pi/5$, amplitude = 8, frequency = $5/(2\pi)$

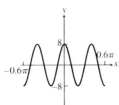

29. Period π; amplitude 1.5; $[-2\pi, 2\pi]$ by $[-2, 2]$

30. Period $2\pi/3$; amplitude 2; $\left[-\dfrac{2\pi}{3}, \dfrac{2\pi}{3}\right]$ by $[-4, 4]$

31. Period π; amplitude 3; $[-2\pi, 2\pi]$ by $[-4, 4]$

32. Period 4π; amplitude 5; $[-4\pi, 4\pi]$ by $[-10, 10]$

33. Period 6; amplitude 4; $[-3, 3]$ by $[-5, 5]$

34. Period 2; amplitude 3; $[-4, 4]$ by $[-5, 5]$

35. Maximum: $2\left(\text{at} -\dfrac{3\pi}{2} \text{ and } \dfrac{\pi}{2}\right)$;

minimum: $-2\left(\text{at} -\dfrac{\pi}{2} \text{ and } \dfrac{3\pi}{2}\right)$.

Zeros: $0, \pm\pi, \pm2\pi$.

36. Maximum: 3 (at 0); minimum: -3 (at $\pm2\pi$). Zeros: $\pm\pi$.

37. Maximum: 1 (at $0, \pm\pi, \pm2\pi$); minimum:

$-1\left(\text{at} \pm\dfrac{\pi}{2} \text{ and } \pm\dfrac{3\pi}{2}\right)$. Zeros: $\pm\dfrac{\pi}{4}, \pm\dfrac{3\pi}{4}, \pm\dfrac{5\pi}{4}, \pm\dfrac{7\pi}{4}$.

38. Maximum: $\dfrac{1}{2}\left(\text{at} -\dfrac{3\pi}{2} \text{ and } \dfrac{\pi}{2}\right)$;

minimum: $-\dfrac{1}{2}\left(\text{at} -\dfrac{\pi}{2} \text{ and } \dfrac{3\pi}{2}\right)$. Zeros: $0, \pm\pi, \pm2\pi$.

39. Maximum: $1\left(\text{at} \pm\dfrac{\pi}{2}, \pm\dfrac{3\pi}{2}\right)$; minimum: -1 (at $0, \pm\pi, \pm2\pi$).

Zeros: $\pm\dfrac{\pi}{4}, \pm\dfrac{3\pi}{4}, \pm\dfrac{5\pi}{4}, \pm\dfrac{7\pi}{4}$.

40. Maximum: $2\left(\text{at} -\dfrac{\pi}{2}, \dfrac{3\pi}{2}\right)$; minimum: $-2\left(\text{at} -\dfrac{3\pi}{2}, \dfrac{\pi}{2}\right)$.

Zeros: $0, \pm\pi, \pm2\pi$.

41. $y = \sin x$ has to be translated left or right by an odd multiple of π. One possibility is $y = \sin(x + \pi)$.

42. $y = \sin x$ has to be translated right by $\dfrac{\pi}{2}$ plus an even multiple of π. One possibility is $y = \sin(x - \pi/2)$.

43. Starting from $y = \sin x$, horizontally shrink by $\dfrac{1}{3}$ and vertically shrink by 0.5. The period is $2\pi/3$.

Possible window: $\left[-\dfrac{2\pi}{3}, \dfrac{2\pi}{3}\right]$ by $\left[-\dfrac{3}{4}, \dfrac{3}{4}\right]$.

44. Starting from $y = \cos x$, horizontally shrink by $\dfrac{1}{4}$ and vertically stretch by 1.5. The period is $\pi/2$.

Possible window: $\left[-\dfrac{\pi}{2}, \dfrac{\pi}{2}\right]$ by $[-2, 2]$.

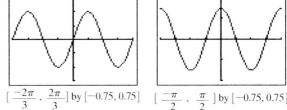

$\left[\dfrac{-2\pi}{3}, \dfrac{2\pi}{3}\right]$ by $[-0.75, 0.75]$ $\left[\dfrac{-\pi}{2}, \dfrac{\pi}{2}\right]$ by $[-0.75, 0.75]$

For #43   **For #44**

45. Starting from $y = \cos x$, horizontally stretch by 3, vertically shrink by $\dfrac{2}{3}$, reflect across x-axis. The period is 6π. Possible window: $[-6\pi, 6\pi]$ by $[-1, 1]$.

46. Starting from $y = \sin x$, horizontally stretch by 5 and vertically shrink by $\dfrac{3}{4}$. The period is 10π. Possible window: $[-10\pi, 10\pi]$ by $[-1, 1]$.

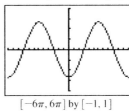
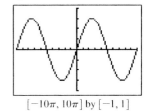

$[-6\pi, 6\pi]$ by $[-1, 1]$ $[-10\pi, 10\pi]$ by $[-1, 1]$

For #45   **For #46**

47. Starting from $y = \cos x$, horizontally shrink by $\dfrac{3}{2\pi}$ and vertically stretch by 3. The period is 3. Possible window: $[-3, 3]$ by $[-3.5, 3.5]$.

48. Starting from $y = \sin x$, horizontally stretch by $\frac{4}{\pi}$, vertically stretch by 2, and reflect across x-axis. The period is 8. Possible window: $[-8, 8]$ by $[-3, 3]$.

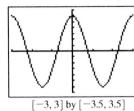
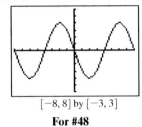

| $[-3, 3]$ by $[-3.5, 3.5]$ | $[-8, 8]$ by $[-3, 3]$ |
| **For #47** | **For #48** |

49. Starting with y_1, vertically stretch by $\frac{5}{3}$.

50. Starting with y_1, translate right $\frac{\pi}{12}$ units and vertically shrink by $\frac{1}{2}$.

51. Starting with y_1, horizontally shrink by $\frac{1}{2}$.

52. Starting with y_1, horizontally stretch by 2 and vertically shrink by $\frac{2}{3}$.

For #53–56, graph the functions or use facts about sine and cosine learned to this point.

53. (a) and (b)

54. (a) and (b)

55. (a) and (b) — both functions equal $\cos x$

56. (a) and (c) — $\sin\left(2x + \frac{\pi}{4}\right)$
$$= \sin\left[\left(2x - \frac{\pi}{4}\right) + \frac{\pi}{2}\right] = \cos\left(2x - \frac{\pi}{4}\right)$$

In #57–60, for $y = a \sin(b(x - h))$, the amplitude is $|a|$, the period is $2\pi/|b|$, and the phase shift is h.

57. One possibility is $y = 3 \sin 2x$.

58. One possibility is $y = 2 \sin(2x/3)$.

59. One possibility is $y = 1.5 \sin 12(x - 1)$.

60. One possibility is $y = 3.2 \sin 14(x - 5)$.

61. Amplitude 2, period 2π, phase shift $\frac{\pi}{4}$, vertical translation 1 unit up.

62. Rewrite as $y = -3.5 \sin\left[2\left(x - \frac{\pi}{4}\right)\right] - 1$.

Amplitude 3.5, period π, phase shift $\frac{\pi}{4}$, vertical translation 1 unit down.

63. Rewrite as $y = 5 \cos\left[3\left(x - \frac{\pi}{18}\right)\right] + 0.5$.

Amplitude 5, period $\frac{2\pi}{3}$, phase shift $\frac{\pi}{18}$, vertical translation $\frac{1}{2}$ units up.

64. Amplitude 3, period 2π, phase shift -3, vertical translation 2 units down.

65. Amplitude 2, period 1, phase shift 0, vertical translation 1 unit up.

66. Amplitude 4, period $\frac{2}{3}$, phase shift 0, vertical translation 2 units down.

67. Amplitude $\frac{7}{3}$, period 2π, phase shift $-\frac{5}{2}$, vertical translation 1 unit down.

68. Amplitude $\frac{2}{3}$, period 8π, phase shift 3, vertical translation 1 unit up.

69. $y = 2 \sin 2x$ ($a = 2, b = 2, h = 0, k = 0$).

70. $y = 3 \sin[2(x + 0.5)]$ ($a = 3, b = 2, h = 0.5, k = 0$).

71. **(a)** There are two points of intersection in that interval.

(b) The coordinates are $(0, 1)$ and $(2\pi, 1.3^{-2\pi})$ $\approx (6.28, 0.19)$. In general, two functions intersect where $\cos x = 1$, i.e., $x = 2n\pi$, n an integer.

72. $a = 4$ and $b = \frac{2\pi}{3.5} = \frac{4\pi}{7}$.

73. The height of the rider is modeled by
$$h = 30 - 25 \cos\left(\frac{2\pi}{40}t\right),$$
where $t = 0$ corresponds to the time when the rider is at the low point. $h = 50$ when $\frac{-4}{5} = \cos\left(\frac{2\pi}{40}t\right)$. Then $\frac{2\pi}{40}t \approx 2.498$, so $t \approx 15.90$ sec.

74. The length L must be the distance traveled in 30 min by an object traveling at 540 ft/sec:
$$L = 1800 \text{ sec} \cdot 540 \frac{\text{ft}}{\text{sec}} = 972,000 \text{ ft, or about 184 miles.}$$

75. **(a)** A model of the depth of the tide is
$$d = 2 \cos\left[\frac{\pi}{6.2}(t - 7.2)\right] + 9,$$
where t is hours since midnight. The first low tide is at 1:00 A.M. ($t = 1$).

(b) At 4:00 A.M. ($t = 4$): about 8.90 ft. At 9:00 P.M. ($t = 21$): about 10.52 ft.

(c) 4:06 A.M. ($t = 4.1$ — halfway between 1:00 A.M. and 7:12 A.M.).

76. **(a)** 1 second.

(b) Each peak corresponds to a heartbeat —there are 60 per minute.

(c)

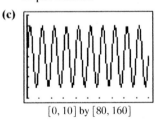

$[0, 10]$ by $[80, 160]$

77. (a) The maximum d is approximately 21.4. The amplitude is $(21.4 - 7.2)/2 = 7.1$.
Scatterplot:

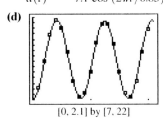

[0, 2.1] by [7, 22]

(b) The period appears to be slightly greater than 0.8, say 0.83.

(c) Since the function has a minimum at $t = 0$, we use an inverted cosine model:
$d(t) = -7.1 \cos(2\pi t/0.83) + 14.3$.

(d)

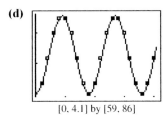

[0, 2.1] by [7, 22]

78. (a) The amplitude is 12.7, half the diameter of the turntable.

(b) The period is 1.8, as can be seen by measuring from minimum to minimum.

(c) Since the function has a minimum at $t = 0$, we use an inverted cosine model:
$d(t) = -12.7 \cos(2\pi t/1.8) + 72.7$.

(d)

[0, 4.1] by [59, 86]

79. One possible answer is $T = 21.5 \cos\left(\dfrac{\pi}{6}(x - 7)\right) + 57.5$.

Start with the general form sinusoidal function $y = a\cos(b(x - h)) + k$, and find the variables a, b, h, and k as follows:

The amplitude is $|a| = \dfrac{79 - 36}{2} = 21.5$. We can arbitrarily choose to use the positive value, so $a = 21.5$.

The period is 12 months. $12 = \dfrac{2\pi}{|b|} \Rightarrow |b| = \dfrac{2\pi}{12} = \dfrac{\pi}{6}$.
Again, we can arbitrarily choose to use the positive value, so $b = \dfrac{\pi}{6}$.

The maximum is at month 7, so the phase shift $h = 7$.

The vertical shift $k = \dfrac{79 + 36}{2} = 57.5$.

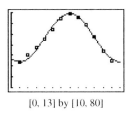

[0, 13] by [10, 80]

80. One possible answer is $y = 24 \cos\left(\dfrac{\pi}{6}(x - 7)\right) + 44$.

Start with the general form sinusoidal function $y = a\cos(b(x - h)) + k$, and find the variables a, b, h, and k as follows:

The amplitude is $|a| = \dfrac{68 - 20}{2} = 24$. We can arbitrarily choose to use the positive value, so $a = 24$.

The period is 12 months. $12 = \dfrac{2\pi}{|b|} \Rightarrow |b| = \dfrac{2\pi}{12} = \dfrac{\pi}{6}$.
Again, we can arbitrarily choose to use the positive value, so $b = \dfrac{\pi}{6}$.

The maximum is at month 7, so the phase shift $h = 7$.

The vertical shift $k = \dfrac{68 + 20}{2} = 44$.

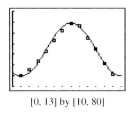

[0, 13] by [10, 80]

81. False. Since $y = \sin 2x$ is a horizontal *stretch* of $y = \sin 4x$ by a factor of 2, $y = \sin 2x$ has twice the period, not half. Remember, the period of $y = \sin bx$ is $2\pi/|b|$.

82. True. Any cosine curve can be converted to a sine curve of the same amplitude and frequency by a phase shift, which can be accomplished by an appropriate choice of C (a multiple of $\pi/2$).

83. The minimum and maximum values differ by twice the amplitude. The answer is D.

84. Because the graph passes through $(6, 0)$, $f(6) = 0$. And 6 plus exactly two periods equals 96, so $f(96) = 0$ also. But $f(0)$ depends on phase and amplitude, which are unknown. The answer is D.

85. For $f(x) = a\sin(bx + c)$, the period is $2\pi/|b|$, which here equals $2\pi/420 = \pi/210$. The answer is C.

86. There are 2 solutions per cycle, and 2000 cycles in the interval. The answer is C.

87. (a)

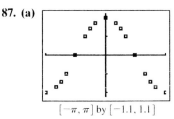

$[-\pi, \pi]$ by $[-1.1, 1.1]$

(b) $\cos x \approx 0.0246x^4 + 0x^3 - 0.4410x^2 + 0x + 0.9703$. The coefficients given as "0" here may show up as very small numbers (e.g., 1.44×10^{-14}) on some calculators. Note that $\cos x$ is an even function, and only the even powers of x have nonzero (or a least "non-small") coefficients.

(c) The Taylor polynomial is
$$1 - \frac{1}{2}x^2 + \frac{1}{24}x^4 = 1 - 0.5000x^2 + 0.04167x^4;$$ the coefficients are fairly similar.

88. (a)

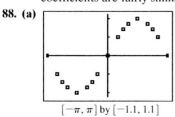

$$[-\pi, \pi] \text{ by } [-1.1, 1.1]$$

(b) $\sin x \approx -0.0872x^3 + 0x^2 + 0.8263x + 0$. The coefficients given as "0" here may show up as very small numbers (e.g., 3.56×10^{-15}) on some calculators. Note that $\sin x$ is an odd function, and only the odd powers of x have nonzero (or a least "non-small") coefficients.

(c) The Taylor polynomial is $x - \frac{1}{6}x^3 = x - 0.16667x^3$; the coefficients are somewhat similar.

89. (a) $p = \dfrac{2\pi}{524\pi} = \dfrac{1}{262}$ sec

(b) $f = 262 \dfrac{1}{\text{sec}}$ ("cycles per sec"), or 262 Hertz (Hz).

(c)

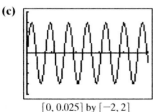

$$[0, 0.025] \text{ by } [-2, 2]$$

90. Since the cursor moves at a constant rate, its distance from the center must be made up of linear pieces as shown (the slope of the line is the rate of motion). A graph of a sinusoid is included for comparison.

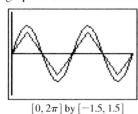

$$[0, 2\pi] \text{ by } [-1.5, 1.5]$$

91. (a) $a - b$ must equal 1.

(b) $a - b$ must equal 2.

(c) $a - b$ must equal k.

92. (a) $a - b$ must equal 1.

(b) $a - b$ must equal 2.

(c) $a - b$ must equal k.

For #93–96, note that A and C are one period apart. Meanwhile, B is located one-fourth of a period to the right of A, and the y-coordinate of B is the amplitude of the sinusoid.

93. The period of this function is π and the amplitude is 3. B and C are located (respectively) $\dfrac{\pi}{4}$ units and π units to the right of A. Therefore, $B = (0, 3)$ and $C = \left(\dfrac{3\pi}{4}, 0\right)$.

94. The period of this function is 2π and the amplitude is 4.5. B and C are located (respectively) $\dfrac{\pi}{2}$ units and 2π units to the right of A. Therefore, $B = \left(\dfrac{3\pi}{4}, 4.5\right)$ and $C = \left(\dfrac{9\pi}{4}, 0\right)$

95. The period of this function is $\dfrac{2\pi}{3}$ and the amplitude is 2. B and C are located respectively $\dfrac{\pi}{6}$ units and $\dfrac{2\pi}{3}$ units to the right of A. Therefore, $B = \left(\dfrac{\pi}{4}, 2\right)$ and $C = \left(\dfrac{3\pi}{4}, 0\right)$

96. The first coordinate of A is the smallest positive x such that $2x - \pi = n\pi$, n and integer, so $x = \dfrac{n+1}{2}\pi$ must equal $\dfrac{\pi}{2}$. The period of this function π is and the amplitude is 3. B and C are located (respectively) $\dfrac{\pi}{4}$ units and π units to the right of A. Therefore, $A = \left(\dfrac{\pi}{2}, 0\right)$, $B = \left(\dfrac{3\pi}{4}, 3\right)$ and $C = \left(\dfrac{3\pi}{2}, 0\right)$:

97. (a) Since $\sin(-\theta) = -\sin\theta$ (because sine is an odd function) $a\sin[-B(x-h)] + k = -a\sin[B(x-h)] + k$. Then any expression with a negative value of b can be rewritten as an expression of the same general form but with a positive coefficient in place of b.

(b) A sine graph can be translated a quarter of a period to the left to become a cosine graph of the same sinusoid. Thus $y = a\sin\left[b\left((x-h) + \dfrac{1}{4}\cdot\dfrac{2\pi}{b}\right)\right] + k$
$= a\sin\left[b\left(x - \left(h - \dfrac{\pi}{2b}\right)\right)\right] + k$ has the same graph as $y = a\cos[b(x-h)] + k$. We therefore choose $H = h - \dfrac{\pi}{2b}$.

(c) The angles $\theta + \pi$ and θ determine diametrically opposite points on the unit circle, so they have point symmetry with respect to the origin. The y-coordinates are therefore opposites, so $\sin(\theta + \pi) = -\sin\theta$.

(d) By the identity in (c). $y = a\sin[b(x-h) + \pi] + k$
$= -a\sin[b(x-h)] + k$. We therefore choose $H = h - \dfrac{\pi}{b}$.

(e) Part (b) shows how to convert $y = a\cos[b(x-h)] + k$ to $y = a\sin[b(x-H)] + k$, and parts (a) and (d) show how to ensure that a and b are positive.

■ Section 4.5 Graphs of Tangent, Cotangent, Secant, and Cosecant

Exploration 1

1. The graphs do not seem to intersect.

2. Set the expressions equal and solve for x:
$$-k \cos x = \sec x$$
$$-k \cos x = 1/\cos x$$
$$-k(\cos x)^2 = 1$$
$$(\cos x)^2 = -1/k$$
Since $k > 0$, this requires that the square of $\cos x$ be negative, which is impossible. This proves that there is no value of x for which the two functions are equal, so the graphs do not intersect.

Quick Review 4.5

1. Period π

2. Period $\dfrac{2\pi}{3}$

3. Period 6π

4. Period 4π

For #5–8, recall that zeros of rational functions are zeros of the numerator, and vertical asymptotes are found at zeros of the denominator (provided the numerator and denominator have no common zeros).

5. Zero: 3. Asymptote: $x = -4$

6. Zero: -5. Asymptote: $x = 1$

7. Zero: -1. Asymptotes: $x = 2$ and $x = -2$

8. Zero: -2. Asymptotes: $x = 0$ and $x = 3$

For #9–10, examine graphs to suggest the answer. Confirm by checking $f(-x) = f(x)$ for even functions and $f(-x) = -f(x)$ for odd functions.

9. Even: $(-x)^2 + 4 = x^2 + 4$

10. Odd: $\dfrac{1}{(-x)} = -\dfrac{1}{x}$

Section 4.5 Exercises

1. The graph of $y = 2 \csc x$ must be vertically stretched by 2 compared to $y = \csc x$, so $y_1 = 2 \csc x$ and $y_2 = \csc x$.

2. The graph of $y = 5 \tan x$ must be vertically stretched by 10 compared to $y = 0.5 \tan x$, so $y_1 = 5 \tan x$ and $y_2 = 0.5 \tan x$.

3. The graph of $y = 3 \csc 2x$ must be vertically stretched by 3 and horizontally shrunk by $\dfrac{1}{2}$ compared to $y = \csc x$, so $y_1 = 3 \csc 2x$ and $y_2 = \csc x$.

4. The graph of $y = \cot(x - 0.5) + 3$ must be translated 3 units up and 0.5 units right compared to $y = \cot x$, so $y_1 = \cot(x - 0.5) + 3$ and $y_2 = \cot x$.

5. The graph of $y = \tan 2x$ results from shrinking the graph of $y = \tan x$ horizontally by a factor of $\dfrac{1}{2}$. There are vertical asymptotes at $x = \ldots, -\dfrac{\pi}{4}, \dfrac{\pi}{4}, \dfrac{3\pi}{4}, \ldots$.

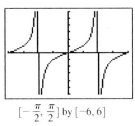

$\left[-\dfrac{\pi}{2}, \dfrac{\pi}{2}\right]$ by $[-6, 6]$

6. The graph of $y = -\cot 3x$ results from shrinking the graph of $y = \cot x$ horizontally by a factor of $\dfrac{1}{3}$ and reflecting it across the x-axis. There are vertical asymptotes at
$$x = \ldots, -\dfrac{2\pi}{3}, -\dfrac{\pi}{3}, 0, \dfrac{\pi}{3}, \ldots$$

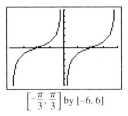

$\left[-\dfrac{\pi}{3}, \dfrac{\pi}{3}\right]$ by $[-6, 6]$

7. The graph of $y = \sec 3x$ results from shrinking the graph of $y = \sec x$ horizontally by a factor of $\dfrac{1}{3}$. There are vertical asymptotes at odd multiples of $\dfrac{\pi}{6}$.

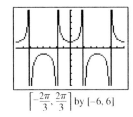

$\left[-\dfrac{2\pi}{3}, \dfrac{2\pi}{3}\right]$ by $[-6, 6]$

8. The graph of $y = \csc 2x$ results from shrinking the graph of $y = \csc x$ horizontally by a factor of $\dfrac{1}{2}$. There are vertical asymptotes at $x = \ldots, -\pi, -\dfrac{\pi}{2}, 0, \dfrac{\pi}{2}, \ldots$.

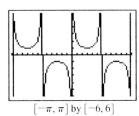

$[-\pi, \pi]$ by $[-6, 6]$

9. The graph of $y = 2 \cot 2x$ results from shrinking the graph of $y = \cot x$ horizontally by a factor of $\frac{1}{2}$ and stretching it vertically by a factor of 2. There are vertical asymptotes at $x = \ldots ., -\pi, -\frac{\pi}{2}, 0, \frac{\pi}{2}, \ldots$

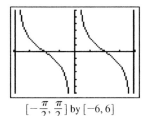

$[-\frac{\pi}{2}, \frac{\pi}{2}]$ by $[-6, 6]$

10. The graph of $y = 3 \tan\left(\frac{x}{2}\right)$ results from stretching the graph of $y = \tan x$ horizontally by a factor of 2 and stretching it vertically by a factor of 3. There are vertical asymptotes at $x = \ldots ., -\pi, \pi, 3\pi, \ldots$

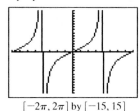

$[-2\pi, 2\pi]$ by $[-15, 15]$

11. The graph of $y = \csc\left(\frac{x}{2}\right)$ results from horizontally stretching the graph of $y = \csc x$ by a factor of 2. There are vertical asymptotes at $x = \ldots ., -4\pi, -2\pi, 0, 2\pi, \ldots$

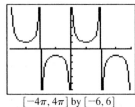

$[-4\pi, 4\pi]$ by $[-6, 6]$

12. The graph of $y = 3 \sec 4x$ results from horizontally shrinking the graph of $y = \sec x$ by a factor of $\frac{1}{4}$ and stretching it vertically by a factor of 3. There are vertical asymptotes at odd multiples of $\frac{\pi}{8}$.

$[-\frac{\pi}{2}, \frac{\pi}{2}]$ by $[-15, 15]$

13. Graph (a); Xmin $= -\pi$ and Xmax $= \pi$
14. Graph (d); Xmin $= -\pi$ and Xmax $= \pi$
15. Graph (c); Xmin $= -\pi$ and Xmax $= \pi$
16. Graph (b); Xmin $= -\pi$ and Xmax $= \pi$

17. Domain: All reals except integer multiples of π
Range: $(-\infty, \infty)$
Continuous on its domain
Decreasing on each interval in its domain
Symmetric with respect to the origin (odd)
Not bounded above or below
No local extrema
No horizontal asymptotes
Vertical asymptotes $x = k\pi$ for all integers k
End behavior: $\lim\limits_{x \to \infty} \cot x$ and $\lim\limits_{x \to -\infty} \cot x$ do not exist.

18. Domain: All reals except odd multiples of $\frac{\pi}{2}$
Range: $(-\infty, -1] \cup [1, \infty)$
Continuous on its domain
On each interval centered at an even multiple of π: decreasing on the left half of the interval and increasing on the right half
On each interval centered at an odd multiple of π: increasing on the left half of the interval and decreasing on the right half
Symmetric with respect to the y-axis (even)
Not bounded above or below
Local minimum 1 at each even multiple of π, local maximum -1 at each odd multiple of π
No horizontal asymptotes
Vertical asymptotes $x = k\pi/2$ for all odd integers k
End behavior: $\lim\limits_{x \to \infty} \sec x$ and $\lim\limits_{x \to -\infty} \sec x$ do not exist.

19. Domain: All reals except integer multiples of π
Range: $(-\infty, -1] \cup [1, \infty)$
Continuous on its domain
On each interval centered at $x = \frac{\pi}{2} + 2k\pi$ (k an integer): decreasing on the left half of the interval and increasing on the right half
On each interval centered at $\frac{3\pi}{2} + 2k\pi$: increasing on the left half of the interval and decreasing on the right half
Symmetric with respect to the origin (odd)
Not bounded above or below
Local minimum 1 at each $x = \frac{\pi}{2} + 2k\pi$, local maximum -1 at each $x = \frac{3\pi}{2} + 2k\pi$, where k is an even integer in both cases
No horizontal asymptotes
Vertical asymptotes: $x = k\pi$ for all integers k
End behavior: $\lim\limits_{x \to \infty} \csc x$ and $\lim\limits_{x \to -\infty} \csc x$ do not exist.

20. Domain: All reals except odd multiples of π
Range: $(-\infty, \infty)$
Continuous on its domain
Increasing on each interval in its domain
Symmetric with respect to the origin (odd)
Not bounded above or below
No local extrema
No horizontal asymptotes
Vertical asymptotes $x = k\pi$ for all odd integers k
End behavior: $\lim\limits_{x \to \infty} \tan(x/2)$ and $\lim\limits_{x \to -\infty} \tan(x/2)$ do not exist.

21. Starting with $y = \tan x$, vertically stretch by 3.

22. Starting with $y = \tan x$, reflect across x-axis.

23. Starting with $y = \csc x$, vertically stretch by 3.

24. Starting with $y = \tan x$, vertically stretch by 2.

25. Starting with $y = \cot x$, horizontally stretch by 2, vertically stretch by 3, and reflect across x-axis.

26. Starting with $y = \sec x$, horizontally stretch by 2, vertically stretch by 2, and reflect across x-axis.

27. Starting with $y = \tan x$, horizontally shrink by $\dfrac{2}{\pi}$ and reflect across x-axis and shift up by 2 units.

28. Starting with $y = \tan x$, horizontally shrink by $\dfrac{1}{\pi}$ and vertically stretch by 2 and shift down by 2 units.

29. $\sec x = 2$

$\cos x = \dfrac{1}{2}$

$x = \dfrac{\pi}{3}$

30. $\csc x = 2$

$\sin x = \dfrac{1}{2}$

$x = \dfrac{5\pi}{6}$

31. $\cot x = -\sqrt{3}$

$\tan x = -\dfrac{\sqrt{3}}{3}$

$x = \dfrac{5\pi}{6}$

32. $\sec x = -\sqrt{2}$

$\cos x = -\dfrac{\sqrt{2}}{2}$

$x = \dfrac{5\pi}{4}$

33. $\csc x = 1$

$\sin x = 1$

$x = \dfrac{5\pi}{2}$

34. $\cot x = 1$

$\tan x = 1$

$x = -\dfrac{3\pi}{4}$

35. $\tan x = 1.3$

$x \approx 0.92$

36. $\sec x = 2.4$

$\cos x = \dfrac{1}{2.4}$

$x \approx 1.14$

37. $\cot x = -0.6$

$\tan x = -\dfrac{1}{0.6}$

$x \approx -1.03 + 2\pi$

≈ 5.25

38. $\csc x = -1.5$

$\sin x = -\dfrac{1}{1.5}$

$x \approx \pi - (-0.73)$

≈ 3.87

39. $\csc x = 2$

$\sin x = \dfrac{1}{2}$

$x \approx 0.52$ or

$x \approx \pi - 0.52$

≈ 2.62

40. $\tan x = 0.3$

$x \approx 0.29$ or

$x \approx \pi + 0.29$

≈ 3.43

41. (a) One explanation: If O is the origin, the right triangles with hypotenuses $\overline{OP_1}$ and $\overline{OP_2}$, and one leg (each) on the x-axis, are congruent, so the legs have the same lengths. These lengths give the magnitudes of the coordinates of P_1 and P_2; therefore, these coordinates differ only in sign. Another explanation: The reflection of point (a, b) across the origin is $(-a, -b)$.

(b) $\tan t = \dfrac{\sin t}{\cos t} = \dfrac{b}{a}$.

(c) $\tan(t - \pi) = \dfrac{\sin(t - \pi)}{\cos(t - \pi)} = \dfrac{-b}{-a} = \dfrac{b}{a} = \tan t$.

(d) Since points on opposite sides of the unit circle determine the same tangent ratio, $\tan(t \pm \pi) = \tan t$ for all numbers t in the domain. Other points on the unit circle yield triangles with different tangent ratios, so no smaller period is possible.

(e) The tangent function repeats every π units; therefore, so does its reciprocal, the cotangent (see also #43).

42. The terminal side passes through $(0, 0)$ and $(\cos x, \sin x)$; the slope is therefore $m = \dfrac{\sin x - 0}{\cos x - 0} = \dfrac{\sin x}{\cos x} = \tan x$.

43. For any x, $\left(\dfrac{1}{f}\right)(x + p) = \dfrac{1}{f(x + p)} = \dfrac{1}{f(x)} = \left(\dfrac{1}{f}\right)(x)$. This is not true for any smaller value of p, since this is the smallest value that works for f.

44. (a), (b) The angles t and $t + \pi$ determine points $(\cos t, \sin t)$ and $(\cos(t + \pi), \sin(t + \pi))$, respectively. These points are on opposite sides of the unit circle, so they are reflections of each other about the origin. The reflection of any point (a, b) about the origin is $(-a, -b)$, so $\cos(t + \pi) = -\cos t$ and $\sin(t + \pi) = -\sin t$.

(c) $\tan(t + \pi) = \dfrac{\sin(t + \pi)}{\cos(t + \pi)} = \dfrac{-\sin t}{-\cos t} = \dfrac{\sin t}{\cos t} = \tan t$. In order to determine that the period of $\tan t$ is π, we would need to show that no $p < \pi$ satisfies $\tan(t + p) = \tan t$ for all t.

45. (a) $d = 350 \sec x = \dfrac{350}{\cos x}$ ft

(b) $d \approx 16{,}831$ ft

46. (a) $x = 800 \cot y = \dfrac{800}{\tan x}$ ft

(b) $x \approx 5{,}051$ ft

(c) $\dfrac{\pi}{20} \cdot \dfrac{180°}{\pi} = 9°$

For #47–50, the equations can be rewritten (as shown), but generally are easiest to solve graphically.

47. $\sin^2 x = \cos x$; $x \approx \pm 0.905$

48. $\cos^2 x = \sin x$; $x \approx 0.666$ or $x \approx 2.475$

49. $\cos^2 x = \dfrac{1}{5}$; $x \approx \pm 1.107$ or $x \approx \pm 2.034$

50. $4 \cos^2 x = \sin x$; $x \approx 1.082$ or $x \approx 2.060$

51. False. $f(x) = \tan x$ is increasing only over intervals on which it is defined, that is, intervals bounded by consecutive asymptotes.

52. True. Asymptotes of the secant function, $\sec x = 1/\cos x$, occur at all odd multiples of $\pi/2$ (where $\cos x = 0$), and these are exactly the zeros of the cotangent function, $\cot x = \cos x/\sin x$.

53. The cotangent curves are shaped like the tangent curves, but they are mirror images. The reflection of $\tan x$ in the x-axis is $-\tan x$. The answer is A.

54. $\sec x$ "just barely" intersects its inverse, $\cos x$, and when $\cos x$ is shifted to produce $\sin x$, that curve and the curve of $\sec x$ do not intersect at all. The answer is E.

55. $y = k/\sin x$ and the range of $\sin x$ is $[-1, 1]$. The answer is D.

56. $y = \csc x = 1/\sin x$ has the same asymptotes as $y = \cos x/\sin x = \cot x$. The answer is C.

57. On the interval $[-\pi, \pi]$, $f > g$ on about $(-0.44, 0) \cup (0.44, \pi)$.

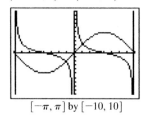

$[-\pi, \pi]$ by $[-10, 10]$

58. On the interval $[-\pi, \pi]$, $f > g$ on about $\left(-\pi, -2.24\right) \cup \left(-\dfrac{\pi}{2}, 0\right) \cup \left(\dfrac{\pi}{2}, 2.24\right)$.

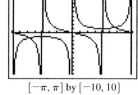

$[-\pi, \pi]$ by $[-10, 10]$

59. $\cot x$ is not defined at 0; the definition of "increasing on (a, b)" requires that the function be defined everywhere in (a, b). Also, choosing $a = -\pi/4$ and $b = \pi/4$, we have $a < b$ but $f(a) = 1 > f(b) = -1$.

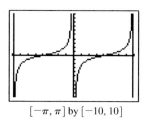

$[-\pi, \pi]$ by $[-10, 10]$

60. They look similar on this window, but they are noticeably different at the edges (near 0 and π). Also, if f were equal to g, then it would follow that $\dfrac{1}{f} = -\cos x = \dfrac{1}{g} = x - \dfrac{\pi}{2}$ on this interval, which we know to be false.

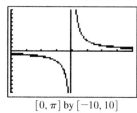

$[0, \pi]$ by $[-10, 10]$

61. $\csc x = \sec\left(x - \dfrac{\pi}{2}\right)$ (or $\csc x = \sec\left(x - \left(\dfrac{\pi}{2} + n\pi\right)\right)$ for any integer n) This is a translation to the right of $\dfrac{\pi}{2}\left(\text{or } \dfrac{\pi}{2} + n\pi\right)$ units.

62. $\cot x = -\tan\left(x - \dfrac{\pi}{2}\right)$ (or $\cot x = -\tan\left(x - \left(\dfrac{\pi}{2} + n\pi\right)\right)$ for any integer n).

This is a translation to the right of $\dfrac{\pi}{2}\left(\text{or } \dfrac{\pi}{2} + n\pi\right)$ units, and a reflection in the x-axis, in either order.

63. $d = 30 \sec x = \dfrac{30}{\cos x}$

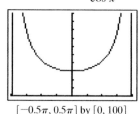

$[-0.5\pi, 0.5\pi]$ by $[0, 100]$

64. (a) For any acute angle θ, $\cos \theta = \sin\left(\dfrac{\pi}{2} - \theta\right)$—the sine of the complement of θ. This can be seen from the right-triangle definition of sine and cosine: if one of the acute angles is θ, then the other acute angle is $\dfrac{\pi}{2} - \theta$, since all three angles in a triangle must add to π. The side opposite the angle θ is the side adjacent to the other acute angle.

(b) $(\cos t, \sin t)$

(c) Using $\triangle ODA \sim \triangle OCB$ (recall "~" means "similar to"), $\dfrac{DA}{OD} = \tan t = \dfrac{BC}{OC} = \dfrac{BC}{1}$, so $BC = \tan t$.

(d) Using $\triangle ODA \sim \triangle OCB$, $\dfrac{OD}{OA} = \cot t = \dfrac{OC}{OB} = \dfrac{1}{OB}$,

so $OB = \dfrac{1}{\cos t} = \sec t$.

(e) $\overline{BC}$ is a tangent segment (part of the tangent line); $\overline{OB}$ is a secant segment (part of a secant line, which crosses the circle at two points). The names "cotangent" and "cosecant" arise in the same way as "cosine"—they are the tangent and secant (respectively) of the complement. That is, just as $\overline{BC}$ and $\overline{OB}$ go with $\angle BOC$ (which has measure t), they also go with $\angle OBC$ (the complement of $\angle BOC$, with measure $\dfrac{\pi}{2} - t$).

65. $0.058\,\dfrac{\text{N}}{\text{m}} = \dfrac{1}{2}(1.5\text{ m})\left(1050\,\dfrac{\text{kg}}{\text{m}^3}\right)\left(9.8\,\dfrac{\text{m}}{\text{sec}^2}\right)$

$(4.7 \times 10^{-6}\text{ m})\sec\phi \approx 0.03627\sec\phi\,\dfrac{\text{kg}}{\text{sec}^2}$, so

$\sec\phi \approx 1.5990$, and $\phi \approx 0.8952$ radians $\approx 51.29°$.

66. (a) $\dfrac{1}{y} = \dfrac{1}{a\sec(bx)} = \dfrac{1}{a}\cdot\dfrac{1}{\sec(bx)} = \dfrac{1}{a}\cos(bx) = \dfrac{1}{a}\sin(bx + \pi/2)$

(b) $y = 0.2\sin\left(\dfrac{1}{6}x + \dfrac{\pi}{2}\right)$

(c) $a = 1/0.2 = 5$ and $b = 1/6$

(d) $y = 5\sec\left(\dfrac{x}{6}\right)$. The scatter plot is shown below, and the fit is very good—so good that you should realize that we made the data up!

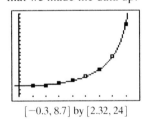

$[-0.3, 8.7]$ by $[2.32, 24]$

■ Section 4.6 Graphs of Composite Trigonometric Functions

Exploration 1

$y = 3\sin x + 2\cos x$

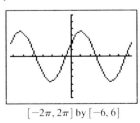

$[-2\pi, 2\pi]$ by $[-6, 6]$
Sinusoid

$y = 2\sin x - 3\cos x$

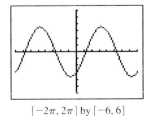

$[-2\pi, 2\pi]$ by $[-6, 6]$
Sinusoid

$y = 2\sin 3x - 4\cos 2x$

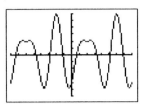

$[-2\pi, 2\pi]$ by $[-6, 6]$
Not a Sinusoid

$y = 2\sin(5x + 1) - 5\cos 5x$

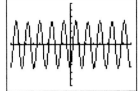

$[-2\pi, 2\pi]$ by $[-6, 6]$
Sinusoid

$y = \cos\left(\dfrac{7x - 2}{5}\right) + \sin\left(\dfrac{7x}{5}\right)$

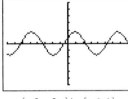
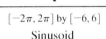

$[-2\pi, 2\pi]$ by $[-6, 6]$
Sinusoid

$y = 3\cos 2x + 2\sin 7x$

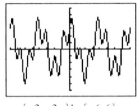

$[-2\pi, 2\pi]$ by $[-6, 6]$
Not a Sinusoid

Quick Review 4.6

1. Domain: $(-\infty, \infty)$; range: $[-3, 3]$
2. Domain: $(-\infty, \infty)$, range: $[-2, 2]$
3. Domain: $[1, \infty)$; range: $[0, \infty)$
4. Domain: $[0, \infty)$; range: $[0, \infty)$
5. Domain: $(-\infty, \infty)$; range: $[-2, \infty)$
6. Domain: $(-\infty, \infty)$; range: $[1, \infty)$
7. As $x \to -\infty$, $f(x) \to \infty$; as $x \to \infty$, $f(x) \to 0$.
8. As $x \to -\infty$, $f(x) \to -\infty$; as $x \to \infty$, $f(x) \to 0$.
9. $f \circ g(x) = (\sqrt{x})^2 - 4 = x - 4$, domain: $[0, \infty)$.
   $g \circ f(x) = \sqrt{x^2 - 4}$, domain: $(-\infty, -2] \cup [2, \infty)$.
10. $f \circ g(x) = (\cos x)^2 = \cos^2 x$, domain: $(-\infty, \infty)$.
    $g \circ f(x) = \cos(x^2)$, domain: $(-\infty, \infty)$.

Section 4.6 Exercises

1. Periodic.

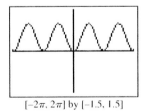

$[-2\pi, 2\pi]$ by $[-1.5, 1.5]$

2. Periodic.

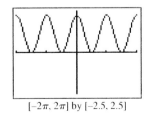

$[-2\pi, 2\pi]$ by $[-2.5, 2.5]$

3. Not periodic.

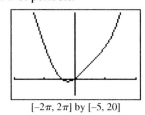

$[-2\pi, 2\pi]$ by $[-5, 20]$

4. Not periodic.

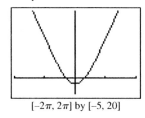

$[-2\pi, 2\pi]$ by $[-5, 20]$

5. Not periodic.

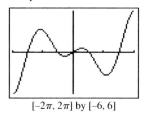

$[-2\pi, 2\pi]$ by $[-6, 6]$

6. Not periodic.

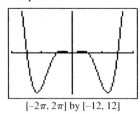

$[-2\pi, 2\pi]$ by $[-12, 12]$

7. Periodic.

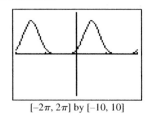

$[-2\pi, 2\pi]$ by $[-10, 10]$

8. Periodic.

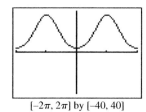

$[-2\pi, 2\pi]$ by $[-40, 40]$

9. Since the period of $\cos x$ is 2π, we have
$\cos^2(x + 2\pi) = (\cos(x + 2\pi))^2 = (\cos x)^2 = \cos^2 x$.
The period is therefore an exact divisor of 2π, and we see graphically that it is π. A graph for $-\pi \le x \le \pi$ is shown:

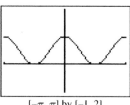

$[-\pi, \pi]$ by $[-1, 2]$

10. Since the period of $\cos x$ is 2π, we have
$\cos^3(x + 2\pi) = (\cos(x + 2\pi))^3 = (\cos x)^3 = \cos^3 x$.
The period is therefore an exact divisor of 2π, and we see graphically that it is 2π. A graph for $-2\pi \le x \le 2\pi$ is shown:

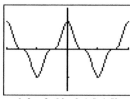

$[-2\pi, 2\pi]$ by $[-1.5, 1.5]$

11. Since the period of $\cos x$ is 2π, we have
$\sqrt{\cos^2(x + 2\pi)} = \sqrt{(\cos(x + 2\pi))^2} = \sqrt{(\cos x)^2}$
$= \sqrt{\cos^2 x}$. The period is therefore an exact divisor of 2π, and we see graphically that it is π. A graph for $-\pi \le x \le \pi$ is shown:

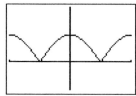

$[-\pi, \pi]$ by $[-1, 2]$

12. Since the period of $\cos x$ is 2π, we have
$|\cos^3(x + 2\pi)| = |(\cos(x + 2\pi))^3| = |(\cos x)^3|$
$= |\cos^3 x|$. The period is therefore an exact divisor of 2π, and we see graphically that it is π. A graph for $-\pi \le x \le \pi$ is shown:

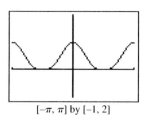

$[-\pi, \pi]$ by $[-1, 2]$

13. Domain: $(-\infty, \infty)$. Range: $[0, 1]$.

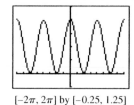

$[-2\pi, 2\pi]$ by $[-0.25, 1.25]$

14. Domain: $(-\infty, \infty)$. Range: $[0, 1]$.

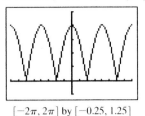

$[-2\pi, 2\pi]$ by $[-0.25, 1.25]$

15. Domain: all $x \neq n\pi$, n an integer. Range: $[0, \infty)$.

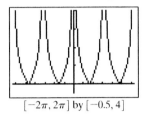

$[-2\pi, 2\pi]$ by $[-0.5, 4]$

16. Domain: $(-\infty, \infty)$. Range: $[-1, 1]$.

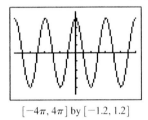

$[-4\pi, 4\pi]$ by $[-1.2, 1.2]$

17. Domain: all $x \neq \dfrac{\pi}{2} + n\pi$, n an integer. Range: $(-\infty, 0]$.

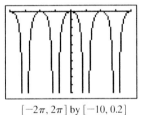

$[-2\pi, 2\pi]$ by $[-10, 0.2]$

18. Domain: $(-\infty, \infty)$. Range: $[-1, 0]$.

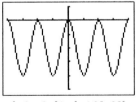

$[-2\pi, 2\pi]$ by $[-1.25, .25]$

In #19–22, the linear equations are found by setting the cosine term equal to ± 1.

19. $2x - 1 \leq y \leq 2x + 1$

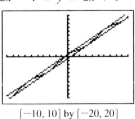

$[-10, 10]$ by $[-20, 20]$

20. $-0.5x \leq y \leq 2 - 0.5x$

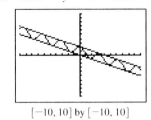

$[-10, 10]$ by $[-10, 10]$

21. $1 - 0.3x \leq y \leq 3 - 0.3x$

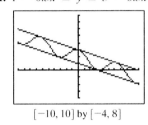

$[-10, 10]$ by $[-4, 8]$

22. $x \leq y \leq x + 2$

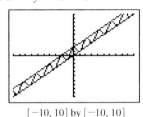

$[-10, 10]$ by $[-10, 10]$

For #23–28, the function $y_1 + y_2$ is a sinusoid if both y_1 and y_2 are sine or cosine functions with the same period.

23. Yes (period 2π) **24.** Yes (period 2π)

25. Yes (period 2) **26.** No

27. No **28.** No

For #29–34, graph the function. Estimate a as the amplitude of the graph (i.e., the height of the maximum). Notice that the value of b is always the coefficient of x in the original functions. Finally, note that $a \sin[b(x - h)] = 0$ when $x = h$, so estimate h using a zero of $f(x)$ where $f(x)$ changes from negative to positive.

29. $A \approx 3.61$, $b = 2$, and $h \approx 0.49$, so $f(x)$ $\approx 3.61 \sin[2(x - 0.49)]$.

30. $A \approx 2.24$, $b = 3$, and $h \approx -0.15$, so $f(x)$ $\approx 2.24 \sin[3(x + 0.15)]$.

31. $A \approx 2.24$, $b = \pi$, and $h \approx 0.35$, so $f(x)$ $\approx 2.24 \sin[\pi(x - 0.35)]$.

32. $A \approx 3.16$, $b = 2\pi$, and $h \approx -0.05$, so $f(x)$ $\approx 3.16 \sin[2\pi(x + 0.05)]$.

33. $A \approx 2.24$, $b = 1$, and $h \approx -1.11$, so $f(x)$ $\approx 2.24 \sin(x + 1.11)$.

34. $A \approx 3.16$, $b = 2$, and $h \approx 0.16$, so $f(x)$ $\approx 3.16 \sin[2(x - 0.16)]$.

35. The period is 2π.

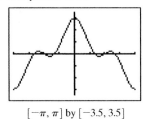

$[-\pi, \pi]$ by $[-3.5, 3.5]$

36. The period is 2π.

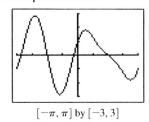

$[-\pi, \pi]$ by $[-3, 3]$

37. The period is 2π.

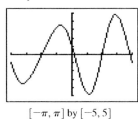

$[-\pi, \pi]$ by $[-5, 5]$

38. The period is 2π.

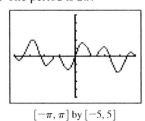

$[-\pi, \pi]$ by $[-5, 5]$

39. (a)   **40.** (d)

41. (c)   **42.** (b)

43. The damping factor is e^{-x}, which goes to zero as x gets large. So damping occurs as $x \to \infty$.

44. The damping factor is x, which goes to zero as x goes to zero (obviously). So damping occurs as $x \to 0$.

45. The amplitude, $\sqrt{5}$, is constant. So there is no damping.

46. The amplitude, π^2, is constant. So there is no damping.

47. The damping factor is x^3, which goes to zero as x goes to zero. So damping occurs as $x \to 0$.

48. The damping factor is $(2/3)^x$, which goes to zero as x gets large. So damping occurs as $x \to \infty$.

49. f oscillates up and down between 1.2^{-x} and -1.2^{-x}. As $x \to \infty$, $f(x) \to 0$.

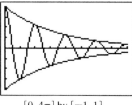

$[0, 4\pi]$ by $[-1, 1]$

50. f oscillates up and down between 2^{-x} and -2^{-x}. As $x \to \infty$, $f(x) \to 0$.

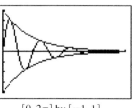

$[0, 2\pi]$ by $[-1, 1]$

51. f oscillates up and down between $\dfrac{1}{x}$ and $-\dfrac{1}{x}$.

As $x \to \infty$, $f(x) \to 0$.

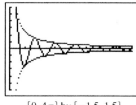

$[0, 4\pi]$ by $[-1.5, 1.5]$

52. f oscillates up and down between e^{-x} and $-e^{-x}$. As $x \to \infty$, $f(x) \to 0$.

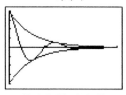

$[0, 1.5\pi]$ by $[-1, 1]$

53. Period 2π: $\sin[3(x + 2\pi)] + 2\cos[2(x + 2\pi)] = \sin(3x + 6\pi) + 2\cos(2x + 4\pi) = \sin 3x + 2\cos 2x$. The graph, shows that no $p < 2\pi$ could be the period.

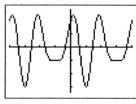

$[-2\pi, 2\pi]$ by $[-3.4, 2.8]$

54. Period 2π: $4\cos[2(x + 2\pi)] - 2\cos[3(x + 2\pi) - 1]$
$= 4\cos(2x + 4\pi) - 2\cos(3x - 1 + 6\pi)$
$= 4\cos 2x - 2\cos(3x - 1)$. The graph, shows that no
$p < 2\pi$ could be the period.

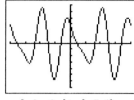

$[-2\pi, 2\pi]$ by $[-7, 6]$

55. Period 2π:
$2\sin[3(x + 2\pi) + 1] - \cos[5(x + 2\pi) - 1]$
$= 2\sin(3x + 1 + 6\pi) - \cos(5x - 1 + 10\pi)$
$= 2\sin(3x + 1) - \cos(5x - 1)$. The graph, shows that
no $p < 2\pi$ could be the period.

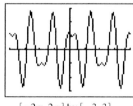

$[-2\pi, 2\pi]$ by $[-3, 3]$

56. Period 2π:
$3\cos[2(x + 2\pi) - 1] - 4\sin[3(x + 2\pi) - 2]$
$= 3\cos(2x - 1 + 4\pi) - 4\sin(3x - 2 + 6\pi)$
$= 3\cos(2x - 1) - 4\sin(3x - 2)$. The graph, shows that
no $p < 2\pi$ could be the period.

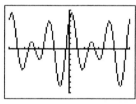

$[-2\pi, 2\pi]$ by $[-8, 7]$

57. Period 2π: $\left|\sin\left[\dfrac{1}{2}(x + 2\pi)\right]\right| + 2 =$
$\left|\sin\left(\dfrac{1}{2}x + \pi\right)\right| + 2 = \left|-\sin\dfrac{1}{2}x\right| + 2 = \left|\sin\dfrac{1}{2}x\right| + 2.$
The graph, shows that no $p < 2\pi$ could be the period.

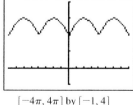

$[-4\pi, 4\pi]$ by $[-1, 4]$

58. Not periodic

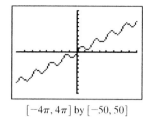

$[-4\pi, 4\pi]$ by $[-50, 50]$

59. Not periodic

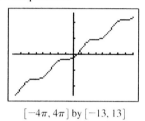

$[-4\pi, 4\pi]$ by $[-13, 13]$

60. Not periodic

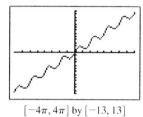

$[-4\pi, 4\pi]$ by $[-13, 13]$

61. Not periodic

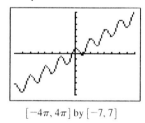

$[-4\pi, 4\pi]$ by $[-7, 7]$

62. Not periodic

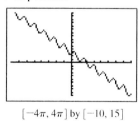

$[-4\pi, 4\pi]$ by $[-10, 15]$

For #63–70, graphs may be useful to suggest the domain and
range.

63. There are no restrictions on the value of x, so the domain
is $(-\infty, \infty)$. Range: $(-\infty, \infty)$.

64. There are no restrictions on the value of x, so the domain
is $(-\infty, \infty)$. Range: $(-\infty, \infty)$.

65. There are no restrictions on the value of x, so the domain
is $(-\infty, \infty)$. Range: $[1, \infty)$.

66. There are no restrictions on the value of x, so the domain
is $(-\infty, \infty)$. Range: $(-\infty, \infty)$.

67. sin x must be nonnegative, so the domain is
$\cdots \cup [-2\pi, -\pi] \cup [0, \pi] \cup [2\pi, 3\pi] \cup \cdots$; that is, all x
with $2n\pi \le x \le (2n + 1)\pi$, n an integer. Range: $[0, 1]$.

68. There are no restrictions on the value of x, so the domain
is $(-\infty, \infty)$. Range: $[-1, 1]$.

69. There are no restrictions on the value of x, since
$|\sin x| \ge 0$, so the domain is $(-\infty, \infty)$. Range: $[0, 1]$.

70. cos x must be nonnegative, so the domain is

$\cdots \cup \left[-\dfrac{5\pi}{2}, -\dfrac{3\pi}{2} \right] \cup \left[-\dfrac{\pi}{2}, \dfrac{\pi}{2} \right] \cup \left[\dfrac{3\pi}{2}, \dfrac{5\pi}{2} \right] \cup \cdots$; that is, all

x with $\dfrac{(4n - 1)\pi}{2} \le x \le \dfrac{(4n + 1)\pi}{2}$, n an integer.
Range: $[0, 1]$.

71. (a)

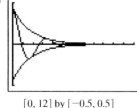

[0, 12] by [−0.5, 0.5]

(b) For $t > 0.51$ (approximately).

72. (a) Using $S(t) = 75(1.04)^t + 4\sin\left(\dfrac{\pi t}{3}\right)$ to estimate sales
(in millions of dollars) t years after 2005, we have

$S(0) = 75(1.04)^0 + 4\sin\left(\dfrac{\pi \cdot 0}{3}\right) = 75$ million dollars.

(b) The approximate annual growth rate is 4%.

(c) In 2013, $t = 8$ so the sales are predicted by

$S(8) = 75(1.04)^8 + 4\sin\left(\dfrac{\pi \cdot 8}{3}\right) \approx 106.1$ million

dollars.

(d) To find the number of years in each economic cycle,
find the period of $\sin\left(\dfrac{\pi x}{3}\right)$, the trigonometric part of

the model. The period of $\sin\left(\dfrac{\pi x}{3}\right)$ is $\dfrac{2\pi}{\pi/3} = 6$, so there

are 6 years in each economic cycle for the company.

73. No. This is suggested by a graph of $y = \sin x^3$; there is no
other section of the graph that looks like the section
between -1 and 1. In particular, there is only one zero of
the function in that interval (at $x = 0$); nowhere else can
we find an interval this long with only one zero.

74. One explanation: The 'v'-shaped section around $x = 0$ is
unique — it does not appear anywhere else on the graph.

75. (a) — this is obtained by adding x to all parts of the
inequality $-1 \le \sin x \le 1$. In the second, after subtracting x from both sides, we are left with $-\sin x \le \sin x$,
which is false when $\sin x$ is negative.

76. (b) — the first is impossible (even ignoring the middle
part) if $x < 0$, since then $-x \not\le x$.

77. Graph (d), shown on $[-2\pi, 2\pi]$ by $[-4, 4]$

78. Graph (a), shown on $[-2\pi, 2\pi]$ by $[-4, 4]$

79. Graph (b), shown on $[-2\pi, 2\pi]$ by $[-4, 4]$

80. Graph (c), shown on $[-2\pi, 2\pi]$ by $[-4, 4]$

81. False. The behavior near zero, with a relative minimum
of 0 at $x = 0$, is not repeated anywhere else.

82. False. If two sinusoids have different periods, the sum of
the sinusoids is not a sinusoid. Example: $\sin x + \sin 3x$.

83. The negative portions of the graph of $y = \sin x$ are
reflected in the x-axis for $y = |\sin x|$. This halves the
period. The answer is B.

84. $f(-x) = (-x)\sin(-x) = x \sin x = f(x)$.
The answer is C.

85. $f(-x) = -x + \sin(-x) = -x - \sin x = -f(x)$.
The answer is D.

86. The sum of two sinusoids is a sinusoid only when the two
sinusoids have the same period. The answer is D.

87. (a) Answers will vary — for example,

on a TI-81: $\dfrac{\pi}{47.5} = 0.0661\ldots \approx 0.07$;

on a TI-82: $\dfrac{\pi}{47} = 0.0668\ldots \approx 0.07$;

on a TI-85: $\dfrac{\pi}{63} = 0.0498\ldots \approx 0.05$;

on a TI-92: $\dfrac{\pi}{119} = 0.0263\ldots \approx 0.03$.

(b) Period: $p = \pi/125 = 0.0251\ldots$. For any of the
TI graphers, there are from 1 to 3 cycles between each
pair of pixels; the graphs produced are therefore inac-
curate, since so much detail is lost.

88. The amplitude is 3 hr 6 min, or 3.1 hr. The period is
365 days (one could also use 365.26 days), so $b = \dfrac{2\pi}{365}$.

The phase shift h is 80 days, so an answer is

$3.1\sin\left[\dfrac{2\pi}{365}(x - 80)\right] + 12$ hours of daylight, where x is
the day of the year.

89. Domain: $(-\infty, \infty)$. Range: $[-1, 1]$. Horizontal asymptote:

$y = 1$. Zeros at $\ln\left(\dfrac{\pi}{2} + n\pi\right)$, n a non-negative integer.

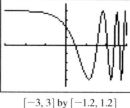

[−3, 3] by [−1.2, 1.2]

90. Period: π. Domain: $x \ne n\pi + \dfrac{\pi}{2}$. Range: $(0, \infty)$. Vertical

asymptotes at missing points of domain: $x = n\pi + \dfrac{\pi}{2}$.

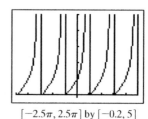

[−2.5π, 2.5π] by [−0.2, 5]

91. Domain: $[0, \infty)$. Range: $(-\infty, \infty)$. Zeros at $n\pi$, n a non-negative integer.

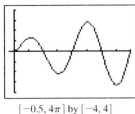

$[-0.5, 4\pi]$ by $[-4, 4]$

92. Domain: $[-2, 2]$. Range: $[0, 2.94]$ (approximately). Zeros at -2 and 2.

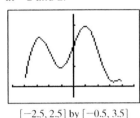

$[-2.5, 2.5]$ by $[-0.5, 3.5]$

93. Domain: $(-\infty, 0) \cup (0, \infty)$. Range: approximately $[-0.22, 1)$. Horizontal asymptote: $y = 0$. Zeros at $n\pi$, n a non-zero integer.

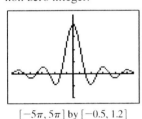

$[-5\pi, 5\pi]$ by $[-0.5, 1.2]$

94. Domain: $(-\infty, 0) \cup (0, \infty)$. Range: $(-\infty, \infty)$. Horizontal asymptote: $y = 0$. Vertical asymptote: $x = 0$. Zeros at $n\pi$, n a non-zero integer.

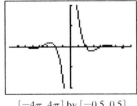

$[-4\pi, 4\pi]$ by $[-0.5, 0.5]$

95. Domain: $(-\infty, 0) \cup (0, \infty)$. Range: approximately $[-0.22, 1)$. Horizontal asymptote: $y = 1$. Zeros at $\dfrac{1}{n\pi}$, n a non-zero integer.

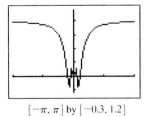

$[-\pi, \pi]$ by $[-0.3, 1.2]$

96. Domain: $(-\infty, 0) \cup (0, \infty)$. Range: $(-\infty, \infty)$. Zeros at $\dfrac{1}{n\pi}$, n a non-zero integer. Note: the graph also suggests the end-behavior asymptote $y = x$.

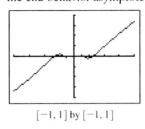

$[-1, 1]$ by $[-1, 1]$

■ Section 4.7 Inverse Trigonometric Functions

Exploration 1

1. $\tan \theta = \dfrac{x}{1} = x$

2. $\tan^{-1} x = \tan^{-1}\left(\dfrac{x}{1}\right) = \theta$

3. $\sqrt{1 + x^2}$ (by the Pythagorean theorem)

4. $\sin(\tan^{-1}(x)) = \sin(\theta) = \dfrac{x}{\sqrt{1 + x^2}}$

5. $\sec(\tan^{-1}(x)) = \sec(\theta) = \sqrt{1 + x^2}$

6. The hypotenuse is positive in either quadrant. The ratios in the six basic trig functions are the same in every quadrant, so the functions are still valid regardless of the sign of x. (Also, the sign of the answer in (4) is negative, as it should be, and the sign of the answer in (5) is negative, as it should be.)

Quick Review 4.7

1. $\sin x$: positive; $\cos x$: positive; $\tan x$: positive

2. $\sin x$: positive; $\cos x$: negative; $\tan x$: negative

3. $\sin x$: negative; $\cos x$: negative; $\tan x$: positive

4. $\sin x$: negative; $\cos x$: positive; $\tan x$: negative

5. $\sin \dfrac{\pi}{6} = \dfrac{1}{2}$ **6.** $\tan \dfrac{\pi}{4} = 1$

7. $\cos \dfrac{2\pi}{3} = -\dfrac{1}{2}$ **8.** $\sin \dfrac{2\pi}{3} = \dfrac{\sqrt{3}}{2}$

9. $\sin \dfrac{-\pi}{6} = -\dfrac{1}{2}$ **10.** $\cos \dfrac{-\pi}{3} = \dfrac{1}{2}$

Section 4.7 Exercises

For #1–12, keep in mind that the inverse sine and inverse tangent functions return values in $\left[-\dfrac{\pi}{2}, \dfrac{\pi}{2}\right]$, and the inverse cosine function gives values in $[0, \pi]$. A calculator may also be useful to suggest the exact answer. (A useful trick is to compute, e.g., $\sin^{-1}(\sqrt{3}/2)\pi$ and observe that this is ≈ 0.333, suggesting the answer $\pi/3$.)

1. $\sin^{-1}\left(\dfrac{\sqrt{3}}{2}\right) = \dfrac{\pi}{3}$ **2.** $\sin^{-1}\left(-\dfrac{1}{2}\right) = -\dfrac{\pi}{6}$

3. $\tan^{-1}(0) = 0$ **4.** $\cos^{-1}(1) = 0$

5. $\cos^{-1}\left(\dfrac{1}{2}\right) = \dfrac{\pi}{3}$

6. $\tan^{-1}(1) = \dfrac{\pi}{4}$

7. $\tan^{-1}(-1) = -\dfrac{\pi}{4}$

8. $\cos^{-1}\left(-\dfrac{\sqrt{3}}{2}\right) = \dfrac{5\pi}{6}$

9. $\sin^{-1}\left(-\dfrac{1}{\sqrt{2}}\right) = -\dfrac{\pi}{4}$

10. $\tan^{-1}(-\sqrt{3}) = -\dfrac{\pi}{3}$

11. $\cos^{-1}(0) = \dfrac{\pi}{2}$

12. $\sin^{-1}(1) = \dfrac{\pi}{2}$

13. approx. $21.22°$

14. approx. $42.07°$

15. approx. $-85.43°$

16. approx. $103.30°$

17. approx. 1.172

18. approx. 1.527

19. approx. -0.478

20. approx. 2.593

21. $y = \tan^{-1}(x^2)$ is equivalent to $\tan y = x^2$, $-\pi/2 < y < \pi/2$. For x^2 to get very large, y has to approach $\pi/2$. So $\displaystyle\lim_{x\to\infty} \tan^{-1}(x^2) = \pi/2$ and $\displaystyle\lim_{x\to-\infty} \tan^{-1}(x^2) = \pi/2$.

22. $y = (\tan^{-1} x)^2$ is equivalent to $x = \tan(\pm\sqrt{y})$, $0 \le y < \pi^2/4$. For x to get very large, in the positive or negative direction, y has to approach $\pi^2/4$. So $\displaystyle\lim_{x\to\infty} (\tan^{-1}x)^2 = \pi^2/4$ and $\displaystyle\lim_{x\to-\infty} (\tan^{-1}x)^2 = \pi^2/4$.

23. $\cos\left(\sin^{-1}\dfrac{1}{2}\right) = \cos\dfrac{\pi}{6} = \dfrac{\sqrt{3}}{2}$

24. $\sin(\tan^{-1} 1) = \sin\dfrac{\pi}{4} = \dfrac{\sqrt{2}}{2}$

25. $\sin^{-1}\left(\cos\dfrac{\pi}{4}\right) = \sin^{-1}\left(\dfrac{\sqrt{2}}{2}\right) = \dfrac{\pi}{4}$

26. $\cos^{-1}\left(\cos\dfrac{7\pi}{4}\right) = \cos^{-1}\left(\dfrac{\sqrt{2}}{2}\right) = \dfrac{\pi}{4}$

27. $\cos\left(2\sin^{-1}\dfrac{1}{2}\right) = \cos\left(2\cdot\dfrac{\pi}{6}\right) = \dfrac{1}{2}$

28. $\sin[\tan^{-1}(-1)] = \sin\left(-\dfrac{\pi}{4}\right) = -\dfrac{\sqrt{2}}{2}$

29. $\arcsin\left(\cos\dfrac{\pi}{3}\right) = \arcsin\dfrac{1}{2} = \dfrac{\pi}{6}$

30. $\arccos\left(\tan\dfrac{\pi}{4}\right) = \arccos 1 = 0$

31. $\cos(\tan^{-1}\sqrt{3}) = \cos\left(\dfrac{\pi}{3}\right) = \dfrac{1}{2}$

32. $\tan^{-1}(\cos\pi) = \tan^{-1}(-1) = -\dfrac{\pi}{4}$

33. Domain: $[-1, 1]$
Range: $[-\pi/2, \pi/2]$
Continuous
Increasing
Symmetric with respect to the origin (odd)
Bounded
Absolute maximum of $\pi/2$, absolute minimum of $-\pi/2$
No asymptotes
No end behavior (bounded domain)

34. Domain: $[-1, 1]$
Range: $[0, \pi]$
Continuous
Decreasing
Neither odd nor even (but symmetric with respect to the point $(0, \pi/2)$)
Bounded
Absolute maximum of π, absolute minimum of 0
No asymptotes
No end behavior (bounded domain)

35. Domain: $(-\infty, \infty)$
Range: $(-\pi/2, \pi/2)$
Continuous
Increasing
Symmetric with respect to the origin (odd)
Bounded
No local extrema
Horizontal asymptotes: $y = \pi/2$ and $y = -\pi/2$
End behavior: $\displaystyle\lim_{x\to\infty} \tan^{-1}x = \pi/2$ and $\displaystyle\lim_{x\to-\infty} \tan^{-1}x = -\pi/2$

36. Domain: $(-\infty, \infty)$
Range: $(0, \pi)$
Continuous
Decreasing
Neither odd nor even (but symmetric with respect to the point $(0, \pi/2)$)
Bounded
No local extrema
Horizontal asymptotes: $y = \pi$ and $y = 0$
End behavior: $\displaystyle\lim_{x\to\infty} \cot^{-1}x = 0$ and $\displaystyle\lim_{x\to-\infty} \cot^{-1}x = \pi$

37. Domain: $\left[-\dfrac{1}{2}, \dfrac{1}{2}\right]$. Range: $\left[-\dfrac{\pi}{2}, \dfrac{\pi}{2}\right]$. Starting from $y = \sin^{-1} x$, horizontally shrink by $\dfrac{1}{2}$.

38. Domain: $\left[-\dfrac{1}{2}, \dfrac{1}{2}\right]$. Range: $[0, 3\pi]$. Starting from $y = \cos^{-1} x$, horizontally shrink by $\dfrac{1}{2}$ and vertically stretch by 3 (either order).

39. Domain: $(-\infty, \infty)$. Range: $\left(-\dfrac{5\pi}{2}, \dfrac{5\pi}{2}\right)$. Starting from $y = \tan^{-1} x$, horizontally stretch by 2 and vertically stretch by 5 (either order).

40. Domain: $[-2, 2]$. Range: $[0, 3\pi]$. Starting from $y = \arccos x = \cos^{-1} x$, horizontally stretch by 2 and vertically stretch by 3 (either order).

41. First set $\theta = \sin^{-1} x$ and solve $\sin\theta = 1$, yielding $\theta = \dfrac{\pi}{2} + 2n\pi$ for integers n. Since $\theta = \sin^{-1} x$ must be in $\left[-\dfrac{\pi}{2}, \dfrac{\pi}{2}\right]$, we have $\sin^{-1} x = \dfrac{\pi}{2}$, so $x = 1$.

42. First set $y = \cos x$ and solve $\cos^{-1} y = 1$, yielding $y = \cos 1$. Then solve $\cos x = \cos 1$, which gives $x = 1 + 2n\pi$ or $x = -1 + 2n\pi$, for all integers n.

43. Divide both sides of the equation by 2, leaving $\sin^{-1} x = \dfrac{1}{2}$, so $x = \sin\dfrac{1}{2} \approx 0.479$.

44. If $\tan^{-1} x = -1$, then $x = \tan(-1) \approx -1.557$.

45. For any x in $[0, \pi]$, $\cos(\cos^{-1}x), = x$. Hence, $x = \dfrac{1}{3}$.

46. For any x in $\left[-\dfrac{\pi}{2}, \dfrac{\pi}{2}\right]$, $\sin^{-1}(\sin x) = x$. Since $\dfrac{\pi}{10}$ is in $\left[-\dfrac{\pi}{2}, \dfrac{\pi}{2}\right]$, $x = \dfrac{\pi}{10}$.

47. Draw a right triangle with horizontal leg 1, vertical leg x (if $x > 0$, draw the vertical leg "up"; if $x < 0$, draw it down), and hypotenuse $\sqrt{1 + x^2}$. The acute angle adjacent to the leg of length 1 has measure $\theta = \tan^{-1} x$ (take $\theta < 0$ if $x < 0$), so $\sin \theta = \sin(\tan^{-1} x) = \dfrac{x}{\sqrt{1 + x^2}}$.

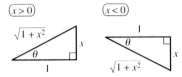

48. Use the same triangles as in #47: draw a triangle with horizontal leg 1, vertical leg x (up or down as $x > 0$ or $x < 0$), and hypotenuse $\sqrt{1 + x^2}$. The acute angle adjacent to the leg of length 1 has measure $\theta = \tan^{-1} x$ (take $\theta < 0$ if $x < 0$), so $\cos \theta = \cos(\tan^{-1} x) = \dfrac{1}{\sqrt{1 + x^2}}$.

49. Draw a right triangle with horizontal leg $\sqrt{1 - x^2}$, vertical leg x (if $x > 0$, draw the vertical leg "up"; if $x < 0$, draw it down), and hypotenuse 1. The acute angle adjacent to the horizontal leg has measure $\theta = \arcsin x$ (take $\theta < 0$ if $x < 0$), so $\tan \theta = \tan(\arcsin x) = \dfrac{x}{\sqrt{1 - x^2}}$.

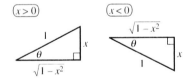

50. Draw a right triangle with horizontal leg x (if $x > 0$, draw the horizontal leg right; if $x < 0$, draw it left), vertical leg $\sqrt{1 - x^2}$, and hypotenuse 1. If $x > 0$, let θ be the acute angle adjacent to the horizontal leg; if $x < 0$, let θ be the supplement of this angle. Then $\theta = \arccos x$, so $\cot \theta = \cot(\arccos x) = \dfrac{x}{\sqrt{1 - x^2}}$.

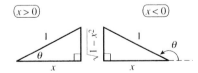

51. Draw a right triangle with horizontal leg 1, vertical leg $2x$ (up or down as $x > 0$ or $x < 0$), and hypotenuse $\sqrt{1 + 4x^2}$. The acute angle adjacent to the leg of length 1 has measure $\theta = \arctan 2x$ (take $\theta < 0$ if $x < 0$), so $\cos \theta = \cos(\arctan 2x) = \dfrac{1}{\sqrt{1 + 4x^2}}$.

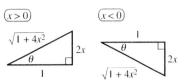

52. Draw a right triangle with horizontal leg $3x$ (if $x > 0$, draw the horizontal leg right; if $x < 0$, draw it left), vertical leg $\sqrt{1 - 9x^2}$, and hypotenuse 1. If $x > 0$, let θ be the acute angle adjacent to the horizontal leg; if $x < 0$, let θ be the supplement of this angle. Then $\theta = \arccos 3x$, so $\sin \theta = \sin(\arccos 3x) = \sqrt{1 - 9x^2}$.

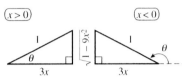

53. (a) Call the smaller (unlabeled) angle in the lower left α; then $\tan \alpha = \dfrac{2}{x}$, or $\alpha = \tan^{-1} \dfrac{2}{x}$ (since α is acute). Also, $\theta + \alpha$ is the measure of one acute angle in the right triangle formed by a line parallel to the floor and the wall; for this triangle $\tan(\theta + \alpha) = \dfrac{14}{x}$. Then $\theta + \alpha = \tan^{-1} \dfrac{14}{x}$ (since $\theta + \alpha$ is acute), so $\theta = \tan^{-1} \dfrac{14}{x} - \alpha = \tan^{-1} \dfrac{14}{x} - \tan^{-1} \dfrac{2}{x}$.

(b) Graph is shown. The actual maximum occurs at $x \approx 5.29$ ft, where $\theta \approx 48.59°$.

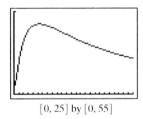

$[0, 25]$ by $[0, 55]$

(c) Either $x \approx 1.83$ or $x \approx 15.31$—these round to 2 ft or 15 ft.

54. (a) θ is one acute angle in the right triangle with leg lengths x (opposite) and 3 (adjacent); thus $\tan \theta = \dfrac{x}{3}$, and $\theta = \tan^{-1} \dfrac{x}{3}$ (since θ is acute).

(b) Graph is shown (using DEGREE mode). Negative values of x correspond to the point Q being "upshore" from P ("into" the picture) instead of downshore (as shown in the illustration). Positive angles are angles that point downshore; negative angles point upshore.

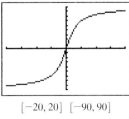

$[-20, 20]$ $[-90, 90]$

(c) $\theta = \tan^{-1} 5 \approx 78.69°$

55. (a) $\theta = \tan^{-1} \dfrac{s}{500}$.

(b) As s changes from 10 to 20 ft, θ changes from about 1.1458° to 2.2906°—it almost exactly doubles (a 99.92% increase). As s changes from 200 to 210 ft, θ changes from about 21.80° to 22.78°—an increase of less than 1°, and a very small relative change (only about 4.25%).

(c) The x-axis represents the height and the y-axis represents the angle: the angle cannot grow past 90° (in fact, it *approaches* but never exactly equals 90°).

56. (a) $\text{Sin}(x)$ exists for all x, but $\sin^{-1}(x)$ is restricted to $[-1, 1]$. The domain of $f(x)$ is $[-1, 1]$. The range is $[-1, 1]$.

(b) Since the domains of $\sin^{-1}(x)$ and $\cos^{-1}(x)$ are $[-1, 1]$, the domain of $g(x)$ is $[-1, 1]$. The range is $\left\{\dfrac{\pi}{2}\right\}$.

(c) Since $|\sin(x)| \le 1$ for all x, $h(x)$ exists for all x and its domain is $(-\infty, \infty)$. The range is $\left[-\dfrac{\pi}{2}, \dfrac{\pi}{2}\right]$.

(d) $\text{Sin}(x)$ exists for all x, but $\cos^{-1}(x)$ is restricted to $[-1, 1]$. The domain of $k(x)$ is $[-1, 1]$. The range is $[0, 1]$.

(e) Since $|\sin(x)| \le 1$ for all x, $q(x)$ exists for all x and its domain is $(-\infty, \infty)$. The range is $[0, \pi]$.

57. False. This is only true for $-1 \le x \le 1$, the domain of the $\sin^{-1}$ function. For $x < -1$ and for $x > 1$, $\sin(\sin^{-1} x)$ is undefined.

58. True. The end behavior of $y = \arctan x$ determines two horizontal asymptotes, since $\lim\limits_{x \to -\infty} \arctan x = -\pi/2$ and $\lim\limits_{x \to \infty} \arctan x = \pi/2$.

59. $\cos(5\pi/6) = -\sqrt{3}/2$, so $\cos^{-1}(-\sqrt{3}/2) = 5\pi/6$. The answer is E.

60. $\sin^{-1}(\sin \pi) = \sin^{-1} 0 = 0$. The answer is C.

61. $\sec(\tan^{-1} x) = \sqrt{1 + \tan^2(\tan^{-1} x)} = \sqrt{1 + x^2}$. The answer is C.

62. The range of $f(x) = \arcsin x = \sin^{-1} x$ is, by definition, $[-\pi/2, \pi/2]$. The answer is E.

63. The cotangent function restricted to the interval $(0, \pi)$ is one-to-one and has an inverse. The unique angle y between 0 and π (non-inclusive) such that $\cot y = x$ is called the inverse cotangent (or arccotangent) of x, denoted $\cot^{-1} x$ or $\text{arccot } x$. The domain of $y = \cot^{-1} x$ is $(-\infty, \infty)$ and the range is $(0, \pi)$.

64. In the triangle below, $A = \sin^{-1} x$ and $B = \cos^{-1} x$. Since A and B are complementary angles, $A + B = \pi/2$. The left-hand side of the equation is only defined for $-1 \le x \le 1$.

65. (a) Domain all reals, range $[-\pi/2, \pi/2]$, period 2π.

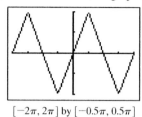

$[-2\pi, 2\pi]$ by $[-0.5\pi, 0.5\pi]$

(b) Domain all reals, range $[0, \pi]$, period 2π.

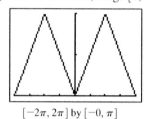

$[-2\pi, 2\pi]$ by $[-0, \pi]$

(c) Domain all reals except $\pi/2 + n\pi$ (n an integer), range $(-\pi/2, \pi/2)$, period π. Discontinuity is not removable.

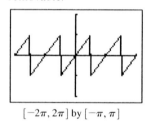

$[-2\pi, 2\pi]$ by $[-\pi, \pi]$

66. (a) Let $\theta = \sin^{-1}(2x)$. Then the adjacent side of the right triangle is $\sqrt{1^2 - (2x)^2} = \sqrt{1 - 4x^2}$.

$$\cos(\theta) = \frac{\sqrt{1 - 4x^2}}{1} = \sqrt{1 - 4x^2}$$

(b) Let $\theta = \tan^{-1}(x)$. Then the hypotenuse is $\sqrt{1 + x^2}$.

$$\sec^2(\theta) = \left(\frac{\sqrt{1 + x^2}}{1}\right)^2 = 1 + x^2$$

(c) Let $\theta = \cos^{-1}(\sqrt{x})$. Then the opposite side of the right triangle is $\sqrt{1^2 - (\sqrt{x})^2} = \sqrt{1 - x}$.

$$\sin(\theta) = \frac{\sqrt{1 - x}}{1} = \sqrt{1 - x}$$

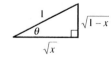

(d) Let $\theta = \cot^{-1}(x)$. Then the hypotenuse is

$$\sqrt{1^2 + x^2} = \sqrt{1 + x^2}. \ -\csc^2(\theta) = -\left(\frac{\sqrt{1 + x^2}}{1}\right)^2$$

$$= -(1 + x^2) = -x^2 - 1.$$

(e) Let $\theta = \sec^{-1}(x^2)$. Then the opposite leg of the right triangle is $\sqrt{(x^2)^2 - 1^2} = \sqrt{x^4 - 1}$.

$$\tan(\theta) = \frac{\sqrt{x^4 - 1}}{1} = \sqrt{x^4 - 1}.$$

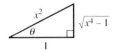

67. $y = \dfrac{\pi}{2} - \tan^{-1} x.$

(Note that $y = \tan^{-1}\left(\dfrac{1}{x}\right)$ does not have the correct range for negative values of x.)

68. (a) $\cos(\sin^{-1} x)$ or $\sin(\cos^{-1} x)$

(b) $\sin(\tan^{-1} x)$ or $\cos(\cot^{-1} x)$

(c) $\tan(\sin^{-1} x)$ or $\cot(\cos^{-1} x)$

69. In order to transform the arctangent function to a function that has horizontal asymptotes at $y = 24$ and $y = 42$, we need to find a and d that will satisfy the equation $y = a \tan^{-1} x + d$. In other words, we are shifting the horizontal asymptotes of $y = \tan^{-1} x$ from $y = -\dfrac{\pi}{2}$ and $y = \dfrac{\pi}{2}$ to the new asymptotes $y = 24$ and $y = 42$.

Solving $y = a \tan^{-1} x + d$ and $y = 24$ for $\tan^{-1} x$ in terms of a and d yields $24 = a \tan^{-1} x + d$; so, $\dfrac{24 - d}{a} = \tan^{-1}x$. We know that $y = 24$ is the lower horizontal asymptote and thus it corresponds to $y = -\dfrac{\pi}{2}$.

So, $\dfrac{24 - d}{a} = \tan^{-1}x = -\dfrac{\pi}{2} \Rightarrow \dfrac{24 - d}{a} = -\dfrac{\pi}{2}$. Solving this for d in terms of a yields $d = 24 + \left(\dfrac{\pi}{2}\right)a.$

Solving $y = a \tan^{-1} x + d$ and $y = 42$ for $\tan^{-1} x$ in terms of a and d yields $42 = a \tan^{-1} x + d$; so,

$\dfrac{42 - d}{a} = \tan^{-1}x$. We know that $y = 42$ is the upper horizontal asymptote and thus it corresponds to $y = \dfrac{\pi}{2}$.

So, $\dfrac{42 - d}{a} = \tan^{-1}x = \dfrac{\pi}{2} \Rightarrow \dfrac{42 - d}{a} = \dfrac{\pi}{2}$. Solving this for d in terms of a yields $d = 42 - \left(\dfrac{\pi}{2}\right)a.$

If $d = 24 + \left(\dfrac{\pi}{2}\right)a$ and $d = 42 - \left(\dfrac{\pi}{2}\right)a$, then

$24 + \left(\dfrac{\pi}{2}\right)a = 42 - \left(\dfrac{\pi}{2}\right)a$. So, $18 = \pi a$, and $a = \dfrac{18}{\pi}$.

Substitute this value for a into either of the two equations for d to get: $d = 24 + \left(\dfrac{\pi}{2}\right)\left(\dfrac{18}{\pi}\right) = 24 + 9 = 33$ or

$d = 42 - \left(\dfrac{\pi}{2}\right)\left(\dfrac{18}{\pi}\right) = 42 - 9 = 33.$

The arctangent function with horizontal asymptotes at $y = 24$ and $y = 42$ will be $y = \dfrac{18}{\pi} \tan^{-1}x + 33.$

70. (a) As in Example 5, θ can only be in Quadrant I or Quadrant IV, so the horizontal side of the triangle can only be positive.

(b) $\tan\left(\sin^{-1}\left(\dfrac{1}{x}\right)\right) = \dfrac{x}{s} = \dfrac{x}{\sqrt{x^4 - x^2}}$

(c) $\sin\left(\cos^{-1}\left(\dfrac{1}{x}\right)\right) = \dfrac{s}{x^2} = \dfrac{\sqrt{x^4 - x^2}}{x^2}$

(See figure below.)

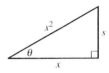

71. (a) The horizontal asymptote of the graph on the left is $y = \dfrac{\pi}{2}.$

(b) The two horizontal asymptotes of the graph on the right are $y = \dfrac{\pi}{2}$ and $y = \dfrac{3\pi}{2}.$

(c) The graph of $y = \cos^{-1}\left(\dfrac{1}{x}\right)$ will look like the graph on the left.

(d) The graph on the left is increasing on both connected intervals.

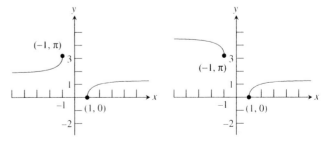

72. (a) The horizontal asymptote of the graph on the left is
$y = 0$.

(b) The two horizontal asymptotes of the graph on the
right are $y = 0$ and $y = \pi$.

(c) The graph of $y = \sin^{-1}\left(\dfrac{1}{x}\right)$ will look like the graph
on the left.

(d) The graph on the left is decreasing on both connected
intervals.

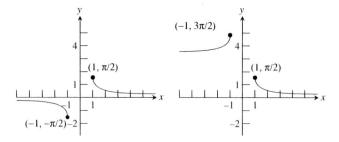

■ Section 4.8 Solving Problems with Trigonometry

Exploration 1

1. The parametrization should produce the unit circle.

2. The grapher is actually graphing the unit circle, but the
y-window is so large that the point never seems to get
above or below the x-axis. It is flattened vertically.

3. Since the grapher is plotting points along the unit circle,
it covers the circle at a constant speed. Toward the
extremes its motion is mostly vertical, so not much horizontal progress (which is all that we see) occurs. Toward
the middle, the motion is mostly horizontal, so it moves
faster.

4. The directed distance of the point from the origin at any
T is exactly $\cos T$, and $d = \cos t$ models simple harmonic
motion.

Quick Review 4.8

1. $b = 15 \cot 31° \approx 24.964$, $c = 15 \csc 31° \approx 29.124$

2. $a = 25 \cos 68° \approx 9.365$, $b = 25 \sin 68° \approx 23.180$

3. $b = 28 \cot 28° - 28 \cot 44° \approx 23.665$,
$c = 28 \csc 28° \approx 59.642$, $a = 28 \csc 44° \approx 40.308$

4. $b = 21 \cot 31° - 21 \cot 48° \approx 16.041$,
$c = 21 \csc 31° \approx 40.774$, $a = 21 \csc 48° \approx 28.258$

5. complement: 58°, supplement: 148°

6. complement: 17°, supplement: 107°

7. 45°

8. 202.5°

9. Amplitude: 3; period: π

10. Amplitude: 4; period: $\pi/2$

Section 4.8 Exercises

All triangles in the supplied figures are right triangles.

1. $\tan 60° = \dfrac{h}{300 \text{ ft}}$, so $h = 300 \tan 60° = 300\sqrt{3}$
≈ 519.62 ft.

2. $\tan 34°13'12'' = \dfrac{h}{100 \text{ ft}}$, so $h = 100 \tan 34°13'12''$
≈ 68.01

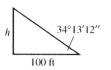

3. Let d be the length of the horizontal leg. Then $\tan 10°$
$= \dfrac{120 \text{ ft}}{d}$, so $d = \dfrac{120}{\tan 10°} = 120 \cot 10° \approx 680.55$ ft.

4. $\tan 14° = \dfrac{90 \text{ ft}}{d}$, so $d = \dfrac{90}{\tan 14°} = 90 \cot 14° \approx 361$ ft.

5. Let ℓ be the wire length (the hypotenuse); then
$\cos 80° = \dfrac{5 \text{ ft}}{\ell}$, so $\ell = \dfrac{5}{\cos 80°} = 5 \sec 80° \approx 28.79$ ft.

Let h be the tower height (the vertical leg); then
$\tan 80° = \dfrac{h}{5 \text{ ft}}$, so $h = 5 \tan 80° \approx 28.36$ ft.

6. $\cos 62° = \dfrac{16 \text{ ft}}{\ell}$, so $\ell = \dfrac{16}{\cos 62°} = 16 \sec 62° \approx 34.08$ ft.

$\tan 62° = \dfrac{h}{16 \text{ ft}}$, so $h = 16 \tan 62° \approx 30.09$ ft.

7. $\tan 80°1'12'' = \dfrac{h}{185 \text{ ft}}$, so $h = 185 \tan 80°1'12'' \approx$
1051 ft.

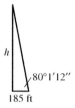

8. Let h be the height of the smokestack; then
$\tan 38° = \dfrac{h}{1580 \text{ ft}}$, so $h = 1580 \tan 38° \approx 1234.43$ ft.

9. $\tan 83°12' = \dfrac{h}{100 \text{ ft}}$, so $h = 100 \tan 83°12' \approx 839$ ft.

10. $\theta = \sin^{-1}\dfrac{32 \text{ ft}}{470 \text{ ft}} \approx 3.9°$

11. $\tan 55° = \dfrac{h}{10 \text{ m}}$, so $h = 10 \tan 55° \approx 14.3$ m

12. $\tan 29°48' = \dfrac{h}{125 \text{ ft}}$, so $h = 125 \tan 29°48' \approx 71.6$ ft

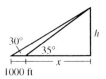

13. $\tan 35° = \dfrac{LP}{4.25 \text{ mi}}$, so $LP = 4.25 \tan 35° \approx 2.98$ mi.

14. $\tan 35° = \dfrac{h}{x}$ and $\tan 30° = \dfrac{h}{x + 1000}$, so $x = h \cot 35°$ and $x + 1000 = h \cot 30°$. Then $h \cot 35° = h \cot 30° - 1000$, so $h = \dfrac{1000}{\cot 30° - \cot 35°} \approx 3290.5$ ft.

15. Let x be the elevation of the bottom of the deck, and h be the height of the deck. Then $\tan 30° = \dfrac{x}{200 \text{ ft}}$ and $\tan 40° = \dfrac{x + h}{200 \text{ ft}}$, so $x = 200 \tan 30°$ ft and $x + h = 200 \tan 40°$ ft. Therefore $h = 200(\tan 40° - \tan 30°) \approx 52.35$ ft.

16. Let d be the distance traveled, and let x be car's ending distance from the base of the building. Then $\tan 15° = \dfrac{100 \text{ ft}}{d + x}$ and $\tan 33° = \dfrac{100 \text{ ft}}{x}$, so $d + x = 100 \cot 15°$ ft and $x = 100 \cot 33°$ ft. Therefore $d = 100(\cot 15° - \cot 33°) \approx 219$ ft.

17. The two legs of the right triangle are the same length (30 knots · 2 hr = 60 naut mi), so both acute angles are 45°. The length of the hypotenuse is the distance: $60\sqrt{2} \approx 84.85$ naut mi. The bearing is $95° + 45° = 140°$.

18. The two legs of the right triangle are 40 knots · 2 hr = 80 naut mi and 40 knots · 4 hr = 160 naut mi. The distance can be found with the Pythagorean Theorem: $d = 80\sqrt{5} \approx 178.885$ naut mi. The acute angle at Fort Lauderdale has measure $\tan^{-1} 2$, so the bearing is $65° + \tan^{-1} 2 \approx 128.435°$ (see figure below)

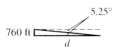

19. The difference in elevations is 1097 ft. If the width of the canyon is w, then $\tan 19° = \dfrac{1097 \text{ ft}}{w}$, so $w = 1097 \cot 19° \approx 3186$ ft.

20. The distance from the base of the tower d satisfies $\tan 1°20' = \dfrac{73 \text{ ft}}{d}$, so $d = 73 \cot 1°20' \approx 3136$ ft.

21. The acute angle in the triangle has measure $180° - 117° = 63°$, so $\tan 63° = \dfrac{\ell}{325 \text{ ft}}$. Then $\ell = 325 \tan 63° \approx 638$ ft.

22. $\tan 17° = \dfrac{h}{12 \text{ mi}}$, so $h = 12 \tan 17° \approx 3.67$ mi.

23. If h is the height of the vertical span, $\tan 15° = \dfrac{h}{36.5 \text{ ft}}$, so $h = 36.5 \tan 15° \approx 9.8$ ft.

24. The distance d satisfies $\tan 5.25° = \dfrac{760 \text{ ft}}{d}$, so $d = 760 \cot 5.25° \approx 8271$ ft.

25. Let d be the distance from the boat to the shore, and let x be the short leg of the smaller triangle. For the two triangles, the larger acute angles are 70° and 80°. Then $\tan 80° = \dfrac{d}{x}$ and $\tan 70° = \dfrac{d}{x + 550}$, or $x = d \cot 80°$ and $x + 550 = d \cot 70°$. Therefore $d = \dfrac{550}{\cot 70° - \cot 80°} \approx 2931$ ft.

26. If t is the time until the boats collide, the law enforcement boat travels $23t$ naut mi. During that same time, the smugglers' craft travels xt naut mi, where x is that craft's speed. These two distances are the legs of a right triangle (shown); then $\tan 15° = \dfrac{xt}{23t} = \dfrac{x}{23}$, so $x = 23 \tan 15° \approx 6.2$ knots.

27. (a) Frequency: $\dfrac{\omega}{2\pi} = \dfrac{16\pi}{2\pi} = 8$ cycles/sec.

   (b) $d = 6 \cos 16\pi t$ inches.

   (c) When $t = 2.85$, $d \approx 1.854$; this is about 4.1 in. left of the starting position (when $t = 0$, $d = 6$).

28. (a) Frequency: $\dfrac{\omega}{2\pi} = \dfrac{\pi}{2\pi} = \dfrac{1}{2}$ cycle/sec.

   (b) $d = 18 \cos \pi t$ cm.

   (c) Since 1 cycle takes 2 sec, there are 30 cycles/min.

29. The frequency is 2 cycles/sec, so $\omega = 2 \cdot 2\pi$
$= 4\pi$ radians/sec. Assuming the initial position is
$d = 3$ cm: $d = 3 \cos 4\pi t$.

30. $\dfrac{\omega}{2\pi} = 528$, so $\omega = 1056\pi$ radians/sec.

31. (a) The amplitude is $a = 25$ ft, the radius of the wheel.

   (b) $k = 33$ ft, the height of the center of the wheel.

   (c) $\dfrac{\omega}{2\pi} = \dfrac{1}{20}$ rotations/sec, so $\omega = \pi/10$ radians/sec.

32. (a) $\dfrac{\omega}{2\pi} = 3$ rpm $= \dfrac{1}{20}$ rotations/sec, so $\omega = \pi/10$.

   One possibility is $h = -8 \cos \dfrac{\pi t}{10} + 9$ m.

   (b)

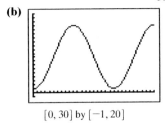

   [0, 30] by [−1, 20]

   (c) $h(4) \approx 6.5$ m; $h(10) = 17$ m.

33. (a) Given a period of 12, we have $12 = \dfrac{2\pi}{|b|}$.

   $12|b| = 2\pi$ so $|b| = \dfrac{2\pi}{12} = \dfrac{\pi}{6}$. We select the positive

   value so $b = \dfrac{\pi}{6}$.

   (b) Using the high temperature of 82 and a low tempera-
   ture of 48, we find $|a| = \dfrac{82 - 48}{2} = \dfrac{34}{2}$ so $|a| = 17$

   and we will select the positive value.

   $k = \dfrac{82 + 48}{2} = 65$

   (c) h is halfway between the times of the minimum and
   maximum. Using the maximum at time $t = 7$ and the

   minimum at time $t = 1$, we have $\dfrac{7 - 1}{2} = 3$. So,

   $h = 1 + 3 = 4$.

   (d) The fit is very good for $y = 17 \sin\left(\dfrac{\pi}{6}(t - 4)\right) + 65$.

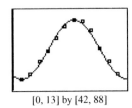

   [0, 13] by [42, 88]

   (e) There are several ways to find when the mean temperature will be 70°. *Graphical solution*: Graph the
   line $t = 70$ with the curve shown above, and find the
   intersection of the two curves. The two intersections
   are at $t \approx 4.57$ and $t \approx 9.43$.

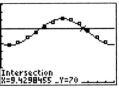

   [0, 13] by [42, 88]

   Algebraic solution: Solve $17 \sin\left(\dfrac{\pi}{6}(t - 4)\right) + 65 = 70$
   for t.

   $$17 \sin\left(\frac{\pi}{6}(t - 4)\right) + 65 = 70$$
   $$\sin\left(\frac{\pi}{6}(t - 4)\right) = \frac{5}{17}$$
   $$\frac{\pi}{6}(t - 4) = \sin^{-1}\left(\frac{5}{17}\right)$$
   $$\frac{\pi}{6}(t - 4) \approx 0.299, 2.842$$
   $$\text{Note: } \sin\theta = \sin(\pi - \theta)$$
   $$t \approx 4.57, 9.43$$

   Using either method to find t, find the day of the year
   as follows: $\dfrac{4.57}{12} \cdot 365 \approx 139$ and $\dfrac{9.43}{12} \cdot 365 \approx 287$.

   These represent May 19 and October 14.

34. (d) All have the correct period, but the others are incorrect
   in various ways. Equation (a) oscillates between −25
   and +25, while equation (b) oscillates between −17
   and +33. Equation (c) is the closest among the incorrect formulas: it has the right maximum and minimum
   values, but it does not have the property that $h(0) = 8$.
   This is accomplished by the horizontal shift in (d).

35. (a) Solve this graphically by finding the zero of the function

   $P = 2t - 7 \sin\left(\dfrac{\pi t}{3}\right)$. The zero occurs at approximately

   2.3. The function is positive to the right of the zero. So,
   the shop began to make a profit in March.

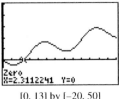

   [0, 13] by [−20, 50]

   (b) Solve this graphically by finding the maximum of the

   function $P = 2t - 7 \sin\left(\dfrac{\pi t}{3}\right)$. The maximum occurs

   at approximately 10.76, so the shop enjoyed its greatest profit in November.

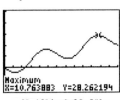

   [0, 13] by [−20, 50]

36. (a) Using the function $W = 220 - 1.5t + 9.81 \sin\left(\dfrac{\pi t}{4}\right)$,

where t is measured in months after January 1 of the first year and W is measured in pounds, we have $t = 0$ at the beginning. This gives

$W = 220 - 1.5(0) + 9.81 \sin\left(\dfrac{\pi \cdot 0}{4}\right) = 220$ pounds.

At the end of two years, $t = 24$, which gives

$W = 220 - 1.5(24) + 9.81 \sin\left(\dfrac{\pi \cdot 24}{4}\right) = 184$ pounds.

(b) Solve this graphically by finding the maximum of the function $W = 220 - 1.5t + 9.81 \sin\left(\dfrac{\pi t}{4}\right)$. The maximum occurs at $t = 1.75$, where $W \approx 227$.

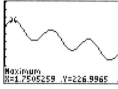

Maximum
X=1.7505259 Y=226.9965
[0, 24] by [150, 250]

(c) Solve this graphically by finding the minimum of the function $W = 220 - 1.5t + 9.81 \sin\left(\dfrac{\pi t}{4}\right)$. The minimum occurs at $t \approx 22.2$, where $W \approx 177$.

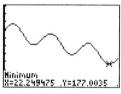

Minimum
X=22.249475 Y=177.0035
[0, 24] by [150, 250]

37. True. The frequency and the period are reciprocals: $f = 1/T$. So the higher the frequency, the shorter the period.

38. False. One nautical mile equals about 1.15 statute miles, and one knot is one nautical mile per hour. So, in the time that the car travels 1 statute mile, the ship travels about 1.15 statute miles. Therefore the ship is traveling faster.

39. If the building height in feet is x, then $\tan 58° = x/50$. So $x = 50 \tan 58° \approx 80$. The answer is D.

40. By the Law of Cosines, the distance is

$c = \sqrt{a^2 + b^2 - 2ab \cos \theta}$

$= \sqrt{40^2 + 20^2 + 2(40)(20) \cos 60°} \approx 53$ naut. mi.

The answer is B.

41. Model the tide level as a sinusoidal function of time, t. 6 hr, 12 min $= 372$ min is a half-period, and the amplitude is half of $13 - 9 = 4$. So use the model $f(t) = 2 \cos(\pi t/372) - 11$ with $t = 0$ at 8:15 PM. This takes on a value of -10 at $t = 124$. The answer is D.

42. The answer is A.

43. (a)

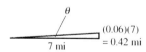

[0, 0.0062] by [−0.5, 1]

(b) The first is the best. This can be confirmed by graphing all three equations.

(c) About $\dfrac{2464}{2\pi} = \dfrac{1232}{\pi} \approx 392$ oscillations/sec.

44. (a) Newborn: about 6 hours. Four-year-old: about 24 hours. Adult: about 24 hours.

(b) The adult sleep cycle is perhaps most like a sinusoid, though one might also pick the newborn cycle. At least one can perhaps say that the four-year-old sleep cycles is *least* like a sinusoid.

45. The 7-gon can be split into 14 congruent right triangles with a common vertex at the center. The legs of these triangles measure a and 2.5. The angle at the center is $\dfrac{2\pi}{14} = \dfrac{\pi}{7}$, so $a = 2.5 \cot \dfrac{\pi}{7} \approx 5.2$ cm

46. The 7-gon can be split into 14 congruent right triangles with a common vertex at the center. The legs of these triangles measure a and 2.5, while the hypotenuse has length r. The angle at the center is $\dfrac{2\pi}{14} = \dfrac{\pi}{7}$, so

$r = 2.5 \csc \dfrac{\pi}{7} \approx 5.8$ cm

47. Choosing point E in the center of the rhombus, we have ΔAEB with right angle at E, and $m\angle EAB = 21°$. Then $AE = 18 \cos 21°$ in., $BE = 18 \sin 21°$ in., so that $AC = 2AE \approx 33.6$ in. and $BD = 2BE \approx 12.9$ in.

48. (a) $BE = 20 \tan 50° \approx 23.8$ ft.

(b) $CD = BE + 45 \tan 20° \approx 40.2$ ft.

(c) $AE + ED = 20 \sec 50° + 45 \sec 20° \approx 79$ ft, so the total distance across the top of the roof is about 158 ft.

49. $\theta = \tan^{-1} 0.06 \approx 3.4$

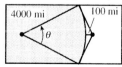

θ
(0.06)(7)
7 mi
= 0.42 mi

50. Observe that there are two (congruent) right triangles with hypotenuse 4100 mi (see figure below). The acute angle adjacent to the 4000 mi leg has measure $\cos^{-1} \dfrac{4000}{4100}$

$= \cos^{-1} \dfrac{40}{41}$, so $\theta = 2 \cos^{-1} \dfrac{40}{41} \approx 25.361°$

≈ 0.4426 radians. The arc length is $s = r\theta$

$\approx (4000 \text{ mi})(0.4426) \approx 1771$ mi.

4000 mi   100 mi
θ

51. (a)

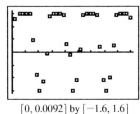

[0, 0.0092] by [−1.6, 1.6]

(b) One pretty good match is
$y = 1.51971 \sin[2467(t - 0.0002)]$ (that is,
$a = 1.51971, b = 2467, h = 0.0002$). Answers will
vary but should be close to these values. A good estimate of a can be found by noting the highest and lowest values of "Pressure" from the data. For the value
of b, note the time between maxima (approx.
$0.0033728 - 0.0008256 = 0.0025472$ sec); this is the
period, so $b \approx \dfrac{2\pi}{0.0025472} \approx 2467$. Finally, since
0.0008256 is the location of the first peak after $t = 0$,
choose h so that $2467(0.0008256 - h) \approx \dfrac{\pi}{2}$. This
gives $h \approx 0.0002$.

(c) Frequency: about $\dfrac{2467}{2\pi} \approx \dfrac{1}{0.0025472} \approx 393$ Hz.
It appears to be a G.

(d) Exercise 41 had $b \approx 2464$, so the frequency is again
about 392 Hz; it also appears to be a G.

■ Chapter 4 Review

1. On the positive y-axis (between quadrants I and II);
$\dfrac{5\pi}{2} \cdot \dfrac{180°}{\pi} = 450°$.

2. Quadrant II; $\dfrac{3\pi}{4} \cdot \dfrac{180°}{\pi} = 135°$.

3. Quadrant III; $-135° \cdot \dfrac{\pi}{180°} = -\dfrac{3\pi}{4}$.

4. Quadrant IV; $-45° \cdot \dfrac{\pi}{180°} = -\dfrac{\pi}{4}$.

5. Quadrant I; $78° \cdot \dfrac{\pi}{180°} = \dfrac{13\pi}{30}$.

6. Quadrant II; $112° \cdot \dfrac{\pi}{180°} = \dfrac{28\pi}{45}$.

7. Quadrant I; $\dfrac{\pi}{12} \cdot \dfrac{180°}{\pi} = 15°$.

8. Quadrant II; $\dfrac{7\pi}{10} \cdot \dfrac{180°}{\pi} = 126°$.

9. $270°$ or $\dfrac{3\pi}{2}$ radians

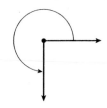

10. $900°$ or 5π radians

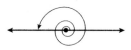

For #11–16, it may be useful to plot the given points and draw
the terminal side to determine the angle. Be sure to make
your sketch on a "square viewing window."

11. $\theta = \tan^{-1}\left(\dfrac{1}{\sqrt{3}}\right) = 30° = \dfrac{\pi}{6}$ radians

12. $\theta = 135° = \dfrac{3\pi}{4}$ radians

13. $\theta = 120° = \dfrac{2\pi}{3}$ radians

14. $\theta = 225° = \dfrac{5\pi}{4}$ radians

15. $\theta = 360° + \tan^{-1}(-2) \approx 296.565 \approx 5.176$ radians

16. $\theta = \tan^{-1} 2 \approx 63.435° \approx 1.107$ radians

17. $\sin 30° = \dfrac{1}{2}$ **18.** $\cos 330° = \dfrac{\sqrt{3}}{2}$

19. $\tan(-135°) = 1$ **20.** $\sec(-135°) = -\sqrt{2}$

21. $\sin \dfrac{5\pi}{6} = \dfrac{1}{2}$ **22.** $\csc \dfrac{2\pi}{3} = \dfrac{2}{\sqrt{3}}$

23. $\sec\left(-\dfrac{\pi}{3}\right) = 2$ **24.** $\tan\left(-\dfrac{2\pi}{3}\right) = \sqrt{3}$

25. $\csc 270° = -1$ **26.** $\sec 180° = -1$

27. $\cot(-90°) = 0$ **28.** $\tan 360° = 0$

29. Reference angle: $\dfrac{\pi}{6} = 30°$; use a 30–60 right triangle with
side lengths $\sqrt{3}$, $(-)1$, and 2 (hypotenuse).
$\sin\left(-\dfrac{\pi}{6}\right) = -\dfrac{1}{2}, \cos\left(-\dfrac{\pi}{6}\right) = \dfrac{\sqrt{3}}{2}, \tan\left(-\dfrac{\pi}{6}\right) = -\dfrac{1}{\sqrt{3}}$;
$\csc\left(-\dfrac{\pi}{6}\right) = -2, \sec\left(-\dfrac{\pi}{6}\right) = \dfrac{2}{\sqrt{3}}; \cot\left(-\dfrac{\pi}{6}\right) = -\sqrt{3}$.

30. Reference angle: $\dfrac{\pi}{4} = 45°$; use a 45–45 right triangle with
side lengths $(-)1, 1$, and $\sqrt{2}$ (hypotenuse).
$\sin \dfrac{19\pi}{4} = \dfrac{1}{\sqrt{2}}, \cos \dfrac{19\pi}{4} = -\dfrac{1}{\sqrt{2}}, \tan \dfrac{19\pi}{4} = -1$;
$\csc \dfrac{19\pi}{4} = \sqrt{2}, \sec \dfrac{19\pi}{4} = -\sqrt{2}; \cot \dfrac{19\pi}{4} = -1$.

31. Reference angle: $45°$; use a 45–45 right triangle with side
lengths $(-)1, (-)1$, and $\sqrt{2}$ (hypotenuse).
$\sin(-135°) = -\dfrac{1}{\sqrt{2}}, \cos(-135°) = -\dfrac{1}{\sqrt{2}}$,
$\tan(-135°) = 1; \csc(-135°) = -\sqrt{2}$,
$\sec(-135°) = -\sqrt{2}, \cot(-135°) = 1$.

32. Reference angle: $60°$; use a 30–60 right triangle with side
lengths $1, \sqrt{3}$, and 2 (hypotenuse).
$\sin 420° = \dfrac{\sqrt{3}}{2}, \cos 420° = \dfrac{1}{2}, \tan 420° = \sqrt{3}$;
$\csc 420° = \dfrac{2}{\sqrt{3}}, \sec 420° = 2, \cot 420° = \dfrac{1}{\sqrt{3}}$.

33. The hypotenuse length is 13 cm, so $\sin \alpha = \dfrac{5}{13}$, $\cos \alpha = \dfrac{12}{13}$, $\tan \alpha = \dfrac{5}{12}$, $\csc \alpha = \dfrac{13}{5}$, $\sec \alpha = \dfrac{13}{12}$, $\cot \alpha = \dfrac{12}{5}$.

For #34–35, since we are using a right triangle, we assume that θ is acute.

34. Draw a right triangle with legs 5 (adjacent) and $\sqrt{7^2 - 5^2} = \sqrt{24} = 2\sqrt{6}$, and hypotenuse 7.
$\sin \theta = \dfrac{2\sqrt{6}}{7}$, $\cos \theta = \dfrac{5}{7}$, $\tan \theta = \dfrac{2\sqrt{6}}{5}$; $\csc \theta = \dfrac{7}{2\sqrt{6}}$, $\sec \theta = \dfrac{7}{5}$, $\cot \theta = \dfrac{5}{2\sqrt{6}}$.

35. Draw a right triangle with legs 8 (adjacent) and 15, and hypotenuse $\sqrt{8^2 + 15^2} = \sqrt{289} = 17$.
$\sin \theta = \dfrac{15}{17}$, $\cos \theta = \dfrac{8}{17}$, $\tan \theta = \dfrac{15}{8}$; $\csc \theta = \dfrac{17}{15}$, $\sec \theta = \dfrac{17}{8}$, $\cot \theta = \dfrac{8}{15}$.

36. $\theta \approx 64.623°$

37. $x \approx 4.075$ radians

38. $x \approx 0.220$ or $x \approx 2.922$ radians

For #39–44, choose whichever of the following formulas is appropriate:

$$a = \sqrt{c^2 - b^2} = c \sin \alpha = c \cos \beta = b \tan \alpha = \dfrac{b}{\tan \beta}$$

$$b = \sqrt{c^2 - a^2} = c \cos \alpha = c \sin \beta = a \tan \beta = \dfrac{a}{\tan \alpha}$$

$$c = \sqrt{a^2 + b^2} = \dfrac{a}{\cos \beta} = \dfrac{a}{\sin \alpha} = \dfrac{b}{\sin \beta} = \dfrac{b}{\cos \alpha}$$

If one angle is given, subtract from 90° to find the other angle. If neither α nor β is given, find the value of one of the trigonometric functions, then use a calculator to approximate the value of one angle, then subtract from 90° to find the other.

39. $a = c \sin \alpha = 15 \sin 35° \approx 8.604$, $b = c \cos \alpha = 15 \cos 35° \approx 12.287$, $\beta = 90° - \alpha = 55°$

40. $a = \sqrt{c^2 - b^2} = \sqrt{10^2 - 8^2} = 6$. For the angles, we know $\cos \alpha = \dfrac{8}{10} = \dfrac{4}{5}$; using a calculator, we find $\alpha \approx 36.87°$, so that $\beta = 90° - \alpha \approx 53.13°$.

41. $b = a \tan \beta = 7 \tan 48° \approx 7.774$, $c = \dfrac{a}{\cos \beta} = \dfrac{7}{\cos 48°} \approx 10.461$, $\alpha = 90° - \beta = 42°$

42. $a = c \sin \alpha = 8 \sin 28° \approx 3.756$, $b = c \cos \alpha \approx 8 \cos 28° = 7.064$, $\beta = 90° - \alpha = 62°$

43. $a = \sqrt{c^2 - b^2} = \sqrt{7^2 - 5^2} = \sqrt{24} = 2\sqrt{6} \approx 4.90$. For the angles, we know $\cos \alpha = \dfrac{5}{7}$; using a calculator, we find $\alpha \approx 44.42°$, so that $\beta = 90° - \alpha \approx 45.58°$.

44. $c = \sqrt{a^2 + b^2} = \sqrt{2.5^2 + 7.3^2} = \sqrt{59.54} \approx 7.716$. For the angles, we know $\tan \alpha = \dfrac{2.5}{7.3}$; using a calculator, we find $\alpha \approx 18.90°$, so that $\beta = 90° - \alpha \approx 71.10°$.

45. $\sin x < 0$ and $\cos x < 0$: Quadrant III

46. $\cos x < 0$ and $\dfrac{1}{\sin x} > 0$: Quadrant II

47. $\sin x > 0$ and $\cos x < 0$: Quadrant II

48. $\dfrac{1}{\cos x} < 0$ and $\dfrac{1}{\sin x} > 0$: Quadrant II

49. The distance $OP = 3\sqrt{5}$, so $\sin \theta = \dfrac{2}{\sqrt{5}}$, $\cos \theta = -\dfrac{1}{\sqrt{5}}$, $\tan \theta = -2$; $\csc \theta = \dfrac{\sqrt{5}}{2}$, $\sec \theta = -\sqrt{5}$, $\cot \theta = -\dfrac{1}{2}$.

50. $OP = \sqrt{193}$, so $\sin \theta = \dfrac{7}{\sqrt{193}}$, $\cos \theta = \dfrac{12}{\sqrt{193}}$, $\tan \theta = \dfrac{7}{12}$; $\csc \theta = \dfrac{\sqrt{193}}{7}$, $\sec \theta = \dfrac{\sqrt{193}}{12}$, $\cot \theta = \dfrac{12}{7}$.

51. $OP = \sqrt{34}$, so $\sin \theta = -\dfrac{3}{\sqrt{34}}$, $\cos \theta = -\dfrac{5}{\sqrt{34}}$, $\tan \theta = \dfrac{3}{5}$; $\csc \theta = -\dfrac{\sqrt{34}}{3}$, $\sec \theta = -\dfrac{\sqrt{34}}{5}$, $\cot \theta = \dfrac{5}{3}$.

52. $OP = \sqrt{97}$, so $\sin \theta = \dfrac{9}{\sqrt{97}}$, $\cos \theta = \dfrac{4}{\sqrt{97}}$, $\tan \theta = \dfrac{9}{4}$; $\csc \theta = \dfrac{\sqrt{97}}{9}$, $\sec \theta = \dfrac{\sqrt{97}}{4}$, $\cot \theta = \dfrac{4}{9}$.

53. Starting from $y = \sin x$, translate left π units.

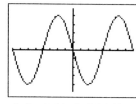

$[-2\pi, 2\pi]$ by $[-1.2, 1.2]$

54. Starting from $y = \cos x$, vertically stretch by 2 then translate up 3 units.

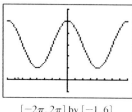

$[-2\pi, 2\pi]$ by $[-1, 6]$

55. Starting from $y = \cos x$, translate left $\dfrac{\pi}{2}$ units, reflect across x-axis, and translate up 4 units.

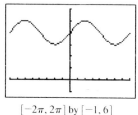

$[-2\pi, 2\pi]$ by $[-1, 6]$

56. Starting from $y = \sin x$, translate right π units, vertically stretch by 3, reflect across x-axis, and translate down 2 units.

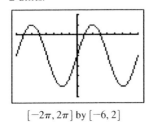

$[-2\pi, 2\pi]$ by $[-6, 2]$

57. Starting from $y = \tan x$, horizontally shrink by $\frac{1}{2}$.

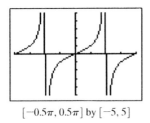

$[-0.5\pi, 0.5\pi]$ by $[-5, 5]$

58. Starting from $y = \cot x$, horizontally shrink by $\frac{1}{3}$, vertically stretch by 2, and reflect across x-axis (in any order).

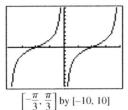

$\left[-\frac{\pi}{3}, \frac{\pi}{3}\right]$ by $[-10, 10]$

59. Starting from $y = \sec x$, horizontally stretch by 2, vertically stretch by 2, and reflect across x-axis (in any order).

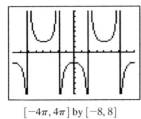

$[-4\pi, 4\pi]$ by $[-8, 8]$

60. Starting from $y = \csc \pi x$, horizontally shrink by $\frac{1}{\pi}$.

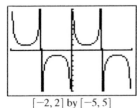

$[-2, 2]$ by $[-5, 5]$

For #61–66, recall that for $y = a \sin[b(x - h)]$ or $y = a \cos[b(x - h)]$, the amplitude is $|a|$, the period is $\frac{2\pi}{|b|}$, and the phase shift is h. The domain is always $(-\infty, \infty)$, and the range is $[-|a|, |a|]$.

61. $f(x) = 2 \sin 3x$. Amplitude: 2; period: $\frac{2\pi}{3}$; phase shift: 0; domain: $(-\infty, \infty)$; range: $[-2, 2]$.

62. $g(x) = 3 \cos 4x$. Amplitude: 3; period: $\frac{\pi}{2}$; phase shift: 0; domain: $(-\infty, \infty)$; range: $[-3, 3]$.

63. $f(x) = 1.5 \sin\left[2\left(x - \frac{\pi}{8}\right)\right]$. Amplitude: 1.5; period: π; phase shift: $\frac{\pi}{8}$; domain: $(-\infty, \infty)$; range: $[-1.5, 1.5]$.

64. $g(x) = -2 \sin\left[3\left(x - \frac{\pi}{9}\right)\right]$. Amplitude: 2; period: $\frac{2\pi}{3}$; phase shift: $\frac{\pi}{9}$; domain: $(-\infty, \infty)$; range: $[-2, 2]$.

65. $y = 4 \cos\left[2\left(x - \frac{1}{2}\right)\right]$. Amplitude: 4; period: π; phase shift: $\frac{1}{2}$; domain: $(-\infty, \infty)$; range: $[-4, 4]$.

66. $g(x) = -2 \cos\left[3\left(x + \frac{1}{3}\right)\right]$. Amplitude: 2; period: $\frac{2\pi}{3}$; phase shift: $-\frac{1}{3}$; domain: $(-\infty, \infty)$; range: $[-2, 2]$.

For #67–68, graph the function. Estimate a as the amplitude of the graph (i.e., the height of the maximum). Notice that the value of b is always the coefficient of x in the original functions. Finally, note that $a \sin[b(x - h)] = 0$ when $x = h$, so estimate h using a zero of $f(x)$ where $f(x)$ changes from negative to positive.

67. $a \approx 4.47$, $b = 1$, and $h \approx 1.11$, so $f(x) \approx 4.47 \sin(x - 1.11)$.

68. $a \approx 3.61$, $b = 2$, and $h \approx -1.08$, so $f(x) \approx 3.61 \sin[2(x + 1.08)]$.

69. $\approx 49.996° \approx 0.873$ radians

70. $\approx 61.380° \approx 1.071$ radians

71. $45° = \frac{\pi}{4}$ radians

72. $60° = \frac{\pi}{3}$ radians

73. Starting from $y = \sin^{-1} x$, horizontally shrink by $\frac{1}{3}$. Domain: $\left[-\frac{1}{3}, \frac{1}{3}\right]$. Range: $\left[-\frac{\pi}{2}, \frac{\pi}{2}\right]$.

74. Starting from $y = \tan^{-1} x$, horizontally shrink by $\frac{1}{2}$. Domain: $(-\infty, \infty)$. Range: $\left(-\frac{\pi}{2}, \frac{\pi}{2}\right)$.

75. Starting from $y = \sin^{-1} x$, translate right 1 unit, horizontally shrink by $\frac{1}{3}$, translate up 2 units. Domain: $\left[0, \frac{2}{3}\right]$. Range: $\left[2 - \frac{\pi}{2}, 2 + \frac{\pi}{2}\right]$.

76. Starting from $y = \cos^{-1} x$, translate left 1 unit, horizontally shrink by $\frac{1}{2}$, translate down 3 units. Domain: $[-1, 0]$. Range: $[-3, \pi - 3]$.

77. $x = \dfrac{5\pi}{6}$

78. $x = \dfrac{\pi}{6}$

79. $x = \dfrac{3\pi}{4}$

80. $\dfrac{5\pi}{3}$

81. $\dfrac{3\pi}{2}$

82. $\dfrac{5\pi}{6}$

83. As $|x| \to \infty$, $\dfrac{\sin x}{x^2} \to 0$.

84. As $x \to \infty$, $\dfrac{3}{5} e^{-x/12} \sin(2x - 3) \to 0$; as $x \to -\infty$, the function oscillates from positive to negative, and tends to ∞ in absolute value.

85. $\tan(\tan^{-1} 1) = \tan \dfrac{\pi}{4} = 1$

86. $\cos^{-1}\left(\cos \dfrac{\pi}{3}\right) = \cos^{-1} \dfrac{1}{2} = \dfrac{\pi}{3}$

87. $\tan(\sin^{-1} \dfrac{3}{5}) = \dfrac{\sin \theta}{\cos \theta}$, where θ is an angle in $\left[-\dfrac{\pi}{2}, \dfrac{\pi}{2}\right]$ with $\sin \theta = \dfrac{3}{5}$. Then $\cos \theta = \sqrt{1 - \sin^2 \theta} = \sqrt{0.64}$ $= 0.80$ and $\tan \theta = 0.75$

88. $\cos^{-1} \cos\left(-\dfrac{\pi}{7}\right) = -\dfrac{\pi}{7}$

89. Periodic; period π. Domain $x \neq \dfrac{\pi}{2} + n\pi, n$ an integer. Range: $[1, \infty)$.

90. Not periodic. Domain: $(-\infty, \infty)$. Range: $[-1, 1]$.

91. Not periodic. Domain: $x \neq \dfrac{\pi}{2} + n\pi, n$ an integer. Range: $[-\infty, \infty)$.

92. Periodic; period 2π. Domain: $(-\infty, \infty)$. Range: approximately $[-5, 4.65]$.

93. $s = r\theta = (2)\left(\dfrac{2\pi}{3}\right) = \dfrac{4\pi}{3}$

94. Draw a right triangle with horizontal leg x (if $x > 0$, draw the horizontal leg right; if $x < 0$, draw it left), vertically leg $\sqrt{1 - x^2}$, and hypotenuse 1. If $x > 0$, let θ be the acute angle adjacent to the horizontal leg; if $x < 0$, let θ be the supplement of this angle. Then $\theta = \cos^{-1} x$, so $\tan \theta = \tan(\cos^{-1} x) = \dfrac{\sqrt{1 - x^2}}{x}$.

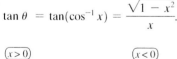

95. $\tan 78° = \dfrac{h}{100 \text{ m}}$, so $h = 100 \tan 78° \approx 470$ m.

96. $\tan 25° = \dfrac{h}{51 \text{ ft}}$, so $h = 51 \tan 25° \approx 23.8$ ft.

97. $\tan 42° = \dfrac{150 \text{ ft}}{x}$ and $\tan 18° = \dfrac{150 \text{ ft}}{d + x}$, so $x = 150 \cot 42°$ and $d + x = 150 \cot 18°$. Then $d = 150 \cot 18° - 150 \cot 42° \approx 295$ ft.

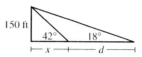

98. $\tan 22° = \dfrac{PQ}{4}$, so $PQ = 4 \tan 22° \approx 1.62$ mi.

99. See figure below.

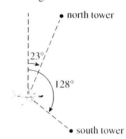

100. $\tan 25° = \dfrac{x}{d}$ and $\tan 33° = \dfrac{x + 855}{d}$, so $x = d \tan 25°$ and $x + 855 = d \tan 33°$. Then $d \tan 25° + 855 = d \tan 33°$, so $d = \dfrac{855}{\tan 33° - \tan 25°} \approx 4670$ ft.

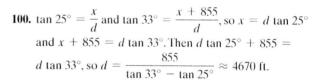

101. $\tan 72°24' = \dfrac{h}{62 \text{ ft}}$, so $h = 62 \tan 72°24' \approx 195.4$ ft

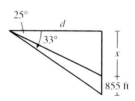

102. Let θ be the angle of elevation. Note that $\sin \theta = \dfrac{h}{75 \text{ ft}}$, so $h = 75 \sin \theta$.

(a) If $\theta = 22°$, then $h = 75 \sin 22° \approx 28$ ft.

(b) If $\theta = 27°$, then $h = 75 \sin 27° \approx 34$ ft.

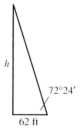

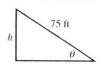

103. $s = r\theta = (44 \text{ in.})\left(6° \cdot \frac{\pi}{180°}\right) = \frac{22\pi}{15} \approx 4.6 \text{ in.}$

104. The blade sweeps out $\frac{110}{360} = \frac{11}{36}$ of a circle; take this fraction of (the area of a 20 in.-radius circle minus the area of a 4 in.-radius circle):

$$A = \frac{11}{36}[\pi(20)^2 - \pi(4)^2] = \frac{352\pi}{3} \approx 368.6 \text{ in}^2$$

105. *Solve algebraically*: Set $T(x) = 32$ and solve for x.

$$37.3 \sin\left[\frac{2\pi}{365}(x - 114)\right] + 26 = 32$$

$$\sin\left[\frac{2\pi}{365}(x - 114)\right] = \frac{6}{37.3}$$

$$\frac{2\pi}{365}(x - 114) = \sin^{-1}\left(\frac{6}{37.3}\right)$$

$$\frac{2\pi}{365}(x - 114) \approx 0.162, 2.98$$

Note: $\sin\theta = \sin(\pi - \theta)$

$$x \approx 123, 287$$

Solve graphically: Graph $T(x) = 32$ and

$$T(x) = 37.3 \sin\left[\frac{2\pi}{365}(x - 114)\right] + 25 \text{ on the same set}$$

of axes, and then determine the intersections.

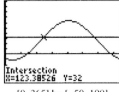 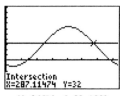

Intersection
X=123.30526 Y=32   Intersection
X=287.11474 Y=32

[0, 365] by [−50, 100]   [0, 365] by [−50, 100]

Using either method, we would expect the average temperature to be 32°F on day 123 (May 3) and day 287 (October 14).

106. Set $h(x) = 0$ and solve for x.

$$0 = 35 \cos\left(\frac{x}{35}\right) + 17$$

$$-\frac{17}{35} = \cos\frac{x}{35}$$

$$\frac{x}{35} = \cos^{-1}\left(-\frac{17}{35}\right) \approx 2.078 \text{ rad}$$

$$x = (35)(2.078)$$

$$x \approx 72.7 \text{ ft.}$$

Chapter 4 Project

Solutions are based on the sample data shown in the table.

1.

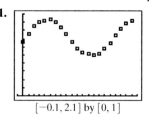

[−0.1, 2.1] by [0, 1]

2. The peak value seems to occur between $x = 0.4$ and $x = 0.5$, so let $h = 0.45$. The difference of the two extreme values is $0.931 - 0.495 = 0.436$, so let $a \approx 0.436/2 \approx 0.22$. The average of the two extreme values is $(0.931 + 0.495)/2 = 0.713$, so let $k = 0.71$. The time interval from $x = 0.5$ to $x = 1.3$, which equals 0.8, is right around a half-period, so let $b = \pi/0.8 \approx 3.93$. Then the equation is $y \approx 0.22 \cos(3.93(x - 0.45)) + 0.71$.

3. The constant a represents half the distance the pendulum bob swings as it moves from its highest point to its lowest point. And k represents the distance from the detector to the pendulum bob when it is in mid-swing.

4. Since the sine and cosine functions differ only by a phase shift, only h would change.

5. The regression yields $y \approx 0.22 \sin(3.87 x - 0.16) + 0.71$. Most calculator/computer regression models are expressed in the form $y = a \sin(bx + f) + k$, where $-f/b = h$ in the equation $y = a \sin(b(x - h)) + k$. Here, the regression equation can be rewritten as $y \approx 0.22 \sin(3.87(x - 0.04)) + 0.71$. The difference in the two values of h for the cosine and sine models is 0.41, which is right around a quarter-period, as it should be.

Chapter 5
Analytic Trigonometry

■ Section 5.1 Fundamental Identities

Exploration 1

1. $\cos\theta = 1/\sec\theta$, $\sec\theta = 1/\cos\theta$, and $\tan\theta = \sin\theta/\cos\theta$

2. $\sin\theta = 1/\csc\theta$ and $\tan\theta = 1/\cot\theta$

3. $\csc\theta = 1/\sin\theta$, $\cot\theta = 1/\tan\theta$, and $\cot\theta = \cos\theta/\sin\theta$

Quick Review 5.1

For #1–4, use a calculator.

1. 1.1760 rad $= 67.380°$

2. 0.9273 rad $= 53.130°$

3. 2.4981 rad $= 143.130°$

4. -0.3948 rad $= -22.620°$

5. $a^2 - 2ab + b^2 = (a - b)^2$

6. $4u^2 + 4u + 1 = (2u + 1)^2$

7. $2x^2 - 3xy - 2y^2 = (2x + y)(x - 2y)$

8. $2v^2 - 5v - 3 = (2v + 1)(v - 3)$

9. $\dfrac{1}{x} \cdot \dfrac{y}{y} - \dfrac{2}{y} \cdot \dfrac{x}{x} = \dfrac{y - 2x}{xy}$

10. $\dfrac{a}{x} \cdot \dfrac{y}{y} + \dfrac{b}{y} \cdot \dfrac{x}{x} = \dfrac{ay + bx}{xy}$

11. $\dfrac{x + y}{\dfrac{1}{x} + \dfrac{1}{y}} = (x + y) \cdot \left(\dfrac{xy}{x + y}\right) = xy$

12. $\dfrac{x}{x - y} \cdot \dfrac{x + y}{x + y} - \dfrac{y}{x + y} \cdot \dfrac{x - y}{x - y} = \dfrac{x^2 + y^2}{x^2 - y^2}$

Section 5.1 Exercises

1. $\sec^2\theta = 1 + \tan^2\theta = 1 + (3/4)^2 = 25/16$, so
$\sec\theta = \pm 5/4$. Then $\cos\theta = 1/\sec\theta = \pm 4/5$. But
$\sin\theta, \tan\theta > 0$ implies $\cos\theta > 0$. So $\cos\theta = 4/5$. Finally,

$$\tan\theta = \frac{3}{4}$$
$$\frac{\sin\theta}{\cos\theta} = \frac{3}{4}$$
$$\sin\theta = \frac{3}{4}\cos\theta = \frac{3}{4}\left(\frac{4}{5}\right) = \frac{3}{5}.$$

2. $\sec^2\theta = 1 + \tan^2\theta = 1 + 3^2 = 10$, so $\sec\theta = \pm\sqrt{10}$.
But $\cos\theta > 0$ implies $\sec\theta > 0$, so $\sec\theta = \sqrt{10}$. Finally,
$$\tan\theta = 3$$
$$\frac{\sec\theta}{\csc\theta} = 3$$
$$\csc\theta = \frac{1}{3}\sec\theta = \frac{1}{3}\sqrt{10} = \frac{\sqrt{10}}{3}.$$

3. $\tan^2\theta = \sec^2\theta - 1 = 4^2 - 1 = 15$, so $\tan\theta = \pm\sqrt{15}$.
But $\sec\theta > 0$, $\sin\theta < 0$ implies $\tan\theta < 0$, so

$\tan\theta = -\sqrt{15}$. And
$\cot\theta = 1/\tan\theta = -1/\sqrt{15} = -\sqrt{15}/15$.

4. $\sin^2\theta = 1 - \cos^2\theta = 1 - (0.8)^2 = 0.36$, so $\sin\theta = \pm 0.6$.
But $\cos\theta > 0$, $\tan\theta < 0$ implies $\sin\theta < 0$,
so $\sin\theta = -0.6$. Finally,
$\tan\theta = \sin\theta/\cos\theta = -0.6/0.8 = -0.75$.

5. $\cos(\pi/2 - \theta) = \sin\theta = 0.45$

6. $\cot\theta = \tan(\pi/2 - \theta) = -5.32$

7. $\cos(-\theta) = \cos\theta = \sin(\pi/2 - \theta)$
$= -\sin(\theta - \pi/2) = -0.73$

8. $\cot(-\theta) = -\cot\theta = -\tan(\pi/2 - \theta)$
$= \tan(\theta - \pi/2) = 7.89$

9. $\tan x \cos x = \dfrac{\sin x}{\cos x} \cdot \cos x = \sin x$

10. $\cot x \tan x = \dfrac{\cos x}{\sin x} \cdot \dfrac{\sin x}{\cos x} = 1$

11. $\sec y \sin\left(\dfrac{\pi}{2} - y\right) = \dfrac{1}{\cos y} \cdot \cos y = 1$

12. $\cot u \sin u = \dfrac{\cos u}{\sin u} \cdot \sin u = \cos u$

13. $\dfrac{1 + \tan^2 x}{\csc^2 x} = \dfrac{\sec^2 x}{\csc^2 x} = \dfrac{1/\cos^2 x}{1/\sin^2 x} = \dfrac{\sin^2 x}{\cos^2 x} = \tan^2 x$

14. $\dfrac{1 - \cos^2\theta}{\sin\theta} = \dfrac{\sin^2\theta}{\sin\theta} = \sin\theta$

15. $\cos x - \cos^3 x = \cos x(1 - \cos^2 x) = \cos x \sin^2 x$

16. $\dfrac{\sin^2 u + \tan^2 u + \cos^2 u}{\sec u} = \dfrac{1 + \tan^2 u}{\sec u} = \dfrac{\sec^2 u}{\sec u} = \sec u$

17. $\sin x \csc(-x) = \sin x \cdot \dfrac{1}{\sin(-x)} = -1$

18. $\sec(-x)\cos(-x) = \dfrac{1}{\cos(-x)} \cdot \cos(-x) = 1$

19. $\cot(-x)\cot\left(\dfrac{\pi}{2} - x\right) = \dfrac{\cos(-x)}{\sin(-x)} \cdot \dfrac{\cos\left(\dfrac{\pi}{2} - x\right)}{\sin\left(\dfrac{\pi}{2} - x\right)}$

$= \dfrac{\cos(-x)}{\sin(-x)} \cdot \dfrac{\sin(x)}{\cos(x)} = -1$

20. $\cot(-x)\tan(-x) = \dfrac{\cos(-x)}{\sin(-x)} \cdot \dfrac{\sin(-x)}{\cos(-x)} = 1$

21. $\sin^2(-x) + \cos^2(-x) = 1$

22. $\sec^2(-x) - \tan^2 x = \sec^2 x - \tan^2 x = 1$

23. $\dfrac{\tan\left(\dfrac{\pi}{2} - x\right)\csc x}{\csc^2 x} = \dfrac{\cot x}{\csc x} = \dfrac{\cos x}{\sin x} \cdot \dfrac{\sin x}{1} = \cos x$

24. $\dfrac{1 + \tan x}{1 + \cot x} \cdot \dfrac{\sin x \cos x}{\sin x \cos x} = \dfrac{\sin x \cos x + \sin^2 x}{\sin x \cos x + \cos^2 x}$

$\quad = \dfrac{\sin x(\cos x + \sin x)}{\cos x(\sin x + \cos x)} = \tan x$

25. $(\sec^2 x + \csc^2 x) - (\tan^2 x + \cot^2 x)$
$\quad = (\sec^2 x - \tan^2 x) + (\csc^2 x - \cot^2 x) = 1 + 1 = 2$

26. $\dfrac{\sec^2 u - \tan^2 u}{\cos^2 v + \sin^2 v} = \dfrac{1}{1} = 1$

27. $(\sin x)(\tan x + \cot x) = (\sin x)\left(\dfrac{\sin x}{\cos x} + \dfrac{\cos x}{\sin x}\right)$

$\quad = \sin x\left(\dfrac{\sin^2 x + \cos^2 x}{(\cos x)(\sin x)}\right) = \dfrac{1}{\cos x} = \sec x$

28. $\sin \theta - \tan \theta \cos \theta + \cos\left(\dfrac{\pi}{2} - \theta\right)$

$\quad = \sin \theta - \dfrac{\sin \theta}{\cos \theta} \cdot \cos \theta + \sin \theta = \sin \theta$

29. $(\sin x)(\cos x)(\tan x)(\sec x)(\csc x)$

$\quad = (\sin x)(\cos x)\left(\dfrac{\sin x}{\cos x}\right)\left(\dfrac{1}{\cos x}\right)\left(\dfrac{1}{\sin x}\right) = \dfrac{\sin x}{\cos x}$

$\quad = \tan x$

30. $\dfrac{(\sec y - \tan y)(\sec y + \tan y)}{\sec y}$

$\quad = \dfrac{\left(\dfrac{1}{\cos y} - \dfrac{\sin y}{\cos y}\right)\left(\dfrac{1}{\cos y} + \dfrac{\sin y}{\cos y}\right)}{\left(\dfrac{1}{\cos y}\right)}$

$\quad = \dfrac{1 + \sin y - \sin y - \sin^2 y}{\cos^2 y} \cdot \dfrac{\cos y}{1} = \dfrac{1 - \sin^2 y}{\cos y}$

$\quad = \dfrac{\cos^2 y}{\cos y} = \cos y$

31. $\dfrac{\tan x}{\csc^2 x} + \dfrac{\tan x}{\sec^2 x}$

$\quad = \left(\dfrac{\sin x}{\cos x}\right)(\sin^2 x) + \left(\dfrac{\sin x}{\cos x}\right) \cdot \cos^2 x$

$\quad = \left(\dfrac{\sin x}{\cos x}\right)(\sin^2 x + \cos^2 x) = \dfrac{\sin x}{\cos x} = \tan x.$

32. $\dfrac{\sec^2 x \csc x}{\sec^2 x + \csc^2 x} = \dfrac{\left(\dfrac{1}{\cos^2 x} \cdot \dfrac{1}{\sin x}\right)}{\left(\dfrac{1}{\cos^2 x}\right) + \left(\dfrac{1}{\sin^2 x}\right)}$

$\quad = \dfrac{1}{\cos^2 x \cdot \sin x} \cdot \dfrac{\cos^2 x \sin^2 x}{\sin^2 x + \cos^2 x} = \dfrac{\sin x}{1} = \sin x$

33. $\dfrac{1}{\sin^2 x} + \dfrac{\sec^2 x}{\tan^2 x} = \csc^2 x + \dfrac{1}{\cos^2 x\left(\dfrac{\sin^2 x}{\cos^2 x}\right)}$

$\quad = \csc^2 x + \dfrac{1}{\sin^2 x} = 2\csc^2 x$

34. $\dfrac{1}{1 - \sin x} + \dfrac{1}{1 + \sin x}$

$\quad = \dfrac{1 + \sin x}{(1 - \sin x)(1 + \sin x)} + \dfrac{1 - \sin x}{(1 - \sin x)(1 + \sin x)}$

$\quad = \dfrac{2}{1 - \sin^2 x} = \dfrac{2}{\cos^2 x} = 2\sec^2 x$

35. $\dfrac{\sin x}{\cot^2 x} - \dfrac{\sin x}{\cos^2 x} = (\sin x)(\tan^2 x) - (\sin x)(\sec^2 x)$

$\quad = (\sin x)(\tan^2 x - \sec^2 x) = (\sin x)(-1) = -\sin x$

36. $\dfrac{1}{\sec x - 1} - \dfrac{1}{\sec x + 1} = \dfrac{\sec x + 1 - \sec x + 1}{\sec^2 x - 1}$

$\quad = \dfrac{2}{\tan^2 x} = 2\cot^2 x$

37. $\dfrac{\sec x}{\sin x} - \dfrac{\sin x}{\cos x} = \dfrac{\sec x \cos x - \sin^2 x}{\sin x \cos x} = \dfrac{1 - \sin^2 x}{\sin x \cos x}$

$\quad = \dfrac{\cos^2 x}{\sin x \cos x} = \dfrac{\cos x}{\sin x} = \cot x$

38. $\dfrac{\sin x}{1 - \cos x} + \dfrac{1 - \cos x}{\sin x} = \dfrac{\sin^2 x + (1 - \cos x)^2}{\sin x(1 - \cos x)}$

$\quad = \dfrac{\sin^2 x + \cos x^2 + 1 - 2\cos x}{\sin x(1 - \cos x)} = \dfrac{2(1 - \cos x)}{\sin x(1 - \cos x)}$

$\quad = 2\csc x$

39. $\cos^2 x + 2\cos x + 1 = (\cos x + 1)^2$

40. $1 - 2\sin x + \sin^2 x = (1 - \sin x)^2$

41. $1 - 2\sin x + (1 - \cos^2 x) = 1 - 2\sin x + \sin^2 x$
$\quad = (1 - \sin x)^2$

42. $\sin x - \cos^2 x - 1 = \sin x + \sin^2 x - 2$
$\quad = (\sin x - 1)(\sin x + 2)$

43. $\cos x - 2\sin^2 x + 1 = \cos x - 2 + 2\cos^2 x + 1$
$\quad = 2\cos^2 x + \cos x - 1 = (2\cos x - 1)(\cos x + 1)$

44. $\sin^2 x + \dfrac{2}{\csc x} + 1 = \sin^2 x + 2\sin x + 1$
$\quad = (\sin x + 1)^2$

45. $4\tan^2 x - \dfrac{4}{\cot x} + \sin x \csc x$

$\quad = 4\tan^2 x - 4\tan x + \sin x \cdot \dfrac{1}{\sin x}$

$\quad = 4\tan^2 x - 4\tan x + 1 = (2\tan x - 1)^2$

46. $\sec^2 x - \sec x + \tan^2 x = \sec^2 x - \sec x + \sec^2 x - 1$
$\quad = 2\sec^2 x - \sec x - 1 = (2\sec x + 1)(\sec x - 1)$

47. $\dfrac{1 - \sin^2 x}{1 + \sin x} = \dfrac{(1 - \sin x)(1 + \sin x)}{1 + \sin x} = 1 - \sin x$

48. $\dfrac{\tan^2 \alpha - 1}{1 + \tan \alpha} = \dfrac{(\tan \alpha - 1)(\tan \alpha + 1)}{1 + \tan \alpha} = \tan \alpha - 1$

49. $\dfrac{\sin^2 x}{1 + \cos x} = \dfrac{1 - \cos^2 x}{1 + \cos x} = \dfrac{(1 - \cos x)(1 + \cos x)}{1 + \cos x}$

$\quad = 1 - \cos x$

50. $\dfrac{\tan^2 x}{\sec x + 1} = \dfrac{\sec^2 x - 1}{\sec x + 1} = \dfrac{(\sec x - 1)(\sec x + 1)}{\sec x + 1}$

$\quad = \sec x - 1$

51. $(\cos x)(2\sin x - 1) = 0$, so either $\cos x = 0$ or

$\quad \sin x = \dfrac{1}{2}$. Then $x = \dfrac{\pi}{2} + n\pi$ or $x = \dfrac{\pi}{6} + 2n\pi$ or

$\quad x = \dfrac{5\pi}{6} + 2n\pi$, n an integer. On the interval:

$\quad x = \left\{\dfrac{\pi}{6}, \dfrac{\pi}{2}, \dfrac{5\pi}{6}, \dfrac{3\pi}{2}\right\}$

52. $(\tan x)(\sqrt{2}\cos x - 1) = 0$, so either $\tan x = 0$ or
$\cos x = \dfrac{1}{\sqrt{2}}$. Then $x = n\pi$ or $x = \pm\dfrac{\pi}{4} + 2n\pi$, n an
integer. On the interval: $x = \left\{0, \dfrac{\pi}{4}, \pi, \dfrac{7\pi}{4}\right\}$

53. $(\tan x)(\sin^2 x - 1) = 0$, so either $\tan x = 0$ or
$\sin^2 x = 1$. Then $x = n\pi$ or $x = \dfrac{\pi}{2} + n\pi$, n an interger.
However, $\tan x$ excludes $x = \dfrac{\pi}{2} + n\pi$, so we have only
$x = n\pi$, n an integer. On the interval: $x = \{0, \pi\}$

54. $(\sin x)(\tan^2 x - 1) = 0$, so either $\sin x = 0$
or $\tan^2 x = 1$.
Then $x = n\pi$ or $x = \dfrac{\pi}{4} + n\dfrac{\pi}{2}$, n an integer. Put another
way, all multiples of $\dfrac{\pi}{4}$ except for $\pm\dfrac{\pi}{2}, \pm\dfrac{3\pi}{2}$, etc.
On the interval: $x = \left\{0, \dfrac{\pi}{4}, \dfrac{3\pi}{4}, \pi, \dfrac{5\pi}{4}, \dfrac{7\pi}{4}\right\}$

55. $\tan x = \pm\sqrt{3}$, so $x = \pm\dfrac{\pi}{3} + n\pi$, n an integer.
On the interval: $x = \left\{\dfrac{\pi}{3}, \dfrac{2\pi}{3}, \dfrac{4\pi}{3}, \dfrac{5\pi}{3}\right\}$

56. $\sin x = \pm\dfrac{1}{\sqrt{2}}$, so $x = \dfrac{\pi}{4} + n\dfrac{\pi}{2}$, n an integer.
On the interval: $x = \left\{\dfrac{\pi}{4}, \dfrac{3\pi}{4}, \dfrac{5\pi}{4}, \dfrac{7\pi}{4}\right\}$

57. $(2\cos x - 1)^2 = 0$, so $\cos x = \dfrac{1}{2}$; therefore
$x = \pm\dfrac{\pi}{3} + 2n\pi$, n an integer.

58. $(2\sin x + 1)(\sin x + 1) = 0$, so $\sin x = -\dfrac{1}{2}$ or
$\sin x = -1$. Then $x = -\dfrac{\pi}{6} + 2n\pi$, $x = -\dfrac{5\pi}{6} + 2n\pi$ or
$x = -\dfrac{\pi}{2} + 2n\pi$, n an integer.

59. $(\sin\theta)(\sin\theta - 2) = 0$, so $\sin\theta = 0$ or $\sin\theta = 2$. Then
$\theta = n\pi$, n an integer.

60. $3\sin t = 2 - 2\sin^2 t$, or $2\sin^2 t + 3\sin t - 2 = 0$. This
factors to $(2\sin t - 1)(\sin t + 2) = 0$, so $\sin t = \dfrac{1}{2}$ or
$\sin t = -2$. Then $t = \dfrac{\pi}{6} + 2n\pi$ or $t = \dfrac{5\pi}{6} + 2n\pi$,
n an integer.

61. $\cos(\sin x) = 1$ if $\sin x = n\pi$. Only $n = 0$ gives a value
between -1 and $+1$, so $\sin x = 0$, or $x = n\pi$, n an
integer.

62. This can be rewritten as $(2\sin x - 1)(\sin x + 2) = 0$, so
$\sin x = \dfrac{1}{2}$ or $\sin x = -2$. Then $x = \dfrac{\pi}{6} + 2n\pi$ or
$x = \dfrac{5\pi}{6} + 2n\pi$, n an integer. See also #60.

63. $\cos^{-1} 0.37 \approx 1.1918$, so the solution set is
$\{\pm 1.1918 + 2n\pi \mid n = 0, \pm 1, \pm 2, \dots\}$.

64. $\cos^{-1} 0.75 \approx 0.7227$, so the solution set is
$\{\pm 0.7227 + 2n\pi \mid n = 0, \pm 1, \pm 2, \dots\}$.

65. $\sin^{-1} 0.30 \approx 0.3047$ and $\pi - 0.3047 \approx 2.8369$, so the
solution set is $\{0.3047 + 2n\pi$ or $2.8369 + 2n\pi \mid n = 0,$
$\pm 1, \pm 2, \dots\}$.

66. $\tan^{-1} 5 \approx 1.3734$, so the solution set is $\{1.3734 + n\pi \mid$
$n = 0, \pm 1, \pm 2, \dots\}$.

67. $\sqrt{0.4} \approx 0.63246$, and $\cos^{-1} 0.63246 \approx 0.8861$, so the solution set is $\{\pm 0.8861 + n\pi \mid n = 0, \pm 1, \pm 2, \dots\}$.

68. $\sqrt{0.4} \approx 0.63246$ and $\sin^{-1} 0.63246 \approx 0.6847$, so the solution set is $\{\pm 0.6847 + n\pi \mid n = 0, \pm 1, \pm 2, \dots\}$.

69. $\sqrt{1 - \cos^2\theta} = |\sin\theta|$

70. $\sqrt{\tan^2\theta + 1} = |\sec\theta|$

71. $\sqrt{9\sec^2\theta - 9} = 3|\tan\theta|$

72. $\sqrt{36 - 36\sin^2\theta} = 6|\cos\theta|$

73. $\sqrt{81\tan^2\theta + 81} = 9|\sec\theta|$

74. $\sqrt{100\sec^2\theta - 100} = 10|\tan\theta|$

75. True. Since cosine is an even function, so is secant, and
thus $\sec(x - \pi/2) = \sec(\pi/2 - x)$, which equals $\csc x$
by one of the cofunction identities.

76. False. The domain of validity does not include values of θ
for which $\cos\theta = 0$ and $\tan\theta = \sin\theta/\cos\theta$ is undefined,
namely all odd integer multiples of $\pi/2$.

77. $\tan x \sec x = \tan x/\cos x = \sin x/\cos^2 x \neq \sin x$. The
answer is D.

78. sine, tangent, cosecant, and cotangent are odd, while
cosine and secant are even. The answer is A.

79. $(\sec\theta + 1)(\sec\theta - 1) = \sec^2\theta - 1 = \tan^2\theta$. The
answer is C.

80. By the quadratic formula, $3\cos^2 x + \cos x - 2 = 0$
implies
$$\cos x = \frac{-1 \pm \sqrt{1 - 4(3)(-2)}}{2(3)}$$
$$= -1 \text{ or } \frac{2}{3}$$
There are three solutions on the interval $(0, 2\pi)$. The
answer is D.

81. $\sin x$, $\cos x = \pm\sqrt{1 - \sin^2 x}$, $\tan x = \pm\dfrac{\sin x}{\sqrt{1 - \sin^2 x}}$,
$\csc x = \dfrac{1}{\sin x}$, $\sec x = \pm\dfrac{1}{\sqrt{1 - \sin^2 x}}$
$\cot x = \pm\dfrac{\sqrt{1 - \sin^2 x}}{\sin x}$

82. $\sin x = \pm\sqrt{1 - \cos^2 x}$, $\cos x$, $\tan x = \pm\dfrac{\sqrt{1 - \cos^2 x}}{\cos x}$,
$\csc x = \pm\dfrac{1}{\sqrt{1 - \cos^2 x}}$, $\sec x = \dfrac{1}{\cos x}$,
$\cot x = \pm\dfrac{\cos x}{\sqrt{1 - \cos^2 x}}$

83. The two functions are parallel to each other, separated by
1 unit for every x. At any x, the distance between the two
graphs is $\sin^2 x - (-\cos^2 x) = \sin^2 x + \cos^2 x = 1$.

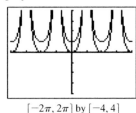

$[-2\pi, 2\pi]$ by $[-4, 4]$

84. The two functions are parallel to each other, separated by 1 unit for every x. At any x, the distance between the two graphs is $\sec^2 x - \tan^2 x = 1$.

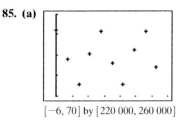

$[-2\pi, 2\pi]$ by $[-4, 4]$

85. (a)

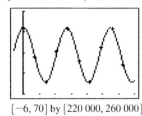

$[-6, 70]$ by $[220\,000, 260\,000]$

(b) The equation is
$$y = 13{,}111 \sin(0.22997x + 1.571) + 238{,}855.$$

$[-6, 70]$ by $[220\,000, 260\,000]$

(c) $(2\pi)/0.22998 \approx 27.32$ days. This is the number of days that it takes the Moon to make one complete orbit of the Earth (known as the Moon's sidereal period).

(d) 225,744 miles

(e) $y = 13{,}111 \cos(-0.22997x) + 238{,}855$, or
$y = 13{,}111 \cos(0.22997x) + 238{,}855$.

86. Answers will vary.

87. Factor the left-hand side:
$$\begin{aligned}
\sin^4 \theta - \cos^4 \theta &= (\sin^2 \theta - \cos^2 \theta)(\sin^2 \theta + \cos^2 \theta) \\
&= (\sin^2 \theta - \cos^2 \theta) \cdot 1 \\
&= \sin^2 \theta - \cos^2 \theta
\end{aligned}$$

88. Any k satisfying $k \geq 2$ or $k \leq -2$.

89. Use the hint:
$$\begin{aligned}
\sin(\pi - x) &= \sin(\pi/2 - (x - \pi/2)) \\
&= \cos(x - \pi/2) && \text{Cofunction identity} \\
&= \cos(\pi/2 - x) && \text{Since cos is even} \\
&= \sin x && \text{Cofunction identity}
\end{aligned}$$

90. Use the hint:
$$\begin{aligned}
\cos(\pi - x) &= \cos(\pi/2 - (x - \pi/2)) \\
&= \sin(x - \pi/2) && \text{Cofunction identity} \\
&= -\sin(\pi/2 - x) && \text{Since sin is odd} \\
&= -\cos x && \text{Cofunction identity}
\end{aligned}$$

91. Since A, B, and C are angles of a triangle, $A + B = \pi - C$. So: $\sin(A + B) = \sin(\pi - C)$
$$= \sin C$$

92. Using the identities from Exercises 69 and 70, we have:
$$\begin{aligned}
\tan(\pi - x) &= \frac{\sin(\pi - x)}{\cos(\pi - x)} \\
&= \frac{\sin x}{-\cos x} \\
&= -\tan x
\end{aligned}$$

■ Section 5.2 Proving Trigonometric Identities

Exploration 1

1. The graphs lead us to conclude that this is not an identity.

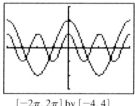

$[-2\pi, 2\pi]$ by $[-4, 4]$

2. For example, $\cos(2 \cdot 0) = 1$, whereas $2\cos(0) = 2$.

3. Yes.

4. The graphs lead us to conclude that this is an identity.

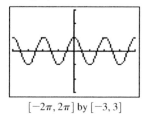

$[-2\pi, 2\pi]$ by $[-3, 3]$

5. No. The graph window can not show the full graphs, so they could differ outside the viewing window. Also, the function values could be so close that the graphs *appear* to coincide.

Quick Review 5.2

1. $\csc x + \sec x = \dfrac{1}{\sin x} + \dfrac{1}{\cos x} = \dfrac{\sin x + \cos x}{\sin x \cos x}$

2. $\tan x + \cot x = \dfrac{\sin x}{\cos x} + \dfrac{\cos x}{\sin x} = \dfrac{\sin^2 x + \cos^2 x}{\sin x \cos x}$
$$= \dfrac{1}{\sin x \cos x}$$

3. $\cos x \cdot \dfrac{1}{\sin x} + \sin x \cdot \dfrac{1}{\cos x} = \dfrac{\cos^2 x + \sin^2 x}{\sin x \cos x}$
$$= \dfrac{1}{\sin x \cos x}$$

4. $\sin\theta\cdot\dfrac{\cos\theta}{\sin\theta} - \cos\theta\cdot\dfrac{\sin\theta}{\cos\theta} = \cos\theta - \sin\theta$

5. $\dfrac{\sin x}{1/\sin x} + \dfrac{\cos x}{1/\cos x} = \sin^2 x + \cos^2 x = 1$

6. $\dfrac{1/\cos\alpha}{\cos\alpha} - \dfrac{\sin\alpha}{\cos^2\alpha/\sin\alpha} = \dfrac{1}{\cos^2\alpha} - \dfrac{\sin^2\alpha}{\cos^2\alpha}$

$= \dfrac{1 - \sin^2\alpha}{\cos^2\alpha} = 1$

7. No. (Any negative x.)

8. Yes.

9. No. (Any x for which $\sin x < 0$, e.g. $x = -\pi/2$.)

10. No. (Any x for which $\tan x < 0$, e.g. $x = -\pi/4$.)

11. Yes.

12. Yes.

Section 5.2 Exercises

1. One possible proof:
$$\dfrac{x^3 - x^2}{x} - (x-1)(x+1) = \dfrac{x(x^2 - x)}{x} - (x^2 - 1)$$
$$= x^2 - x - (x^2 - 1)$$
$$= -x + 1$$
$$= 1 - x$$

2. One possible proof:
$$\dfrac{1}{x} - \dfrac{1}{2} = \dfrac{1}{x}\left(\dfrac{2}{2}\right) - \dfrac{1}{2}\left(\dfrac{x}{x}\right)$$
$$= \dfrac{2}{2x} - \dfrac{x}{2x}$$
$$= \dfrac{2 - x}{2x}$$

3. One possible proof:
$$\dfrac{x^2 - 4}{x - 2} - \dfrac{x^2 - 9}{x + 3}$$
$$= \dfrac{(x+2)(x-2)}{x-2} - \dfrac{(x+3)(x-3)}{x+3}$$
$$= x + 2 - (x - 3)$$
$$= 5$$

4. One possible proof:
$$(x-1)(x+2) - (x+1)(x-2)$$
$$= x^2 + x - 2 - (x^2 - x - 2)$$
$$= x^2 + x - 2 - x^2 + x + 2$$
$$= 2x$$

5. $\dfrac{\sin^2 x + \cos^2 x}{\csc x} = \dfrac{1}{\csc x} = \sin x$. Yes.

6. $\dfrac{\tan x}{\sec x} = \dfrac{\sin x}{\cos x}\cdot\dfrac{\cos x}{1} = \sin x$. Yes.

7. $\cos x\cdot\cot x = \dfrac{\cos x}{1}\cdot\dfrac{\cos x}{\sin x} = \dfrac{\cos^2 x}{\sin x}$. No.

8. $\cos\left(x - \dfrac{\pi}{2}\right) = \cos\left(\dfrac{\pi}{2} - x\right) = \sin x$. Yes.

9. $(\sin^3 x)(1 + \cot^2 x) = (\sin^3 x)(\csc^2 x) = \dfrac{\sin^3 x}{\sin^2 x} = \sin x$. Yes.

10. No. Confirm graphically.

11. $(\cos x)(\tan x + \sin x\cot x)$
$$= \cos x\cdot\dfrac{\sin x}{\cos x} + \cos x\sin x\cdot\dfrac{\cos x}{\sin x} = \sin x + \cos^2 x$$

12. $(\sin x)(\cot x + \cos x\tan x)$
$$= \sin x\cdot\dfrac{\cos x}{\sin x} + \sin x\cos x\cdot\dfrac{\sin x}{\cos x} = \cos x + \sin^2 x$$

13. $(1 - \tan x)^2 = 1 - 2\tan x + \tan^2 x$
$$= (1 + \tan^2 x) - 2\tan x = \sec^2 x - 2\tan x$$

14. $(\cos x - \sin x)^2 = \cos^2 x - 2\sin x\cos x + \sin^2 x$
$$= (\cos^2 x + \sin^2 x) - 2\sin x\cos x = 1 - 2\sin x\cos x$$

15. One possible proof:
$$\dfrac{(1 - \cos u)(1 + \cos u)}{\cos^2 u} = \dfrac{1 - \cos^2 u}{\cos^2 u}$$
$$= \dfrac{\sin^2 u}{\cos^2 u}$$
$$= \tan^2 u$$

16. $\tan x + \sec x = \dfrac{\sin x}{\cos x} + \dfrac{1}{\cos x} = \dfrac{\sin x + 1}{\cos x}$
$$= \dfrac{\cos x(\sin x + 1)}{\cos^2 x} = \dfrac{\cos x(\sin x + 1)}{1 - \sin^2 x} = \dfrac{\cos x}{1 - \sin x}$$

17. $\dfrac{\cos^2 x - 1}{\cos x} = \dfrac{-\sin^2 x}{\cos x} = -\dfrac{\sin x}{\cos x}\cdot\sin x = -\tan x\sin x$

18. $\dfrac{\sec^2\theta - 1}{\sin\theta} = \dfrac{\tan^2\theta}{\sin\theta} = \dfrac{1}{\sin\theta}\cdot\left(\dfrac{\sin\theta}{\cos\theta}\right)^2 = \dfrac{\sin\theta}{\cos^2\theta}$
$$= \dfrac{\sin\theta}{1 - \sin^2\theta}$$

19. Multiply out the expression on the left side.

20. $\dfrac{1}{1 - \cos x} + \dfrac{1}{1 + \cos x} = \dfrac{(1 + \cos x) + (1 - \cos x)}{(1 - \cos x)(1 + \cos x)}$
$$= \dfrac{2}{1 - \cos^2 x} = \dfrac{2}{\sin^2 x} = 2\csc^2 x$$

21. $(\cos t - \sin t)^2 + (\cos t + \sin t)^2$
$$= \cos^2 t - 2\cos t\sin t + \sin^2 t + \cos^2 t$$
$$+ 2\cos t\sin t + \sin^2 t = 2\cos^2 t + 2\sin^2 t = 2$$

22. $\sin^2\alpha - \cos^2\alpha = (1 - \cos^2\alpha) - \cos^2\alpha = 1 - 2\cos^2\alpha$

23. $\dfrac{1 + \tan^2 x}{\sin^2 x + \cos^2 x} = \dfrac{\sec^2 x}{1} = \sec^2 x$

24. $\dfrac{1}{\tan\beta} + \tan\beta = \dfrac{\cos\beta}{\sin\beta} + \dfrac{\sin\beta}{\cos\beta} = \dfrac{\cos^2\beta + \sin^2\beta}{\cos\beta\sin\beta}$
$$= \dfrac{1}{\cos\beta\sin\beta} = \sec\beta\csc\beta$$

25. $\dfrac{\cos\beta}{1 + \sin\beta} = \dfrac{\cos^2\beta}{\cos\beta(1 + \sin\beta)} = \dfrac{1 - \sin^2\beta}{\cos\beta(1 + \sin\beta)}$
$$= \dfrac{(1 - \sin\beta)(1 + \sin\beta)}{\cos\beta(1 + \sin\beta)} = \dfrac{1 - \sin\beta}{\cos\beta}$$

26. One possible proof:
$$\dfrac{\sec x + 1}{\tan x} = \dfrac{(\sec x + 1)(\sec x - 1)}{\tan x(\sec x - 1)}$$
$$= \dfrac{\sec^2 x - 1}{\tan x(\sec x - 1)}$$
$$= \dfrac{\tan^2 x}{\tan x(\sec x - 1)} = \dfrac{\dfrac{\sin x}{\cos x}}{\dfrac{1}{\cos x} - 1}\cdot\dfrac{\cos x}{\cos x}$$
$$= \dfrac{\sin x}{1 - \cos x}$$

27. $\dfrac{\tan^2 x}{\sec x + 1} = \dfrac{\sec^2 x - 1}{\sec x + 1} = \sec x - 1 = \dfrac{1}{\cos x} - 1$

$\quad = \dfrac{1 - \cos x}{\cos x}$

28. $\dfrac{\cot v - 1}{\cot v + 1} = \dfrac{\cot v - 1}{\cot v + 1} \cdot \dfrac{\tan v}{\tan v} = \dfrac{\cot v \tan v - \tan v}{\cot v \tan v + \tan v}$

$\quad = \dfrac{1 - \tan v}{1 + \tan v}$ (Note: $\cot v \tan v = \dfrac{\cos v}{\sin v} \cdot \dfrac{\sin v}{\cos v} = 1$)

29. $\cot^2 x - \cos^2 x = \left(\dfrac{\cos x}{\sin x}\right)^2 - \cos^2 x$

$\quad = \dfrac{\cos^2 x(1 - \sin^2 x)}{\sin^2 x} = \cos^2 x \cdot \dfrac{\cos^2 x}{\sin^2 x}$

$\quad = \cos^2 x \cot^2 x$

30. $\tan^2 \theta - \sin^2 \theta = \left(\dfrac{\sin \theta}{\cos \theta}\right)^2 - \sin^2 \theta$

$\quad = \dfrac{\sin^2 \theta(1 - \cos^2 \theta)}{\cos^2 \theta} = \sin^2 \theta \cdot \dfrac{\sin^2 \theta}{\cos^2 \theta}$

$\quad = \sin^2 \theta \tan^2 \theta$

31. $\cos^4 x - \sin^4 x = (\cos^2 x + \sin^2 x)(\cos^2 x - \sin^2 x)$

$\quad = 1(\cos^2 x - \sin^2 x) = \cos^2 x - \sin^2 x$

32. $\tan^4 t + \tan^2 t = \tan^2 t(\tan^2 t + 1) = (\sec^2 t - 1)(\sec^2 t)$

$\quad = \sec^4 t - \sec^2 t$

33. $(x \sin \alpha + y \cos \alpha)^2 + (x \cos \alpha - y \sin \alpha)^2$

$\quad = (x^2 \sin^2 \alpha + 2xy \sin \alpha \cos \alpha + y^2 \cos^2 \alpha)$

$\quad\quad + (x^2 \cos^2 \alpha - 2xy \cos \alpha \sin \alpha + y^2 \sin^2 \alpha)$

$\quad = x^2 \sin^2 \alpha + y^2 \cos^2 \alpha + x^2 \cos^2 \alpha + y^2 \sin^2 \alpha$

$\quad = (x^2 + y^2)(\sin^2 \alpha + \cos^2 \alpha) = x^2 + y^2$

34. $\dfrac{1 - \cos \theta}{\sin \theta} = \dfrac{1 - \cos^2 \theta}{\sin \theta(1 + \cos \theta)} = \dfrac{\sin^2 \theta}{\sin \theta(1 + \cos \theta)}$

$\quad = \dfrac{\sin \theta}{1 + \cos \theta}$

35. $\dfrac{\tan x}{\sec x - 1} = \dfrac{\tan x(\sec x + 1)}{\sec^2 x - 1} = \dfrac{\tan x(\sec x + 1)}{\tan^2 x}$

$\quad = \dfrac{\sec x + 1}{\tan x}$. See also #26.

36. $\dfrac{\sin t}{1 + \cos t} + \dfrac{1 + \cos t}{\sin t} = \dfrac{\sin^2 t + (1 + \cos t)^2}{(\sin t)(1 + \cos t)}$

$\quad = \dfrac{\sin^2 t + 1 + 2 \cos t + \cos^2 t}{(\sin t)(1 + \cos t)} = \dfrac{2 + 2 \cos t}{(\sin t)(1 + \cos t)}$

$\quad = \dfrac{2}{\sin t} = 2 \csc t$

37. $\dfrac{\sin x - \cos x}{\sin x + \cos x} = \dfrac{(\sin x - \cos x)(\sin x + \cos x)}{(\sin x + \cos x)^2}$

$= \dfrac{\sin^2 x - \cos^2 x}{\sin^2 x + 2 \sin x \cos x + \cos^2 x} = \dfrac{\sin^2 x - (1 - \sin^2 x)}{1 + 2 \sin x \cos x}$

$\quad = \dfrac{2 \sin^2 x - 1}{1 + 2 \sin x \cos x}$

38. $\dfrac{1 + \cos x}{1 - \cos x} = \dfrac{1 + \cos x}{1 - \cos x} \cdot \dfrac{\sec x}{\sec x} = \dfrac{\sec x + \cos x \sec x}{\sec x - \cos x \sec x}$

$\quad = \dfrac{\sec x + 1}{\sec x - 1}$ (Note: $\cos x \sec x = \cos x \cdot \dfrac{1}{\cos x} = 1$.)

39. $\dfrac{\sin t}{1 - \cos t} + \dfrac{1 + \cos t}{\sin t} = \dfrac{\sin^2 t + (1 + \cos t)(1 - \cos t)}{(\sin t)(1 - \cos t)}$

$\quad = \dfrac{\sin^2 t + 1 - \cos^2 t}{(\sin t)(1 - \cos t)} = \dfrac{1 - \cos^2 t + 1 - \cos^2 t}{(\sin t)(1 - \cos t)}$

$\quad = \dfrac{2(1 - \cos^2 t)}{(\sin t)(1 - \cos t)} = \dfrac{2(1 + \cos t)}{\sin t}$

40. $\dfrac{\sin A \cos B + \cos A \sin B}{\cos A \cos B - \sin A \sin B}$

$\quad = \left(\dfrac{\dfrac{1}{\cos A \cos B}}{\dfrac{1}{\cos A \cos B}}\right) \cdot \dfrac{\sin A \cos B + \cos A \sin B}{\cos A \cos B - \sin A \sin B}$

$\quad = \dfrac{\dfrac{\sin A}{\cos A} + \dfrac{\sin B}{\cos B}}{1 - \dfrac{\sin A}{\cos A} \dfrac{\sin B}{\cos B}} = \dfrac{\tan A + \tan B}{1 - \tan A \tan B}$

41. $\sin^2 x \cos^3 x = \sin^2 x \cos^2 x \cos x$

$\quad = \sin^2 x(1 - \sin^2 x)\cos x = (\sin^2 x - \sin^4 x)\cos x$

42. $\sin^5 x \cos^2 x = \sin^4 x \cos^2 x \sin x$

$\quad = (\sin^2 x)^2 \cos^2 x \sin x = (1 - \cos^2 x)^2 \cos^2 x \sin x$

$\quad = (1 - 2 \cos^2 x + \cos^4 x)\cos^2 x \sin x$

$\quad = (\cos^2 x - 2 \cos^4 x + \cos^6 x)\sin x$

43. $\cos^5 x = \cos^4 x \cos x = (\cos^2 x)^2 \cos x$

$\quad = (1 - \sin^2 x)^2 \cos x = (1 - 2 \sin^2 x + \sin^4 x) \cos x$

44. $\sin^3 x \cos^3 x = \sin^3 x \cos^2 x \cos x$

$\quad = \sin^3 x (1 - \sin^2 x)\cos x = (\sin^3 x - \sin^5 x)\cos x$

45. $\dfrac{\tan x}{1 - \cot x} + \dfrac{\cot x}{1 - \tan x}$

$\quad = \dfrac{\tan x}{1 - \cot x} \cdot \dfrac{\sin x}{\sin x} + \dfrac{\cot x}{1 - \tan x} \cdot \dfrac{\cos x}{\cos x}$

$\quad = \left(\dfrac{\sin^2 x/\cos x}{\sin x - \cos x} + \dfrac{\cos^2 x/\sin x}{\cos x - \sin x}\right)\dfrac{\sin x \cos x}{\sin x \cos x}$

$\quad = \dfrac{\sin^3 x - \cos^3 x}{\sin x \cos x(\sin x - \cos x)}$

$\quad = \dfrac{\sin^2 x + \sin x \cos x + \cos^2 x}{\sin x \cos x}$

$\quad = \dfrac{1 + \sin x \cos x}{\sin x \cos x} = \dfrac{1}{\sin x \cos x} + 1 = \csc x \sec x + 1.$

This involves rewriting $a^3 - b^3$ as
$(a - b)(a^2 + ab + b^2)$, where $a = \sin x$ and $b = \cos x$.

46. $\dfrac{\cos x}{1 + \sin x} + \dfrac{\cos x}{1 - \sin x}$

$\quad = \dfrac{(\cos x)[(1 - \sin x) + (1 + \sin x)]}{(1 + \sin x)(1 - \sin x)} = \dfrac{2 \cos x}{1 - \sin^2 x}$

$\quad = \dfrac{2 \cos x}{\cos^2 x} = 2 \sec x$

47. $\dfrac{2\tan x}{1-\tan^2 x}+\dfrac{1}{2\cos^2 x-1}$

$=\dfrac{2\tan x}{1-\tan^2 x}\cdot\dfrac{\cos^2 x}{\cos^2 x}+\dfrac{1}{\cos^2 x-\sin^2 x}$

$=\dfrac{2\sin x\cos x}{\cos^2 x-\sin^2 x}+\dfrac{\cos^2 x+\sin^2 x}{\cos^2 x-\sin^2 x}$

$=\dfrac{2\sin x\cos x+\cos^2 x+\sin^2 x}{(\cos x-\sin x)(\cos x+\sin x)}$

$=\dfrac{(\cos x+\sin x)^2}{(\cos x-\sin x)(\cos x+\sin x)}=\dfrac{\cos x+\sin x}{\cos x-\sin x}$

48. $\dfrac{1-3\cos x-4\cos^2 x}{\sin^2 x}=\dfrac{(1+\cos x)(1-4\cos x)}{1-\cos^2 x}$

$=\dfrac{(1+\cos x)(1-4\cos x)}{(1+\cos x)(1-\cos x)}=\dfrac{1-4\cos x}{1-\cos x}$

49. $\cos^3 x=(\cos^2 x)(\cos x)=(1-\sin^2 x)(\cos x)$

50. $\sec^4 x=(\sec^2 x)(\sec^2 x)=(1+\tan^2 x)(\sec^2 x)$

51. $\sin^5 x=(\sin^4 x)(\sin x)=(\sin^2 x)^2(\sin x)$
$\qquad=(1-\cos^2 x)^2(\sin x)$
$\qquad=(1-2\cos^2 x+\cos^4 x)(\sin x)$

52. (b) — divide through by $\cos x$: $\dfrac{1+\sin x}{\cos x}$

$=\dfrac{1}{\cos x}+\dfrac{\sin x}{\cos x}=\sec x+\tan x.$

53. (d) — multiply out: $(1+\sec x)(1-\cos x)$
$=1-\cos x+\sec x-\sec x\cos x$
$=1-\cos x+\dfrac{1}{\cos x}-\dfrac{1}{\cos x}\cdot\cos x$
$=1-\cos x+\dfrac{1}{\cos x}-1=\dfrac{1-\cos^2 x}{\cos x}=\dfrac{\sin^2 x}{\cos x}$
$=\dfrac{\sin x}{\cos x}\cdot\sin x=\tan x\sin x.$

54. (a) — put over a common denominator:

$\sec^2 x+\csc^2 x=\left(\dfrac{1}{\cos x}\right)^2+\left(\dfrac{1}{\sin x}\right)^2$

$=\dfrac{\sin^2 x+\cos^2 x}{\cos^2 x\sin^2 x}=\dfrac{1}{\cos^2 x\sin^2 x}=\left(\dfrac{1}{\cos x}\cdot\dfrac{1}{\sin x}\right)^2$

$=\sec^2 x\csc^2 x.$

55. (c) — put over a common denominator:

$\dfrac{1}{1+\sin x}+\dfrac{1}{1-\sin x}=\dfrac{1-\sin x+1+\sin x}{1-\sin^2 x}$

$=\dfrac{2}{\cos^2 x}=2\sec^2 x.$

56. (e) — multiply and divide by $\sin x\cos x$: $\dfrac{1}{\tan x+\cot x}$

$=\dfrac{\sin x\cos x}{\left(\dfrac{\sin x}{\cos x}+\dfrac{\cos x}{\sin x}\right)(\sin x\cos x)}=\dfrac{\sin x\cos x}{\sin^2 x+\cos^2 x}$

$=\dfrac{\sin x\cos x}{1}=\sin x\cos x.$

57. (b) — multiply and divide by $\sec x+\tan x$:

$\dfrac{1}{\sec x-\tan x}\cdot\dfrac{\sec x+\tan x}{\sec x+\tan x}=\dfrac{\sec x+\tan x}{\sec^2 x-\tan^2 x}$

$=\dfrac{\sec x+\tan x}{1}.$

58. False. There are numbers in the domain of both sides of the equation for which equality does not hold, namely all negative real numbers. For example, $\sqrt{(-3)^2}=3$, not -3.

59. True. If x is in the domain of both sides of the equation, then $x\geq 0$. The equation $(\sqrt{x})^2=x$ holds for all $x\geq 0$, so it is an identity.

60. By the definition of identity, all three must be true. The answer is E.

61. A proof is

$\dfrac{\sin x}{1-\cos x}=\dfrac{\sin x}{1-\cos x}\cdot\dfrac{1+\cos x}{1+\cos x}$

$\qquad=\dfrac{\sin x\,(1+\cos x)}{1-\cos^2 x}$

$\qquad=\dfrac{\sin x\,(1+\cos x)}{\sin^2 x}$

$\qquad=\dfrac{1+\cos x}{\sin x}$

The answer is E.

62. One possible proof:

$\tan\theta+\sec\theta=\dfrac{\sin\theta}{\cos\theta}+\dfrac{1}{\cos\theta}$

$\qquad=\dfrac{\sin\theta+1}{\cos\theta}$

$\qquad=\dfrac{\sin\theta+1}{\cos\theta}\cdot\dfrac{\sin\theta-1}{\sin\theta-1}$

$\qquad=\dfrac{\sin^2\theta-1}{\cos\theta\,(\sin\theta-1)}$

$\qquad=\dfrac{-\cos^2\theta}{\cos\theta\,(\sin\theta-1)}$

$\qquad=\dfrac{-\cos\theta}{\sin\theta-1}$

$\qquad=\dfrac{\cos\theta}{1-\sin\theta}$

The answer is C.

63. k must equal 1, so $f(x)\neq 0$. The answer is B.

64. $\cos x$; $\sin x\cot x=\sin x\cdot\dfrac{\cos x}{\sin x}=\cos x$

65. $\sin x$; $\cos x\tan x=\cos x\cdot\dfrac{\sin x}{\cos x}=\sin x$

66. 1; $\dfrac{\sin x}{\csc x}+\dfrac{\cos x}{\sec x}=\dfrac{\sin x}{1/\sin x}+\dfrac{\cos x}{1/\cos x}$
$=\sin^2 x+\cos^2 x=1$

67. 1; $\dfrac{\csc x}{\sin x}-\dfrac{\cot x\csc x}{\sec x}=\dfrac{1/\sin x}{\sin x}-\dfrac{\cos x/\sin^2 x}{1/\cos x}$
$=\dfrac{1}{\sin^2 x}-\dfrac{\cos^2 x}{\sin^2 x}=\dfrac{1-\cos^2 x}{\sin^2 x}=\dfrac{\sin^2 x}{\sin^2 x}=1$

68. $\cos x$; $\dfrac{\sin x}{\tan x}=\dfrac{\sin x}{\sin x/\cos x}=\cos x.$

69. 1; $(\sec^2 x)(1-\sin^2 x)=\left(\dfrac{1}{\cos x}\right)^2(\cos^2 x)=1$

70. Since the sum of the logarithms is the logarithm of the product, and since the product of the absolute values of all six basic trig functions is 1, the logarithms sum to $\ln 1$, which is 0.

71. If A and B are complementary angles, then
$$\sin^2 A + \sin^2 B = \sin^2 A + \sin^2(\pi/2 - A)$$
$$= \sin^2 A + \cos^2 A$$
$$= 1$$

72. Check Exercises 11–51 for correct identities.

73. Multiply and divide by $1 - \sin t$ under the radical:

$$\sqrt{\frac{1 - \sin t}{1 + \sin t} \cdot \frac{1 - \sin t}{1 - \sin t}} = \sqrt{\frac{(1 - \sin t)^2}{1 - \sin^2 t}}$$

$$= \sqrt{\frac{(1 - \sin t)^2}{\cos^2 t}} = \frac{|1 - \sin t|}{|\cos t|} \text{ since } \sqrt{a^2} = |a|.$$

Now, since $1 - \sin t \geq 0$, we can dispense with the absolute value in the numerator, but it must stay in the denominator.

74. Multiply and divide by $1 + \cos t$ under the radical:

$$\sqrt{\frac{1 + \cos t}{1 - \cos t} \cdot \frac{1 + \cos t}{1 + \cos t}} = \sqrt{\frac{(1 + \cos t)^2}{1 - \cos^2 t}}$$

$$= \sqrt{\frac{(1 + \cos t)^2}{\sin^2 t}} = \frac{|1 + \cos t|}{|\sin t|} \text{ since } \sqrt{a^2} = |a|.$$

Now, since $1 + \cos t \geq 0$, we can dispense with the absolute value in the numerator, but it must stay in the denominator.

75. $\sin^6 x + \cos^6 x = (\sin^2 x)^3 + \cos^6 x$
$= (1 - \cos^2 x)^3 + \cos^6 x$
$= (1 - 3\cos^2 x + 3\cos^4 x - \cos^6 x) + \cos^6 x$
$= 1 - 3\cos^2 x(1 - \cos^2 x) = 1 - 3\cos^2 x \sin^2 x.$

76. Note that $a^3 - b^3 = (a - b)(a^2 + ab + b^2)$. Also note that $a^2 + ab + b^2 = a^2 + 2ab + b^2 - ab$
$= (a + b)^2 - ab$. Taking $a = \cos^2 x$ and $b = \sin^2 x$, we have $\cos^6 x - \sin^6 x$
$= (\cos^2 x - \sin^2 x)(\cos^4 x + \cos^2 x \sin^2 x + \sin^4 x)$
$= (\cos^2 x - \sin^2 x)[(\cos^2 x + \sin^2 x)^2 - \cos^2 x \sin^2 x]$
$= (\cos^2 x - \sin^2 x)(1 - \cos^2 x \sin^2 x).$

77. One possible proof: $\ln|\tan x| = \ln\dfrac{|\sin x|}{|\cos x|}$

$= \ln|\sin x| - \ln|\cos x|.$

78. One possible proof:
$\ln|\sec \theta + \tan \theta| + \ln|\sec \theta - \tan \theta| = \ln|\sec^2 \theta - \tan^2 \theta|$
$= \ln 1$
$= 0$

79. (a) They are not equal. Shown is the window $[-2\pi, 2\pi,]$ by $[-2, 2]$; graphing on nearly any viewing window does not show any apparent difference — but using TRACE, one finds that the y coordinates are not identical. Likewise, a table of values will show slight differences; for example, when $x = 1$, $y_1 = 0.53988$ while $y_2 = 0.54030$

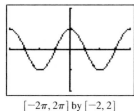

$[-2\pi, 2\pi]$ by $[-2, 2]$

(b) One choice for h is 0.001 (shown). The function y_3 is a combination of three sinusoidal functions $(1000 \sin(x + 0.001), 1000 \sin x, \text{ and } \cos x)$, all with period 2π.

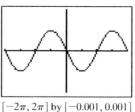

$[-2\pi, 2\pi]$ by $[-0.001, 0.001]$

80. (a) $\cosh^2 x - \sinh^2 x = \dfrac{1}{4}(e^x + e^{-x})^2 - \dfrac{1}{4}(e^x - e^{-x})^2$

$= \dfrac{1}{4}[e^{2x} + 2 + e^{-2x} - (e^{2x} - 2 + e^{-2x})]$

$= \dfrac{1}{4}(4) = 1.$

(b) $1 - \tanh^2 x = 1 - \dfrac{\sinh^2 x}{\cosh^2 x} = \dfrac{\cosh^2 x - \sinh^2 x}{\cosh^2 x}$

$= \dfrac{1}{\cosh^2 x}$, using the result from (a). This equals $\text{sech}^2 x.$

(c) $\coth^2 x - 1 = \dfrac{\cosh^2 x}{\sinh^2 x} - 1 = \dfrac{\cosh^2 x - \sinh^2 x}{\sinh^2 x}$

$= \dfrac{1}{\sinh^2 x}$, using the result from (a). This equals $\text{csch}^2 x.$

81. In the decimal window, the x coordinates used to plot the graph on the calculator are (e.g.) 0, 0.1, 0.2, 0.3, etc. — that is, $x = n/10$, where n is an integer. Then $10\pi x = \pi n$, and the sine of integer multiples of π is 0; therefore, $\cos x + \sin 10\pi x = \cos x + \sin \pi n = \cos x + 0$

$= \cos x.$ However, for other choices of x, such as $x = \dfrac{1}{\pi}$,

we have $\cos x + \sin 10\pi x = \cos x + \sin 10 \neq \cos x.$

■ Section 5.3 Sum and Difference Identities

Exploration 1

1. $\sin(u + v) = -1$, $\sin u + \sin v = 1$. No.

2. $\cos(u + v) = 1$, $\cos u + \cos v = 2$. No.

3. $\tan(\pi/3 + \pi/3) = -\sqrt{3}$, $\tan \pi/3 + \tan \pi/3 = 2\sqrt{3}$. (Many other answers are possible.)

Quick Review 5.3

1. $15° = 45° - 30°$

2. $75° = 45° + 30°$

3. $165° = 180° - 15° = 180° + 30° - 45° = 210° - 45°$

4. $\dfrac{\pi}{12} = 2 \cdot \dfrac{\pi}{6} - \dfrac{\pi}{4} = \dfrac{\pi}{3} - \dfrac{\pi}{4}$

5. $\dfrac{5\pi}{12} = 4 \cdot \dfrac{\pi}{6} - \dfrac{\pi}{4} = \dfrac{2\pi}{3} - \dfrac{\pi}{4}$

6. $\dfrac{7\pi}{12} = \dfrac{4\pi}{12} + \dfrac{3\pi}{12} = \dfrac{\pi}{3} + \dfrac{\pi}{4}$

7. No. $(f(x) + f(y) = \ln x + \ln y = \ln(xy)$
$= f(xy) \neq f(x + y))$

8. No. $(f(x + y) = e^{x+y} = e^x e^y$
$= f(x) f(y) \neq f(x + y))$

9. Yes. $(f(x + y) = 32(x + y) = 32x + 32y$
$= f(x) + f(y))$

10. No. $(f(x + y) = x + y + 10$
$= f(x) + y \neq f(x) + f(y))$

Section 5.3 Exercises

1. $\sin 15° = \sin(45° - 30°)$
$= \sin 45° \cos 30° - \cos 45° \sin 30°$
$= \dfrac{\sqrt{2}}{2} \cdot \dfrac{\sqrt{3}}{2} - \dfrac{\sqrt{2}}{2} \cdot \dfrac{1}{2} = \dfrac{\sqrt{6} - \sqrt{2}}{4}$

2. $\tan 15° = \tan(45° - 30°) = \dfrac{\tan 45° - \tan 30°}{1 + \tan 45° \tan 30°}$
$= \dfrac{1 - \sqrt{3}/3}{1 + \sqrt{3}/3} = \dfrac{3 - \sqrt{3}}{3 + \sqrt{3}} = \dfrac{(3 - \sqrt{3})^2}{9 - 3} = 2 - \sqrt{3}$

3. $\sin 75° = \sin(45° + 30°)$
$= \sin 45° \cos 30° + \cos 45° \sin 30°$
$= \dfrac{\sqrt{2}}{2} \cdot \dfrac{\sqrt{3}}{2} + \dfrac{\sqrt{2}}{2} \cdot \dfrac{1}{2} = \dfrac{\sqrt{6} + \sqrt{2}}{4}$

4. $\cos 75° = \cos(45° + 30°)$
$= \cos 45° \cos 30° - \sin 45° \sin 30°$
$= \dfrac{\sqrt{2}}{2} \cdot \dfrac{\sqrt{3}}{2} - \dfrac{\sqrt{2}}{2} \cdot \dfrac{1}{2} = \dfrac{\sqrt{6} - \sqrt{2}}{4}$

5. $\cos \dfrac{\pi}{12} = \cos\left(\dfrac{\pi}{3} - \dfrac{\pi}{4}\right) = \cos \dfrac{\pi}{3} \cos \dfrac{\pi}{4} + \sin \dfrac{\pi}{3} \sin \dfrac{\pi}{4}$
$= \dfrac{1}{2} \cdot \dfrac{\sqrt{2}}{2} + \dfrac{\sqrt{3}}{2} \cdot \dfrac{\sqrt{2}}{2} = \dfrac{\sqrt{2} + \sqrt{6}}{4}$

6. $\sin \dfrac{7\pi}{12} = \sin\left(\dfrac{\pi}{3} + \dfrac{\pi}{4}\right) = \sin \dfrac{\pi}{3} \cos \dfrac{\pi}{4} + \cos \dfrac{\pi}{3} \sin \dfrac{\pi}{4}$
$= \dfrac{\sqrt{3}}{2} \cdot \dfrac{\sqrt{2}}{2} + \dfrac{1}{2} \cdot \dfrac{\sqrt{2}}{2} = \dfrac{\sqrt{6} + \sqrt{2}}{4}$

7. $\tan \dfrac{5\pi}{12} = \tan\left(\dfrac{2\pi}{3} - \dfrac{\pi}{4}\right) = \dfrac{\tan(2\pi/3) - \tan(\pi/4)}{1 + \tan(2\pi/3)\tan(\pi/4)}$
$= \dfrac{-\sqrt{3} - 1}{1 - \sqrt{3}} = \dfrac{\sqrt{3} + 1}{\sqrt{3} - 1} = \dfrac{(\sqrt{3} + 1)^2}{3 - 1} = 2 + \sqrt{3}$

8. $\tan \dfrac{11\pi}{12} = \tan\left(\dfrac{2\pi}{3} + \dfrac{\pi}{4}\right) = \dfrac{\tan(2\pi/3) + \tan(\pi/4)}{1 - \tan(2\pi/3)\tan(\pi/4)}$
$= \dfrac{-\sqrt{3} + 1}{1 + \sqrt{3}} = \dfrac{1 - \sqrt{3}}{1 + \sqrt{3}} = \dfrac{(1 - \sqrt{3})^2}{1 - 3} = \sqrt{3} - 2$

9. $\cos \dfrac{7\pi}{12} = \cos\left(\dfrac{5\pi}{6} - \dfrac{\pi}{4}\right)$
$= \cos \dfrac{5\pi}{6} \cos \dfrac{\pi}{4} + \sin \dfrac{5\pi}{6} \sin \dfrac{\pi}{4} = -\dfrac{\sqrt{3}}{2} \cdot \dfrac{\sqrt{2}}{2} + \dfrac{1}{2} \cdot \dfrac{\sqrt{2}}{2}$
$= \dfrac{\sqrt{2} - \sqrt{6}}{4}$

10. $\sin\left(-\dfrac{\pi}{12}\right) = \sin\left(\dfrac{\pi}{6} - \dfrac{\pi}{4}\right)$
$= \sin \dfrac{\pi}{6} \cos \dfrac{\pi}{4} - \cos \dfrac{\pi}{6} \sin \dfrac{\pi}{4} = \dfrac{1}{2} \cdot \dfrac{\sqrt{2}}{2} - \dfrac{\sqrt{3}}{2} \cdot \dfrac{\sqrt{2}}{2}$
$= \dfrac{\sqrt{2} - \sqrt{6}}{4}$

In #11–22, match the given expression with the sum and difference identities.

11. $\sin(42° - 17°) = \sin 25°$

12. $\cos(94° - 18°) = \cos 76°$

13. $\sin\left(\dfrac{\pi}{5} + \dfrac{\pi}{2}\right) = \sin \dfrac{7\pi}{10}$

14. $\sin\left(\dfrac{\pi}{3} - \dfrac{\pi}{7}\right) = \sin \dfrac{4\pi}{21}$

15. $\tan(19° + 47°) = \tan 66°$

16. $\tan\left(\dfrac{\pi}{5} - \dfrac{\pi}{3}\right) = \tan -\dfrac{2\pi}{15}$

17. $\cos\left(\dfrac{\pi}{7} - x\right) = \cos\left(x - \dfrac{\pi}{7}\right)$

18. $\cos\left(x + \dfrac{\pi}{7}\right)$

19. $\sin(3x - x) = \sin 2x$

20. $\cos(7y + 3y) = \cos 10y$

21. $\tan(2y + 3x)$

22. $\tan(3\alpha - 2\beta)$

23. $\sin\left(x - \dfrac{\pi}{2}\right) = \sin x \cos \dfrac{\pi}{2} - \cos x \sin \dfrac{\pi}{2}$
$= \sin x \cdot 0 - \cos x \cdot 1 = -\cos x$

24. Using the difference identity for the tangent function, we encounter $\tan \dfrac{\pi}{2}$, which is undefined. However, we can compute $\tan\left(x - \dfrac{\pi}{2}\right) = \dfrac{\sin(x - \pi/2)}{\cos(x - \pi/2)}$. From #23, $\sin\left(x - \dfrac{\pi}{2}\right) = -\cos x$. Since the cosine function is even, $\cos\left(x - \dfrac{\pi}{2}\right) = \cos\left(\dfrac{\pi}{2} - x\right) = \sin x$ (see Example 2, or #25). Therefore this simplifies to $\dfrac{-\cos x}{\sin x} = -\cot x$.

25. $\cos\left(x - \dfrac{\pi}{2}\right) = \cos x \cos \dfrac{\pi}{2} + \sin x \sin \dfrac{\pi}{2}$
$= \cos x \cdot 0 + \sin x \cdot 1 = \sin x$

26. The simplest way is to note that
$\left(\dfrac{\pi}{2} - x\right) - y = \dfrac{\pi}{2} - x - y = \dfrac{\pi}{2} - (x + y)$, so that
$\cos\left[\left(\dfrac{\pi}{2} - x\right) - y\right] = \cos\left[\dfrac{\pi}{2} - (x + y)\right]$. Now use Example 2 to conclude that $\cos\left[\dfrac{\pi}{2} - (x + y)\right]$
$= \sin(x + y)$.

27. $\sin\left(x + \dfrac{\pi}{6}\right) = \sin x \cos \dfrac{\pi}{6} + \cos x \sin \dfrac{\pi}{6}$
$= \sin x \cdot \dfrac{\sqrt{3}}{2} + \cos x \cdot \dfrac{1}{2}$

28. $\cos\left(x - \dfrac{\pi}{4}\right) = \cos x \cos \dfrac{\pi}{4} + \sin x \sin \dfrac{\pi}{4}$
$= \cos x \cdot \dfrac{\sqrt{2}}{2} + \sin x \cdot \dfrac{\sqrt{2}}{2} = \dfrac{\sqrt{2}}{2}(\cos x + \sin x)$

29. $\tan\left(\theta + \dfrac{\pi}{4}\right) = \dfrac{\tan\theta + \tan(\pi/4)}{1 - \tan\theta\tan(\pi/4)} = \dfrac{\tan\theta + 1}{1 - \tan\theta \cdot 1}$

$= \dfrac{1 + \tan\theta}{1 - \tan\theta}$

30. $\cos\left(\theta + \dfrac{\pi}{2}\right) = \cos\theta\cos\dfrac{\pi}{2} - \sin\theta\sin\dfrac{\pi}{2}$

$= \cos\theta \cdot 0 - \sin\theta \cdot 1 = -\sin\theta$

31. Equations B and F.

32. Equations C and E.

33. Equations D and H.

34. Equations A and G.

35. Rewrite as $\sin 2x\cos x - \cos 2x\sin x = 0$; the left side equals $\sin(2x - x) = \sin x$, so $x = n\pi$, n an integer.

36. Rewrite as $\cos 3x\cos x - \sin 3x\sin x = 0$; the left side equals $\cos(3x + x) = \cos 4x$, so $4x = \dfrac{\pi}{2} + n\pi$; then

$x = \dfrac{\pi}{8} + n\dfrac{\pi}{4}$, n an integer.

37. $\sin\left(\dfrac{\pi}{2} - u\right) = \sin\dfrac{\pi}{2}\cos u - \cos\dfrac{\pi}{2}\sin u$

$= 1 \cdot \cos u - 0 \cdot \sin u = \cos u.$

38. Using the difference identity for the tangent function, we encounter $\tan\dfrac{\pi}{2}$, which is undefined. However, we can

compute $\tan\left(\dfrac{\pi}{2} - u\right) = \dfrac{\sin(\pi/2 - u)}{\cos(\pi/2 - u)} = \dfrac{\cos u}{\sin u} = \cot u.$ Or, use #24, and the fact that the tangent function is odd.

39. $\cot\left(\dfrac{\pi}{2} - u\right) = \dfrac{\cos(\pi/2 - u)}{\sin(\pi/2 - u)} = \dfrac{\sin u}{\cos u} = \tan u$ using the first two cofunction identities.

40. $\sec\left(\dfrac{\pi}{2} - u\right) = \dfrac{1}{\cos(\pi/2 - u)} = \dfrac{1}{\sin u} = \csc u$ using the first cofunction identity.

41. $\csc\left(\dfrac{\pi}{2} - u\right) = \dfrac{1}{\sin(\pi/2 - u)} = \dfrac{1}{\cos u} = \sec u$ using the second cofunction identity.

42. $\cos\left(x + \dfrac{\pi}{2}\right) = \cos x\cos\left(\dfrac{\pi}{2}\right) - \sin x\sin\left(\dfrac{\pi}{2}\right)$

$= \cos x \cdot 0 - \sin x \cdot 1$

$= -\sin x$

43. To write $y = 3\sin x + 4\cos x$ in the form $y = a\sin(bx + c)$, rewrite the formula using the formula for the sine of a sum:

$y = a((\sin bx\cos c) + (\cos bx\sin c))$

$= a\sin bx\cos c + a\cos bx\sin c$

$= (a\cos c)\sin bx + (a\sin c)\cos bx.$

Then compare the coefficients: $a\cos c = 3$, $b = 1$, $a\sin c = 4$.

Solve for a as follows:

$(a\cos c)^2 + (a\sin c)^2 = 3^2 + 4^2$

$a^2\cos^2 c + a^2\sin^2 c = 25$

$a^2(\cos^2 c + \sin^2 c) = 25$

$a^2 = 25$

$a = \pm 5$

If we choose a to be positive, then $\cos c = 3/5$ and $\sin c = 4/5$. $c = \cos^{-1}(3/5) = \sin^{-1}(4/5)$. So the sinusoid is $y = 5\sin(x + \cos^{-1}(3/5)) \approx 5\sin(x + 0.9273)$.

44. Follow the steps shown in Exercise 43 (using the formula for the sine of a difference) to compare the coefficients in $y = (a\cos c)\sin bx - (a\sin c)\cos bx$ to the coefficients in $y = 5\sin x - 12\cos x$: $a\cos c = 5$, $b = 1$, $a\sin c = 12$.

Solve for a as follows:

$(a\cos c)^2 + (a\sin c)^2 = 5^2 + 12^2$

$a^2(\cos^2 c + \sin^2 c) = 169$

$a = \pm 13$

If we choose a to be positive, then $\cos c = 5/13$ and $\sin c = 12/13$. So the sinusoid is $y = 13\sin(x - \cos^{-1}(5/13)) \approx 13\sin(x - 1.176)$.

45. Follow the steps shown in Exercise 43 to compare the coefficients in $y = (a\cos c)\sin bx + (a\sin c)\cos bx$ to the coefficients in $y = \cos 3x + 2\sin 3x$: $a\cos c = 2$, $b = 3$, $a\sin c = 1$.

Solve for a as follows:

$(a\cos c)^2 + (a\sin c)^2 = 1^2 + 2^2$

$a^2(\cos^2 c + \sin^2 c) = 5$

$a = \pm\sqrt{5}$

If we choose a to be positive, then $\cos c = 2/\sqrt{5}$ and $\sin c = 1/\sqrt{5}$. So the sinusoid is $y = \sqrt{5}\sin(3x - \cos^{-1}(2/\sqrt{5})) \approx 2.236\sin(3x - 0.4636)$.

46. Follow the steps shown in Exercise 43 to compare the coefficients in $y = (a\cos c)\sin bx + (a\sin c)\cos bx$ to the coefficients in $y = 3\cos 2x - 2\sin 2x$ $= -2\sin 2x + 3\cos 2x$: $a\cos c = -2$, $b = 2$, $a\sin c = 3$.

Solve for a as follows:

$(a\cos c)^2 + (a\sin c)^2 = (-2)^2 + 3^2$

$a^2(\cos^2 c + \sin^2 c) = 13$

$a = \pm\sqrt{13}$

If we choose a to be negative, then $\cos c = 2/\sqrt{13}$ and $\sin c = -3/\sqrt{13}$. So the sinusoid is $y = -\sqrt{13}\sin(2x - \cos^{-1}(2/\sqrt{13}))$

$\approx -3.606\sin(2x - 0.9828)$.

47. $\sin(x - y) + \sin(x + y)$

$= (\sin x\cos y - \cos x\sin y) + (\sin x\cos y + \cos x\sin y)$

$= 2\sin x\cos y$

48. $\cos(x - y) + \cos(x + y)$

$= (\cos x\cos y + \sin x\sin y) + (\cos x\cos y - \sin x\sin y)$

$= 2\cos x\cos y$

49. $\cos 3x = \cos[(x + x) + x]$

$= \cos(x + x)\cos x - \sin(x + x)\sin x$

$= (\cos x\cos x - \sin x\sin x)\cos x$

$\quad - (\sin x\cos x + \cos x\sin x)\sin x$

$= \cos^3 x - \sin^2 x\cos x - 2\cos x\sin^2 x$

$= \cos^3 x - 3\sin^2 x\cos x$

50. $\sin 3u = \sin[(u + u) + u] = \sin(u + u)\cos u + \cos(u + u)\sin u = (\sin u\cos u + \cos u\sin u)\cos u + (\cos u\cos u - \sin u\sin u)\sin u = 2\cos^2 u\sin u + \cos^2 u\sin u - \sin^3 u = 3\cos^2 u\sin u - \sin^3 u$

51. $\cos 3x + \cos x = \cos(2x + x) + \cos(2x - x)$; use #48 with x replaced with $2x$ and y replaced with x.

52. $\sin 4x + \sin 2x = \sin(3x + x) + \sin(3x - x)$; use #47 with x replaced with $3x$ and y replaced with x.

53. $\tan(x + y)\tan(x - y)$

$= \left(\dfrac{\tan x + \tan y}{1 - \tan x \tan y}\right) \cdot \left(\dfrac{\tan x - \tan y}{1 + \tan x \tan y}\right)$

$= \dfrac{\tan^2 x - \tan^2 y}{1 - \tan^2 x \tan^2 y}$ since both the numerator and

denominator are factored forms for differences of squares.

54. $\tan 5u \tan 3u = \tan(4u + u)\tan(4u - u)$; use #53 with $x = 4u$ and $y = u$.

55. $\dfrac{\sin(x + y)}{\sin(x - y)}$

$= \dfrac{\sin x \cos y + \cos x \sin y}{\sin x \cos y - \cos x \sin y}$

$= \dfrac{\sin x \cos y + \cos x \sin y}{\sin x \cos y - \cos x \sin y} \cdot \dfrac{1/(\cos x \cos y)}{1/(\cos x \cos y)}$

$= \dfrac{(\sin x \cos y)/(\cos x \cos y) + (\cos x \sin y)/(\cos x \cos y)}{(\sin x \cos y)/(\cos x \cos y) - (\cos x \sin y)/(\cos x \cos y)}$

$= \dfrac{(\sin x/\cos x) + (\sin y/\cos y)}{(\sin x/\cos x) - (\sin y/\cos y)}$

$= \dfrac{\tan x + \tan y}{\tan x - \tan y}$

56. True. If $B = \pi - A$, then $\cos A + \cos B$

$= \cos A + \cos(\pi - A)$

$= \cos A + \cos \pi \cos A + \sin \pi \sin A$

$= \cos A + (-1)\cos A + (0)\sin A = 0$.

57. False. For example, $\cos 3\pi + \cos 4\pi = 0$, but 3π and 4π are not supplementary. And even though $\cos(3\pi/2) + \cos(3\pi/2) = 0$, $3\pi/2$ is not supplementary with itself.

58. If $\cos A \cos B = \sin A \sin B$, then $\cos(A + B) = \cos A \cos B - \sin A \sin B = 0$. The answer is A.

59. $y = \sin x \cos 2x + \cos x \sin 2x = \sin(x + 2x) = \sin 3x$. The answer is A.

60. $\sin 15° = \sin(45° - 30°)$

$= \sin 45° \cos 30° - \cos 45° \sin 30°$

$= \dfrac{\sqrt{2}}{2}\left(\dfrac{\sqrt{3}}{2}\right) - \dfrac{\sqrt{2}}{2}\left(\dfrac{1}{2}\right)$

$= \dfrac{\sqrt{6} - \sqrt{2}}{4}$

The answer is D.

61. For all u, v, $\tan(u + v) = \dfrac{\tan u + \tan v}{1 - \tan u \tan v}$. The answer is B.

62. $\tan(u + v) = \dfrac{\sin(u + v)}{\cos(u + v)}$

$= \dfrac{\sin u \cos v + \cos u \sin v}{\cos u \cos v - \sin u \sin v}$

$= \dfrac{\dfrac{\sin u \cos v}{\cos u \cos v} + \dfrac{\cos u \sin v}{\cos u \cos v}}{\dfrac{\cos u \cos v}{\cos u \cos v} - \dfrac{\sin u \sin v}{\cos u \cos v}}$

$= \dfrac{\dfrac{\sin u}{\cos u} + \dfrac{\sin v}{\cos v}}{1 - \dfrac{\sin u \sin v}{\cos u \cos v}}$

$= \dfrac{\tan u + \tan v}{1 - \tan u \tan v}$

63. $\tan(u - v) = \dfrac{\sin(u - v)}{\cos(u - v)}$

$= \dfrac{\sin u \cos v - \cos u \sin v}{\cos u \cos v + \sin u \sin v}$

$= \dfrac{\dfrac{\sin u \cos v}{\cos u \cos v} - \dfrac{\cos u \sin v}{\cos u \cos v}}{\dfrac{\cos u \cos v}{\cos u \cos v} + \dfrac{\sin u \sin v}{\cos u \cos v}}$

$= \dfrac{\dfrac{\sin u}{\cos u} - \dfrac{\sin v}{\cos v}}{1 + \dfrac{\sin u \sin v}{\cos u \cos v}}$

$= \dfrac{\tan u - \tan v}{1 + \tan u \tan v}$

64. The identity would involve $\tan\left(\dfrac{\pi}{2}\right)$, which does not exist.

$\tan\left(x + \dfrac{\pi}{2}\right) = \dfrac{\sin\left(x + \dfrac{\pi}{2}\right)}{\cos\left(x + \dfrac{\pi}{2}\right)}$

$= \dfrac{\sin x \cos \dfrac{\pi}{2} + \cos x \sin \dfrac{\pi}{2}}{\cos x \cos \dfrac{\pi}{2} - \sin x \sin \dfrac{\pi}{2}}$

$= \dfrac{\sin x \cdot 0 + \cos x \cdot 1}{\cos x \cdot 0 - \sin x \cdot 1}$

$= -\cot x$

65. The identity would involve $\tan\left(\dfrac{3\pi}{2}\right)$, which does not exit.

$\tan\left(x - \dfrac{3\pi}{2}\right) = \dfrac{\sin\left(x - \dfrac{3\pi}{2}\right)}{\cos\left(x - \dfrac{3\pi}{2}\right)}$

$= \dfrac{\sin x \cos \dfrac{3\pi}{2} - \cos x \sin \dfrac{3\pi}{2}}{\cos x \cos \dfrac{3\pi}{2} + \sin x \sin \dfrac{3\pi}{2}}$

$= \dfrac{\sin x \cdot 0 - \cos x \cdot (-1)}{\cos x \cdot 0 + \sin x \cdot (-1)}$

$= -\cot x$

66. $\dfrac{\sin(x + h) - \sin x}{h} = \dfrac{\sin x \cos h + \cos x \sin h - \sin x}{h}$

$= \dfrac{\sin x(\cos h - 1) + \cos x \sin h}{h}$

$= \sin x\left(\dfrac{\cos h - 1}{h}\right) + \cos x \dfrac{\sin h}{h}$

67.
$$\frac{\cos(x + h) - \cos x}{h} = \frac{\cos x \cos h - \sin x \sin h - \cos x}{h}$$
$$= \frac{\cos x(\cos h - 1) - \sin x \sin h}{h}$$
$$= \cos x\left(\frac{\cos h - 1}{h}\right) - \sin x \frac{\sin h}{h}$$

68. The coordinates of all 24 points must be
$\left(\cos\left(\frac{k\pi}{12}\right), \sin\left(\frac{k\pi}{12}\right)\right)$ for $k = 0, 1, 2, ..., 23$. We only
need to find the coordinates of those points in Quadrant I,
because the remaining points are symmetric. We already
know the coordinates for the cases when $k = 0, 2, 3, 4, 6$
since these correspond to the special angles.

$k = 1: \cos\left(\frac{\pi}{12}\right) = \cos\left(\frac{\pi}{3} - \frac{\pi}{4}\right) = \cos\left(\frac{\pi}{3}\right)\cos\left(\frac{\pi}{4}\right)$
$\qquad + \sin\left(\frac{\pi}{3}\right)\sin\left(\frac{\pi}{4}\right) = \frac{1}{2} \cdot \frac{\sqrt{2}}{2} + \frac{\sqrt{3}}{2} \cdot \frac{\sqrt{2}}{2}$
$\qquad = \frac{\sqrt{2} + \sqrt{6}}{4}$

$\sin\left(\frac{\pi}{12}\right) = \sin\left(\frac{\pi}{3} - \frac{\pi}{4}\right) = \sin\left(\frac{\pi}{3}\right)\cos\left(\frac{\pi}{4}\right)$
$\qquad - \sin\left(\frac{\pi}{4}\right)\cos\left(\frac{\pi}{3}\right) = \frac{\sqrt{3}}{2} \cdot \frac{\sqrt{2}}{2} - \frac{\sqrt{2}}{2} \cdot \frac{1}{2}$
$\qquad = \frac{\sqrt{6} - \sqrt{2}}{4}$

$k = 5: \cos\left(\frac{5\pi}{12}\right) = \cos\left(\frac{3\pi}{4} - \frac{\pi}{3}\right)$
$\qquad = \cos\left(\frac{3\pi}{4}\right)\cos\left(\frac{\pi}{3}\right) + \sin\left(\frac{3\pi}{4}\right)\sin\left(\frac{\pi}{3}\right)$
$\qquad = -\frac{\sqrt{2}}{2} \cdot \frac{1}{2} + \frac{\sqrt{2}}{2} \cdot \frac{\sqrt{3}}{2} = \frac{\sqrt{6} - \sqrt{2}}{4}$

$\sin\left(\frac{5\pi}{12}\right) = \sin\left(\frac{3\pi}{4} - \frac{\pi}{3}\right)$
$\qquad = \sin\left(\frac{3\pi}{4}\right)\cos\left(\frac{\pi}{3}\right) - \sin\left(\frac{\pi}{3}\right)\cos\left(\frac{3\pi}{4}\right)$
$\qquad = \frac{\sqrt{2}}{2} \cdot \frac{1}{2} - \frac{\sqrt{3}}{2} \cdot \left(-\frac{\sqrt{2}}{2}\right) = \frac{\sqrt{2} + \sqrt{6}}{4}$

Coordinates in the first quadrant are $(1, 0)$,
$\left(\frac{\sqrt{2} + \sqrt{6}}{4}, \frac{\sqrt{6} - \sqrt{2}}{4}\right), \left(\frac{\sqrt{3}}{2}, \frac{1}{2}\right), \left(\frac{\sqrt{2}}{2}, \frac{\sqrt{2}}{2}\right),$
$\left(\frac{1}{2}, \frac{\sqrt{3}}{2}\right), \left(\frac{\sqrt{6} - \sqrt{2}}{4}, \frac{\sqrt{2} + \sqrt{6}}{4}\right), (0, 1)$

69. $\sin(A + B) = \sin(\pi - C)$
$\qquad = \sin\pi\cos C - \cos\pi\sin C$
$\qquad = 0 \cdot \cos C - (-1)\sin C$
$\qquad = \sin C$

70. $\cos C = \cos(\pi - (A + B))$
$\qquad = \cos\pi\cos(A + B) + \sin\pi\sin(A + B)$
$\qquad = (-1)(\cos A \cos B - \sin A \sin B)$
$\qquad\quad + 0 \cdot \sin(A + B)$
$\qquad = \sin A \sin B - \cos A \cos B$

71. $\tan A + \tan B + \tan C = \frac{\sin A}{\cos A} + \frac{\sin B}{\cos B} + \frac{\sin C}{\cos C}$
$\qquad = \frac{\sin A(\cos B \cos C) + \sin B(\cos A \cos C)}{\cos A \cos B \cos C}$
$\qquad\quad + \frac{\sin C(\cos A \cos B)}{\cos A \cos B \cos C}$
$\qquad = \frac{\cos C(\sin A \cos B + \cos A \sin B) + \sin C(\cos A \cos B)}{\cos A \cos B \cos C}$
$\qquad = \frac{\cos C \sin(A + B) + \sin C(\cos(A + B) + \sin A \sin B)}{\cos A \cos B \cos C}$
$\qquad = \frac{\cos C \sin(\pi - C) + \sin C(\cos(\pi - C) + \sin A \sin B)}{\cos A \cos B \cos C}$
$\qquad = \frac{\cos C \sin C + \sin C(-\cos C) + \sin C \sin A \sin B}{\cos A \cos B \cos C}$
$\qquad = \frac{\sin A \sin B \sin C}{\cos A \cos B \cos C}$
$\qquad = \tan A \tan B \tan C$

72. $\cos A \cos B \cos C - \sin A \sin B \cos C$
$\qquad - \sin A \cos B \sin C - \cos A \sin B \sin C$
$\qquad = \cos A(\cos B \cos C - \sin B \sin C)$
$\qquad\quad - \sin A(\sin B \cos C + \cos B \sin C)$
$\qquad = \cos A \cos(B + C) - \sin A \sin(B + C)$
$\qquad = \cos(A + B + C)$
$\qquad = \cos\pi$
$\qquad = -1$

73. This equation is easier to deal with after rewriting it as
$\cos 5x \cos 4x + \sin 5x \sin 4x = 0$. The left side of this
equation is the expanded form of $\cos(5x - 4x)$, which of
course equals $\cos x$; the graph shown is simply $y = \cos x$.
The equation $\cos x = 0$ is easily solved on the interval
$[-2\pi, 2\pi]: x = \pm\frac{\pi}{2}$ or $x = \pm\frac{3\pi}{2}$. The original graph is so
crowded that one cannot see where crossings occur.

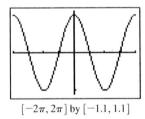

$[-2\pi, 2\pi]$ by $[-1.1, 1.1]$

74. $x = a\cos\left(\frac{2\pi t}{T} + \delta\right)$
$\qquad = a\left[\cos\left(\frac{2\pi t}{T}\right)\cos\delta - \sin\left(\frac{2\pi t}{T}\right)\sin\delta\right]$
$\qquad = (a\cos\delta)\cos\left(\frac{2\pi t}{T}\right) + (-a\sin\delta)\sin\left(\frac{2\pi t}{T}\right)$

75. $B = B_{in} + B_{ref}$
$\qquad = \frac{E_0}{c}\cos\left(\omega t - \frac{\omega x}{c}\right) + \frac{E_0}{c}\cos\left(\omega t + \frac{\omega x}{c}\right)$
$\qquad = \frac{E_0}{c}\left(\cos\omega t \cos\frac{\omega x}{c} + \sin\omega t \sin\frac{\omega x}{c}\right.$
$\qquad\qquad + \cos\omega t \cos\frac{\omega x}{c} - \sin\omega t \sin\frac{\omega x}{c}\bigg)$
$\qquad = \frac{E_0}{c}\left(2\cos\omega t \cos\frac{\omega x}{c}\right) = 2\frac{E_0}{c}\cos\omega t \cos\frac{\omega x}{c}$

■ Section 5.4 Multiple-Angle Identities

Exploration 1

1. $\sin^2 \dfrac{\pi}{8} = \dfrac{1 - \cos(\pi/4)}{2}$

$\qquad = \dfrac{1 - (\sqrt{2}/2)}{2} \cdot \dfrac{2}{2}$

$\qquad = \dfrac{2 - \sqrt{2}}{4}$

2. $\sin \dfrac{\pi}{8} = \pm\sqrt{\dfrac{2 - \sqrt{2}}{4}} = \dfrac{\sqrt{2 - \sqrt{2}}}{2}.$

We take the positive square root because $\dfrac{\pi}{8}$ is a first-quadrant angle.

3. $\sin^2 \dfrac{9\pi}{8} = \dfrac{1 - \cos(9\pi/4)}{2}$

$\qquad = \dfrac{1 - (\sqrt{2}/2)}{2} \cdot \dfrac{2}{2}$

$\qquad = \dfrac{2 - \sqrt{2}}{4}$

4. $\sin \dfrac{9\pi}{8} = \pm\sqrt{\dfrac{2 - \sqrt{2}}{4}} = \dfrac{-\sqrt{2 - \sqrt{2}}}{2}.$

We take the negative square root because $\dfrac{\pi}{8}$ is a third-quadrant angle.

Quick Review 5.4

1. $\tan x = 1$ when $x = \dfrac{\pi}{4} + n\pi$, n an integer

2. $\tan x = -1$ when $x = -\dfrac{\pi}{4} + n\pi$, n an integer

3. Either $\cos x = 0$ or $\sin x = 1$. The latter implies the former, so $x = \dfrac{\pi}{2} + n\pi$, n an integer.

4. Either $\sin x = 0$ or $\cos x = -1$. The latter implies the former, so $x = n\pi$, n an integer.

5. $\sin x = -\cos x$ when $x = -\dfrac{\pi}{4} + n\pi$, n an integer

6. $\sin x = \cos x$ when $x = \dfrac{\pi}{4} + n\pi$, n an integer

7. Either $\sin x = \dfrac{1}{2}$ or $\cos x = -\dfrac{1}{2}$. Then $x = \dfrac{\pi}{6} + 2n\pi$ or $x = \dfrac{5\pi}{6} + 2n\pi$ or $x = \pm\dfrac{2\pi}{3} + 2n\pi$, n an integer.

8. Either $\sin x = -1$ or $\cos x = \dfrac{\sqrt{2}}{2}$. Then $x = \dfrac{3\pi}{2} + 2n\pi$ or $x = \pm\dfrac{\pi}{4} + 2n\pi$, n an integer.

9. The trapezoid can be viewed as a rectangle and two triangles; the area is then $A = (2)(3) + \dfrac{1}{2}(1)(3) + \dfrac{1}{2}(2)(3)$

$\qquad = 10.5$ square units.

10. View the triangle as two right triangles with hypotenuse 3, one leg 1, and the other leg — the height — equal to $\sqrt{3^2 - 1^2} = \sqrt{8} = 2\sqrt{2}$

Section 5.4 Exercises

1. $\cos 2u = \cos(u + u) = \cos u \cos u - \sin u \sin u$
$\qquad = \cos^2 u - \sin^2 u$

2. Starting with the result of #1: $\cos 2u = \cos^2 u - \sin^2 u$
$\qquad = \cos^2 u - (1 - \cos^2 u) = 2\cos^2 u - 1$

3. Starting with the result of #1: $\cos 2u = \cos^2 u - \sin^2 u$
$\qquad = (1 - \sin^2 u) - \sin^2 u = 1 - 2\sin^2 u$

4. $\tan 2u = \tan(u + u) = \dfrac{\tan u + \tan u}{1 - \tan u \tan u} = \dfrac{2\tan u}{1 - \tan^2 u}$

5. $2 \sin x \cos x - 2 \sin x = 0$, so $2 \sin x(\cos x - 1) = 0$; $\sin x = 0$ or $\cos x = 1$ when $x = 0$ or $x = \pi$.

6. $2 \sin x \cos x - \sin x = 0$
$\sin x(2 \cos x - 1) = 0$,
So $\sin x = 0$ or $\cos x = \dfrac{1}{2}$
when $x = 0,\ \pi,\ \dfrac{\pi}{3},$ or $\dfrac{5\pi}{3}.$

7. $2 \sin^2 x + \sin x - 1 = 0$, so $(2 \sin x - 1)(\sin x + 1)$
$= 0$; $\sin x = \dfrac{1}{2}$ or $\sin x = -1$ when $x = \dfrac{\pi}{6}$,
$x = \dfrac{5\pi}{6}$ or $x = \dfrac{3\pi}{2}.$

8. $2 \cos^2 x - \cos x - 1 = 0$, so $(2 \cos x + 1)(\cos x - 1)$
$= 0$; $\cos x = -\dfrac{1}{2}$ or $\cos x = 1$ when $x = 0$,
$x = \dfrac{2\pi}{3}$ or $x = \dfrac{4\pi}{3}.$

9. $2 \sin x \cos x - \dfrac{\sin x}{\cos x} = 0$, so $\dfrac{\sin x}{\cos x}(2 \cos^2 x - 1) = 0$, or
$\dfrac{\sin x \cos 2x}{\cos x} = 0$. Then $\sin x = 0$ or $\cos 2x = 0$
(but $\cos x \neq 0$), so $x = 0$, $x = \dfrac{\pi}{4}$, $x = \dfrac{3\pi}{4}$, $x = \pi$,
$x = \dfrac{5\pi}{4}$ or $x = \dfrac{7\pi}{4}.$

10. $\cos^2 x - \cos x - 1 = 0$, so $\cos x = \dfrac{1 \pm \sqrt{5}}{2}$. Only
$\dfrac{1 - \sqrt{5}}{2}$ is in $[-1, 1]$, so $x = \cos^{-1}\left(\dfrac{1 - \sqrt{5}}{2}\right) \approx 2.2370$
or $x = 2\pi - \cos^{-1}\left(\dfrac{1 - \sqrt{5}}{2}\right) \approx 4.0461$

For #11–14, any one of the last several expressions given is an answer to the question. In some cases, other answers are possible, as well.

11. $\sin 2\theta + \cos \theta = 2 \sin \theta \cos \theta + \cos \theta$
$\qquad = (\cos \theta)(2 \sin \theta + 1)$

12. $\sin 2\theta + \cos 2\theta = 2 \sin \theta \cos \theta + \cos^2 \theta - \sin^2 \theta$
$\qquad = 2 \sin \theta \cos \theta + 2 \cos^2 \theta - 1$
$\qquad = 2 \sin \theta \cos \theta + 1 - 2 \sin^2 \theta$

13. $\sin 2\theta + \cos 3\theta$
$\qquad = 2 \sin \theta \cos \theta + \cos 2\theta \cos \theta - \sin 2\theta \sin \theta$
$\qquad = 2 \sin \theta \cos \theta + (\cos^2\theta - \sin^2 \theta) \cos \theta - 2 \sin^2 \theta \cos \theta$
$\qquad = 2 \sin \theta \cos \theta + \cos^3 \theta - 3 \sin^2 \theta \cos \theta$
$\qquad = 2 \sin \theta \cos \theta + 4 \cos^3 \theta - 3 \cos \theta$

14. $\sin 3\theta + \cos 2\theta$
$= \sin 2\theta \cos \theta + \cos 2\theta \sin \theta + \cos^2 \theta - \sin^2\theta$
$= 2 \sin \theta \cos^2 \theta + (\cos^2 \theta - \sin^2 \theta) \sin \theta + \cos^2 \theta - \sin^2 \theta$
$= 3 \sin \theta \cos^2 \theta - \sin^3 \theta + \cos^2 \theta - \sin^2 \theta$

15. $\sin 4x = \sin 2(2x) = 2 \sin 2x \cos 2x$

16. $\cos 6x = \cos 2(3x) = 2 \cos^2 3x - 1$

17. $2 \csc 2x = \dfrac{2}{\sin 2x} = \dfrac{2}{2 \sin x \cos x}$
$= \dfrac{1}{\sin^2 x} \cdot \dfrac{\sin x}{\cos x} = \csc^2 x \tan x$

18. $2 \cot 2x = \dfrac{2}{\tan 2x} = \dfrac{2(1 - \tan^2 x)}{2 \tan x} = \dfrac{1}{\tan x} - \tan x$
$= \cot x - \tan x$

19. $\sin 3x = \sin 2x \cos x + \cos 2x \sin x = 2 \sin x \cos^2 x$
$+ (2 \cos^2 x - 1) \sin x = (\sin x)(4 \cos^2 x - 1)$

20. $\sin 3x = \sin 2x \cos x + \cos 2x \sin x$
$= 2 \sin x \cos^2 x + (1 - 2 \sin^2 x) \sin x$
$= (\sin x)(2 \cos^2 x + 1 - 2 \sin^2 x)$
$= (\sin x)(3 - 4 \sin^2 x)$

21. $\cos 4x = \cos 2(2x) = 1 - 2 \sin^2 2x$
$= 1 - 2(2 \sin x \cos x)^2 = 1 - 8 \sin^2 x \cos^2 x$

22. $\sin 4x = \sin 2(2x) = 2 \sin 2x \cos 2x$
$= 2(2 \sin x \cos x)(2 \cos^2 x - 1)$
$= (4 \sin x \cos x)(2 \cos^2 x - 1)$

23. $2 \cos^2 x + \cos x - 1 = 0$, so $\cos x = -1$ or $\cos x = \dfrac{1}{2}$,
$x = \dfrac{\pi}{3}, x = \pi$ or $x = \dfrac{5\pi}{3}$

24. $\cos 2x + \sin x = 1 - 2 \sin^2 x + \sin x = 0$, so
$\sin x = 1$ or $\sin x = -\dfrac{1}{2}, x = \dfrac{\pi}{2}, x = \dfrac{7\pi}{6}$, or $x = \dfrac{11\pi}{6}$.

25. $\cos 3x = \cos 2x \cos x - \sin 2x \sin x$
$= (1 - 2 \sin^2 x) \cos x$
$\quad - (2 \sin x \cos x) \sin x$
$= \cos x - 2 \sin^2 x \cos x$
$\quad - 2 \sin^2 x \cos x$
$= \cos x - 4 \sin^2 x \cos x$
Thus the left side can be written as $2(\cos x)(1 - 2 \sin^2 x)$
$= 2 \cos x \cos 2x$. This equals 0 in $[0, 2\pi)$ when
$x = \dfrac{\pi}{4}, x = \dfrac{\pi}{2}, x = \dfrac{3\pi}{4}, x = \dfrac{5\pi}{4}, x = \dfrac{3\pi}{2}$, or $x = \dfrac{7\pi}{4}$.

26. Using #19, this become $4 \sin x \cos^2 x = 0$, so $x = 0$,
$x = \dfrac{\pi}{2}, x = \pi$, or $x = \dfrac{3\pi}{2}$.

27. $\sin 2x + \sin 4x = \sin 2x + 2 \sin 2x \cos 2x$
$= (\sin 2x)(1 + 2 \cos 2x) = 0$. Then $\sin 2x = 0$ or
$\cos 2x = -\dfrac{1}{2}$; the solutions in $[0, 2\pi)$ are
$x = 0, x = \dfrac{\pi}{3}, x = \dfrac{\pi}{2}$,
$x = \dfrac{2\pi}{3}, x = \pi, x = \dfrac{4\pi}{3}, x = \dfrac{3\pi}{2}$, or $x = \dfrac{5\pi}{3}$.

28. With $u = 2x$, this becomes $\cos u + \cos 2u = 0$, the same
as #23. This means $u = \dfrac{\pi}{3}, u = \pi, u = \dfrac{5\pi}{3}$, etc. —
i.e., $2x = \dfrac{\pi}{3} + n \dfrac{2\pi}{3}$. Then $x = \dfrac{\pi}{6}, x = \dfrac{\pi}{2}, x = \dfrac{5\pi}{6}$,
$x = \dfrac{7\pi}{6}, x = \dfrac{3\pi}{2}, x = \dfrac{11\pi}{6}$.

29. Using results from #25, $\sin 2x - \cos 3x$
$= (2 \sin x \cos x) - (\cos x - 4 \sin^2 x \cos x)$
$= (\cos x)(4 \sin^2 x + 2 \sin x - 1) = 0$.
$\cos x = 0$ when $x = \dfrac{\pi}{2}$ or $x = \dfrac{3\pi}{2}$, while the second
factor equals zero when $\sin x = \dfrac{-1 \pm \sqrt{5}}{4}$. It turns
out — as can be observed by noting, e.g., that
$\sin^{-1}\left(\dfrac{-1 + \sqrt{5}}{4}\right) \approx 0.31415926$ — that this means
$x = 0.1\pi, x = 0.9\pi, x = 1.3\pi$, or $x = 1.7\pi$.

30. Using #14, the left side can be rewritten as
$3 \sin x \cos^2 x - \sin^3 x + \cos^2 x - \sin^2 x$.
Replacing $\cos^2 x$ with $1 - \sin^2 x$ gives
$-4 \sin^3 x - 2 \sin^2 x + 3 \sin x + 1$
$= (\sin x + 1)(-4 \sin^2 x + 2 \sin x + 1)$.
This equals 0 when $\sin x = -1$ $\left(x = \dfrac{3\pi}{2}\right)$, and
when $\sin x = \dfrac{1 \pm \sqrt{5}}{4}$. These values turn out to be
$x = 0.3\pi, x = 0.7\pi, x = 1.1\pi$, and $x = 1.9\pi$,
as can be observed by noting, e.g., that
$\sin^{-1}\left(\dfrac{1 - \sqrt{5}}{4}\right) \approx -0.31415926$.

31. $\sin 15° = \pm\sqrt{\dfrac{1 - \cos 30°}{2}} = \pm\sqrt{\dfrac{1}{2}\left(1 - \dfrac{\sqrt{3}}{2}\right)}$
$= \pm\dfrac{1}{2}\sqrt{2 - \sqrt{3}}$. Since $\sin 15° > 0$, take the positive
square root.

32. $\tan 195° = \dfrac{1 - \cos 390°}{\sin 390°} = \dfrac{1 - \sqrt{3}/2}{1/2} = 2 - \sqrt{3}$. Note
that $\tan 195° = \tan 15°$.

33. $\cos 75° = \pm\sqrt{\dfrac{1 + \cos 150°}{2}} = \pm\sqrt{\dfrac{1}{2}\left(1 - \dfrac{\sqrt{3}}{2}\right)}$
$= \pm\dfrac{1}{2}\sqrt{2 - \sqrt{3}}$. Since $\cos 75° > 0$, take the positive
square root.

34. $\sin \dfrac{5\pi}{12} = \pm\sqrt{\dfrac{1 - \cos(5\pi/6)}{2}} = \pm\sqrt{\dfrac{1}{2}\left(1 + \dfrac{\sqrt{3}}{2}\right)}$
$= \pm\dfrac{1}{2}\sqrt{2 + \sqrt{3}}$. Since $\sin \dfrac{5\pi}{12} > 0$, take the positive
square root.

35. $\tan \dfrac{7\pi}{12} = \dfrac{1 - \cos(7\pi/6)}{\sin(7\pi/6)} = \dfrac{1 + \sqrt{3}/2}{-1/2} = -2 - \sqrt{3}$.

36. $\cos \dfrac{\pi}{8} = \pm\sqrt{\dfrac{1 + \cos(\pi/4)}{2}} = \pm\sqrt{\dfrac{1}{2}\left(1 + \dfrac{\sqrt{2}}{2}\right)}$
$= \pm\dfrac{1}{2}\sqrt{2 + \sqrt{2}}$. Since $\cos \dfrac{\pi}{8} > 0$, take the positive
square root.

37. (a) Starting from the right side: $\frac{1}{2}(1 - \cos 2u)$

$$= \frac{1}{2}[1 - (1 - 2\sin^2 u)] = \frac{1}{2}(2\sin^2 u) = \sin^2 u.$$

(b) Starting from the right side: $\frac{1}{2}(1 + \cos 2u)$

$$= \frac{1}{2}[1 + (2\cos^2 u - 1)] = \frac{1}{2}(2\cos^2 u) = \cos^2 u.$$

38. (a) $\tan^2 u = \dfrac{\sin^2 u}{\cos^2 u} = \dfrac{(1 - \cos 2u)/2}{(1 + \cos 2u)/2} = \dfrac{1 - \cos 2u}{1 + \cos 2u}$

(b) The equation is false when $\tan u$ is a negative number. It would be an identity if it were written as

$$|\tan u| = \sqrt{\frac{1 - \cos u}{1 + \cos u}}.$$

39. $\sin^4 x = (\sin^2 x)^2 = \left[\dfrac{1}{2}(1 - \cos 2x)\right]^2$

$$= \frac{1}{4}(1 - 2\cos 2x + \cos^2 2x)$$

$$= \frac{1}{4}\left[1 - 2\cos 2x + \frac{1}{2}(1 + \cos 4x)\right]$$

$$= \frac{1}{8}(2 - 4\cos 2x + 1 + \cos 4x)$$

$$= \frac{1}{8}(3 - 4\cos 2x + \cos 4x)$$

40. $\cos^3 x = \cos x \cos^2 x = \cos x \cdot \dfrac{1}{2}(1 + \cos 2x)$

$$= \frac{1}{2}(\cos x)(1 + \cos 2x)$$

41. $\sin^3 2x = \sin 2x \sin^2 2x = \sin 2x \cdot \dfrac{1}{2}(1 - \cos 4x)$

$$= \frac{1}{2}(\sin 2x)(1 - \cos 4x)$$

42. $\sin^5 x = (\sin x)(\sin^2 x)^2 = (\sin x)\left[\dfrac{1}{2}(1 - \cos 2x)\right]^2$

$$= \frac{1}{4}(\sin x)(1 - 2\cos 2x + \cos^2 2x)$$

$$= \frac{1}{4}(\sin x)\left[1 - 2\cos 2x + \frac{1}{2}(1 + \cos 4x)\right]$$

$$= \frac{1}{8}(\sin x)(2 - 4\cos 2x + 1 + \cos 4x)$$

$$= \frac{1}{8}(\sin x)(3 - 4\cos 2x + \cos 4x).$$

Alternatively, take $\sin^5 x = \sin x \sin^4 x$ and apply the result of #39.

43. $\cos^2 x = \dfrac{1 - \cos x}{2}$, so $2\cos^2 x + \cos x - 1 = 0$. Then

$\cos x = -1$ or $\cos x = \dfrac{1}{2}$. In the interval $[0, 2\pi)$, $x = \dfrac{\pi}{3}$,

$x = \pi$, or $x = \dfrac{5\pi}{3}$. General solution: $= \pm\dfrac{\pi}{3} + 2n\pi$ or

$x = \pi + 2n\pi$, n an integer.

44. $1 - \cos^2 x = \dfrac{1 + \cos x}{2}$, so $2\cos^2 x + \cos x - 1 = 0$.

Then $\cos x = -1$ or $\cos x = \dfrac{1}{2}$. In the interval $[0, 2\pi)$,

$x = \dfrac{\pi}{3}$, $x = \pi$, or $x = \dfrac{5\pi}{3}$. General solution:

$x = \pm\dfrac{\pi}{3} + 2n\pi$ or $x = \pi + 2n\pi$, n an integer.

45. The right side equals $\tan^2(x/2)$; the only way that $\tan(x/2) = \tan^2(x/2)$ is if either $\tan(x/2) = 0$ or $\tan(x/2) = 1$. In $[0, 2\pi)$, this happens when $x = 0$ or

$x = \dfrac{\pi}{2}$. The general solution is $x = 2n\pi$ or

$x = \dfrac{\pi}{2} + 2n\pi$, n an integer.

46. $\dfrac{1 - \cos x}{2} = 2\cos^2 x - 1$, so $4\cos^2 x + \cos x - 3 = 0$,

or $(4\cos x - 3)(\cos x + 1) = 0$. Then $\cos x = -1$ or

$\cos x = \dfrac{3}{4}$. Let $\alpha = \cos^{-1}\left(\dfrac{3}{4}\right) \approx 0.7227$. In the interval

$[0, 2\pi)$, $x = \alpha$, $x = \pi$, or $x = 2\pi - \alpha$. General solution:
$x = \pm\alpha + 2n\pi$ or $x = \pi + 2n\pi$, n an integer.

47. False. For example, $f(x) = 2\sin x$ has period 2π and $g(x) = \cos x$ has period 2π, but the product $f(x)g(x) = 2\sin x \cos x = \sin 2x$ has period π.

48. True. $\cos^2 x = \dfrac{1 + \cos 2x}{2}$

$$= \frac{1}{2} + \frac{1}{2}\cos 2x$$

$$= \frac{1}{2}\sin\left(\frac{\pi}{2} - 2x\right) + \frac{1}{2}$$

$$= \frac{1}{2}\sin\left(-2\left(x - \frac{\pi}{4}\right)\right) + \frac{1}{2}$$

The last expression is in the form for a sinusoid.

49. $f(2x) = \sin 2x = 2\sin x \cos x = 2f(x)g(x)$. The answer is D.

50. $\sin 22.5° = \sin\left(\dfrac{45°}{2}\right)$

$$= \sqrt{\frac{1 - \cos 45°}{2}}$$

$$= \sqrt{\frac{1 - \sqrt{2}/2}{2}}$$

$$= \sqrt{\frac{2 - \sqrt{2}}{4}}$$

$$= \frac{\sqrt{2 - \sqrt{2}}}{2}$$

The answer is E.

51. $\sin 2x = \cos x$

$2\sin x \cos x = \cos x$

$2\sin x = 1$ or $\cos x = 0$

$\sin x = \dfrac{1}{2}$ or $\cos x = 0$

$x = \dfrac{\pi}{6}$ or $\dfrac{5\pi}{6}$ $x = \dfrac{\pi}{2}$ or $\dfrac{3\pi}{2}$

The answer is E.

52. $\sin^2 x - \cos^2 x = 1 - 2\cos^2 x$, which has the same period as the function $\cos^2 x$, namely π. The answer is C.

53. **(a)** In the figure, the triangle with side lengths $x/2$ and R is a right triangle, since R is given as the perpendicular distance. Then the tangent of the angle $\theta/2$ is the ratio "opposite over adjacent": $\tan\dfrac{\theta}{2} = \dfrac{x/2}{R}$ Solving for x gives the desired equation. The central angle θ is $2\pi/n$ since one full revolution of 2π radians is divided evenly into n sections.

(b) $5.87 \approx 2R\tan\dfrac{\theta}{2}$, where $\theta = 2\pi/11$, so

$$R \approx 5.87/(2\tan\dfrac{\pi}{11}) \approx 9.9957. \; R = 10.$$

54. **(a)**

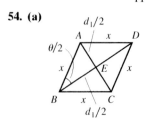

Call the center of the rhombus E. Consider right $\triangle ABE$, with legs $d_2/2$ and $d_1/2$, and hypotenuse length x. $\angle ABE$ has measure $\theta/2$, and using "sine equals $\dfrac{\text{opp}}{\text{hyp}}$" and "cosine equals $\dfrac{\text{adj}}{\text{hyp}}$," we have

$$\cos\frac{\theta}{2} = \frac{d_2/2}{x} = \frac{d_2}{2x} \text{ and } \sin\frac{\theta}{2} = \frac{d_1/2}{x} = \frac{d_1}{2x}.$$

(b) Use the double angle formula for the sine function:

$$\sin\theta = \sin 2\left(\frac{\theta}{2}\right) = 2\sin\frac{\theta}{2}\cos\frac{\theta}{2} = 2\frac{d_1}{2x}\cdot\frac{d_2}{2x} = \frac{d_1 d_2}{2x^2}$$

55. **(a)**

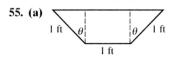

The volume is 10 ft times the area of the end. The end is made up of two identical triangles, with area $\dfrac{1}{2}(\sin\theta)(\cos\theta)$ each, and a rectangle with area $(1)(\cos\theta)$. The total volume is then $10\cdot(\sin\theta\cos\theta + \cos\theta) = 10(\cos\theta)(1 + \sin\theta)$.

Considering only $-\dfrac{\pi}{2} \le \theta \le \dfrac{\pi}{2}$, the maximum value occurs when $\theta \approx 0.52$ (in fact, it happens exactly at $\theta = \dfrac{\pi}{6}$). The maximum value is about 12.99 ft³.

56. **(a)**

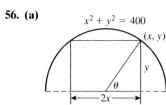

The height of the tunnel is y, and the width is $2x$, so the area is $2xy$. The x- and y-coordinates of the vertex are $20\cos\theta$ and $20\sin\theta$, so the area is $2(20\cos\theta)(20\sin\theta) = 400(2\cos\theta\sin\theta) = 400\sin 2\theta$.

(b) Considering $0 \le \theta \le \dfrac{\pi}{2}$, the maximum area occurs when $\theta = \dfrac{\pi}{4}$, or about 0.79. This gives

$$x = 20\cos\frac{\pi}{4} = 10\sqrt{2}, \text{ or about } 14.14, \text{ for a width of}$$

about 28.28, and a height of $y = 10\sqrt{2} \approx 14.14$

57. $\csc 2u = \dfrac{1}{\sin 2u} = \dfrac{1}{2\sin u\cos u} = \dfrac{1}{2}\cdot\dfrac{1}{\sin u}\cdot\dfrac{1}{\cos u}$

$\qquad = \dfrac{1}{2}\csc u\sec u$

58. $\cot 2u = \dfrac{1}{\tan 2u} = \dfrac{1 - \tan^2 u}{2\tan u}$

$\qquad = \left(\dfrac{1 - \tan^2 u}{2\tan u}\right)\left(\dfrac{\cot^2 u}{\cot^2 u}\right) = \dfrac{\cot^2 u - 1}{2\cot u}$

59. $\sec 2u = \dfrac{1}{\cos 2u} = \dfrac{1}{1 - 2\sin^2 u}$

$\qquad = \left(\dfrac{1}{1 - 2\sin^2 u}\right)\left(\dfrac{\csc^2 u}{\csc^2 u}\right) = \dfrac{\csc^2 u}{\csc^2 u - 2}$

60. $\sec 2u = \dfrac{1}{\cos 2u} = \dfrac{1}{2\cos^2 u - 1}$

$\qquad = \left(\dfrac{1}{2\cos^2 u - 1}\right)\left(\dfrac{\sec^2 u}{\sec^2 u}\right) = \dfrac{\sec^2 u}{2 - \sec^2 u}$

61. $\sec 2u = \dfrac{1}{\cos 2u} = \dfrac{1}{\cos^2 u - \sin^2 u}$

$\qquad = \left(\dfrac{1}{\cos^2 u - \sin^2 u}\right)\left(\dfrac{\sec^2 u\csc^2 u}{\sec^2 u\csc^2 u}\right)$

$\qquad = \dfrac{\sec^2 u\csc^2 u}{\csc^2 u - \sec^2 u}$

62. The second equation cannot work for any values of x for which $\sin x < 0$, since the square root cannot be negative. The first is correct since a double angle identity for the cosine gives $\cos 2x = 1 - 2\sin^2 x$; solving for $\sin x$ gives

$$\sin^2 x = \frac{1}{2}(1 - \cos 2x), \text{ so that}$$

$$\sin x = \pm\sqrt{\frac{1}{2}(1 - \cos 2x)}. \text{ The absolute value of both}$$

sides removes the "$\pm$."

63. **(a)** The following is a scatter plot of the days past January 1 as x-coordinates (L1) and the time (in 24 hour mode) as y-coordinates (L2) for the time of day that astronomical twilight began in northeastern Mali in 2005.

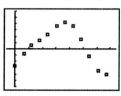

$[-30, 370]$ by $[-60, 60]$

(b) The sine regression curve through the points defined by L1 and L2 is $y = 41.656 \sin(0.015x - 0.825) - 1.473$. This is a fairly good fit, but not really as good as one might expect from data generated by a sinusoidal physical model.

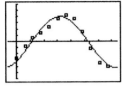

[−30, 370] by [−60, 60]

(c) Using the formula L2 − Y1(L1) (where Y1 is the sine regression curve), the residual list is:
{3.64, 7.56, 3.35, −5.94, −9.35, −3.90, 5.12, 9.43, 3.90, −4.57, −9.72, −3.22}.

(d) The following is a scatter plot of the days past January 1 as x-coordinates (L1) and the residuals (the difference between the actual number of minutes (L2) and the number of minutes predicted by the regression curve (Y1)) as y-coordinates (L3) for the time of day that astronomical twilight began in northeastern Mali in 2005.

The sine regression curve through the points defined by L1 and L3 is
$y = 8.856 \sin(0.0346x + 0.576) - 0.331$. (Note: Round L3 to 2 decimal places to obtain this answer.) This is another fairly good fit, which indicates that the residuals are not due to chance. There is a periodic variation that is most probably due to physical causes.

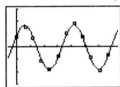

[−30, 370] by [−15, 15]

(e) The first regression indicates that the data are periodic and nearly sinusoidal. The second regression indicates that the *variation* of the data around the predicted values is also periodic and nearly sinusoidal. Periodic variation around periodic models is a predictable consequence of bodies orbiting bodies, but ancient astronomers had a difficult time reconciling the data with their simpler models of the universe.

■ Section 5.5 The Law of Sines

Exploration 1

1. If $BC \leq AB$, the segment will not reach from point B to the dotted line. On the other hand, if $BC > AB$, then a circle of radius BC will intersect the dotted line in a unique point. (Note that the line only extends to the left of point A.)

2. A circle of radius BC will be tangent to the dotted line at C if $BC = h$, thus determining a unique triangle. It will miss the dotted line entirely if $BC < h$, thus determining zero triangles.

3. The second point (C_2) is the reflection of the first point (C_1) on the other side of the altitude.

4. $\sin C_2 = \sin(\pi - C_1) = \sin \pi \cos C_1 - \cos \pi \sin C_1$
   $= \sin C_1$.

5. If $BC \geq AB$, then BC can only extend to the right of the altitude, thus determining a unique triangle.

Quick Review 5.5

1. $a = bc/d$

2. $b = ad/c$

3. $c = ad/b$

4. $d = bc/a$

5. $\dfrac{7 \sin 48°}{\sin 23°} \approx 13.314°$

6. $\dfrac{9 \sin 121°}{\sin 14°} \approx 31.888°$

7. $x = \sin^{-1} 0.3 \approx 17.458°$

8. $x = 180° - \sin^{-1} 0.3 \approx 162.542°$

9. $x = 180° - \sin^{-1}(-0.7) \approx 224.427°$

10. $x = 360° + \sin^{-1}(-0.7) \approx 315.573°$

Section 5.5 Exercises

1. Given: $b = 3.7$, $B = 45°$, $A = 60°$ — an AAS case.
   $C = 180° - (A + B) = 75°$;
   $$\frac{a}{\sin A} = \frac{b}{\sin B} \Rightarrow a = \frac{b \sin A}{\sin B} = \frac{3.7 \sin 60°}{\sin 45°} \approx 4.5;$$
   $$\frac{b}{\sin B} = \frac{c}{\sin C} \Rightarrow c = \frac{b \sin C}{\sin B} = \frac{3.7 \sin 75°}{\sin 45°} \approx 5.1$$

2. Given: $c = 17$, $B = 15°$, $C = 120°$ — an AAS case.
   $A = 180° - (B + C) = 45°$;
   $$\frac{a}{\sin A} = \frac{c}{\sin C} \Rightarrow a = \frac{c \sin A}{\sin C} = \frac{17 \sin 45°}{\sin 120°} \approx 13.9;$$
   $$\frac{b}{\sin B} = \frac{c}{\sin C} \Rightarrow b = \frac{c \sin B}{\sin C} = \frac{17 \sin 15°}{\sin 120°} \approx 5.1$$

3. Given: $A = 100°$, $C = 35°$, $a = 22$ — an AAS case.
   $B = 180° - (A + C) = 45°$;
   $$b = \frac{a \sin B}{\sin A} = \frac{22 \sin 45°}{\sin 100°} \approx 15.8;$$
   $$c = \frac{a \sin C}{\sin A} = \frac{22 \sin 35°}{\sin 100°} \approx 12.8$$

4. Given: $A = 81°$, $B = 40°$, $b = 92$ — an AAS case.
   $C = 180° - (A + B) = 59°$;
   $$a = \frac{b \sin A}{\sin B} = \frac{92 \sin 81°}{\sin 40°} \approx 141.4;$$
   $$c = \frac{b \sin C}{\sin B} = \frac{92 \sin 59°}{\sin 40°} \approx 122.7$$

5. Given: $A = 40°$, $B = 30°$, $b = 10$ — an AAS case.
   $C = 180° - (A + B) = 110°$;
   $$a = \frac{b \sin A}{\sin B} = \frac{10 \sin 40°}{\sin 30°} \approx 12.9;$$
   $$c = \frac{b \sin C}{\sin B} = \frac{10 \sin 110°}{\sin 30°} \approx 18.8$$

6. Given: $A = 50°$, $B = 62°$, $a = 4$ — an AAS case.
   $C = 180° - (A + B) = 68°$;
   $$b = \frac{a \sin B}{\sin A} = \frac{4 \sin 62°}{\sin 50°} \approx 4.6;$$
   $$c = \frac{a \sin C}{\sin A} = \frac{4 \sin 68°}{\sin 50°} \approx 4.8$$

7. Given: $A = 33°, B = 70°, b = 7$ — an AAS case.

$C = 180° - (A + B) = 77°$;

$a = \dfrac{b \sin A}{\sin B} = \dfrac{7 \sin 33°}{\sin 70°} \approx 4.1$;

$c = \dfrac{b \sin C}{\sin B} = \dfrac{7 \sin 77°}{\sin 70°} \approx 7.3$

8. Given: $B = 16°, C = 103°, c = 12$ — an AAS case.

$A = 180° - (B + C) = 61°$;

$a = \dfrac{c \sin A}{\sin C} = \dfrac{12 \sin 61°}{\sin 103°} \approx 10.8$;

$b = \dfrac{c \sin B}{\sin C} = \dfrac{12 \sin 16°}{\sin 103°} \approx 3.4$

9. Given: $A = 32°, a = 17, b = 11$ — an SSA case.

$h = b \sin A \approx 5.8; h < b < a$, so there is one triangle.

$B = \sin^{-1}\left(\dfrac{b \sin A}{a}\right) = \sin^{-1}(0.342...) \approx 20.1°$

$C = 180° - (A + B) \approx 127.9°$;

$c = \dfrac{a \sin C}{\sin A} = \dfrac{17 \sin 127.9°}{\sin 32°} \approx 25.3$

10. Given: $A = 49°, a = 32, b = 28$ — an SSA case.

$h = b \sin A \approx 21.1; h < b < a$, so there is one triangle.

$B = \sin^{-1}\left(\dfrac{b \sin A}{a}\right) = \sin^{-1}(0.660...) \approx 41.3°$

$C = 180° - (A + B) = 89.7°$;

$c = \dfrac{a \sin C}{\sin A} = \dfrac{32 \sin 89.7°}{\sin 49°} \approx 42.4$

11. Given: $B = 70°, b = 14, c = 9$ — an SSA case.

$h = c \sin B \approx 8.5; h < c < b$, so there is one triangle.

$C = \sin^{-1}\left(\dfrac{c \sin B}{b}\right) = \sin^{-1}(0.604...) \approx 37.2°$

$A = 180° - (B + C) \approx 72.8°$;

$a = \dfrac{b \sin A}{\sin B} = \dfrac{14 \sin 72.8°}{\sin 70°} \approx 14.2$

12. Given: $C = 103°, b = 46, c = 61$ — an SSA case.

$h = b \sin C \approx 44.8; h < b < c$, so there is one triangle.

$B = \sin^{-1}\left(\dfrac{b \sin C}{c}\right) = \sin^{-1}(0.734...) \approx 47.3°$

$A = 180° - (B + C) = 29.7°$;

$a = \dfrac{c \sin A}{\sin C} = \dfrac{61 \sin 29.7°}{\sin 103°} \approx 31.0$

13. Given: $A = 36°, a = 2, b = 7. h = b \sin A \approx 4.1$;

$a < h$, so no triangle is formed.

14. Given: $B = 82°, b = 17, c = 15. h = c \sin B \approx 14.9$;

$h < c < b$, so there is one triangle.

15. Given: $C = 36°, a = 17, c = 16. h = a \sin C \approx 10.0$;

$h < c < a$, so there are two triangles.

16. Given: $A = 73°, a = 24, b = 28. h = b \sin A \approx 26.8$;

$a < h$, so no triangle is formed.

17. Given: $C = 30°, a = 18, c = 9. h = a \sin C = 9$;

$h = c$, so there is one triangle.

18. Given: $B = 88°, b = 14, c = 62. h = c \sin B \approx 62.0$;

$b < h$, so no triangle is formed.

19. Given: $A = 64°, a = 16, b = 17. h = b \sin A \approx 15.3$;

$h < a < b$, so there are two triangles.

$B_1 = \sin^{-1}\left(\dfrac{b \sin A}{a}\right) = \sin^{-1}(0.954...) \approx 72.7°$

$C_1 = 180° - (A + B_1) \approx 43.3°$;

$c_1 = \dfrac{a \sin C_1}{\sin A} = \dfrac{16 \sin 43.3°}{\sin 64°} \approx 12.2$

Or (with B obtuse):

$B_2 = 180° - B_1 \approx 107.3°$;

$C_2 = 180° - (A + B_2) \approx 8.7°$;

$c_2 = \dfrac{a \sin C_2}{\sin A} \approx 2.7$

20. Given: $B = 38°, b = 21, c = 25. h = c \sin B \approx 15.4$;

$h < b < c$, so there are two triangles.

$C_1 = \sin^{-1}\left(\dfrac{c \sin B}{b}\right) = \sin^{-1}(0.732...) \approx 47.1°$

$A_1 = 180° - (B + C_1) \approx 94.9°$;

$a_1 = \dfrac{b \sin A_1}{\sin B} = \dfrac{21 \sin 94.9°}{\sin 38°} \approx 34.0$

Or (with C obtuse):

$C_2 = 180° - C_1 \approx 132.9°$;

$A_2 = 180° - (B + C_2) \approx 9.1°$;

$a_2 = \dfrac{b \sin A_2}{\sin B} \approx 5.4$

21. Given: $C = 68°, a = 19, c = 18. h = a \sin C \approx 17.6$;

$h < c < a$, so there are two triangles.

$A_1 = \sin^{-1}\left(\dfrac{a \sin C}{c}\right) = \sin^{-1}(0.978...) \approx 78.2°$

$B_1 = 180° - (A + C) \approx 33.8°$;

$b_1 = \dfrac{c \sin B_1}{\sin C} = \dfrac{18 \sin 33.8°}{\sin 68°} \approx 10.8$

Or (with A obtuse):

$A_2 = 180° - A_1 \approx 101.8°$;

$B_2 = 180° - (A_2 + C) \approx 10.2°$;

$b_2 = \dfrac{c \sin B_2}{\sin C} \approx 3.4$

22. Given: $B = 57°, a = 11, b = 10. h = a \sin B \approx 9.2$;

$h < b < a$, so there are two triangles.

$A_1 = \sin^{-1}\left(\dfrac{a \sin B}{b}\right) = \sin^{-1}(0.922...) \approx 67.3°$

$C_1 = 180° - (A_1 + B) \approx 55.7°$;

$c_1 = \dfrac{b \sin C_1}{\sin B} = \dfrac{10 \sin 55.7°}{\sin 57°} \approx 9.9$

Or (with A obtuse):

$A_2 = 180° - A_1 \approx 112.7°$;

$C_2 = 180° - (A_2 + B) \approx 10.3°$;

$c_2 = \dfrac{b \sin C_2}{\sin B} \approx 2.1$

23. $h = 10 \sin 42° \approx 6.691$, so:

(a) $6.691 < b < 10$.

(b) $b \approx 6.691$ or $b \geq 10$.

(c) $b < 6.691$

24. $h = 12 \sin 53° \approx 9.584$, so:

(a) $9.584 < c < 12$.

(b) $c \approx 9.584$ or $c \geq 12$.

(c) $c < 9.584$

25. (a) No: this is an SAS case

(b) No: only two pieces of information given.

26. (a) Yes: this is an AAS case.

$B = 180° - (A + C) = 32°;$

$b = \dfrac{a \sin B}{\sin A} = \dfrac{81° \sin 32°}{\sin 29°} \approx 88.5;$

$c = \dfrac{a \sin C}{\sin A} = \dfrac{81 \sin 119°}{\sin 29°} \approx 146.1$

(b) No: this is an SAS case.

27. Given: $A = 61°$, $a = 8$, $b = 21$ — an SSA case.

$h = b \sin A = 18.4$; $a < h$, so no triangle is formed.

28. Given: $B = 47°$, $a = 8$, $b = 21$ — an SSA case.

$h = a \sin B \approx 5.9$; $h < a < b$, so there is one triangle.

$A = \sin^{-1}\left(\dfrac{a \sin B}{b}\right) = \sin^{-1}(0.278\ldots) \approx 16.2°$

$C = 180° - (A + B) = 116.8°;$

$c = \dfrac{b \sin C}{\sin B} = \dfrac{21 \sin 116.8°}{\sin 47°} \approx 25.6$

29. Given: $A = 136°$, $a = 15$, $b = 28$ — an SSA case.

$h = b \sin A \approx 19.5$; $a < h$, so no triangle is formed.

30. Given: $C = 115°$, $b = 12$, $c = 7$ — an SSA case.

$h = b \sin C \approx 10.9$; $c < h$, so no triangle is formed.

31. Given: $B = 42°$, $c = 18$, $C = 39°$ — an AAS case.

$A = 180° - (B + C) = 99°;$

$a = \dfrac{c \sin A}{\sin C} = \dfrac{18 \sin 99°}{\sin 39°} \approx 28.3;$

$b = \dfrac{c \sin B}{\sin C} = \dfrac{18 \sin 42°}{\sin 39°} \approx 19.1$

32. Given: $A = 19°$, $b = 22$, $B = 47°$ — an AAS case.

$C = 180° - (A + B) = 114°;$

$a = \dfrac{b \sin A}{\sin B} = \dfrac{22 \sin 19°}{\sin 47°} \approx 9.8;$

$c = \dfrac{b \sin C}{\sin B} = \dfrac{22 \sin 114°}{\sin 47°} \approx 27.5$

33. Given: $C = 75°$, $b = 49$, $c = 48$. — an SSA case.

$h = b \sin C \approx 47.3$; $h < c < b$, so there are two triangles.

$B_1 = \sin^{-1}\left(\dfrac{b \sin C}{c}\right) = \sin^{-1}(0.986\ldots) \approx 80.4°$

$A_1 = 180° - (B + C) \approx 24.6°;$

$a_1 = \dfrac{c \sin A_1}{\sin C} = \dfrac{48 \sin 24.6°}{\sin 75°} \approx 20.7$

Or (with B obtuse):

$B_2 = 180° - B_1 \approx 99.6°;$

$A_2 = 180° - (B_2 + C) \approx 5.4°;$

$a_2 = \dfrac{c \sin A_2}{\sin C} \approx 4.7$

34. Given: $A = 54°$, $a = 13$, $b = 15$. — an SSA case.

$h = b \sin A \approx 12.1$; $h < a < b$, so there are two triangles.

$B_1 = \sin^{-1}\left(\dfrac{b \sin A}{a}\right) = \sin^{-1}(0.933\ldots) \approx 69.0°$

$C_1 = 180° - (A + B_1) \approx 57.0°;$

$c_1 = \dfrac{a \sin C_1}{\sin A} = \dfrac{13 \sin 57.0°}{\sin 54°} \approx 13.5$

Or (with B obtuse):

$B_2 = 180° - B_1 \approx 111.0°;$

$C_2 = 180° - (A + B_2) \approx 15.0°;$

$c_2 = \dfrac{a \sin C_2}{\sin A} \approx 4.2$

35. Cannot be solved by law of sines (an SAS case).

36. Cannot be solved by law of sines (an SAS case).

37. Given: $c = AB = 56$, $A = 72°$, $B = 53°$ — an ASA case, so $C = 180° - (A + B) = 55°$

(a) $AC = b = \dfrac{c \sin B}{\sin C} = \dfrac{56 \sin 53°}{\text{in } 55°} \approx 54.6$ ft.

(b) $h = b \sin A(\ = \ a \sin B) \approx 51.9$ ft.

38. Given: $c = 25$, $A = 90° - 38° = 52°$, $B = 90° - 53° = 37°$ — an ASA case, so $C = 180° - (A + B) = 91°$ and

$a = \dfrac{c \sin A}{\sin C} = \dfrac{25 \sin 52°}{\sin 91°} \approx 19.7$ mi.

$b = \dfrac{c \sin B}{\sin C} = \dfrac{25 \sin 37°}{\sin 91°} \approx 15.0$ mi,

and finally $h = b \sin A = a \sin B \approx 11.9$ mi.

39. Given: $c = 16$, $C = 90° - 62 = 28°$, $B = 90° + 15° = 105°$ — an AAS case. $A = 180° - (B + C) = 47°$, so

$a = \dfrac{c \sin A}{\sin C} = \dfrac{16 \sin 47°}{\sin 28°} \approx 24.9$ ft.

40. Given: $c = 2.32$, $A = 28°$, $B = 37°$ — an ASA case. $C = 180° - (A + B) = 115°;$

$a = \dfrac{c \sin A}{\sin C} = \dfrac{2.32 \sin 28°}{\sin 115°} \approx 1.2$ mi.

$b = \dfrac{c \sin B}{\sin C} = \dfrac{2.32 \sin 37°}{\sin 115°} \approx 1.5$ mi.

Therefore, the altitude is $h = b \sin A \approx (1.5) \sin 28°$ ≈ 0.7 mi — or $a \sin B \approx (1.2) \sin 37°$ mi ≈ 0.7 mi.

41.

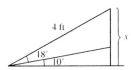

The length of the brace is the leg of the larger triangle.

$\sin 28° = \dfrac{x}{4}$, so $x = 1.9$ ft.

42.

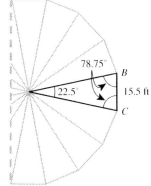

The center of the wheel (A) and two adjacent chairs (B and C) form a triangle with $a = 15.5$, $A = \dfrac{360°}{16}$ $= 22.5°$, and $B = C = 78.75°$. This is an ASA case, so the radius is $b = c = \dfrac{a \sin B}{\sin A} = \dfrac{15.5 \sin 78.75°}{\sin 22.5°} \approx 39.7$ ft.

Alternatively, let D be the midpoint of $\overline{BC}$, and consider right $\triangle ABD$, with $m\angle BAD = 11.25°$ and $BD = 7.75$ ft; then r is the hypotenuse of this triangle, so

$r = \dfrac{7.75}{\sin 11.25°} \approx 39.7$ ft.

43. Consider the triangle with vertices at the top of the flag-pole (A) and the two observers (B and C). Then $a = 600$, $B = 19°$, and $C = 21°$ (an ASA case), so
$$A = 180° - (B + C) = 140°;$$
$$b = \frac{a \sin B}{\sin A} = \frac{600 \sin 19°}{\sin 140°} \approx 303.9;$$
$$c = \frac{a \sin C}{\sin A} = \frac{600 \sin 21°}{\sin 140°} \approx 334.5$$
and finally $h = b \sin C = c \sin B \approx 108.9$ ft.

44. Consider the triangle with vertices at the top of the tree (A) and the two observers (B and C). Then $a = 400$, $B = 15°$, and $C = 20°$ (an ASA case), so
$$A = 180° - (B + C) = 145°;$$
$$b = \frac{a \sin B}{\sin A} = \frac{400 \sin 15°}{\sin 145°} \approx 180.5;$$
$$c = \frac{a \sin C}{\sin A} = \frac{400 \sin 20°}{\sin 145°} \approx 238.5;$$
and finally $h = b \sin C = c \sin B \approx 61.7$ ft.

45. Given: $c = 20$, $B = 52°$, $C = 33°$ — an AAS case.
$A = 180° - (B + C) = 95°$, so
$$a = \frac{c \sin A}{\sin C} = \frac{20 \sin 95°}{\sin 33°} \approx 36.6 \text{ mi, and}$$
$$b = \frac{c \sin B}{\sin C} = \frac{20 \sin 52°}{\sin 33°} \approx 28.9 \text{ mi.}$$

46. We use the mean (average) measurements for A, B, and AB, which are $79.7°$, $83.9°$, and 25.9 feet, respectively. This gives $16.4°$ for angle C. By the Law of Sines,
$$AC = \frac{25.9 \sin 83.9°}{\sin 16.4°} \approx 91.2 \text{ feet.}$$

47. True. By the law of sines, $\dfrac{\sin A}{a} = \dfrac{\sin B}{b}$,
which is equivalent to $\dfrac{\sin A}{\sin B} = \dfrac{a}{b}$ (since $\sin A$, $\sin B \neq 0$).

48. False. By the law of sines, the third side of the triangle measures $\dfrac{10 \sin 100°}{\sin 40°}$, which is about 15.32 inches. That makes the perimeter about $10 + 10 + 15.32 = 35.32$, which is less than 36 inches.

49. The third angle is $32°$. By the Law of Sines,
$$\frac{\sin 32°}{12.0} = \frac{\sin 53°}{x}, \text{ which can be solved for } x.$$
The answer is C.

50. With SSA, the known side opposite the known angle sometimes has two different possible positions. The answer is D.

51. The longest side is opposite the largest angle, while the shortest side is opposite the smallest angle. By the Law of Sines, $\dfrac{\sin 50°}{9.0} = \dfrac{\sin 70°}{x}$, which can be solved for x.
The answer is A.

52. Because $BC > AB$, only one triangle is possible. The answer is B.

53. (a) Given any triangle with side lengths a, b, and c, the law of sines says that $\dfrac{\sin A}{a} = \dfrac{\sin B}{b} = \dfrac{\sin C}{c}$.
But we can also find another triangle(using ASA) with two angles the same as the first (in which case the third angle is also the same) and a different side

length — say, a'. Suppose that $a' = ka$ for some constant k. Then for this new triangle, we have
$$\frac{\sin A}{a'} = \frac{\sin B}{b'} = \frac{\sin C}{c'}. \text{ Since } \frac{\sin A}{a'} = \frac{\sin A}{ka} =$$
$\dfrac{1}{k} \cdot \dfrac{\sin A}{a}$, we can see that $\dfrac{\sin B}{b'} = \dfrac{1}{k} \cdot \dfrac{\sin B}{b}$,
so that $b' = kb$ and similarly, $c' = kc$. So for any choice of a positive constant k, we can create a triangle with angles A, B, and C.

(b) Possible answers: $a = 1, b = \sqrt{3}, c = 2$ (or any set of three numbers proportional to these).

(c) Any set of three identical numbers.

54. In each proof, assume that sides a, b, and c are opposite angles A, B, and C, and that c is the hypotenuse.

(a) $\dfrac{\sin A}{a} = \dfrac{\sin 90°}{c}$
$$\frac{\sin A}{a} = \frac{1}{c}$$
$$\sin A = \frac{a}{c} = \frac{opp}{hyp}$$

(b) $\dfrac{\sin B}{b} = \dfrac{\sin 90°}{c}$
$$\frac{\cos(\pi/2 - B)}{b} = \frac{1}{c}$$
$$\cos A = \frac{b}{c} = \frac{adj}{hyp}$$

(c) $\dfrac{\sin A}{a} = \dfrac{\sin B}{b}$
$$\frac{\sin A}{\sin B} = \frac{a}{b}$$
$$\frac{\sin A}{\cos A} = \frac{a}{b}$$
$$\tan A = \frac{a}{b} = \frac{opp}{adj}$$

55. (a) $h = AB \sin A$

(b) $BC < AB \sin A$

(c) $BC \geq AB$ or $BC = AB \sin A$

(d) $AB \sin A < BC < AB$

56. Drawing the line suggested in the hint, and extending $\overline{BC}$ to meet that line at, say, D, gives right $\triangle ADC$ and right $\triangle ADB$.

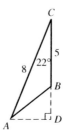

Then $AD = 8 \sin 22° \approx 3.0$ and $DC = 8 \cos 22° \approx 7.4$, so $DB = DC - 5$ and
$$c = AB = \sqrt{AD^2 + DB^2} \approx 3.9. \text{ Finally,}$$
$$A = (90° - 22°) - \sin^{-1}\left(\frac{DB}{AB}\right) \approx 29.1° \text{ and}$$
$$B = 180° - A - C \approx 128.9°.$$

57. Given: $c = 4.1, B = 25°, C = 36.5° - 25° = 11.5°$. An AAS case: $A = 180° - (B + C) = 143.5°$, so

$$AC = b = \frac{c \sin B}{\sin C} = \frac{4.1 \sin 25°}{\sin 11.5°} \approx 8.7 \text{ mi, and}$$

$$BC = a = \frac{c \sin A}{\sin C} = \frac{4.1 \sin 143.5°}{\sin 11.5°} \approx 12.2 \text{ mi.}$$

The height is $h = a \sin 25° = b \sin 36.5° \approx 5.2$ mi.

■ Section 5.6   The Law of Cosines

Exploration 1

1. The semiperimeters are 154 and 150.
$$A = \sqrt{154(154 - 115)(154 - 81)(154 - 112)}$$
$$+ \sqrt{150(150 - 112)(150 - 102)(150 - 86)}$$
$$= 8475.742818 \text{ paces}^2$$

2. 41,022.59524 square feet

3. 0.0014714831 square miles

4. 0.94175 acres

5. The estimate of "a little over an acre" seems questionable, but the roughness of their measurement system does not provide firm evidence that it is incorrect. If Jim and Barbara wish to make an issue of it with the owner, they would be well-advised to get some more reliable data.

6. Yes. In fact, any polygonal region can be subdivided into triangles.

Quick Review 5.6

1. $A = \cos^{-1}\left(\frac{3}{5}\right) \approx 53.130°$

2. $C = \cos^{-1}(-0.23) \approx 103.297°$

3. $A = \cos^{-1}(-0.68) \approx 132.844°$

4. $C = \cos^{-1}\left(\frac{1.92}{3}\right) \approx 50.208°$

5. (a) $\cos A = \dfrac{81 - x^2 - y^2}{-2xy} = \dfrac{x^2 + y^2 - 81}{2xy}$.

(b) $A = \cos^{-1}\left(\dfrac{x^2 + y^2 - 81}{2xy}\right)$

6. (a) $\cos A = \dfrac{y^2 - x^2 - 25}{-10} = \dfrac{x^2 - y^2 + 25}{10}$

(b) $A = \cos^{-1}\left(\dfrac{x^2 - y^2 + 25}{10}\right)$

7. One answer: $(x - 1)(x - 2) = x^2 - 3x + 2$.
Generally: $(x - a)(x - b) = x^2 - (a + b)x + ab$ for any two positive numbers a and b.

8. One answer: $(x - 1)(x + 1) = x^2 - 1$.
Generally, $(x - a)(x + b) = x^2 - (a - b)x - ab$ for any two positive numbers a and b.

9. One answer: $(x - i)(x + i) = x^2 + 1$

10. One answer: $(x - 1)^2 = x^2 - 2x + 1$.
Generally: $(x - a)^2 = x^2 - 2ax + a^2$ for any positive number a.

Section 5.6 Exercises

1. Given: $B = 131°, c = 8, a = 13$ — an SAS case.
$$b = \sqrt{a^2 + c^2 - 2ac \cos B} \approx \sqrt{369.460} \approx 19.2;$$
$$C = \cos^{-1}\left(\frac{a^2 + b^2 - c^2}{2ab}\right) \approx \cos^{-1}(0.949) \approx 18.3°;$$
$$A = 180° - (B + C) \approx 30.7°.$$

2. Given: $C = 42°, b = 12, a = 14$ — an SAS case.
$$c = \sqrt{a^2 + b^2 - 2ab \cos C} \approx \sqrt{90.303} \approx 9.5;$$
$$A = \cos^{-1}\left(\frac{b^2 + c^2 - a^2}{2bc}\right) \approx \cos^{-1}(0.167) \approx 80.3°;$$
$$B = 180° - (A + C) \approx 57.7°.$$

3. Given: $a = 27, b = 19, c = 24$ — an SSS case.
$$A = \cos^{-1}\left(\frac{b^2 + c^2 - a^2}{2bc}\right) \approx \cos^{-1}(0.228) \approx 76.8°;$$
$$B = \cos^{-1}\left(\frac{a^2 + c^2 - b^2}{2ac}\right) \approx \cos^{-1}(0.728) \approx 43.2°;$$
$$C = 180° - (A + B) \approx 60°.$$

4. Given: $a = 28, b = 35, c = 17$ — an SSS case.
$$A = \cos^{-1}\left(\frac{b^2 + c^2 - a^2}{2bc}\right) \approx \cos^{-1}(0.613) \approx 52.2°;$$
$$B = \cos^{-1}\left(\frac{a^2 + c^2 - b^2}{2ac}\right) \approx \cos^{-1}(-0.159) \approx 99.2°;$$
$$C = 180° - (A + B) \approx 28.6°.$$

5. Given: $A = 55°, b = 12, c = 7$ — an SAS case.
$$a = \sqrt{b^2 + c^2 - 2bc \cos A} \approx \sqrt{96.639} \approx 9.8;$$
$$B = \cos^{-1}\left(\frac{a^2 + c^2 - b^2}{2ac}\right) \approx \cos^{-1}(0.011) \approx 89.3°;$$
$$C = 180° - (A + B) \approx 35.7°.$$

6. Given: $B = 35°, a = 43, c = 19$ — an SAS case.
$$b = \sqrt{a^2 + c^2 - 2ac \cos B} \approx \sqrt{871.505} \approx 29.5;$$
$$C = \cos^{-1}\left(\frac{a^2 + b^2 - c^2}{2ab}\right) \approx \cos^{-1}(0.929) \approx 21.7°;$$
$$A = 180° - (B + C) \approx 123.3°.$$

7. Given: $a = 12, b = 21, C = 95°$ — an SAS case.
$$c = \sqrt{a^2 + b^2 - 2ab \cos C} \approx \sqrt{628.926} \approx 25.1;$$
$$A = \cos^{-1}\left(\frac{b^2 + c^2 - a^2}{2bc}\right) \approx \cos^{-1}(0.879) \approx 28.5°;$$
$$B = 180° - (A + C) \approx 56.5°.$$

8. Given: $b = 22, c = 31, A = 82°$ — an SAS case.
$$a = \sqrt{b^2 + c^2 - 2bc \cos A} \approx \sqrt{1255.167} \approx 35.4;$$
$$B = \cos^{-1}\left(\frac{a^2 + c^2 - b^2}{2ac}\right) \approx \cos^{-1}(0.788) \approx 37.9°;$$
$$C = 180° - (A + B) \approx 60.1°.$$

9. No triangles possible $(a + c = b)$

10. No triangles possible $(a + b < c)$

11. Given: $a = 3.2, b = 7.6, c = 6.4$ — an SSS case.
$$A = \cos^{-1}\left(\frac{b^2 + c^2 - a^2}{2bc}\right) \approx \cos^{-1}(0.909) \approx 24.6°;$$
$$B = \cos^{-1}\left(\frac{a^2 + c^2 - b^2}{2ac}\right) \approx \cos^{-1}(-0.160) \approx 99.2°;$$
$$C = 180° - (A + B) \approx 56.2°.$$

12. No triangles possible ($a + b < c$)

Exercises 13–16 are SSA cases, and can be solved with either the Law of Sines or the Law of Cosines. The law of cosines solution is shown.

13. Given: $A = 42°$, $a = 7$, $b = 10$ — an SSA case. Solve the quadratic equation $7^2 = 10^2 + c^2 - 2(10)c \cos 42°$, or $c^2 - (14.862...)c + 51 = 0$; there are two positive solutions: ≈ 9.487 *or* 5.376. Since $\cos B = \dfrac{a^2 + c^2 - b^2}{2ac}$:

$c_1 \approx 9.487$, $B_1 \approx \cos^{-1}(0.294) \approx 72.9°$, and
$C_1 = 180° - (A + B_1) \approx 65.1°$,
or
$c_2 \approx 5.376$, $B_2 \approx \cos^{-1}(-0.294) \approx 107.1°$, and
$C_2 = 180° - (A + B_2) \approx 30.9°$.

14. Given: $A = 57°$, $a = 11$, $b = 10$ — an SSA case. Solve the quadratic equation $11^2 = 10^2 + c^2 - 2(10)C \cos 57°$, or $c^2 - (10.893)c - 21 = 0$; there is one positive solution $c = 12.564$. Since $\cos B = \dfrac{a^2 + c^2 - b^2}{2ac}$,
$B \approx \cos^{-1}(0.647) \approx 49.7°$ and $C = 180° - (A + B) \approx 73.3°$.

15. Given: $A = 63°$, $a = 8.6$, $b = 11.1$ — an SSA case. Solve the quadratic equation
$8.6^2 = 11.1^2 + c^2 - 2(11.1)c \cos 63°$, or
$c^2 - (10.079)c + 49.25 = 0$; there are no real solutions, so there is no triangle.

16. Given: $A = 71°$, $a = 9.3$, $b = 8.5$ — an SSA case. Solve the quadratic equation
$9.3^2 = 8.5^2 + c^2 - 2(8.5)c \cos 71°$, or
$c^2 - (5.535)c - 14.24 = 0$; there is one positive solution: $c \approx 7.447$. Since $\cos B = \dfrac{a^2 + c^2 - b^2}{2ac}$,
$B \approx \cos^{-1}(0.503) \approx 59.8°$ and $C = 180° - (A + B) \approx 49.2°$.

17. Given: $A = 47°$, $b = 32$, $c = 19$ — an SAS case.
$a = \sqrt{b^2 + c^2 - 2bc \cos A} \approx \sqrt{555.689} \approx 23.573$,
so Area $\approx \sqrt{49431.307} \approx 222.33$ ft^2 (using Heron's formula). Or, use $A = \dfrac{1}{2}bc \sin A$.

18. Given: $A = 52°$, $b = 14$, $c = 21$ — an SAS case.
$a = \sqrt{b^2 + c^2 - 2bc \cos A} \approx \sqrt{274.991} \approx 16.583$,
so Area $\approx \sqrt{13418.345} \approx 115.84$ m^2 (using Heron's formula). Or, use $A = \dfrac{1}{2}bc \sin A$.

19. Given: $B = 101°$, $a = 10$, $c = 22$ — an SAS case.
$b = \sqrt{a^2 + c^2 - 2ac \cos B} \approx \sqrt{667.955} \approx 25.845$,
so Area $\approx \sqrt{11659.462} \approx 107.98$ cm^2 (using Heron's formula). Or, use $A = \dfrac{1}{2}ac \sin B$.

20. Given: $C = 112°$, $a = 1.8$, $b = 5.1$ — an SAS case.
$c = \sqrt{a^2 + b^2 - 2ab \cos C} \approx \sqrt{36.128} \approx 6.011$,
so Area $\approx \sqrt{18.111} \approx 4.26$ in.^{2} (using Heron's formula). Or, use $A = \dfrac{1}{2}ab \sin C$.

For #21–28, a triangle can be formed if $a + b < c$, $a + c < b$, and $b + c < a$.

21. $s = \dfrac{17}{2}$; Area $= \sqrt{66.9375} \approx 8.18$

22. $s = \dfrac{21}{2}$; Area $= \sqrt{303.1875} \approx 17.41$

23. No triangle is formed ($a + b = c$).

24. $s = 27$; Area $= \sqrt{12,960} = 36\sqrt{10} \approx 113.84$

25. $a = 36.4$; Area $= \sqrt{46,720.3464} \approx 216.15$

26. No triangle is formed ($a + b < c$)

27. $s = 42.1$; Area $= \sqrt{98,629.1856} \approx 314.05$

28. $s = 23.8$; Area $\sqrt{10,269.224} \approx 101.34$

29. Let $a = 4$, $b = 5$, and $c = 6$. The largest angle is opposite the largest side, so we call it C. Since
$\cos C = \dfrac{a^2 + b^2 - c^2}{2ab}$, $C = \cos^{-1}\left(\dfrac{1}{8}\right) \approx 82.819°$
≈ 1.445 radians.

30. The shorter diagonal splits the parallelogram into two (congruent) triangles with $a = 26$, $B = 39°$, and $c = 18$.
The diagonal has length $b = \sqrt{a^2 + c^2 - 2ac \cos B}$
$\approx \sqrt{272.591} \approx 16.5$ ft.

31. Following the method of Example 3, divide the hexagon into 6 triangles. Each has two 12-inch sides that form a 60° angle.
$6 \times \dfrac{1}{2}(12)(12)\sin 60° = 216\sqrt{3} \approx 374.1$ square inches

32. Following the method of Example 3, divide the nonagon into 9 triangles. Each has two 10-inch sides that form a 40° angle.
$9 \times \dfrac{1}{2}(10)(10)\sin 40° \approx 289.3$ square inches

33.

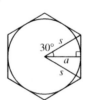

In the figure, $a = 12$ and so $s = 12 \sec 30° = 8\sqrt{3}$. The area of the hexagon is
$6 \times \dfrac{1}{2}(8\sqrt{3})(8\sqrt{3})\sin 60° = 288\sqrt{3}$
≈ 498.8 square inches.

34.

In the figure, $a = 10$ and so $s = 10 \sec 20°$. The area of the nonagon is
$9 \times \dfrac{1}{2}(10 \sec 20°)(10 \sec 20°)\sin 40°$
≈ 327.6 square inches.

35. Given: $C = 54°$, $BC = a = 160$, $AC = b = 110$ — an SAS case. $AB = c = \sqrt{a^2 + b^2 - 2ab \cos C}$
$\approx \sqrt{17,009.959} \approx 130.42$ ft.

36. **(a)** The home-to-second segment is the hypotenuse of a right triangle, so the distance from the pitcher's rubber to second base is $90\sqrt{2} - 60.5 \approx 66.8$ ft. This is a bit more than
$c = \sqrt{60.5^2 + 90^2 - 2(60.5)(90) \cos 45°}$
$\approx \sqrt{4059.857} \approx 63.7$ ft.

(b) $B = \cos^{-1}\left(\dfrac{a^2 + c^2 - b^2}{2ac}\right) \approx \cos^{-1}(-0.049)$
$\approx 92.8°$.

37. **(a)** $c = \sqrt{40^2 + 60^2 - 2(40)(60) \cos 45°}$
$\approx \sqrt{1805.887} \approx 42.5$ ft.

(b) The home-to-second segment is the hypotenuse of a right triangle, so the distance from the pitcher's rubber to second base is $60\sqrt{2} - 40 \approx 44.9$ ft.

(c) $B = \cos^{-1}\left(\dfrac{a^2 + c^2 - b^2}{2ac}\right) \approx \cos^{-1}(-0.057)$
$\approx 93.3°$.

38. Given: $a = 175$, $b = 860$, and $C = 78°$. An SAS case, so
$AB = c = \sqrt{a^2 + b^2 - 2ab \cos C} \approx \sqrt{707,643.581}$
≈ 841.2 ft.

39. **(a)** Using right $\triangle ACE$, $m\angle CAE = \tan^{-1}\left(\dfrac{6}{18}\right)$
$= \tan^{-1}\left(\dfrac{1}{3}\right) \approx 18.435°$.

(b) Using $A \approx 18.435°$, we have an SAS case, so
$DF = \sqrt{9^2 + 12^2 - 2(9)(12) \cos A} \approx \sqrt{20.084}$
≈ 4.5 ft.

(c) $EF = \sqrt{18^2 + 12^2 - 2(18)(12) \cos A} \approx \sqrt{58.168}$
≈ 7.6 ft.

40. After two hours, the planes have traveled 700 and 760 miles, and the angle between them is 22.5°, so the
distance is $\sqrt{700^2 + 760^2 - 2(700)(760) \cos 22.5°}$
$\approx \sqrt{84,592.177} \approx 290.8$ mi.

41. $AB = \sqrt{73^2 + 65^2 - 2(73)(65) \cos 8°}$
$\approx \sqrt{156.356} \approx 12.5$ yd.

42. $m\angle HAB = 135°$, so
$HB = \sqrt{20^2 + 20^2 - 2(20)(20) \cos 135°}$
$\approx \sqrt{1365.685} \approx 37.0$ ft.
Note that $\overline{AB}$ is the hypotenuse of an equilateral right
triangle with leg length $\dfrac{20}{\sqrt{2}} = 10\sqrt{2}$, and $\overline{HC}$ is the
hypotenuse of an equilateral right triangle with leg length
$20 + 10\sqrt{2}$, so $HC = \sqrt{2(20 + 10\sqrt{2})^2} \approx 48.3$ ft.
Finally, using right $\triangle HAD$ with leg lengths
$HA = 20$ ft and $AD = HC \approx 48.3$ ft, we have
$HD = \sqrt{HA^2 + AD^2} \approx 52.3$ ft.

43. $AB = c = \sqrt{2^2 + 3^2} = \sqrt{13}$, $AC = b = \sqrt{1^2 + 3^2}$
$= \sqrt{10}$, and $BC = a = \sqrt{1^2 + 2^2} = \sqrt{5}$, so
$m\angle CAB = A = \cos^{-1}\left(\dfrac{b^2 + c^2 - a^2}{2bc}\right)$
$= \cos^{-1}\left(\dfrac{9}{\sqrt{130}}\right) \approx 37.9°$.

44. $\triangle ABC$ is a right triangle ($C = 90°$), with $BC = a$
$= \sqrt{2^2 + 2^2} = 2\sqrt{2}$ and $AC = b = 1$, so $AB = c$
$= \sqrt{a^2 + b^2} = 3$ and $B = m\angle ABC = \sin^{-1}\left(\dfrac{1}{3}\right)$
$\approx 19.5°$.

45. True. By the Law of Cosines, $b^2 + c^2 - 2bc \cos A = a^2$, which is a positive number. Since $b^2 + c^2 - 2bc \cos A > 0$, it follows that $b^2 + c^2 > 2bc \cos A$.

46. True. The diagonal opposite angle θ splits the parallelogram into two congruent triangles, each with area $\dfrac{1}{2} ab \sin \theta$.

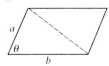

47. Following the method of Example 3, divide the dodecagon into 12 triangles. Each has two 12-inch sides that form a 30° angle.
$12 \times \dfrac{1}{2} (12)(12) \sin 30° = 432$
The answer is B.

48. The semiperimeter is $s = (7 + 8 + 9)/2 = 12$. Then by Heron's Formula, $A = \sqrt{12(12 - 7)(12 - 8)(12 - 9)}$
$= 12\sqrt{5}$. The answer is B.

49. After 30 minutes, the first boat has traveled 12 miles and the second has traveled 16 miles. By the Law of Cosines, the two boats are $\sqrt{12^2 + 16^2 - 2(12)(16) \cos 110°} \approx 23.05$ miles apart. The answer is C.

50. By the Law of Cosines, $12^2 = 17^2 + 25^2 - 2(17)(25)$
$\cos \theta$, so $\theta = \cos^{-1}\left(\dfrac{17^2 + 25^2 - 12^2}{2(17)(25)}\right) \approx 25.06°$.
The answer is E.

51. Consider that a n-sided regular polygon inscribed within a circle can divide into n equilateral triangles, each with equal area of $\dfrac{r^2}{2} \sin \dfrac{360°}{n}$. (The two equal sides of the equilateral triangle are of length r, the radius of the circle.) Then, the area of the polygon is exactly $\dfrac{nr^2}{2} \sin \dfrac{360°}{n}$.

52. **(a)** $\dfrac{b^2 + c^2 - a^2}{2abc} = \dfrac{b^2 + c^2 - (b^2 + c^2 - 2bc \cos A)}{2abc}$ Law of Cosines
$= \dfrac{2bc \cos A}{2abc}$
$= \dfrac{\cos A}{a}$

(b) The identity in (a) has two other equivalent forms:
$\dfrac{\cos B}{b} = \dfrac{a^2 + c^2 - b^2}{2abc}$
$\dfrac{\cos C}{c} = \dfrac{a^2 + b^2 - c^2}{2abc}$

We use them all in the proof:

$$\frac{\cos A}{a} + \frac{\cos B}{b} + \frac{\cos C}{c}$$

$$= \frac{b^2 + c^2 - a^2}{2abc} + \frac{a^2 + c^2 - b^2}{2abc} + \frac{a^2 + b^2 - c^2}{2abc}$$

$$= \frac{b^2 + c^2 - a^2 + a^2 + c^2 - b^2 + a^2 + b^2 - c^2}{2abc}$$

$$= \frac{a^2 + b^2 + c^2}{2abc}$$

53. (a) Ship A: $\dfrac{30.2 - 15.1}{1 \text{ hr}} = 15.1$ knots;

Ship B: $\dfrac{37.2 - 12.4}{2 \text{ hrs}} = 12.4$ knots

(b) $\cos A = \dfrac{b^2 + c^2 - a^2}{2bc}$

$$= \frac{(15.1)^2 + (12.4)^2 - (8.7)^2}{2(15.1)(12.4)}$$

$$A = 35.18°$$

(c) $c^2 = a^2 + b^2 - 2ab \cos C$

$$= (49.6)^2 + (60.4)^2 - 2(49.6)(60.4) \cos (35.18°)$$

$$\approx 1211.04, \text{ so the boats are 34.8 nautical miles}$$
apart at noon.

54. Use the area formula and the Law of Sines:

$$A_\Delta = \frac{1}{2} ab \sin C$$

$$= \frac{1}{2} a \left(\frac{a \sin B}{\sin A} \right) \sin C \left(\text{Law of Sines} \Rightarrow b = \frac{a \sin B}{\sin A} \right)$$

$$= \frac{a^2 \sin B \sin C}{2 \sin a}$$

55. Let P be the center of the circle. Then,

$$\cos P = \frac{5^2 + 5^2 - 7^2}{2(5)(5)} = 0.02 \text{ , so } P \approx 88.9°. \text{ The area}$$

of the segment is $\pi r^2 \cdot \dfrac{88.9°}{360°} \approx 25\pi \cdot (0.247) \approx 19.39 \text{ in}^2$.

The area of the triangle, however, is $\dfrac{1}{2}(5)(5) \sin (88.9)$

$\approx 12.50 \text{ in}^2$, so the area of the shaded region is approx. 6.9 in^2.

■ Chapter 5 Review

1. $2 \sin 100° \cos 100° = \sin 200°$

2. $\dfrac{2 \tan 40°}{1 - \tan^2 40°} = \tan 80°$

3. 1; the expression simplifies to $(\cos 2\theta)^2 + (2 \sin \theta \cos \theta)^2 = (\cos 2\theta)^2 + (\sin 2\theta)^2 = 1$.

4. $\cos^2 2x$; the expression can be rewritten $1 - (2 \sin x \cos x)^2 = 1 - (\sin 2x)^2 = \cos^2 2x$.

5. $\cos 3x = \cos(2x + x) = \cos 2x \cos x - \sin 2x \sin x$
$$= (\cos^2 x - \sin^2 x) \cos x - (2 \sin x \cos x) \sin x$$
$$= \cos^3 x - 3 \sin^2 x \cos x$$
$$= \cos^3 x - 3(1 - \cos^2 x)\cos x$$
$$= \cos^3 x - 3 \cos x + 3 \cos^3 x$$
$$= 4 \cos^3 x - 3 \cos x$$

6. $\cos^2 2x - \cos^2 x = (1 - \sin^2 2x) - (1 - \sin^2 x)$
$$= \sin^2 x - \sin^2 2x$$

7. $\tan^2 x - \sin^2 x = \sin^2 x \left(\dfrac{1 - \cos^2 x}{\cos^2 x} \right)$

$$= \sin^2 x \cdot \frac{\sin^2 x}{\cos^2 x} = \sin^2 x \tan^2 x$$

8. $2 \sin \theta \cos^3 \theta + 2 \sin^3 \theta \cos \theta$
$$= (2 \sin \theta \cos \theta)(\cos^2 \theta + \sin^2 \theta)$$
$$= (2 \sin \theta \cos \theta)(1) = \sin 2\theta.$$

9. $\csc x - \cos x \cot x = \dfrac{1}{\sin x} - \cos x \cdot \dfrac{\cos x}{\sin x}$

$$= \frac{1 - \cos^2 x}{\sin x} = \frac{\sin^2 x}{\sin x} = \sin x$$

10. $\dfrac{\tan \theta + \sin \theta}{2 \tan \theta} = \dfrac{1 + \cos \theta}{2} = \left(\pm \sqrt{\dfrac{1 + \cos \theta}{2}} \right)^2$

$$= \left(\cos \frac{\theta}{2} \right)^2$$

11. Recall that $\tan \theta \cot \theta = 1$. $\dfrac{1 + \tan \theta}{1 - \tan \theta} + \dfrac{1 + \cot \theta}{1 - \cot \theta}$

$$= \frac{(1 + \tan \theta)(1 - \cot \theta) + (1 + \cot \theta)(1 - \tan \theta)}{(1 - \tan \theta)(1 - \cot \theta)}$$

$$= \frac{(1 + \tan \theta - \cot \theta - 1) + (1 + \cot \theta - \tan \theta - 1)}{(1 - \tan \theta)(1 - \cot \theta)}$$

$$= \frac{0}{(1 - \tan \theta)(1 - \cot \theta)} = 0$$

12. $\sin 3\theta = \sin(2\theta + \theta) = \sin 2\theta \cos \theta + \cos 2\theta \sin \theta$
$$= 2 \sin \theta \cos^2 \theta + (\cos^2 \theta - \sin^2 \theta) \sin \theta$$
$$= 3 \sin \theta \cos^2 \theta - \sin^3 \theta$$

13. $\cos^2 \dfrac{t}{2} = \left[\pm \sqrt{\dfrac{1}{2}(1 + \cos t)} \right]^2 = \dfrac{1}{2}(1 + \cos t)$

$$= \left(\frac{1 + \cos t}{2} \right) \left(\frac{\sec t}{\sec t} \right) = \frac{1 + \sec t}{2 \sec t}$$

14. $\dfrac{\tan^3 \gamma - \cot^3 \gamma}{\tan^2 \gamma + \csc^2 \gamma}$

$$= \frac{(\tan \gamma - \cot \gamma)(\tan^2 \gamma + \tan \gamma \cot \gamma + \cot^2 \gamma)}{\tan^2 \gamma + \csc^2 \gamma}$$

$$= \frac{(\tan \gamma - \cot \gamma)(\tan^2 \gamma + 1 + \cot^2 \gamma)}{\tan^2 \gamma + \csc^2 \gamma}$$

$$= \frac{(\tan \gamma - \cot \gamma)(\tan^2 \gamma + \csc^2 \gamma)}{\tan^2 \gamma + \csc^2 \gamma} = \tan \gamma - \cot \gamma$$

15. $\dfrac{\cos \phi}{1 - \tan \phi} + \dfrac{\sin \phi}{1 - \cot \phi}$

$$= \left(\frac{\cos \phi}{1 - \tan \phi} \right) \left(\frac{\cos \phi}{\cos \phi} \right) + \left(\frac{\sin \phi}{1 - \cot \phi} \right) \left(\frac{\sin \phi}{\sin \phi} \right)$$

$$= \frac{\cos^2 \phi}{\cos \phi - \sin \phi} + \frac{\sin^2 \phi}{\sin \phi - \cos \phi} = \frac{\cos^2 \phi - \sin^2 \phi}{\cos \phi - \sin \phi}$$

$$= \cos \phi + \sin \phi$$

16. $\dfrac{\cos(-z)}{\sec(-z) + \tan(-z)} = \dfrac{\cos(-z)}{[1 + \sin(-z)]/\cos(-z)}$

$$= \frac{\cos^2(-z)}{1 + \sin(-z)} = \frac{\cos^2 z}{1 - \sin z} = \frac{1 - \sin^2 z}{1 - \sin z} = 1 + \sin z$$

17. $\sqrt{\dfrac{1-\cos y}{1+\cos y}} = \sqrt{\dfrac{(1-\cos y)^2}{(1+\cos y)(1-\cos y)}}$

$= \sqrt{\dfrac{(1-\cos y)^2}{1-\cos^2 y}} = \sqrt{\dfrac{(1-\cos y)^2}{\sin^2 y}}$

$= \dfrac{|1-\cos y|}{|\sin y|} = \dfrac{1-\cos y}{|\sin y|}$ — since $1-\cos y \geq 0$,

we can drop that absolute value.

18. $\sqrt{\dfrac{1-\sin \gamma}{1+\sin \gamma}} = \sqrt{\dfrac{(1-\sin \gamma)(1+\sin \gamma)}{(1+\sin \gamma)^2}}$

$= \sqrt{\dfrac{1-\sin^2 \gamma}{(1+\sin \gamma)^2}} = \sqrt{\dfrac{\cos^2 \gamma}{(1+\sin \gamma)^2}}$

$= \dfrac{|\cos \gamma|}{|1+\sin \gamma|} = \dfrac{|\cos \gamma|}{1+\sin \gamma}$ — since $1+\sin \gamma \geq 0$,

we can drop that absolute value.

19. $\tan\left(u + \dfrac{3\pi}{4}\right) = \dfrac{\tan u + \tan(3\pi/4)}{1 - \tan u \tan(3\pi/4)}$

$= \dfrac{\tan u + (-1)}{1 - \tan u(-1)} = \dfrac{\tan u - 1}{1 + \tan u}$

20. $\dfrac{1}{4}\sin 4\gamma = \dfrac{1}{4}\sin 2(2\gamma) = \dfrac{1}{4}(2\sin 2\gamma \cos 2\gamma)$

$= \dfrac{1}{2}(2\sin \gamma \cos \gamma)(\cos^2 \gamma - \sin^2 \gamma)$

$= \sin \gamma \cos^3 \gamma - \cos \gamma \sin^3 \gamma$

21. $\tan\dfrac{1}{2}\beta = \dfrac{1-\cos \beta}{\sin \beta} = \dfrac{1}{\sin \beta} - \dfrac{\cos \beta}{\sin \beta} = \csc \beta - \cot \beta$

22. Let $\theta = \arctan t$, so that $\tan \theta = t$. Then

$\tan 2\theta = \dfrac{2\tan \theta}{1 - \tan^2 \theta} = \dfrac{2t}{1 - t^2}$. Note also that since

$-1 < t < 1, -\dfrac{\pi}{4} < \theta < \dfrac{\pi}{4}$, and therefore $-\dfrac{\pi}{2} < 2\theta < \dfrac{\pi}{2}$.

That means that 2θ is in the range of the arctan function,

and so $2\theta = \arctan\dfrac{2t}{1 - t^2}$, or equivalently

$\theta = \dfrac{1}{2}\arctan\dfrac{2t}{1 - t^2}$ — and of course, $\theta = \arctan t$.

23. Yes: $\sec x - \sin x \tan x = \dfrac{1}{\cos x} - \dfrac{\sin^2 x}{\cos x}$

$= \dfrac{1 - \sin^2 x}{\cos x} = \dfrac{\cos^2 x}{\cos x} = \cos x$.

24. Yes: $(\sin^2 \alpha - \cos^2 a)(\tan^2 \alpha + 1)$

$= (\sin^2 \alpha - \cos^2 \alpha)(\sec^2 \alpha)$

$= \dfrac{\sin^2 \alpha - \cos^2 \alpha}{\cos^2 \alpha} = \dfrac{\sin^2 \alpha}{\cos^2 \alpha} - 1 = \tan^2 \alpha - 1$.

25. Many answers are possible, for example,

$\sin 3x + \cos 3x$

$= (3\sin x - 4\sin^3 x) + (4\cos^3 x - 3\cos x)$

$= 3(\sin x - \cos x) - 4(\sin^3 x - \cos^3 x)$

$= (\sin x - \cos x)[3 - 4(\sin^2 x + \sin x \cos x + \cos^2 x)]$

$= (\sin x - \cos x)(3 - 4 - 4\sin x \cos x)$

$= (\cos x - \sin x)(1 + 4\sin x \cos x)$. Check

other answers with a grapher.

26. Many answers are possible, for example,

$\sin 2x + \cos 3x = 2\sin x \cos x + 4\cos^3 x - 3\cos x$

$= \cos x(2\sin x + 4\cos^2 x - 3)$

$= \cos x(2\sin x + 1 - 4\sin^2 x)$. Check other answers

with a grapher.

27. Many answers are possible, for example,

$\cos^2 2x - \sin 2x = 1 - \sin^2 2x - \sin 2x$

$= 1 - 4\sin^2 x \cos^2 x - 2\sin x \cos x$. Check other

answers with a grapher.

28. Many answers are possible, for example (using Review

Exercise #12), $\sin 3x - 3\sin 2x$

$= 3\cos^2 x \sin - \sin^3 x - 6\sin x \cos x$

$= \sin x(3\cos^2 x - \sin^2 x - 6\cos x)$

$= \sin x(4\cos^2 x - 1 - 6\cos x)$. Check other answers

with a grapher.

In #29–33, n represents any integer.

29. $\sin 2x = 0.5$ when $2x = \dfrac{\pi}{6} + 2n\pi$ or $2x = \dfrac{5\pi}{6} + 2n\pi$,

so $x = \dfrac{\pi}{12} + n\pi$ or $x = \dfrac{5\pi}{12} + n\pi$.

30. $\cos x = \dfrac{\sqrt{3}}{2}$ when $x = \pm\dfrac{\pi}{6} + 2n\pi$

31. $\tan x = -1$ when $x = -\dfrac{\pi}{4} + n\pi$

32. If $\sin^{-1} x = \dfrac{\sqrt{2}}{2}$, then $x = \sin\dfrac{\sqrt{2}}{2}$.

33. If $\tan^{-1} x = 1$, then $x = \tan 1$.

34.
$$2\cos 2x = 1$$
$$\cos 2x = \dfrac{1}{2}$$
$$2\cos^2 x - 1 = \dfrac{1}{2}$$
$$\cos^2 x = \dfrac{3}{4}$$
$$\cos x = \pm\dfrac{\sqrt{3}}{2}$$

So $x = \dfrac{\pi}{6} + 2n\pi$ or $x = \dfrac{5\pi}{6} + 2n\pi$ for n any integer.

35. $x \approx 1.12$ or $x \approx 5.16$

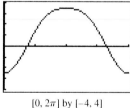

[0, 2π] by [−4, 4]

36. $x \approx 0.14$ or $x \approx 3.79$

[0, 2π] by [−3, 2]

37. $x \approx 1.15$

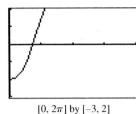

[0, 2π] by [−3, 2]

38. $x \approx 1.85$ or $x \approx 3.59$

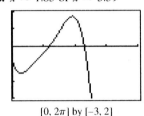

[0, 2π] by [−3, 2]

39. $\cos x = \dfrac{1}{2}$, so $x = \dfrac{\pi}{3}$ or $x = \dfrac{5\pi}{3}$.

40. $\sin 3x = (\sin x)(4 \cos^2 x - 1)$. This equation becomes $(\sin x)(4 \cos^2 x - 1) = \sin x$, or $2(\sin x)(2 \cos^2 x - 1) = 0$, so $\sin x = 0$ or $\cos x = \pm\dfrac{\sqrt{2}}{2}$; $x = 0$, $x = \dfrac{\pi}{4}$, $x = \dfrac{3\pi}{4}$, $x = \pi$, $x = \dfrac{5\pi}{4}$, or $x = \dfrac{7\pi}{4}$.

41. The left side factors to $(\sin x - 3)(\sin x + 1) = 0$; only $\sin x = -1$ is possible, so $x = \dfrac{3\pi}{2}$.

42. $2 \cos^2 t - 1 = \cos t$, or $2 \cos^2 t - \cos t - 1 = 0$, or $(2 \cos t + 1)(\cos t - 1) = 0$. Then $\cos t = -\dfrac{1}{2}$ or $\cos t = 1$: $t = 0$, $t = \dfrac{2\pi}{3}$ or $t = \dfrac{4\pi}{3}$.

43. $\sin(\cos x) = 1$ only if $\cos x = \dfrac{\pi}{2} + 2n\pi$. No choice of n gives a value in $[-1, 1]$, so there are no solutions.

44. $\cos(2x) + 5 \cos x - 2 = 2 \cos^2 x - 1 + 5 \cos x - 2 = 2 \cos^2 x + 5 \cos x - 3 = 0$. $(2 \cos x - 1)(\cos x + 3) = 0$, so $\cos(x) = \dfrac{1}{2}$ and $\cos(x) = -3$. The latter is extraneous so $x = \left\{ \dfrac{\pi}{3}, \dfrac{5\pi}{3} \right\}$

For #45–48, use graphs to suggest the intervals. To find the endpoints of the intervals, treat the inequalities as equations and solve.

45. $\cos 2x = \dfrac{1}{2}$ has solutions $x = \dfrac{\pi}{6}$, $x = \dfrac{5\pi}{6}$, $x = \dfrac{7\pi}{6}$, and $x = \dfrac{11\pi}{6}$ in interval $[0, 2\pi)$. The solution set for the inequality is, $0 \leq x < \dfrac{\pi}{6}$ or $\dfrac{5\pi}{6} < x < \dfrac{7\pi}{6}$ or $\dfrac{11\pi}{6} < x < 2\pi$; that is, $\left[0, \dfrac{\pi}{6} \right) \cup \left(\dfrac{5\pi}{6}, \dfrac{7\pi}{6} \right) \cup \left(\dfrac{11\pi}{6}, 2\pi \right)$.

46. $2 \sin x \cos x = 2 \cos x$ is equivalent to $(\cos x)(\sin x - 1) = 0$, so the solutions in $(0, 2\pi]$ are $x = \dfrac{\pi}{2}$ and $x = \dfrac{3\pi}{2}$. The solution set for the inequality is $\dfrac{\pi}{2} < x < \dfrac{3\pi}{2}$; that is, $\left(\dfrac{\pi}{2}, \dfrac{3\pi}{2} \right)$.

47. $\cos x = \dfrac{1}{2}$ has solutions $x = \dfrac{\pi}{3}$ and $x = \dfrac{5\pi}{3}$ in the interval $[0, 2\pi)$. The solution set for the inequality is $\dfrac{\pi}{3} < x < \dfrac{5\pi}{3}$; that is, $\left(\dfrac{\pi}{3}, \dfrac{5\pi}{3} \right)$.

48. $\tan x = \sin x$ is equivalent to $(\sin x)(\cos x - 1) = 0$, so the only solution in $\left(-\dfrac{\pi}{2}, \dfrac{\pi}{2} \right)$ is $x = 0$. The solution set for the inequality is $-\dfrac{\pi}{2} < x < 0$; that is, $\left(-\dfrac{\pi}{2}, 0 \right)$.

49. $y = 5 \sin (3x + \cos^{-1}(3/5)) \approx 5 \sin (3x + 0.9273)$

50. $y = 13 \sin (2x - \cos^{-1}(5/13)) \approx 13 \sin (2x - 1.176)$

51. Given: $A = 79°$, $B = 33°$, $a = 7$ — an AAS case.
$C = 180° - (A + B) = 68°$
$b = \dfrac{a \sin B}{\sin A} = \dfrac{7 \sin 33°}{\sin 79°} \approx 3.9$;
$c = \dfrac{a \sin C}{\sin A} = \dfrac{7 \sin 68°}{\sin 79°} \approx 6.6$.

52. Given: $a = 5$, $b = 8$, $B = 110°$ — an SSA case. Using the Law of Sines: $h = a \sin B = 4.7$; $h < a < b$, so there is one triangle.
$A = \sin^{-1}\left(\dfrac{a \sin B}{b} \right) \approx \sin^{-1}(0.587) \approx 36.0°$;
$C = 180° - (A + B) \approx 34.0°$;
$c = \dfrac{b \sin C}{\sin B} \approx \dfrac{8 \sin 34.0°}{\sin 110°} \approx 4.8$.
Using Law of Cosines: Solve the quadratic equation $8^2 = 5^2 + c^2 - 2(5)c \cos 110°$, or $c^2 + (3.420)c - 39 = 0$; there is one positive solution: $c \approx 4.8$. Since $\cos A = \dfrac{b^2 + c^2 - a^2}{2bc}$:
$A \approx \cos^{-1}(0.809) \approx 36.0°$ and $C = 180° - (A + B) \approx 34.0°$.

53. Given: $a = 8$, $b = 3$, $B = 30°$ — an SSA case. Using the Law of Sines: $h = a \sin B = 4$; $b < h$, so no triangle is formed. Using the Law of Cosines: Solve the quadratic equation $3^2 = 8^2 + c^2 - 2(8)c \cos 30°$, or $c^2 - (8\sqrt{3})c + 55 = 0$; there are no real solutions.

54. Given: $a = 14.7$, $A = 29.3°$, $C = 33°$ — an AAS case.
$B = 180° - (A + C) = 117.7°$, and
$b = \dfrac{a \sin B}{\sin A} = \dfrac{14.7 \sin 117.7°}{\sin 29.3°} \approx 26.6$;
$c = \dfrac{a \sin C}{\sin A} = \dfrac{14.7 \sin 33°}{\sin 29.3°} \approx 16.4$.

55. Given: $A = 34°$, $B = 74°$, $c = 5$ — an ASA case.
$C = 180° - (A + B) = 72°$;
$a = \dfrac{c \sin A}{\sin C} = \dfrac{5 \sin 34°}{\sin 72°} \approx 2.9$;
$b = \dfrac{c \sin B}{\sin C} = \dfrac{5 \sin 74°}{\sin 72°} \approx 5.1$.

56. Given: $c = 41$, $A = 22.9°$, $C = 55.1°$ — an AAS case.
$B = 180° - (A + C) = 102°$;
$$a = \frac{c \sin A}{\sin C} = \frac{41 \sin 22.9°}{\sin 55.1°} \approx 19.5;$$
$$b = \frac{c \sin B}{\sin C} = \frac{41 \sin 102°}{\sin 55.1°} \approx 48.9.$$

57. Given: $a = 5$, $b = 7$, $c = 6$ — an SSS case.
$$A = \cos^{-1}\left(\frac{b^2 + c^2 - a^2}{2bc}\right) \approx \cos^{-1}(0.714) \approx 44.4°;$$
$$B = \cos^{-1}\left(\frac{a^2 + c^2 - b^2}{2ac}\right) \approx \cos^{-1}(0.2) \approx 78.5°;$$
$$C = 180° - (A + B) \approx 57.1°.$$

58. Given: $A = 85°$, $a = 6$, $b = 4$ — an SSA case. Using the Law of Sines: $h = b \sin A \approx 4.0$; $h < b < a$, so there is one triangle.
$$B = \sin^{-1}\left(\frac{b \sin A}{a}\right) \approx \sin^{-1}(0.664) \approx 41.6°;$$
$$C = 180° - (A + B) \approx 53.4°;$$
$$c = \frac{a \sin C}{\sin A} = \frac{6 \sin 53.4°}{\sin 85°} \approx 4.8.$$

Using the Law of Cosines: Solve the quadratic equation $6^2 = 4^2 + c^2 - 2(4)c \cos 85°$, or $c^2 - (0.697)c - 20 = 0$; there is one positive solution:
$c \approx 4.8$. Since $\cos B = \frac{a^2 + c^2 - b^2}{2ac}$:
$B \approx \cos^{-1}(0.747) \approx 41.6°$ and $C = 180° - (A + B)$
$\approx 53.4°$.

59. $s = \frac{1}{2}(3 + 5 + 6) = 7$;
$$\text{Area} = \sqrt{s(s - a)(s - b)(s - c)}$$
$$= \sqrt{7(7 - 3)(7 - 5)(7 - 6)}$$
$$= \sqrt{56} \approx 7.5$$

60. $c \approx 7.672$ so area $\approx \sqrt{528.141} \approx 23.0$ (using Heron's formula). Or, use $A = \frac{1}{2}ab \sin C$.

61. $h = 12 \sin 28° \approx 5.6$, so:

  (a) $\approx 5.6 < b < 12$.

  (b) $b \approx 5.6$ or $b \geq 12$.

  (c) $b < 5.6$.

62. (a) $C = 180° - (A + B) = 45°$, so
$$AC = b = \frac{c \sin B}{\sin C} = \frac{80 \sin 65°}{\sin 45°} \approx 102.5 \text{ ft.}$$

  (b) The distance across the canyon is $b \sin A \approx 96.4$ ft.

63. Given: $c = 1.75$, $A = 33°$, $B = 37°$ — an ASA case, so
$C = 180° - (A + B) = 110°$;
$$a = \frac{c \sin A}{\sin C} = \frac{1.75 \sin 33°}{\sin 110°} \approx 1.0;$$
$$b = \frac{c \sin B}{\sin C} = \frac{1.75 \sin 37°}{\sin 110°} \approx 1.1,$$
and finally, the height is $h = b \sin A = a \sin b \approx 0.6$ mi.

64. Given: $C = 70°$, $a = 225$, $b = 900$ — an SAS case, so
$AB = c = \sqrt{a^2 + b^2 - 2ab \cos C}$
$\approx \sqrt{722,106.841} \approx 849.77$ ft.

65. Let $a = 8$, $b = 9$, and $c = 10$. The largest angle is opposite the largest side, so we call it C.
Since $\cos C = \frac{a^2 + b^2 - c^2}{2ab}$, $C = \cos^{-1}\left(\frac{5}{16}\right)$
$\approx 71.790°$, 1.253 rad.

66. The shorter diagonal splits the parallelogram into two (congruent) triangles with $a = 15$, $B = 40°$, and $c = 24$. The shorter diagonal has length $b = \sqrt{a^2 + b^2 - 2ac \cos B} \approx \sqrt{249.448} \approx 15.794$ ft. Since adjacent angles are supplementary, the other angle is $140°$. The longer diagonal splits the parallelogram into (two) congruent triangles with $a = 15$, $B = 140°$, and $c = 24$, so the longer diagonal length is $b = \sqrt{a^2 + c^2 - 2ac \cos B} \approx \sqrt{1352.552} \approx 36.777$ ft.

67. (a) The point (x, y) has coordinates $(\cos \theta, \sin \theta)$, so the bottom is $b_1 = 2$ units wide, the top is $b_2 = 2x = 2 \cos \theta$ units wide, and the height is $h = y = \sin \theta$ units. Either use the formula for the area of a trapezoid, $A = \frac{1}{2}(b_1 + b_2)h$, or notice that the trapezoid can be split into two triangles and a rectangle. Either way:
$A(\theta) = \sin \theta + \sin \theta \cos \theta = \sin \theta(1 + \cos \theta)$
$= \sin \theta + \frac{1}{2} \sin 2\theta.$

  (b) The maximizing angle is $\theta = \frac{\pi}{3} = 60°$; the maximum area is $\frac{3}{4}\sqrt{3} \approx 1.30$ square units.

68. (a) Substituting the values of a and b:
$$S(\theta) = 6.825 + 0.63375(-\cot \theta + \sqrt{3} \cdot \csc \theta)$$
$$= 6.825 + \frac{0.63375(\sqrt{3} - \cos \theta)}{\sin \theta}$$

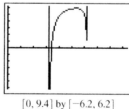

[0, 9.4] by [−6.2, 6.2]

  (b) Considering only angles between 0 and π, the minimum occurs when $\theta \approx 0.96 \approx 54.74°$.

  (c) The minimum value of S is approximately $S(0.96) \approx 7.72$ in.^{2}

69. (a) Split the quadrilateral in half to leave two (identical) right triangles, with one leg 4000 mi, hypotenuse $4000 + h$ mi, and one acute angle $\theta/2$.
Then $\cos \frac{\theta}{2} = \frac{4000}{4000 + h}$; solve for h to leave
$$h = \frac{4000}{\cos(\theta/2)} - 4000 = 4000 \sec \frac{\theta}{2} - 4000 \text{ miles.}$$

  (b) $\cos \frac{\theta}{2} = \frac{4000}{4200}$, so $\theta = 2 \cos^{-1}\left(\frac{20}{21}\right) \approx 0.62 \approx 35.51°$.

70. Rewrite the left side of the equation as follows:

$\sin x - \sin 2x + \sin 3x$

$= \sin x - 2\sin x \cos x + \sin(2x + x)$

$= \sin x - 2\sin x \cos x + \sin 2x \cos x + \cos 2x \sin x$

$= \sin x - 2\sin x \cos x + 2\sin x \cos^2 x +$
$\quad (\cos^2 x - \sin^2 x)\sin x$

$= \sin x - 2\sin x \cos x + 2\sin x \cos^2 x +$
$\quad \sin x \cos^2 x - \sin^3 x$

$= \sin x - 2\sin x \cos x + 3\sin x \cos^2 x - \sin^3 x$

$= \sin x\,(1 - 2\cos x + 3\cos^2 x - \sin^2 x)$

$= \sin x\,((1 - \sin^2 x) - 2\cos x + 3\cos^2 x)$

$= \sin x\,(\cos^2 x - 2\cos x + 3\cos^2 x)$

$= \sin x\,(4\cos^2 x - 2\cos x)$

$= 2\sin x \cos x\,(2\cos x - 1)$

$= \sin 2x\,(2\cos x - 1)$

So $\sin 2x = 0$ or $2\cos x - 1 = 0$. So $x = n\dfrac{\pi}{2}$ or $x = \pm\dfrac{\pi}{3} + 2n\pi$, n an integer.

71. The hexagon is made up of 6 equilateral triangles; using Heron's formula (or some other method), we find that each triangle has area $\sqrt{24(24-16)^3}$ $= \sqrt{12{,}288} = 64\sqrt{3}$. The hexagon's area is therefore, $384\sqrt{3}$ cm^2, and the radius of the circle is 16 cm, so the area of the circle is 256π cm^2, and the area outside the hexagon is $256\pi - 384\sqrt{3} \approx 139.140$ cm^2.

72. The pentagon is made up of 5 triangles with base length 12 cm and height $\dfrac{6}{\tan 36°} \approx 8.258$ cm, so its area is about 247.749 cm^2. The radius of the circle is the height of those triangles, so the desired area is about $247.749 - \pi(8.258)^2 \approx 33.51$ cm^2.

73. The volume of a cylinder with radius r and height h is $V = \pi r^2 h$, so the wheel of cheese has volume $\pi(9^2)(5) = 405\pi$ cm^3; a $15°$ wedge would have fraction $\dfrac{15}{360} = \dfrac{1}{24}$ of that volume, or $\dfrac{405\pi}{24} \approx 53.01$ cm^3.

74. (a) $\dfrac{1}{2}(\cos(u-v) - \cos(u+v))$

$= \dfrac{1}{2}(\cos u \cos v + \sin u \sin v$
$\quad - (\cos u \cos v - \sin u \sin v))$

$= \dfrac{1}{2}(2\sin u \sin v)$

$= \sin u \sin v$

(b) $\dfrac{1}{2}(\cos(u-v) + \cos(u+v))$

$= \dfrac{1}{2}(\cos u \cos v + \sin u \sin v + \cos u \cos v$
$\quad - \sin u \sin v)$

$= \dfrac{1}{2}(2\cos u \cos v)$

$= \cos u \cos v$

(c) $\dfrac{1}{2}(\sin(u+v) + \sin(u-v))$

$= \dfrac{1}{2}(\sin u \cos v + \cos u \sin v + \sin u \cos v$
$\quad - \cos u \sin v)$

$= \dfrac{1}{2}(2\sin u \cos v)$

$= \sin u \cos v$

75. (a) By the product-to-sum formula in 74 (c),

$2\sin\dfrac{u+v}{2}\cos\dfrac{u-v}{2}$

$= 2\cdot\dfrac{1}{2}\left(\sin\dfrac{u+v+u-v}{2}\right.$
$\qquad\qquad \left. + \sin\dfrac{u+v-(u-v)}{2}\right)$

$= \sin u + \sin v$

(b) By the product-to-sum formula in 74 (c),

$2\sin\dfrac{u-v}{2}\cos\dfrac{u+v}{2}$

$= 2\cdot\dfrac{1}{2}\left(\sin\dfrac{u-v+u+v}{2}\right.$
$\qquad\qquad \left. + \sin\dfrac{u-v-(u+v)}{2}\right)$

$= \sin u + \sin(-v)$

$= \sin u - \sin v$

(c) By the product-to-sum formula in 74 (b),

$2\cos\dfrac{u+v}{2}\cos\dfrac{u-v}{2}$

$= 2\cdot\dfrac{1}{2}\left(\cos\dfrac{u+v-(u-v)}{2}\right.$
$\qquad\qquad \left. + \cos\dfrac{u+v+u-v}{2}\right)$

$= \cos v + \cos u$

$= \cos u + \cos v$

(d) By the product-to-sum formula in 74 (a),

$-2\sin\dfrac{u+v}{2}\sin\dfrac{u-v}{2}$

$= -2\cdot\dfrac{1}{2}\left(\cos\dfrac{u+v-(u-v)}{2}\right.$
$\qquad\qquad \left. - \cos\dfrac{u+v+u-v}{2}\right)$

$= -(\cos v - \cos u)$

$= \cos u - \cos v$

76. Pat faked the data. The Law of Cosines can be solved to show that $x = 12\sqrt{\dfrac{2}{1-\cos\theta}}$. Only Carmen's values are consistent with the formula.

77. (a) Any inscribed angle that intercepts an arc of $180°$ is a right angle.

(b) Two inscribed angles that intercept the same arc are congruent.

(c) In right $\triangle A'BC$, $\sin A' = \dfrac{opp}{hyp} = \dfrac{a}{d}$.

(d) Because $\angle A'$ and $\angle A$ are congruent, $\dfrac{\sin A}{a} = \dfrac{\sin A'}{a} = \dfrac{a/d}{a} = \dfrac{1}{d}$.

(e) Of course. They both equal $\dfrac{\sin A}{a}$ by the Law of Sines.

Chapter 5 Project

1.

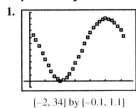

[–2, 34] by [–0.1, 1.1]

2. We set the amplitude as half the difference between the maximum value, 1.00, and the minimum value, 0.00, so $a = 0.5$. And we set the average value as the average of the maximum and minimum values, so $k = 0.5$. Since $\cos(b(x - h))$ takes on its maximum value at h, we set $h = 29$. Experimenting with the graph suggests that b should be about $2\pi/30.5$. So the equation is

$$y \approx 0.5 \cos\left(\frac{2\pi}{30.5}(x - 29)\right) + 0.5.$$

5. Using the identities from Questions 3 and 4 together,

$$y \approx 0.5 \cos\left(\frac{2\pi}{30.5}(x - 29)\right) + 0.5$$
$$= 0.5 \cos\left(\frac{2\pi}{30.5}(29 - x)\right) + 0.5$$
$$= 0.5 \sin\left(\frac{\pi}{2} - \frac{2\pi}{30.5}(29 - x)\right) + 0.5$$
$$= 0.5 \sin\left(\frac{2\pi}{30.5}(x - 21.375)\right) + 0.5,$$

which is equivalent to
$y \approx 0.5 \sin(0.21x - 4.4) + 0.5$.
Sinusoidal regression yields
$y \approx 0.5 \sin(0.21x + 1.87) + 0.49$.

Chapter 6
Applications of Trigonometry

■ Section 6.1 Vectors in the Plane

Exploration 1

1. Use the HMT rule, which states that if an arrow has initial point (x_1, y_1) and terminal point (x_2, y_2), it represents the vector $\langle x_2 - x_1, y_2 - y_1 \rangle$. If the initial point is $(2, 3)$ and the terminal point is $(7, 5)$, the vector is $\langle 7 - 2, 5 - 3 \rangle = \langle 5, 2 \rangle$.

2. Use the HMT rule, which states that if an arrow has initial point (x_1, y_1) and terminal point (x_2, y_2), it represents the vector $\langle x_2 - x_1, y_2 - y_1 \rangle$. If the initial point is $(3, 5)$ and the terminal point is (x_2, y_2), the vector is $\langle x_2 - 3, y_2 - 5 \rangle$. Using the given vector $\langle -3, 6 \rangle$, we have $x_2 - 3 = -3$ and $y_2 - 5 = 6$.
$x_2 - 3 = -3 \Rightarrow x_2 = 0; y_2 - 5 = 6 \Rightarrow y_2 = 11$.
The terminal point is $(0, 11)$.

3. Use the HMT rule, which states that if an arrow has initial point (x_1, y_1) and terminal point (x_2, y_2), it represents the vector $\langle x_2 - x_1, y_2 - y_1 \rangle$. If the initial point P is $(4, -3)$ and the terminal point Q is (x_2, y_2), the vector $\overrightarrow{PQ}$ is $\langle x_2 - 4, y_2 - (-3) \rangle$. Using the given vector $\overrightarrow{PQ}\langle 2, -4 \rangle$, we have $x_2 - 4 = 2$ and $y_2 + 3 = -4$.
$x_2 - 4 = 2 \Rightarrow x_2 = 6; y_2 + 3 = -4 \Rightarrow y_2 = -7$.
The point Q is $(6, -7)$.

4. Use the HMT rule, which states that if an arrow has initial point (x_1, y_1) and terminal point (x_2, y_2), it represents the vector $\langle x_2 - x_1, y_2 - y_1 \rangle$. If the initial point P is (x_1, y_1) and the terminal point Q is $(4, -3)$, the vector $\overrightarrow{PQ}$ is $\langle 4 - x_1, -3 - y_1 \rangle$. Using the given vector $\overrightarrow{PQ}\langle 2, -4 \rangle$, we have $4 - x_1 = 2$ and $-3 - y_1 = -4$.
$4 - x_1 = 2 \Rightarrow x_1 = 2; -3 - y_1 = -4 \Rightarrow y_1 = 1$.
The point P is $(2, 1)$.

Quick Review 6.1

1. $x = 9 \cos 30° = \dfrac{9\sqrt{3}}{2}, y = 9 \sin 30° = 4.5$

2. $x = 15 \cos 120° = -7.5, y = 15 \sin 120° = \dfrac{15\sqrt{3}}{2}$

3. $x = 7 \cos 220° \approx -5.36, y = 7 \sin 220° \approx -4.5$

4. $x = 6 \cos(-50°) \approx 3.86, y = 6 \sin(-50°) \approx -4.60$

For #5–6, use a calculator.

5. $\theta \approx 33.85°$

6. $\theta \approx 104.96°$

For #7–10, the angle determined by $P(x, y)$ involves $\tan^{-1}(y/x)$. Since this will always be between $-180°$ and $+180°$, you may need to add $180°$ or $360°$ to put the angle in the correct quadrant.

7. $\theta = \tan^{-1}\left(\dfrac{9}{5}\right) \approx 60.95°$

8. $\theta = 360° + \tan^{-1}\left(-\dfrac{7}{5}\right) \approx 305.54°$

9. $\theta = 180° + \tan^{-1}\left(\dfrac{5}{2}\right) \approx 248.20°$

10. After 3 hours, the ship has traveled $(3)(42 \sin 40°)$ naut mi east and $(3)(42 \cos 40°)$ naut mi north. Five hours later, it is $(3)(42 \sin 40°) + (5)(42 \sin 125°) \approx 253.013$ naut mi east and $(3)(42 \cos 40°) + (5)(42 \cos 125°) \approx -23.929$ naut mi north (about 23.93 naut mi south) of Port Norfolk.

   Bearing: $180° + \tan^{-1}\left(-\dfrac{253.013}{23.929}\right) \approx 95.40°$

   Distance: $\sqrt{(253.013)^2 + (-23.929)^2} \approx 254.14$ naut mi.

Section 6.1 Exercises

For #1–4, recall that two vectors are equivalent if they have the same magnitude and direction. If R has coordinates (a, b) and S has coordinates (c, d), then the magnitude of $\overrightarrow{RS}$ is $|\overrightarrow{RS}| = \sqrt{(c - a)^2 + (d - b)^2} = RS$, the distance from R to S. The direction of $\overrightarrow{RS}$ is determined by the coordinates $(c - a, d - b)$.

1. If $R = (-4, 7)$ and $S = (-1, 5)$, then, using the HMT rule, $\overrightarrow{RS} = \langle -1 - (-4), 5 - 7 \rangle = \langle 3, -2 \rangle$.
If $P = (0, 0)$ and $Q = (3, -2)$, then, using the HMT rule, $\overrightarrow{PQ} = \langle 3 - 0, -2 - 0 \rangle = \langle 3, -2 \rangle$.
Both vectors represent $\langle 3, -2 \rangle$ by the HMT rule.

2. If $R = (7, -3)$ and $S = (4, -5)$, then, using the HMT rule, $\overrightarrow{RS} = \langle 4 - 7, -5 - (-3) \rangle = \langle -3, -2 \rangle$.
If $P = (0, 0)$ and $Q = (-3, -2)$, then, using the HMT rule, $\overrightarrow{PQ} = \langle -3 - 0, -2 - 0 \rangle = \langle -3, -2 \rangle$.
Both vectors represent $\langle -3, -2 \rangle$ by the HMT rule.

3. If $R = (2, 1)$ and $S = (0, -1)$, then, using the HMT rule, $\overrightarrow{RS} = \langle 0 - 2, -1 - 1 \rangle = \langle -2, -2 \rangle$.
If $P = (1, 4)$ and $Q = (-1, 2)$, then, using the HMT rule, $\overrightarrow{PQ} = \langle -1 - 1, 2 - 4 \rangle = \langle -2, -2 \rangle$.
Both vectors represent $\langle -2, -2 \rangle$ by the HMT rule.

4. If $R = (-2, -1)$ and $S = (2, 4)$, then, using the HMT rule, $\overrightarrow{RS} = \langle 2 - (-2), 4 - (-1) \rangle = \langle 4, 5 \rangle$.
If $P = (-3, -1)$ and $Q = (1, 4)$, then, using the HMT rule, $\overrightarrow{PQ} = \langle 1 - (-3), 4 - (-1) \rangle = \langle 4, 5 \rangle$.
Both vectors represent $\langle 4, 5 \rangle$ by the HMT rule.

5. $\overrightarrow{PQ} = \langle 3 - (-2), 4 - 2 \rangle = \langle 5, 2 \rangle$,
$|\overrightarrow{PQ}| = \sqrt{5^2 + 2^2} = \sqrt{29}$

6. $\overrightarrow{RS} = \langle 2 - (-2), -8 - 5 \rangle = \langle 4, -13 \rangle,$
$|\overrightarrow{RS}| = \sqrt{4^2 + (-13)^2} = \sqrt{185}$

7. $\overrightarrow{QR} = \langle -2 - 3, 5 - 4 \rangle = \langle -5, 1 \rangle,$
$|\overrightarrow{QR}| = \sqrt{(-5)^2 + 1^2} = \sqrt{26}$

8. $\overrightarrow{PS} = \langle 2 - (-2), -8 - 2 \rangle = \langle 4, -10 \rangle,$
$|\overrightarrow{PS}| = \sqrt{4^2 + (-10)^2} = \sqrt{116} = 2\sqrt{29}$

9. $2\overrightarrow{QS} = 2\langle 2 - 3, -8 - 4 \rangle = \langle -2, -24 \rangle,$
$|2\overrightarrow{QS}| = \sqrt{(-2)^2 + (-24)^2} = \sqrt{580} = 2\sqrt{145}$

10. $(\sqrt{2})\overrightarrow{PR} = \sqrt{2}\langle -2 - (-2), 5 - 2 \rangle = \langle 0, 3\sqrt{2} \rangle,$
$|\sqrt{2}\overrightarrow{QR}| = \sqrt{0^2 + (3\sqrt{2})^2} = 3\sqrt{2}$

11. $3\overrightarrow{QR} + \overrightarrow{PS} = 3\langle -5, 1 \rangle + \langle 4, -10 \rangle = \langle -11, -7 \rangle,$
$|3\overrightarrow{QR} + \overrightarrow{PS}| = \sqrt{(-11)^2 + (-7)^2} = \sqrt{170}$

12. $\overrightarrow{PS} - 3\overrightarrow{PQ} = \langle 4, -10 \rangle - 3\langle 5, 2 \rangle = \langle -11, -16 \rangle,$
$|\overrightarrow{PS} - 3\overrightarrow{PQ}| = \sqrt{(-11)^2 + (-16)^2} = \sqrt{377}$

13. $\langle -1, 3 \rangle + \langle 2, 4 \rangle = \langle 1, 7 \rangle$

14. $\langle -1, 3 \rangle - \langle 2, 4 \rangle = \langle -3, -1 \rangle$

15. $\langle -1, 3 \rangle - \langle 2, -5 \rangle = \langle -3, 8 \rangle$

16. $3\langle 2, 4 \rangle = \langle 6, 12 \rangle$

17. $2\langle -1, 3 \rangle + 3\langle 2, -5 \rangle = \langle 4, -9 \rangle$

18. $2\langle -1, 3 \rangle - 4\langle 2, 4 \rangle = \langle -10, -10 \rangle$

19. $-2\langle -1, 3 \rangle - 3\langle 2, 4 \rangle = \langle -4, -18 \rangle$

20. $-\langle -1, 3 \rangle - \langle 2, 4 \rangle = \langle -1, -7 \rangle$

21. $\dfrac{\mathbf{u}}{|\mathbf{u}|} = \left\langle \dfrac{-2}{\sqrt{(-2)^2 + 4^2}}, \dfrac{4}{\sqrt{(-2)^2 + 4^2}} \right\rangle$
$\approx -0.45\mathbf{i} + 0.89\mathbf{j}$

22. $\dfrac{\mathbf{v}}{|\mathbf{v}|} = \left\langle \dfrac{1}{\sqrt{1^2 + (-1)^2}}, \dfrac{-1}{\sqrt{1^2 + (-1)^2}} \right\rangle$
$\approx 0.71\mathbf{i} - 0.71\mathbf{j}$

23. $\dfrac{\mathbf{w}}{|\mathbf{w}|} = \left\langle \dfrac{-1}{\sqrt{(-1)^2 + (-2)^2}}, \dfrac{-2}{\sqrt{(-1)^2 + (-2)^2}} \right\rangle$
$\approx -0.45\mathbf{i} - 0.89\mathbf{j}$

24. $\dfrac{\mathbf{w}}{|\mathbf{w}|} = \left\langle \dfrac{5}{\sqrt{5^2 + 5^2}}, \dfrac{5}{\sqrt{5^2 + 5^2}} \right\rangle \approx 0.71\mathbf{i} + 0.71\mathbf{j}$

For #25–28, the unit vector in the direction of $\mathbf{v} = \langle a, b \rangle$ is

$\dfrac{1}{|\mathbf{v}|}\mathbf{v} = \left\langle \dfrac{a}{\sqrt{a^2 + b^2}}, \dfrac{b}{\sqrt{a^2 + b^2}} \right\rangle$

$= \dfrac{a}{\sqrt{a^2 + b^2}}\mathbf{i} + \dfrac{b}{\sqrt{a^2 + b^2}}\mathbf{j}.$

25. (a) $\left\langle \dfrac{2}{\sqrt{5}}, \dfrac{1}{\sqrt{5}} \right\rangle$

(b) $\dfrac{2}{\sqrt{5}}\mathbf{i} + \dfrac{1}{\sqrt{5}}\mathbf{j}$

26. (a) $\left\langle -\dfrac{3}{\sqrt{13}}, \dfrac{2}{\sqrt{13}} \right\rangle$

(b) $-\dfrac{3}{\sqrt{13}}\mathbf{i} + \dfrac{2}{\sqrt{13}}\mathbf{j}$

27. (a) $\left\langle -\dfrac{4}{\sqrt{41}}, -\dfrac{5}{\sqrt{41}} \right\rangle$

(b) $-\dfrac{4}{\sqrt{41}}\mathbf{i} + \left(-\dfrac{5}{\sqrt{41}} \right)\mathbf{j} = -\dfrac{4}{\sqrt{41}}\mathbf{i} - \dfrac{5}{\sqrt{41}}\mathbf{j}$

28. (a) $\left\langle \dfrac{3}{5}, -\dfrac{4}{5} \right\rangle$

(b) $\dfrac{3}{5}\mathbf{i} + \left(-\dfrac{4}{5} \right)\mathbf{j} = \dfrac{3}{5}\mathbf{i} - \dfrac{4}{5}\mathbf{j}.$

29. $\mathbf{v} = \langle 18\cos 25°, 18\sin 25° \rangle \approx \langle 16.31, 7.61 \rangle$

30. $\mathbf{v} = \langle 14\cos 55°, 14\sin 55° \rangle \approx \langle 8.03, 11.47 \rangle$

31. $\mathbf{v} = \langle 47\cos 108°, 47\sin 108° \rangle \approx \langle -14.52, 44.70 \rangle$

32. $\mathbf{v} = \langle 33\cos 136°, 33\sin 136° \rangle \approx \langle -23.74, 22.92 \rangle$

33. $|\mathbf{u}| = \sqrt{3^2 + 4^2} = 5, \alpha = \cos^{-1}\left(\dfrac{3}{5} \right) \approx 53.13°$

34. $|\mathbf{u}| = \sqrt{(-1)^2 + 2^2} = \sqrt{5}, \alpha = \cos^{-1}\left(\dfrac{-1}{\sqrt{5}} \right) \approx 116.57°$

35. $|\mathbf{u}| = \sqrt{3^2 + (-4)^2} = 5, \alpha = 360° - \cos^{-1}\left(\dfrac{3}{5} \right)$
$\approx 306.87°$

36. $|\mathbf{u}| = \sqrt{(-3)^2 + (-5)^2} = \sqrt{34},$
$\alpha = 360° - \cos^{-1}\left(\dfrac{-3}{\sqrt{34}} \right) \approx 239.04°$

37. Since $(7\cos 135°)\mathbf{i} + (7\sin 135°)\mathbf{j} = (|\mathbf{u}|\cos\alpha)\mathbf{i} + (|\mathbf{u}|\sin\alpha)\mathbf{j}, |\mathbf{u}| = 7$ and $\alpha = 135°.$

38. Since $(2\cos 60°)\mathbf{i} + (2\sin 60°)\mathbf{j} = (|\mathbf{u}|\cos\alpha)\mathbf{i} + (|\mathbf{u}|\sin\alpha)\mathbf{j}, |\mathbf{u}| = 2$ and $\alpha = 60°.$

For #39–40, first find the unit vector in the direction of $\mathbf{u}$. Then multiply by the magnitude of $\mathbf{v}, |\mathbf{v}|$.

39. $\mathbf{v} = |\mathbf{v}| \cdot \dfrac{\mathbf{u}}{|\mathbf{u}|} = 2\left\langle \dfrac{3}{\sqrt{3^2 + (-3)^2}}, \dfrac{-3}{\sqrt{3^2 + (-3)^2}} \right\rangle$
$= 2\left\langle \dfrac{\sqrt{2}}{2}, \dfrac{-\sqrt{2}}{2} \right\rangle = \langle \sqrt{2}, -\sqrt{2} \rangle$

40. $\mathbf{v} = |\mathbf{v}| \cdot \dfrac{\mathbf{u}}{|\mathbf{u}|} = 5\left\langle \dfrac{-5}{\sqrt{(-5)^2 + 7^2}}, \dfrac{7}{\sqrt{(-5)^2 + 7^2}} \right\rangle$
$\approx 5\langle -0.58, 0.81 \rangle = \langle -2.91, 4.07 \rangle$

41. A bearing of $335°$ corresponds to a direction angle of $115°$.
$\mathbf{v} = 530\langle \cos 115°, \sin 115° \rangle \approx \langle -223.99, 480.34 \rangle$

42. A bearing of $170°$ corresponds to a direction angle of $-80°$.
$\mathbf{v} = 460\langle \cos(-80°), \sin(-80°) \rangle \approx \langle 79.88, -453.01 \rangle$

43. (a) A bearing of $340°$ corresponds to a direction angle of $110°$. $\mathbf{v} = 325\langle \cos 110°, \sin 110° \rangle \approx \langle -111.16, 305.40 \rangle$

(b) The wind bearing of $320°$ corresponds to a direction angle of $130°$. The wind vector is
$\mathbf{w} = 40\langle \cos 130°, \sin 130° \rangle \approx \langle -25.71, 30.64 \rangle$.
Actual velocity vector: $\mathbf{v} + \mathbf{w} \approx \langle -136.87, 336.04 \rangle$.
Actual speed: $\|\mathbf{v} + \mathbf{w}\| \approx \sqrt{136.87^2 + 336.04^2}$
≈ 362.84 mph.

Actual direction: $\theta = 180° + \tan^{-1}\left(\dfrac{336.04}{-136.87} \right)$
$\approx 112.16°$, so the bearing is about $337.84°$.

44. (a) A bearing of 170° corresponds to a direction angle of $-80°$:
$$\mathbf{v} = 460 \langle \cos(-80°), \sin(-80°) \rangle \approx \langle 79.88, -453.01 \rangle.$$

(b) The wind bearing of 200° corresponds to a direction angle of $-110°$. The wind vector is
$$\mathbf{w} = 80 \langle \cos(-110°), \sin(-110°) \rangle \approx \langle -27.36, -75.18 \rangle.$$
Actual velocity vector: $\mathbf{v} + \mathbf{w} \approx \langle 52.52, -528.19 \rangle$.
Actual speed: $\|\mathbf{v} + \mathbf{w}\| \approx \sqrt{52.52^2 + 528.19^2}$
≈ 530.79 mph.

Actual direction: $\theta = 180° + \tan^{-1}\left(-\dfrac{52.52}{528.19}\right)$
$\approx -84.32°$, so the bearing is about 174.32°.

45. (a) $\mathbf{v} = 10 \langle \cos 70°, \sin 70° \rangle \approx \langle 3.42, 9.40 \rangle$

(b) The horizontal component is the (constant) horizontal speed of the basketball as it travels toward the basket. The vertical component is the vertical velocity of the basketball, affected by both the initial speed and the downward pull of gravity.

46. (a) $\mathbf{v} = 2.5 \langle \cos 15°, \sin 15° \rangle \approx \langle 2.41, 0.65 \rangle$

(b) The horizontal component is the force moving the box forward. The vertical component is the force moving the box upward against the pull of gravity.

47. We need to choose $\mathbf{w} = \langle a, b \rangle = k \langle \cos 33°, \sin 33° \rangle$, so that $k \cos(33° - 15°) = k \cos 18° = 2.5$. (Redefine "horizontal" to mean the parallel to the inclined plane; then the towing vector makes an angle of 18° with the "horizontal.") Then $k = \dfrac{2.5}{\cos 18°} \approx 2.63$ lb, so that
$\mathbf{w} \approx \langle 2.20, 1.43 \rangle$.

48. Juana's force can be represented by
$23 \langle \cos 18°, \sin 18° \rangle \approx \langle 21.87, 7.11 \rangle$, while Diego's force is $27 \langle \cos(-15)°, \sin(-15°) \rangle \approx \langle 26.08, -6.99 \rangle$. Their total force is therefore $\langle 47.95, 0.12 \rangle$, so Corporal must be pulling with an equal force in the opposite direction: $\langle -47.95, -0.12 \rangle$. The magnitude of Corporal's force is about 47.95 lb.

49. $\mathbf{F} = \langle 50 \cos 45°, 50 \sin 45° \rangle + \langle 75 \cos(-30°),$
$75 \sin(-30°) \rangle \approx \langle 100.31, -2.14 \rangle$, so $|\mathbf{F}| \approx 100.33$ lb
and $\theta \approx -1.22°$.

50. $\mathbf{F} = 100 \langle \cos 50°, \sin 50° \rangle + 50 \langle \cos 160°, \sin 160° \rangle$
$+ 80 \langle \cos(-20), \sin(-20°) \rangle \approx \langle 92.47, 66.34 \rangle$, so
$|\mathbf{F}| \approx 113.81$ lb and $\theta \approx 35.66°$.

51. Ship heading: $\langle 12 \cos 90°, 12 \sin 90° \rangle = \langle 0, 12 \rangle$
Current heading: $\langle 4 \cos 225°, 4 \sin 225° \rangle \approx \langle -2.83, -2.83 \rangle$
The ship's actual velocity vector is $\langle -2.83, 9.17 \rangle$, so its speed is $\approx \sqrt{(-2.83)^2 + 9.17^2} \approx 9.6$ mph and the direction angle is $\cos^{-1}\left(\dfrac{-2.83}{9.6}\right) \approx 107.14°$, so the bearing is about 342.86°.

52. Let $\mathbf{v} = \langle 0, 20 \rangle$ be the velocity of the boat and $\mathbf{w} = \langle 8, 0 \rangle$ be the velocity vector of the current. If the boat travels t minutes to reach the opposite shore, then its position, in vector form, must be
$$\langle 0, 20t \rangle + \langle 8t, 0 \rangle = \langle 8t, 20t \rangle = \langle 8t, 1 \rangle.$$
So $20t = 1 \Rightarrow t = \dfrac{1}{20} \Rightarrow 8t = 0.4$ mi. The boat meets the shore 0.4 mi downstream.

53. Let w be the speed of the ship. The ship's velocity (in still water) is $\langle w \cos 270°, w \sin 270° \rangle = \langle 0, -w \rangle$. Let z be the speed of the current. Then, the current velocity is $\langle z \cos 135°, z \sin 135° \rangle \approx \langle -0.71z, 0.71z \rangle$. The position of the ship after two hours is $\langle 20 \cos 240°, 20 \sin 240° \rangle \approx \langle -10, -17.32 \rangle$. Putting all this together we have:
$2\langle 0, -w \rangle + 2\langle -0.71z, 0.71z \rangle = \langle -10, -17.32 \rangle$,
$\langle -1.42z, -2w + 1.42z \rangle = \langle -10, -17.32 \rangle$, so $z \approx 7.07$ and $w \approx 13.66$. The speed of the ship is about 13.66 mph, and the speed of the current is about 7.07 mph.

54. Let $\mathbf{u} = \langle u_1, u_2 \rangle$, $\mathbf{v} = \langle v_1, v_2 \rangle$, and $\mathbf{w} = \langle w_1, w_2 \rangle$.

(a) $\mathbf{u} + \mathbf{v} = \langle u_1, u_2 \rangle + \langle v_1, v_2 \rangle = \langle u_1 + v_1, u_2 + v_2 \rangle$
$= \langle v_1 + u_1, v_2 + u_2 \rangle = \langle v_1, v_2 \rangle + \langle u_1, u_2 \rangle = \mathbf{v} + \mathbf{u}$

(b) $(\mathbf{u} + \mathbf{v}) + \mathbf{w} = \langle u_1 + v_1, u_2 + v_2 \rangle + \langle w_1, w_2 \rangle$
$= \langle u_1 + v_1 + w_1, u_2 + v_2 + w_2 \rangle$
$= \langle u_1, u_2 \rangle + \langle v_1 + w_1, v_2 + w_2 \rangle$
$= \mathbf{u} + (\mathbf{v} + \mathbf{w})$

(c) $\mathbf{u} + \mathbf{0} = \langle u_1, u_2 \rangle + \langle 0, 0 \rangle = \langle u_1 + 0, u_2 + 0 \rangle$
$= \langle u_1, u_2 \rangle = \mathbf{u}$

(d) $\mathbf{u} + (-\mathbf{u}) = \langle u_1, u_2 \rangle + \langle -u_1, -u_2 \rangle$
$= \langle u_1 + (-u_1), u_2 + (-u_2) \rangle = \langle 0, 0 \rangle = \mathbf{0}$

(e) $a(\mathbf{u} + \mathbf{v}) = a\langle u_1 + v_1, u_2 + v_2 \rangle$
$= \langle a(u_1 + v_1), a(u_2 + v_2) \rangle$
$= \langle au_1 + av_1, au_2 + av_2 \rangle = \langle au_1, au_2 \rangle + \langle av_1, av_2 \rangle$
$= a \langle u_1, u_2 \rangle + a \langle v_1, v_2 \rangle = a\mathbf{u} + a\mathbf{v}$

(f) $(a + b)\mathbf{u} = \langle (a + b)u_1, (a + b)u_2 \rangle$
$= \langle au_1 + bu_1, au_2 + bu_2 \rangle$
$= \langle au_1, au_2 \rangle + \langle bu_1, bu_2 \rangle = a \langle u_1, u_2 \rangle + b \langle u_1, u_2 \rangle$
$= a\mathbf{u} + b\mathbf{u}$

(g) $(ab)\mathbf{u} = \langle (ab)u_1, (ab)u_2 \rangle = \langle a(bu_1), a(bu_2) \rangle$
$= a \langle bu_1, bu_2 \rangle = a(b\mathbf{u})$

(h) $a\mathbf{0} = a \langle 0, 0 \rangle = \langle a0, a0 \rangle = \langle 0, 0 \rangle = \mathbf{0}$
$0\mathbf{u} = 0 \langle u_1, u_2 \rangle = \langle 0u_1, 0u_2 \rangle = \langle 0, 0 \rangle = \mathbf{0}$

(i) $(1)\mathbf{u} = \langle (1)u_1, (1)u_2 \rangle = \langle u_1, u_2 \rangle = \mathbf{u}$
$(-1)\mathbf{u} = \langle (-1)u_1, (-1)u_2 \rangle = \langle -u_1, -u_2 \rangle = -\mathbf{u}$

(j) $|a\mathbf{u}| = |\langle au_1, au_2 \rangle| = \sqrt{(au_1)^2 + (au_2)^2}$
$= \sqrt{a^2 u_1^2 + a^2 u_2^2} = \sqrt{a^2(u_1^2 + u_2^2)}$
$= |a|\sqrt{u_1^2 + u_2^2} = |a| \, |\mathbf{u}|$

55. True. Vectors $\mathbf{u}$ and $-\mathbf{u}$ have the same length but opposite directions. Thus, the length of $-\mathbf{u}$ is also 1.

56. False. $1/\mathbf{u}$ is not a vector at all.

57. $|\langle 2, -1 \rangle| = \sqrt{2^2 + (-1)^2} = \sqrt{5}$
The answer is D.

58. $\mathbf{u} - \mathbf{v} = \langle -2, 3 \rangle - \langle 4, -1 \rangle$
$= \langle -2 - 4, 3 - (-1) \rangle$
$= \langle -6, 4 \rangle$
The answer is E.

59. The x-component is $3 \cos 30°$, and the y-component is $3 \sin 30°$. The answer is A.

60. $|\mathbf{v}| = \sqrt{(-1)^2 + 3^2} = \sqrt{10}$, so the unit vector is $\langle -1, 3 \rangle / \sqrt{10}$. The answer is C.

61. (a) Let A be the point (a_1, a_2) and B be the point (b_1, b_2). Then $\overrightarrow{OA}$ is the vector $\langle a_1, a_2 \rangle$ and $\overrightarrow{OB}$ is the vector $\langle b_1, b_2 \rangle$.

So, $\overrightarrow{BA} = \langle a_1 - b_1, a_2 - b_2 \rangle$
$= \langle a_1, a_2 \rangle - \langle b_1, b_2 \rangle$
$= \overrightarrow{OA} - \overrightarrow{OB}$

(b) $x\,\overrightarrow{OA} + y\,\overrightarrow{OB} = x(\overrightarrow{OC} + \overrightarrow{CA}) + y(\overrightarrow{OC} + \overrightarrow{CB})$
(from part (a))
$= x\,\overrightarrow{OC} + x\,\overrightarrow{CA} + y\,\overrightarrow{OC} + y\,\overrightarrow{CB}$
$= (x + y)\,\overrightarrow{OC} + x\,\overrightarrow{CA} + y\,\overrightarrow{CB}$
$= \overrightarrow{OC} + x\,\overrightarrow{CA} + y\,\overrightarrow{CB}$ (since $x + y = 1$)
$= \overrightarrow{OC} + y\,\dfrac{|\overrightarrow{BC}|}{|\overrightarrow{CA}|} \cdot \overrightarrow{CA} + y\,\overrightarrow{CB}$ $\left(\text{since } x = y\dfrac{|\overrightarrow{BC}|}{|\overrightarrow{CA}|}\right)$
$= \overrightarrow{OC} + y\left(|\overrightarrow{BC}| \cdot \dfrac{\overrightarrow{CA}}{|\overrightarrow{CA}|} + \overrightarrow{CB}\right)$

$\dfrac{\overrightarrow{CA}}{|\overrightarrow{CA}|}$ is a unit vector, and $\overrightarrow{BC}$ points in the same direction.

$= \overrightarrow{OC} + y\left(|\overrightarrow{BC}| \cdot \dfrac{\overrightarrow{BC}}{|\overrightarrow{BC}|} + \overrightarrow{CB}\right)$
$= \overrightarrow{OC} + y\left(\overrightarrow{BC} + \overrightarrow{CB}\right)$
$= \overrightarrow{OC}$

62. (a) By Exercise 61, $\overrightarrow{OM_1} = x\,\overrightarrow{OA} + y\,\overrightarrow{OB}$, where $x + y = 1$. Since M_1 is the midpoint, $|\overrightarrow{BM_1}| = |\overrightarrow{M_1A}|$. We know from Exercise 61, however that $\dfrac{|\overrightarrow{BM_1}|}{|\overrightarrow{M_1A}|} = 1 = \dfrac{x}{y}$. So $x = y = \dfrac{1}{2}$. As a result, $\overrightarrow{OM_1} = \dfrac{1}{2}\,\overrightarrow{OA} + \dfrac{1}{2}\,\overrightarrow{OB}$. The proof for $\overrightarrow{OM_2}$ and $\overrightarrow{OM_3}$ are similar.

(b) $2\,\overrightarrow{OM_1} + \overrightarrow{OC} = 2\left(\dfrac{1}{2}\,\overrightarrow{OA} + \dfrac{1}{2}\,\overrightarrow{OB}\right) + \overrightarrow{OC}$
$= \overrightarrow{OA} + \overrightarrow{OB} + \overrightarrow{OC}$. Use the same method for the other proofs.

(c) Part (b) implies that $2\,\overrightarrow{OM_1} + \overrightarrow{OC} = 2\,\overrightarrow{OM_2} + \overrightarrow{OA}$
$= 2\,\overrightarrow{OM_3} + \overrightarrow{OB}$. Each of the three vectors lies along a different median (that is, if nonzero, the three vectors have three different directions). Hence they can only be equal if all are equal to **0**. Thus $2\,\overrightarrow{OM_1} = -\overrightarrow{OC}, 2\,\overrightarrow{OM_2} = -\overrightarrow{OA}$, and $2\,\overrightarrow{OM_3} = -\overrightarrow{OB}$, so $\dfrac{|\overrightarrow{OM_1}|}{|\overrightarrow{OC}|} = \dfrac{|\overrightarrow{OM_2}|}{|\overrightarrow{OA}|} = \dfrac{|\overrightarrow{OM_3}|}{|\overrightarrow{OB}|} = \dfrac{1}{2}$.

63. Use the result of Exercise 61. First we show that if C is on the line segment AB, then there is a real number t so that $\dfrac{|\overrightarrow{BC}|}{|\overrightarrow{CA}|} = \dfrac{t}{1 - t}$. (Convince yourself that $t = \dfrac{BC}{BC + CA}$ works.) Then $\overrightarrow{OC} = t\,\overrightarrow{OA} + (1 - t)\,\overrightarrow{OB}$. A similar argument can be used in the cases where B is on the line segment AC or A is on the line segment BC.

Suppose there is a real number t so that
$\overrightarrow{OC} = t\,\overrightarrow{OA} + (1 - t)\,\overrightarrow{OB}$. We also know
$\overrightarrow{OC} = \overrightarrow{OB} + \overrightarrow{BC}$ and $\overrightarrow{OC} = \overrightarrow{OA} + \overrightarrow{AC}$. So we have
$t\,\overrightarrow{OA} + (1 - t)\overrightarrow{OB} = \overrightarrow{OB} + \overrightarrow{BC}$ and
$t\,\overrightarrow{OA} + (1 - t)\overrightarrow{OB} = \overrightarrow{OA} + \overrightarrow{AC}$. Therefore,
$t\,(\overrightarrow{OA} - \overrightarrow{OB}) = \overrightarrow{BC}$ and $(t - 1)(\overrightarrow{OA} - \overrightarrow{OB}) = \overrightarrow{AC}$.
Hence $\overrightarrow{BC}$ and $\overrightarrow{AC}$ have the same or opposite directions, so C must lie on the line L through the two points A and B.

64.

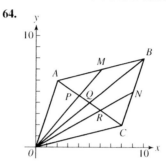

The line segment OM is a median of $\triangle ABO$ since M is a midpoint of AB. The line segment AQ is a median of $\triangle ABO$ since diagonals of a parallelogram bisect each other. By the result of Exercise 62, since P is the intersection point of 2 medians, $\dfrac{AP}{PQ} = \dfrac{2}{1}$. Similarly, $\dfrac{CR}{RQ} = \dfrac{2}{1}$. This implies that $AP = PR = RC$, so the diagonal has been trisected.

■ Section 6.2 Dot Product of Vectors

Exploration 1

1. $\mathbf{u} = \langle -2 - x, 0 - y \rangle = \langle -2 - x, -y \rangle$
$\mathbf{v} = \langle 2 - x, 0 - y \rangle = \langle 2 - x, -y \rangle$

2. $\mathbf{u} \cdot \mathbf{v} = (-2 - x)(2 - x) + (-y)(-y) = -4 + x^2 + y^2$
$= -4 + 4 = 0$

Therefore, $\theta = 90°$.

3. Answers will vary.

Quick Review 6.2

1. $|\mathbf{u}| = \sqrt{2^2 + (-3)^2} = \sqrt{13}$

2. $|\mathbf{u}| = \sqrt{(-3)^2 + (-4)^2} = 5$

3. $|\mathbf{u}| = \sqrt{\cos^2 35° + \sin^2 35°} = 1$

4. $|\mathbf{u}| = 2\sqrt{\cos^2 75° + \sin^2 75°} = 2$

5. $\overrightarrow{AB} = \langle 1 - (-2), \sqrt{3} - 0 \rangle = \langle 3, \sqrt{3} \rangle$

6. $\overrightarrow{AB} = \langle 1 - 2, \sqrt{3} - 0 \rangle = \langle -1, \sqrt{3} \rangle$

7. $\overrightarrow{AB} = \langle 1 - 2, -\sqrt{3} - 0 \rangle = \langle -1, -\sqrt{3} \rangle$

8. $\overrightarrow{AB} = \langle 1 - (-2), -\sqrt{3} - 0 \rangle = \langle 3, -\sqrt{3} \rangle$

9. $\mathbf{u} = |\mathbf{u}| \cdot \dfrac{\mathbf{v}}{|\mathbf{v}|} = \dfrac{2 \cdot \langle 2, 3 \rangle}{\sqrt{2^2 + 3^2}} = \dfrac{\langle 4, 6 \rangle}{\sqrt{13}}$
$= \left\langle \dfrac{4}{\sqrt{13}}, \dfrac{6}{\sqrt{13}} \right\rangle$

10. $\mathbf{u} = |\mathbf{u}| \cdot \dfrac{\mathbf{v}}{|\mathbf{v}|} = \dfrac{3 \cdot \langle -4, 3 \rangle}{\sqrt{(-4)^2 + 3^2}} = \dfrac{\langle -12, 9 \rangle}{5}$
$= \left\langle -\dfrac{12}{5}, \dfrac{9}{5} \right\rangle$

Section 6.2 Exercises

1. $60 + 12 = 72$

2. $-40 + 26 = -14$

3. $-12 - 35 = -47$

4. $10 - 56 = -46$

5. $12 + 18 = 30$

6. $-16 - 28 = -44$

7. $-14 + 0 = -14$

8. $0 + 33 = 33$

9. $|\mathbf{u}| = \sqrt{\mathbf{u} \cdot \mathbf{u}} = \sqrt{25 + 144} = 13$

10. $|\mathbf{u}| = \sqrt{\mathbf{u} \cdot \mathbf{u}} = \sqrt{64 + 225} = 17$

11. $|\mathbf{u}| = \sqrt{\mathbf{u} \cdot \mathbf{u}} = \sqrt{16} = 4$

12. $|\mathbf{u}| = \sqrt{\mathbf{u} \cdot \mathbf{u}} = \sqrt{9} = 3$

13. $\mathbf{u} \cdot \mathbf{v} = 4 - 15 = -11, |\mathbf{u}| = \sqrt{16 + 9} = 5,$
    $|\mathbf{v}| = \sqrt{1 + 25} = \sqrt{26}, \theta = \cos^{-1}\left(\dfrac{-11}{5\sqrt{26}}\right) \approx 115.6°$

14. $\mathbf{u} \cdot \mathbf{v} = -6 + 6 = 0, \theta = 90°$

15. $\mathbf{u} \cdot \mathbf{v} = -6 + 15 = 9,$
    $|\mathbf{u}| = \sqrt{4 + 9} = \sqrt{13},$
    $|\mathbf{u}| = \sqrt{9 + 25} = \sqrt{34},$
    $\theta = \cos^{-1}\left(\dfrac{9}{\sqrt{13} \cdot \sqrt{34}}\right) \approx 64.65°$

16. $\mathbf{u} \cdot \mathbf{v} = -30 - 2 = -32, |\mathbf{u}| = \sqrt{25 + 4} = \sqrt{29},$
    $|\mathbf{v}| = \sqrt{36 + 1} = \sqrt{37},$
    $\theta = \cos^{-1}\left(\dfrac{-32}{\sqrt{29} \cdot \sqrt{37}}\right) \approx 167.66°$

17. $\mathbf{u} \cdot \mathbf{v} = -6 - 6\sqrt{3}, |\mathbf{u}| = \sqrt{9 + 9} = \sqrt{18},$
    $|\mathbf{v}| = \sqrt{4 + 12} = \sqrt{16} = 4,$
    $\theta = \cos^{-1}\left(\dfrac{-6 - 6\sqrt{3}}{\sqrt{18} \cdot 4}\right) = 165°$

18. $\mathbf{u} \cdot \mathbf{v} = 0, \theta = 90°$

19. $\mathbf{u}$ has direction angle $\dfrac{\pi}{4}$ and $\mathbf{v}$ has direction angle $\dfrac{3\pi}{2}$
    (which is equivalent to $-\dfrac{\pi}{2}$), so the angle between the
    vectors is $\dfrac{\pi}{4} - \left(-\dfrac{\pi}{2}\right) = \dfrac{3\pi}{4}$ or $135°$.

20. $\mathbf{u}$ has direction angle $\dfrac{\pi}{3}$ and $\mathbf{v}$ has direction angle $\dfrac{5\pi}{6}$,
    so the angle between the vectors is $\dfrac{5\pi}{6} - \dfrac{\pi}{3} = \dfrac{\pi}{2}$ or $90°$.

21. $\mathbf{u} \cdot \mathbf{v} = -24 + 20 = -4, |\mathbf{u}| = \sqrt{64 + 25} = \sqrt{89},$
    $|\mathbf{v}| = \sqrt{9 + 16} = 5,$
    $\theta = \cos^{-1}\left(\dfrac{-4}{5\sqrt{89}}\right) \approx 94.86°$

22. $\mathbf{u} \cdot \mathbf{v} = 3 - 72 = -69, |\mathbf{u}| = \sqrt{9 + 64} = \sqrt{73},$
    $|\mathbf{v}| = \sqrt{1 + 81} = \sqrt{82},$
    $\theta = \cos^{-1}\left(\dfrac{-69}{\sqrt{73} \cdot \sqrt{82}}\right) \approx 153.10°$

23. $\mathbf{u} \cdot \mathbf{v} = \langle 2, 3 \rangle \cdot \left\langle \dfrac{3}{2}, -1 \right\rangle = 2\left(\dfrac{3}{2}\right) + 3(-1)$
    $= 3 - 3 = 0$
    Since $\mathbf{u} \cdot \mathbf{v} = 0$, $\mathbf{u}$ and $\mathbf{v}$ are orthogonal.

24. $\mathbf{u} \cdot \mathbf{v} = \langle -4, -1 \rangle \cdot \langle 1, -4 \rangle = -4(1) + (-1)(-4)$
    $= -4 + 4 = 0$
    Since $\mathbf{u} \cdot \mathbf{v} = 0$, $\mathbf{u}$ and $\mathbf{v}$ are orthogonal.

For #25–28, first find $\text{proj}_\mathbf{v}\mathbf{u}$. Then use the fact that $\mathbf{u} \cdot \mathbf{v} = 0$ when $\mathbf{u}$ and $\mathbf{v}$ are orthogonal.

25. $\text{proj}_\mathbf{v}\mathbf{u} = \left(\dfrac{\langle -8, 3 \rangle \cdot \langle -6, -2 \rangle}{36 + 4}\right)\langle -6, -2 \rangle$
    $= \left(\dfrac{42}{40}\right)\langle -6, -2 \rangle = \dfrac{21}{20}\langle -6, -2 \rangle$
    $= -\dfrac{21}{10}\langle 3, 1 \rangle$
    $\mathbf{u} = -\dfrac{21}{10}\langle 3, 1 \rangle + \dfrac{17}{10}\langle -1, 3 \rangle$

26. $\text{proj}_\mathbf{v}\mathbf{u} = \left(\dfrac{\langle 3, -7 \rangle \cdot \langle -2, -6 \rangle}{4 + 36}\right)\langle -2, -6 \rangle$
    $= \left(\dfrac{36}{40}\right)\langle -2, -6 \rangle = -\dfrac{9}{5}\langle 1, 3 \rangle$
    $\mathbf{u} = -\dfrac{9}{5}\langle 1, 3 \rangle + \dfrac{8}{5}\langle 3, -1 \rangle$

27. $\text{proj}_\mathbf{v}\mathbf{u} = \left(\dfrac{\langle 8, 5 \rangle \cdot \langle -9, -2 \rangle}{81 + 4}\right)\langle -9, -2 \rangle$
    $= \left(\dfrac{-82}{85}\right)\langle -9, -2 \rangle = \dfrac{82}{85}\langle 9, 2 \rangle$
    $\mathbf{u} = \dfrac{82}{85}\langle 9, 2 \rangle + \dfrac{29}{85}\langle -2, 9 \rangle$

28. $\text{proj}_\mathbf{v}\mathbf{u} = \left(\dfrac{\langle -2, 8 \rangle \cdot \langle 9, -3 \rangle}{81 + 9}\right)\langle 9, -3 \rangle$
    $= \left(\dfrac{-42}{90}\right)\langle 9, -3 \rangle = \dfrac{7}{5}\langle -3, 1 \rangle$
    $\mathbf{u} = \dfrac{7}{5}\langle -3, 1 \rangle + \dfrac{1}{5}\langle 11, 33 \rangle$

29.

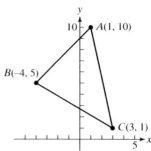

$\overrightarrow{CA} \cdot \overrightarrow{CB} = \langle 1 - 3, 10 - 1 \rangle \cdot \langle -4 - 3, 5 - 1 \rangle$
$= \langle -2, 9 \rangle \cdot \langle -7, 4 \rangle = 14 + 36 = 50,$

$|\overrightarrow{CA}| = \sqrt{4 + 81} = \sqrt{85}, |\overrightarrow{CB}| = \sqrt{49 + 16} = \sqrt{65},$

$C = \cos^{-1}\left(\dfrac{40}{\sqrt{85} \cdot \sqrt{65}}\right) \approx 47.73°$

$\overrightarrow{BC} \cdot \overrightarrow{BA} = \langle 7, -4 \rangle \cdot \langle 1 - (-4), 10 - 5 \rangle$
$= \langle 7, -4 \rangle \cdot \langle 5, 5 \rangle = 35 - 20 = 15,$

$|\overrightarrow{BC}| = \sqrt{65}, |\overrightarrow{BA}| = \sqrt{50}, B = \cos^{-1}\left(\dfrac{15}{\sqrt{65} \cdot \sqrt{50}}\right)$

$\approx 74.74°$
$A = 180° - B - C \approx 180° - 74.74° - 47.73° = 57.53°$

30.

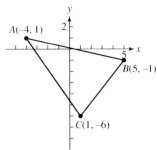

$$\overrightarrow{CA} \cdot \overrightarrow{CB} = \langle -4 - 1, 1 - (-6) \rangle \cdot \langle 5 - 1, -1 - (-6) \rangle$$
$$= \langle -5, 7 \rangle \cdot \langle 4, 5 \rangle = -20 + 35 = 15,$$
$$|\overrightarrow{CA}| = \sqrt{25 + 49} = \sqrt{74}, |\overrightarrow{CB}| = \sqrt{16 + 25} = \sqrt{41},$$
$$C = \cos^{-1}\left(\frac{15}{\sqrt{74} \cdot \sqrt{41}}\right) \approx 74.20°$$
$$\overrightarrow{BA} \cdot \overrightarrow{BC} = \langle -4 - 5, 1 - (-1) \rangle \cdot \langle 1 - 5, -6 - (-1) \rangle$$
$$= \langle -9, 2 \rangle \cdot \langle -4, -5 \rangle = 36 - 10 = 26,$$
$$|\overrightarrow{BA}| = \sqrt{81 + 4} = \sqrt{85}, |\overrightarrow{BC}| = \sqrt{41},$$
$$B = \cos^{-1}\left(\frac{26}{\sqrt{85} \cdot \sqrt{41}}\right) \approx 63.87°$$
$$A = 180° - B - C \approx 180° - 63.87° - 74.20° = 41.93°$$

For #31–32, use the relationship $\mathbf{u} \cdot \mathbf{v} = |\mathbf{u}| \, |\mathbf{v}| \cos \theta$.

31. $\mathbf{u} \cdot \mathbf{v} = 3 \cdot 8 \cos 150° \approx -20.78$

32. $\mathbf{u} \cdot \mathbf{v} = 12 \cdot 40 \cos\left(\dfrac{\pi}{3}\right) = 240$

For #33–38, vectors are orthogonal if $\mathbf{u} \cdot \mathbf{v} = 0$ and are parallel if $\mathbf{u} = k\mathbf{v}$ for some constant k.

33. Parallel: $-2\left\langle -\dfrac{10}{4}, -\dfrac{3}{2} \right\rangle = \left\langle \dfrac{10}{2}, 3 \right\rangle = \langle 5, 3 \rangle$

34. Neither: $\mathbf{u} \cdot \mathbf{v} = \dfrac{40}{3} \neq 0$ and
$$\frac{3}{5}\mathbf{v} = \frac{3}{5}\left\langle \frac{10}{3}, \frac{4}{3} \right\rangle = \left\langle 2, \frac{4}{5} \right\rangle \neq \mathbf{u}$$

35. Neither: $\mathbf{u} \cdot \mathbf{v} = -120 \neq 0$ and
$$\frac{-15}{4}\mathbf{v} = \frac{-15}{4}\langle -4, 5 \rangle = \left\langle 15, \frac{-75}{4} \right\rangle \neq \mathbf{u}$$

36. Orthogonal: $\mathbf{u} \cdot \mathbf{v} = -60 + 60 = 0$

37. Orthogonal: $\mathbf{u} \cdot \mathbf{v} = -60 + 60 = 0$

38. Parallel: $-\dfrac{1}{2}\mathbf{v} = -\dfrac{1}{2}\langle -4, 14 \rangle = \langle 2, -7 \rangle = \mathbf{u}$

For #39–42 part (b), first find the direction(s) of $\overrightarrow{AP}$ and then find the unit vectors. Then find P by adding the coordinates of A to the components of a unit vector.

39. (a) A is $(4, 0)$ and B is $(0, -3)$.

(b) The line is parallel to
$$\overrightarrow{AB} = \langle 0 - 4, -3 - 0 \rangle = \langle -4, -3 \rangle, \text{ so the direction}$$
of $\overrightarrow{AP}$ is $\mathbf{u} = \langle 3, -4 \rangle$ or $\mathbf{v} = \langle -3, 4 \rangle$.

$$\overrightarrow{AP} = \frac{\mathbf{u}}{|\mathbf{u}|} = \frac{\langle 3, -4 \rangle}{\sqrt{9 + 16}} = \left\langle \frac{3}{5}, -\frac{4}{5} \right\rangle \text{ or}$$

$$\overrightarrow{AP} = \frac{\mathbf{v}}{|\mathbf{v}|} = \frac{\langle -3, 4 \rangle}{\sqrt{9 + 16}} = \left\langle -\frac{3}{5}, \frac{4}{5} \right\rangle.$$

So, P is $(4.6, -0.8)$ or $(3.4, 0.8)$.

40. (a) A is $(-5, 0)$ and B is $(0, 2)$.

(b) The line is parallel to
$$\overrightarrow{AB} = \langle 0 - (-5), 2 - 0 \rangle = \langle 5, 2 \rangle, \text{ so the direction}$$
of $\overrightarrow{AP}$ is $\mathbf{u} = \langle -2, 5 \rangle$ or $\mathbf{v} = \langle 2, -5 \rangle$.

$$\overrightarrow{AP} = \frac{\mathbf{u}}{|\mathbf{u}|} = \frac{\langle -2, 5 \rangle}{\sqrt{4 + 25}} = \left\langle -\frac{2}{\sqrt{29}}, \frac{5}{\sqrt{29}} \right\rangle \text{ or}$$

$$\overrightarrow{AP} = \frac{\mathbf{v}}{|\mathbf{v}|} = \frac{\langle 2, -5 \rangle}{\sqrt{29}} = \left\langle \frac{2}{\sqrt{29}}, -\frac{5}{\sqrt{29}} \right\rangle.$$

So P is $\left(-5 - \dfrac{2}{\sqrt{29}}, \dfrac{5}{\sqrt{29}} \right) \approx (-5.37, 0.93)$ or
$$\left(-5 + \frac{2}{\sqrt{29}}, -\frac{5}{\sqrt{29}} \right) \approx (-4.63, -0.93).$$

41. (a) A is $(7, 0)$ and B is $(0, -3)$.

(b) The line is parallel to
$$\overrightarrow{AB} = \langle 0 - 7, -3 - 0 \rangle = \langle -7, -3 \rangle, \text{ so the direction}$$
of $\overrightarrow{AP}$ is $\mathbf{u} = \langle 3, -7 \rangle$ or $\mathbf{v} = \langle -3, 7 \rangle$.

$$\overrightarrow{AP} = \frac{\mathbf{u}}{|\mathbf{u}|} = \frac{\langle 3, -7 \rangle}{\sqrt{9 + 49}} = \left\langle \frac{3}{\sqrt{58}}, -\frac{7}{\sqrt{58}} \right\rangle \text{ or}$$

$$\overrightarrow{AP} = \frac{\mathbf{v}}{|\mathbf{v}|} = \frac{\langle -3, 7 \rangle}{\sqrt{58}} = \left\langle -\frac{3}{\sqrt{58}}, \frac{7}{\sqrt{58}} \right\rangle.$$

So P is $\left(7 + \dfrac{3}{\sqrt{58}}, -\dfrac{7}{\sqrt{58}} \right) \approx (-7.39, 0.92)$ or
$$\left(7 - \frac{3}{\sqrt{58}}, \frac{7}{\sqrt{58}} \right) \approx (6.61, 0.92).$$

42. (a) A is $(6, 0)$ and B is $(0, 3)$.

(b) The line is parallel to
$$\overrightarrow{AB} = \langle 0 - 6, 3 - 0 \rangle = \langle -6, 3 \rangle, \text{ so the direction}$$
of $\overrightarrow{AP}$ is $\mathbf{u} = \langle 3, 6 \rangle$ or $\mathbf{v} = \langle -3, -6 \rangle$.

$$\overrightarrow{AP} = \frac{\mathbf{u}}{|\mathbf{u}|} = \frac{\langle 3, 6 \rangle}{\sqrt{9 + 36}} = \frac{\langle 3, 6 \rangle}{3\sqrt{5}} = \left\langle \frac{1}{\sqrt{5}}, \frac{2}{\sqrt{5}} \right\rangle \text{ or}$$

$$\overrightarrow{AP} = \frac{\mathbf{v}}{|\mathbf{v}|} = \frac{\langle -3, -6 \rangle}{\sqrt{9 + 36}} = \frac{\langle -3, -6 \rangle}{3\sqrt{5}}$$
$$= \left\langle -\frac{1}{\sqrt{5}}, -\frac{2}{\sqrt{5}} \right\rangle. \text{ So } P \text{ is } \left(6 + \frac{1}{\sqrt{5}}, \frac{2}{\sqrt{5}} \right)$$
$$\approx (6.45, 0.89) \text{ or } \left(6 - \frac{1}{\sqrt{5}}, -\frac{2}{\sqrt{5}} \right) \approx (5.55, -0.89).$$

43. $2v_1 + 3v_2 = 10$, $v_1{}^2 + v_2{}^2 = 17$. Since $v_1 = 5 - \dfrac{3}{2}v_2$,
$$\left(5 - \frac{3}{2}v_2 \right)^2 + v_2{}^2 = 17, \ 25 - 15v_2 + \frac{9}{4}v_2{}^2 + v_2{}^2 = 17,$$
$$\frac{13}{4}v_2{}^2 - 15v_2 + 8 = 0, \ 13v_2{}^2 - 60v_2 + 32 = 0,$$
$$(v_2 - 4)(13v_2 - 8) = 0, \text{ so } v_2 = 4 \text{ or } v_2 = \frac{8}{13}.$$

Therefore, $\mathbf{v} \approx \langle -1, 4 \rangle$ or $\mathbf{v} = \left\langle \dfrac{53}{13}, \dfrac{8}{13} \right\rangle \approx \langle 4.07, 0.62 \rangle$.

44. $-2v_1 + 5v_2 = -11, v_1^2 + v_2^2 = 10.$ Since $v_1 = \frac{5}{2}v_2 + \frac{11}{2}$,

$$\left(\frac{1}{2}(5v_2 + 11)\right)^2 + v_2^2 = 10,$$

$$\frac{25v_2^2}{4} + \frac{110v_2}{4} + \frac{121}{4} + v_2^2 = 10,$$

$$\frac{29}{4}v_2^2 + \frac{110}{4}v_2 + \frac{81}{4} = 0, 29v_2^2 + 110v_2 + 81 = 0,$$

$(v_2 + 1)(29v_2 + 81) = 0$, so $v_2 = -1$ or $v_2 = -\frac{81}{29}$.

Therefore, $\mathbf{v} = \langle 3, -1 \rangle$ or $\mathbf{v} = \left\langle -\frac{43}{29}, -\frac{81}{29} \right\rangle$

$\approx \langle -1.48, -2.79 \rangle$.

45. $\mathbf{v} = (\cos 60°)\mathbf{i} + (\sin 60°)\mathbf{j} = \frac{1}{2}\mathbf{i} + \frac{\sqrt{3}}{2}\mathbf{j}$

$\mathbf{F_1} = \text{proj}_\mathbf{v}\mathbf{F} = (\mathbf{F}\cdot\mathbf{v})\mathbf{v} = \left(-160\mathbf{j}\cdot\left(\frac{1}{2}\mathbf{i} + \frac{\sqrt{3}}{2}\mathbf{j}\right)\right)\mathbf{v}$

$= -80\sqrt{3}\left(\frac{1}{2}\mathbf{i} + \frac{\sqrt{3}}{2}\mathbf{j}\right) = -40\sqrt{3}\mathbf{i} - 120\mathbf{j}.$

The magnitude of the force is

$|\mathbf{F_1}| = \sqrt{(-40\sqrt{3})^2 + (-120)^2} = \sqrt{19{,}200}$
≈ 138.56 pounds.

46. In this case, $\mathbf{F} = -125\mathbf{j}$ and $\mathbf{v}$ remains the same as in Example 6.

$\mathbf{F_1} = \text{proj}_\mathbf{v}\mathbf{F} = (\mathbf{F}\cdot\mathbf{v})\mathbf{v} = -125\left(\frac{\sqrt{2}}{2}\right)\mathbf{v} = 62.5(\mathbf{i} + \mathbf{j}).$

The magnitude of the force is $|\mathbf{F_1}| = 62.5\sqrt{2} \approx 88.39$ pounds.

47. (a) $\mathbf{v} = (\cos 12°)\mathbf{i} + (\sin 12°)\mathbf{j}$
$\mathbf{F} = -2000\mathbf{j}$
$\mathbf{F_1} = \text{proj}_\mathbf{v}\mathbf{F} = (\mathbf{F}\cdot\mathbf{v})\mathbf{v}$
$= (\langle 0, -2000 \rangle \cdot \langle \cos 12°, \sin 12° \rangle) \langle \cos 12°, \sin 12° \rangle$
$= (-2000 \sin 12°)\langle \cos 12°, \sin 12° \rangle.$
Since $\langle \cos 12°, \sin 12° \rangle$ is a unit vector, the magnitude of the force being extended is
$|\mathbf{F_1}| = 2000 \sin 12° \approx 415.82$ pounds.

(b) We are looking for the gravitational force exerted perpendicular to the street. A unit vector perpendicular to the street is $\mathbf{w} = \langle \cos(-78°), \sin(-78°) \rangle$, so $\mathbf{F_2} = \text{proj}_\mathbf{w}\mathbf{F} = (\mathbf{F}\cdot\mathbf{w})\mathbf{w}$
$= (-2000 \sin(-78°)) \langle \cos(-78°), \sin(-78°) \rangle$
Since $\langle \cos(-78°), \sin(-78°) \rangle$ is a unit vector, the magnitude of the force perpendicular to the street is $-2000 \sin(-78°) \approx 1956.30$ pounds.

48. We want to determine "how much" of the 60 pound force is projected along the inclined plane.
$\mathbf{F} = 60 \langle \cos 43°, \sin 43° \rangle \approx \langle 43.88, 40.92 \rangle$ and
$\mathbf{v} = \langle \cos 18°, \sin 18° \rangle \approx \langle 0.95, 0.31 \rangle$
$$\text{proj}_\mathbf{v}\mathbf{F} = \frac{(\langle 43.88, 40.92 \rangle \cdot \langle 0.95, 0.31 \rangle)\langle 0.95, 0.31 \rangle}{(\sqrt{1})^2}$$
$$\approx \frac{54.38\langle 0.95, 0.31 \rangle}{1} \approx \langle 51.72, 16.80 \rangle.$$ The magnitude of this force is $|\mathbf{F_1}| = \sqrt{(51.72)^2 + (16.80)^2}$
≈ 54.38 pounds. Of note, it is also possible to evaluate this problem considering the x-axis parallel to the inclined plane and the y-axis perpendicular to the plane. In this

case $\mathbf{F} = 60 \langle \cos 25°, \sin 25° \rangle \approx \langle 54.38, 25.36 \rangle$. Since we only want the force in the x-direction, we immediately find our answer of about 54.38 pounds.

49. Since the car weighs 2600 pounds, the force needed to lift the car is $\langle 0, 2600 \rangle$.
$W = \mathbf{F} \cdot \overrightarrow{AB} = \langle 0, 2600 \rangle \cdot \langle 0, 5.5 \rangle = 14{,}300$ foot-pounds

50. Since the potatoes weigh 100 pounds, the force needed to lift the potatoes is $\langle 0, 100 \rangle$.
$W = \mathbf{F} \cdot \overrightarrow{AB} = \langle 0, 100 \rangle \cdot \langle 0, 3 \rangle = 300$ foot-pounds

51. $\mathbf{F} = 12 \cdot \frac{\langle 1, 2 \rangle}{|\langle 1, 2 \rangle|} = \frac{12}{\sqrt{5}}\langle 1, 2 \rangle$
$W = \mathbf{F} \cdot \overrightarrow{AB} = \frac{12}{\sqrt{5}}\langle 1, 2 \rangle \cdot \langle 4, 0 \rangle = \frac{48}{\sqrt{5}}$
≈ 21.47 foot-pounds

52. $\mathbf{F} = 24 \cdot \frac{\langle 4, 5 \rangle}{|\langle 4, 5 \rangle|} = \frac{24}{\sqrt{4^2 + 5^2}}\langle 4, 5 \rangle \approx \frac{24}{\sqrt{41}}\langle 4, 5 \rangle$
$W = \mathbf{F} \cdot \overrightarrow{AB} = \frac{24}{\sqrt{41}}\langle 5, 0 \rangle = \frac{120}{\sqrt{41}}$
$= \mathbf{F} \cdot \overrightarrow{AB} = \frac{24}{\sqrt{41}}\langle 4, 5 \rangle \cdot \langle 5, 0 \rangle = \frac{480}{\sqrt{41}}$
≈ 74.96 foot-pounds

53. $\mathbf{F} = 30 \cdot \frac{\langle 2, 2 \rangle}{|\langle 2, 2 \rangle|} = \frac{30}{\sqrt{2^2 + 2^2}}\langle 2, 2 \rangle = 15\sqrt{2}\langle 1, 1 \rangle$

Since we want to move 3 feet along the line $y = \frac{1}{2}x$, we solve for x and y by using the Pythagorean theorem:
$x^2 + y^2 = 3^2, x^2 + \left(\frac{1}{2}x\right)^2 = 9, \frac{5}{4}x^2 = 9,$

$x = \frac{6}{\sqrt{5}}, y = \frac{3}{\sqrt{5}}$

$\overrightarrow{AB} = \left\langle \frac{6}{\sqrt{5}}, \frac{3}{\sqrt{5}} \right\rangle$

$W = \mathbf{F} \cdot \overrightarrow{AB} = \langle 15\sqrt{2}, 15\sqrt{2} \rangle \cdot \left\langle \frac{6}{\sqrt{5}}, \frac{3}{\sqrt{5}} \right\rangle$

$= 135\sqrt{\frac{2}{5}} = 27\sqrt{10} \approx 85.38$ foot-pounds

54. $\mathbf{F} = 50 \cdot \frac{\langle 2, 3 \rangle}{|\langle 2, 3 \rangle|} = \frac{50}{\sqrt{2^2 + 3^2}}\langle 2, 3 \rangle = \frac{50}{\sqrt{13}}\langle 2, 3 \rangle$
Since we want to move the object 5 feet along the line $y = x$, we solve for x and y by using the Pythagorean theorem: $x^2 + y^2 = 5^2, x^2 + x^2 = 25, 2x^2 = 25,$
$x = 2.5\sqrt{2}, y = 2.5\sqrt{2}.$
$\overrightarrow{AB} = \langle 2.5\sqrt{2}, 2.5\sqrt{2} \rangle.$
$W = \mathbf{F} \cdot \overrightarrow{AB} = \frac{50}{\sqrt{13}}\langle 2, 3 \rangle \cdot \langle 2.5\sqrt{2}, 2.5\sqrt{2} \rangle = 625\sqrt{\frac{2}{13}}$
≈ 245.15 foot-pounds

55. $W = \mathbf{F} \cdot \overrightarrow{AB} = |\mathbf{F}||\overrightarrow{AB}| \cos\theta = 200\sqrt{13}\cos 30°$
$= 200\sqrt{13} \cdot \frac{\sqrt{3}}{2} = 100\sqrt{39} \approx 624.5$ foot-pounds

56. $\overrightarrow{AB} = \langle 4, 3 \rangle - \langle -1, 1 \rangle = \langle 5, 2 \rangle$
$W = \mathbf{F} \cdot \overrightarrow{AB} = |\mathbf{F}||\overrightarrow{AB}| \cos\theta = 75\sqrt{29}\cos 60°$
$= 75\sqrt{29} \cdot \frac{1}{2} = \frac{75\sqrt{29}}{2} \approx 201.9$ foot-pounds

57. (a) Let $\mathbf{u} = \langle u_1, u_2 \rangle$, $\mathbf{v} = \langle v_1, v_2 \rangle$, and $\mathbf{w} = \langle w_1, w_2 \rangle$.
$\mathbf{0} \cdot u = \langle 0, 0 \rangle \cdot \langle u_1, u_2 \rangle = 0 \cdot u_1 + 0 \cdot u_2 = 0$

(b) $\mathbf{u} \cdot (\mathbf{v} + \mathbf{w}) = \langle u_1, u_2 \rangle \cdot (\langle v_1, v_2 \rangle + \langle w_1, w_2 \rangle)$
$= \langle u_1, u_2 \rangle \cdot \langle v_1 + w_1, v_2 + w_2 \rangle$
$= u_1(v_1 + w_1) + u_2(v_2 + w_2)$
$= u_1 v_1 + u_2 v_2 + u_1 w_1 + u_2 w_2$
$= \langle u_1, u_2 \rangle \cdot \langle v_1, v_2 \rangle + \langle u_1, u_2 \rangle \cdot \langle w_1, w_2 \rangle$
$= \mathbf{u} \cdot \mathbf{v} + \mathbf{u} \cdot \mathbf{w}$

(c) $(\mathbf{u} + \mathbf{v}) \cdot \mathbf{w} = (\langle u_1, u_2 \rangle + \langle v_1, v_2 \rangle) \cdot \langle w_1, w_2 \rangle$
$= \langle u_1 + v_1, u_2 + v_2 \rangle \cdot \langle w_1, w_2 \rangle$
$= (u_1 + v_1) w_1 + (u_2 + v_2) w_2$
$= u_1 w_1 + u_2 w_2 + v_1 w_1 + v_2 w_2$
$= \langle u_1, u_2 \rangle \cdot \langle w_1, w_2 \rangle + \langle v_1, v_2 \rangle \cdot \langle w_1, w_2 \rangle$
$= \mathbf{u} \cdot \mathbf{w} + \mathbf{v} \cdot \mathbf{w}$

(d) $(c\mathbf{u}) \cdot \mathbf{v} = (c \langle u_1, u_2 \rangle) \cdot \langle v_1, v_2 \rangle = \langle cu_1, cu_2 \rangle \cdot \langle v_1, v_2 \rangle$
$= cu_1 v_1 + cu_2 v_2 = \langle u_1, u_2 \rangle \cdot \langle cv_1, cv_2 \rangle = \mathbf{u} \cdot (c\mathbf{v})$
$= c(u_1 v_1 + u_2 v_2) = c(\langle u_1, u_2 \rangle \cdot \langle v_1, v_2 \rangle) = c(\mathbf{u} \cdot \mathbf{v})$

58. (a) When we evaluate the projection of $\mathbf{u}$ onto $\mathbf{v}$ we are actually trying to determine "how much" of $\mathbf{u}$ is "going" in the direction of $\mathbf{v}$. Using Figure 6.19, imagine that $\mathbf{v}$ runs along our x-axis, with the y-axis perpendicular to it. Written in component form, $\mathbf{u} = (|\mathbf{u}| \cos \theta, |\mathbf{u}| \sin \theta)$ and we see that the projection of $\mathbf{u}$ onto $\mathbf{v}$ is exactly $|\mathbf{u}| \cos \theta$ times $\mathbf{v}$'s unit vector $\dfrac{\mathbf{v}}{|\mathbf{v}|}$. Thus, $\text{proj}_{\mathbf{v}} \mathbf{u} = |\mathbf{u}| \cos \theta \cdot \dfrac{\mathbf{v}}{|\mathbf{v}|}$
$= |\mathbf{u}| \left(\dfrac{\mathbf{u} \cdot \mathbf{v}}{|\mathbf{u}| \, |\mathbf{v}|} \right) \dfrac{\mathbf{v}}{|\mathbf{v}|} = \dfrac{(\mathbf{u} \cdot \mathbf{v})}{|\mathbf{v}|} \dfrac{\mathbf{v}}{|\mathbf{v}|} = \left(\dfrac{\mathbf{u} \cdot \mathbf{v}}{|\mathbf{v}|^2} \right) \mathbf{v}$

(b) Recall Figure 6.19 and let $\mathbf{w}_1$ be $\overrightarrow{PR} = \text{proj}_{\mathbf{v}} \mathbf{u}$ and $\mathbf{w}_2 = \overrightarrow{RQ} = \mathbf{u} - \text{proj}_{\mathbf{v}} \mathbf{u}$. Then, $(\mathbf{u} - \text{proj}_{\mathbf{v}} \mathbf{u}) \cdot (\text{proj}_{\mathbf{v}} \mathbf{u}) = \mathbf{w}_2 \cdot \mathbf{w}_1$. Since $\mathbf{w}_1$ and $\mathbf{w}_2$ are perpendicular, $\mathbf{w}_1 \cdot \mathbf{w}_2 = 0$.

59.

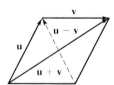

As the diagram indicates, the long diagonal of the parallelogram can be expressed as the vector $\mathbf{u} + \mathbf{v}$ while the short diagonal can be expressed as the vector $\mathbf{u} - \mathbf{v}$. The sum of the squares of the diagonals is
$|\mathbf{u} + \mathbf{v}|^2 + |\mathbf{u} - \mathbf{v}|^2 = (\mathbf{u} + \mathbf{v}) \cdot (\mathbf{u} + \mathbf{v})$
$+ (\mathbf{u} - \mathbf{v}) \cdot (\mathbf{u} - \mathbf{v}) = \mathbf{u} \cdot \mathbf{u} + \mathbf{u} \cdot \mathbf{v} + \mathbf{v} \cdot \mathbf{u} + \mathbf{v} \cdot \mathbf{v}$
$+ \mathbf{u} \cdot \mathbf{u} - \mathbf{u} \cdot \mathbf{v} - \mathbf{u} \cdot \mathbf{v} + \mathbf{v} \cdot \mathbf{v} = 2|\mathbf{u}|^2 + 2|\mathbf{v}|^2$
$+ 2\mathbf{u} \cdot \mathbf{v} - 2\mathbf{u} \cdot \mathbf{v} = 2|\mathbf{u}|^2 + 2|\mathbf{v}|^2$, which is the sum of the squares of the sides.

60. Let $\mathbf{u} = \langle u_1, u_2 \rangle$.
$(\mathbf{u} \cdot \mathbf{i})\mathbf{i} + (\mathbf{u} \cdot \mathbf{j})\mathbf{j}$
$= (\langle u_1, u_2 \rangle \cdot \langle 1, 0 \rangle)\mathbf{i} + (\langle u_1, u_2 \rangle \cdot \langle 0, 1 \rangle)\mathbf{j}$
$= (u_1)\mathbf{i} + (u_2)\mathbf{j}$
$= u_1 \mathbf{i} + u_2 \mathbf{j}$
$= \langle u_1, u_2 \rangle$
$= \mathbf{u}$

61. False. If either $\mathbf{u}$ or $\mathbf{v}$ is the zero vector, then $\mathbf{u} \cdot \mathbf{v} = 0$ and so $\mathbf{u}$ and $\mathbf{v}$ are orthogonal, but they do not count as perpendicular.

62. True. $\mathbf{u} \cdot \mathbf{u} = |\mathbf{u}|^2 = (1)^2 = 1$.

63. $\mathbf{u} \cdot \mathbf{v} = 0$, so the vectors are perpendicular. The answer is D.

64. $\mathbf{u} \cdot \mathbf{v} = \langle 4, -5 \rangle \cdot \langle -2, -3 \rangle$
$= 4(-2) + (-5)(-3)$
$= -8 + 15$
$= 7$
The answer is C.

65. $\text{proj}_{\mathbf{v}} \mathbf{u} = \left(\dfrac{\mathbf{u} \cdot \mathbf{v}}{|\mathbf{v}|^2} \right) \mathbf{v}$
$= \left(\dfrac{3 + 0}{2^2} \right) \langle 2, 0 \rangle$
$= \left(\dfrac{3}{4} \right) \langle 2, 0 \rangle$
$= \left\langle \dfrac{3}{2}, 0 \right\rangle$
The answer is A.

66. The unit vector in the direction of $\mathbf{u}$ is $\dfrac{1}{\sqrt{2}} \langle -1, 1 \rangle$. The force is represented by 5 times the unit vector. The answer is B.

67. (a) $2 \cdot 0 + 5 \cdot 2 = 10$ and $2 \cdot 5 + 5 \cdot 0 = 10$

(b) $\overrightarrow{AP} = \langle 3 - 0, 7 - 2 \rangle = \langle 3, 5 \rangle$
$\overrightarrow{AB} = \langle 5 - 0, 0 - 2 \rangle = \langle 5, -2 \rangle$
$\mathbf{w}_1 = \text{proj}_{\overrightarrow{AB}} \overrightarrow{AP} = \left(\dfrac{\langle 3, 5 \rangle \cdot \langle 5, -27 \rangle}{5^2 + (-2)^2} \right) \langle 5, -2 \rangle$
$= \left(\dfrac{15 - 10}{29} \right) \langle 5, -2 \rangle = \dfrac{5}{29} \langle 5, -2 \rangle$
$\mathbf{w}_2 = \overrightarrow{AP} - \text{proj}_{\overrightarrow{AB}} \overrightarrow{AP}$
$= \langle 3, 5 \rangle - \dfrac{5}{29} \langle 5, -2 \rangle$
$= \left\langle 3 - \dfrac{25}{29}, 5 + \dfrac{10}{29} \right\rangle = \dfrac{1}{29} \langle 62, 155 \rangle$

(c) $\mathbf{w}_2$ is a vector from a point on $\overrightarrow{AB}$ to point P. Since $\mathbf{w}_2$ is perpendicular to $\overrightarrow{AB}$, $|\mathbf{w}_2|$ is the shortest distance from $\overrightarrow{AB}$ to P.
$|\mathbf{w}_2| = \sqrt{\left(\dfrac{62}{29} \right)^2 + \left(\dfrac{155}{29} \right)^2} = \sqrt{\dfrac{27{,}869}{29^2}} = \dfrac{31\sqrt{29}}{29}$

(d) Consider Figure 6.19. To find the distance from a point P to a line L, we must first find $\mathbf{u}_1 = \text{proj}_{\mathbf{v}} \mathbf{u}$. In this case,
$\text{proj}_{\overrightarrow{AB}} \overrightarrow{AP} = \left(\dfrac{\langle x_0, y_0 - 2 \rangle \cdot \langle 5, -2 \rangle}{(\sqrt{5^2 + (-2)^2})^2} \right) \langle 5, -2 \rangle$
$= \left(\dfrac{5x_0 - 2y_0 + 4}{29} \right) \langle 5, -2 \rangle$
$= \left\langle \dfrac{25x_0 - 10y_0 + 20}{29}, \dfrac{-10x_0 + 4y_0 - 8}{29} \right\rangle$ and
$\overrightarrow{AP} - \text{proj}_{\overrightarrow{AB}} \overrightarrow{AP} = \langle x_0, y_0 - 2 \rangle$
$- \left\langle \dfrac{25x_0 - 10y_0 + 20}{29}, \dfrac{-10x_0 + 4y_0 - 8}{29} \right\rangle$
$= \dfrac{1}{29} (\langle 29x_0, 29(y_0 - 2) \rangle$
$- \langle 25x_0 - 10y_0 + 20, -10x_0 + 4y_0 - 8 \rangle)$
$= \dfrac{1}{29} \langle 4x_0 + 10y_0 - 20, 10x_0 + 25y_0 - 50 \rangle$

So, the distance is the magnitude of this vector.

$$d = \frac{1}{29}\sqrt{(4x_0 + 10y_0 - 20)^2 + (10x_0 + 25y_0 - 50)^2}$$

$$= \frac{\sqrt{2^2(2x_0 + 5y_0 - 10)^2 + 5^2(2x_0 + 5y_0 - 10)^2}}{29}$$

$$= \frac{\sqrt{29(2x_0 + 5y_0 - 10)^2}}{29}$$

$$= \frac{|(2x_0 + 5y_0 - 10)|}{\sqrt{29}}$$

(c) In the general case, $\overrightarrow{AB} = \left\langle \dfrac{c}{a}, \dfrac{-c}{b} \right\rangle$ and

$\overrightarrow{AP} = \left\langle x_0, y_0 - \dfrac{c}{b} \right\rangle$, so $\text{proj}_{\overrightarrow{AB}}\, \overrightarrow{AP}$

$$= \frac{\left(\dfrac{x_0 c}{a} - \dfrac{(bcy_0 - c^2)}{b^2} \right)\left\langle \dfrac{c}{a}, -\dfrac{c}{b} \right\rangle}{\left| \dfrac{c}{a} \right|^2 + \left| -\dfrac{c}{b} \right|^2}$$

$$= \left\langle \frac{b^2 x_0 - aby_0 + ac}{a^2 + b^2}, \frac{-abx_0 + a^2 y_0 - \dfrac{a^2 c}{b}}{a^2 + b^2} \right\rangle$$

$\overrightarrow{AP} - \text{proj}_{\overrightarrow{AB}}\, \overrightarrow{AP} = \left\langle x_0, y_0 - \dfrac{c}{b} \right\rangle$

$$- \left\langle \frac{b^2 x_0 - aby_0 + ac}{a^2 + b^2}, \frac{-abx_0 + a^2 y_0 - \dfrac{a^2 c}{b}}{a^2 + b^2} \right\rangle$$

$$= \left\langle \frac{a^2 x_0 + aby_0 - ac}{a^2 + b^2}, \frac{abx_0 + b^2 y_0 - bc}{a^2 + b^2} \right\rangle$$

The magnitude of this vector, $\left| \overrightarrow{AP} - \text{proj}_{\overrightarrow{AB}}\, \overrightarrow{AP} \right|$, is

the distance from point P to L: $\dfrac{ax_0 + by_0 - c}{\sqrt{a^2 + b^2}}$.

68. (a) Yes, if $\mathbf{v} = \langle 0, 0 \rangle$ or $t = n\pi$, $n = $ any integer

(b) Yes, if $\mathbf{u} = \langle 0, 0 \rangle$ or $t = \dfrac{n\pi}{2}$, $n = $ odd integer

(c) Generally, no, because $\sin t \neq \cos t$ for most t.

Exceptions, however, would occur when $t = \dfrac{\pi}{4} + n\pi$,

$n = $ any integer, or if $\mathbf{u} = \langle 0, 0 \rangle$ and/or $\mathbf{v} = \langle 0, 0 \rangle$.

69. One possible answer:
If $a\mathbf{u} + b\mathbf{v} = c\mathbf{u} + d\mathbf{v}$
$a\mathbf{u} - c\mathbf{u} + b\mathbf{v} - d\mathbf{v} = 0$
$(a - c)\mathbf{u} + (b - d)\mathbf{v} = 0$
Since $\mathbf{u}$ and $\mathbf{v}$ are not parallel, the only way for this equality to hold true for all vectors $\mathbf{u}$ and $\mathbf{v}$ is if $(a - c) = 0$ and $(b - d) = 0$, which indicates that $a = c$ and $b = d$.

■ Section 6.3 Parametric Equations and Motion

Exploration 1

1.

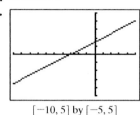

$[-10, 5]$ by $[-5, 5]$

2. $0.5(17) + 1.5 = 10$, so the point $(17, 10)$ is on the graph, $t = -8$

3. $0.5(-23) + 1.5 = -10$, so the point $(-23, -10)$ is on the graph, $t = 12$.

4. $x = a = 1 - 2t$, $2t = 1 - a$, $t = \dfrac{1}{2} - \dfrac{a}{2}$.
Alternatively, $b = 2 - t$, so $t = 2 - b$.

5. Choose Tmin and Tmax so that
Tmin ≤ -2 and Tmax ≥ 5.5.

Exploration 2

1. It looks like the line in Figure 6.32.

2. The graph is a vertical line segment that extends from $(400, 0)$ to $(400, 20)$.

3. For 19° and 20°, the ball does not clear the fence, as shown below.

19°:

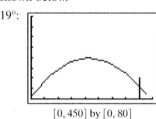

$[0, 450]$ by $[0, 80]$

20°:

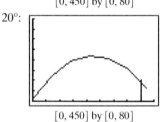

$[0, 450]$ by $[0, 80]$

For 21° and 22°, the ball clears the fence, as shown below.

21°

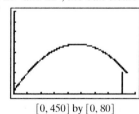

$[0, 450]$ by $[0, 80]$

22°:

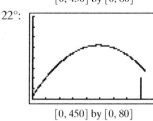

$[0, 450]$ by $[0, 80]$

Quick Review 6.3

1. (a) $\overrightarrow{OA} = \langle -3, -2 \rangle$

   (b) $\overrightarrow{OB} = \langle 4, 6 \rangle$

   (c) $\overrightarrow{AB} = \langle 4 - (-3), 6 - (-2) \rangle = \langle 7, 8 \rangle$

2. (a) $\overrightarrow{OA} = \langle -1, 3 \rangle$

   (b) $\overrightarrow{OB} = \langle 4, -3 \rangle$

   (c) $\overrightarrow{AB} = \langle 4 - (-1), -3 - 3 \rangle = \langle 5, -6 \rangle$

3. $m = \dfrac{6 - (-2)}{4 - (-3)} = \dfrac{8}{7}$

   $y + 2 = \dfrac{8}{7}(x + 3)$ or $y - 6 = \dfrac{8}{7}(x - 4)$

4. $m = \dfrac{-3 - 3}{4 - (-1)} = -\dfrac{6}{5}$

   $y - 3 = -\dfrac{6}{5}(x + 1)$ or $y + 3 = -\dfrac{6}{5}(x - 4)$

5. Graph $y = \pm\sqrt{8x}$.

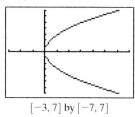

[−3, 7] by [−7, 7]

6. Graph $y = \pm\sqrt{-5x}$.

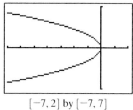

[−7, 2] by [−7, 7]

7. $x^2 + y^2 = 4$

8. $(x + 2)^2 + (y - 5)^2 = 9$

9. $\dfrac{600 \text{ rotations}}{1 \text{ min}} \cdot \dfrac{1 \text{ min}}{60 \text{ sec}} \cdot \dfrac{2\pi \text{ rad}}{1 \text{ rotation}} = 20\pi$ rad/sec

10. $\dfrac{700 \text{ rotations}}{1 \text{ min}} \cdot \dfrac{1 \text{ min}}{60 \text{ sec}} \cdot \dfrac{2\pi \text{ rad}}{1 \text{ rotation}} = \dfrac{70}{3}\pi$ rad/sec

Section 6.3 Exercises

1. (b) $[-5, 5]$ by $[-5, 5]$

2. (d) $[-5, 5]$ by $[-5, 5]$

3. (a) $[-5, 5]$ by $[-5, 5]$

4. (c) $[-10, 10]$ by $[-12, 10]$

5. (a)

t	−2	−1	0	1	2
x	0	1	2	3	4
y	$-\dfrac{1}{2}$	−2	undef.	4	$\dfrac{5}{2}$

(b)

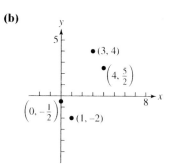

6. (a)

t	0	$\dfrac{\pi}{2}$	π	$\dfrac{3\pi}{2}$	2π
x	1	0	−1	0	1
y	0	1	0	−1	0

(b)

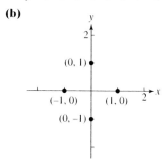

7.

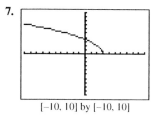

[−10, 10] by [−10, 10]

8.

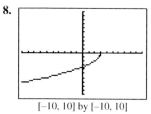

[−10, 10] by [−10, 10]

9.

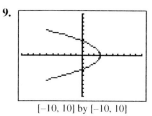

[−10, 10] by [−10, 10]

10.

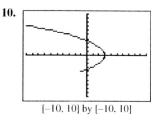

[−10, 10] by [−10, 10]

11. $x = 1 + y$, so $y = x - 1$: line through $(0, -1)$ and $(1, 0)$

12. $t = y - 5$, so $x = 2 - 3(y - 5)$; $y = -\frac{1}{3}x + \frac{17}{3}$: line through $\left(0, \frac{17}{3}\right)$ and $(17, 0)$

13. $t = \frac{1}{2}x + \frac{3}{2}$, so $y = 9 - 4\left(\frac{1}{2}x + \frac{3}{2}\right)$; $y = -2x + 3$, $3 \le x \le 7$: line segment with endpoints $(3, -3)$ and $(7, -11)$

14. $t = y - 2$, so $x = 5 - 3(y - 2)$; $y = -\frac{1}{3}x + \frac{11}{3}$, $-4 \le x \le 8$: line segment with endpoints $(8, 1)$ and $(-4, 5)$

15. $x = (y - 1)^2$: parabola that opens to right with vertex at $(0, 1)$

16. $y = x^2 - 3$: parabola that opens upward with vertex at $(0, -3)$

17. $y = x^3 - 2x + 3$: cubic polynomial

18. $x = 2y^2 - 1$; parabola that opens to right with vertex at $(0, -1)$

19. $x = 4 - y^2$; parabola that opens to left with vertex at $(4, 0)$

20. $t = 2x$, so $y = 16x^3 - 3$: cubic, $-1 \le x \le 1$

21. $t = x + 3$, so $y = \frac{2}{x + 3}$, on domain: $[-8, -3) \cup (-3, 2]$

22. $t = x - 2$, so $y = \frac{4}{x - 2}$, $x \ge 4$

23. $x^2 + y^2 = 25$, circle of radius 5 centered at $(0, 0)$

24. $x^2 + y^2 = 16$, circle of radius 4 centered at $(0, 0)$

25. $x^2 + y^2 = 4$, three-fourths of a circle of radius 2 centered at $(0, 0)$ (not in Quadrant II)

26. $x^2 + y^2 = 9$, semicircle of radius 3, $y \ge 0$ only

27. $\overrightarrow{OA} = \langle -2, 5\rangle$, $\overrightarrow{OB} = \langle 4, 2\rangle$, $\overrightarrow{OP} = \langle x, y\rangle$
$\overrightarrow{OP} - \overrightarrow{OA} = t(\overrightarrow{OB} - \overrightarrow{OA})$
$\langle x + 2, y - 5\rangle = t\langle 6, -3\rangle$
$x + 2 = 6t \Rightarrow x = 6t - 2$
$y - 5 = 3t \Rightarrow y = -3t + 5$

28. $\overrightarrow{OA} = \langle -3, -3\rangle$, $\overrightarrow{OB} = \langle 5, 1\rangle$, $\overrightarrow{OP} = \langle x, y\rangle$
$\overrightarrow{OP} - \overrightarrow{OA} = t(\overrightarrow{OB} - \overrightarrow{OA})$
$\langle x + 3, y + 3\rangle = t\langle 8, 4\rangle$
$x + 3 = 8t \Rightarrow x = 8t - 3$
$y + 3 = 4t \Rightarrow y = 4t - 3$

For #29–32, many answers are possible; one or two of the simplest are given.

29. Two possibilities are $x = t + 3$, $y = 4 - \frac{7}{3}t, 0 \le t \le 3$, or $x = 3t + 3$, $y = 4 - 7t$, $0 \le t \le 1$.

30. Two possibilities are $x = 5 - t$, $y = 2 - \frac{6}{7}t$, $0 \le t \le 7$, or $x = 5 - 7t$, $y = 2 - 6t, 0 \le t \le 1$.

31. One possibility is $x = 5 + 3 \cos t$, $y = 2 + 3 \sin t$, $0 \le t \le 2\pi$.

32. One possibility is $x = -2 + 2 \cos t$, $y = -4 + 2 \sin t$, $0 \le t \le 2\pi$.

33. In Quadrant I, we need $x > 0$ and $y > 0$, so $2 - |t| > 0$ and $t - 0.5 > 0$. Then $-2 < t < 2$ and $t > 0.5$, so $0.5 < t < 2$. This is not changed by the additional requirement that $-3 \le t \le 3$.

34. In Quadrant II, we need $x < 0$ and $y > 0$, so $2 - |t| < 0$ and $t - 0.5 > 0$. Then $(t < -2$ or $t > 2)$ and t > 0.5, so $t > 2$. With the additional requirement that $-3 \le t \le 3$, this becomes $2 < t \le 3$.

35. In Quadrant III, we need $x < 0$ and $y < 0$, so $2 - |t| < 0$ and $t - 0.5 < 0$. Then $(t < -2$ or $t > 2)$ and $t < 0.5$, so $t < -2$. With the additional requirement that $-3 \le t \le 3$, this becomes $-3 \le t < -2$.

36. In Quadrant IV, we need $x > 0$ and $y < 0$, so $2 - |t| > 0$ and $t - 0.5 < 0$. Then $-2 < t < 2$ and $t < 0.5$, so $-2 < t < 0.5$. This is not changed by the additional requirement that $-3 \le t \le 3$.

37. **(a)** One good window is $[-20, 300]$ by $[-1, 10]$. If your grapher allows, use "Simultaneous" rather than "Sequential" plotting. Note that 100 yd is 300 ft. To show the whole race, use $0 \le t \le 13$ (upper limit may vary), since Ben finishes in 12.916 sec. Note that it is the *process* of graphing (during which one observes Ben passing Jerry and crossing "the finish line" first), not the final product (which is two horizontal lines) which is needed; for that reason, no graph is shown here.

(b) After 3 seconds, Jerry is at $20(3) = 60$ ft and Ben is at $24(3) - 10 = 62$ ft. Ben is ahead by 2 ft.

38. **(a)** If your grapher allows, use "Simultaneous" rather than "Sequential" plotting. To see the whole race, use $0 \le t \le 5.1$ (upper limit may vary), since the faster runner reaches the flag after 5.1 sec. Note that it is the *process* of graphing, not the final product (which shows a horizontal line) which is needed; for that reason, no graph is shown here.

(b) The faster runner (who is coming from the left in the simulation) arrives at $t = 5.1$ sec. At this instant, the slower runner is 4.1 ft away from the flag; the slower runner doesn't reach the flag until $t = 5.5$ sec. This can be observed from the simulation, or by solving algebraically $x_1 = 50$ and $x_2 = 50$.

39. **(a)** $y = -16t^2 + v_0t + s_0 = -16t^2 + 0t + 1000 = -16t^2 + 1000$

(b) Graph and trace: $x = 1$ and $y = -16t^2 + 1000$ with $0 \le t \le 6$, on the window $[0, 2]$ by $[0, 1200]$. Use something like 0.2 or less for Tstep. This graph will appear as a vertical line from $(1, 424)$ to $(1, 1000)$; it is not shown here because the simulation is accomplished by the *tracing*, not by the *picture*.

(c) When $t = 4$, $y = -16(4)^2 + 1000 = 744$ ft; the food containers are 744 ft above the ground after 4 sec.

40. **(a)** $y = -16t^2 + v_0t + s_0 = -16t^2 + 80t + 5$

(b) Graph and trace: $x = 6$ and $y = -16t^2 + 80t + 5$ with $0 \le t \le 5.1$ (upper limit may vary) on $[0, 7]$ by $[0, 120]$. This graph will appear as a vertical line from about $(6, 0)$ to about $(6, 105)$. Tracing shows how the ball begins at a height of 5 ft, rises to over 100 ft, then falls back to the ground.

(c) Graph $x = t$ and $y = -16t^2 + 80t + 5$ with $0 \le t \le 5.1$ (upper limit may vary).

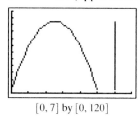

[0, 7] by [0, 120]

(d) When $t = 4$, $y = -16(4)^2 + 80(4) + 5 = 69$ ft. The ball is 69 ft above the ground after 4 sec.

(e) From the graph in (b), when $t = 2.5$ sec, the ball is at its maximum height of 105 ft.

41. Possible answers:

(a) $0 < t < \dfrac{\pi}{2}$ (t in radians)

(b) $0 < t < \pi$

(c) $\dfrac{\pi}{2} < t < \dfrac{3\pi}{2}$

42. (a) Both pairs of equations can be changed to $x^2 + y^2 = 9$ — a circle centered at the origin with radius 3. Also, when one chooses a point on this circle and swaps the x and y coordinates, one obtains another point on the same circle.

(b) The first begins at the right side (when $t = 0$) and traces the circle counterclockwise. The second begins at the top (when $t = 0$) and traces the circle clockwise.

43. (a) $x = 400$ when $t \approx 2.80$ — about 2.80 sec.

(b) When $t \approx 2.80$ sec, $y \approx 7.18$ ft.

(c) Reaching up, the outfielder's glove should be at or near the height of the ball as it approaches the wall. If hit at an angle of 20°, the ball would strike the wall about 19.74 ft up (after 2.84 sec) — the outfielder could not catch this.

44. (a) No: $x = (120 \cos 30°)t$; this equals 350 when $t \approx 3.37$. At this time, the ball is at a height of $y = -16t^2 + (120 \sin 30°)t + 4 \approx 24.59$ ft.

(b) The ball hits the wall about 24.59 ft up when $t \approx 3.37$ (see part a) — not catchable.

45. (a) Yes: $x = (5 + 120 \cos 30°)t$; this equals 350 when $t \approx 3.21$. At this time, the ball is at a height of $y = -16t^2 + (120 \sin 30°)t + 4 \approx 31.59$ ft.

(b) The ball clears the wall with about 1.59 ft to spare (when $t \approx 3.21$).

46. For Linda's ball, $x_1 = (45 \cos 44°)t$ and $y_1 = -16t^2 + (45 \sin 44°)t + 5$. For Chris's ball, $x_2 = 78 - (41 \cos 39°)t$ and $y_2 = -16t^2 + (41 \sin 39°)t + 5$. Find (graphically) the minimum of $d(t) = \sqrt{(x_1 - x_2)^2 + (y_1 - y_2)^2}$. It occurs when $t \approx 1.21$ sec; the minimum distance is about 6.60 ft.

47. No: $x = (30 \cos 70°)t$ and $y = -16t^2 + (30 \sin 70°)t + 3$. The dart lands when $y = 0$, which happens when $t \approx 1.86$ sec. At this point, the dart is about 19.11 ft from Tony, just over 10 in. short of the target.

48. Yes: $x = (25 \cos 55°)t$ and $y = -16t^2 + (25 \sin 55°)t + 4$. The dart lands when $y = 0$, which happens when $t \approx 1.45$ sec. At this point, the dart is about 20.82 ft from Sue, inside the target.

49. The parametric equations for this motion are $x = (v + 160 \cos 20°)t$ and $y = -16t^2 + (160 \sin 20°)t + 4$, where v is the velocity of the wind (in ft/sec) — it should be positive if the wind is in the direction of the hit, and negative if the wind is against the ball.

To solve this algebraically, eliminate the parameter t as follows:

$$t = \frac{x}{v + 160 \cos 20°}. \text{ So } y = -16\left(\frac{x}{v + 160 \cos 20°}\right)^2$$
$$+ 160 \sin 20°\left(\frac{x}{v + 160 \cos 20°}\right) + 4.$$

Substitute $x = 400$ and $y = 30$:

$$30 = -16\left(\frac{400}{v + 160 \cos 20°}\right)^2$$
$$+ 160 \sin 20°\left(\frac{400}{v + 160 \cos 20°}\right) + 4.$$

Let $u = \dfrac{400}{v + 160 \cos 20°}$, so the equation becomes $-16u^2 + 54.72u - 26 = 0$. Using the quadratic formula, we find that $u = \dfrac{-54.72 \pm \sqrt{54.72^2 - 4(-16)(-26)}}{-32} \approx$ 0.57, 2.85. Solving $0.57 = \dfrac{400}{v + 160 \cos 20°}$ and $2.85 = \dfrac{400}{v + 160 \cos 20°}$, $v \approx 551$, $v \approx -10$. A wind speed of 551 ft/sec (375.7 mph) is unrealistic, so we eliminate that solution. So the wind will be blowing against the ball in order for the ball to hit within a few inches of the top of the wall.

To verify this graphically, graph the equation

$$30 = -16\left(\frac{400}{v + 160 \cos 20°}\right)^2$$
$$+ 160 \sin 20°\left(\frac{400}{v + 160 \cos 20°}\right) + 4, \text{ and find}$$

the zero.

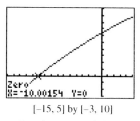

[-15, 5] by [-3, 10]

50. Assuming the course is level, the ball hits the ground when $y = -16t^2 + (180 \sin \theta)t$ equals 0, which happens when $t = \dfrac{180 \sin \theta}{16} = 11.25 \sin \theta$ sec. At that time, the ball has traveled $x = (180 \cos \theta)t = 2025(\cos \theta)(\sin \theta)$ feet. The answers are therefore approximately:

(a) 506.25 ft.

(b) 650.82 ft.

(c) 775.62 ft.

(d) 876.85 ft.

51. $x = 35 \cos\left(\dfrac{\pi}{6}t\right)$ and $y = 50 + 35 \sin\left(\dfrac{\pi}{6}t\right)$

52. $t = \dfrac{1}{5}x + \dfrac{2}{5}$, $y = 3 + 3\left(\dfrac{1}{5}x + \dfrac{2}{5}\right) = \dfrac{3}{5}x + \dfrac{21}{5}$

Since $3 = \dfrac{3}{5}(-2) + \dfrac{21}{5} = \dfrac{15}{5} = 3$ and

$6 = \dfrac{3}{5}(3) + \dfrac{21}{5} = \dfrac{30}{5} = 6$, both $(-2, 3)$ and $(3, 6)$ are

on the line.

53. (a) When $t = \pi$ (or 3π, or 5π, etc.), $y = 2$. This corresponds to the highest points on the graph.

(b) The x-intercepts occur where $y = 0$, which happens when $t = 0, 2\pi, 4\pi$, etc. The x coordinates at those times are (respectively) $0, 2\pi, 4\pi$, etc., so these are 2π units apart.

54. (a)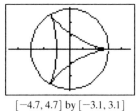

$[-4.7, 4.7]$ by $[-3.1, 3.1]$

(b) All 2's should be changed to 3's.

55. The particle begins at -10, moves right to $+2.25$ (at $t = 1.5$), then changes direction and ends at -4.

56. The particle begins at -5, moves right to $+4$ (at time $t = 2$), then changes direction and returns to -5.

57. The particle begins at -5, moves right to about $+0.07$ (at time $t \approx 0.15$), changes direction and moves left to about -20.81 (at time $t \approx 4.5$), then changes direction and ends at $+7$.

58. The particle begins at -10, moves right to about $+0.88$ (at $t \approx 0.46$), changes direction and moves left to about -6.06 (at time $t \approx 2.9$), then changes direction and ends at $+20$.

59. True. Eliminate t from the first set:

$t = x_1 + 1$
$y_1 = 3(x_1 + 1) + 1$
$y_1 = 3x_1 + 4$

Eliminate t from the second set:

$t = \dfrac{3}{2}x_2 + 2$

$y_2 = 2\left(\dfrac{3}{2}x_2 + 2\right)$

$y_2 = 3x_2 + 4$

Both sets correspond to the rectangular equation $y = 3x + 4$.

60. True. $x = 0$ and $y = 1$ when $t = 1$, and $x = 2$ and $y = 5$ when $t = 3$. Eliminating t,

$t = x + 1$.
$y = 2(x + 1) - 1$.
$y = 2x + 1$, $0 \le x \le 2, 1 \le y \le 5$.

61. $x = (-1)^2 - 4 = -3$, $y = -1 + \dfrac{1}{-1} = -2$

The answer is A.

62. The parametrization describes a circle of radius 2, centered at the origin and t represents the angle traveled counterclockwise from $(1, 0)$. The answer is A.

63. Set $-16t^2 + 80t + 7$ equal to 91 and solve either graphically or using the quadratic formula. The answer is D.

64. The equations are both linear, so the answer is either (a), (b), or (c). Since t has a minimum value and no maximum value, the answer is C.

65. (a)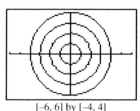

$[-6, 6]$ by $[-4, 4]$

(b) $x^2 + y^2 = (a \cos t)^2 + (a \sin t)^2$
$\qquad\qquad = a^2 \cos^2 t + a^2 \sin^2 t$
$\qquad\qquad = a^2$

The radius of the circles are $a = \{1, 2, 3, 4\}$, centered at $(0, 0)$.

(c)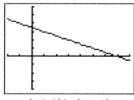

$[-6, 6]$ by $[-4, 4]$

(d) $x - h = a \cos t$ and $y - k = a \sin t$, so
$(x - h)^2 + (y - k)^2$
$\quad = (a \cos t)^2 + (a \sin t)^2$
$\quad = a^2 \cos^2 t + a^2 \sin^2 t$
$\quad = a^2$

The graph is the circle of radius a centered at (h, k).

(e) If $(x + 1)^2 + (y - 4)^2 = 9$, then $a = 3$, $h = -1$, and $k = 4$.

As a result, $x = 3 \cos t - 1$ and $y = 3 \sin t + 4$.

66. (a)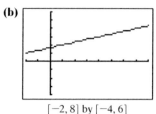

$[-2, 8]$ by $[-4, 6]$

(b)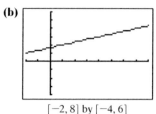

$[-2, 8]$ by $[-4, 6]$

(c) $t = \dfrac{1}{a}x - \dfrac{b}{a}$, $\quad y = c\left(\dfrac{1}{a}x - \dfrac{b}{a}\right) + d$

$\qquad = \dfrac{c}{a}x - \dfrac{b - ad}{a}$, $a \ne 0$.

(d) Slope: $\dfrac{c}{a}$, if $a \neq 0$;

  y-intercept: $\left(0, \dfrac{-b + ad}{a}\right)$, if $a \neq 0$;

  x-intercept: $\left(\dfrac{b - ad}{c}, 0\right)$, if $c \neq 0$.

(e) The line will be horizontal if $c = 0$. The line will be vertical if $a = 0$.

67. (a) Jane is traveling in a circle of radius 20 feet and center $(0, 20)$, which yields $x_1 = 20 \cos{(nt)}$ and $y_1 = 20 + 20 \sin{(nt)}$. Since the Ferris wheel is making one revolution (2π) every 12 seconds,

$$2\pi = 12n, \text{ so } n = \frac{2\pi}{12} = \frac{\pi}{6}.$$

Thus,

$$x_1 = 20 \cos\left(\frac{\pi}{6}t\right) \text{ and } y_1 = 20 + 20 \sin\left(\frac{\pi}{6}t\right), \text{ in}$$

radian mode.

(b) Since the ball was released at 75 ft in the positive x-direction and gravity acts in the negative y-direction at 16 ft/s², we have $x_2 = at + 75$ and $y_2 = -16t^2 + bt$, where a is the initial speed of the ball in the x-direction and b is the initial speed of the ball in the y-direction. The initial velocity vector of the ball is $60 \langle \cos 120°, \sin 120° \rangle = \langle -30, 30\sqrt{3} \rangle$, so $a = -30$ and $b = 30\sqrt{3}$. As a result $x_2 = -30t + 75$ and $y_2 = -16t^2 + 30\sqrt{3}t$ are the parametric equations for the ball.

(c)

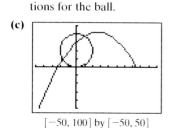

$[-50, 100]$ by $[-50, 50]$

Our graph shows that Jane and the ball will be close to each other but not at the exact same point at $t = 2.1$ seconds.

(d) $d(t) = \sqrt{(x_1 - x_2)^2 + (y_1 - y_2)^2}$

$$= \sqrt{\left(20 \cos\left(\frac{\pi}{6}t\right) + 30t - 75\right)^2 + \left(20 + 20 \sin\left(\frac{\pi}{6}t\right) + 16t^2 - (30\sqrt{3})t\right)^2}$$

(e)

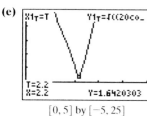

$[0, 5]$ by $[-5, 25]$

The minimum distance occurs at $t = 2.2$, when $d(t) = 1.64$ feet.

68. Assuming that the bottom of the ferris wheel and the ball's initial position are at the same height, the position of Matthew is $x_1 = 71 \cos\left(\frac{\pi}{10}t\right)$ and $y_1 = 71 + 71 \sin\left(\frac{\pi}{10}t\right)$. The ball's position is $x_2 = 90 + (88 \cos 100)t$ and $y_2 = -16t^2 + (88 \sin 100)t$. Find (graphically) the minimum of $d(t) = \sqrt{(x_1 - x_2)^2 + (y_1 - y_2)^2}$. It occurs when $t \approx 2.19$ sec; the minimum distance is about 3.47 ft.

69. Chang's position: $x_1 = 20 \cos\left(\frac{\pi}{6}t\right)$ and $y_1 = 20 + 20 \sin\left(\frac{\pi}{6}t\right)$. Kuan's position: $x_2 = 15 + 15 \cos\left(\frac{\pi}{4}t\right)$ and $y_2 = 15 + 15 \sin\left(\frac{\pi}{4}t\right)$.

Find (graphically) the minimum of $d(t) = \sqrt{(x_1 - x_2)^2 + (y_1 - y_2)^2}$. It occurs when $t \approx 21.50$ sec; the minimum distance is about 4.11 ft.

70. Chang's position: $x_1 = 20 \cos\left(\frac{\pi}{6}t\right)$ and $y_1 = 20 + 20 \sin\left(\frac{\pi}{6}t\right)$. Kuan's position: $x_2 = 15 + 15 \sin\left(\frac{\pi}{4}t\right)$ and $y_2 = 15 - 15 \cos\left(\frac{\pi}{4}t\right)$. Find (graphically) the minimum of $d(t) = \sqrt{(x_1 - x_2)^2 + (y_1 - y_2)^2}$. It occurs when $t \approx 12.32$ sec; the minimum distance is about 10.48 ft.

71. (a) $x(0) = 0c + (1 - 0)a = a$ and $y(0) = 0d + (1 - 0)b = b$

  (b) $x(1) = 1c + (1 - 1)a = c$ and $y(1) = 1d + (1 - 1)b = d$

72. $x(0.5) = 0.5c + (1 - 0.5)a = 0.5(a + c) = (a + c)/2$, while $y(0.5) = (b + d)/2$ — the correct coordinates for the midpoint.

73. Since the relationship between x and y is linear and one unit of time $(t = 1)$ separates the two points,

$t = \dfrac{1}{3} \approx 0.33$ will divide the segment into three equal

pieces. Similarly, $t = \dfrac{1}{4} = 0.25$ will divide the segment

into four equal pieces.

■ Section 6.4 Polar Coordinates

Exploration 1

2. $\left(2, \dfrac{\pi}{3}\right) = (1, \sqrt{3})$

  $\left(-1, \dfrac{\pi}{2}\right) = (0, -1)$

  $(2, \pi) = (-2, 0)$

  $\left(-5, \dfrac{3\pi}{2}\right) = (0, 5)$

  $(3, 2\pi) = (3, 0)$

3. $(-1, -\sqrt{3}) = \left(-2, \dfrac{\pi}{3}\right)$

$(0, 2) = \left(2, \dfrac{\pi}{2}\right)$

$(3, 0) = (3, 0)$

$(-1, 0) = (1, \pi)$

$(0, -4) = \left(4, \dfrac{3\pi}{2}\right)$

Quick Review 6.4

1. (a) Quadrant II

(b) Quadrant III

2. (a) Quadrant I

(b) Quadrant III

3. Possible answers: $7\pi/4, -9\pi/4$

4. Possible answers: $7\pi/3, -5\pi/3$

5. Possible answers: $520°, -200°$

6. Possible answers: $240°, -480°$

7. $(x - 3)^2 + y^2 = 4$

8. $x^2 + (y + 4)^2 = 9$

9. $a^2 = 12^2 + 10^2 - 2(12)(10)\cos 60°$

$a \approx 11.14$

10. $a^2 = 9^2 + 6^2 - 2(9)(6)\cos 40°$

$a \approx 5.85$

Section 6.4 Exercises

1. $\left(-\dfrac{3}{2}, \dfrac{3\sqrt{3}}{2}\right)$

2. $(2\sqrt{2}, 2\sqrt{2})$

3. $(-1, -\sqrt{3})$

4. $\left(-\dfrac{\sqrt{2}}{2}, \dfrac{\sqrt{2}}{2}\right)$

5. (a)

θ	$\dfrac{\pi}{4}$	$\dfrac{\pi}{2}$	$\dfrac{5\pi}{6}$	π	$\dfrac{4\pi}{3}$	2π
r	$\dfrac{3\sqrt{2}}{2}$	3	1.5	0	$\dfrac{-3\sqrt{3}}{2}$	0

(b)

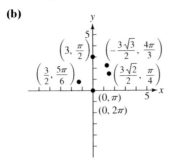

6. (a)

θ	$\dfrac{\pi}{4}$	$\dfrac{\pi}{2}$	$\dfrac{5\pi}{6}$	π	$\dfrac{4\pi}{3}$	2π
r	$2\sqrt{2}$	2	4	undefined	$\dfrac{-4\sqrt{3}}{2}$	undefined

(b)

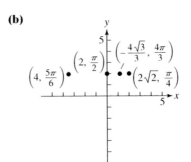

7.

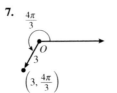

8. $\left(2, \dfrac{5\pi}{6}\right)$

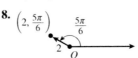

9.

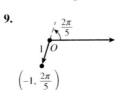

10. $\left(-3, \dfrac{17\pi}{10}\right)$

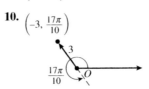

11.

12.

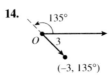

13.

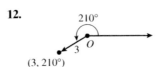

14.

15. $\left(\dfrac{3}{4}, \dfrac{3}{4}\sqrt{3}\right)$

16. $\left(\dfrac{5}{4}\sqrt{2}, \dfrac{5}{4}\sqrt{2}\right)$

17. $(-2.70, 1.30)$

18. $(1.62, 1.18)$

19. $(2, 0)$

20. $(0, 1)$

21. $(0, -2)$

22. $(-3, 0)$

23. $\left(2, \dfrac{\pi}{6} + 2n\pi \right)$ and $\left(-2, \dfrac{\pi}{6} + (2n + 1)\pi \right)$, n an integer

24. $\left(1, -\dfrac{\pi}{4} + 2n\pi \right)$ and $\left(-1, -\dfrac{\pi}{4} + (2n + 1)\pi \right)$, n an integer

25. $(1.5, -20° + 360n°)$ and $(-1.5, 160° + 360n°)$, n an integer

26. $(-2.5, 50° + 360n°)$ and $(2.5, 230° + 360n°)$, n an integer

27. (a) $\left(\sqrt{2}, \dfrac{\pi}{4} \right)$ or $\left(-\sqrt{2}, \dfrac{5\pi}{4} \right)$

(b) $\left(\sqrt{2}, \dfrac{\pi}{4} \right)$ or $\left(-\sqrt{2}, -\dfrac{3\pi}{4} \right)$

(c) The answers from (a), and also $\left(\sqrt{2}, \dfrac{9\pi}{4} \right)$ or $\left(-\sqrt{2}, \dfrac{13\pi}{4} \right)$

28. (a) $(\sqrt{10}, \tan^{-1} 3) \approx (\sqrt{10}, 1.25)$ or $(-\sqrt{10}, \tan^{-1} 3 + \pi) \approx (-\sqrt{10}, 4.39)$

(b) $(\sqrt{10}, \tan^{-1} 3) \approx (\sqrt{10}, 1.25)$ or $(-\sqrt{10}, \tan^{-1} 3 - \pi) \approx (-\sqrt{10}, -1.89)$

(c) The answers from (a), and also $(\sqrt{10}, \tan^{-1} 3 + 2\pi) \approx (\sqrt{10}, 7.53)$ or $(-\sqrt{10}, \tan^{-1} 3 + 3\pi) \approx (-\sqrt{10}, 10.67)$

29. (a) $(\sqrt{29}, \tan^{-1}(-2.5) + \pi) \approx (\sqrt{29}, 1.95)$ or $(-\sqrt{29}, \tan^{-1}(-2.5) + 2\pi) \approx (-\sqrt{29}, 5.09)$

(b) $(-\sqrt{29}, \tan^{-1}(-2.5)) \approx (-\sqrt{29}, -1.19)$ or $(\sqrt{29}, \tan^{-1}(-2.5) + \pi) \approx (\sqrt{29}, 1.95)$

(c) The answers from (a), plus $(\sqrt{29}, \tan^{-1}(-2.5) + 3\pi) \approx (\sqrt{29}, 8.23)$ or $(-\sqrt{29}, \tan^{-1}(-2.5) + 4\pi) \approx (-\sqrt{29}, 11.38)$

30. (a) $(-\sqrt{5}, \tan^{-1} 2) \approx (-\sqrt{5}, 1.11)$ or $(\sqrt{5}, \tan^{-1} 2 + \pi) \approx (\sqrt{5}, 4.25)$

(b) $(-\sqrt{5}, \tan^{-1} 2) \approx (-\sqrt{5}, 1.11)$ or $(\sqrt{5}, \tan^{-1} 2 - \pi) \approx (\sqrt{5}, -2.03)$

(c) The answers from (a), plus $(-\sqrt{5}, \tan^{-1} 2 + 2\pi) \approx (-\sqrt{5}, 7.39)$ or $(\sqrt{5}, \tan^{-1} 2 + 3\pi) \approx (\sqrt{5}, 10.53)$

31. (b)

32. (d)

33. (c)

34. (a)

35. $x = 3$ — a vertical line

36. $y = -2$ — a horizontal line

37. $r^2 + 3r \sin \theta = 0$, or $x^2 + y^2 + 3y = 0$. Completing the square gives $x^2 + \left(y + \dfrac{3}{2} \right)^2 = \dfrac{9}{4}$ — a circle centered at $\left(0, -\dfrac{3}{2} \right)$ with radius $\dfrac{3}{2}$.

38. $r^2 + 4r \cos \theta = 0$, or $x^2 + y^2 + 4x = 0$. Completing the square gives $(x + 2)^2 + y^2 = 4$ — a circle centered at $(-2, 0)$ with radius 2

39. $r^2 - r \sin \theta = 0$, or $x^2 + y^2 - y = 0$. Completing the square gives $x^2 + \left(y - \dfrac{1}{2} \right)^2 = \dfrac{1}{4}$ — a circle centered at $\left(0, \dfrac{1}{2} \right)$ with radius $\dfrac{1}{2}$.

40. $r^2 - 3r \cos \theta = 0$, or $x^2 + y^2 - 3x = 0$. Completing the square gives $\left(x - \dfrac{3}{2} \right)^2 + y^2 = \dfrac{9}{4}$ — a circle centered at $\left(\dfrac{3}{2}, 0 \right)$ with radius $\dfrac{3}{2}$.

41. $r^2 - 2r \sin \theta + 4r \cos \theta = 0$, or $x^2 + y^2 - 2y + 4x = 0$. Completing the square gives $(x + 2)^2 + (y - 1)^2 = 5$ — a circle centered at $(-2, 1)$ with radius $\sqrt{5}$.

42. $r^2 - 4r \cos \theta + 4r \sin \theta = 0$, or $x^2 + y^2 - 4x + 4y = 0$. Completing the square gives $(x - 2)^2 + (y + 2)^2 = 8$ — a circle centered at $(2, -2)$ with radius $2\sqrt{2}$.

43. $r = 2/\cos \theta = 2 \sec \theta$ — a vertical line

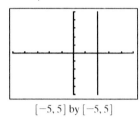

$[-5, 5]$ by $[-5, 5]$

44. $r = 5/\cos \theta = 5 \sec \theta$

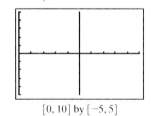

$[0, 10]$ by $[-5, 5]$

45. $r = \dfrac{5}{2 \cos \theta - 3 \sin \theta}$

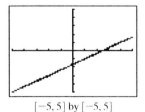

$[-5, 5]$ by $[-5, 5]$

46. $r = \dfrac{2}{3 \cos \theta + 4 \sin \theta}$

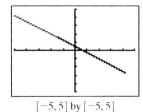

$[-5, 5]$ by $[-5, 5]$

47. $r^2 - 6r \cos \theta = 0$, so $r = 6 \cos \theta$

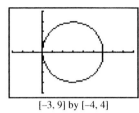

[-3, 9] by [-4, 4]

48. $r^2 - 2r \sin \theta = 0$, so $r = 2 \sin \theta$

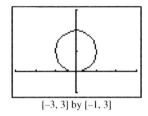

[-3, 3] by [-1, 3]

49. $r^2 + 6r \cos \theta + 6r \sin \theta = 0$, so $r = -6 \cos \theta - 6 \sin \theta$

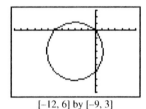

[-12, 6] by [-9, 3]

50. $r^2 - 2r \cos \theta + 8r \sin \theta = 0$, so $r = 2 \cos \theta - 8 \sin \theta$

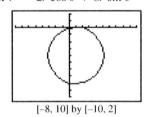

[-8, 10] by [-10, 2]

51. $d = \sqrt{4^2 + 2^2 - 2 \cdot 4 \cdot 2 \cos(12° - 72°)}$
$= \sqrt{20 - 16 \cos 60°} = \sqrt{12} = 2\sqrt{3}$ mi

52. $d = \sqrt{3^2 + 5^2 - 2 \cdot 3 \cdot 5 \cos(170° - 150°)}$
$= \sqrt{34 - 30 \cos 20°} \approx 2.41$ mi

53. Using the Pythagorean theorem, the center-to-vertex distance is $\dfrac{a}{\sqrt{2}}$. The four vertices are then $\left(\dfrac{a}{\sqrt{2}}, \dfrac{\pi}{4}\right)$, $\left(\dfrac{a}{\sqrt{2}}, \dfrac{3\pi}{4}\right)$, $\left(\dfrac{a}{\sqrt{2}}, \dfrac{5\pi}{4}\right)$, and $\left(\dfrac{a}{\sqrt{2}}, \dfrac{7\pi}{4}\right)$. Other polar coordinates for these points are possible, of course.

54. The vertex on the x-axis has polar coordinates $(a, 0)$. All other vertices must also be a units from the origin; their coordinates are $\left(a, \dfrac{2\pi}{5}\right)$, $\left(a, \dfrac{4\pi}{5}\right)$, $\left(a, \dfrac{6\pi}{5}\right)$, and $\left(a, \dfrac{8\pi}{5}\right)$. Other polar coordinates for these points are possible, of course.

55. False. Point (r, θ) is the same as point $(r, \theta + 2n\pi)$ for any integer n. So each point has an infinite number of distinct polar coordinates.

56. True. For (r_1, θ) and $(r_2, \theta + \pi)$ to represent the same point, $(r_2, \theta + \pi)$ has to be the reflection across the orgin of $(r_1, \theta + \pi)$, and this is accomplished by setting $r_2 = -r_1$.

57. For point (r, θ), changing the sign on r and adding 3π to θ constitutes a twofold reflection across the orgin. The answer is C.

58. The rectangular coordinates are
$(-2 \cos(-\pi/3), -2 \sin(-\pi/3)) = (-1, \sqrt{3})$.
The answer is C.

59. For point (r, θ), changing the sign on r and subtracting $180°$ from θ constitutes a twofold reflection across the origin. The answer is A.

60. $(-2, 2)$ lies in Quadrant III, whereas $(-2\sqrt{2}, 135°)$ lies in Quadrant IV. The answer is E.

61. (a) If $\theta_1 - \theta_2$ is an odd integer multiple of π, then the distance is $|r_1 + r_2|$. If $\theta_1 - \theta_2$ is an even integer multiple of π, then the distance is $|r_1 - r_2|$.

(b) Consider the triangle formed by O_1, P_1, and P_2 (ensuring that the angle at the origin is less than $180°$), then by the Law of Cosines,
$\overline{P_1 P_2}^2 = \overline{OP_1}^2 + \overline{OP_2}^2 - 2 \cdot \overline{OP_1} \cdot \overline{OP_2} \cos \theta$,
where θ is the angle between $\overline{OP_1}$ and $\overline{OP_2}$. In polar coordinates, this formula translates very nicely into $d^2 = r_1^2 + r_2^2 - 2r_1 r_2 \cos(\theta_2 - \theta_1)$ (or $\cos(\theta_1 - \theta_2)$ since $\cos(\theta_2 - \theta_1) = \cos(\theta_1 - \theta_2)$), so
$d = \sqrt{r_1^2 + r_2^2 - 2r_1 r_2 \cos(\theta_2 - \theta_1)}$.

(c) Yes. If $\theta_1 - \theta_2$ is an odd integer multiple of π, then $\cos(\theta_1 - \theta_2) = -1 \Rightarrow d = \sqrt{r_1^2 + r_2^2 + 2r_1 r_2}$ $= |r_1 + r_2|$. If $\theta_1 - \theta_2$ is an even integer multiple of π, then $\cos(\theta_1 - \theta_2) = 1 \Rightarrow$ $d = \sqrt{r_1^2 + r_2^2 - 2r_1 r_2} = |r_1 - r_2|$.

62. (a) The right half of a circle centered at $(0, 2)$ of radius 2.

(b) Three quarters of the same circle, starting at $(0, 0)$ and moving counterclockwise.

(c) The full circle (plus another half circle found through the TRACE function).

(d) 4 counterclockwise rotations of the same circle.

63. $d = \sqrt{2^2 + 5^2 - 2(2)(5) \cos 120°} \approx 6.24$

64. $d = \sqrt{4^2 + 6^2 - 2(4)(6) \cos 45°} \approx 4.25$

65. $d = \sqrt{(-3)^2 + (-5)^2 - 2(-3)(-5) \cos 135°} \approx 7.43$

66. $d = \sqrt{6^2 + 8^2 - 2(6)(8) \cos 30°} \approx 4.11$

67. Since $x = r \cos \theta$ and $y = r \sin \theta$, the parametric equation would be $x = f(\theta) \cos(\theta)$ and $y = f(\theta) \sin(\theta)$.

68. $x = 2 \cos^2 \theta$
$y = 2(\cos \theta)(\sin \theta)$

69. $x = 5(\cos \theta)(\sin \theta)$
$y = 5 \sin^2 \theta$

70. $x = 2(\cos \theta)(\sec \theta) = 2$
$y = 2(\sin \theta)(\sec \theta) = 2 \tan \theta$

71. $x = 4(\cos \theta)(\csc \theta) = 4 \cot \theta$
$y = 4(\sin \theta)(\csc \theta) = 4$

■ Section 6.5 Graphs of Polar Equations

Exploration 1

Answers will vary.

Exploration 2

1. If $r^2 = 4\cos(2\theta)$, then r does not exist when $\cos(2\theta) < 0$. Since $\cos(2\theta) < 0$ whenever θ is in the interval $\left(\dfrac{\pi}{4} + n\pi, \dfrac{3\pi}{4} + n\pi\right)$, n is any integer, the domain of r does not include these intervals.

2. $-r\sqrt{\cos(2\theta)}$ draws the same graph, but in the opposite direction.

3. $(r)^2 - 4\cos(-2\theta) = r^2 - 4\cos(2\theta)$
(since $\cos(\theta) = \cos(-\theta)$)

4. $(-r)^2 - 4\cos(-2\theta) = r^2 - 4\cos(2\theta)$

5. $(-r)^2 - 4\cos(2\theta) = r^2 - 4\cos(2\theta)$

Quick Review 6.5

For #1–4, use your grapher's TRACE function to solve.

1. Minimum: -3 at $x = \left\{\dfrac{\pi}{2}, \dfrac{3\pi}{2}\right\}$; Maximum: 3 at $x = \{0, \pi, 2\pi\}$

2. Minimum: -1 at $x = \pi$; Maximum: 5 at $x = \{0, 2\pi\}$

3. Minimum: 0 at $x = \left\{\dfrac{\pi}{4}, \dfrac{3\pi}{4}, \dfrac{5\pi}{4}, \dfrac{7\pi}{4}\right\}$; Maximum: 2 at $x = \{0, \pi, 2\pi\}$

4. Minimum: 0 at $x = \dfrac{\pi}{2}$; Maximum: 6 at $x = \dfrac{3\pi}{2}$

5. (a) No   **(b)** No   **(c)** Yes

6. (a) No   **(b)** Yes   **(c)** No

7. $\sin(\pi - \theta) = \sin\theta$

8. $\cos(\pi - \theta) = -\cos\theta$

9. $\cos 2(\pi + \theta) = \cos(2\pi + 2\theta) = \cos 2\theta$
$= \cos^2\theta - \sin^2\theta$

10. $\sin 2(\pi + \theta) = \sin(2\pi + 2\theta) = \sin 2\theta$
$= 2\sin\theta\cos\theta$

Section 6.5 Exercises

1. (a)

θ	0	$\pi/4$	$\pi/2$	$3\pi/4$	π	$5\pi/4$	$3\pi/2$	$7\pi/4$
r	3	0	-3	0	3	0	-3	0

(b)

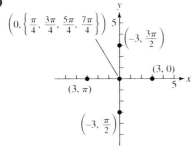

2. (a)

θ	0	$\pi/6$	$\pi/3$	$\pi/2$	$2\pi/3$	$5\pi/6$	π
r	0	2	0	-2	0	2	0

(b)

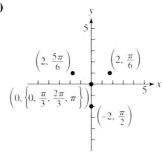

3. $k = \pi$

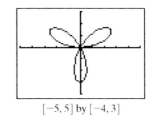

$[-5, 5]$ by $[-4, 3]$

4. $k = 2\pi$

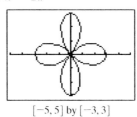

$[-5, 5]$ by $[-3, 3]$

5. $k = 2\pi$

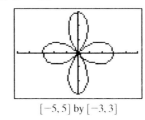

$[-5, 5]$ by $[-3, 3]$

6. $k = \pi$

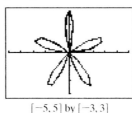

$[-5, 5]$ by $[-3, 3]$

7. r_1 is not shown (this is a 12-petal rose). r_2 is not shown (this is a 6-petal rose), r_3 is graph (b).

8. $6\cos 2\theta \sin 2\theta = 3(2\cos u \sin u)$ where $u = 2\theta$; this equals $3\sin 2u = 3\sin 4\theta$. $r = 3\sin 4\theta$ is the equation for the eight-petal rose shown in graph (a).

9. Graph (b) is $r = 2 - 2\cos\theta$: Taking $\theta = 0$ and $\theta = \dfrac{\pi}{2}$, we get $r = 2$ and $r = 4$ from the first equation, and $r = 0$ and $r = 2$ from the second. No graph matches the first of these (r, θ) pairs, but (b) matches the latter (and any others one might choose).

10. Graph (c) is $r = 2 + 3\cos\theta$: Taking $\theta = 0$, we get $r = -1$ from the other equation, which matches nothing. Any (r, θ) pair from the first equation matches (c), however.

11. Graph (a) is $r = 2 - 2\sin\theta$ — where $\theta = \dfrac{\pi}{2}$, $2 + 2\cos\theta = 2$, but $\left(2, \dfrac{\pi}{2}\right)$ is clearly not on graph (a); meanwhile $2 - 2\sin\dfrac{\pi}{2} = 0$, and $\left(0, \dfrac{\pi}{2}\right)$ (the origin) is part of graph (a).

12. Graph (d) is $r = 2 - 1.5\sin\theta$ — where $\theta = \dfrac{\pi}{2}$, $2 + 1.5\cos\theta = 2$, but $\left(2, \dfrac{\pi}{2}\right)$ is clearly not on graph (d); meanwhile $2 - 1.5\sin\dfrac{\pi}{2} = 0.5$, and $\left(0.5, \dfrac{\pi}{2}\right)$ is part of graph (d).

13. Symmetric about the y-axis: replacing (r, θ) with $(r, \pi - \theta)$ gives the same equation, since $\sin(\pi - \theta) = \sin\theta$.

14. Symmetric about the x-axis: replacing (r, θ) with $(r, -\theta)$ gives the same equation, since $\cos(-\theta) = \cos\theta$.

15. Symmetric about the x-axis: replacing (r, θ) with $(r, -\theta)$ gives the same equation, since $\cos(-\theta) = \cos\theta$.

16. Symmetric about the y-axis: replacing (r, θ) with $(r, \pi - \theta)$ gives the same equation, since $\sin(\pi - \theta) = \sin\theta$.

17. All three symmetries. Polar axis: replacing (r, θ) with $(r, -\theta)$ gives the same equation, since $\cos(-2\theta) = \cos 2\theta$. y-axis: replacing (r, θ) with $(r, \pi - \theta)$ gives the same equation, since $\cos[2(\pi - \theta)] = \cos(2\pi - 2\theta)$ $= \cos(-2\theta) = \cos 2\theta$. Pole: replacing (r, θ) with $(r, \theta + \pi)$ gives the same equation, since $\cos[2(\theta + \pi)]$ $= \cos(2\theta + 2\pi) = \cos 2\theta$.

18. Symmetric about the y-axis: replacing (r, θ) with $(-r, -\theta)$ gives the same equation, since $\sin(-3\theta) = -\sin 3\theta$.

19. Symmetric about the y-axis: replacing (r, θ) with $(r, \pi - \theta)$ gives the same equation, since $\sin(\pi - \theta) = \sin\theta$.

20. Symmetric about the x-axis: replacing (r, θ) with $(r, -\theta)$ gives the same equation, since $\cos(-\theta) = \cos\theta$.

21. Maximum r is 5 — when $\theta = 2n\pi$ for any integer n.

22. Maximum r is 5 (actually, -5) — when $\theta = \dfrac{3\pi}{2} + 2n\pi$ for any integer n.

23. Maximum r is 3 (along with -3) — when $\theta = 2n\pi/3$ for any integer n.

24. Maximum r is 4 (along with -4) — when $\theta = n\pi/4$ for any odd integer n.

25. Domain: All reals
Range: $[-3, 3]$
Symmetric about the x-axis, y-axis, and origin
Continuous
Bounded
Maximum r-value: 3
No asymptotes

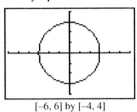

[–6, 6] by [–4, 4]

26. Domain: All reals
Range: $[-2, 2]$
Symmetric about the x-axis, y-axis, and origin
Continuous
Bounded
Maximum r-value: 2
No asymptotes

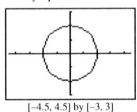

[–4.5, 4.5] by [–3, 3]

27. Domain: $\theta = \pi/3 + n\pi$, n is an integer
Range: $(-\infty, \infty)$
Symmetric about the origin
Continuous
Unbounded
Maximum r-value: none
No asymptotes

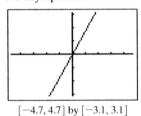

[–4.7, 4.7] by [–3.1, 3.1]

28. Domain: $\theta = -\pi/4 + n\pi$, n is an integer
Range: $(-\infty, \infty)$
Symmetric about the origin
Continuous
Unbounded
Maximum r-value: none
No asymptotes

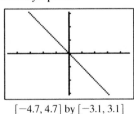

[–4.7, 4.7] by [–3.1, 3.1]

29. Domain: All reals
Range: $[-2, 2]$
Symmetric about the y-axis
Continuous
Bounded
Maximum r-value: 2
No asymptotes

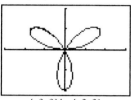

[-3, 3] by [-2, 2]

30. Domain: All reals
Range: $[-3, 3]$
Symmetric about the x-axis, y-axis, and origin
Continuous
Bounded
Maximum r-value: 3
No asymptotes

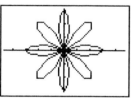

[-4.7, 4.7] by [-3.1, 3.1]

31. Domain: All reals
Range: $[1, 9]$
Symmetric about the y-axis
Continuous
Bounded
Maximum r-value: 9
No asymptotes

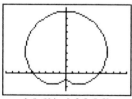

[-9, 9] by [-2.5, 9.5]

32. Domain: All reals
Range: $[1, 11]$
Symmetric about the x-axis
Continuous
Bounded
Maximum r-value: 11
No asymptotes

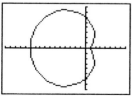

[-16, 8] by [-8, 8]

33. Domain: All reals
Range: $[0, 8]$
Symmetric about the x-axis
Continuous
Bounded
Maximum r-value: 8
No asymptotes

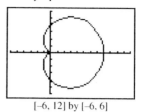

[-6, 12] by [-6, 6]

34. Domain: All reals
Range: $[0, 10]$
Symmetric about the y-axis
Continuous
Bounded
Maximum r-value: 10
No asymptotes

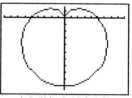

[-9, 9] by [-10.5, 1.5]

35. Domain: All reals
Range: $[3, 7]$
Symmetric about the x-axis
Continuous
Bounded
Maximum r-value: 7
No asymptotes

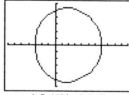

[-7, 11] by [-6, 6]

36. Domain: All reals
Range: $[2, 4]$
Symmetric about the y-axis
Continuous
Bounded
Maximum r-value: 4
No asymptotes

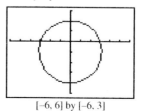

[-6, 6] by [-6, 3]

37. Domain: All reals
Range: $[-3, 7]$
Symmetric about the x-axis
Continuous
Bounded
Maximum r-value: 7
No asymptotes

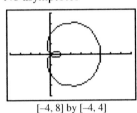

[−4, 8] by [−4, 4]

38. Domain: All reals
Range: $[-1, 7]$
Symmetric about the y-axis
Continuous
Bounded
Maximum r-value: 7
No asymptotes

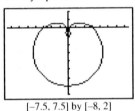

[−7.5, 7.5] by [−8, 2]

39. Domain: All reals
Range: $[0, 2]$
Symmetric about the x-axis
Continuous
Bounded
Maximum r-value: 2
No asymptotes

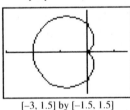

[−3, 1.5] by [−1.5, 1.5]

40. Domain: All reals
Range: $[1, 3]$
Symmetric about the y-axis
Continuous
Bounded
Maximum r-value: 3
No asymptotes

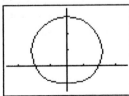

[−3.75, 3.75] by [−1.5, 3.5]

41. Domain: All reals
Range: $[0, \infty)$

Continuous
No symmetry
Unbounded
Maximum r-value: none
No asymptotes
Graph for $\theta \geq 0$:

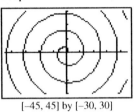

[−45, 45] by [−30, 30]

42. Domain: All reals
Range: $[0, \infty)$
Continuous
No symmetry
Unbounded
Maximum r-value: none
No asymptotes
Graph for $\theta \geq 0$:

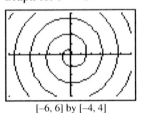

[−6, 6] by [−4, 4]

43. Domain: $\left[0, \dfrac{\pi}{2}\right] \cup \left[\dfrac{3\pi}{2}, 2\pi\right]$

Range: $[0, 1]$
Symmetric about the origin
Continuous on each interval in domain
Bounded
Maximum r-value: 1
No asymptotes

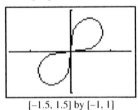

[−1.5, 1.5] by [−1, 1]

44. Domain: $\left[0, \dfrac{\pi}{4}\right] \cup \left[\dfrac{3\pi}{4}, \dfrac{5\pi}{4}\right] \cup \left[\dfrac{7\pi}{4}, 2\pi\right]$

Range: $[0, 3]$
Symmetric about the x-axis, y-axis, and origin
Continuous on each interval in domain
Bounded
Maximum r-value: 3
No asymptotes

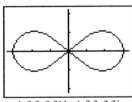

[−3.3, 3.3] by [−2.2, 2.2]

For #45–48, recall that the petal length is the maximum
r-value over the interval that creates the petal.

45. $r = -2$ when $\theta = \left\{ \dfrac{3\pi}{4}, \dfrac{7\pi}{4} \right\}$ and $r = 6$ when

$\theta = \left\{ \dfrac{\pi}{4}, \dfrac{5\pi}{4} \right\}$. There are four petals with lengths $\{6, 2, 6, 2\}$.

46. $r = -2$ when $\theta = \{0, \pi\}$ and $r = 8$ when

$\theta = \left\{ \dfrac{\pi}{2}, \dfrac{3\pi}{2} \right\}$. There are four petals with lengths $\{2, 8, 2, 8\}$.

47. $r = -3$ when $\theta = \left\{ 0, \dfrac{2\pi}{5}, \dfrac{4\pi}{5}, \dfrac{6\pi}{5}, \dfrac{8\pi}{5} \right\}$ and

$r = 5$ when $\theta = \left\{ \dfrac{\pi}{5}, \dfrac{3\pi}{5}, \pi, \dfrac{7\pi}{5}, \dfrac{9\pi}{5} \right\}$.

There are ten petals with lengths $\{3, 5, 3, 5, 3, 5, 3, 5, 3, 5\}$.

48. $r = 7$ when $\theta = \left\{ \dfrac{\pi}{10}, \dfrac{\pi}{2}, \dfrac{9\pi}{10}, \dfrac{13\pi}{10}, \dfrac{17\pi}{10} \right\}$ and

$r = -1$ when $\theta = \left\{ \dfrac{3\pi}{10}, \dfrac{7\pi}{10}, \dfrac{11\pi}{10}, \dfrac{3\pi}{2}, \dfrac{19\pi}{10} \right\}$.

There are ten petals with lengths $\{7, 1, 7, 1, 7, 1, 7, 1, 7, 1\}$.

49. r_1 and r_2 produce identical graphs — r_1 begins at $(1, 0)$
and r_2 begins at $(-1, 0)$.

50. r_1 and r_3 produce identical graphs — r_1 begins at $(3, 0)$
and r_2 begins at $(1, 0)$.

51. r_2 and r_3 produce identical graphs — r_1 begins at $(3, 0)$
and r_3 begins at $(-3, 0)$.

52. r_1 and r_2 produce identical graphs — r_1 begins at $(2, 0)$
and r_2 begins at $(-2, 0)$.

53. (a) A 4-petal rose curve with 2 short petals of length
1 and 2 long petals of length 3.

(b) Symmetric about the origin.

(c) Maximum r-value: 3.

54. (a) A 4-petal rose curve with petals of about length 1, 3.3,
and 4 units.

(b) Symmetric about the y-axis.

(c) Maximum r-value: 4.

55. (a) A 6-petal rose curve with 3 short petals of length
2 and 3 long petals of length 4.

(b) Symmetric about the x-axis.

(c) Maximum r-value: 4.

56. (a) A 6-petal rose curve with 3 short petals of length 2
and 3 long petals of length 4.

(b) Symmetric about the y-axis.

(c) Maximum r-value: 4.

57. Answers will vary but generally students should find that
a controls the length of the rose petals and n controls
both the number of rose petals and symmetry. If n is odd,
n rose petals are formed, with the cosine curve symmetric
about the polar x-axis and sine curve symmetric about the
y-axis. If n is even, $2n$ rose petals are formed, with both
the cosine and sine functions having symmetry about the
polar x-axis, y-axis, and origin.

58. Symmetry about y-axis: $r - 3 \sin(4\theta) = 0 \Rightarrow$
$-r - 3 \sin(4(-\theta)) = -r + 3 \sin(4\theta)$ (since $\sin(\theta)$ is
odd, i.e., $\sin(-\theta) = -\sin(\theta)) = r - 3 \sin(4\theta) = 0$.
Symmetry about the origin: $r - 3 \sin(4\theta) = 0$
$\Rightarrow r - 3 \sin(4\theta + 4\pi) = r - 3 \sin(4\theta) = 0$.

59.

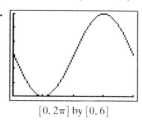

$[0, 2\pi]$ by $[0, 6]$

$y = 3 - 3 \sin x$ has minimum and maximum values of 0
and 6 on $[0, 2\pi]$. So the range of the polar function
$r = 3 - 3 \sin \theta$ is also $[0, 6]$.

60.

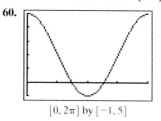

$[0, 2\pi]$ by $[-1, 5]$

$y = 2 + 3 \cos x$ has minimum and maximum values of
-1 and 5 on $[0, 2\pi]$. So the range of the polar function
$r = 2 + 3 \cos \theta$ is also $[-1, 5]$.

In general, this works because any polar graph can also be
plotted using rectangular coordinates. Here, we have y
representing r and x representing θ on a rectangular coordinate graph. Since y is exactly equal to r, the range of y
and range of r will be exactly the same.

61. False. The spiral $r = \theta$ is unbounded, since a point on the
curve can be found at any arbitrarily large distance from
the origin by setting θ numerically equal to that distance.

62. True. If point (r, θ) satisfies the equation $r = 2 + \cos\theta$, then
point $(r, -\theta)$ does also, since $2 + \cos(-\theta) = 2 + \cos\theta = r$.

63. With $r = a \cos n\theta$, if n is even there are $2n$ petals.
The answer is D.

64. The four petals lie along the x- and y-axis, because $\cos 2\theta$
takes on its extreme values at multiples of $\pi/2$.
The answer is D.

65. When $\cos \theta = -1, r = 5$. The answer is B.

66. With $r = a \sin n\theta$, if n is odd there are n petals.
The answer is B.

67. (a) Symmetry about the polar x-axis: $r - a \cos(n\theta) = 0$
$\Rightarrow r - a \cos(-n\theta) = r - a \cos(n\theta)$ (since $\cos(\theta)$
is even, i.e., $\cos(\theta) = \cos(-\theta)$ for all $\theta) = 0$.

(b) No symmetry about y-axis: $r - a \cos(n\theta) = 0 \Rightarrow$
$-r - a \cos(-n\theta) = -r - a \cos(n\theta)$ (since $\cos(\theta)$
is even) $\neq r - a \cos(n\theta)$ unless $r = 0$. As a result,
the equation is not symmetric about the y-axis.

(c) No symmetry about origin: $r - a \cos(n\theta) = 0 \Rightarrow$
$-r - a \cos(n\theta) \neq -r - a \cos(n\theta)$ unless $r = 0$.
As a result, the equation is not symmetric about
the origin.

(d) Since $|\cos(n\theta)| \leq 1$ for all θ, the maximum r-value
is $|a|$.

(e) Domain: All reals
Range: $[-|a|, |a|]$
Symmetric about the x-axis
Continuous
Bounded
Maximum r-value: 2
No asymptotes

68. (a) Symmetry about the y-axis: $r - a \sin (n\theta) = 0 \Rightarrow$ $-r - a \sin (-n\theta) = -r + a \sin (n\theta)$ (since $\sin (\theta)$ is odd, $\sin (-\theta) = -\sin (\theta)) = -1(r - a \sin (n\theta))$ $= (-1)(0) = 0$.

(b) Not symmetric about polar x-axis: $r - a \sin (n\theta) = 0$ $\Rightarrow r - a \sin (-n\theta) = r + a \sin (n\theta)$. The two functions are equal only when $-\sin (n\theta) = \sin (n\theta) = 0$, or $\theta = \{0, \pi\}$, so $r - a \sin (n\theta)$ is not symmetric about the polar x-axis.

(c) Not symmetric about origin: $r - a \sin (n\theta) \Rightarrow$ $-r - a \sin (n\theta) = -(r + a \sin (n\theta))$. The two functions are equal only when $r = 0$, so $r - a \sin (n\theta))$ is not symmetric about the origin.

(d) Since $|\sin (n\theta)| \leq 1$ for all θ, the maximum r-value is $|a|$.

(e) Domain: All reals
Range: $[-|a|, |a|]$
Symmetric about y-axis
Continuous
Bounded
Maximum r-value: $|a|$
No asymptotes

69. (a) For r_1: $0 \leq \theta \leq 4\pi$ (or any interval that is 4π units long). For r_2: same answer.

(b) r_1: 10 (overlapping) petals. r_2: 14 (overlapping) petals.

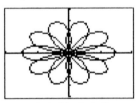

[−4, 4] by [−4, 4]

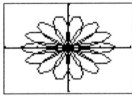

[−4, 4] by [−4, 4]

70. Starting with the graph of r_1, if we rotate clockwise (centered at the origin) by $\pi/12$ radians ($15°$), we get the graph of r_2; rotating r_1 clockwise by $\pi/4$ radians ($45°$) gives the graph of r_3.

(a)

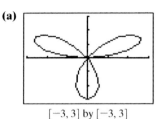

[−3, 3] by [−3, 3]

(b)

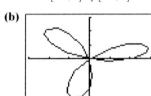

[−3, 3] by [−3, 3]

(c)

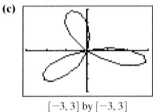

[−3, 3] by [−3, 3]

71. Starting with the graph of r_1, if we rotate counterclockwise (centered at the origin) by $\pi/4$ radians ($45°$), we get the graph of r_2; rotating r_1 counterclockwise by $\pi/3$ radians ($60°$) gives the graph of r_3.

(a)

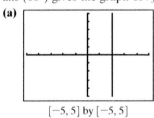

[−5, 5] by [−5, 5]

(b)

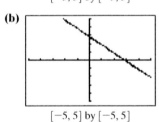

[−5, 5] by [−5, 5]

(c)

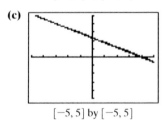

[−5, 5] by [−5, 5]

72. Starting with the graph of r_1, if we rotate clockwise (centered at the origin) by $\pi/4$ radians ($45°$), we get the graph of r_2; rotating r_1 clockwise by $\pi/3$ radians ($60°$) gives the graph of r_3.

(a)

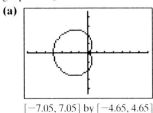

$[-7.05, 7.05]$ by $[-4.65, 4.65]$

(b)

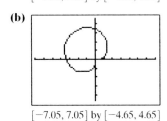

$[-7.05, 7.05]$ by $[-4.65, 4.65]$

(c)

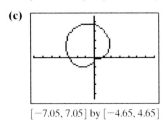

$[-7.05, 7.05]$ by $[-4.65, 4.65]$

73. The second graph is the result of rotating the first graph clockwise (centered at the origin) through an angle of α. The third graph results from rotating the first graph counterclockwise through the same angle. One possible explanation: the radius r achieved, for example, when $\theta = 0$ in the first equation is achieved instead when $\theta = -\alpha$ for the second equation, and when $\theta = \alpha$ for the third equation.

■ Section 6.6 DeMoivre's Theorem and *n*th Roots

Quick Review 6.6

1. Using the quadratic equation to find the roots of $x^2 + 13 = 4x$, we have $x^2 - 4x + 13 = 0$ with $a = 1$, $b = -4$, and $c = 13$.

$$x = \frac{-(-4) \pm \sqrt{(-4)^2 - 4(1)(13)}}{2(1)}$$

$$= \frac{4 \pm \sqrt{16 - 52}}{2} = \frac{4 \pm \sqrt{-36}}{2} = \frac{4 \pm 6i}{2}$$

$$x = \frac{4 + 6i}{2} = \frac{4}{2} + \frac{6i}{2} = 2 + 3i \text{ and}$$

$$x = \frac{4 - 6i}{2} = \frac{4}{2} - \frac{6i}{2} = 2 - 3i$$

The roots are $2 + 3i$ and $2 - 3i$.

2. Using the quadratic equation to find the roots of $5(x^2 + 1) = 6x$, we have $5x^2 - 6x + 5 = 0$ with $a = 5$, $b = -6$, and $c = 5$.

$$x = \frac{-(-6) \pm \sqrt{(-6)^2 - 4(5)(5)}}{2(5)}$$

$$= \frac{6 \pm \sqrt{36 - 100}}{10} = \frac{6 \pm \sqrt{-64}}{10} = \frac{6 \pm 8i}{10}$$

$$x = \frac{6 + 8i}{10} = \frac{6}{10} + \frac{8i}{10} = 0.6 + 0.8i \text{ and}$$

$$x = \frac{6 - 8i}{10} = \frac{6}{10} + \frac{8i}{10} = 0.6 - 0.8i$$

The roots are $0.6 + 0.8i$ and $0.6 - 0.8i$.

3. $(1 + i)^5 = (1 + i) \cdot [(1 + i)^2]^2 = (1 + i) \cdot (2i)^2$
$= -4(1 + i) = -4 - 4i$

4. $(1 - i)^4 = [(1 - i)^2]^2 = (-2i)^2 = -4 = -4 + 0i$

For #5–8, use the given information to find a point P on the terminal side of the angle, which in turn determines the quadrant of the terminal side.

5. $P(-\sqrt{3}, 1)$, in quadrant II: $\theta = \dfrac{5\pi}{6}$

6. $P(1, -1)$, in quadrant IV: $\theta = \dfrac{7\pi}{4}$

7. $P(-1, -\sqrt{3},)$, in quadrant III: $\theta = \dfrac{4\pi}{3}$

8. $P(-1, -1)$, in quadrant III: $\theta = \dfrac{5\pi}{4}$

9. $x^3 = 1$ when $x = 1$

10. $x^4 = 1$ when $x = \pm 1$

Section 6.6 Exercises

1.

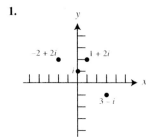

2.

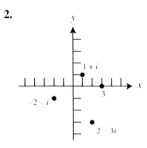

For #3–12, $a + bi = r(\cos \theta + i \sin \theta)$, where $r = |a + bi| = \sqrt{a^2 + b^2}$ and θ is chosen so that $\cos \theta = \dfrac{a}{\sqrt{a^2 + b^2}}$

and $\sin \theta = \dfrac{b}{\sqrt{a^2 + b^2}}$.

3. $r = |3i| = 3$; $\cos\theta = 0$ and $\sin\theta = 1$, so $\theta = \dfrac{\pi}{2}$:

$$3i = 3\left(\cos\frac{\pi}{2} + i\sin\frac{\pi}{2}\right)$$

4. $r = |-2i| = 2$; $\cos\theta = 0$ and $\sin\theta = -1$, so $\theta = \dfrac{3\pi}{2}$:

$$-2i = 2\left(\cos\frac{3\pi}{2} + i\sin\frac{3\pi}{2}\right)$$

5. $r = |2 + 2i| = 2\sqrt{2}$; $\cos\theta = \dfrac{\sqrt{2}}{2}$ and $\sin\theta = \dfrac{\sqrt{2}}{2}$,

so $\theta = \dfrac{\pi}{4}$: $2 + 2i = 2\sqrt{2}\left(\cos\dfrac{\pi}{4} + i\sin\dfrac{\pi}{4}\right)$

6. $r = |\sqrt{3} + i| = 2$; $\cos\theta = \dfrac{\sqrt{3}}{2}$ and $\sin\theta = \dfrac{1}{2}$,

so $\theta = \dfrac{\pi}{6}$: $\sqrt{3} + i = 2\left(\cos\dfrac{\pi}{6} + i\sin\dfrac{\pi}{6}\right)$

7. $r = |-2 + 2i\sqrt{3}| = 4$; $\cos\theta = -\dfrac{1}{2}$ and $\sin\theta = \dfrac{\sqrt{3}}{2}$,

so $\theta = \dfrac{2\pi}{3}$: $-2 + 2i\sqrt{3} = 4\left(\cos\dfrac{2\pi}{3} + i\sin\dfrac{2\pi}{3}\right)$

8. $r = |3 - 3i| = 3\sqrt{2}$; $\cos\theta = \dfrac{\sqrt{2}}{2}$ and $\sin\theta = -\dfrac{\sqrt{2}}{2}$,

so $\theta = \dfrac{7\pi}{4}$: $3 - 3i = 3\sqrt{2}\left(\cos\dfrac{7\pi}{4} + i\sin\dfrac{7\pi}{4}\right)$

9. $r = |3 + 2i| = \sqrt{13}$; $\cos\theta = \dfrac{3}{\sqrt{13}}$ and

$\sin\theta = \dfrac{2}{\sqrt{13}}$, so $\theta \approx 0.588$: $3 + 2i$

$\approx \sqrt{13}(\cos 0.59 + i\sin 0.59)$

10. $r = |4 - 7i| = \sqrt{65}$; $\cos\theta = \dfrac{4}{\sqrt{65}}$ and

$\sin\theta = -\dfrac{7}{\sqrt{65}}$, so $\theta \approx 5.232$: $4 - 7i$

$\approx \sqrt{65}(\cos 5.23 + i\sin 5.23)$

11. $r = 3$; $30° = \dfrac{\pi}{6}$; $3\left(\cos\dfrac{\pi}{6} + i\sin\dfrac{\pi}{6}\right)$

12. $r = 3$; $225° = \dfrac{5\pi}{4}$; $4\left(\cos\dfrac{5\pi}{4} + i\sin\dfrac{5\pi}{4}\right)$

13. $3\left(\dfrac{\sqrt{3}}{2} - \dfrac{1}{2}i\right) = \dfrac{3}{2}\sqrt{3} - \dfrac{3}{2}i$

14. $8\left(-\dfrac{\sqrt{3}}{2} - \dfrac{1}{2}i\right) = -4\sqrt{3} - 4i$

15. $5\left(\dfrac{1}{2} - \dfrac{\sqrt{3}}{2}i\right) = \dfrac{5}{2} - \dfrac{5}{2}\sqrt{3}\,i$

16. $5\left(\dfrac{\sqrt{2}}{2} - \dfrac{\sqrt{2}}{2}i\right) = \dfrac{5}{2}\sqrt{2} + \dfrac{5}{2}\sqrt{2}\,i$

17. $\sqrt{2}\left(-\dfrac{\sqrt{3}}{2} - \dfrac{1}{2}i\right) = \dfrac{\sqrt{6}}{2} - \dfrac{\sqrt{2}}{2}i$

18. $\approx 2.56 + 0.68i$

19. $(2\cdot 7)[\cos(25° + 130°) + i\sin(25° + 130°)]$
$= 14(\cos 155° + i\sin 155°)$

20. $(\sqrt{2}\cdot 0.5)[\cos(188° - 19°) + i\sin(118° - 19°)]$

$= \dfrac{\sqrt{2}}{2}(\cos 99° + i\sin 99°)$

21. $(5\cdot 3)\left[\cos\left(\dfrac{\pi}{4} + \dfrac{5\pi}{3}\right) + i\sin\left(\dfrac{\pi}{4} + \dfrac{5\pi}{3}\right)\right]$

$= 15\left(\cos\dfrac{23\pi}{12} + i\sin\dfrac{23\pi}{12}\right)$

22. $\left(\sqrt{3}\cdot\dfrac{1}{3}\right)\left[\cos\left(\dfrac{3\pi}{4} + \dfrac{\pi}{6}\right) + i\sin\left(\dfrac{3\pi}{4} + \dfrac{\pi}{6}\right)\right]$

$= \dfrac{\sqrt{3}}{3}\left(\cos\dfrac{11\pi}{12} + i\sin\dfrac{11\pi}{12}\right)$

23. $\dfrac{2}{3}[\cos(30° - 60°) + i\sin(30° - 60°)]$

$= \dfrac{2}{3}[\cos(-30°) + i\sin(-30°)] = \dfrac{2}{3}(\cos 30° - i\sin 30°)$

24. $\dfrac{5}{2}[\cos(220° - 115°) + i\sin(220° - 115°)]$

$= \dfrac{5}{2}(\cos 105° + i\sin 105°)$

25. $\dfrac{6}{3}[\cos(5\pi - 2\pi) + i\sin(5\pi - 2\pi)]$

$= 2(\cos 3\pi + i\sin 3\pi) = 2(\cos\pi + i\sin\pi)$

26. $1\left[\cos\left(\dfrac{\pi}{2} - \dfrac{\pi}{4}\right) + i\sin\left(\dfrac{\pi}{2} - \dfrac{\pi}{4}\right)\right] = \cos\dfrac{\pi}{4} + i\sin\dfrac{\pi}{4}$

27. (a) $3 - 2i \approx \sqrt{13}[\cos(5.695) + i\sin(5.695)]$

and $1 + i = \sqrt{2}\left(\cos\dfrac{\pi}{4} + i\sin\dfrac{\pi}{4}\right)$, so

$\sqrt{13}[\cos(5.695) + i\sin(5.695)]\cdot\sqrt{2}\left[\cos\dfrac{\pi}{4} + i\sin\dfrac{\pi}{4}\right]$

$= \sqrt{26}\left[\cos\left(5.695 + \dfrac{\pi}{4}\right) + i\sin\left(5.695 + \dfrac{\pi}{4}\right)\right] = 5 + i$

$\dfrac{\sqrt{13}[\cos(5.695) + i\sin(5.695)]}{\sqrt{2}[\cos(\pi/4) + i\sin(\pi/4)]}$

$\approx \sqrt{6.5}\left[\cos\left(5.695 - \dfrac{\pi}{4}\right) + i\sin\left(5.695 - \dfrac{\pi}{4}\right)\right]$

$= \dfrac{1}{2} - \dfrac{5}{2}i$

(b) $(3 - 2i)(1 + i) = 3 + 3i - 2i - 2i^2 = 5 + i$

$\dfrac{3 - 2i}{1 + i} = \dfrac{3 - 2i}{1 + i}\cdot\dfrac{1 - i}{1 - i} = \dfrac{1 - 5i}{2} = \dfrac{1}{2} - \dfrac{5}{2}i$

28. (a) $1 - i = \sqrt{2}\left(\cos\dfrac{7\pi}{4} + i\sin\dfrac{7\pi}{4}\right)$

and $\sqrt{3} + i = 2\left(\cos\dfrac{\pi}{6} + i\sin\dfrac{\pi}{6}\right)$, so

$\sqrt{2}\left(\cos\dfrac{7\pi}{4} + i\sin\dfrac{7\pi}{4}\right) \cdot 2\left(\cos\dfrac{\pi}{6} + i\sin\dfrac{\pi}{6}\right)$

$= 2\sqrt{2}\left(\cos\dfrac{23\pi}{12} + \sin\dfrac{23\pi}{12}\right) \approx 2.73 - 0.73i$

$\dfrac{\sqrt{2}[\cos(7\pi/4) + i\sin(7\pi/4)]}{2[\cos(\pi/6) + i\sin(\pi/6)]}$

$= \dfrac{1}{\sqrt{2}}\left(\cos\dfrac{19\pi}{12} + i\sin\dfrac{19\pi}{12}\right) \approx 0.18 - 0.68i$

(b) $(1 - i)(\sqrt{3} + i) = \sqrt{3} + i - \sqrt{3}i - i^2$

$(1 + \sqrt{3}) + (1 - \sqrt{3})i \approx 2.73 - 0.73i$

$\dfrac{1 - i}{\sqrt{3} + i} = \dfrac{1 - i}{\sqrt{3} + i} \cdot \dfrac{\sqrt{3} - i}{\sqrt{3} - i} = \dfrac{(1 - i)(\sqrt{3} - i)}{4}$

$= \dfrac{1}{4}\left[\sqrt{3} - 1 - (\sqrt{3} + 1)i\right] \approx 0.18 - 0.68i$

29. (a) $3 + i \approx \sqrt{10}[\cos(0.321) + i\sin(0.321)]$

and $5 - 3i \approx \sqrt{34}[\cos(-0.540) + i\sin(-0.540)]$, so

$\sqrt{10}[\cos(0.321) + i\sin(0.321)] \cdot \sqrt{34}[\cos(-0.540)$

$+ i\sin(-0.540)]$

$= 2\sqrt{85}[\cos(-0.219) + i\sin(-0.219)] = 18 - 4i$

$\dfrac{\sqrt{10}[\cos(0.321) + i\sin(0.321)]}{\sqrt{34}[\cos(-0.540) + i\sin(-0.540)]}$

$\approx \sqrt{\dfrac{5}{17}}[\cos(0.862) + i\sin(0.862)]$

$\approx 0.35 + 0.41i$

(b) $(3 + i)(5 - 3i) = 15 - 9i + 5i - 3i^2 = 18 - 4i$

$\dfrac{3 + i}{5 - 3i} = \dfrac{3 + i}{5 - 3i} \cdot \dfrac{5 + 3i}{5 + 3i} = \dfrac{(3 + i)(5 + 3i)}{34}$

$\dfrac{1}{17}(6 + 7i) \approx 0.35 + 0.41i$

30. (a) $2 - 3i \approx \sqrt{13}[\cos(-0.982) + i\sin(-0.982)]$,

and $1 - \sqrt{3}i = 2\left[\cos\left(-\dfrac{\pi}{3}\right) + i\sin\left(-\dfrac{\pi}{3}\right)\right]$, so

$\sqrt{13}[\cos(-0.983) + i\sin(-0.983)] \cdot 2\left[\cos\left(-\dfrac{\pi}{3}\right)\right.$

$\left. + i\sin\left(-\dfrac{\pi}{3}\right)\right] = 2\sqrt{13}\left[\cos\left(-0.983 - \dfrac{\pi}{3}\right)\right.$

$\left. + i\sin\left(-0.983 - \dfrac{\pi}{3}\right)\right]$

$\approx -3.20 - 6.46i$

$\dfrac{\sqrt{13}[\cos(-0.983) + i\sin(-0.983)]}{2[\cos(-\pi/3) + i\sin(-\pi/3)]}$

$\approx \dfrac{\sqrt{13}}{2}[\cos(0.064) + i\sin(0.064)]$

$\approx 1.80 + 0.12i$

(b) $(2 - 3i)(1 - \sqrt{3}i) = 2 - 2\sqrt{3}i - 3i + 3\sqrt{3}i^2$

$= (2 - 3\sqrt{3}) - (2\sqrt{3} + 3)i \approx -3.196 - 6.464i$

$\dfrac{2 - 3i}{1 - \sqrt{3}i} = \dfrac{2 - 3i}{1 - \sqrt{3}i} \cdot \dfrac{1 + \sqrt{3}i}{1 + \sqrt{3}i}$

$= \dfrac{(2 - 3i)(1 + \sqrt{3}i)}{4}$

$= \dfrac{1}{4}\left[2 + 3\sqrt{3} + (2\sqrt{3} - 3)i\right] \approx 1.80 + 0.12i$

31. $\left(\cos\dfrac{\pi}{4} + i\sin\dfrac{\pi}{4}\right)^3 = \cos\dfrac{3\pi}{4} + i\sin\dfrac{3\pi}{4}$

$= -\dfrac{\sqrt{2}}{2} + i\dfrac{\sqrt{2}}{2}$

32. $\left[3\left(\cos\dfrac{3\pi}{2} + i\sin\dfrac{3\pi}{2}\right)\right]^5 = 243\left(\cos\dfrac{15\pi}{2} + i\sin\dfrac{15\pi}{2}\right)$

$= 243i$

33. $\left[2\left(\cos\dfrac{3\pi}{4} + i\sin\dfrac{3\pi}{4}\right)\right]^3 = 8\left(\cos\dfrac{9\pi}{4} + i\sin\dfrac{9\pi}{4}\right)$

$= 4\sqrt{2} + 4\sqrt{2}i$

34. $\left[6\left(\cos\dfrac{5\pi}{6} + i\sin\dfrac{5\pi}{6}\right)\right]^4$

$= 1296\left(\cos\dfrac{20\pi}{6} + i\sin\dfrac{20\pi}{6}\right)$

$= -648 - 648\sqrt{3}i$

35. $(1 + i)^5 = \left[\sqrt{2}\left(\cos\dfrac{\pi}{4} + i\sin\dfrac{\pi}{4}\right)\right]^5$

$= (\sqrt{2})^5\left(\cos\dfrac{5\pi}{4} + i\sin\dfrac{5\pi}{4}\right)$

$= 4\sqrt{2}\left(\cos\dfrac{5\pi}{4} + i\sin\dfrac{5\pi}{4}\right) = -4 - 4i$

36. $(3 + 4i)^{20}$

$= \left\{5\left[\cos\tan^{-1}\left(\dfrac{4}{3}\right) + i\sin\tan^{-1}\left(\dfrac{4}{3}\right)\right]\right\}^{20}$

$= 5^{20}\left\{\cos\left[20\tan^{-1}\left(\dfrac{4}{3}\right)\right] + i\sin\left[20\tan^{-1}\left(\dfrac{4}{3}\right)\right]\right\}$

$= 5^{20}[\cos(5.979) + i\sin(5.979)] \approx 5^{20}(0.95 - 0.30i)$

37. $(1 - \sqrt{3}i)^3 = \left[2\left(\cos\dfrac{5\pi}{3} + i\sin\dfrac{5\pi}{3}\right)\right]^3$

$= 8(\cos 5\pi + i\sin 5\pi) = 8(\cos\pi + i\sin\pi) = -8$

38. $\left(\dfrac{1}{2} + i\dfrac{\sqrt{3}}{2}\right)^3 = \left(\cos\dfrac{\pi}{3} + i\sin\dfrac{\pi}{3}\right)^3$

$= \cos\pi + i\sin\pi = -1$

For #39–44, the cube roots of $r(\cos\theta + i\sin\theta)$ are

$= \sqrt[3]{r}\left(\cos\dfrac{\theta + 2k\pi}{3} + i\sin\dfrac{\theta + 2k\pi}{3}\right), k = 0, 1, 2.$

39. $\sqrt[3]{2}\left(\cos\dfrac{2k\pi + 2\pi}{3} + i\sin\dfrac{2k\pi + 2\pi}{3}\right)$

$= \sqrt[3]{2}\left(\cos\dfrac{2\pi(k + 1)}{3} + i\sin\dfrac{2\pi(k + 1)}{3}\right),$

$k = 0, 1, 2$:

$\sqrt[3]{2}\left(\cos\dfrac{2\pi}{3} + i\sin\dfrac{2\pi}{3}\right) = \sqrt[3]{2}\left(-\dfrac{1}{2} + \dfrac{\sqrt{3}}{2}i\right)$

$= \dfrac{1 + \sqrt{3}i}{\sqrt[3]{4}}.$

$\sqrt[3]{2}\left(\cos\dfrac{4\pi}{3} + i\sin\dfrac{4\pi}{3}\right)$

$= \sqrt[3]{2}\left(-\dfrac{1}{2} - \dfrac{\sqrt{3}}{2}i\right) = \dfrac{-1 - \sqrt{3}i}{\sqrt[3]{4}},$

$\sqrt[3]{2}(\cos 2\pi + i\sin 2\pi) = \sqrt[3]{2}$

40. $\sqrt[3]{2}\left(\cos\dfrac{2k\pi + \pi/4}{3} + i\sin\dfrac{2k\pi + \pi/4}{3}\right)$

$= \sqrt[3]{2}\left(\cos\dfrac{\pi(8k + 1)}{12} + i\sin\dfrac{\pi(8k + 1)}{12}\right),$

$k = 0, 1, 2$:

$$\sqrt[3]{2}\left(\cos\frac{\pi}{12} + i\sin\frac{\pi}{12}\right),$$

$$\sqrt[3]{2}\left(\cos\frac{3\pi}{4} + i\sin\frac{3\pi}{4}\right)$$

$$= \sqrt[3]{2}\left(-\frac{1}{\sqrt{2}} + \frac{1}{\sqrt{2}}i\right) = \frac{-1+i}{\sqrt[6]{2}},$$

$$\sqrt[3]{2}\left(\cos\frac{17\pi}{12} + i\sin\frac{17\pi}{12}\right)$$

41. $\sqrt[3]{3}\left(\cos\dfrac{2k\pi + 4\pi/3}{3} + i\sin\dfrac{2k\pi + 4\pi/3}{3}\right)$

$$= \sqrt[3]{3}\left(\cos\frac{2\pi(3k+2)}{9} + i\sin\frac{2\pi(3k+2)}{9}\right),$$

$k = 0, 1, 2$:

$$\sqrt[3]{3}\left(\cos\frac{4\pi}{9} + i\sin\frac{4\pi}{9}\right), \sqrt[3]{3}\left(\cos\frac{10\pi}{9} + i\sin\frac{10\pi}{9}\right),$$

$$\sqrt[3]{3}\left(\cos\frac{16\pi}{9} + i\sin\frac{16\pi}{9}\right)$$

42. $\sqrt[3]{27}\left(\cos\dfrac{2k\pi + 11\pi/6}{3} + i\sin\dfrac{2k\pi + 11\pi/6}{3}\right)$

$$= 3\left(\cos\frac{\pi(12k+11)}{18} + i\sin\frac{\pi(12k+11)}{18}\right),$$

$k = 0, 1, 2$:

$$3\left(\cos\frac{11\pi}{18} + i\sin\frac{11\pi}{18}\right), 3\left(\cos\frac{23\pi}{18} + i\sin\frac{23\pi}{18}\right),$$

$$3\left(\cos\frac{35\pi}{18} + i\sin\frac{35\pi}{18}\right)$$

43. $3 - 4i \approx 5(\cos 5.355 + i\sin 5.355)$

$$\sqrt[3]{5}\left(\cos\frac{2k\pi + 5.355}{3} + i\sin\frac{2k\pi + 5.355}{3}\right)$$

$k = 0, 1, 2$:

$$\approx \sqrt[3]{5}(\cos 1.79 + i\sin 1.79),$$

$$\approx \sqrt[3]{5}(\cos 3.88 + i\sin 3.88),$$

$$\approx \sqrt[3]{5}(\cos 5.97 + i\sin 5.97)$$

44. $-2 + 2i = 2\sqrt{2}\left(\cos\dfrac{3\pi}{4} + i\sin\dfrac{3\pi}{4}\right)$. Note that

$\sqrt[3]{2\sqrt{2}} = \sqrt{2}$.

$$\sqrt{2}\left(\cos\frac{2k\pi + 3\pi/4}{3} + i\sin\frac{2k\pi + 3\pi/4}{3}\right)$$

$$= \sqrt{2}\left(\cos\frac{\pi(8k+3)}{12} + i\sin\frac{\pi(8k+3)}{12}\right),$$

$k = 0, 1, 2$:

$$\sqrt{2}\left(\cos\frac{\pi}{4} + i\sin\frac{\pi}{4}\right) = \sqrt{2}\left(\frac{\sqrt{2}}{2} + \frac{i\sqrt{2}}{2}\right) = 1 + i,$$

$$\sqrt{2}\left(\cos\frac{11\pi}{12} + i\sin\frac{11\pi}{12}\right),$$

$$\sqrt{2}\left(\cos\frac{19\pi}{12} + i\sin\frac{19\pi}{12}\right)$$

For #45–50, the fifth roots of $r(\cos\theta + i\sin\theta)$ are

$$\sqrt[5]{r}\left(\cos\frac{\theta + 2k\pi}{5} + i\sin\frac{\theta + 2k\pi}{5}\right), k = 0, 1, 2, 3, 4.$$

45. $\cos\dfrac{2k\pi + \pi}{5} + i\sin\dfrac{2k\pi + \pi}{5}$

$$= \cos\frac{\pi(2k+1)}{5} + i\sin\frac{\pi(2k+1)}{5}, k = 0, 1, 2, 3, 4:$$

$$\cos\frac{\pi}{5} + i\sin\frac{\pi}{5}, \cos\frac{3\pi}{5} + i\sin\frac{3\pi}{5}, -1,$$

$$\cos\frac{7\pi}{5} + i\sin\frac{7\pi}{5}, \cos\frac{9\pi}{5} + i\sin\frac{9\pi}{5}$$

46. $\sqrt[5]{32}\left(\cos\dfrac{2k\pi + \pi/2}{5} + i\sin\dfrac{2k\pi + \pi/2}{5}\right)$

$$= 2\left(\cos\frac{\pi(4k+1)}{10} + i\sin\frac{\pi(4k+1)}{10}\right),$$

$k = 0, 1, 2, 3, 4$:

$$2\left(\cos\frac{\pi}{10} + i\sin\frac{\pi}{10}\right), 2\left(\cos\frac{\pi}{2} + i\sin\frac{\pi}{2}\right) = 2i,$$

$$2\left(\cos\frac{9\pi}{10} + i\sin\frac{9\pi}{10}\right), 2\left(\cos\frac{13\pi}{10} + i\sin\frac{13\pi}{10}\right),$$

$$2\left(\cos\frac{17\pi}{10} + i\sin\frac{17\pi}{10}\right)$$

47. $\sqrt[5]{2}\left(\cos\dfrac{2k\pi + \pi/6}{5} + i\sin\dfrac{2k\pi + \pi/6}{5}\right)$

$$= \sqrt[5]{2}\left(\cos\frac{\pi(12k+1)}{30} + \sin\frac{\pi(12k+1)}{30}\right),$$

$k = 0, 1, 2, 3, 4$:

$$\sqrt[5]{2}\left(\cos\frac{\pi}{30} + i\sin\frac{\pi}{30}\right), \sqrt[5]{2}\left(\cos\frac{13\pi}{30} + i\sin\frac{13\pi}{30}\right),$$

$$\sqrt[5]{2}\left(\cos\frac{5\pi}{6} + i\sin\frac{5\pi}{6}\right), \sqrt[5]{2}\left(\cos\frac{37\pi}{30} + i\sin\frac{37\pi}{30}\right),$$

$$\sqrt[5]{2}\left(\cos\frac{49\pi}{30} + i\sin\frac{49\pi}{30}\right)$$

48. $\sqrt[5]{2}\left(\cos\dfrac{2k\pi + \pi/4}{5} + i\sin\dfrac{2k\pi + \pi/4}{5}\right)$

$$= \sqrt[5]{2}\left(\cos\frac{\pi(8k+1)}{20} + i\sin\frac{\pi(8k+1)}{20}\right),$$

$k = 0, 1, 2, 3, 4$:

$$\sqrt[5]{2}\left(\cos\frac{\pi}{20} + i\sin\frac{\pi}{20}\right), \sqrt[5]{2}\left(\cos\frac{9\pi}{20} + i\sin\frac{9\pi}{20}\right),$$

$$\sqrt[5]{2}\left(\cos\frac{17\pi}{20} + i\sin\frac{17\pi}{20}\right), \sqrt[5]{2}\left(\cos\frac{5\pi}{4} + i\sin\frac{5\pi}{4}\right) =$$

$$\sqrt[5]{2}\left(-\frac{1}{\sqrt{2}} - \frac{1}{\sqrt{2}}i\right) = \frac{-2^{1/5} - 2^{1/5}i}{2^{1/2}} =$$

$$\frac{-1-i}{2^{3/10}} = \frac{-1-i}{\sqrt[10]{8}},$$

$$\sqrt[5]{2}\left(\cos\frac{33\pi}{20} + i\sin\frac{33\pi}{20}\right)$$

49. $\sqrt[5]{2}\left(\cos\dfrac{2k\pi + \pi/2}{5} + i\sin\dfrac{2k\pi + \pi/2}{5}\right)$

$$= \sqrt[5]{2}\left(\cos\frac{\pi(4k+1)}{10} + i\sin\frac{\pi(4k+1)}{10}\right),$$

$k = 0, 1, 2, 3, 4$:

$$\sqrt[5]{2}\left(\cos\frac{\pi}{10} + i\sin\frac{\pi}{10}\right), \sqrt[5]{2}\left(\cos\frac{\pi}{2} + i\sin\frac{\pi}{2}\right) = \sqrt[5]{2}i,$$

$$\sqrt[5]{2}\left(\cos\frac{9\pi}{10} + i\sin\frac{9\pi}{10}\right), \sqrt[5]{2}\left(\cos\frac{13\pi}{10} + i\sin\frac{13\pi}{10}\right),$$

$$\sqrt[5]{2}\left(\cos\frac{17\pi}{10} + i\sin\frac{17\pi}{10}\right)$$

50. $\sqrt[5]{2}\left(\cos\dfrac{2k\pi + \pi/3}{5} + i\sin\dfrac{2k\pi + \pi/3}{5}\right)$

$= \sqrt[5]{2}\left(\cos\dfrac{\pi(6k+1)}{15} + i\sin\dfrac{\pi(6k+1)}{15}\right),$

$k = 0, 1, 2, 3, 4:$

$\sqrt[5]{2}\left(\cos\dfrac{\pi}{15} + i\sin\dfrac{\pi}{15}\right),\ \sqrt[5]{2}\left(\cos\dfrac{7\pi}{15} + i\sin\dfrac{7\pi}{15}\right),$

$\sqrt[5]{2}\left(\cos\dfrac{13\pi}{15} + i\sin\dfrac{13\pi}{15}\right),\ \sqrt[5]{2}\left(\cos\dfrac{19\pi}{15} + i\sin\dfrac{19\pi}{15}\right),$

$\sqrt[5]{2}\left(\cos\dfrac{5\pi}{3} + i\sin\dfrac{5\pi}{3}\right) = 2^{1/5}\left(\dfrac{1}{2} - \dfrac{\sqrt{3}i}{2}\right) =$

$\dfrac{1 - \sqrt{3}i}{2^{4/5}} = \dfrac{1 - \sqrt{3}i}{\sqrt[5]{16}}$

For #51–56, the *n*th roots of $r(\cos\theta + i\sin\theta)$ are

$\sqrt[n]{r}\left(\cos\dfrac{\theta + 2k\pi}{n} + i\sin\dfrac{\theta + 2k\pi}{n}\right),\ k = 0, 1, 2, \ldots, n-1.$

51. $1 + i = \sqrt{2}\left(\cos\dfrac{\pi}{4} + i\sin\dfrac{\pi}{4}\right),$ so the roots are

$\sqrt[4]{\sqrt{2}}\left(\cos\dfrac{2k\pi + \pi/4}{4} + i\sin\dfrac{2k\pi + \pi/4}{4}\right)$

$= \sqrt[8]{2}\left(\cos\dfrac{\pi(8k+1)}{16} + i\sin\dfrac{\pi(8k+1)}{16}\right),$

$k = 0, 1, 2, 3:$

$\sqrt[8]{2}\left(\cos\dfrac{\pi}{16} + i\sin\dfrac{\pi}{16}\right),\ \sqrt[8]{2}\left(\cos\dfrac{9\pi}{16} + i\sin\dfrac{9\pi}{16}\right),$

$\sqrt[8]{2}\left(\cos\dfrac{17\pi}{16} + i\sin\dfrac{17\pi}{16}\right),\ \sqrt[8]{2}\left(\cos\dfrac{25\pi}{16} + i\sin\dfrac{25\pi}{16}\right)$

52. $1 - i = \sqrt{2}\left(\cos\dfrac{7\pi}{4} + i\sin\dfrac{7\pi}{4}\right),$ so the roots are

$\sqrt[6]{\sqrt{2}}\left(\cos\dfrac{2k\pi + 7\pi/4}{6} + i\sin\dfrac{2k\pi + 7\pi/4}{6}\right)$

$= \sqrt[12]{2}\left(\cos\dfrac{\pi(8k+7)}{24} + i\sin\dfrac{\pi(8k+7)}{24}\right),$

$k = 0, 1, 2, 3, 4, 5:$

$\sqrt[12]{2}\left(\cos\dfrac{7\pi}{24} + i\sin\dfrac{7\pi}{24}\right),\ \sqrt[12]{2}\left(\cos\dfrac{5\pi}{8} + i\sin\dfrac{5\pi}{8}\right),$

$\sqrt[12]{2}\left(\cos\dfrac{23\pi}{24} + i\sin\dfrac{23\pi}{24}\right),\ \sqrt[12]{2}\left(\cos\dfrac{31\pi}{24} + i\sin\dfrac{31\pi}{24}\right),$

$\sqrt[12]{2}\left(\cos\dfrac{13\pi}{8} + i\sin\dfrac{13\pi}{8}\right),\ \sqrt[12]{2}\left(\cos\dfrac{47\pi}{24} + i\sin\dfrac{47\pi}{24}\right)$

53. $2 + 2i = 2\sqrt{2}\left(\cos\dfrac{\pi}{4} + i\sin\dfrac{\pi}{4}\right),$ so the roots are

$\sqrt[3]{2\sqrt{2}}\left(\cos\dfrac{2k\pi + \pi/4}{3} + i\sin\dfrac{2k\pi + \pi/4}{3}\right)$

$= \sqrt{2}\left(\cos\dfrac{\pi(8k+1)}{12} + i\sin\dfrac{\pi(8k+1)}{12}\right),\ k = 0, 1, 2:$

$\sqrt{2}\left(\cos\dfrac{\pi}{12} + i\sin\dfrac{\pi}{12}\right),\ -1 + i,$

$\sqrt{2}\left(\cos\dfrac{17\pi}{12} + i\sin\dfrac{17\pi}{12}\right)$

54. $-2 + 2i = 2\sqrt{2}\left(\cos\dfrac{3\pi}{4} + i\sin\dfrac{3\pi}{4}\right),$ so the roots are

$\sqrt[4]{2\sqrt{2}}\left(\cos\dfrac{2k\pi + 3\pi/4}{4} + i\sin\dfrac{2k\pi + 3\pi/4}{4}\right)$

$= \sqrt[8]{8}\left(\cos\dfrac{\pi(8k+3)}{16} + i\sin\dfrac{\pi(8k+3)}{16}\right),$

$k = 0, 1, 2, 3:$

$\sqrt[8]{8}\left(\cos\dfrac{3\pi}{16} + i\sin\dfrac{3\pi}{16}\right),\ \sqrt[8]{8}\left(\cos\dfrac{11\pi}{16} + i\sin\dfrac{11\pi}{16}\right),$

$\sqrt[8]{8}\left(\cos\dfrac{19\pi}{16} + i\sin\dfrac{19\pi}{16}\right),\ \sqrt[8]{8}\left(\cos\dfrac{27\pi}{16} + i\sin\dfrac{27\pi}{16}\right)$

55. $-2i = 2\left(\cos\dfrac{3\pi}{2} + i\sin\dfrac{3\pi}{2}\right),$ so the roots are

$\sqrt[6]{2}\left(\cos\dfrac{2k\pi + 3\pi/2}{6} + i\sin\dfrac{2k\pi + 3\pi/2}{6}\right)$

$= \sqrt[6]{2}\left(\cos\dfrac{\pi(4k+3)}{12} + i\sin\dfrac{\pi(4k+3)}{12}\right),$

$k = 0, 1, 2, 3, 4, 5:$

$\dfrac{1+i}{\sqrt[6]{4}},\ \sqrt[6]{2}\left(\cos\dfrac{7\pi}{12} + i\sin\dfrac{7\pi}{12}\right),$

$\sqrt[6]{2}\left(\cos\dfrac{11\pi}{12} + i\sin\dfrac{11\pi}{12}\right),\ \sqrt[6]{2}\left(\cos\dfrac{5\pi}{4} + i\sin\dfrac{5\pi}{4}\right),$

$\sqrt[6]{2}\left(\cos\dfrac{19\pi}{12} + i\sin\dfrac{19\pi}{12}\right),\ \sqrt[6]{2}\left(\cos\dfrac{23\pi}{12} + i\sin\dfrac{23\pi}{12}\right)$

56. $32 = 32(\cos 0 + i\sin 0),$ so the roots are

$\sqrt[5]{32}\left(\cos\dfrac{2k\pi + 0}{5} + i\sin\dfrac{2k\pi + 0}{5}\right)$

$= 2\left(\cos\dfrac{2k\pi}{5} + i\sin\dfrac{2k\pi}{5}\right),\ k = 0, 1, 2, 3, 4:$

$2(\cos 0 + i\sin 0) = 2,\ 2\left(\cos\dfrac{2\pi}{5} + i\sin\dfrac{2\pi}{5}\right),$

$2\left(\cos\dfrac{4\pi}{5} + i\sin\dfrac{4\pi}{5}\right),\ 2\left(\cos\dfrac{6\pi}{5} + i\sin\dfrac{6\pi}{5}\right),$

$2\left(\cos\dfrac{8\pi}{5} + i\sin\dfrac{8\pi}{5}\right)$

For #57–60, the *n*th roots of unity are

$\cos\dfrac{2k\pi}{n} + i\sin\dfrac{2k\pi}{n},\ k = 0, 1, 2, \ldots, n-1.$

57. $1, -\dfrac{1}{2} \pm \dfrac{\sqrt{3}}{2}i;$

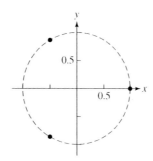

58. $\pm 1, \pm i$

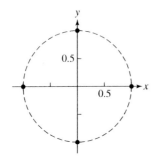

60. $1, -1$

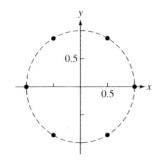

59. $\pm 1, \dfrac{1}{2} \pm \dfrac{\sqrt{3}}{2}i, -\dfrac{1}{2} \pm \dfrac{\sqrt{3}}{2}i$

61. $z = (1 + \sqrt{3}i)^3 = \left[2\left(\cos\dfrac{\pi}{3} + i\sin\dfrac{\pi}{3}\right)\right]^3$

$= 8(\cos\pi + i\sin\pi) = -8$; the cube roots are -2 and $1 \pm \sqrt{3}i$.

62. $z = (-2 - 2i)^4 = \left[2\sqrt{2}\left(\cos\dfrac{5\pi}{4} + i\sin\dfrac{5\pi}{4}\right)\right]^4$

$= 64(\cos 5\pi + i\sin 5\pi) = -64$; the fourth roots are $2 \pm 2i$ and $-2 \pm 2i$.

63. $\dfrac{z_1}{z_2} = \dfrac{r_1(\cos\theta_1 + i\sin\theta_1)}{r_2(\cos\theta_2 + i\sin\theta_2)} = \dfrac{r_1}{r_2} \cdot \dfrac{\cos\theta_1 + i\sin\theta_1}{\cos\theta_2 + i\sin\theta_2} \cdot \dfrac{\cos\theta_2 - i\sin\theta_2}{\cos\theta_2 - i\sin\theta_2}$

$= \dfrac{r_1}{r_2} \cdot \dfrac{\cos\theta_1\cos\theta_2 + \sin\theta_1\sin\theta_2 + i(\sin\theta_1\cos\theta_2 - \cos\theta_1\sin\theta_2)}{(\cos\theta_2)^2 + (\sin\theta_2)^2}$

$= \dfrac{r_1}{r_2} \cdot [\cos\theta_1\cos\theta_2 + \sin\theta_1\sin\theta_2 + i(\sin\theta_1\cos\theta_2 - \cos\theta_1\sin\theta_2)].$

Now use the angle difference formulas:

$\cos(\theta_1 - \theta_2) = \cos\theta_1\cos\theta_2 + \sin\theta_1\sin\theta_2$ and $\sin(\theta_1 - \theta_2) = \sin\theta_1\cos\theta_2 - \cos\theta_1\sin\theta_2$.

So $\dfrac{z_1}{z_2} = \dfrac{r_1}{r_2}[\cos(\theta_1 - \theta_2) + i\sin(\theta_1 - \theta_2)].$

64. The n nth roots are given by $\sqrt[n]{r}\left(\cos\dfrac{2k\pi + \theta}{n} + i\sin\dfrac{2k\pi + \theta}{n}\right)$, $k = 0, 1, 2, \ldots n - 1$:

$\sqrt[n]{r}\left(\cos\dfrac{\theta}{n} + i\sin\dfrac{\theta}{n}\right)$, $\sqrt[n]{r}\left(\cos\dfrac{\theta + 2\pi}{n} + i\sin\dfrac{\theta + 2\pi}{n}\right)$,

$\sqrt[n]{r}\left(\cos\dfrac{\theta + 4\pi}{n} + i\sin\dfrac{\theta + 4\pi}{n}\right), \ldots, \sqrt[n]{r}\left(\cos\dfrac{\theta + 2(n - 1)\pi}{n} + i\sin\dfrac{\theta + 2(n - 1)\pi}{n}\right)$.

The angles between successive values in this list differ by $\dfrac{2\pi}{n}$ radians, while the first and last roots differ by $2\pi - \dfrac{2\pi}{n}$, which also makes the angle between them $\dfrac{2\pi}{n}$. Also, the modulus of each root is $\sqrt[n]{r}$, placing it at that distance from the origin, on the circle with radius $\sqrt[n]{r}$.

65. False. If $z = r(\cos\theta + i\sin\theta)$, then it is also true that $z = r[\cos(\theta + 2n\pi) + i\sin(\theta + 2n\pi)]$ for any integer n.

For example, here are two trigonometric forms for $1 + i$: $\sqrt{2}\left(\cos\dfrac{\pi}{4} + i\sin\dfrac{\pi}{4}\right)$, $\sqrt{2}\left(\cos\dfrac{9\pi}{4} + i\sin\dfrac{9\pi}{4}\right)$.

66. True. $i^3 = i^2 \cdot i = -i$, so i is a cube root of $-i$.

67. $2\left(\cos\dfrac{2\pi}{3} + i\sin\dfrac{2\pi}{3}\right) = 2\left(-\dfrac{1}{2} + i\dfrac{\sqrt{3}}{2}\right) = -1 + \sqrt{3}i$

The answer is B.

68. Any complex number has n distinct nth roots, so $1 + i$ has five 5th roots. The answer is E.

69. $\sqrt{2}\left(\cos\dfrac{\pi}{4} + i\sin\dfrac{\pi}{4}\right) \cdot \sqrt{2}\left(\cos\dfrac{7\pi}{4} + i\sin\dfrac{7\pi}{4}\right)$

$= (\sqrt{2}\cdot\sqrt{2})\left[\cos\left(\dfrac{\pi}{4} + \dfrac{7\pi}{4}\right) + i\sin\left(\dfrac{\pi}{4} + \dfrac{7\pi}{4}\right)\right]$

$= 2(\cos 2\pi + i\sin 2\pi)$

$= 2$

The answer is A.

70. $(\sqrt{i})^4 = [(\sqrt{i})^2]^2 = i^2 = -1 \neq 1$; The answer is E.

71. (a) $a + bi = r(\cos\theta + i\sin\theta)$, where $r = \sqrt{a^2 + b^2}$ and $\theta = \tan^{-1}\left(\dfrac{b}{a}\right)$. Then $a + (-bi) = r'(\cos\theta' + i\sin\theta')$, where

$r' = \sqrt{a^2 + (-b)^2}$ and $\theta' = \tan^{-1}\left(\dfrac{-b}{a}\right)$. Since $r' = \sqrt{a^2 + b^2} = r$ and $\theta' = \tan^{-1}\left(\dfrac{-b}{a}\right) = -\tan^{-1}\left(\dfrac{b}{a}\right) = -\theta$, we

have $a - bi = r(\cos(-\theta) + i\sin(-\theta))$

(b) $z\cdot\bar{z} = r[\cos\theta + i\sin\theta]\cdot r[\cos(-\theta) + i\sin(-\theta)]$

$= r^2[\cos\theta\cos(-\theta) + i(\sin(-\theta))(\cos\theta) + i(\sin\theta)(\cos(-\theta)) - (\sin\theta)(\sin(-\theta))]$

Since $\sin\theta$ is an odd function (i.e., $\sin(-\theta) = -\sin(\theta)$) and $\cos\theta$ is an even function (i.e., $\cos(-\theta) = \cos\theta$), we have

$z\cdot\bar{z} = r^2[\cos^2\theta - i(\sin\theta)(\cos\theta) + i(\sin\theta)(\cos\theta) + \sin^2\theta]$

$= r^2[\cos^2\theta + \sin^2\theta]$

$= r^2$

(c) $\dfrac{z}{\bar{z}} = \dfrac{r[\cos\theta + i\sin\theta]}{r[\cos(-\theta) + i\sin(-\theta)]} = \cos[\theta - (-\theta)] + i\sin[\theta - (-\theta)]$

$= \cos(2\theta) + i\sin(2\theta)$

(d) $-z = -(a + bi) = -a + (-bi) = r(\cos\theta + i\sin\theta)$, where $r = \sqrt{(-a^2) + (-b)^2}$ and

$\theta = \tan^{-1}\left(\dfrac{-b}{-a}\right) = \tan^{-1}\left(\dfrac{b}{a}\right)$.

Recall, however, that $(-a, -b)$ is in the quadrant directly opposite the quadrant that holds (a, b) (i.e., if (a, b) is in Quadrant I, $(-a, -b)$ is in Quadrant III, and if (a, b) is in Quadrant II, $(-a, -b)$ is in Quadrant IV). Thus, $-z = \sqrt{a^2 + b^2}\,(\cos(\theta + \pi) + i\sin(\theta + \pi)) = r(\cos(\theta + \pi) + i\sin(\theta + \pi))$.

72. (a) $|z| = \sqrt{(r\cos\theta)^2 + (r\sin\theta)^2}$

$= \sqrt{r^2\cos^2\theta + r^2\sin^2\theta}$

$= |r|\sqrt{\cos^2\theta + \sin^2\theta}$

$= |r|$

(b) $|z_1\cdot z_2| = |[r_1\cos\theta_1 + (r_1\sin\theta_1)i]\cdot[r_2\cos\theta_2 + (r_2\sin\theta_2)i]|$

$= |r_1 r_2\cos\theta_1\cos\theta_2 + (r_1 r_2\cos\theta_1\sin\theta_2)i + (r_1 r_2\sin\theta_1\cos\theta_2)i + (r_1 r_2\sin\theta_1\theta_2)i^2|$

$= |r_1 r_2[\cos\theta_1\cos\theta_2 - \sin\theta_1\sin\theta_2 + (\cos\theta_1\sin\theta_2 + \sin\theta_1\cos\theta_2)i]|$

$= |r_1 r_2[\cos(\theta_1 + \theta_2) + (\sin(\theta_1 + \theta_2))i]|$

$= \sqrt{(r_1 r_2)^2[\cos^2(\theta_1 + \theta_2) + \sin^2(\theta_1 + \theta_2)]}$

$= \sqrt{(r_1 r_2)^2}$

$= |r_1|\cdot|r_2|$

$= |z_1|\cdot|z_1|$ by part (a)

73. (a)
```
25√(2)*(cos(-π/4)
)+isin(-π/4))*14
*(cos(π/3)+isin(
π/3))
    478.11+128.11i
■
```

(c)
```
(cos(3π/4)+isin(
3π/4))^8
    1.00+2.00ᴇ-13i
```

(b)
```
2√(2)*(cos(135)+
isin(135))/(6*(c
os(300)+isin(300
)))
    -.46-.12i
```

74. (a)

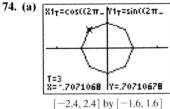

$[-2.4, 2.4]$ by $[-1.6, 1.6]$

(b) Yes. $6\pi/8, 10\pi/8, 14\pi/8$

(c) For fifth and seventh roots of unity, all of the roots except the complex number 1 generate the corresponding roots of unity. For the sixth roots of unity, only $2\pi/6$ and $10\pi/6$ generate the sixth roots of unity.

(d) $2\pi k/n$ generates the nth roots of unity if and only if k and n have no common factors other than 1.

75. Using $\tan^{-1}\left(\dfrac{1}{\sqrt{2}}\right) \approx 0.62$, we have

$\sqrt{2} + i \approx \sqrt{3}\,(\cos 0.62 + i \sin 0.62)$, so graph
$x(t) = (\sqrt{3})^t \cos(0.62t)$ and
$y(t) = (\sqrt{3})^t \sin(0.62t)$.
Use Tmin $= 0$, Tmax $= 4$, Tstep $= 1$.
Shown is $[-7, 2]$ by $[-0, 6]$.

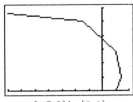

$[-7, 2]$ by $[0, 6]$

76. $-1 + i = \sqrt{2}\left(\cos\dfrac{3\pi}{4} + i \sin\dfrac{3\pi}{4}\right)$, so graph

$x(t) = (\sqrt{2})^t \cos(0.75\pi t)$ and $y(t) = (\sqrt{2})^t \sin(0.75\pi t)$
Use Tmin $= 0$, Tmax $= 4$, Tstep $= 1$.
Shown is $[-5, 3]$ by $[-3, 3]$.

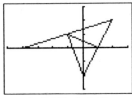

$[-5, 3]$ by $[-3, 3]$

77. Suppose that $z_1 = r_1(\cos\theta_1 + i\sin\theta_1)$ and $z_2 = r_2(\cos\theta_2 + i\sin\theta_2)$. Each triangle's angle at the origin has the same measure: For the smaller triangle, this angle has measure θ_1; for the larger triangle, the side from the origin out to z_2 makes an angle of θ_2 with the x-axis, while the side from the origin to z_1z_2 makes an angle of $\theta_1 + \theta_2$, so that the angle between is θ_1 as well.

The corresponding side lengths for the sides adjacent to these angles have the same ratio: two longest side have lengths $|z_1| = r_1$ (for the smaller) and $|z_1z_2| = r_1r_2$, for a ratio of r_2. For the other two sides, the lengths are 1 and r_2, again giving a ratio of r_2. Finally, the Law of Sines can be used to show that the remaining side have the same ratio.

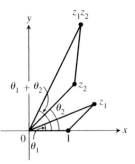

78. Construct an angle with vertex at z_2, and one ray from z_2 to 0, congruent to the angle formed by 0, 1, and z_1, with vertex 1. Also, be sure that this new angle is oriented in the appropriate direction: e.g., if z_1 is located "counter-clockwise" from 1 then the points on this new ray should also be located counterclockwise from z_2. Now similarly construct an angle with vertex at 0, and one ray from 0 to z_2, congruent to the angle formed by 1, 0, and z_1, with vertex 0. the intersection of the two newly constructed rays is z_1z_2.

79. The solutions are the cube roots of 1:
$$\cos\left(\frac{2\pi k}{3}\right) + i\sin\left(\frac{2\pi k}{3}\right), k = 0, 1, 2 \text{ or}$$
$$1, -\frac{1}{2} + \frac{\sqrt{3}}{2}i, -\frac{1}{2} - \frac{\sqrt{3}}{2}i$$

80. The solutions are the fourth roots of 1:
$$\cos\left(\frac{\pi k}{2}\right) + i\sin\left(\frac{\pi k}{2}\right), k = 0, 1, 2, 3 \text{ or}$$
$$-1, 1, -i, i$$

81. The solutions are the cube roots of -1:
$$\cos\left(\frac{\pi + 2\pi k}{3}\right) + i\sin\left(\frac{\pi + 2\pi k}{3}\right), k = 0, 1, 2 \text{ or}$$
$$-1, \frac{1}{2} + \frac{\sqrt{3}}{2}i, \frac{1}{2} - \frac{\sqrt{3}}{2}i$$

82. The solutions are the fourth roots of -1:
$$\cos\left(\frac{\pi + 2\pi k}{4}\right) + i\sin\left(\frac{\pi + 2\pi k}{4}\right), k = 0, 1, 2, 3 \text{ or}$$
$$\frac{\sqrt{2}}{2} + \frac{\sqrt{2}}{2}i, \frac{\sqrt{2}}{2} - \frac{\sqrt{2}}{2}i, -\frac{\sqrt{2}}{2} + \frac{\sqrt{2}}{2}i, -\frac{\sqrt{2}}{2} - \frac{\sqrt{2}}{2}i$$

83. The solutions are the fifth roots of -1:
$$\cos\left(\frac{\pi + 2\pi k}{5}\right) + i\sin\left(\frac{\pi + 2\pi k}{5}\right), k = 0, 1, 2, 3, 4, \text{ or}$$
$$-1, \approx 0.81 + 0.59i, 0.81 - 0.59i, -0.31 + 0.95i, -0.31 - 0.95i$$

84. The solutions are the fifth roots of 1:
$$\cos\left(\frac{2\pi k}{5}\right) + i\sin\left(\frac{2\pi k}{5}\right), k = 0, 1, 2, 3, 4 \text{ or}$$
$$1, \approx 0.31 + 0.95i, 0.31 - 0.95i, -0.81 + 0.59i, -0.81 - 0.59i$$

■ Chapter 6 Review

1. $\mathbf{u} - \mathbf{v} = \langle 2 - 4, -1 - 2\rangle = \langle -2, -3\rangle$

2. $2\mathbf{u} - 3\mathbf{w} = \langle 4 - 3, -2 + 9\rangle = \langle 1, 7\rangle$

3. $|\mathbf{u} + \mathbf{v}| = \sqrt{(2 + 4)^2 + (-1 + 2)^2} = \sqrt{37}$

4. $|\mathbf{w} - 2\mathbf{u}| = \sqrt{(1 - 4)^2 + (-3 + 2)^2} = \sqrt{10}$

5. $\mathbf{u} \cdot \mathbf{v} = 8 - 2 = 6$

6. $\mathbf{u} \cdot \mathbf{w} = 2 + 3 = 5$

7. $3\overrightarrow{AB} = 3\langle 3 - 2, 1 - (-1)\rangle = \langle 3, 6\rangle$;
$|3\overrightarrow{AB}| = \sqrt{3^2 + 6^2} = \sqrt{45} = 3\sqrt{5}$

8. $\overrightarrow{AB} + \overrightarrow{CD} = \langle 3 - 2, 1 - (-1)\rangle + \langle 1 - (-4), -5 - 2\rangle$
$= \langle 6, -5\rangle; |\overrightarrow{AB} + \overrightarrow{CD}| = \sqrt{6^2 + 5^2} = \sqrt{61}$

9. $\overrightarrow{AC} + \overrightarrow{BD} = \langle -4 - 2, 2 - (-1)\rangle + \langle 1 - 3, -5 - 1\rangle$
$= \langle -8, -3\rangle; |\overrightarrow{AC} + \overrightarrow{BD}| = \sqrt{8^2 + 3^2} = \sqrt{73}$

10. $\overrightarrow{CD} - \overrightarrow{AB} = \langle 1 - (-4), -5 - 2\rangle - \langle 3 - 2, 1 - (-1)\rangle$
$= \langle 4, -9\rangle; |\overrightarrow{CD} + \overrightarrow{AB}| = \sqrt{4^2 + 9^2} = \sqrt{97}$

11. (a) $\dfrac{\overrightarrow{AB}}{|\overrightarrow{AB}|} = \dfrac{\langle -2, 1\rangle}{\sqrt{(-2)^2 + 1^2}} = \dfrac{\langle -2, 1\rangle}{\sqrt{5}} = \left\langle -\dfrac{2}{\sqrt{5}}, \dfrac{1}{\sqrt{5}}\right\rangle$

(b) $-3 \cdot \dfrac{\overrightarrow{AB}}{|\overrightarrow{BA}|} = -3\left\langle \dfrac{-2}{\sqrt{5}}, \dfrac{1}{\sqrt{5}}\right\rangle = \left\langle \dfrac{6}{\sqrt{5}}, -\dfrac{3}{\sqrt{5}}\right\rangle$

12. (a) $\dfrac{\overrightarrow{AB}}{|\overrightarrow{AB}|} = \dfrac{\langle 2, 0\rangle}{\sqrt{2^2 + 0^2}} = \dfrac{\langle 2, 0\rangle}{2} = \langle 1, 0\rangle$

(b) $-3 \cdot \dfrac{\overrightarrow{AB}}{|\overrightarrow{BA}|} = -3\langle 1, 0\rangle = \langle -3, 0\rangle$

For #13–14, the direction angle θ of $\langle a, b\rangle$ has $\tan \theta = \dfrac{b}{a}$; start with $\tan^{-1}\left(\dfrac{b}{a}\right)$, and add (or subtract) $180°$ if the angle is not in the correct quadrant. The angle between two vectors is the absolute value of the difference between their angles; if this difference is greater than $180°$, subtract it from $360°$.

13. (a) $\theta_u = \tan^{-1}\left(\dfrac{3}{4}\right) \approx 0.64, \theta_r = \tan^{-1}\left(\dfrac{5}{2}\right) \approx 1.19$

(b) $\theta_r - \theta_u \approx 0.55$.

14. (a) $\theta_u = \pi + \tan^{-1}(-2) = \cos^{-1}\left(-\dfrac{1}{\sqrt{5}}\right) \approx 2.03$,

$\theta_r = \tan^{-1}\left(\dfrac{2}{3}\right) \approx 0.59$

(b) $\theta_u - \theta_r \approx 1.45$

15. $(-2.5\cos 25°, -2.5\sin 25°) \approx (-2.27, -1.06)$

16. $(-3.1\cos 135°, -3.1\sin 135°) = (1.55\sqrt{2}, -1.55\sqrt{2})$

17. $(2\cos(-\pi/4), 2\sin(-\pi/4)) = (\sqrt{2}, -\sqrt{2})$

18. $(3.6\cos(3\pi/4), 3.6\sin(3\pi/4)) = (-1.8\sqrt{2}, 1.8\sqrt{2})$

19. $\left(1, -\dfrac{2\pi}{3} + (2n + 1)\pi\right)$ and $\left(-1, -\dfrac{2\pi}{3} + 2n\pi\right)$, n an integer

20. $\left(2, \dfrac{5\pi}{6} + (2n + 1)\pi\right)$ and $\left(-2, \dfrac{5\pi}{6} + 2n\pi\right)$, n an integer

21. (a) $\left(-\sqrt{13}, \pi + \tan^{-1}\left(-\dfrac{3}{2}\right)\right) \approx (-\sqrt{13}, 2.16)$ or

$\left(\sqrt{13}, 2\pi + \tan^{-1}\left(-\dfrac{3}{2}\right)\right) \approx (\sqrt{13}, 5.30)$

(b) $\left(\sqrt{13}, \tan^{-1}\left(-\dfrac{3}{2}\right)\right) \approx (\sqrt{13}, -0.98)$ or

$\left(-\sqrt{13}, \pi + \tan^{-1}\left(-\dfrac{3}{2}\right)\right) \approx (-\sqrt{13}, 2.16)$

(c) The answers from (a), and also
$\left(-\sqrt{13}, 3\pi + \tan^{-1}\left(-\dfrac{3}{2}\right)\right) \approx (-\sqrt{13}, 8.44)$ or

$\left(\sqrt{13}, 4\pi + \tan^{-1}\left(-\dfrac{3}{2}\right)\right) \approx (\sqrt{13}, 11.58)$

22. (a) $(-10, 0)$ or $(10, \pi)$ or $(-10, 2\pi)$

(b) $(10, -\pi)$ or $(-10, 0)$ or $(10, \pi)$

(c) The answers from (a), and also $(10, 3\pi)$ or $(-10, 4\pi)$

23. (a) $(5, 0)$ or $(-5, \pi)$ or $(5, 2\pi)$

(b) $(-5, -\pi)$ or $(5, 0)$ or $(-5, \pi)$

(c) The answers from (a), and also $(-5, 3\pi)$ or $(5, 4\pi)$

24. (a) $\left(-2, \dfrac{\pi}{2}\right)$ or $\left(2, \dfrac{3\pi}{2}\right)$

(b) $\left(2, -\dfrac{\pi}{2}\right)$ or $\left(-2, \dfrac{\pi}{2}\right)$

(c) The answers from (a), and also $\left(-2, \dfrac{5\pi}{2}\right)$
or $\left(2, \dfrac{7\pi}{2}\right)$

25. $t = -\dfrac{1}{5}x + \dfrac{3}{5}$, so $y = 4 + 3\left(-\dfrac{1}{5}x + \dfrac{3}{5}\right)$
$= -\dfrac{3}{5}x + \dfrac{29}{5}$:

Line through $\left(0, \dfrac{29}{5}\right)$ with slope $m = -\dfrac{3}{5}$

26. $t = x - 4$, so $y = -8 - 5(x - 4) = -5x + 12$,
$1 \leq x \leq 9$: segment from $(1, 7)$ to $(9, -33)$.

27. $t = y + 1$, so $x = 2(y + 1)^2 + 3$: Parabola that opens to right with vertex at $(3, -1)$.

28. $x^2 + y^2 = (3\cos t)^2 + (3\sin t)^2 =$
$9\cos^2 t + 9\sin^2 t = 9$, so $x^2 + y^2 = 9$: Circle of radius 3 centered at $(0, 0)$.

29. $x + 1 = e^{2t}, t = \dfrac{\ln(x + 1)}{2}$, so $y = e^{\frac{1}{2}\ln(x+1)} = e^{\ln\sqrt{x+1}}$
$= \sqrt{x + 1}$: square root function starting at $(-1, 0)$

30. $t = \sqrt[3]{x}$, so $y = \ln(\sqrt[3]{x}) = \ln x^{1/3} = \dfrac{1}{3}\ln x$: the
logarithmic function, with asymptote at $x = 0$

31. $m = \dfrac{4 - (-2)}{3 - (-1)} = \dfrac{6}{4} = \dfrac{3}{2}$, so $\Delta x = 2$ when $\Delta y = 3$.
One possibility for the parametrization of the line is:
$x = 2t + 3, y = 3t + 4$.

32. $m = \dfrac{1 - 3}{5 - (-2)} = \dfrac{-2}{7}$, so $\Delta x = 7$ when $\Delta y = -2$.
One possibility for the parametrization of the segment is:
$x = 7t + 5, y = -2t + 1, -1 \leq t \leq 0$. Another possibility is $x = 7t - 2, y = -2t + 3, 0 \leq t \leq 1$.

33. $a = -3, b = 4, |z_1| = \sqrt{3^2 + 4^2} = 5$

34. $z_1 = 5\left\{\cos\left[\cos^{-1}\left(-\dfrac{3}{5}\right)\right] + i\sin\left[\cos^{-1}\left(-\dfrac{3}{5}\right)\right]\right\}$
$\approx 5[\cos(2.21) + i\sin(2.21)]$

35. $6(\cos 30° + i\sin 30°) = 6\left(\dfrac{\sqrt{3}}{2} + \dfrac{1}{2}i\right) = 3\sqrt{3} + 3i$

36. $3(\cos 150° + i\sin 150°) = 3\left(-\dfrac{\sqrt{3}}{2} + \dfrac{1}{2}i\right)$
$= -1.5\sqrt{3} + 1.5i$

37. $2.5\left(\cos\dfrac{4\pi}{3} + i\sin\dfrac{4\pi}{3}\right) = 2.5\left(-\dfrac{1}{2} - \dfrac{\sqrt{3}}{2}i\right)$
$= -1.25 - 1.25\sqrt{3}\,i$

38. $4\,(\cos 2.5 + i\sin 2.5) \approx -3.20 + 2.39i$

39. $3 - 3i = 3\sqrt{2}\left(\cos\dfrac{7\pi}{4} + i\sin\dfrac{7\pi}{4}\right)$. Other

representations would use angles $\dfrac{7\pi}{4} + 2n\pi$, n an integer.

40. $-1 + i\sqrt{2} = \sqrt{3}\left\{\cos\left[\cos^{-1}\left(-\dfrac{1}{\sqrt{3}}\right)\right]\right.$

$\left. + i\sin\left[\cos^{-1}\left(-\dfrac{1}{\sqrt{3}}\right)\right]\right\} \approx \sqrt{3}[\cos (2.19)$

$+ i\sin (2.19)]$. Other representations would use
angles $2.19 + 2n\pi$, n an integer.

41. $3 - 5i = \sqrt{34}\left\{\cos\left[\tan^{-1}\left(-\dfrac{5}{3}\right)\right]\right.$

$\left. + i\sin\left[\tan^{-1}\left(-\dfrac{5}{3}\right)\right]\right\}$

$\approx \sqrt{34}\,[\cos (-1.03) + i\sin(-1.03)]$

$\approx \sqrt{34}[\cos (5.25) + i\sin (5.25)]$

Other representations would use angles $\approx 5.25 + 2n\pi$,
n an integer.

42. $-2 - 2i = 2\sqrt{2}\left(\cos\dfrac{5\pi}{4} + i\sin\dfrac{5\pi}{4}\right)$. Other

representations would use angles $\dfrac{5\pi}{4} + 2n\pi$, n an integer.

43. $z_1 z_2 = (3)(4)\,[\cos (30° + 60°) + i\sin (30° + 60°)]$
$= 12\,(\cos 90° + i\sin 90°)$

$z_1/z_2 = \dfrac{3}{4}\,[\cos (30° - 60°) + i\sin (30° - 60°)]$

$= \dfrac{3}{4}\,[\cos (-30°) + i\sin (-30°)]$

$= \dfrac{3}{4}\,(\cos 330° + i\sin 330°)$

44. $z_1 z_2 = (5)(-2)\,[\cos (20° + 45°) + i\sin (20° + 45°)]$
$= -10\,(\cos 65° + i\sin 65°)$
$= 10\,(\cos 245° + i\sin 245°)$

$z_1/z_2 = \dfrac{5}{-2}\,[\cos (20° - 45°) + i\sin (20° - 45°)]$

$= -2.5[\cos (-25°) + i\sin (-25°)]$
$= 2.5\,(\cos 155° + i\sin 155°)$

45. (a) $\left[3\left(\cos\dfrac{\pi}{4} + i\sin\dfrac{\pi}{4}\right)\right]^5 = 3^5\left(\cos\dfrac{5\pi}{4} + i\sin\dfrac{5\pi}{4}\right)$

$= 243\left(\cos\dfrac{5\pi}{4} + i\sin\dfrac{5\pi}{4}\right)$

(b) $-\dfrac{243\sqrt{2}}{2} - \dfrac{243\sqrt{2}}{2}i$

46. (a) $\left[2\left(\cos\dfrac{\pi}{12} + i\sin\dfrac{\pi}{12}\right)\right]^8 = 2^8\left(\cos\dfrac{2\pi}{3} + i\sin\dfrac{2\pi}{3}\right)$

$= 256\left(\cos\dfrac{2\pi}{3} + i\sin\dfrac{2\pi}{3}\right)$

(b) $-128 + 128\sqrt{3}\,i$

47. (a) $\left[5\left(\cos\dfrac{5\pi}{3} + i\sin\dfrac{5\pi}{3}\right)\right]^3 = 5^3\,(\cos 5\pi + i\sin 5\pi)$

$= 125\,(\cos \pi + i\sin \pi)$

(b) $-125 + 0i = -125$

48. (a) $\left[7\left(\cos\dfrac{\pi}{24} + i\sin\dfrac{\pi}{24}\right)\right]^6 = 7^6\left(\cos\dfrac{\pi}{4} + i\sin\dfrac{\pi}{4}\right)$

$= 117,649\left(\cos\dfrac{\pi}{4} + i\sin\dfrac{\pi}{4}\right)$

(b) $\dfrac{117,649\sqrt{2}}{2} + \dfrac{117,649\sqrt{2}}{2}i$

For #49–52, the nth roots of $r\,(\cos \theta + i\sin \theta)$ are

$\sqrt[n]{r}\left(\cos\dfrac{2k\pi + \theta}{n} + i\sin\dfrac{2k\pi + \theta}{n}\right)$, $k = 0, 1, 2, \ldots,$

$n - 1$.

49. $3 + 3i = 3\sqrt{2}\left(\cos\dfrac{\pi}{4} + i\sin\dfrac{\pi}{4}\right)$, so the roots are

$\sqrt[4]{3\sqrt{2}}\left(\cos\dfrac{2k\pi + \pi/4}{4} + i\sin\dfrac{2k\pi + \pi/4}{4}\right)$

$= \sqrt[8]{18}\left(\cos\dfrac{\pi(8k + 1)}{16} + i\sin\dfrac{\pi(8k + 1)}{16}\right),$

$k = 0, 1, 2, 3:$

$\sqrt[8]{18}\left(\cos\dfrac{\pi}{16} + i\sin\dfrac{\pi}{16}\right),$

$\sqrt[8]{18}\left(\cos\dfrac{9\pi}{16} + i\sin\dfrac{9\pi}{16}\right),$

$\sqrt[8]{18}\left(\cos\dfrac{17\pi}{16} + i\sin\dfrac{17\pi}{16}\right),$

$\sqrt[8]{18}\left(\cos\dfrac{25\pi}{16} + i\sin\dfrac{25\pi}{16}\right)$

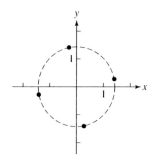

50. $8 = 8\,(\cos 0 + i\sin 0)$, so the roots are

$\sqrt[3]{8}\left(\cos\dfrac{2k\pi + 0}{3} + i\sin\dfrac{2k\pi + 0}{3}\right)$

$= 2\left(\cos\dfrac{2k\pi}{3} + i\sin\dfrac{2k\pi}{3}\right), k = 0, 1, 2:$

$2\,(\cos 0 + i\sin 0) = 2,$

$2\left(\cos\dfrac{2\pi}{3} + i\sin\dfrac{2\pi}{3}\right),$

$2\left(\cos\dfrac{4\pi}{3} + i\sin\dfrac{4\pi}{3}\right)$

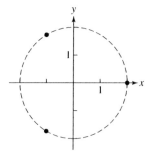

51. $1 = \cos 0 + i \sin 0$, so the roots are
$$\cos \frac{2k\pi + 0}{5} + i \sin \frac{2k\pi + 0}{5} = \cos \frac{2k\pi}{5} + i \sin \frac{2k\pi}{5},$$
$k = 0, 1, 2, 3, 4$:
$$\cos 0 + i \sin 0 = 1, \cos \frac{2\pi}{5} + i \sin \frac{2\pi}{5},$$
$$\cos \frac{4\pi}{5} + i \sin \frac{4\pi}{5}, \cos \frac{6\pi}{5} + i \sin \frac{6\pi}{5}$$
$$\cos \frac{8\pi}{5} + i \sin \frac{8\pi}{5}$$

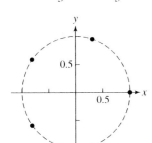

52. $-1 = 1 (\cos \pi + i \sin \pi)$, so the roots are
$$\cos \frac{2k\pi + \pi}{6} + i \sin \frac{2k\pi + \pi}{6}$$
$$= \cos \frac{\pi(2k + 1)}{6} + i \sin \frac{\pi(2k + 1)}{6},$$
$k = 0, 1, 2, 3, 4, 5$:
$$\cos \frac{\pi}{6} + i \sin \frac{\pi}{6}, \cos \frac{\pi}{2} + i \sin \frac{\pi}{2} = i,$$
$$\cos \frac{5\pi}{6} + i \sin \frac{5\pi}{6}, \cos \frac{7\pi}{6} + i \sin \frac{7\pi}{6},$$
$$\cos \frac{3\pi}{2} + i \sin \frac{3\pi}{2} = -i, \cos \frac{11\pi}{6} + i \sin \frac{11\pi}{6}$$

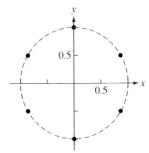

53. Graph (b)

54. Not shown

55. Graph (a)

56. Not shown

57. Not shown

58. Graph (d)

59. Graph (c)

60. Not shown

61. $x^2 + y^2 = 4$ — a circle with center $(0, 0)$ and radius 2

62. $r^2 + 2r \sin \theta = x^2 + y^2 + 2y = 0$. Completing the square: $x^2 + (y^2 + 1)^2 = 1$ — a circle of radius 1 with center $(0, -1)$

63. $r^2 + 3r \cos \theta + 2r \sin \theta = x^2 + y^2 + 3x + 2y = 0$. Completing the square: $\left(x + \frac{3}{2} \right)^2 + (y + 1)^2 = \frac{13}{4}$ — a circle of radius $\frac{\sqrt{13}}{2}$ with center $\left(-\frac{3}{2}, -1 \right)$

64. $1 - \frac{3}{r \cos \theta} = 1 - \frac{3}{x} = 0 \Rightarrow x - 3 = 0, x = 3$ — a vertical line through $(3, 0)$

65. $r = \frac{-4}{\sin \theta} = -4 \csc \theta$

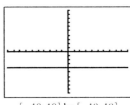

$[-10, 10]$ by $[-10, 10]$

66. $r = \frac{5}{\cos \theta} = 5 \sec \theta$

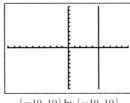

$[-10, 10]$ by $[-10, 10]$

67. $(r \cos \theta - 3)^2 + (r \sin \theta + 1)^2 = 10$, so $r^2(\cos^2 \theta + \sin^2 \theta) + r(-6 \cos \theta + 2 \sin \theta) + 10 = 10$, or $r = 6 \cos \theta - 2 \sin \theta$

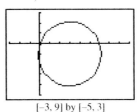

$[-3, 9]$ by $[-5, 3]$

68. $2r \cos \theta - 3r \sin \theta = 4, r = \frac{4}{2 \cos \theta - 3 \sin \theta}$

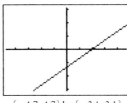

$[-4.7, 4.7]$ by $[-3.1, 3.1]$

69.

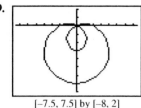

[−7.5, 7.5] by [−8, 2]

Domain: All reals
Range: [−3, 7]
Symmetric about the y-axis
Continuous
Bounded
Maximum r-value: 7
No asymptotes

70.

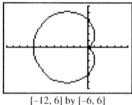

[−12, 6] by [−6, 6]

Domain: All reals
Range: [0, 8]
Symmetric about the x-axis
Continuous
Bounded
Maximum r-value: 8
No asymptotes

71.

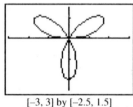

[−3, 3] by [−2.5, 1.5]

Domain: All reals
Range: [−2, 2]
Symmetric about the y-axis
Continuous
Bounded
Maximum r-value: 2
No asymptotes

72.

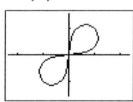

[−2.35, 2.35] by [−1.55, 1.55]

Domain: $\left[0, \dfrac{\pi}{2}\right] \cup \left[\pi, \dfrac{3\pi}{2}\right]$

Range: $[0, \sqrt{2}]$
Symmetric about the origin
Bounded
Maximum r-value: $\sqrt{2}$
No asymptotes

73. (a) $r = a \sec \theta \Rightarrow \dfrac{r}{\sec \theta} = a \Rightarrow r \cos \theta = a \Rightarrow x = a.$

(b) $r = b \csc \theta \Rightarrow \dfrac{r}{\csc \theta} = b \Rightarrow r \sin \theta = b \Rightarrow y = b.$

(c) $y = mx + b \Rightarrow r \sin \theta = mr \cos \theta + b \Rightarrow$

$r(\sin \theta - m \cos \theta) = b \Rightarrow r = \dfrac{b}{\sin \theta - m \cos \theta}.$

The domain of r is any value of θ for which
$\sin \theta \neq m \cos \theta \Rightarrow \tan \theta \neq m \Rightarrow \theta \neq \arctan(m).$

(d)

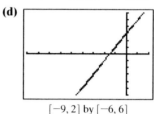

[−9, 2] by [−6, 6]

74. (a) $\mathbf{v} = 540 \langle \sin 80°, \cos 80° \rangle \approx \langle 531.80, 93.77 \rangle$

(b) The wind vector is $\mathbf{w} = 55 \langle \sin 100°, \cos 100° \rangle$
$\approx \langle 54.16, -9.55 \rangle$. Actual velocity vector:
$\mathbf{v} + \mathbf{w} \approx \langle 585.96, 84.22 \rangle$. Actual speed: $\|\mathbf{v} + \mathbf{w}\|$
$\approx \sqrt{585.96^2 + 84.22^2} \approx 591.98$ mph. Actual
bearing: $\tan^{-1}\left(\dfrac{585.96}{84.22}\right) \approx 82.82°$

75. (a) $\mathbf{v} = 480 \langle \sin 285°, \cos 285° \rangle \approx \langle -463.64, 124.23 \rangle$

(b) The wind vector is $\mathbf{w} = 30 \langle \sin 265°, \cos 265° \rangle$
$\approx \langle -29.89, -2.61 \rangle$. Actual velocity vector:
$\mathbf{v} + \mathbf{w} \approx \langle -493.53, 121.62 \rangle$. Actual speed: $\|\mathbf{v} + \mathbf{w}\|$
$\approx \sqrt{493.53^2 + 121.62^2} \approx 508.29$ mph. Actual
bearing: $360° + \tan^{-1}\left(\dfrac{-493.53}{121.62}\right) \approx 283.84°$

76. $\mathbf{F} = \langle 120 \cos 20°, 120 \sin 20° \rangle + \langle 300 \cos(-5°),$
$300 \sin(-5°) \rangle \approx \langle 411.62, 14.90 \rangle$, so
$\|\mathbf{F}\| \approx \sqrt{411.62^2 + 14.90^2} \approx 411.89$ lb and
$\theta = \tan^{-1}\left(\dfrac{14.90}{411.62}\right) \approx 2.07°$

77.

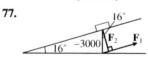

$\mathbf{F}_1$ Force to keep car from going downhill

$\mathbf{F}_2$ Force perpendicular to the street

(a) $\mathbf{F}_1 = -3000 \sin 16° \approx -826.91$, so the force required to keep the car from rolling down the hill is approximately 826.91 pounds.

(b) $\mathbf{F}_2 = -3000 \cos 16° \approx 2883.79$, so the force perpendicular to the street is approximately 2883.79 pounds.

78. $\mathbf{F} = 36 \cdot \dfrac{\langle 3, 5 \rangle}{\sqrt{3^2 + 5^2}} = \dfrac{\langle 108, 180 \rangle}{\sqrt{34}}$

Since $\overrightarrow{AB} = \langle 10, 0 \rangle$, $\mathbf{F} \cdot \overrightarrow{AB} = (10)\left(\dfrac{108}{\sqrt{34}}\right) + 0$

$= \dfrac{1080}{\sqrt{34}} \approx 185.22$ foot-pounds.

79. (a) $h = -16t^2 + v_0 t + s_0 = -16t^2 + 245t + 200$

(b) Graph and trace: $x = 17$ and $y = -16t^2 + 245t + 200$ with $0 \le t \le 16.1$ (upper limit may vary) on $[0, 18]$ by $[0, 1200]$. This graph will appear as a vertical line from about $(17, 0)$ to about $(17, 1138)$. Tracing shows how the arrow begins at a height of 200 ft, rises to over 1000 ft, then falls back to the ground.

(c) Graph $x = t$ and $y = -16t^2 + 245t + 200$ with $0 \le t \le 16.1$ (upper limit may vary).

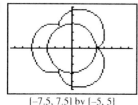

$[0, 18]$ by $[0, 1200]$

(d) When $t = 4$, $h = 924$ ft.

(e) When $t \approx 7.66$, the arrow is at its peak: about 1138 ft.

(f) The arrow hits the ground ($h = 0$) after about 16.09 sec.

80. $x = 35 \cos\left(\dfrac{\pi}{10}t\right)$, $y = 50 + 35 \sin\left(\dfrac{\pi}{10}t\right)$, assuming the wheel turns counterclockwise.

81. $x = 40 \sin\left(\dfrac{2\pi}{15}t\right)$, $y = 50 - 40 \cos\left(\dfrac{2\pi}{15}t\right)$, assuming the wheel turns counterclockwise.

82. $x = -40 \sin\left(\dfrac{\pi}{9}t\right)$, $y = 50 + 40 \cos\left(\dfrac{\pi}{9}t\right)$, assuming the wheel turns counterclockwise.

83. (a)

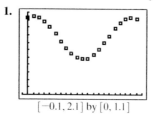

$[-7.5, 7.5]$ by $[-5, 5]$

(b) All 4's should be changed to 5's.

84. $x = (66 \cos 5°)t$ and $y = -16t^2 + (66 \sin 5°)t + 4$. $y = 0$ when $t \approx 0.71$ sec (and also when $t \approx -0.352$, but that is not appropriate in this problem). When $t \approx 0.71$ sec, $x \approx 46.75$ ft.

85. $x = (66 \cos 12°)t$ and $y = -16t^2 + (66 \sin 12°)t + 3.5$. $y = 0$ when $t \approx 1.06$ sec (and also when $t \approx -0.206$, but that is not appropriate in this problem). When $t \approx 1.06$ sec, $x \approx 68.65$ ft.

86. $x = (70 \cos 45°)t$ and $y = -16t^2 + (70 \sin 45°)t$. The ball traveled 40 yd (120 ft) horizontally after about 2.42 sec, at which point it is about 25.96 ft above the ground, so it clears the crossbar.

87. If we assume that the initial height is 0 ft, then $x = (85 \cos 56°)t$ and $y = -16t^2 + (85 \sin 56°)t$. [If the assumed initial height is something other than 0 ft, add that amount to y.]

(a) Find graphically: the maximum y value is about 77.59 ft (after about 2.20 seconds).

(b) $y = 0$ when $t \approx 4.404$ sec

88. $x = (v_0 \cos 30°)t$ and $y = -16t^2 + (v_0 \sin 30°)t + 2.5$. v_0 must be (at least) just over 125 ft/sec. This can be found graphically (by trial-and-error), or algebraically: the ball is 400 ft from the plate (i.e., $x = 400$) when
$$t = \frac{400}{v_0 \cos 30°} = \frac{800/\sqrt{3}}{v_0}$$
Substitute this value of t in the parametric equation for y. Then solve to see what value of v_0 makes y equal to 15 ft.

$$-16\left(\frac{800}{\sqrt{3}v_0}\right)^2 + v_0 \sin 30°\left(\frac{800}{\sqrt{3}v_0}\right) + 2.5 = 15$$

$$\frac{-16(640,000)}{3v_0^2} + \frac{400}{\sqrt{3}} = 12.5$$

$$\frac{-16(640,000)}{3} + \frac{400v_0^2}{\sqrt{3}} = 12.5v_0^2$$

$$\frac{-16(640,000)}{3} = v_0^2\left(12.5 - \frac{400}{\sqrt{3}}\right)$$

$$\frac{-16(640,000)}{3\left(12.5 - \dfrac{400}{\sqrt{3}}\right)} = v_0^2$$

$$\pm 125.004 \approx v_0$$

The negative root doesn't apply to this problem, so the initial velocity needed is just over 125 ft/sec.

89. Kathy's position: $x_1 = 60 \cos\left(\dfrac{\pi}{6}t\right)$ and

$y_1 = 60 + 60 \sin\left(\dfrac{\pi}{6}t\right)$

Ball's position:
$x_2 = -80 + (100 \cos 70°)t$ and
$y_2 = -16t^2 + (100 \sin 70°)t$
Find (graphically) the minimum of
$d(t) = \sqrt{(x_1 - x_2)^2 + (y_1 - y_2)^2}$. It occurs when $t \approx 2.64$ sec; the minimum distance is about 17.65 ft.

90. $x = (20 \cos 50°)t$ and $y = -16t^2 + (20 \sin 50°)t + 5$. $y = 0$ when $t = 1.215$ sec (and also when $t = -0.257$, but that is not appropriate in this problem). When $t = 1.215$ sec, $x = 15.62$ ft. The dart falls several feet short of the target.

Chapter 6 Project

Answers are based on the sample data shown in the table.

1.

$[-0.1, 2.1]$ by $[0, 1.1]$

2. Sinusoidal regression produces $y \approx 0.28 \sin(3.46x + 1.20) + 0.75$ or, with a phase shift of 2π, $y \approx 0.28 \sin(3.46x - 5.09) + 0.75$ $\approx 0.28 \sin(3.46(x - 1.47)) + 0.75$.

3.

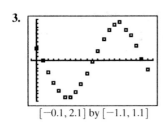

$[-0.1, 2.1]$ by $[-1.1, 1.1]$

5.

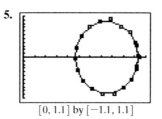

$[0, 1.1]$ by $[-1.1, 1.1]$

The curve $y \approx 0.9688 \cos(3.46(x - 1.47))$ closely fits the data.

4. The distance and velocity both vary sinusoidally, with the same period but a phase shift of 90° — like the x- and y-coordinates of a point moving around a circle. A scatter plot of distance versus time should have the shape of a circle (or ellipse).

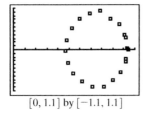

$[0, 1.1]$ by $[-1.1, 1.1]$

Chapter 7
Systems and Matrices

■ Section 7.1 Solving Systems of Two Equations

Exploration 1

1.

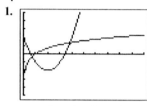

[0, 10] by [−5, 5]

2.

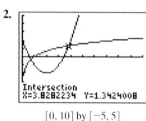   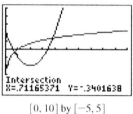

[0, 10] by [−5, 5]   [0, 10] by [−5, 5]

3. The function ln x is only defined for $x > 0$, so all solutions must be positive. As x approaches infinity, $x^2 - 4x + 2$ is going to infinity much more quickly than ln x is going to infinity, hence will always be larger than ln x for x-values greater than 4.

Quick Review 7.1

1. $3y = 5 - 2x$

$$y = \frac{5}{3} - \frac{2}{3}x$$

2. $x(y + 1) = 4$

$$y + 1 = \frac{4}{x}, x \neq 0$$

$$y = \frac{4}{x} - 1$$

3. $(3x + 2)(x - 1) = 0$

$3x + 2 = 0$ or $x - 1 = 0$

$3x = -2$ $\qquad x = 1$

$$x = -\frac{2}{3}$$

4. $x = \dfrac{-5 \pm \sqrt{5^2 - 4(2)(-10)}}{4}$

$$= \frac{-5 \pm \sqrt{105}}{4}$$

$$x = \frac{-5 + \sqrt{105}}{4}, \frac{-5 - \sqrt{105}}{4}$$

5. $x^3 - 4x = 0$

$x(x^2 - 4) = 0$

$x(x - 2)(x + 2) = 0$

$x = 0, x = 2, x = -2$

6. $x^3 + x^2 - 6x = 0$

$x(x^2 + x - 6) = 0$

$x(x + 3)(x - 2) = 0$

$x = 0, x = -3, x = 2$

7. $m = -\dfrac{4}{5}, y - 2 = -\dfrac{4}{5}(x + 1)$

$$y = -\frac{4}{5}x - \frac{4}{5} + 2$$

$$y = \frac{-4x + 6}{5}$$

8. $m = \dfrac{5}{4}, \quad y - 2 = \dfrac{5}{4}(x + 1)$

$$y = \frac{5}{4}x + \frac{5}{4} + 2$$

$$y = \frac{5x + 13}{4}$$

9. $-2(2x + 3y) = -2(5)$

$-4x - 6y = -10$

10.

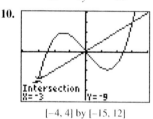   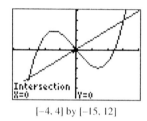

[−4, 4] by [−15, 12]   [−4, 4] by [−15, 12]

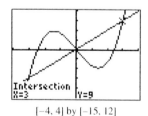

[−4, 4] by [−15, 12]

Section 7.1 Exercises

1. (a) No: $5(0) - 2(4) \neq 8$.

  (b) Yes: $5(2) - 2(1) = 8$ and $2(2) - 3(1) = 1$.

  (c) No: $2(-2) - 3(-9) \neq 1$.

2. (a) Yes: $-3 = 2^2 - 6(2) + 5$ and $-3 = 2(2) - 7$.

  (b) No: $-5 \neq 1^2 - 6(1) + 5$.

  (c) Yes: $5 = 6^2 - 6(6) + 5$ and $5 = 2(6) - 7$.

In #3–12, there may be more than one good way to choose the variable for which the substitution will be made. One approach is given. In most cases, the solution is only shown up to the point where the value of the first variable is found.

3. $(x, y) = (9, -2)$: Since $y = -2$, we have $x - 4 = 5$, so $x = 9$.

4. $(x, y) = (3, -17)$: Since $x = 3$, we have $3 - y = 20$, so $y = -17$.

5. $(x, y) = \left(\dfrac{50}{7}, -\dfrac{10}{7}\right)$: $y = 20 - 3x$,

so $x - 2(20 - 3x) = 10$, or $7x = 50$, so $x = \dfrac{50}{7}$.

6. $(x, y) = \left(-\dfrac{23}{5}, \dfrac{23}{5}\right)$: $y = -x$,

so $2x + 3x = -23$, or $x = -\dfrac{23}{5}$.

7. $(x, y) = \left(-\dfrac{1}{2}, 2\right)$: $x = (3y - 7)/2$,

so $2(3y - 7) + 5y = 8$, or $11y = 22$, so $y = 2$.

8. $(x, y) = (-3, 2)$: $x = (5y - 16)/2$, so
$1.5(5y - 16) + 2y = -5$, or $9.5y = 19$, so $y = 2$.

9. No solution: $x = 3y + 6$, so $-2(3y + 6) + 6y = 4$,
or $-12 = 4$ — not true.

10. There are infinitely many solutions, any pair $(x, 3x + 2)$:
From the first equation, $y = 3x + 2$, so $-9x +$
$3(3x + 2) = 6$, or $6 = 6$ — always true.

11. $(x, y) = (\pm3, 9)$; The second equation gives $y = 9$,
so, $x^2 = 9$, or $x = \pm3$.

12. $(x, y) = (0, -3)$ or $(x, y) = (4, 1)$: Since $x = y + 3$,
we have $y + 3 - y^2 = 3y$, or $y^2 + 2y - 3 = 0$.
Therefore $y = -3$ or $y = 1$.

13. $(x, y) = \left(-\dfrac{3}{2}, \dfrac{27}{2}\right)$ or $(x, y) = \left(\dfrac{1}{3}, \dfrac{2}{3}\right)$:

$6x^2 + 7x - 3 = 0$, so $x = -\dfrac{3}{2}$ or $x = \dfrac{1}{3}$. Substitute these

values into $y = 6x^2$.

14. $(x, y) = (-4, 28)$ or $(x, y) = \left(\dfrac{5}{2}, 15\right)$:

$2x^2 + 3x - 20 = 0$, so $x = -4$ or $x = \dfrac{5}{2}$.

Substitute these values into $y = 2x^2 + x$.

15. $(x, y) = (0, 0)$ or $(x, y) = (3, 18)$: $3x^2 = x^3$, so $x = 0$ or
$x = 3$. Substitute these values into $y = 2x^2$.

16. $(x, y) = (0, 0)$ or $(x, y) = (-2, -4)$: $x^3 + 2x^2 = 0$, so
$x = 0$ or $x = -2$. Substitute these values into $y = -x^2$.

17. $(x, y) = \left(\dfrac{-1 + 3\sqrt{89}}{10}, \dfrac{3 + \sqrt{89}}{10}\right)$ and

$\left(\dfrac{-1 - 3\sqrt{89}}{10}, \dfrac{3 - \sqrt{89}}{10}\right)$: $x - 3y = -1$, so $x = 3y + 1$.

Substitute $x = 3y + 1$ into $x^2 + y^2 = 9$:
$(3y - 1)^2 + y^2 = 9 \Rightarrow 10y^2 - 6y - 8 = 0$. Using the

quadratic formula, we find that $y = \dfrac{3 \pm \sqrt{89}}{10}$.

18. $(x, y) = \left(\dfrac{52 + 7\sqrt{871}}{65}, \dfrac{91 - 4\sqrt{871}}{65}\right)$

$\approx (3.98, -0.42)$ or

$(x, y) = \left(\dfrac{52 - 7\sqrt{871}}{65}, \dfrac{91 + 4\sqrt{871}}{65}\right)$

$\approx (-2.38, 3.22)$: $\dfrac{1}{16}(13 - 7y)^2 + y^2 = 16$, so

$65y^2 - 182y - 87 = 0$. Then $y = \dfrac{1}{65}(91 \pm 4\sqrt{871})$.

Substitute into $x = \dfrac{1}{4}(13 - 7y)$ to get

$$x = \frac{1}{65}(52 \mp 7\sqrt{871}).$$

In the following, $\mathbf{E_1}$ and $\mathbf{E_2}$ refer to the first and second
equations, respectively.

19. $(x, y) = (8, -2)$: $\mathbf{E_1} + \mathbf{E_2}$ leaves $2x = 16$,
so $x = 8$.

20. $(x, y) = (3, 4)$: $2\mathbf{E_1} + \mathbf{E_2}$ leaves $5x = 15$,
so $x = 3$.

21. $(x, y) = (4, 2)$: $2\mathbf{E_1} + \mathbf{E_2}$ leaves $11x = 44$,
so $x = 44$.

22. $(x, y) = (-2, 3)$: $4\mathbf{E_1} + 5\mathbf{E_2}$ leaves $31x = -62$,
so $x = -2$.

23. No solution: $3\mathbf{E_1} + 2\mathbf{E_2}$ leaves $0 = -72$, which is false.

24. There are infinitely many solutions, any pair $\left(x, \dfrac{1}{2}x - 2\right)$:

$\mathbf{E_1} + 2\mathbf{E_2}$ leaves $0 = 0$, which is always true. As long as
(x, y) satisfies one equation, it will also satisfy the other.

25. There are infinitely many solutions, any pair $\left(x, \dfrac{2}{3}x - \dfrac{5}{3}\right)$:

$3\mathbf{E_1} + \mathbf{E_2}$ leaves $0 = 0$, which is always true. As long as
(x, y) satisfies one equation, it will also satisfy the other.

26. No solution: $2\mathbf{E_1} + \mathbf{E_2}$ leaves $0 = 11$, which is false.

27. $(x, y) = (0, 1)$ or $(x, y) = (3, -2)$

28. $(x, y) = (1.5, 1)$

29. No solution

30. $(x, y) = (0, -4)$ or $(x, y) = (\pm\sqrt{7}, 3) \approx (\pm2.65, 3)$

31. One solution

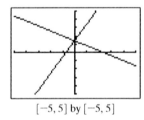

$[-5, 5]$ by $[-5, 5]$

32. No solution

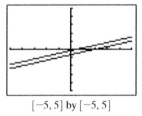

$[-5, 5]$ by $[-5, 5]$

33. Infinitely many solutions

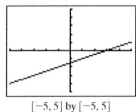

$[-5, 5]$ by $[-5, 5]$

34. One solution

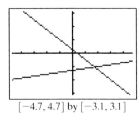

$[-4.7, 4.7]$ by $[-3.1, 3.1]$

35. $(x, y) \approx (0.69, -0.37)$

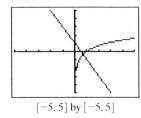

$[-5, 5]$ by $[-5, 5]$

36. $(x, y) \approx (1.13, 1.27)$

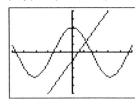

37. $(x, y) \approx (-2.32, -3.16)$ or $(0.47, -1.77)$ or $(1.85, -1.08)$

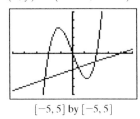

$[-5, 5]$ by $[-5, 5]$

38. $(x, y) \approx (-0.70, -2.40)$ or $(5.70, 10.40)$

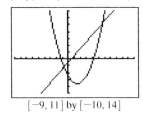

$[-9, 11]$ by $[-10, 14]$

39. $(x, y) = (-1.2, 1.6)$ or $(2, 0)$

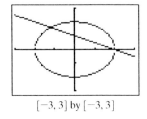

$[-3, 3]$ by $[-3, 3]$

40. $(x, y) \approx (-1.2, -1.6)$ or $(2, 0)$

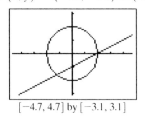

$[-4.7, 4.7]$ by $[-3.1, 3.1]$

41. $(x, y) \approx (2.05, 2.19)$ or $(-2.05, 2.19)$

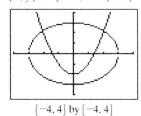

$[-4, 4]$ by $[-4, 4]$

42. $(x, y) \approx (2.05, -2.19)$ or $(-2.05, -2.19)$

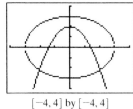

$[-4, 4]$ by $[-4, 4]$

43. $(x, p) = (3.75, 143.75)$: $200 - 15x = 50 + 25x$, so $40x = 150$.

44. $(x, p) = (130, 5.9)$: $15 - 0.07x = 2 + 0.03x$, so $0.10x = 13$.

45. In this problem, the graphs are representative of the expenditures (in billions of dollars) for benefits and administrative costs from federal hospital and medical insurance trust funds for several years, where x is the number of years past 1980.

(a) The following is a scatter plot of the data with the quadratic regression equation $y = -0.0938x^2 + 15.0510x - 28.2375$ superimposed on it.

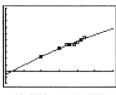

$[0, 30]$ by $[-100, 500]$

(b) The following is a scatter plot of the data with the logistic regression equation $y = \dfrac{353.6473}{(1 + 8.6873e^{-0.1427x})}$ superimposed on it.

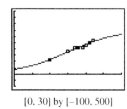

$[0, 30]$ by $[-100, 500]$

(c) Quadratic regression model

Graphical solution: Graph the line $y = 300$ with the quadratic regression curve
$y = -0.0938x^2 + 15.0510x - 28.2375$ and find the intersection of the two curves. The two intersect at $x \approx 26.03$. The expenditures will be 300 billion dollars sometime in the year 2006.

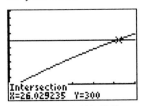

[0, 30] by [-100, 500]

Another graphical solution would be to find where the graph of the difference of the two curves is equal to 0. Note: The quadratic and the line intersect in two points, but the second point is an unrealistic answer. This would be sometime in the year 2114.

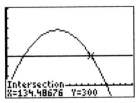

[0, 200] by [-100, 800]

Algebraic solution: Solve
$300 = -0.0938x^2 + 15.0510x - 28.2375$ for x.
Use the quadratic formula to solve the equation
$-0.0938x^2 + 15.0510x - 328.2375 = 0$.
$a = -0.0938 \qquad b = 15.0510 \qquad c = -328.2375$

$$x = \frac{-(15.0510) \pm \sqrt{(15.0510)^2 - 4(-0.0938)(-328.2375)}}{2(-0.0938)}$$

$$x = \frac{-(15.0510) \pm \sqrt{226.5326 - 123.1547}}{-0.1876}$$

$$= \frac{-(15.0510) \pm 10.1675}{-0.1876}$$

$x \approx 26.03$ and $x \approx 134.43$
We select $x = 26.03$, which indicates that the expenditures will be 300 billion dollars sometime in the year 2006.

Logistic regression model

Graphical solution: Graph the line $y = 300$ with the logistic regression curve $y = \dfrac{353.6473}{(1 + 8.6873e^{-0.1427x})}$ and find the intersection of the two curves. The two intersect at $x \approx 27.21$.
The expenditures will be 300 billion dollars sometime in the year 2007.

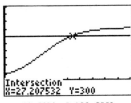

[0, 50] by [-100, 500]

Another graphical solution would be to find where the graph of the difference of the two curves is equal to 0.

Algebraic solution: Solve $300 = \dfrac{353.6473}{(1 + 8.6873e^{-0.1427x})}$ for x.

$$300(1 + 8.86873e^{-0.1427x}) = 353.6473$$

$$8.8687e^{-0.1427x} = \frac{353.6473}{300} - 1$$

$$8.8687e^{-0.1427x} = 1.1788 - 1 = 0.1788$$

$$e^{-0.1427x} = \frac{0.1788}{8.8687} = 0.0202$$

$$-0.1427x = \ln 0.0202$$

$$x = \frac{\ln 0.0202}{-0.1427} \approx 27.34$$

The expenditures will be 300 billion dollars sometime in the year 2007.

(d) The long-range implication of using the quadratic regression equation is that the expenditures will eventually fall to zero.
(The graph of the function is a parabola with vertex at about (80, 576) and it opens downward. So, eventually the curve will cross the x-axis and the expenditures will be 0. This will happen when $x \approx 158$.)

(e) The long-range implication of using the logistic regression equation is that the expenditures will eventually level off at about 354 billion dollars.
(We notice that as x gets larger, $e^{-0.1427x}$ approaches 0. Therefore, the denominator of the function approaches 1 and the function itself approaches 353.65, which is about 354.)

46. In this problem, the graphs are representative of the total personal income (in billions of dollars) for residents of the states of (a) Iowa and (b) Nevada for several years, where x is the number of years past 1990.

(a) The following is a scatter plot of the Iowa data with the linear regression equation $y = 2.8763x + 48.4957$ superimposed on it.

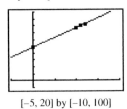

[-5, 20] by [-10, 100]

(b) The following is a scatter plot of the Nevada data with the linear regression equation $y = 3.5148x + 25.0027$ superimposed on it.

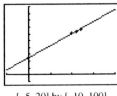

[-5, 20] by [-10, 100]

(c) *Graphical solution:* Graph the two linear equations $y = 2.8763x + 48.4957$ and $y = 3.5148x + 25.0027$ on the same axes and find the point of intersection. The two curves intersect at $x \approx 36.8$.

The personal incomes of the two states will be the same sometime in the year 2026.

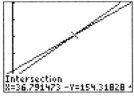

[–5, 70] by [–10, 250]

Another graphical solution would be to find where the graph of the difference of the two curves is equal to 0.

Algebraic solution:
Solve $2.8763x + 48.4957 = 3.5148x + 25.0027$ for x.
$$2.8763x + 48.4957 = 3.5148x + 25.0027$$
$$0.6385x = 23.4930$$
$$x = \frac{23.4930}{0.6385} \approx 36.8$$

The personal incomes of the two states will be the same sometime in the year 2026.

47. In this problem, the graphs are representative of the population (in thousands) of the states of Arizona and Massachusetts for several years, where x is the number of years past 1980.

(a) The following is a scatter plot of the Arizona data with the linear regression equation $y = 127.6351x + 2587.0010$ superimposed on it.

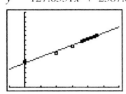

[–5, 30] by [0, 8000]

(b) The following is a scatter plot of the Massachusetts data with the linear regression equation $y = 31.3732x + 5715.9742$ superimposed on it.

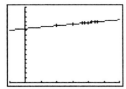

[–5, 30] by [0, 8000]

(c) *Graphical solution:* Graph the two linear equations $y = 127.6351x + 2587.0010$ and $y = 31.3732x + 5715.9742$ on the same axes and find the point of intersection. The two curves intersect at $x \approx 32.5$.
The population of the two states will be the same sometime in the year 2012.

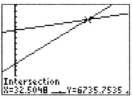

[–5, 50] by [0, 8000]

Another graphical solution would be to find where the graph of the difference of the two curves is equal to 0.

Algebraic solution:
Solve $127.6351x + 2587.0010 = 31.3732x + 5715.9742$ for x.
$$127.6351x + 2587.0010 = 31.3732x + 5715.9742$$
$$96.2619x = 3128.9732$$
$$x = \frac{3128.9732}{96.2619} \approx 32.5$$

The population of the two states will be the same sometime in the year 2012.

48. (a) None: the line never crosses the circle.
One: the line touches the circle at only one point—a tangent line.
Two: the line intersects the circle at two points.

(b) None: the parabola never crosses the circle.
One, two, three, or four: the parabola touches the circle in one, two, three or four points.

49. $200 = 2(x + y)$ and $500 = xy$. Then $y = 100 - x$, so $500 = x(100 - x)$, and therefore $x = 50 \pm 20\sqrt{5}$, and $y = 50 \mp 20\sqrt{5}$. Both answers correspond to a rectangle with approximate dimensions 5.28 m $\times$ 94.72 m.

50. $220 = 2(x + y)$ and $3000 = xy$. Then $y = 110 - x$, so $3000 = x(110 - x)$, and therefore $x = 50$ or 60. That means $y = 60$ or 50; the rectangle has dimensions 50 yd $\times$ 60 yd.

51. If r is Hank's rowing speed (in miles per hour) and c is the speed of the current, $\frac{24}{60}(r - c) = 1$ and $\frac{13}{60}(r + c) = 1$. Therefore $r = c + \frac{5}{2}$ (from the first equation); substituting gives $\frac{13}{60}\left(2c + \frac{5}{2}\right) = 1$, so $2c = \frac{60}{13} - \frac{5}{2} = \frac{55}{26}$, and $c = \frac{55}{52} \approx 1.06$ mph. Finally, $r = c + \frac{5}{2} = \frac{185}{52} \approx 3.56$ mph.

52. If x is airplane's speed (in miles per hour) and y is the wind speed, $4.4(x - y) = 2500$ and $3.75(x + y) = 2500$. Therefore $x = y + 568.18$; substituting gives $3.75(2y + 568.18) = 2500$, so $2y = 98.48$, and $y = 49.24$ mph. Finally, $x = y + 568.18 = 617.42$ mph.

53. $m + \ell = 1.74$ and $\ell = m + 0.16$, so $2m + 0.16 = 1.74$. Then $m = \$0.79$ (79 cents) and $\ell = \$0.95$ (95 cents).

54. $p + c = 5$ and $1.70p + 4.55c = 2.80 \cdot 5$. Then
$1.70(5 - c) + 4.55c = 14$, so $2.85c = 5.5$. That means
$c = \dfrac{110}{57} \approx 1.93$ lb of cashews and $p = \dfrac{175}{57} \approx 3.07$ lb of
peanuts.

55. $4 = -a + b$ and $6 = 2a + b$, so $b = a + 4$ and
$6 = 3a + 4$. Then $a = \dfrac{2}{3}$ and $b = \dfrac{14}{3}$.

56. $2a - b = 8$ and $-4a - 6b = 8$, so $b = 2a - 8$ and
$8 = -4a - 6(2a - 8) = -16a + 48$. Then
$a = \dfrac{40}{16} = \dfrac{5}{2}$ and $b = -3$.

57. (a) Let $C(x)$ = the amount charged by each rental
company, and let x = the number of miles driven
by Pedro.
Company A: $C(x) = 40 + 0.10x$
Company B: $C(x) = 25 + 0.15x$
Solving these two equations for x,
$$40 + 0.10x = 25 + 0.15x$$
$$15 = 0.05x$$
$$300 = x$$
Pedro can drive 300 miles to be charged the same
amount by the two companies.

(b) One possible answer: If Pedro is making only a short
trip, Company B is better because the flat fee is less.
However, if Pedro drives the rental van over 300 miles,
Company A's plan is more economical for his needs.

58. (a) Let $S(x)$ = Stephanie's salary, and let x = total sales
from household appliances sold weekly.
Plan A: $S(x) = 300 + 0.05x$
Plan B: $S(x) = 600 + 0.01x$
Solving these equations, we find:
$$300 + 0.05x = 600 + 0.01x$$
$$0.04x = 300$$
$$x = 7500$$
Stephanie's sales must be exactly \$7500 for the plans
to provide the same salary.

(b) One possible answer: If Stephanie expects that her
sales will generally be above \$7500 each week, then
Plan A provides a better salary. If she believes that
sales will not reach \$7500/week, however, Plan B will
maximize her salary.

59. False. A system of two linear equations in two variables
has either 0, 1, or infinitely many solutions.

60. False. The system would have no solutions, because any
solution of the original system would have to be a solution of $7 = 0$, which has no solutions.

61. Using $(x, y) = (3, -2)$,
$$2(3) - 3(-2) = 12$$
$$3 + 2(-2) = -1$$
The answer is C.

62. A parabola and a circle can intersect in at most 4 places.
The answer is E.

63. Two parabolas can intersect in 0, 1, 2, 3, or 4 places, or
infinitely many places if the parabolas completely
coincide. The answer is D.

64. When the solution process leads to an identity (an equation that is true for all (x, y), the original system has
infinitely many solutions. The answer is E.

65. (a)
$$\frac{x^2}{4} + \frac{y^2}{9} = 1$$
$$9x^2 + 4y^2 = 36$$
$$4y^2 = 36 - 9x^2$$
$$y^2 = \frac{36 - 9x^2}{4}$$
$$y = \frac{3}{2}\sqrt{4 - x^2}, \ y = -\frac{3}{2}\sqrt{4 - x^2}$$

(b)

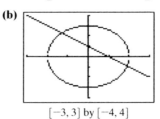

$[-3, 3]$ by $[-4, 4]$

$(x, y) \approx (-1.29, 2.29)$ or $(1.91, -0.91)$

(c) $\dfrac{(-1.29)^2}{4} + \dfrac{(2.29)^2}{9} \approx 0.9987 \approx 1$ and
$(-1.29) + (2.29) = 1$, so the first solution checks.
$\dfrac{(1.91)^2}{4} + \dfrac{(-0.91)^2}{9} \approx 1.004 \approx 1$ and
$(1.91) + (-0.91) = 1$, so the second solution checks.

66. (a)
$$\frac{x^2}{4} - \frac{y^2}{9} = 1$$
$$-9x^2 + 4y^2 = -36$$
$$4y^2 = 9x^2 - 36$$
$$y^2 = \frac{9x^2 - 36}{4}$$
$$y = \frac{3}{2}\sqrt{x^2 - 4}, \ y = -\frac{3}{2}\sqrt{x^2 - 4}$$

(b)

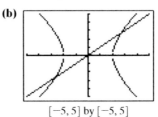

$[-5, 5]$ by $[-5, 5]$

$(x, y) \approx (2.68, 2.68)$ or $(-2.68, -2.68)$

(c) $\dfrac{(2.68)^2}{4} - \dfrac{(2.68)^2}{9} = \dfrac{(-2.68)^2}{4} - \dfrac{(-2.68)^2}{9}$
$\approx 0.9976 \approx 1$, so both solutions check.

67. Subtract the second equation from the first, leaving
$-3y = -10$, or $y = \dfrac{10}{3}$. Then $x^2 = 4 - \dfrac{10}{3} = \dfrac{2}{3}$, so
$x = \pm\sqrt{\dfrac{2}{3}}$.

68. Add the two equations to get $2x^2 = 2$, so $x^2 = 1$, and
therefore $x = \pm 1$. Then $y = 0$.

69. The vertex of the parabola $R = (100 - 4x)x$
$= 4x(25 - x)$ has first coordinate $x = 12.5$ units.

70. The local maximum of $R = x(80 - x^2) = 80x - x^3$
has first coordinate $x \approx 5.16$ units.

■ Section 7.2 Matrix Algebra

Exploration 1

1. $a_{11} = 3(1) - (1) = 2$ Set $i = j = 1$.
$a_{12} = 3(1) - (2) = 1$ Set $i = 1, j = 2$.
$a_{21} = 3(2) - (1) = 5$ Set $i = 2, j = 1$.
$a_{22} = 3(2) - (2) = 4$ Set $i = j = 2$.

So, $A = \begin{bmatrix} 2 & 1 \\ 5 & 4 \end{bmatrix}$. Similar computations show that

$B = \begin{bmatrix} -1 & 2 \\ 2 & 5 \end{bmatrix}$.

2. The additive inverse of A is $-A$ and
$-A = \begin{bmatrix} -2 & -1 \\ -5 & -4 \end{bmatrix}$.

$A + (-A) = \begin{bmatrix} 2 & 1 \\ 5 & 4 \end{bmatrix} + \begin{bmatrix} -2 & -1 \\ -5 & -4 \end{bmatrix} = \begin{bmatrix} 0 & 0 \\ 0 & 0 \end{bmatrix} = [0]$

The order of $[0]$ is 2×2.

3. $3A - 2B = 3\begin{bmatrix} 2 & 1 \\ 5 & 4 \end{bmatrix} - 2\begin{bmatrix} -1 & 2 \\ 2 & 5 \end{bmatrix}$

$= \begin{bmatrix} 6 & 3 \\ 15 & 12 \end{bmatrix} - \begin{bmatrix} -2 & 4 \\ 4 & 10 \end{bmatrix} = \begin{bmatrix} 8 & -1 \\ 11 & 2 \end{bmatrix}$

Exploration 2

1. $\det(A) = -a_{12}\,a_{21}\,a_{33} + a_{13}\,a_{21}\,a_{32} + a_{11}\,a_{22}\,a_{33}$
$- a_{13}\,a_{22}\,a_{31} - a_{11}\,a_{23}\,a_{32} + a_{12}\,a_{23}\,a_{31}$
Each element contains an element from each row and each column due to a definition of a determinant. Regardless of the row or column "picked" to apply the definition, all other elements of the matrix are eventually factored into the multiplication.

2. $\begin{vmatrix} a_{11} & a_{12} & a_{13} \\ a_{21} & a_{22} & a_{23} \\ a_{31} & a_{32} & a_{33} \end{vmatrix} = a_{11}(-1)^2\begin{vmatrix} a_{22} & a_{23} \\ a_{32} & a_{33} \end{vmatrix}$

$+ a_{12}(-1)^3\begin{vmatrix} a_{21} & a_{23} \\ a_{31} & a_{33} \end{vmatrix} + a_{13}(-1)^4\begin{vmatrix} a_{21} & a_{22} \\ a_{31} & a_{32} \end{vmatrix}$

$= a_{11}(a_{22}a_{33} - a_{23}a_{32}) - a_{12}(a_{21}a_{33} - a_{23}a_{31})$
$+ a_{13}(a_{21}a_{32} - a_{22}a_{31})$
$= a_{11}a_{22}a_{33} - a_{11}a_{23}a_{32} - a_{12}a_{21}a_{33} + a_{12}a_{23}a_{31}$
$+ a_{13}a_{21}a_{32} - a_{13}a_{22}a_{31}$
The two expressions are exactly equal.

3. Recall that A_{ij} is $(-1)^{i+j}M_{ij}$ where M_{ij} is the determinant of the matrix obtained by deleting the row and column containing a_{ij}. Let $A = k \times k$ square matrix with zeros in the ith row. Then: $\det(A) =$

$i\text{th row} \rightarrow \begin{vmatrix} a_{11} & a_{12} & \cdots & a_{1k} \\ a_{21} & a_{22} & \cdots & a_{2k} \\ \vdots & \vdots & & \vdots \\ 0 & 0 & \cdots & 0 \\ \vdots & \vdots & & \vdots \\ a_{k1} & a_{k2} & \cdots & a_{kk} \end{vmatrix}$

$= 0 \cdot A_{i1} + 0 \cdot A_{i2} + \cdots + 0 \cdot A_{ik} = 0 + 0 + \cdots + 0$
$= 0$

Quick Review 7.2

1. (a) $(3, 2)$

(b) $(x, -y)$

2. (a) $(-3, -2)$

(b) $(-x, y)$

3. (a) $(-2, 3)$

(b) (y, x)

4. (a) $(2, -3)$

(b) $(-y, -x)$

5. $(3 \cos \theta, 3 \sin \theta)$

6. $(r \cos \theta, r \sin \theta)$

7. $\sin(\alpha + \beta) = \sin \alpha \cos \beta + \cos \alpha \sin \beta$

8. $\sin(\alpha - \beta) = \sin \alpha \cos \beta - \cos \alpha \sin \beta$

9. $\cos(\alpha + \beta) = \cos \alpha \cos \beta - \sin \alpha \sin \beta$

10. $\cos(\alpha - \beta) = \cos \alpha \cos \beta + \sin \alpha \sin \beta$

Section 7.2 Exercises

1. 2×3; not square

2. 2×2; square

3. 3×2; not square

4. 1×3; not square

5. 3×1; not square

6. 1×1; square

7. $a_{13} = 3$

8. $a_{24} = -1$

9. $a_{32} = 4$

10. $a_{33} = -1$

11. (a) $\begin{bmatrix} 3 & 0 \\ -3 & 1 \end{bmatrix}$

(b) $\begin{bmatrix} 1 & 6 \\ 1 & 9 \end{bmatrix}$

(c) $\begin{bmatrix} 6 & 9 \\ -3 & 15 \end{bmatrix}$

(d) $2A - 3B = 2\begin{bmatrix} 2 & 3 \\ -1 & 5 \end{bmatrix} - 3\begin{bmatrix} 1 & -3 \\ -2 & -4 \end{bmatrix} =$
$\begin{bmatrix} 4 & 6 \\ -2 & 10 \end{bmatrix} - \begin{bmatrix} 3 & -9 \\ -6 & -12 \end{bmatrix} = \begin{bmatrix} 1 & 15 \\ 4 & 22 \end{bmatrix}$

12. (a) $\begin{bmatrix} 1 & 1 & 2 \\ 3 & 1 & 1 \\ 6 & -3 & 0 \end{bmatrix}$

(b) $\begin{bmatrix} -3 & -1 & 2 \\ 5 & 1 & -3 \\ -2 & 3 & 2 \end{bmatrix}$

(c) $\begin{bmatrix} -3 & 0 & 6 \\ 12 & 3 & -3 \\ 6 & 0 & 3 \end{bmatrix}$

(d) $2A - 3B = 2\begin{bmatrix} -1 & 0 & 2 \\ 4 & 1 & -1 \\ 2 & 0 & 1 \end{bmatrix} - 3\begin{bmatrix} 2 & 1 & 0 \\ -1 & 0 & 2 \\ 4 & -3 & -1 \end{bmatrix}$

$= \begin{bmatrix} -2 & 0 & 4 \\ 8 & 2 & -2 \\ 4 & 0 & 2 \end{bmatrix} - \begin{bmatrix} 6 & 3 & 0 \\ -3 & 0 & 6 \\ 12 & -9 & -3 \end{bmatrix}$

$= \begin{bmatrix} -8 & -3 & 4 \\ 11 & 2 & -8 \\ -8 & 9 & 5 \end{bmatrix}$

13. (a) $\begin{bmatrix} 1 & 1 \\ -2 & 0 \\ -1 & 0 \end{bmatrix}$

(b) $\begin{bmatrix} -7 & 1 \\ 2 & -2 \\ 5 & 2 \end{bmatrix}$

(c) $\begin{bmatrix} -9 & 3 \\ 0 & -3 \\ 6 & 3 \end{bmatrix}$

(d) $2A - 3B = 2\begin{bmatrix} -3 & 1 \\ 0 & -1 \\ 2 & 1 \end{bmatrix} - 3\begin{bmatrix} 4 & 0 \\ -2 & 1 \\ -3 & -1 \end{bmatrix}$

$= \begin{bmatrix} -6 & 2 \\ 0 & -2 \\ 4 & 2 \end{bmatrix} - \begin{bmatrix} 12 & 0 \\ -6 & 3 \\ -9 & -3 \end{bmatrix} = \begin{bmatrix} -18 & 2 \\ 6 & -5 \\ 13 & 5 \end{bmatrix}$

14. (a) $\begin{bmatrix} 3 & 1 & 4 & 1 \\ 3 & 0 & 1 & 0 \end{bmatrix}$

(b) $\begin{bmatrix} 7 & -5 & 2 & 1 \\ -5 & 0 & 3 & 4 \end{bmatrix}$

(c) $\begin{bmatrix} 15 & -6 & 9 & 3 \\ -3 & 0 & 6 & 6 \end{bmatrix}$

(d) $2A - 3B = 2\begin{bmatrix} 5 & -2 & 3 & 1 \\ -1 & 0 & 2 & 2 \end{bmatrix} -$

$3\begin{bmatrix} -2 & 3 & 1 & 0 \\ 4 & 0 & -1 & -2 \end{bmatrix}$

$= \begin{bmatrix} 10 & -4 & 6 & 2 \\ -2 & 0 & 4 & 4 \end{bmatrix} -$

$\begin{bmatrix} -6 & 9 & 3 & 0 \\ 12 & 0 & -3 & -6 \end{bmatrix}$

$= \begin{bmatrix} 16 & -13 & 3 & 2 \\ -14 & 0 & 7 & 10 \end{bmatrix}$

15. (a) $\begin{bmatrix} -3 \\ 1 \\ 4 \end{bmatrix}$

(b) $\begin{bmatrix} -1 \\ 1 \\ -4 \end{bmatrix}$

(c) $\begin{bmatrix} -6 \\ 3 \\ 0 \end{bmatrix}$

(d) $2A - 3B = 2\begin{bmatrix} -2 \\ 1 \\ 0 \end{bmatrix} - 3\begin{bmatrix} -1 \\ 0 \\ 4 \end{bmatrix} = \begin{bmatrix} -4 \\ 2 \\ 0 \end{bmatrix} - \begin{bmatrix} -3 \\ 0 \\ 12 \end{bmatrix}$

$= \begin{bmatrix} -1 \\ 2 \\ -12 \end{bmatrix}$

16. (a) $[0 \quad 0 \quad -2 \quad 3]$

(b) $[-2 \quad -4 \quad 2 \quad 3]$

(c) $[-3 \quad -6 \quad 0 \quad 9]$

(d) $2A - 3B = 2[-1 \quad -2 \quad 0 \quad 3] - 3[1 \quad 2 \quad -2 \quad 0]$
$= [-2 \quad -4 \quad 0 \quad 6] - [3 \quad 6 \quad -6 \quad 0]$
$= [-5 \quad -10 \quad 6 \quad 6]$

17. (a) $AB = \begin{bmatrix} (2)(1) + (3)(-2) & (2)(-3) + (3)(-4) \\ (-1)(1) + (5)(-2) & (-1)(-3) + (5)(-4) \end{bmatrix} = \begin{bmatrix} -4 & -18 \\ -11 & -17 \end{bmatrix}$

(b) $BA = \begin{bmatrix} (1)(2) + (-3)(-1) & (1)(3) + (-3)(5) \\ (-2)(2) + (-4)(-1) & (-2)(3) + (-4)(5) \end{bmatrix} = \begin{bmatrix} 5 & -12 \\ 0 & -26 \end{bmatrix}$

18. (a) $AB = \begin{bmatrix} (1)(5) + (-4)(-2) & (1)(1) + (-4)(-3) \\ (2)(5) + (6)(-2) & (2)(1) + (6)(-3) \end{bmatrix} = \begin{bmatrix} 13 & 13 \\ -2 & -16 \end{bmatrix}$

(b) $BA = \begin{bmatrix} (5)(1) + (1)(2) & (5)(-4) + (1)(6) \\ (-2)(1) + (-3)(2) & (-2)(-4) + (-3)(6) \end{bmatrix} = \begin{bmatrix} 7 & -14 \\ -8 & -10 \end{bmatrix}$

19. (a) $AB = \begin{bmatrix} (2)(1) + (0)(-3) + (1)(0) & (2)(2) + (0)(1) + (1)(-2) \\ (1)(1) + (4)(-3) + (-3)(0) & (1)(2) + (4)(1) + (-3)(-2) \end{bmatrix} = \begin{bmatrix} 2 & 2 \\ -11 & 12 \end{bmatrix}$

(b) $BA = \begin{bmatrix} (1)(2) + (2)(1) & (1)(0) + (2)(4) & (1)(1) + (2)(-3) \\ (-3)(2) + (1)(1) & (-3)(0) + (1)(4) & (-3)(1) + (1)(-3) \\ (0)(2) + (-2)(1) & (0)(0) + (-2)(4) & (0)(1) + (-2)(-3) \end{bmatrix} = \begin{bmatrix} 4 & 8 & -5 \\ -5 & 4 & -6 \\ -2 & -8 & 6 \end{bmatrix}$

20. (a) $AB = \begin{bmatrix} (1)(5) + (0)(0) + (-2)(-1) + (3)(4) & (1)(-1) + (0)(2) + (-2)(3) + (3)(2) \\ (2)(5) + (1)(0) + (4)(-1) + (-1)(4) & (2)(-1) + (1)(2) + (4)(3) + (-1)(2) \end{bmatrix} = \begin{bmatrix} 19 & -1 \\ 2 & 10 \end{bmatrix}$

(b) $BA = \begin{bmatrix} (5)(1) + (-1)(2) & (5)(0) + (-1)(1) & (5)(-2) + (-1)(4) & (5)(3) + (-1)(-1) \\ (0)(1) + (2)(2) & (0)(0) + (2)(1) & (0)(-2) + (2)(4) & (0)(3) + (2)(-1) \\ (-1)(1) + (3)(2) & (-1)(0) + (3)(1) & (-1)(-2) + (3)(4) & (-1)(3) + (3)(-1) \\ (4)(1) + (2)(2) & (4)(0) + (2)(1) & (4)(-2) + (2)(4) & (4)(3) + (2)(-1) \end{bmatrix}$

$= \begin{bmatrix} 3 & -1 & -14 & 16 \\ 4 & 2 & 8 & -2 \\ 5 & 3 & 14 & -6 \\ 8 & 2 & 0 & 10 \end{bmatrix}$

21. (a) $AB = \begin{bmatrix} (-1)(2) + (0)(-1) + (2)(4) & (-1)(1) + (0)(0) + (2)(-3) & (-1)(0) + (0)(2) + (2)(-1) \\ (4)(2) + (1)(-1) + (-1)(4) & (4)(1) + (1)(0) + (-1)(-3) & (4)(0) + (1)(2) + (-1)(-1) \\ (2)(2) + (0)(-1) + (1)(4) & (2)(1) + (0)(0) + (1)(-3) & (2)(0) + (0)(2) + (1)(-1) \end{bmatrix}$

$= \begin{bmatrix} 6 & -7 & -2 \\ 3 & 7 & 3 \\ 8 & -1 & -1 \end{bmatrix}$

(b) $BA = \begin{bmatrix} (2)(-1) + (1)(4) + (0)(2) & (2)(0) + (1)(1) + (0)(0) & (2)(2) + (1)(-1) + (0)(1) \\ (-1)(-1) + (0)(4) + (2)(2) & (-1)(0) + (0)(1) + (2)(0) & (-1)(2) + (0)(-1) + (2)(1) \\ (4)(-1) + (-3)(4) + (-1)(2) & (4)(0) + (-3)(1) + (-1)(0) & (4)(2) + (-3)(-1) + (-1)(1) \end{bmatrix}$

$= \begin{bmatrix} 2 & 1 & 3 \\ 5 & 0 & 0 \\ -18 & -3 & 10 \end{bmatrix}$

22. (a) $AB = \begin{bmatrix} (-2)(4) + (3)(0) + (0)(-1) & (-2)(-1) + (3)(2) + (0)(3) & (-2)(2) + (3)(3) + (0)(-1) \\ (1)(4) + (-2)(0) + (4)(-1) & (1)(-1) + (-2)(2) + (4)(3) & (1)(2) + (-2)(3) + (4)(-1) \\ (3)(4) + (2)(0) + (1)(-1) & (3)(-1) + (2)(2) + (1)(3) & (3)(2) + (2)(3) + (1)(-1) \end{bmatrix}$

$= \begin{bmatrix} -8 & 8 & 5 \\ 0 & 7 & -8 \\ 11 & 4 & 11 \end{bmatrix}$

(b) $BA = \begin{bmatrix} (4)(-2) + (-1)(1) + (2)(3) & (4)(3) + (-1)(-2) + (2)(2) & (4)(0) + (-1)(4) + (2)(1) \\ (0)(-2) + (2)(1) + (3)(3) & (0)(3) + (2)(-2) + (3)(2) & (0)(0) + (2)(4) + (3)(1) \\ (-1)(-2) + (3)(1) + (-1)(3) & (-1)(3) + (3)(-2) + (-1)(2) & (-1)(0) + (3)(4) + (-1)(1) \end{bmatrix}$

$= \begin{bmatrix} -3 & 18 & -2 \\ 11 & 2 & 11 \\ 2 & -11 & 11 \end{bmatrix}$

23. (a) $AB = [(2)(-5) + (-1)(4) + (3)(2)] = [-8]$

(b) $BA = \begin{bmatrix} (-5)(2) & (-5)(-1) & (-5)(3) \\ (4)(2) & (4)(-1) & (4)(3) \\ (2)(2) & (2)(-1) & (2)(3) \end{bmatrix} = \begin{bmatrix} -10 & 5 & -15 \\ 8 & -4 & 12 \\ 4 & -2 & 6 \end{bmatrix}$

24. (a) $AB = \begin{bmatrix} (-2)(-1) & (-2)(2) & (-2)(4) \\ (3)(-1) & (3)(2) & (3)(4) \\ (-4)(-1) & (-4)(2) & (-4)(4) \end{bmatrix} = \begin{bmatrix} 2 & -4 & -8 \\ -3 & 6 & 12 \\ 4 & -8 & -16 \end{bmatrix}$

(b) $BA = [(-1)(-2) + (2)(3) + (4)(-4)] = [-8]$

25. (a) AB is not possible.

(b) $BA = [(-3)(-1) + (5)(3) \quad (-3)(2) + (5)(4)] = [18 \; 14]$

26. (a) $AB = \begin{bmatrix} (-1)(5) + (3)(2) & (-1)(-6) + (3)(3) \\ (0)(5) + (1)(2) & (0)(-6) + (1)(3) \\ (1)(5) + (0)(2) & (1)(-6) + (0)(3) \\ (-3)(5) + (-1)(2) & (-3)(-6) + (-1)(3) \end{bmatrix} = \begin{bmatrix} 1 & 15 \\ 2 & 3 \\ 5 & -6 \\ -17 & 15 \end{bmatrix}$

(b) BA is not possible.

27. (a) $AB = \begin{bmatrix} (0)(1) + (0)(2) + (1)(-1) & (0)(2) + (0)(0) + (1)(3) & (0)(1) + (0)(1) + (1)(4) \\ (0)(1) + (1)(2) + (0)(-1) & (0)(2) + (1)(0) + (0)(3) & (0)(1) + (1)(1) + (0)(4) \\ (1)(1) + (0)(2) + (0)(-1) & (1)(2) + (0)(0) + (0)(3) & (1)(1) + (0)(1) + (0)(4) \end{bmatrix} = \begin{bmatrix} -1 & 3 & 4 \\ 2 & 0 & 1 \\ 1 & 2 & 1 \end{bmatrix}$

(b) $BA = \begin{bmatrix} (1)(0) + (2)(0) + (1)(1) & (1)(0) + (2)(1) + (1)(0) & (1)(1) + (2)(0) + (1)(0) \\ (2)(0) + (0)(0) + (1)(1) & (2)(0) + (0)(1) + (1)(0) & (2)(1) + (0)(0) + (1)(0) \\ (-1)(0) + (3)(0) + (4)(1) & (-1)(0) + (3)(1) + (4)(0) & (-1)(1) + (3)(0) + (4)(0) \end{bmatrix} = \begin{bmatrix} 1 & 2 & 1 \\ 1 & 0 & 2 \\ 4 & 3 & -1 \end{bmatrix}$

28. (a) $AB = \begin{bmatrix} 0 + 0 - 3 + 0 & 0 + 0 + 2 + 0 & 0 + 0 + 1 + 0 & 0 + 0 + 3 + 0 \\ 0 + 2 + 0 + 0 & 0 + 1 + 0 + 0 & 0 + 0 + 0 + 0 & 0 - 1 + 0 + 0 \\ -1 + 0 + 0 + 0 & 2 + 0 + 0 + 0 & 3 + 0 + 0 + 0 & -4 + 0 + 0 + 0 \\ 0 + 0 + 0 + 4 & 0 + 0 + 0 + 0 & 0 + 0 + 0 + 2 & 0 + 0 + 0 - 1 \end{bmatrix} = \begin{bmatrix} -3 & 2 & 1 & 3 \\ 2 & 1 & 0 & -1 \\ -1 & 2 & 3 & -4 \\ 4 & 0 & 2 & -1 \end{bmatrix}$

(b) $BA = \begin{bmatrix} 0 + 0 + 3 + 0 & 0 + 2 + 0 + 0 & -1 + 0 + 0 + 0 & 0 + 0 + 0 - 4 \\ 0 + 0 + 0 + 0 & 0 + 1 + 0 + 0 & 2 + 0 + 0 + 0 & 0 + 0 + 0 - 1 \\ 0 + 0 + 1 + 0 & 0 + 2 + 0 + 0 & -3 + 0 + 0 + 0 & 0 + 0 + 0 + 3 \\ 0 + 0 + 2 + 0 & 0 + 0 + 0 + 0 & 4 + 0 + 0 + 0 & 0 + 0 + 0 - 1 \end{bmatrix} = \begin{bmatrix} 3 & 2 & -1 & -4 \\ 0 & 1 & 2 & -1 \\ 1 & 2 & -3 & 3 \\ 2 & 0 & 4 & -1 \end{bmatrix}$

In #29–32, use the fact that two matrices are equal only if all entries are equal.

29. $a = 5, b = 2$

30. $a = 3, b = -1$

31. $a = -2, b = 0$

32. $a = 1, b = 6$

33. $AB = \begin{bmatrix} (2)(0.8) + (1)(-0.6) & (2)(-0.2) + (1)(0.4) \\ (3)(0.8) + (4)(-0.6) & (3)(-0.2) + (4)(0.4) \end{bmatrix} = \begin{bmatrix} 1 & 0 \\ 0 & 1 \end{bmatrix}$,

$BA = \begin{bmatrix} (0.8)(2) + (-0.2)(3) & (0.8)(1) + (-0.2)(4) \\ (-0.2)(2) + (0.4)(3) & (0.6)(1) + (-0.4)(4) \end{bmatrix} = \begin{bmatrix} 1 & 0 \\ 0 & 1 \end{bmatrix}$, so A and B are inverses.

34. $AB = \begin{bmatrix} (-2)(0) + (1)(0.25) + 3(0.25) & (-2)(1) + (1)(0.5) + (3)(0.5) & (-2)(-2) + (1)(-0.25) + (3)(-1.25) \\ (1)(0) + (2)(0.25) + (-2)(0.25) & (1)(1) + (2)(0.5) + (-2)(0.5) & (1)(-2) + (2)(-0.25) + (-2)(-1.25) \\ (0)(0) + (1)(0.25) + (-1)(0.25) & (0)(1) + (1)(0.5) + (-1)(0.5) & (0)(-2) + (1)(-0.25) + (-1)(-1.25) \end{bmatrix}$

$= \begin{bmatrix} 1 & 0 & 0 \\ 0 & 1 & 0 \\ 0 & 0 & 1 \end{bmatrix}$

$BA = \begin{bmatrix} (0)(-2) + (1)(1) + (-2)(0) & (0)(1) + (1)(2) + (-2)(1) \\ (0.25)(-2) + (0.5)(1) + (-0.25)(0) & (0.25)(1) + (0.5)(2) + (-0.25)(1) \\ (0.25)(-2) + (0.5)(1) + (-1.25)(0) & (0.25)(1) + (0.5)(2) + (-1.25)(1) \end{bmatrix}$

$\begin{matrix} (0)(3) + (1)(-2) + (-2)(-1) \\ (0.25)(3) + (0.5)(-2) + (-0.25)(-1) \\ (0.25)(3) + (0.5)(-2) + (-1.25)(-1) \end{matrix}$

$= \begin{bmatrix} 1 & 0 & 0 \\ 0 & 1 & 0 \\ 0 & 0 & 1 \end{bmatrix}$, so A and B are inverses.

35. $\begin{bmatrix} 2 & 3 \\ 2 & 2 \end{bmatrix}^{-1} = \dfrac{1}{(2)(2) - (2)(3)} \begin{bmatrix} 2 & -3 \\ -2 & 2 \end{bmatrix}$

$= -\dfrac{1}{2} \begin{bmatrix} 2 & -3 \\ -2 & 2 \end{bmatrix} = \begin{bmatrix} -1 & 1.5 \\ 1 & -1 \end{bmatrix}$

36. No inverse: The determinant is $(6)(5) - (10)(3) = 0$.

37. No inverse: The determinant (found with a calculator) is 0.

38. Using a calculator: $\begin{bmatrix} 2 & 3 & -1 \\ -1 & 0 & 4 \\ 0 & 1 & 1 \end{bmatrix}^{-1}$

$= \begin{bmatrix} 1 & 1 & -3 \\ -0.25 & -0.5 & 1.75 \\ 0.25 & 0.5 & -0.75 \end{bmatrix}$;

to confirm, carry out the multiplication.

39. $A = \begin{bmatrix} 1 & -1 & 1 & -1 \\ -1 & 1 & -1 & 1 \\ 1 & -1 & 1 & -1 \\ -1 & 1 & -1 & 1 \end{bmatrix}$;

No inverse, $\det(A) = 0$ (found using a calculator)

40. $B = \begin{bmatrix} 0 & 1 & 2 \\ 1 & 0 & 1 \\ 2 & 1 & 0 \end{bmatrix}$

$B^{-1} = \begin{bmatrix} -0.25 & 0.5 & 0.25 \\ 0.5 & -1.0 & 0.5 \\ 0.25 & 0.5 & -0.25 \end{bmatrix}$

(found using a calculator, use multiplication to confirm)

41. Use row 2 or column 2 since they have the greatest number of zeros. Using column 2:

$\begin{vmatrix} 2 & 1 & 1 \\ -1 & 0 & 2 \\ 1 & 3 & -1 \end{vmatrix} = (1)(-1)^3 \begin{vmatrix} -1 & 2 \\ 1 & -1 \end{vmatrix}$

$+ (0)(-1)^4 \begin{vmatrix} 2 & 1 \\ 1 & -1 \end{vmatrix} + (3)(-1)^5 \begin{vmatrix} 2 & 1 \\ -1 & 2 \end{vmatrix}$

$= (-1)(1 - 2) + 0 + (-3)(4 + 1)$

$= 1 + 0 - 15$

$= -14$

42. Use row 1 or 4 or column 2 or 3 since they have the greatest number of zeros. Using column 3:

$\begin{vmatrix} 1 & 0 & 2 & 0 \\ 0 & 1 & 2 & 3 \\ 1 & -1 & 0 & 2 \\ 1 & 0 & 0 & 3 \end{vmatrix} = (2)(-1)^4 \begin{vmatrix} 0 & 1 & 3 \\ 1 & -1 & 2 \\ 1 & 0 & 3 \end{vmatrix}$

$+ (2)(-1)^5 \begin{vmatrix} 1 & 0 & 0 \\ 1 & -1 & 2 \\ 1 & 0 & 3 \end{vmatrix} + 0 + 0$

$= 2 \cdot \left[0 + 1(-1)^3 \begin{vmatrix} 1 & 3 \\ 0 & 3 \end{vmatrix} + 1(-1)^4 \begin{vmatrix} 1 & 3 \\ -1 & 2 \end{vmatrix} \right]$

$- 2 \left[1(-1)^2 \begin{vmatrix} -1 & 2 \\ 0 & 3 \end{vmatrix} + 0 + 0 \right]$

$= 2((-1)(3 - 0) + (1)(2 + 3)) - 2((1)(-3 - 0))$

$= 2(-3 + 5) - 2(-3)$

$= 4 + 6$

$= 10$

43. $3X = B - A$

$X = \dfrac{B-A}{3} = \dfrac{1}{3}\left(\begin{bmatrix}4\\2\end{bmatrix} - \begin{bmatrix}1\\3\end{bmatrix}\right) = \dfrac{1}{3}\begin{bmatrix}3\\-1\end{bmatrix} = \begin{bmatrix}1\\-\frac{1}{3}\end{bmatrix}$

44. $2X = B - A$

$X = \dfrac{B-A}{2} = \dfrac{1}{2}\left(\begin{bmatrix}1 & 4\\1 & -1\end{bmatrix} - \begin{bmatrix}-1 & 2\\0 & 3\end{bmatrix}\right)$

$= \dfrac{1}{2}\begin{bmatrix}2 & 2\\1 & -4\end{bmatrix}$

$= \begin{bmatrix}1 & 1\\\frac{1}{2} & -2\end{bmatrix}$

45. (a) The entries a_{ij} and a_{ji} are the same because each gives the distance between the same two cities.

(b) The entries a_{ii} are all 0 because the distance between a city and itself is 0.

46. $B = \begin{bmatrix}1.1\cdot120 & 1.1\cdot70\\1.1\cdot150 & 1.1\cdot110\\1.1\cdot80 & 1.1\cdot160\end{bmatrix} = \begin{bmatrix}132 & 77\\165 & 121\\88 & 176\end{bmatrix}$

$B = 1.1A$

47. (a) $B^T A = [\$0.80 \quad \$0.85 \quad \$1.00]\begin{bmatrix}100 & 60\\120 & 70\\200 & 120\end{bmatrix}$

$\begin{bmatrix}0.80(100) & 0.80(60)\\ +0.85(120) & +0.85(70)\\ 1(200) & +1(120)\end{bmatrix}$

$= [382 \quad 227.50]$

(b) b_{1j} in matrix $B^T A$ represents the income Happy Valley Farms makes at grocery store j, selling all three types of eggs.

48. (a) $SP = \begin{bmatrix}16 & 10 & 8 & 12\\12 & 0 & 10 & 14\\4 & 12 & 0 & 8\end{bmatrix}\begin{bmatrix}\$180 & \$269.99\\\$275 & \$399.99\\\$355 & \$499.99\\\$590 & \$799.99\end{bmatrix}$

$= \begin{bmatrix}\$15,550 & \$21,919.54\\\$8,070 & \$11,439.74\\\$8,740 & \$12,279.76\end{bmatrix}$

(b) The wholesale and retail values of all the inventory at store i are represented by a_{i1} and a_{i2}, respectively, in the matrix SP.

49. (a) Total revenue = sum of (price charged)(number sold)
$= AB^T$ or BA^T

(b) Profit = Total revenue $-$ Total Cost
$= AB^T - CB^T$
$= (A - C)B^T$

50. (a) $B = [6 \quad 7 \quad 14]$

(b) $BR = [6 \quad 7 \quad 14]\begin{bmatrix}5 & 22 & 14 & 7 & 17\\7 & 20 & 10 & 9 & 21\\6 & 27 & 8 & 5 & 13\end{bmatrix}$
$= [163 \quad 650 \quad 266 \quad 175 \quad 431]$

(c) $C = \begin{bmatrix}\$1,600\\\$900\\\$500\\\$100\\\$1,000\end{bmatrix}$

(d) $RC = \begin{bmatrix}5 & 22 & 14 & 7 & 17\\7 & 20 & 10 & 9 & 21\\6 & 27 & 8 & 5 & 13\end{bmatrix}\begin{bmatrix}\$1,600\\\$900\\\$500\\\$100\\\$1,000\end{bmatrix}$

$= \begin{bmatrix}\$52,500\\\$56,100\\\$51,400\end{bmatrix}$

(e) $BRC = (BR)C$

$= [163 \quad 650 \quad 266 \quad 175 \quad 431]\begin{bmatrix}\$1,600\\\$900\\\$500\\\$100\\\$1,000\end{bmatrix}$

$= [\$1,427,300]$

This is the building contractor's total cost of building all 27 houses.

51. (a) $[x' \quad y'] = [x \quad y]\begin{bmatrix}\cos\alpha & -\sin\alpha\\\sin\alpha & \cos\alpha\end{bmatrix}$,
$x, y = 1, \alpha = 30°$

$= [1 \quad 1]\begin{bmatrix}\frac{\sqrt{3}}{2} & -\frac{1}{2}\\\frac{1}{2} & \frac{\sqrt{3}}{2}\end{bmatrix}$

$= \begin{bmatrix}\frac{\sqrt{3}+1}{2} & \frac{\sqrt{3}-1}{2}\end{bmatrix} \approx [1.37 \quad 0.37]$

(b) $[x \quad y] = [x' \quad y']\begin{bmatrix}\cos\alpha & \sin\alpha\\-\sin\alpha & \cos\alpha\end{bmatrix}$,
$x', y' = 1, \alpha = 30°$

$= [1 \quad 1]\begin{bmatrix}\frac{\sqrt{3}}{2} & \frac{1}{2}\\-\frac{1}{2} & \frac{\sqrt{3}}{2}\end{bmatrix}$

$= \begin{bmatrix}\frac{\sqrt{3}-1}{2} & \frac{\sqrt{3}+1}{2}\end{bmatrix} \approx [0.37 \quad 1.37]$

52. Answers will vary. One possible answer is given.

(a) $A + B = [a_{ij} + b_{ij}] = [b_{ij} + a_{ij}] = B + A$

(b) $(A + B) + C = [a_{ij} + b_{ij}] + C = [a_{ij} + b_{ij} + c_{ij}]$
$= [a_{ij} + (b_{ij} + c_{ij})] = A + [b_{ij} + c_{ij}]$
$= A + (B + C)$

(c) $A(B + C) = A[b_{ij} + c_{ij}] = \left[\sum_k a_{ik}(b_{kj} + c_{kj})\right]$

(following the rules of matrix multiplication)

$= \left[\sum_k (a_{ik}b_{kj} + a_{ik}c_{kj})\right]$

$= \left[\sum_k a_{ik}b_{kj} + \sum_k a_{ik}c_{kj}\right]$

$= \left[\sum_k a_{ik}b_{kj}\right] + \left[\sum_k a_{ik}c_{kj}\right] = AB + AC$

(d) $(A - B)C = [a_{ij} - b_{ij}]C = [\sum_k (a_{ik} - b_{ik})c_{ki}]$

$= [\sum_k (a_{ik}c_{ki} + b_{ik}c_{ki})]$

$= [\sum_k a_{ik}c_{ki} - \sum_k b_{ik}c_{ki}]$

$= [\sum_k a_{ik}c_{ki}] - [\sum_k b_{ik}c_{ki}]$

$= AC - BC$

53. Answers will vary. One possible answer is provided for each.

(a) $c(A + B) = c[a_{ij} + b_{ij}] = [ca_{ij} + cb_{ij}] = cA + cB$

(b) $(c + d)A = (c + d)[a_{ij}] = c[a_{ij}] + d[a_{ij}]$
$= cA + dA$

(c) $c(dA) = c[da_{ij}] = [cda_{ij}] = cd[a_{ij}] = cdA$

(d) $1 \cdot A = 1 \cdot [a_{ij}] = [a_{ij}] = A$

54. One possible answer: If the definition of determinant is followed, the evaluation of the determinant of any $n \times n$ square matrix ($n > 2$) eventually involves the evaluation of a number of 2×2 sub-determinants. The determinant of the 2×2 matrix serves as the building block for all other determinants.

56. $AI_n = \begin{bmatrix} a_{11} & a_{12} & \cdots & a_{1n} \\ a_{21} & a_{22} & \cdots & a_{2n} \\ \vdots & \vdots & & \vdots \\ a_{n1} & a_{n2} & \cdots & a_{nn} \end{bmatrix} \begin{bmatrix} 1 & 0 & \cdots & 0 \\ 0 & 1 & \cdots & 0 \\ \vdots & \vdots & \ddots & \vdots \\ 0 & 0 & \cdots & 1 \end{bmatrix}$

$= \begin{bmatrix} a_{11} + 0 \cdot a_{12} + \ldots + 0 \cdot a_{1n} & 0 \cdot a_{11} + a_{12} + 0 \cdot a_{13} + \ldots + 0 \cdot a_{1n} & \cdots & 0 \cdot a_{11} + 0 \cdot a_{12} + \ldots + a_{1n} \\ a_{21} + 0 \cdot a_{22} + \ldots + 0 \cdot a_{2n} & 0 \cdot a_{21} + a_{22} + 0 \cdot a_{23} + \ldots + 0 \cdot a_{2n} & \cdots & 0 \cdot a_{21} + 0 \cdot a_{22} + \ldots + a_{2n} \\ \vdots & \vdots & & \vdots \\ a_{n1} + 0 \cdot a_{n2} + \ldots + 0 \cdot a_{nn} & 0 \cdot a_{n1} + a_{n2} + 0 \cdot a_{n3} + \ldots + 0 \cdot a_{nn} & \cdots & 0 \cdot a_{n1} + 0 \cdot a_{n2} + \ldots + a_{nn} \end{bmatrix}$

$= \begin{bmatrix} a_{11} & a_{12} & \cdots & a_{1n} \\ a_{21} & a_{22} & \cdots & a_{2n} \\ \vdots & \vdots & & \vdots \\ a_{n1} & a_{n2} & \cdots & a_{nn} \end{bmatrix} = A$

Use a similar process to show that $I_n A = A$.

57. If (x, y) is reflected across the y-axis, then $(x, y) \Rightarrow (-x, y)$.

$[x' \quad y'] = [x \quad y]\begin{bmatrix} -1 & 0 \\ 0 & 1 \end{bmatrix}$

58. If (x, y) is reflected across the line $y = x$, then $(x, y) \Rightarrow (y, x)$.

$[x' \quad y'] = [x \quad y]\begin{bmatrix} 0 & 1 \\ 1 & 0 \end{bmatrix}$

59. If (x, y) is reflected across the line $y = -x$, then $(x, y) \Rightarrow (-y, -x)$.

$[x' \quad y'] = [x \quad y]\begin{bmatrix} 0 & -1 \\ -1 & 0 \end{bmatrix}$

60. If (x, y) is vertically stretched (or shrunk) by a factor of a, then $(x, y) \Rightarrow (x, ay)$.

$[x' \quad y'] = [x \quad y]\begin{bmatrix} 1 & 0 \\ 0 & a \end{bmatrix}$

55. $A \cdot A^{-1} = \begin{bmatrix} a & b \\ c & d \end{bmatrix} \left(\dfrac{1}{ad - bc}\right)\begin{bmatrix} d & -b \\ -c & a \end{bmatrix}$

$= \left(\dfrac{1}{ad - bc}\right)\begin{bmatrix} a & b \\ c & d \end{bmatrix}\begin{bmatrix} d & -b \\ -c & a \end{bmatrix}$

(since $\dfrac{1}{ad - bc}$ is a scalar)

$= \left(\dfrac{1}{ad - bc}\right)\begin{bmatrix} ad - bc & -ab + ba \\ cd - cd & -bc + ad \end{bmatrix} = \left(\dfrac{1}{ad - bc}\right)$

$\begin{bmatrix} ad - bc & 0 \\ 0 & ad - bc \end{bmatrix}$

$= \begin{bmatrix} \dfrac{ad - bc}{ad - bc} & 0 \\ 0 & \dfrac{ad - bc}{ad - bc} \end{bmatrix}$

$= \begin{bmatrix} 1 & 0 \\ 0 & 1 \end{bmatrix} = I_2$

61. If (x, y) is horizontally stretched (or shrunk) by a factor of c, then $(x, y) \Rightarrow (cx, y)$.

$[x' \quad y'] = [x \quad y]\begin{bmatrix} c & 0 \\ 0 & 1 \end{bmatrix}$

62. False. A square matrix A has an inverse if and only if $\det A \neq 0$.

63. False. The determinant can be negative. For example, the determinant of $A = \begin{bmatrix} 1 & 0 \\ 2 & -1 \end{bmatrix}$ is $1(-1) - 2(0) = -1$.

64. $2(-1) - (-3)(4) = 10$. The answer is C.

65. The matrix AB has the same number of rows as A and the same number of columns as B. The answer is B.

66. $\begin{bmatrix} 2 & 7 \\ 1 & 4 \end{bmatrix}^{-1} = \dfrac{1}{2(4) - 1(7)}\begin{bmatrix} 4 & -7 \\ -1 & 2 \end{bmatrix} = \begin{bmatrix} 4 & -7 \\ -1 & 2 \end{bmatrix}$
. The answer is E.

67. The value in row 1, column 3 is 3. The answer is D.

68. (a) Recall that A_{ij} is $(-1)^{i+j}M_{ij}$ where M_{ij} is the determinant of the matrix obtained by deleting the row and column containing a_{ij}. Let $A = 3 \times 3$ square matrix. Then:

$$\det(A) = \begin{vmatrix} a_{11} & a_{12} & a_{13} \\ a_{21} & a_{22} & a_{23} \\ a_{31} & a_{32} & a_{33} \end{vmatrix}$$

$$= a_{11}A_{11} + a_{12}A_{12} + a_{13}A_{13}$$
$$= a_{11}|A_{11}| - a_{12}|A_{12}| + a_{13}|A_{13}|$$

Now let B be the matrix A with rows 1 and 2 interchanged. Then:

$$\det(B) = \begin{vmatrix} a_{21} & a_{22} & a_{23} \\ a_{11} & a_{12} & a_{13} \\ a_{31} & a_{32} & a_{33} \end{vmatrix}$$

$$= a_{11}B_{21} + a_{12}B_{22} + a_{13}B_{23}$$
$$= -a_{11}|A_{11}| + a_{12}|A_{12}| - a_{13}|A_{13}|$$
$$= (-1)(a_{11}|A_{11}| - a_{12}|A_{12}| + a_{13}|A_{13}|)$$
$$= -\det(A)$$

To generalize, we would say that by the definition of a determinant, the determinant of any $k \times k$ square matrix is ultimately dependent upon a series of 3×3 determinants. (In the 4×4 case, for example, we would have the expansion — using the first row — of $a_{11}A_{11} + a_{12}A_{12} + a_{13}A_{13} + a_{14}A_{14}$. If a row of matrix A is interchanged with another, the elements of all of matrix A's 3×3 matrices will be affected, resulting in a sign change to the determinant.

(b) Let A be a $k \times k$ square matrix with two rows exactly the same, and B be the matrix A with those exact same rows interchanged. From #4, we know that $\det(A) = -\det(B)$. However, since $A = B$ element-wise (i.e., $a_{ij} = b_{ij}$ for $1 \le i, j \le k$), we also know that $\det(A) = \det(B)$. These two properties can hold true only when $\det(A) = \det(B) = 0$.

(c) Let $A = 3 \times 3$ square matrix. Then:
$$\det(A) = a_{11}a_{22}a_{33} - a_{11}a_{23}a_{32} - a_{12}a_{21}a_{33}$$
$$+ a_{12}a_{23}a_{31} + a_{13}a_{21}a_{32} - a_{13}a_{22}a_{31}$$

Now, let B be the 3×3 square matrix A, with the following exception: the first row of B is replaced with k times the second row of A *plus* the first row of A. Then:

$$\det(B) = \begin{vmatrix} a_{11} + ka_{21} & a_{12} + ka_{22} & a_{13} + ka_{23} \\ a_{21} & a_{22} & a_{23} \\ a_{31} & a_{32} & a_{33} \end{vmatrix}$$

$$= (a_{11} + ka_{21})\begin{vmatrix} a_{22} & a_{23} \\ a_{32} & a_{33} \end{vmatrix} - (a_{12} + ka_{22})\begin{vmatrix} a_{21} & a_{23} \\ a_{31} & a_{33} \end{vmatrix}$$
$$+ (a_{13} + ka_{23})\begin{vmatrix} a_{21} & a_{22} \\ a_{31} & a_{32} \end{vmatrix}$$

$$= a_{11}\begin{vmatrix} a_{22} & a_{23} \\ a_{32} & a_{33} \end{vmatrix} + ka_{21}\begin{vmatrix} a_{22} & a_{23} \\ a_{32} & a_{33} \end{vmatrix} - a_{12}\begin{vmatrix} a_{21} & a_{23} \\ a_{31} & a_{33} \end{vmatrix}$$
$$- ka_{22}\begin{vmatrix} a_{21} & a_{23} \\ a_{31} & a_{33} \end{vmatrix} + a_{13}\begin{vmatrix} a_{21} & a_{22} \\ a_{31} & a_{32} \end{vmatrix} + ka_{23}\begin{vmatrix} a_{21} & a_{22} \\ a_{31} & a_{32} \end{vmatrix}$$

$$= a_{11}(a_{22}a_{33} - a_{23}a_{32}) - a_{12}(a_{21}a_{33} - a_{23}a_{31})$$
$$+ a_{13}(a_{21}a_{32} - a_{22}a_{31}) + ka_{21}(a_{22}a_{33} - a_{23}a_{32})$$
$$- ka_{22}(a_{21}a_{33} - a_{23}a_{31}) + ka_{23}(a_{21}a_{32} - a_{22}a_{31})$$
$$= a_{11}a_{22}a_{33} - a_{11}a_{23}a_{32} - a_{12}a_{21}a_{33} + a_{12}a_{23}a_{31}$$
$$+ a_{13}a_{21}a_{32} - a_{13}a_{22}a_{31} + ka_{21}a_{22}a_{33} - ka_{21}a_{23}a_{32}$$

$$- ka_{21}a_{22}a_{33} + ka_{22}a_{23}a_{31} + ka_{21}a_{22}a_{32} - ka_{22}a_{23}a_{31}$$
$$= a_{11}a_{22}a_{33} - a_{11}a_{23}a_{32} - a_{12}a_{21}a_{33} + a_{12}a_{23}a_{31}$$
$$+ a_{13}a_{21}a_{32} - a_{13}a_{22}a_{31} + 0$$
$$= \det(A).$$

This result holds in general.

69. (a) Let $A = [a_{ij}]$ be an $n \times n$ matrix and let B be the same as matrix A, except that the ith row of B is the ith row of A multiplied by the scalar c. Then:

$$\det(B) = \begin{vmatrix} a_{11} & a_{12} & \ldots & a_{1n} \\ a_{21} & a_{22} & \ldots & a_{2n} \\ & \vdots & & \\ ca_{i1} & ca_{i2} & \ldots & ca_{in} \\ & \vdots & & \\ a_{n1} & a_{n2} & \ldots & a_{nn} \end{vmatrix}$$

ith row $\rightarrow$

$$= ca_{i1}(-1)^{i+1}|A_{i1}| + ca_{i2}(-1)^{i+2}|A_{i2}| + \ldots$$
$$+ ca_{in}(-1)^{in}|A_{in}|$$
$$= c(a_{i1}(-1)^{i+1}|A_{i1}| + a_{i2}(-1)^{i+2}|A_{i2}| + \ldots$$
$$+ a_{in}(-1)^{i+n}|A_{in}|)$$
$$= c\det(A) \text{ (by definition of determinant)}$$

(b) Use the 2×2 case as an example

$$\det(A) = \begin{vmatrix} a_{11} & 0 \\ a_{21} & a_{22} \end{vmatrix} = a_{11}a_{22} - 0 = a_{11}a_{22}$$

which is the product of the diagonal elements. Now consider the general case where A is an $n \times n$ matrix. Then:

$$\det(A) = \begin{vmatrix} a_{11} & 0 & 0 & \ldots & 0 \\ a_{21} & a_{22} & 0 & \ldots & 0 \\ \vdots & \vdots & & & \vdots \\ a_{n1} & a_{n2} & & \ldots & a_{nn} \end{vmatrix}$$

$$= a_{11}(-1)^2 \begin{vmatrix} a_{22} & 0 & 0 & \ldots & 0 \\ a_{32} & a_{33} & 0 & \ldots & 0 \\ \vdots & \vdots & & & \vdots \\ a_{n2} & a_{n3} & a_{n4} & \ldots & a_{nn} \end{vmatrix}$$

$$= a_{11}(a_{22})(-1)^2 \begin{vmatrix} a_{33} & 0 & \ldots & 0 \\ a_{43} & a_{44} & \ldots & 0 \\ \vdots & \vdots & & \vdots \\ a_{n3} & a_{n4} & \ldots & a_{nn} \end{vmatrix}$$

$$= a_{11}a_{22} \ldots a_{n-2\ n-2}(-1)^2 \begin{vmatrix} a_{n-1\ n-1} & 0 \\ a_{n\ n-1} & a_{nn} \end{vmatrix}$$

$$= a_{11}a_{22} \ldots a_{n-2\ n-2}a_{n-1\ n-1}a_{nn}, \text{ which is}$$

exactly the product of the diagonal elements (by induction).

70. (a)
$$\begin{vmatrix} 1 & x & y \\ 1 & x_1 & y_1 \\ 1 & x_2 & y_2 \end{vmatrix} = 1(-1)^2 \begin{vmatrix} x_1 & y_1 \\ x_2 & y_2 \end{vmatrix} + x(-1)^3 \begin{vmatrix} 1 & y_1 \\ 1 & y_2 \end{vmatrix}$$
$$+ y(-1)^4 \begin{vmatrix} 1 & x_1 \\ 1 & x_2 \end{vmatrix}$$

$$= (x_1 y_2 - y_1 x_2) - x(y_2 - y_1) + y(x_2 - x_1)$$

Since $(y_2 - y_1)$ is not a power of x and $(x_2 - x_1)$ is not a power of y, the equation is linear.

(b) If $(x, y) = (x_1, y_1)$, then det(A)
$$= x_1y_2 - x_2y_1 - x_1y_2 + x_1y_1 + x_2y_1 - x_1y_1$$
$= 0$, so (x_1, y_1) lies on the line.
If $(x, y) = (x_2, y_2)$, then, det(A)
$$= x_1y_2 - x_2y_1 - x_2y_2 + x_2y_1 + x_2y_2 - x_1y_2 = 0,$$
so (x_2, y_2) lies on the line.

(c) $\begin{vmatrix} 1 & x_3 & y_3 \\ 1 & x_1 & y_1 \\ 1 & x_2 & y_2 \end{vmatrix} = 0$

(d) $\begin{vmatrix} 1 & x_3 & y_3 \\ 1 & x_1 & y_1 \\ 1 & x_2 & y_2 \end{vmatrix} \neq 0$

71. (a) $A \cdot A^{-1} = \begin{bmatrix} \cos\alpha & -\sin\alpha \\ \sin\alpha & \cos\alpha \end{bmatrix} \begin{bmatrix} \cos\alpha & \sin\alpha \\ -\sin\alpha & \cos\alpha \end{bmatrix}$

$= \begin{bmatrix} \cos^2\alpha + \sin^2\alpha \\ \sin\alpha\cos\alpha - \cos\alpha\sin\alpha \end{bmatrix}$

$\begin{matrix} \cos\alpha\sin\alpha - \sin\alpha\cos\alpha \\ \sin^2\alpha + \cos^2\alpha \end{matrix} \bigg] = \begin{bmatrix} 1 & 0 \\ 0 & 1 \end{bmatrix} = I_2$

(b) From the diagram, we know that:
$x = r\cos\theta \qquad y = r\sin\theta$
$x' = r\cos(\theta - \alpha) \qquad y' = r\sin(\theta - \alpha)$
or $\cos(\theta - \alpha) = \dfrac{x'}{r} \qquad \sin(\theta - \alpha) = \dfrac{y'}{r}$

From algebra, we know that:
$x = r\cos(\theta + \alpha - \alpha) = r\cos(\alpha + (\theta - \alpha))$ and
$y = r\sin(\theta + \alpha - \alpha) = r\sin(\alpha + (\theta - \alpha))$

Using the trigonometric properties and substitution, we have:
$x = r(\cos\alpha\cos(\theta - \alpha) - \sin\alpha\sin(\theta - \alpha))$
$= r\cos\alpha\cos(\theta - \alpha) - r\sin\alpha\sin(\theta - \alpha)$
$= (r\cos\alpha)\left(\dfrac{x'}{r}\right) - (r\sin\alpha)\left(\dfrac{y'}{r}\right)$
$= x'\cos\alpha - y'\sin\alpha$
$y = r(\sin\alpha\cos(\theta - \alpha) + \cos\alpha\sin(\theta - \alpha))$
$= r\sin\alpha\cos(\theta - \alpha) + r\cos\alpha\sin(\theta - \alpha)$
$= (r\sin\alpha)\left(\dfrac{x'}{r}\right) + (r\cos\alpha)\left(\dfrac{y'}{r}\right)$
$= x'\sin\alpha + y'\cos\alpha.$

(c) $\begin{bmatrix} x & y \end{bmatrix} = \begin{bmatrix} x' & y' \end{bmatrix} \begin{bmatrix} \cos\alpha & \sin\alpha \\ -\sin\alpha & \cos\alpha \end{bmatrix}$
which is $\begin{bmatrix} x' & y' \end{bmatrix} A^{-1}$, the inverse of A.

72. (a) $\det(xI_2 - A) = \det\begin{bmatrix} x - a_{11} & -a_{12} \\ -a_{21} & x - a_{22} \end{bmatrix}$

$= (x - a_{11})(x - a_{22}) - (a_{12})(a_{21})$
$= x^2 - a_{22}x - a_{11}x + a_{11}a_{22} - a_{12}a_{21}$
$= x^2 + (-a_{22} - a_{11})x + (a_{11}a_{22} - a_{12}a_{21})$
$f(x)$ is a polynomial of degree 2.

(b) They are equal.

(c) The coefficient of x is the opposite of the sum of the elements of the main diagonal in A.

(d) $f(A) = \det(AI - A) = \det(A - A)$
$= \det([0]) = 0.$

73. $\det(xI_3 - A) = \begin{vmatrix} x - a_{11} & -a_{12} & -a_{13} \\ -a_{21} & x - a_{22} & -a_{23} \\ -a_{31} & -a_{32} & x - a_{33} \end{vmatrix}$

$= (x - a_{11})(-1)^2\begin{vmatrix} x - a_{22} & -a_{23} \\ -a_{32} & x - a_{33} \end{vmatrix}$

$+ (-a_{12})(-1)^3\begin{vmatrix} -a_{21} & -a_{23} \\ -a_{31} & x - a_{33} \end{vmatrix}$

$+ (-a_{13})(-1)^4\begin{vmatrix} -a_{21} & x - a_{22} \\ -a_{31} & -a_{32} \end{vmatrix}$

$= (x - a_{11})((x - a_{22})(x - a_{33}) - a_{23}a_{32})$
$\quad + a_{12}((-a_{21})(x - a_{33}) - a_{23}a_{31})$
$\quad - a_{13}(a_{21}a_{32} + (a_{31})(x - a_{22}))$
$= (x - a_{11})(x^2 - a_{33}x - a_{22}x + a_{22}a_{33} - a_{23}a_{32})$
$\quad + a_{12}(-a_{21}x + a_{21}a_{33} - a_{23}a_{31})$
$\quad - a_{13}(a_{21}a_{32} + a_{31}x - a_{22}a_{31})$
$= x^3 - a_{33}x^2 - a_{22}x^2 + a_{22}a_{33}x - a_{23}a_{32}x - a_{11}x^2$
$\quad + a_{11}a_{33}x + a_{11}a_{22}x - a_{11}a_{22}a_{33} + a_{11}a_{23}a_{32} - a_{12}a_{21}x$
$\quad + a_{12}a_{21}a_{33} - a_{12}a_{23}a_{31} - a_{13}a_{21}a_{32} - a_{13}a_{31}x$
$\quad + a_{13}a_{22}a_{31}$
$= x^3 + (-a_{33} - a_{22} - a_{11})x^2 + (a_{22}a_{33} - a_{23}a_{32} + a_{11}a_{33}$
$\quad + a_{11}a_{22} - a_{12}a_{21} - a_{13}a_{31})x + (-a_{11}a_{22}a_{33} + a_{11}a_{23}a_{32}$
$\quad + a_{12}a_{21}a_{33} - a_{12}a_{23}a_{31} - a_{13}a_{21}a_{32} + a_{13}a_{22}a_{31})$

(b) The constant term equals $-\det(A)$.

(c) The coefficient of x^2 is the opposite of the sum of the elements of the main diagonal in A.

(d) $f(A) = \det(AI - A) = \det(A - A)$
$= \det([0]) = 0$

■ Section 7.3 Multivariate Linear Systems and Row Operations

Exploration 1

1. $x + y + z$ must equal the total number of liters in the mixture, namely 60 L.

2. $0.15x + 0.35y + 0.55z$ must equal total amount of acid in the mixture; since the mixture must be 40% acid and have 60 L of solution, the total amount of acid must be $0.40(60) = 24$ L.

3. The number of liters of 35% solution, y, must equal twice the number of liters of 55% solution, z. Hence $y = 2z$.

4. $\begin{bmatrix} 1 & 1 & 1 \\ 0.15 & 0.35 & 0.55 \\ 0 & 1 & -2 \end{bmatrix}\begin{bmatrix} x \\ y \\ z \end{bmatrix} = \begin{bmatrix} 60 \\ 24 \\ 0 \end{bmatrix}$

$A = \begin{bmatrix} 1 & 1 & 1 \\ 0.15 & 0.35 & 0.55 \\ 0 & 1 & -2 \end{bmatrix}, X = \begin{bmatrix} x \\ y \\ z \end{bmatrix}, B = \begin{bmatrix} 60 \\ 24 \\ 0 \end{bmatrix}$

5. $X = A^{-1}B = \begin{bmatrix} 3.75 \\ 37.5 \\ 18.75 \end{bmatrix}$

6. 3.75 L of 15% acid, 37.5 L of 35% acid, and 18.75 L of 55% acid are required to make 60 L of a 40% acid solution.

Quick Review 7.3

1. $(40)(0.32) = 12.8$ liters

2. $(60)(0.14) = 8.4$ milliliters

3. $(50)(1 - 0.24) = 38$ liters

4. $(80)(1 - 0.70) = 24$ milliliters

5. $(-1, 6)$

6. $(0, -1)$

7. $y = w - z + 1$

8. $x = 2z - w + 3$

9. $\begin{bmatrix} 1 & 3 \\ -2 & -2 \end{bmatrix}^{-1} = \begin{bmatrix} -0.5 & -0.75 \\ 0.5 & 0.25 \end{bmatrix}$

10. $\begin{bmatrix} 0 & 0 & 2 \\ -2 & 1 & 3 \\ 0 & 2 & -2 \end{bmatrix}^{-1} = \begin{bmatrix} 1 & -0.5 & 0.25 \\ 0.5 & 0 & 0.5 \\ 0.5 & 0 & 0 \end{bmatrix}$

Section 7.3 Exercises

1. $x - 3y + z = 0$ (1)
$\qquad 2y + 3z = 1$ (2)
$\qquad\qquad z = -2$ (3)
Use $z = -2$ in equation (2).
$2y + 3(-2) = 1$
$\qquad 2y = 7$
$\qquad y = \dfrac{7}{2}$
Use $z = -2$, $y = 7/2$ in equation (1).
$x - 3\left(\dfrac{7}{2}\right) + (-2) = 0$
$\qquad\qquad x = \dfrac{25}{2}$
So the solution is $(25/2, 7/2, -2)$.

2. $3x - y + 2z = -2$ (1)
$\qquad y + 3z = 3$ (2)
$\qquad\quad 2z = 4$ (3)
From equation (3), $z = 2$. Use this in equation (2).
$y + 3(2) = 3$
$\qquad y = -3$
Use $z = 2$, $y = -3$ in equation (1).
$3x - (-3) + 2(2) = -2$
$\qquad\qquad 3x = -9$
$\qquad\qquad x = -3$
So the solution is $(-3, -3, 2)$.

3.
$x - y + z = 0$
$2x \qquad - 3z = -1$
$-x - y + 2z = -1$

$x - y + z = 0$
$-2y + z = -3$ $\diagdown$ $2x - 3z = -1$
$-x - y + 2z = -1$ $-2(-x - y + 2z = -1)$

$x - y + z = 0$
$-2y + z = -3$ $\diagdown$ $x - y + z = 0$
$-2y + 3z = -1$ $-x - y + 2z = -1$

$x - y + z = 0$
$-2y + z = -3$
$\qquad 2z = 2$ $\diagdown$ $-1(-2y + z = -3)$
$\qquad\qquad\qquad -2y + 3z = -1$

$x - y + z = 0$
$y - \dfrac{1}{2}z = \dfrac{3}{2}$ ———— $-\dfrac{1}{2}(-2y + z = -3)$
$\qquad z = 1$ ———— $\dfrac{1}{2}(2z = 2)$

$y - \dfrac{1}{2}(1) = \dfrac{3}{2}$; $y = 2$
$x - 2 + 1 = 0$; $x = 1$
The solution is $(1, 2, 1)$.

4.
$2x - y = 0$
$x + 3y - z = -3$
$\qquad 3y + z = 8$

$-7y + 2z = 6$ $\diagdown$ $2x - y = 0$
$x + 3y - z = -3$ $-2(x + 3y - z = -3)$
$\qquad 3y + z = 8$

$\dfrac{13}{3}z = \dfrac{74}{3}$ $\diagdown$ $-7y + 2z = 6$
$x + 3y - z = -3$ $\dfrac{7}{3}(3y + z = 8)$
$\qquad 3y + z = 8$

$x + 3y - z = -3$
$y + \dfrac{1}{3}z = \dfrac{8}{3}$ ———— $\dfrac{1}{3}(3y + z = 8)$
$\qquad z = \dfrac{74}{13}$ ———— $\dfrac{3}{13}\left(\dfrac{13}{3}z = \dfrac{74}{3}\right)$

$y + \dfrac{1}{3}\left(\dfrac{74}{13}\right) = \dfrac{8}{3}$; $y = \dfrac{10}{13}$
$x + 3\left(\dfrac{10}{13}\right) - \dfrac{74}{13} = -3$; $x = \dfrac{5}{13}$
The solution is $(5/13, 10/13, 74/13)$.

5.
$x + y + z = -3$
$4x - y = -5$
$-3x + 2y + z = 4$

$x + y + z = -3$
$4x - y = -5$
$-4x + y = 7$ $\diagdown$ $-1(x + y + z = -3)$
$\qquad\qquad\qquad -3x + 2y + z = 4$

$x + y + z = -3$
$4x - y = -5$
$\qquad 0 = 2$ $\diagdown$ $4x - y = -5$
$\qquad\qquad\qquad -4x + y = 7$
The system has no solution.

6.
$x + y - 3z = -1$
$2x - 3y + z = 4$
$3x - 7y + 5z = 4$

$x + y - 3z = -1$
$-5y + 7z = 6$ $\diagdown$ $-2(x + y - 3z = -1)$
$3x - 7y + 5z = 4$ $2x - 3y + z = 4$

$x + y - 3z = -1$
$-5y + 7z = 6$
$-10y + 14z = 7$ $\diagdown$ $-3(x + y - 3z = -1)$
$\qquad\qquad\qquad 3x - 7y + 5z = 4$

$x + y - 3z = -1$
$-5y + 7z = 6$
$\qquad 0 = -5$ $\diagdown$ $-2(-5y + 7z = 6)$
$\qquad\qquad\qquad -10y + 14z = 7$
The system has no solution.

7. $x + y - z = 4$
  $y + w = -4$
  $x - y = 1$
  $x + z + w = 1$
  $2y - z = 3$ ◄——— $x + y - z = 4$
  $y + w = -4$ $-1(x - y = 1)$
  $x - y = 1$
  $x + z + w = 1$

  $2y - z = 3$
  $y + w = -4$
  $x - y = 1$
  $y + z + w = 0$ ◄——— $-1(x - y = 1)$
                    $x + z + w = 1$

  $-z - 2w = 11$ ◄——— $2y - z = 3$
  $y + w = -4$ $-2(y + w = -4)$
  $x - y = 1$
  $y + z + w = 0$

  $-z - 2w = 11$
  $y + w = -4$
  $x - y = 1$
  $z = 4$ ◄——— $-1(y + w = -4)$
              $-y + z + w = 0$

  $x - y = 1$
  $y + w = -4$
  $w + \dfrac{1}{2}z = -\dfrac{11}{2}$ ——— $-\dfrac{1}{2}(-z - 2w = 11)$
  $z = 4$

  $w + \dfrac{1}{2}(4) = -\dfrac{11}{2}; w = -\dfrac{15}{2}$

  $y + \left(-\dfrac{15}{2}\right) = -4; y = \dfrac{7}{2}$

  $x - \dfrac{7}{2} = 1; x = \dfrac{9}{2}$

  So the solution is $\left(\dfrac{9}{2}, \dfrac{7}{2}, 4, -\dfrac{15}{2}\right)$.

8. $\dfrac{1}{2}x - y + z - w = 1$

  $-x + y + z + 2w = -3$
  $x - z = 2$
  $y + w = 0$

$\dfrac{1}{2}x - y + z - w = 1$
  $y + 2w = -1$ ◄ $\begin{array}{l} -x + y + z + 2w = -3 \\ x - z = 2 \end{array}$
  $x - z = 2$
  $y + w = 0$

$\dfrac{1}{2}x - y + z - w = 1$
  $y + 2w = -1$ ◄——— $y + 2w = -1$
  $w = -1$ $-1(y + w = 0)$
  $x - z = 2$
  $y + w = 0$

  $-y + \dfrac{3}{2}z - w = 0$ ◄ $\begin{array}{l} \dfrac{1}{2}x - y + z - w = 1 \\ -\dfrac{1}{2}(x - z = 2) \end{array}$
  $w = -1$
  $x - z = 2$
  $y + w = 0$

  $x - z = 2$
  $z - \dfrac{2}{3}y - \dfrac{2}{3}w = 0$ ——— $-\dfrac{2}{3}\left(-y + \dfrac{3}{2}z - w = 0\right)$
  $y + w = 0$
  $w = -1$

  $y + (-1) = 0; y = 1$
  $z - \dfrac{2}{3}(1) - \dfrac{2}{3}(-1) = 0; z = 0$
  $x - 0 = 2; x = 2$
  So the solution is $(2, 1, 0, -1)$.

9. $\begin{bmatrix} 2 & -6 & 4 \\ 1 & 2 & -3 \\ 0 & -8 & 4 \end{bmatrix}$

10. $\begin{bmatrix} 1 & -3 & 2 \\ 1 & 2 & -3 \\ -3 & 1 & -2 \end{bmatrix}$

11. $\begin{bmatrix} 0 & -10 & 10 \\ 1 & 2 & -3 \\ -3 & 1 & -2 \end{bmatrix}$

12. $\begin{bmatrix} 2 & -6 & 4 \\ 3 & -4 & 1 \\ -3 & 1 & -2 \end{bmatrix}$

13. R_{12}

14. $(2)R_2 + R_1$

15. $(-3)R_2 + R_3$

16. $(1/4)R_3$

For #17–20, answers will vary depending on the exact sequence of row operations used. One possible sequence of row operations (not necessarily the shortest) is given. The answers shown are not necessarily the ones that might be produced by a grapher or other technology. In some cases, they are not the ones given in the text answers.

17. $\begin{bmatrix} 1 & 3 & -1 \\ 2 & 1 & 4 \\ -3 & 0 & 1 \end{bmatrix} \xrightarrow[(3)R_1 + R_3]{(-2)R_1 + R_2} \begin{bmatrix} 1 & 3 & -1 \\ 0 & -5 & 6 \\ 0 & 9 & -2 \end{bmatrix} \xrightarrow[(-1/5)R_2]{(9/5)R_2 + R_3} \begin{bmatrix} 1 & 3 & -1 \\ 0 & 1 & -1.2 \\ 0 & 0 & 8.8 \end{bmatrix} \xrightarrow{(5/44)R_3} \begin{bmatrix} 1 & 3 & -1 \\ 0 & 1 & -1.2 \\ 0 & 0 & 1 \end{bmatrix}$

18. $\begin{bmatrix} 1 & 2 & -3 \\ -3 & -6 & 10 \\ -2 & -4 & 7 \end{bmatrix} \xrightarrow[(2)R_1 + R_3]{(3)R_1 + R_2} \begin{bmatrix} 1 & 2 & -3 \\ 0 & 0 & 1 \\ 0 & 0 & 1 \end{bmatrix} \xrightarrow{(-1)R_2 + R_3} \begin{bmatrix} 1 & 2 & -3 \\ 0 & 0 & 1 \\ 0 & 0 & 0 \end{bmatrix}$

19. $\begin{bmatrix} 1 & 2 & 3 & -4 \\ -2 & 6 & -6 & 2 \\ 3 & 12 & 6 & 12 \end{bmatrix} \xrightarrow[(-3)R_1 + R_3]{(2)R_1 + R_2} \begin{bmatrix} 1 & 2 & 3 & -4 \\ 0 & 10 & 0 & -6 \\ 0 & 6 & -3 & 24 \end{bmatrix} \xrightarrow[(-1/3)R_3]{(1/10)R_2} \begin{bmatrix} 1 & 2 & 3 & -4 \\ 0 & 1 & 0 & -0.6 \\ 0 & -2 & 1 & -8 \end{bmatrix} \xrightarrow{(2)R_2 + R_3}$

$\begin{bmatrix} 1 & 2 & 3 & -4 \\ 0 & 1 & 0 & -0.6 \\ 0 & 0 & 1 & -9.2 \end{bmatrix}$

20. $\begin{bmatrix} 3 & 6 & 9 & -6 \\ 2 & 5 & 5 & -3 \end{bmatrix} \xrightarrow{(1/3)R_1} \begin{bmatrix} 1 & 2 & 3 & -2 \\ 2 & 5 & 5 & -3 \end{bmatrix} \xrightarrow{(-2)R_1 + R_2} \begin{bmatrix} 1 & 2 & 3 & -2 \\ 0 & 1 & -1 & 1 \end{bmatrix}$

In #21–24, reduced row echelon format is essentially unique, though the sequence of steps may vary from those shown.

21. $\begin{bmatrix} 1 & 0 & 2 & 1 \\ 3 & 2 & 4 & 7 \\ 2 & 1 & 3 & 4 \end{bmatrix} \xrightarrow[(-2)R_1 + R_3]{(-3)R_1 + R_2} \begin{bmatrix} 1 & 0 & 2 & 1 \\ 0 & 2 & -2 & 4 \\ 0 & 1 & -1 & 2 \end{bmatrix} \xrightarrow{(1/2)R_2} \begin{bmatrix} 1 & 0 & 2 & 1 \\ 0 & 1 & -1 & 2 \\ 0 & 1 & -1 & 2 \end{bmatrix} \xrightarrow{(-1)R_2 + R_3} \begin{bmatrix} 1 & 0 & 2 & 1 \\ 0 & 1 & -1 & 2 \\ 0 & 0 & 0 & 0 \end{bmatrix}$

22. $\begin{bmatrix} 1 & -2 & 2 & 1 & 1 \\ 3 & -5 & 6 & 3 & -1 \\ -2 & 4 & -3 & -2 & 5 \\ 3 & -5 & 6 & 4 & -3 \end{bmatrix} \xrightarrow[(2)R_1 + R_3]{(-3)R_1 + R_2} \begin{bmatrix} 1 & -2 & 2 & 1 & 1 \\ 0 & 1 & 0 & 0 & -4 \\ 0 & 0 & 1 & 0 & 7 \\ 3 & -5 & 6 & 4 & -3 \end{bmatrix} \xrightarrow[(2)R_2 + R_1]{(-3)R_1 + R_4} \begin{bmatrix} 1 & 0 & 2 & 1 & -7 \\ 0 & 1 & 0 & 0 & -4 \\ 0 & 0 & 1 & 0 & 7 \\ 0 & 1 & 0 & 1 & -6 \end{bmatrix}$

$\xrightarrow[(-2)R_3 + R_1]{(-1)R_2 + R_4} \begin{bmatrix} 1 & 0 & 0 & 1 & -21 \\ 0 & 1 & 0 & 0 & -4 \\ 0 & 0 & 1 & 0 & 7 \\ 0 & 0 & 0 & 1 & -2 \end{bmatrix} \xrightarrow{(-1)R_4 + R_1} \begin{bmatrix} 1 & 0 & 0 & 0 & -19 \\ 0 & 1 & 0 & 0 & -4 \\ 0 & 0 & 1 & 0 & 7 \\ 0 & 0 & 0 & 1 & -2 \end{bmatrix}$

23. $\begin{bmatrix} 1 & 2 & 3 & 1 \\ -3 & -5 & -7 & -4 \end{bmatrix} \xrightarrow{(3)R_1 + R_2} \begin{bmatrix} 1 & 2 & 3 & 1 \\ 0 & 1 & 2 & -1 \end{bmatrix} \xrightarrow{(-2)R_2 + R_1} \begin{bmatrix} 1 & 0 & -1 & 3 \\ 0 & 1 & 2 & -1 \end{bmatrix}$

24. $\begin{bmatrix} 3 & -6 & 3 & -3 \\ 2 & -4 & 2 & -2 \\ -3 & 6 & -3 & 3 \end{bmatrix} \xrightarrow{(1/3)R_1} \begin{bmatrix} 1 & -2 & 1 & -1 \\ 2 & -4 & 2 & -2 \\ -3 & 6 & -3 & 3 \end{bmatrix} \xrightarrow[(3)R_1 + R_3]{(-2)R_1 + R_2} \begin{bmatrix} 1 & -2 & 1 & -1 \\ 0 & 0 & 0 & 0 \\ 0 & 0 & 0 & 0 \end{bmatrix}$

25. $\begin{bmatrix} 2 & -3 & 1 & 1 \\ -1 & 1 & -4 & -3 \\ 3 & 0 & -1 & 2 \end{bmatrix}$

26. $\begin{bmatrix} 3 & -4 & 1 & -1 & 1 \\ 1 & 0 & 1 & -2 & 4 \end{bmatrix}$

27. $\begin{bmatrix} 2 & -5 & 1 & -1 & -3 \\ 1 & 0 & -2 & 1 & 4 \\ 0 & 2 & -3 & -1 & 5 \end{bmatrix}$

28. $\begin{bmatrix} 3 & -2 & 5 \\ -1 & 5 & 7 \end{bmatrix}$

In #29–32, the variable names (x, y, etc.) are arbitrary.

29. $3x + 2y = -1$
$-4x + 5y = 2$

30. $x - z + 2w = -3$
$2x + y - w = 4$
$-x + y + 2z = 0$

31. $2x + z = 3$
$-x + y = 2$
$2y - 3z = -1$

32. $2x + y - 2z = 4$
$-3x + 2z = -1$

33. $\begin{bmatrix} 1 & -2 & 1 & 8 \\ 2 & 1 & -3 & -9 \\ -3 & 1 & 3 & 5 \end{bmatrix} \xrightarrow[(3)R_1 + R_3]{(-2)R_1 + R_2} \begin{bmatrix} 1 & -2 & 1 & 8 \\ 0 & 5 & -5 & -25 \\ 0 & -5 & 6 & 29 \end{bmatrix} \xrightarrow[(1/5)R_2]{(1)R_2 + R_3} \begin{bmatrix} 1 & -2 & 1 & 8 \\ 0 & 1 & -1 & -5 \\ 0 & 0 & 1 & 4 \end{bmatrix}$

$x - 2y + z = 8$
$\quad y - z = -5$
$\qquad\quad z = 4$
$y - 4 = -5; y = -1$
$x - 2(-1) + 4 = 8; x = 2$
So the solution is $(2, -1, 4)$.

34. $\begin{bmatrix} 3 & 7 & -11 & 44 \\ 1 & 2 & -3 & 12 \\ 4 & 9 & -13 & 53 \end{bmatrix} \xrightarrow[\;(-4)R_2 + R_3\;]{(-3)R_2 + R_1} \begin{bmatrix} 0 & 1 & -2 & 8 \\ 1 & 2 & -3 & 12 \\ 0 & 1 & -1 & 5 \end{bmatrix} \xrightarrow[\;R_{12}\;]{(-1)R_1 + R_3} \begin{bmatrix} 1 & 2 & -3 & 12 \\ 0 & 1 & -2 & 8 \\ 0 & 0 & 1 & -3 \end{bmatrix}$

$x + 2y - 3z = 12$
$\qquad y - 2z = 8$
$\qquad\qquad z = -3$
$y - 2(-3) = 8; y = 2$
$x + 2(2) - 3(-3) = 12; x = -1$
So the solution is $(-1, 2, -3)$.

35. $(x, y, z) = (-2, 3, 1)$: $\begin{bmatrix} 1 & 2 & -1 & 3 \\ 3 & 7 & -3 & 12 \\ -2 & -4 & 3 & -5 \end{bmatrix} \xrightarrow[\;(2)R_1 + R_3\;]{(-3)R_1 + R_2} \begin{bmatrix} 1 & 2 & -1 & 3 \\ 0 & 1 & 0 & 3 \\ 0 & 0 & 1 & 1 \end{bmatrix} \xrightarrow[\;(1)R_3 + R_1\;]{(-2)R_2 + R_1} \begin{bmatrix} 1 & 0 & 0 & -2 \\ 0 & 1 & 0 & 3 \\ 0 & 0 & 1 & 1 \end{bmatrix}$

36. $(x, y, z) = (7, 6, 3)$: $\begin{bmatrix} 1 & -2 & 1 & -2 \\ 2 & -3 & 2 & 2 \\ 4 & -8 & 5 & -5 \end{bmatrix} \xrightarrow[\;(-4)R_1 + R_3\;]{(-2)R_1 + R_2} \begin{bmatrix} 1 & -2 & 1 & -2 \\ 0 & 1 & 0 & 6 \\ 0 & 0 & 1 & 3 \end{bmatrix} \xrightarrow[\;(-1)R_3 + R_1\;]{(2)R_2 + R_1} \begin{bmatrix} 1 & 0 & 0 & 7 \\ 0 & 1 & 0 & 6 \\ 0 & 0 & 1 & 3 \end{bmatrix}$

37. No solution: $\begin{bmatrix} 1 & 1 & 3 & 2 \\ 3 & 4 & 10 & 5 \\ 1 & 2 & 4 & 3 \end{bmatrix} \xrightarrow[\;(-1)R_1 + R_3\;]{(-3)R_1 + R_2} \begin{bmatrix} 1 & 1 & 3 & 2 \\ 0 & 1 & 1 & -1 \\ 0 & 1 & 1 & 1 \end{bmatrix} \xrightarrow{(-1)R_2 + R_3} \begin{bmatrix} 1 & 1 & 3 & 2 \\ 0 & 1 & 1 & -1 \\ 0 & 0 & 0 & 2 \end{bmatrix}$

38. $(x, y, z) = (z + 2, -z - 1, z)$ — the final matrix translates to $x - z = 2$ and $y + z = -1$.

$\begin{bmatrix} 1 & 0 & -1 & 2 \\ -2 & 1 & 3 & -5 \\ 2 & 1 & -1 & 3 \end{bmatrix} \xrightarrow[\;(-2)R_1 + R_3\;]{(2)R_1 + R_2} \begin{bmatrix} 1 & 0 & -1 & 2 \\ 0 & 1 & 1 & -1 \\ 0 & 1 & 1 & -1 \end{bmatrix} \xrightarrow{(-1)R_2 + R_3} \begin{bmatrix} 1 & 0 & -1 & 2 \\ 0 & 1 & 1 & -1 \\ 0 & 0 & 0 & 0 \end{bmatrix}$

39. $(x, y, z) = (2 - z, 1 + z, z)$ — the final matrix translates to $x + z = 2$ and $y - z = 1$.

$\begin{bmatrix} 1 & 0 & 1 & 2 \\ 2 & 1 & 1 & 5 \end{bmatrix} \xrightarrow{(-2)R_1 + R_2} \begin{bmatrix} 1 & 0 & 1 & 2 \\ 0 & 1 & -1 & 1 \end{bmatrix}$

40. $(x, y, z) = (z + 53, z - 26, z)$ — the final matrix translates to $x - z = 53$ and $y - z = -26$.

$\begin{bmatrix} 1 & 2 & -3 & 1 \\ -3 & -5 & 8 & -29 \end{bmatrix} \xrightarrow{(3)R_1 + R_2} \begin{bmatrix} 1 & 2 & -3 & 1 \\ 0 & 1 & -1 & -26 \end{bmatrix} \xrightarrow{(-2)R_2 + R_1} \begin{bmatrix} 1 & 0 & -1 & 53 \\ 0 & 1 & -1 & -26 \end{bmatrix}$

41. No solution: $\begin{bmatrix} 1 & 2 & 4 \\ 3 & 4 & 5 \\ 2 & 3 & 4 \end{bmatrix} \xrightarrow[\;(-2)R_1 + R_3\;]{(-3)R_1 + R_2} \begin{bmatrix} 1 & 2 & 4 \\ 0 & -2 & -7 \\ 0 & -1 & -4 \end{bmatrix} \xrightarrow{(1/2)R_2} \begin{bmatrix} 1 & 2 & 4 \\ 0 & -1 & -7/2 \\ 0 & -1 & -4 \end{bmatrix}$

42. $(x, y) = (1, 2)$: $\begin{bmatrix} 1 & 1 & 3 \\ 2 & 3 & 8 \\ 2 & 2 & 6 \end{bmatrix} \xrightarrow[\;(-2)R_1 + R_3\;]{(-2)R_1 + R_2} \begin{bmatrix} 1 & 1 & 3 \\ 0 & 1 & 2 \\ 0 & 0 & 0 \end{bmatrix} \xrightarrow{(-1)R_2 + R_1} \begin{bmatrix} 1 & 0 & 1 \\ 0 & 1 & 2 \\ 0 & 0 & 0 \end{bmatrix}$

43. $(x, y, z) = (z + w + 2, 2z - w - 1, z, w)$ — the final matrix translates to $x - z - w = 2$ and $y - 2z + w = -1$.

$\begin{bmatrix} 1 & 1 & -3 & 0 & 1 \\ 1 & 0 & -1 & -1 & 2 \\ 2 & 1 & -4 & -1 & 3 \end{bmatrix} \xrightarrow[\;(-2)R_2 + R_3\;]{(-1)R_2 + R_1} \begin{bmatrix} 0 & 1 & -2 & 1 & -1 \\ 1 & 0 & -1 & -1 & 2 \\ 0 & 1 & -2 & 1 & -1 \end{bmatrix} \xrightarrow[\;R_{12}\;]{(-1)R_1 + R_3} \begin{bmatrix} 1 & 0 & -1 & -1 & 2 \\ 0 & 1 & -2 & 1 & -1 \\ 0 & 0 & 0 & 0 & 0 \end{bmatrix}$

44. $(x, y, z) = (z - w, w + 3, z, w)$ — the final matrix translates to $x - z + w = 0$ and $y - w = 3$.

$\begin{bmatrix} 1 & -1 & -1 & 2 & -3 \\ 2 & -1 & -2 & 3 & -3 \\ 1 & -2 & -1 & 3 & -6 \end{bmatrix} \xrightarrow[\;(-1)R_1 + R_3\;]{(-2)R_1 + R_2} \begin{bmatrix} 1 & -1 & -1 & 2 & -3 \\ 0 & 1 & 0 & -1 & 3 \\ 0 & -1 & 0 & 1 & -3 \end{bmatrix} \xrightarrow[\;(1)R_2 + R_3\;]{(1)R_2 + R_1} \begin{bmatrix} 1 & 0 & -1 & 1 & 0 \\ 0 & 1 & 0 & -1 & 3 \\ 0 & 0 & 0 & 0 & 0 \end{bmatrix}$

45. $\begin{bmatrix} 2 & 5 \\ 1 & -2 \end{bmatrix} \begin{bmatrix} x \\ y \end{bmatrix} = \begin{bmatrix} -3 \\ 1 \end{bmatrix}$

46. $\begin{bmatrix} 5 & -7 & 1 \\ 2 & -3 & -1 \\ 1 & 1 & 1 \end{bmatrix} \begin{bmatrix} x \\ y \\ z \end{bmatrix} = \begin{bmatrix} 2 \\ 3 \\ -3 \end{bmatrix}$

47. $3x - y = -1$
$\quad 2x + 4y = 3$

48. $\quad\; x - 3z = 3$
$\quad 2x - y + 3z = -1$
$-2x + 3y - 4z = 2$

49. $(x, y) = (-2, 3)$:

$$\begin{bmatrix} x \\ y \end{bmatrix} = \begin{bmatrix} 2 & -3 \\ 4 & 1 \end{bmatrix}^{-1} \begin{bmatrix} -13 \\ -5 \end{bmatrix} = \frac{1}{14} \begin{bmatrix} 1 & 3 \\ -4 & 2 \end{bmatrix} \begin{bmatrix} -13 \\ -5 \end{bmatrix} = \frac{1}{14} \begin{bmatrix} -28 \\ 42 \end{bmatrix} = \begin{bmatrix} -2 \\ 3 \end{bmatrix}.$$

50. $(x, y) = (1, -1.5)$:

$$\begin{bmatrix} x \\ y \end{bmatrix} = \begin{bmatrix} 1 & 2 \\ 3 & -4 \end{bmatrix}^{-1} \begin{bmatrix} -2 \\ 9 \end{bmatrix} = -\frac{1}{10} \begin{bmatrix} -4 & -2 \\ -3 & 1 \end{bmatrix} \begin{bmatrix} -2 \\ 9 \end{bmatrix} = -\frac{1}{10} \begin{bmatrix} -10 \\ 15 \end{bmatrix} = \begin{bmatrix} 1 \\ -1.5 \end{bmatrix}.$$

51. $(x, y, z) = (-2, -5, -7)$; $\begin{bmatrix} x \\ y \\ z \end{bmatrix} = \begin{bmatrix} 2 & -1 & 1 \\ 1 & 2 & -3 \\ 3 & -2 & 1 \end{bmatrix}^{-1} \begin{bmatrix} -6 \\ 9 \\ -3 \end{bmatrix} = \begin{bmatrix} -2 \\ -5 \\ -7 \end{bmatrix}$

52. $(x, y, z) = (3, -0.5, 0.5)$; $\begin{bmatrix} x \\ y \\ z \end{bmatrix} = \begin{bmatrix} 1 & 4 & -2 \\ 2 & 1 & 1 \\ -3 & 3 & -5 \end{bmatrix}^{-1} \begin{bmatrix} 0 \\ 6 \\ -13 \end{bmatrix} = \begin{bmatrix} 3 \\ -0.5 \\ 0.5 \end{bmatrix}$

53. $(x, y, z, w) = (-1, 2, -2, 3)$; $\begin{bmatrix} x \\ y \\ z \\ w \end{bmatrix} = \begin{bmatrix} 2 & -1 & 1 & 1 \\ 1 & 2 & -3 & 1 \\ 3 & -1 & -1 & 2 \\ -2 & 3 & 1 & -3 \end{bmatrix}^{-1} \begin{bmatrix} -3 \\ 12 \\ 3 \\ -3 \end{bmatrix} = \begin{bmatrix} -1 \\ 2 \\ -2 \\ 3 \end{bmatrix}$

54. $(x, y, z, w) = (4, -2, 1, -3)$; $\begin{bmatrix} x \\ y \\ z \\ w \end{bmatrix} = \begin{bmatrix} 2 & 1 & 2 & 0 \\ 3 & 2 & -1 & -1 \\ -2 & 1 & 0 & -3 \\ 4 & -3 & 2 & -5 \end{bmatrix}^{-1} \begin{bmatrix} 8 \\ 10 \\ -1 \\ 39 \end{bmatrix} = \begin{bmatrix} 4 \\ -2 \\ 1 \\ -3 \end{bmatrix}$

55. $(x, y, z) = (0, -10, 1)$: Solving up from the bottom gives $z = 1$; then $y - 2 = -12$, so $y = -10$; then $2x + 10 = 10$, so $x = 0$.

$$\begin{array}{llll} 2x - y = 10 & & 2x - y = 10 & & 2x - y = 10 \\ x - z = -1 \Rightarrow 2\mathbf{E}_2 - \mathbf{E}_1 \Rightarrow & y - 2z = -12 & & y - 2z = -12 \\ y + z = -9 & & y + z = -9 \Rightarrow \mathbf{E}_3 - \mathbf{E}_2 \Rightarrow & 3z = 3 \end{array}$$

56. $(x, y, z) = (-2, 0, 0.5)$: Solving up from the bottom gives $z = 0.5$; then $y - (5.5)(0.5) = 247 - 2.75$, so $y = 0$; then $1.25x + 0.5 = -2$, so $x = -2$.

$$\begin{array}{ll} 1.25x + z = -2 & 1.25x + z = -2 \\ y - 5.5z = -2.75 & y - 5.5z = -2.75 \\ 3x - 1.5y = -6 \Rightarrow \mathbf{E}_3 - 2.4\mathbf{E}_1 + 1.5\mathbf{E}_2 \Rightarrow & -10.65z = -5.325 \end{array}$$

57. $(x, y, z, w) = (3, 3, -2, 0)$: Solving up from the bottom gives $w = 0$; then $-z + 0 = 2$, so $z = -2$; then $-3y + 4 = -5$, so $y = 3$; then $x + 6 - 4 = 5$, so $x = 3$.

$$\begin{array}{llll} x + 2y + 2z + w = 5 & & x + 2y + 2z + w = 5 & \\ 2x + y + 2z = 5 \Rightarrow \mathbf{E}_2 - 2\mathbf{E}_1 \Rightarrow & -3y - 2z - 2w = -5 & \\ 3x + 3y + 3z + 2w = 12 \Rightarrow \mathbf{E}_3 - 3\mathbf{E}_1 \Rightarrow & -3y - 3z - w = -3 \Rightarrow \mathbf{E}_3 - \mathbf{E}_2 \Rightarrow \\ x + z + w = 1 \Rightarrow \mathbf{E}_4 - \mathbf{E}_1 \Rightarrow & -2y - z = -4 \Rightarrow 3\mathbf{E}_4 - 2\mathbf{E}_2 \Rightarrow \end{array}$$

$$\begin{array}{ll} x + 2y + 2z + w = 5 & x + 2y + 2z + w = 5 \\ -3y - 2z - 2w = -5 & -3y - 2z - 2w = -5 \\ -z + w = 2 & -z + w = 2 \\ z + 4w = -2 \Rightarrow \mathbf{E}_4 + \mathbf{E}_3 \Rightarrow & 5w = 0 \end{array}$$

58. $(x, y, z, w) = (-1, 2, 4, -1)$: Solving up from the bottom gives $w = -1$; then $-z + 2 = -2$, so $z = 4$; then $-y + 4 - 2 = 0$, so $y = 2$; then $x - 2 - 1 = -4$, so $x = -1$.

$$\begin{array}{lll} x - y + w = -4 & x - y + w = -4 & x - y + w = -4 \\ -2x + y + z = 8 \Rightarrow \mathbf{E}_2 + 2\mathbf{E}_1 \Rightarrow & -y + z + 2w = 0 & -y + z + 2w = 0 \\ 2x - 2y - z = -10 \Rightarrow \mathbf{E}_3 - 2\mathbf{E}_1 \Rightarrow & -z - 2w = -2 & -z - 2w = -2 \\ -2x + z + w = 5 \Rightarrow \mathbf{E}_4 + 2\mathbf{E}_1 \Rightarrow & -2y + z + 3w = -3 \Rightarrow \mathbf{E}_4 - 2\mathbf{E}_2 - \mathbf{E}_3 \Rightarrow & w = -1 \end{array}$$

59. $(x, y, z) = \left(2 - \frac{3}{2}z, -\frac{1}{2}z - 4, z \right)$: z can be anything; once z is chosen, we have $2y + z = -8$, so $y = -\frac{1}{2}z - 4$; then

$x - \left(-\frac{1}{2}z - 4 \right) + z = 6$, so $x = 2 - \frac{3}{2}z$

$$\begin{array}{ll} x - y + z = 6 & x - y + z = 6 \\ x + y + 2z = -2 \Rightarrow \mathbf{E}_2 - \mathbf{E}_1 \Rightarrow & 2y + z = -8 \end{array}$$

60. $(x, y, z) = \left(\dfrac{1}{5}z - 1, \dfrac{3}{5}z - 2, z\right)$: z can be anything; once z is chosen, we have $5y - 3z = -10$, so $y = \dfrac{3}{5}z - 2$; then

$x - 2\left(\dfrac{3}{5}z - 2\right) + z = 3$, so $x = \dfrac{1}{5}z - 1$.

$$\begin{array}{ll} x - 2y + z = 3 & x - 2y + z = 3 \\ 2x + y - z = -4 \Rightarrow \mathbf{E}_2 - 2\mathbf{E}_1 \Rightarrow & 5y - 3z = -10 \end{array}$$

61. $(x, y, z, w) = (-1 - 2w, w + 1, -w, w)$: w can be anything; once w is chosen, we have $-z - w = 0$, so $z = -w$; then $y - w = 1$, so $y = w + 1$; then $x + (w + 1) + (-w) + 2w = 0$, so $x = -1 - 2w$.

$$\begin{array}{lll} 2x + y + z + 4w = -1 \Rightarrow \mathbf{E}_1 - 2\mathbf{E}_3 \Rightarrow & -y - z = -1 \Rightarrow \mathbf{E}_1 + \mathbf{E}_2 \Rightarrow & -z - w = 0 \\ x + 2y + z + w = 1 \;\;\Rightarrow \mathbf{E}_2 - \mathbf{E}_3 \;\;\Rightarrow & y - w = 1 & y - w = 1 \\ x + y + z + 2w = 0 & x + y + z + 2w = 0 & x + y + z + 2w = 0 \end{array}$$

62. $(x, y, z, w) = (w, 1 - 2w, -w - 1, w)$: w can be anything; once w is chosen, we have $-z - w = 1$, so $z = -w - 1$; then $y + 2w = 1$, so $y = 1 - 2w$; then $x + (1 - 2w) + 2(-w - 1) + 3w = -1$, so $x = w$.

$$\begin{array}{lll} 2x + 3y + 3z + 7w = 0 \Rightarrow \mathbf{E}_1 - 2\mathbf{E}_3 \Rightarrow & y - z + w = 2 \Rightarrow \mathbf{E}_1 - \mathbf{E}_2 \Rightarrow & -z - w = 1 \\ x + 2y + 2z + 5w = 0 \Rightarrow \mathbf{E}_2 - \mathbf{E}_3 \Rightarrow & y + 2w = 1 & y + 2w = 1 \\ x + y + 2z + 3w = -1 & x + y + 2z + 3w = -1 & x + y + 2z + 3w = -1 \end{array}$$

63. $(x, y, z, w) = (-w - 2, 0.5 - z, z, w)$: z and w can be anything; once they are chosen, we have $-y - z = -0.5$, so $y = 0.5 - z$; then since $y + z = 0.5$ we have $x + 0.5 + w = -1.5$, so $x = -w - 2$.

$$\begin{array}{ll} 2x + y + z + 2w = -3.5 \Rightarrow \mathbf{E}_1 - 2\mathbf{E}_2 \Rightarrow & -y - z = -0.5 \\ x + y + z + w = -1.5 & x + y + z + w = -1.5 \end{array}$$

64. $(x, y, z, w) = (z - 3w + 1, 2w - 2z + 4, z, w)$: z and w can be anything; once they are chosen, we have $-y - 2z + 2w = -4$, so $y = 2w - 2z + 4$; then $x + (2w - 2z + 4) + z + w = 5$, so $x = z - 3w + 1$.

$$\begin{array}{ll} 2x + y + 4w = 6 \Rightarrow \mathbf{E}_1 - 2\mathbf{E}_2 \Rightarrow & -y - 2z + 2w = -4 \\ x + y + z + w = 5 & x + y + z + w = 5 \end{array}$$

65. No solution: $\mathbf{E}_1 + \mathbf{E}_3$ gives $2x + 2y - z + 5w = 3$, which contradicts $\mathbf{E}_4$.

66. $(x, y, z, w) = (1, 1 - w, 6w - 2, w)$: Note first that $\mathbf{E}_4$ is the same as $\mathbf{E}_1$, so we ignore it. w can be anything, while $x = 1$. Once w is chosen, we have $1 + y + w = 2$, so $y = 1 - w$; then $2(1 - w) + z - 4w = 0$, so $z = 6w - 2$.

$$\begin{array}{lll} x + y + w = 2 & x + y + w = 2 & x + y + w = 2 \\ x + 4y + z - 2w = 3 \Rightarrow \mathbf{E}_2 - \mathbf{E}_1 \Rightarrow & 3y + z - 3w = 1 \Rightarrow \mathbf{E}_2 - \mathbf{E}_1 - \mathbf{E}_3 & -x = -1 \\ x + 3y + z - 3w = 2 \Rightarrow \mathbf{E}_3 - \mathbf{E}_1 \Rightarrow & 2y + z - 4w = 0 & 2y + z - 4w = 0 \end{array}$$

67. $f(x) = 2x^2 - 3x - 2$: We have $f(-1) = a(-1)^2 + b(-1) + c = a - b + c = 3$, $f(1) = a + b + c = -3$, and $f(2) = 4a + 2b + c = 0$. Solving this system gives $(a, b, c) = (2, -3, -2)$.

$$\begin{array}{lll} a - b + c = 3 & a - b + c = 3 & a - b + c = 3 \\ a + b + c = -3 \Rightarrow \mathbf{E}_2 - \mathbf{E}_1 \Rightarrow & 2b = -6 & 2b = -6 \\ 4a + 2b + c = 0 \;\;\Rightarrow \mathbf{E}_3 - 4\mathbf{E}_1 \Rightarrow & 6b - 3c = -12 \Rightarrow \mathbf{E}_3 - 3\mathbf{E}_2 \Rightarrow & -3c = 6 \end{array}$$

68. $f(x) = 3x^3 - x^2 + 2x - 5$: We have $f(-2) = -8a + 4b - 2c + d = -37$, $f(-1) = -a + b - c + d = -11$, $f(0) = d = -5$, and $f(2) = 8a + 4b + 2c + d = 19$. Solving this system gives $(a, b, c, d) = (3, -1, 2, -5)$.

$$\begin{array}{lll} -8a + 4b - 2c + d = -37 & -8a + 4b - 2c + d = -37 \Rightarrow \mathbf{E}_1 - 8\mathbf{E}_2 \Rightarrow & -4b + 6c - 7d = 51 \\ -a + b - c + d = -11 & -a + b - c + d = -11 & -a + b - c + d = -11 \\ d = -5 & d = -5 & d = -5 \\ 8a + 4b + 2c + d = 19 \Rightarrow \mathbf{E}_4 - \mathbf{E}_1 \Rightarrow & 8b + 2d = -18 & 8b + 2d = -18 \end{array}$$

69. $f(x) = (-c - 3)x^2 + x + c$, for any c — or $f(x) = ax^2 + x + (-a - 3)$, for any a: We have $f(-1) = a - b + c = -4$ and $f(1) = a + b + c = -2$. Solving this system gives $(a, b, c) = (-c - 3, 1, c) = (a, 1, -a - 3)$. Note that when $c = -3$ (or $a = 0$), this is simply the line through $(-1, -4)$ and $(1, -2)$.

$$\begin{array}{ll} a - b + c = -4 & a - b + c = -4 \\ a + b + c = -2 \Rightarrow \mathbf{E}_2 - \mathbf{E}_1 \Rightarrow & 2b = 2 \end{array}$$

70. $f(x) = (4 - c)x^3 - x^2 + cx - 1$, for any c — or $f(x) = ax^3 - x^2 + (4 - a)x - 1$, for any a: We have $f(-1) = -a + b - c + d = -6$, $f(0) = d = -1$, and $f(1) = a + b + c + d = 2$. Solving this system gives $(a, b, c, d) = (4 - c, -1, c, -1) = (a, -1, 4 - a, -1)$. Note that when $c = 4$ (or $a = 0$), this is simply the parabola through the given points.

$$\begin{array}{ll} -a + b - c + d = -6 & -a + b - c + d = -6 \\ d = -1 & d = -1 \\ a + b + c + d = 2 \Rightarrow \mathbf{E}_3 + \mathbf{E}_1 \Rightarrow & 2b + 2d = -4 \end{array}$$

71. In this problem, the graphs are representative of the population (in thousands) of the cities of Corpus Christi, TX, and Garland, TX, for several years, where x is the number of years past 1980.

(a) The following is a scatter plot of the Corpus Christi data with the linear regression equation $y = 2.0735x + 234.0268$ superimposed on it.

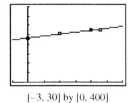

[−3, 30] by [0, 400]

(b) The following is a scatter plot of the Garland data with the linear regression equation $y = 3.5302x + 141.7246$ superimposed on it.

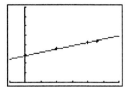

[−3, 30] by [0, 400]

(c) *Graphical solution:* Graph the two linear equations $y = 2.0735x + 234.0268$ and $y = 3.5302x + 141.7246$ on the same axis and find their point of intersection. The two curves intersect at $x \approx 63.4$. So, the population of the two cities will be the same sometime in the year 2043.

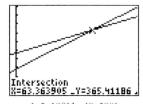

Intersection
X=63.363905 Y=365.41186
[−5, 100] by [0, 500]

Another graphical solution would be to find where the graph of the difference of the two curves is equal to 0.

Algebraic solution:
Solve $2.0735x + 234.0268 = 3.5302x + 141.7246$ for x.
$$2.0735x + 234.0268 = 3.5302x + 141.7246$$
$$1.4567x = 92.3022$$
$$x = \frac{92.3022}{1.4567} \approx 63.4$$
The population of the two cities will be the same sometime in the year 2043.

72. In this problem, the graphs are representative of the population (in thousands) of the cities of Anaheim, CA, and Anchorage, AK, for several years, where x is the number of years past 1970.

(a) The following is a scatter plot of the Anaheim data with the linear regression equation $y = 5.1670x + 166.2935$ superimposed on it.

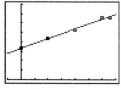

[−3, 35] by [0, 400]

(b) The following is a scatter plot of the Anchorage data with the linear regression equation $y = 6.3140x + 78.3593$ superimposed on it.

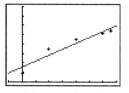

[−3, 35] by [0, 400]

(c) *Graphical solution:* Graph the two linear equations $y = 5.1670x + 166.2935$ and $y = 6.3140x + 78.3593$ on the same axis and find their point of intersection. The two curves intersect at $x \approx 76.7$.
The population of the two cities will be the same sometime in the year 2046.

Intersection
X=76.664676 Y=562.42122
[−5, 120] by [0, 800]

Another graphical solution would be to find where the graph of the difference of the two curves is equal to 0.

Algebraic solution:
Solve $5.1670x + 166.2935 = 6.3140x + 78.3593$ for x.
$$5.1670x + 166.2935 = 6.3140x + 78.3593$$
$$1.147x = 87.9342$$
$$x = \frac{87.9342}{1.147} \approx 76.7$$
The population of the two cities will be the same sometime in the year 2046.

73. $(x, y, z) = (825, 410, 165)$, where x is the number of children, y is the number of adults, and z is the number of senior citizens.

$$\begin{aligned} x + y + z &= 1400 \\ 25x + 100y + 75z &= 74{,}000 \Rightarrow \mathbf{E_2} - 75\mathbf{E_1} \Rightarrow \\ x - y - z &= 250 \quad \Rightarrow \mathbf{E_3} + \mathbf{E_1} \Rightarrow \end{aligned}$$

$$\begin{aligned} x + y + z &= 1400 \\ -50x + 25y &= -31{,}000 \\ 2x &= 1650 \end{aligned}$$

74. $(x, y, z) = \left(\dfrac{160}{11}, \dfrac{320}{11}, \dfrac{400}{11}\right) \approx (14.55, 29.09, 36.36)$ (all amounts in grams), where x is the amount of 22% alloy, y is the

amount of 30% alloy, and z is the amount of 42% alloy.

$$
\begin{array}{rclcrclcrcl}
x + y + z &=& 80 & & x + y + z &=& 80 & & x + y + z &=& 80 \\
0.22x + 0.30y + 0.42z &=& 27.2 \Rightarrow 50\mathbf{E}_2 - 11\mathbf{E}_1 \Rightarrow & & 4y + 10z &=& 480 & & 4y + 10z &=& 480 \\
2x - y &=& 0 \quad \Rightarrow \quad \mathbf{E}_3 - 2\mathbf{E}_1 \Rightarrow & & -3y - 2z &=& -160 \Rightarrow 4\mathbf{E}_3 + 3\mathbf{E}_2 \Rightarrow & & 22z &=& 800
\end{array}
$$

75. $(x, y, z) = (14{,}500, 5500, 60{,}000)$ (all amounts in dollars), where x is the amount invested in CDs, y is the amount in bonds, and z is the amount in the growth fund.

$$
\begin{array}{rclcrcl}
x + y + z &=& 80{,}000 & & x + y + z &=& 80{,}000 \\
0.067x + 0.093y + 0.156z &=& 10{,}843 \Rightarrow 1000\mathbf{E}_2 - 67\mathbf{E}_1 \Rightarrow & & 26y + 89z &=& 5{,}483{,}000 \\
3x + 3y - z &=& 0 \quad \Rightarrow \quad \mathbf{E}_3 - 3\mathbf{E}_1 \Rightarrow & & -4z &=& -240{,}000
\end{array}
$$

76. $(x, y, z) = (z - 9000, 29{,}000 - 2z, z)$ (all amounts in dollars). The amounts cannot be determined: if z dollars are invested at 10% ($9000 \le z \le 14{,}500$), then $z - 9000$ dollars invested at 6% and $29{,}000 - 2z$ invested at 8% satisfy all conditions.

$$
\begin{array}{rclcrclcrcl}
x + y + z &=& 20{,}000 & & x + y + z &=& 20{,}000 & & x + y + z &=& 20{,}000 \\
0.06x + 0.08y + 0.10z &=& 1780 \Rightarrow \quad 50\mathbf{E}_2 \Rightarrow & & 3x + 4y + 5z &=& 89{,}000 \Rightarrow \mathbf{E}_2 - 3\mathbf{E}_1 \Rightarrow & & y + 2z &=& 29{,}000 \\
-x + z &=& 9000 \Rightarrow \mathbf{E}_3 + 4\mathbf{E}_1 \Rightarrow & & 3x + 4y + 5z &=& 89{,}000 & & & &
\end{array}
$$

77. $(x, y, z) \approx (0, 38{,}983.05, 11{,}016.95)$: If z dollars are invested in the growth fund, then $y = \dfrac{1}{295}(21{,}250{,}000 - 885z) \approx$

$72{,}033.898 - 3z$ dollars must be invested in bonds, and $x \approx 2z - 22{,}033.898$ dollars are invested in CDs. Since $x \ge 0$, we see that $z \ge 11016.95$ (approximately); the minimum value of z requires that $x = 0$ (this is logical, since if we wish to minimize z, we should put the rest of our money in bonds, since bonds have a better return than CDs). Then $y \approx 72{,}033.898 - 3z = 38{,}983.05$.

$$
\begin{array}{rclcrcl}
x + y + z &=& 50{,}000 & & x + y + z &=& 50{,}000 \\
0.0575x + 0.087y + 0.146z &=& 5000 \Rightarrow 10{,}000\mathbf{E}_2 - 575\mathbf{E}_1 \Rightarrow & & 295y + 885z &=& 21{,}250{,}000
\end{array}
$$

78. $(x, y, z) = (0, 28.8, 11.2)$: If z liters of the 50% solution are used, then $y = \dfrac{1}{15}(880 - 40z) = \dfrac{8}{3}(22 - z)$ liters of 25%

solution must be used, and $x = \dfrac{5}{3}z - \dfrac{56}{3}$ liters of 10% solution are needed. Since $x \ge 0$, we see that $z \ge 11.2$ liters;

the minimum value of z requires that $x = 0$. Then $y = \dfrac{8}{3}(22 - z) = 28.8$ liters.

$$
\begin{array}{rclcrcl}
x + y + z &=& 40 & & x + y + z &=& 40 \\
0.10x + 0.25y + 0.50z &=& 12.8 \Rightarrow 100\mathbf{E}_2 - 10\mathbf{E}_1 \Rightarrow & & 15y + 40z &=& 880
\end{array}
$$

79. 22 nickels, 35 dimes, and 17 quarters:

$$
\begin{bmatrix} 1 & 1 & 1 & 74 \\ 5 & 10 & 25 & 885 \\ 1 & -1 & 1 & 4 \end{bmatrix}
\xrightarrow[\;(-1)R_1 + R_3\;]{\;(-5)R_1 + R_2\;}
\begin{bmatrix} 1 & 1 & 1 & 74 \\ 0 & 5 & 20 & 515 \\ 0 & -2 & 0 & -70 \end{bmatrix}
\xrightarrow[\;(-1/2)R_2\;]{\;R_{23}\;}
\begin{bmatrix} 1 & 1 & 1 & 74 \\ 0 & 1 & 0 & 35 \\ 0 & 5 & 20 & 515 \end{bmatrix}
\xrightarrow[\;(-5)R_2 + R_3\;]{\;(-1)R_2 + R_1\;}
$$

$$
\begin{bmatrix} 1 & 0 & 1 & 39 \\ 0 & 1 & 0 & 35 \\ 0 & 0 & 20 & 340 \end{bmatrix}
\xrightarrow{\;(1/20)R_3\;}
\begin{bmatrix} 1 & 0 & 1 & 39 \\ 0 & 1 & 0 & 35 \\ 0 & 0 & 1 & 17 \end{bmatrix}
\xrightarrow{\;(-1)R_3 + R_1\;}
\begin{bmatrix} 1 & 0 & 0 & 22 \\ 0 & 1 & 0 & 35 \\ 0 & 0 & 1 & 17 \end{bmatrix}
$$

80. 27 one-dollar bills, 18 fives, and 6 tens:

$$
\begin{bmatrix} 1 & 1 & 1 & 51 \\ 1 & 5 & 10 & 177 \\ 0 & 1 & -3 & 0 \end{bmatrix}
\xrightarrow[\;(-1)R_3 + R_1\;]{\;(-1)R_1 + R_2\;}
\begin{bmatrix} 1 & 0 & 4 & 51 \\ 0 & 4 & 9 & 126 \\ 0 & 1 & -3 & 0 \end{bmatrix}
\xrightarrow[\;R_{23}\;]{\;(-4)R_3 + R_2\;}
\begin{bmatrix} 1 & 0 & 4 & 51 \\ 0 & 1 & -3 & 0 \\ 0 & 0 & 21 & 126 \end{bmatrix}
\xrightarrow{\;(1/21)R_3\;}
$$

$$
\begin{bmatrix} 1 & 0 & 4 & 51 \\ 0 & 1 & -3 & 0 \\ 0 & 0 & 1 & 6 \end{bmatrix}
\xrightarrow[\;(3)R_3 + R_2\;]{\;(-4)R_3 + R_1\;}
\begin{bmatrix} 1 & 0 & 0 & 27 \\ 0 & 1 & 0 & 18 \\ 0 & 0 & 1 & 6 \end{bmatrix}
$$

81. $(x, p) = \left(\dfrac{16}{3}, \dfrac{220}{3}\right): \begin{bmatrix} x \\ p \end{bmatrix} = \begin{bmatrix} 5 & 1 \\ -10 & 1 \end{bmatrix}^{-1} \begin{bmatrix} 100 \\ 20 \end{bmatrix}$

$= \dfrac{1}{15}\begin{bmatrix} 1 & -1 \\ 10 & 5 \end{bmatrix}\begin{bmatrix} 100 \\ 20 \end{bmatrix} = \dfrac{1}{15}\begin{bmatrix} 80 \\ 1100 \end{bmatrix} = \dfrac{1}{3}\begin{bmatrix} 16 \\ 220 \end{bmatrix}$

82. $(x, p) = \left(\dfrac{10}{3}, 110\right): \begin{bmatrix} x \\ p \end{bmatrix} = \begin{bmatrix} 12 & 1 \\ -24 & 1 \end{bmatrix}^{-1} \begin{bmatrix} 150 \\ 30 \end{bmatrix}$

$= \dfrac{1}{36}\begin{bmatrix} 1 & -1 \\ 24 & 12 \end{bmatrix}\begin{bmatrix} 150 \\ 30 \end{bmatrix} = \dfrac{1}{36}\begin{bmatrix} 120 \\ 3960 \end{bmatrix} = \dfrac{1}{3}\begin{bmatrix} 10 \\ 330 \end{bmatrix}$

83. Adding one row to another is the same as multiplying that first row by 1 and then adding it to the other, so that it falls into the category of the second type of elementary row operations. Also, it corresponds to adding one equation to another in the original system.

84. Subtracting one row from another is the same as multiplying that first row by -1 and then adding it to the other, so that it falls into the category of the second type of elementary row operations. Also, it corresponds to subtracting one equation from another.

85. False. For a nonzero square matrix to have an inverse, the determinant of the matrix must not be equal to zero.

86. False. The statement holds only for a system that has exactly one solution. For example, $\begin{bmatrix} 1 & 0 & 1 & 0 \\ 0 & 1 & 1 & 1 \\ 0 & 0 & 0 & 2 \end{bmatrix}$ could be the reduced row echelon form for a system that has no solution.

90. $\begin{bmatrix} 1 & 2 & -1 & 8 \\ -1 & 3 & 2 & 3 \\ 2 & -1 & 3 & -19 \end{bmatrix} \xrightarrow[(-2)R_1 + R_3]{(1)R_1 + R_2} \begin{bmatrix} 1 & 2 & -1 & 8 \\ 0 & 5 & 1 & 11 \\ 0 & -5 & 5 & -35 \end{bmatrix} \xrightarrow[(1/6)R_3]{(1)R_2 + R_3} \begin{bmatrix} 1 & 2 & -1 & 8 \\ 0 & 5 & 1 & 11 \\ 0 & 0 & 1 & -4 \end{bmatrix} \xrightarrow[(1)R_3 + R_1]{(-1)R_3 + R_2}$

$\begin{bmatrix} 1 & 2 & 0 & 4 \\ 0 & 5 & 0 & 15 \\ 0 & 0 & 1 & -4 \end{bmatrix} \xrightarrow[(-2)R_2 + R_1]{(1/5)R_2} \begin{bmatrix} 1 & 0 & 0 & -2 \\ 0 & 1 & 0 & 3 \\ 0 & 0 & 1 & -4 \end{bmatrix}$

The answer is E.

91. (a) The planes can intersect at exactly one point

   (b) At least two planes are parallel, or else the line of each pair of intersecting planes is parallel to the third plane.

   (c) Two or more planes can coincide, or else all three planes can intersect along a single line.

92. Starting with any matrix in row echelon form, one can perform the operation $kR_i + R_j$, for any constant k, with $i > j$, and obtain another matrix in row echelon form. As a simple example, $\begin{bmatrix} 1 & 1 & 1 \\ 0 & 1 & 1 \end{bmatrix}$ and $\begin{bmatrix} 1 & 2 & 2 \\ 0 & 1 & 1 \end{bmatrix}$ are two equivalent matrices (the second can be obtained from the first via $R_2 + R_1$), both of which are in row echelon form.

93. (a) $C(x) = (x - 3)(x - 5) - (-1)(-2)$
   $= x^2 - 8x + 13$.

   (b)
   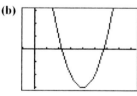
   $[-1, 8.4]$ by $[-3.1, 3.1]$

   (c) $C(x) = 0$ when $x = 4 \pm \sqrt{13}$ — approx. 2.27 and 5.73.

   (d) $\det A = 13$, and the y-intercept is $(0, 13)$. This is the case because $C(0) = (3)(5) - (1)(2) = \det A$.

   (e) $a_{11} + a_{22} = 3 + 5 = 8$. The eigenvalues add to $(4 - \sqrt{13}) + (4 + \sqrt{13}) = 8$, also.

94. (a) $C(x) = (x - 2)^2 - (-5)(-1) = x^2 - 4x - 1$.

   (b)
   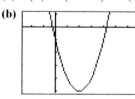
   $[-2.7, 6.7]$ by $[-5.1, 1.1]$

   (c) $C(x) = 0$ when $2 \pm \sqrt{5}$ — approx. -0.24 and 4.24.

   (d) $\det A = -1$, and the y-intercept is $(0, -1)$. This is the case because $C(0) = (2)(2) - (-5)(-1) = \det A$.

   (e) $a_{11} + a_{22} = 2 + 2 = 4$. The eigenvalues add to $(2 - \sqrt{5}) + (2 + \sqrt{5}) = 4$, also.

87. $2(3) - (-1)(2) = 8$. The answer is D.

88. The augmented matrix has the variable coefficients in the first three columns and the constants in the last column. The answer is A.

89. Twice the first row was added to the second row. The answer is D.

■ Section 7.4 Partial Fractions

Exploration 1

1. (a) $25 - 1 = A_1(5 - 5) + A_2(5 + 3)$
   $24 = 8 A_2$
   $3 = A_2$

   (b) $-15 - 1 = A_1(-3 - 5) + A_2(-3 + 3)$
   $-16 = -8 A_1$
   $2 = A_1$

2. (a) $-4 + 4 + 4 = A_1(2 - 2)^2 + 2 A_2(2 - 2) + 2 A_3$
   $4 = 2 A_3$
   $2 = A_3$

   (b) $0 + 0 + 4 = A_1(0 - 2)^2 + 0 \cdot A_2(0 - 2) + 0 \cdot A_3$
   $4 = 4 A_1$
   $1 = A_1$

   (c) Suppose $x = 3$
   $-9 + 6 + 4 = 1 \cdot (3 - 2)^2 + 2 \cdot 3(3 - 2) + 3A_2$
   $1 = 1 + 6 + 3A_2$
   $-6 = 3A_2$
   $-2 = A_2$

Quick Review 7.4

1. $\dfrac{(x - 3) + 2(x - 1)}{(x - 1)(x - 3)} = \dfrac{3x - 5}{(x - 1)(x - 3)}$
   $= \dfrac{3x - 5}{x^2 - 4x + 3}$

2. $\dfrac{5(x + 1) - 2(x + 4)}{(x + 4)(x + 1)} = \dfrac{3x - 3}{(x + 4)(x + 1)}$
   $= \dfrac{3(x - 1)}{x^2 + 5x + 4}$

3. $\dfrac{(x + 1)^2 + 3x(x + 1) + x}{x(x + 1)^2} = \dfrac{4x^2 + 6x + 1}{x(x + 1)^2}$
   $= \dfrac{4x^2 + 6x + 1}{x^3 + 2x^2 + x}$

4. $\dfrac{3(x^2 + 1) - (x + 1)}{(x^2 + 1)^2} = \dfrac{3x^2 - x + 2}{(x^2 + 1)^2}$

5. $\begin{array}{r|rrrr} -2 & 3 & -6 & -2 & 7 \\ & & -6 & 0 & 4 \\ \hline & 3 & 0 & -2 & 3 \end{array}$

   $\dfrac{f(x)}{d(x)} = 3x^2 - 2 + \dfrac{3}{x - 2}$

6.

$$x^2 + x - 6 \overline{) 2x^3 + 3x^2 - 14x - 8}$$

with work:

$2x + 1$

$\underline{2x^3 + 2x^2 - 12x}$

$x^2 - 2x - 8$

$\underline{x^2 + x - 6}$

$-3x - 2$

$$\frac{f(x)}{d(x)} = 2x + 1 - \frac{3x + 2}{x^2 + x - 6}$$

7. Possible real rational zeros:

$$\frac{\pm 1, \ \pm 2, \ \pm 3, \ \pm 4, \ \pm 6, \ \pm 12}{\pm 1}$$

From a graph, $x = -1$ and $x = 3$ seem reasonable:

$$
\begin{array}{r|rrrr}
1 & 1 & -2 & 1 & -8 & -12 \\
  &   & 1 & -3 & 4 & -12 \\
\hline
  & 1 & -3 & 4 & -12 & 0 \\
\end{array}
$$

$$
\begin{array}{r|rrrr}
-3 & 1 & -3 & 4 & -12 \\
   &   & -3 & 0 & -12 \\
\hline
   & 1 & 0 & 4 & 0 \\
\end{array}
$$

$x^4 - 2x^2 + x^2 - 8x + 12 = (x + 1)(x - 3)(x^2 + 4)$

8. Possible real rational zeros: $\dfrac{\pm 1, \ \pm 2, \ \pm 5, \ \pm 10}{\pm 1}$ From a

graph, $x = -1, x = -2$ and $x = 5$ seem reasonable:

$$
\begin{array}{r|rrrr}
1 & 1 & -1 & -15 & -23 & -10 \\
  &   & 1 & -2 & -13 & -10 \\
\hline
  & 1 & -2 & -13 & -10 & 0 \\
\end{array}
$$

$$
\begin{array}{r|rrrr}
2 & 1 & -2 & -13 & -10 \\
  &   & 2 & -8 & -10 \\
\hline
  & 1 & -4 & -5 & 0 \\
\end{array}
$$

$$
\begin{array}{r|rrr}
-5 & 1 & -4 & -5 \\
   &   & -5 & -5 \\
\hline
   & 1 & 1 & 0 \\
\end{array}
$$

$x^4 - x^3 - 15x^2 - 23x - 10 = (x + 1)^2(x + 2)(x - 5)$

In #9–10, equate coefficients.

9. $A = 3, B = -1, C = 1$

10. $A = -2, B = 2, C = -1, D = -5$

Section 7.4 Exercises

1. $\dfrac{x^2 - 7}{x(x^2 - 4)} = \dfrac{A_1}{x} + \dfrac{A_2}{x - 2} + \dfrac{A_3}{x + 2}$

2. $\dfrac{x^4 + 3x^2 - 1}{(x^2 + x + 1)^2(x^2 - x + 1)}$

$= \dfrac{B_1 x + C_1}{x^2 + x + 1} + \dfrac{B_2 x + C_2}{(x^2 + x + 1)^2} + \dfrac{B_3 x + C_3}{x^2 - x + 1}$

3. $\dfrac{x^5 - 2x^4 + x - 1}{x^3(x - 1)^2(x^2 + 9)}$

$= \dfrac{A_1}{x} + \dfrac{A_2}{x^2} + \dfrac{A_3}{x^3} + \dfrac{A_4}{x - 1} + \dfrac{A_5}{(x - 1)^2} + \dfrac{B_1 x + C_1}{x^2 + 9}$

4. $\dfrac{x^2 + 3x + 2}{(x^3 - 1)^3} = \dfrac{x^2 + 3x + 2}{(x - 1)^3(x^2 + x + 1)^3}$

$= \dfrac{A_1}{x - 1} + \dfrac{A_2}{(x - 1)^2} + \dfrac{A_3}{(x - 1)^3} + \dfrac{B_1 x + C_1}{x^2 + x + 1}$

$+ \dfrac{B_2 x + C_2}{(x^2 + x + 1)^2} + \dfrac{B_3 x + C_3}{(x^2 + x + 1)^3}$

5. $\dfrac{-3}{x + 4} + \dfrac{4}{x - 2}$: $x + 22 = A(x - 2) + B(x + 4)$

$= (A + B)x + (-2A + 4B)$

$\begin{matrix} A + B = 1 \\ -2A + 4B = 22 \end{matrix} \Rightarrow \begin{bmatrix} A \\ B \end{bmatrix} = \begin{bmatrix} 1 & 1 \\ -2 & 4 \end{bmatrix}^{-1} \begin{bmatrix} 1 \\ 22 \end{bmatrix} = \begin{bmatrix} -3 \\ 4 \end{bmatrix}$

6. $\dfrac{2}{x + 3} - \dfrac{1}{x}$: $x - 3 = Ax + B(x + 3)$

$= (A + B)x + 3B$

$\begin{matrix} A + B = 1 \\ 0 + 3B = -3 \end{matrix} \Rightarrow \begin{bmatrix} A \\ B \end{bmatrix} = \begin{bmatrix} 1 & 1 \\ 0 & 3 \end{bmatrix}^{-1} \begin{bmatrix} 1 \\ -3 \end{bmatrix} = \begin{bmatrix} 2 \\ -1 \end{bmatrix}$

7. $\dfrac{3}{x^2 + 1} + \dfrac{2x - 1}{(x^2 + 1)^2}$: $3x^2 + 2x + 2$

$= (Ax + B)(x^2 + 1) + (Cx + D)$

$= Ax^3 + Bx^2 + (A + C)x + (B + D)$

$\begin{matrix} A & & & = 0 \\ & B & & = 3 \\ A & & + C & = 2 \\ & B & + D = 2 \end{matrix} \Rightarrow \begin{bmatrix} A \\ B \\ C \\ D \end{bmatrix}$

$= \begin{bmatrix} 1 & 0 & 0 & 0 \\ 0 & 1 & 0 & 0 \\ 1 & 0 & 1 & 0 \\ 0 & 1 & 0 & 1 \end{bmatrix}^{-1} \begin{bmatrix} 0 \\ 3 \\ 2 \\ 2 \end{bmatrix} = \begin{bmatrix} 0 \\ 3 \\ 2 \\ -1 \end{bmatrix}$

8. $\dfrac{1}{x} + \dfrac{2}{x^2} - \dfrac{1}{x + 2}$: $4x + 4$

$= Ax(x + 2) + B(x + 2) + Cx^2$

$= (A + C)x^2 + (2A + B)x + (2B)$

$\begin{matrix} A & & + C = 0 \\ 2A & + B & = 4 \\ & 2B & = 4 \end{matrix} \Rightarrow \begin{bmatrix} A \\ B \\ C \end{bmatrix}$

$= \begin{bmatrix} 1 & 0 & 1 \\ 2 & 1 & 0 \\ 0 & 2 & 0 \end{bmatrix}^{-1} \begin{bmatrix} 0 \\ 4 \\ 4 \end{bmatrix} = \begin{bmatrix} 1 \\ 2 \\ -1 \end{bmatrix}$

9. $\dfrac{1}{x - 2} + \dfrac{2}{(x - 2)^2} + \dfrac{1}{(x - 2)^3}$: $x^2 - 2x + 1$

$= A(x - 2)^2 + B(x - 2) + C$

$= Ax^2 + (-4A + B)x + (4A - 2B + C)$

$\begin{matrix} A & & = 1 \\ -4A & + B & = -2 \\ 4A & - 2B + C & = 1 \end{matrix} \Rightarrow \begin{bmatrix} 1 & 0 & 0 & 1 \\ -4 & 1 & 0 & -2 \\ 4 & -2 & 1 & 1 \end{bmatrix}$

Using a grapher, we find that the reduced row echelon form of the augmented matrix is:

$\begin{bmatrix} 1 & 0 & 0 & 1 \\ 0 & 1 & 0 & 2 \\ 0 & 0 & 1 & 1 \end{bmatrix} \Rightarrow \begin{bmatrix} A \\ B \\ C \end{bmatrix} = \begin{bmatrix} 1 \\ 2 \\ 1 \end{bmatrix}$

10. $\dfrac{-3x + 7}{x^2 + 4} + \dfrac{8x - 17}{x^2 + 9}$:

$5x^3 - 10x^2 + 5x - 5$
$= (Ax + B)(x^2 + 9) + (Cx + D)(x^2 + 4)$
$= (A + C)x^3 + (B + D)x^2 + (9A + 4C)x$
$+ (9B + 4D)$

$$
\begin{array}{rrrcr}
A & + C & & = & 5 \\
 & B & + D & = & -10 \\
9A & + 4C & & = & 5 \\
 & 9B & + 4D & = & -5
\end{array}
\Rightarrow
$$

$$
\begin{bmatrix}
1 & 0 & 1 & 0 & 5 \\
0 & 1 & 0 & 1 & -10 \\
9 & 0 & 4 & 0 & 5 \\
0 & 9 & 0 & 4 & -5
\end{bmatrix}
$$

Using a grapher, we find that the reduced row echelon form of the augmented matrix is:

$$
\begin{bmatrix}
1 & 0 & 0 & 0 & -3 \\
0 & 1 & 0 & 0 & 7 \\
0 & 0 & 1 & 0 & 8 \\
0 & 0 & 0 & 1 & -17
\end{bmatrix}
\Rightarrow
\begin{bmatrix} A \\ B \\ C \\ D \end{bmatrix}
=
\begin{bmatrix} -3 \\ 7 \\ 8 \\ -17 \end{bmatrix}
$$

11. $\dfrac{2}{x + 3} - \dfrac{1}{(x + 3)^2} + \dfrac{3x - 1}{x^2 + 2} + \dfrac{x + 2}{(x^2 + 2)^2}$:

$5x^5 + 22x^4 + 36x^3 + 53x^2 + 71x + 20$
$= A(x + 3)(x^2 + 2)^2 + B(x^2 + 2)^2$
$+ (Cx + D)(x + 3)^2(x^2 + 2) + (Ex + F)(x + 3)^2$
$= (A + C)x^5 + (3A + B + 6C + D)x^4$
$+ (4A + 11C + 6D + E)x^3 + (12A + 4B + 12C$
$+ 11D + 6E + F)x^2 + (4A + 18C + 12D + 9E$
$+ 6F)x + (12A + 4B + 18D + 9F)$

$$
\begin{array}{rrrrrrcr}
A & & + C & & & & = & 5 \\
3A & + B & + 6C & + D & & & = & 22 \\
4A & & + 11C & + 6D & + E & & = & 36 \\
12A & + 4B & + 12C & + 11D & + 6E & + F & = & 53 \\
4A & & + 18C & + 12D & + 9E & + 6F & = & 71 \\
12A & + 4B & & + 18D & & + 9F & = & 20
\end{array}
\Rightarrow
$$

$$
\begin{bmatrix}
1 & 0 & 1 & 0 & 0 & 0 & 5 \\
3 & 1 & 6 & 1 & 0 & 0 & 22 \\
4 & 0 & 11 & 6 & 1 & 0 & 36 \\
12 & 4 & 12 & 11 & 6 & 1 & 53 \\
4 & 0 & 18 & 12 & 9 & 6 & 71 \\
12 & 4 & 0 & 18 & 0 & 9 & 20
\end{bmatrix}
$$

Using a grapher, we find that the reduced row echelon form of the augmented matrix is:

$$
\begin{bmatrix}
1 & 0 & 0 & 0 & 0 & 0 & 2 \\
0 & 1 & 0 & 0 & 0 & 0 & -1 \\
0 & 0 & 1 & 0 & 0 & 0 & 3 \\
0 & 0 & 0 & 1 & 0 & 0 & -1 \\
0 & 0 & 0 & 0 & 1 & 0 & 1 \\
0 & 0 & 0 & 0 & 0 & 1 & 2
\end{bmatrix}
\Rightarrow
\begin{bmatrix} A \\ B \\ C \\ D \\ E \\ F \end{bmatrix}
=
\begin{bmatrix} 2 \\ -1 \\ 3 \\ -1 \\ 1 \\ 2 \end{bmatrix}
$$

12. $\dfrac{-2}{x - 1} + \dfrac{3}{(x - 1)^2} + \dfrac{1}{x + 4} + \dfrac{3}{(x + 4)^2}$:

$-x^3 - 6x^2 - 5x + 87 = A(x - 1)(x + 4)^2$
$+ B(x + 4)^2 + C(x - 1)^2(x + 4) + D(x - 1)^2$
$= (A + C)x^3 + (7A + B + 2C + D)x^2$
$+ (8A + 8B - 7C - 2D)x$
$+ (-16A + 16B + 4C + D)$

$$
\begin{array}{rrrrcr}
A & & + C & & = & -1 \\
7A & + B & + 2C & + D & = & -6 \\
8A & + 8B & - 7C & - 2D & = & -5 \\
-16A & + 16B & + 4C & + D & = & 87
\end{array}
\Rightarrow
$$

$$
\begin{bmatrix}
1 & 0 & 1 & 0 & -1 \\
7 & 1 & 2 & 1 & -6 \\
8 & 8 & -7 & -2 & -5 \\
-16 & 16 & 4 & 1 & 87
\end{bmatrix}
$$

Using a grapher, we find that the reduced row echelon form of the augmented matrix is:

$$
\begin{bmatrix}
1 & 0 & 0 & 0 & -2 \\
0 & 1 & 0 & 0 & 3 \\
0 & 0 & 1 & 0 & 1 \\
0 & 0 & 0 & 1 & 3
\end{bmatrix}
\Rightarrow
\begin{bmatrix} A \\ B \\ C \\ D \end{bmatrix}
=
\begin{bmatrix} -2 \\ 3 \\ 1 \\ 3 \end{bmatrix}
$$

13. $\dfrac{2}{(x - 5)(x - 3)} = \dfrac{A_1}{x - 5} + \dfrac{A_2}{x - 3}$, so

$2 = A_1(x - 3) + A_2(x - 5)$. With $x = 5$, we see that
$2 = 2A_1$, so $A_1 = 1$; with $x = 3$ we have $2 = -2A_2$, so
$A_2 = -1$: $\dfrac{1}{x - 5} - \dfrac{1}{x - 3}$.

14. $\dfrac{4}{(x + 3)(x + 7)} = \dfrac{A_1}{x + 3} + \dfrac{A_2}{x + 7}$, so

$4 = A_1(x + 7) + A_2(x + 3)$. With $x = -3$, we see that
$4 = 4A_1$, so $A_1 = 1$; with $x = -7$ we have $4 = -4A_2$,
so $A_2 = -1$: $\dfrac{1}{x + 3} - \dfrac{1}{x + 7}$.

15. $\dfrac{4}{x^2 - 1} = \dfrac{A_1}{x - 1} + \dfrac{A_2}{x + 1}$, so

$4 = A_1(x + 1) + A_2(x - 1)$. With $x = 1$, we see that
$4 = 2A_1$, so $A_1 = 2$; with $x = -1$ we have $4 = -2A_2$, so
$A_2 = -2$: $\dfrac{2}{x - 1} - \dfrac{2}{x + 1}$.

16. $\dfrac{6}{x^2 - 9} = \dfrac{A_1}{x - 3} + \dfrac{A_2}{x + 3}$, so

$6 = A_1(x + 3) + A_2(x - 3)$. With $x = 3$, we see that
$6 = 6A_1$, so $A_1 = 1$; with $x = -3$ we have $6 = -6A_2$, so
$A_2 = -1$: $\dfrac{1}{x - 3} - \dfrac{1}{x + 3}$.

17. $\dfrac{1}{x^2 + 2x} = \dfrac{A_1}{x} + \dfrac{A_2}{x + 2}$, so $1 = A_1(x + 2) + A_2x$.

With $x = 0$, we see that $1 = 2A_1$, so $A_1 = \dfrac{1}{2}$; with

$x = -2$, we have $1 = -2A_2$, so $A_2 = -\dfrac{1}{2}$:

$\dfrac{1/2}{x} - \dfrac{1/2}{x + 2} = \dfrac{1}{2x} - \dfrac{1/2}{x + 2}$.

18. $\dfrac{-6}{x^2 - 3x} = \dfrac{A_1}{x} + \dfrac{A_2}{x - 3}$, so

$-6 = A_1(x - 3) + A_2x$. With $x = 0$, we see that
$-6 = -3A_1$, so $A_1 = 2$; with $x = 3$ we have $-6 = 3A_2$,
so

$A_2 = -2$: $\dfrac{-2}{x - 3} + \dfrac{2}{x}$.

19. $\dfrac{-x + 10}{x^2 + x - 12} = \dfrac{A_1}{x - 3} + \dfrac{A_2}{x + 4}$, so $-x + 10$

$= A_1(x + 4) + A_2(x - 3)$. With $x = 3$, we see that $7 = 7A_1$, so $A_1 = 1$; with $x = -4$ we have $14 = -7A_2$, so $A_2 = -2$: $\dfrac{1}{x - 3} - \dfrac{2}{x + 4}$.

20. $\dfrac{7x - 7}{x^2 - 3x - 10} = \dfrac{A_1}{x - 5} + \dfrac{A_2}{x + 2}$, so $7x - 7$

$= A_1(x + 2) + A_2(x - 5)$. With $x = 5$, we see that $28 = 7A_1$, so $A_1 = 4$; with $x = -2$ we have $-21 = -7A_2$, so $A_2 = 3$: $\dfrac{4}{x - 5} + \dfrac{3}{x + 2}$.

21. $\dfrac{x + 17}{2x^2 + 5x - 3} = \dfrac{A_1}{x + 3} + \dfrac{A_2}{2x - 1}$, so $x + 17$
$= A_1(2x - 1) + A_2(x + 3)$. With $x = -3$, we see that $14 = -7A_1$, so $A_1 = -2$; with $x = \dfrac{1}{2}$ we have $\dfrac{35}{2} = \dfrac{7}{2}A_2$, so $A_2 = 5$: $\dfrac{-2}{x + 3} + \dfrac{5}{2x - 1}$.

22. $\dfrac{4x - 11}{2x^2 - x - 3} = \dfrac{A_1}{x + 1} + \dfrac{A_2}{2x - 3}$, so $4x - 11$
$= A_1(2x - 3) + A_2(x + 1)$. With $x = -1$, we see that $-15 = -5A_1$, so $A_1 = 3$; with $x = \dfrac{3}{2}$ we have $-5 = \dfrac{5}{2}A_2$, so $A_2 = -2$: $\dfrac{3}{x + 1} - \dfrac{2}{2x - 3}$.

23. $\dfrac{2x^2 + 5}{(x^2 + 1)^2} = \dfrac{B_1x + C_1}{x^2 + 1} + \dfrac{B_2x + C_2}{(x^2 + 1)^2}$, so $2x^2 + 5$
$= (B_1x + C_1)(x^2 + 1) + B_2x + C_2$. Expanding the right side leaves $2x^2 + 5 = B_1x^3 + C_1x^2 + (B_1 + B_2)x + C_1 + C_2$; equating coefficients reveals that $B_1 = 0, C_1 = 2, B_1 + B_2 = 0$, and $C_1 + C_2 = 5$.
This means that $B_2 = 0$ and $C_2 = 3$: $\dfrac{2}{x^2 + 1} + \dfrac{3}{(x^2 + 1)^2}$.

24. $\dfrac{3x^2 + 4}{(x^2 + 1)^2} = \dfrac{B_1x + C_1}{x^2 + 1} + \dfrac{B_2x + C_2}{(x^2 + 1)^2}$, so $3x^2 + 4$
$= (B_1x + C_1)(x^2 + 1) + B_2x + C_2$. Expanding the right side leaves $3x^2 + 4 = B_1x^3 + C_1x^2 + (B_1 + B_2)x + C_1 + C_2$; equating coefficients reveals that $B_1 = 0, C_1 = 3, B_1 + B_2 = 0$, and $C_1 + C_2 = 4$.
This means that $B_2 = 0$ and $C_2 = 1$: $\dfrac{3}{x^2 + 1} + \dfrac{1}{(x^2 + 1)^2}$.

25. The denominator factors into $x(x - 1)^2$, so
$\dfrac{x^2 - x + 2}{x^3 - 2x^2 + x} = \dfrac{A_1}{x} + \dfrac{A_2}{x - 1} + \dfrac{A_3}{(x - 1)^2}$. Then
$x^2 - x + 2 = A_1(x - 1)^2 + A_2x(x - 1) + A_3x$. With $x = 0$, we have $2 = A_1$; with $x = 1$, we have $2 = A_3$; with $x = 2$, we have $4 = A_1 + 2A_2 + 2A_3 = 2 + 2A_2 + 4$,
so $A_2 = -1$: $\dfrac{2}{x} - \dfrac{1}{x - 1} + \dfrac{2}{(x - 1)^2}$.

26. The denominator factors into $x(x - 3)^2$, so
$\dfrac{-6x + 25}{x^3 - 6x^2 + 9x} = \dfrac{A_1}{x} + \dfrac{A_2}{x - 3} + \dfrac{A_3}{(x - 3)^2}$. Then
$-6x + 25 = A_1(x - 3)^2 + A_2x(x - 3) + A_3x$. With

$x = 0$, we have $25 = 9A_1$; so $A_1 = \dfrac{25}{9}$; with $x = 3$, we have $7 = 3A_3$; so $A_3 = \dfrac{7}{3}$; with $x = 4$, we have
$1 = A_1 + 4A_2 + 4A_3 = \dfrac{25}{9} + 4A_2 + \dfrac{28}{3}$, so
$A_2 = -\dfrac{25}{9}$: $\dfrac{7/3}{(x - 3)^2} - \dfrac{25/9}{x - 3} + \dfrac{25/9}{x}$.

27. $\dfrac{3x^2 - 4x + 3}{x^3 - 3x^2} = \dfrac{A_1}{x} + \dfrac{A_2}{x^2} + \dfrac{A_3}{x - 3}$. Then
$3x^2 - 4x + 3 = A_1x(x - 3) + A_2(x - 3) + A_3x^2$.
With $x = 0$, we have $3 = -3A_2$, so $A_2 = -1$; with $x = 3$, we have $18 = 9A_3$, so $A_3 = 2$; with $x = 1$, we have $2 = -2A_1 - 2A_2 + A_3 = -2A_1 + 2 + 2$, so
$A_1 = 1$: $\dfrac{1}{x} - \dfrac{1}{x^2} + \dfrac{2}{x - 3}$.

28. $\dfrac{5x^2 + 7x - 4}{x^3 + 4x^2} = \dfrac{A_1}{x} + \dfrac{A_2}{x^2} + \dfrac{A_3}{x + 4}$. Then
$5x^2 + 7x - 4 = A_1x(x + 4) + A_2(x + 4) + A_3x^2$.
With $x = 0$, we have $-4 = 4A_2$, so $A_2 = -1$; with $x = -4$, we have $48 = 16A_3$, so $A_3 = 3$; with $x = 1$, we have $8 = 5A_1 + 5A_2 + A_3 = 5A_1 - 5 + 3$, so
$A_1 = 2$: $\dfrac{2}{x} - \dfrac{1}{x^2} + \dfrac{3}{x + 4}$.

29. $\dfrac{2x^3 + 4x - 1}{(x^2 + 2)^2} = \dfrac{B_1x + C_1}{x^2 + 2} + \dfrac{B_2x + C_2}{(x^2 + 2)^2}$. Then
$2x^3 + 4x - 1 = (B_1x + C_1)(x^2 + 2) + B_2x + C_2$.
Expanding the right side and equating coefficients reveals that $B_1 = 2, C_1 = 0, 2B_1 + B_2 = 4$, and $2C_1 + C_2 = -1$.
This means than $B_2 = 0$ and $C_2 = -1$:
$\dfrac{2x}{x^2 + 2} - \dfrac{1}{(x^2 + 2)^2}$.

30. $\dfrac{3x^3 + 6x - 1}{(x^2 + 2)^2} = \dfrac{B_1x + C_1}{x^2 + 2} + \dfrac{B_2x + C_2}{(x^2 + 2)^2}$. Then
$3x^3 + 6x - 1 = (B_1x + C_1)(x^2 + 2) + B_2x + C_2$.
Expanding the right side and equating coefficients reveals that $B_1 = 3, C_1 = 0, 2B_1 + B_2 = 6$, and $2C_1 + C_2 = -1$.
This means than $B_2 = 0$ and $C_2 = -1$:
$\dfrac{3x}{x^2 + 2} - \dfrac{1}{(x^2 + 2)^2}$.

31. The denominator factors into $(x - 1)(x^2 + x + 1)$, so
$\dfrac{x^2 + 3x + 2}{x^3 - 1} = \dfrac{A}{x - 1} + \dfrac{Bx + C}{x^2 + x + 1}$. Then
$x^2 + 3x + 2 = A(x^2 + x + 1) + (Bx + C)(x - 1)$.
With $x = 1$, we have $6 = 3A$, so $A = 2$; with $x = 0$, $2 = A - C$, so $C = 0$. Finally, with $x = 2$, we have
$12 = 7A + 2B$, so $B = -1$: $\dfrac{2}{x - 1} - \dfrac{x}{x^2 + x + 1}$.

32. The denominator factors into $(x + 1)(x^2 - x + 1)$, so
$\dfrac{2x^2 - 4x + 3}{x^3 + 1} = \dfrac{A}{x + 1} + \dfrac{Bx + C}{x^2 - x + 1}$. Then
$2x^2 - 4x + 3 = A(x^2 - x + 1) + (Bx + C)(x + 1)$.
With $x = -1$, we have $9 = 3A$, so $A = 3$; with $x = 0$, $3 = A + C$, so $C = 0$. Finally, with $x = -2$, we have
$19 = 7A + 2B$, so $B = -1$: $\dfrac{3}{x + 1} - \dfrac{x}{x^2 - x + 1}$.

In #33–36, find the quotient and remainder via long division or other methods (note in particular that if the degree of the numerator and denominator are the same, the quotient is the ratio of the leading coefficients). Use the usual methods to find the partial fraction decomposition.

33. $\dfrac{2x^2 + x + 3}{x^2 - 1} = 2 + \dfrac{x + 5}{x^2 - 1}; \dfrac{r(x)}{h(x)} = \dfrac{x + 5}{x^2 - 1}$

$= \dfrac{A_1}{x - 1} + \dfrac{A_2}{x + 1}$, so $x + 5 = A_1(x + 1)$

$+ A_2(x - 1)$. With $x = 1$ and $x = -1$ (respectively), we find that $A_1 = 3$ and $A_2 = -2$: $\dfrac{3}{x - 1} - \dfrac{2}{x + 1}$.

Graph of $\dfrac{2x^2 + x + 3}{x^2 - 1}$:

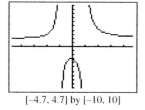

$[-4.7, 4.7]$ by $[-10, 10]$

Graph of $y = 2$:

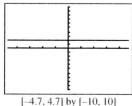

$[-4.7, 4.7]$ by $[-10, 10]$

Graph of $\dfrac{3}{x - 1}$:

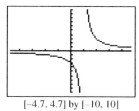

$[-4.7, 4.7]$ by $[-10, 10]$

Graph of $-\dfrac{2}{x + 1}$:

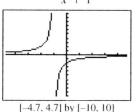

$[-4.7, 4.7]$ by $[-10, 10]$

34. $\dfrac{3x^2 + 2x}{x^2 - 4} = 3 + \dfrac{2x + 12}{x^2 - 4}; \dfrac{r(x)}{h(x)} = \dfrac{2x + 12}{x^2 - 4}$

$= \dfrac{A_1}{x - 2} + \dfrac{A_2}{x + 2}$, so $2x + 12 = A_1(x + 2)$

$+ A_2(x - 2)$. With $x = 2$ and $x = -2$ (respectively), we find that $A_1 = 4$ and $A_2 = -2$: $\dfrac{4}{x - 2} - \dfrac{2}{x + 2}$.

Graph of $\dfrac{3x^2 + 2x}{x^2 - 4}$:

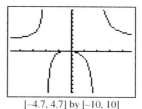

$[-4.7, 4.7]$ by $[-10, 10]$

Graph of $y = 3$:

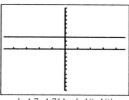

$[-4.7, 4.7]$ by $[-10, 10]$

Graph of $\dfrac{4}{x - 2}$:

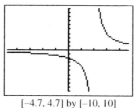

$[-4.7, 4.7]$ by $[-10, 10]$

Graph of $-\dfrac{2}{x + 2}$:

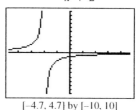

$[-4.7, 4.7]$ by $[-10, 10]$

35. $\dfrac{x^3 - 2}{x^2 + x} = x - 1 + \dfrac{x - 2}{x^2 + x}; \dfrac{r(x)}{h(x)} = \dfrac{x - 2}{x^2 + x}$

$= \dfrac{A_1}{x + 1} + \dfrac{A_2}{x}$, so $x - 2 = A_1x + A_2(x + 1)$. With $x = -1$ and $x = 0$ (respectively), we find that $A_1 = 3$ and $A_2 = -2$: $\dfrac{3}{x + 1} - \dfrac{2}{x}$.

Graph of $y = \dfrac{x^3 - 2}{x^2 + x}$:

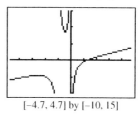

$[-4.7, 4.7]$ by $[-10, 15]$

Graph of $y = x - 1$:

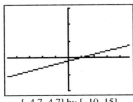

[−4.7, 4.7] by [−10, 15]

Graph of $y = \dfrac{3}{x + 1}$:

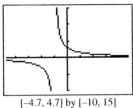

[−4.7, 4.7] by [−10, 15]

Graph of $y = -\dfrac{2}{x}$:

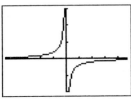

[−4.7, 4.7] by [−10, 15]

36. $\dfrac{x^3 + 2}{x^2 - x} = x + 1 + \dfrac{x + 2}{x^2 - x}; \dfrac{r(x)}{h(x)} = \dfrac{x + 2}{x^2 - x}$

$= \dfrac{A_1}{x - 1} + \dfrac{A_2}{x}$, so $x + 2 = A_1 x + A_2(x - 1)$. With

$x = 1$ and $x = 0$ (respectively), we find that $A_1 = 3$ and

$A_2 = -2$: $\dfrac{3}{x - 1} - \dfrac{2}{x}$ (note the similarity to #35).

Graph of $y = \dfrac{x^3 + 2}{x^2 - x}$:

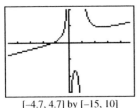

[−4.7, 4.7] by [−15, 10]

Graph of $y = x + 1$:

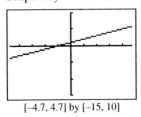

[−4.7, 4.7] by [−15, 10]

Graph of $y = \dfrac{3}{x - 1}$:

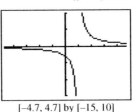

[−4.7, 4.7] by [−15, 10]

Graph of $y = -\dfrac{2}{x}$:

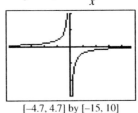

[−4.7, 4.7] by [−15, 10]

37. (c)

38. (f)

39. (d)

40. (b)

41. (a)

42. (e)

43. $\dfrac{-1}{ax} + \dfrac{1}{a(x - a)}$:

$1 = A(x - a) + Bx = (A + B)x - aA$

$\begin{aligned} A + B &= 0 \\ -aA &= 1 \end{aligned}$

Since $A = -\dfrac{1}{a}, -\dfrac{1}{a} + B = 0, B = \dfrac{1}{a}$

$\begin{bmatrix} A \\ B \end{bmatrix} = \begin{bmatrix} -\dfrac{1}{a} \\ \dfrac{1}{a} \end{bmatrix}$

44. $\dfrac{1}{(b - 2)(x - 2)} - \dfrac{1}{(b - 2)(x - b)}$:

$-1 = A(x - b) + B(x - 2) = (A + B)x + (-bA - 2B)$

$\begin{aligned} A + B &= 0 \\ -bA - 2B &= -1 \end{aligned} \Rightarrow \begin{bmatrix} 1 & 1 & 0 \\ -b & -2 & -1 \end{bmatrix}$

$\begin{bmatrix} 1 & 1 & 0 \\ 0 & b - 2 & -1 \end{bmatrix} \Rightarrow \begin{bmatrix} 1 & 1 & 0 \\ 0 & 1 & \dfrac{-1}{b - 2} \end{bmatrix} \Rightarrow$

$\begin{bmatrix} 1 & 0 & \dfrac{1}{b - 2} \\ 0 & 1 & \dfrac{-1}{b - 2} \end{bmatrix} \Rightarrow \begin{bmatrix} A \\ B \end{bmatrix} = \begin{bmatrix} \dfrac{1}{b - 2} \\ \dfrac{-1}{b - 2} \end{bmatrix}$

45. $\dfrac{-3}{(b-a)(x-a)} + \dfrac{3}{(b-a)(x-b)}$:

$3 = A(x-b) + B(x-a) = (A+B)x + (-bA - aB)$

$\begin{aligned} A + B &= 0 \\ -bA - aB &= 3 \end{aligned} \Rightarrow \begin{bmatrix} 1 & 1 & 0 \\ -b & -a & 3 \end{bmatrix} \Rightarrow$

$\begin{bmatrix} 1 & 1 & 0 \\ 0 & b-a & 3 \end{bmatrix} \Rightarrow \begin{bmatrix} 1 & 1 & 0 \\ 0 & 1 & \dfrac{3}{b-a} \end{bmatrix} \Rightarrow$

$\begin{bmatrix} 1 & 0 & \dfrac{-3}{b-a} \\ 0 & 1 & \dfrac{3}{b-a} \end{bmatrix} \Rightarrow \begin{bmatrix} A \\ B \end{bmatrix} = \begin{bmatrix} \dfrac{-3}{b-a} \\ \dfrac{3}{b-a} \end{bmatrix}$

46. $\dfrac{-1}{a(x+a)} + \dfrac{1}{a(x-a)}$:

$2 = A(x-a) + B(x+a) = (A+B)x + (-aA + aB)$

$\begin{aligned} A + B &= 0 \\ -aA + aB &= 2 \end{aligned} \Rightarrow \begin{bmatrix} 1 & 1 & 0 \\ -a & a & 2 \end{bmatrix} \Rightarrow$

$\begin{bmatrix} 1 & 1 & 0 \\ 0 & 2a & 2 \end{bmatrix} \Rightarrow \begin{bmatrix} 1 & 1 & 0 \\ 0 & 1 & \dfrac{1}{a} \end{bmatrix} \Rightarrow$

$\begin{bmatrix} 1 & 0 & -\dfrac{1}{a} \\ 0 & 1 & \dfrac{1}{a} \end{bmatrix} \Rightarrow \begin{bmatrix} A \\ B \end{bmatrix} = \begin{bmatrix} -\dfrac{1}{a} \\ \dfrac{1}{a} \end{bmatrix}$

47. True. The behavior of $f(x)$ near $x = 3$ is the same as the behavior of $y = \dfrac{1}{x-3}$, and $\displaystyle\lim_{x\to 3}\dfrac{1}{x-3} = -\infty$.

48. True. The behavior of $f(x)$ for $|x|$ large is the same as the behavior of $y = -1$, and $\displaystyle\lim_{x\to\infty}(-1) = -1$.

49. The denominator factor x^2 calls for the terms $\dfrac{A_1}{x}$ and $\dfrac{A_2}{x^2}$ in the partial fraction decomposition, and the denominator factor $x^2 + 2$ calls for the term $\dfrac{B_1 x + C_1}{x^2 + 2}$. The answer is E.

50. The denominator factor $(x+3)^2$ calls for terms $\dfrac{A_1}{x+3}$ and $\dfrac{A_2}{(x+3)^2}$ in the partial fraction decomposition, and the denominator factor $(x^2+4)^2$ calls for the terms $\dfrac{B_1 x + C_1}{x^2+4}$ and $\dfrac{B_2 x + C_2}{(x^2+4)^2}$. The answer is C.

51. The y-intercept is -1, and because the denominators are both of degree 1, the expression changes sign at each asymptote. The answer is B.

52. The y-intercept is $\dfrac{3}{4}$, and the expression changes sign at the $x = 1$ asymptote but is negative on both sides of the $x = -2$ asymptote. The answer is E.

53. (a) $x = 1$: $1 + 4 + 1 = A(1 + 1) + (B + C)(0)$
$$6 = 2A$$
$$A = 3$$

(b) $x = i$: $-1 + 4i + 1 = 3(-1 + 1) + (Bi + C)(i - 1)$
$$4i = (Bi + C)(i - 1)$$
$$4i = -B - Bi + Ci - C$$

$\begin{aligned} -B - C &= 0 \\ -Bi + Ci &= 4i \end{aligned} \Rightarrow \begin{aligned} B + C &= 0 \\ B - C &= -4 \end{aligned} \Rightarrow$

$\begin{bmatrix} 1 & 1 & 0 \\ 1 & -1 & -4 \end{bmatrix} \Rightarrow \begin{bmatrix} 1 & 1 & 0 \\ 0 & -2 & -4 \end{bmatrix} \Rightarrow \begin{bmatrix} 1 & 1 & 0 \\ 0 & 1 & 2 \end{bmatrix} \Rightarrow$

$\begin{bmatrix} 1 & 0 & -2 \\ 0 & 1 & 2 \end{bmatrix} \Rightarrow \begin{bmatrix} B \\ C \end{bmatrix} = \begin{bmatrix} -2 \\ 2 \end{bmatrix}$

$x = -i$:
$-1 - 4i + 1 = A(-1 - 1) + (-Bi + C)(-i - 1)$
$$-4i = -B + Bi - Ci - C,\text{ which is the}$$
same as above.

$$B = -2, C = 2$$

54. One possible answer: For any two polynomials to be equal over the entire range of real or complex numbers, the coefficients of each power must be equal. (For example $2x^3 = 2x^2$ only when $x = 0$ and $x = 1$: at all other values of x, the functions are *not* equal).

55. $y = \dfrac{b}{(x-1)^2}$ has a greater effect on $f(x)$ at $x = 1$.

56. Using partial fractions, $f(x) = \dfrac{2}{x-1} + \dfrac{-1}{(x-1)^2}$ while $g(x) = \dfrac{2}{x-1} + \dfrac{5}{(x-1)^2}$. Near $x = 1$, the term $\dfrac{-1}{(x-1)^2}$ dominates $f(x)$; at the same value of x, the term $\dfrac{5}{(x-1)^2}$ dominates $g(x)$. Near $x = 1$, then, we expect $f(x)$ to approach $-\infty$ and $g(x)$ to approach $+\infty$.

■ Section 7.5 Systems of Inequalities in Two Variables

Quick Review 7.5

1. x-intercept: $(3, 0)$; y-intercept: $(0, -2)$

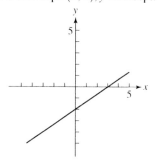

2. x-intercept: $(6, 0)$; y-intercept: $(0, 3)$

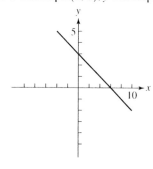

3. x-intercept: $(20, 0)$; y-intercept: $(0, 50)$

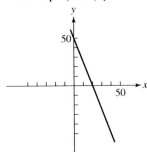

4. x-intercept: $(30, 0)$; y-intercept: $(0, -20)$

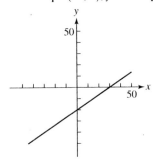

For #5–9, a variety of methods could be used. One is shown.

5. $\begin{bmatrix} 4 & 1 & 180 \\ 1 & 1 & 90 \end{bmatrix} \Rightarrow \begin{bmatrix} 1 & \frac{1}{4} & 45 \\ 0 & 1 & 60 \end{bmatrix} \Rightarrow \begin{bmatrix} 1 & 0 & 30 \\ 0 & 1 & 60 \end{bmatrix} \Rightarrow \begin{bmatrix} x \\ y \end{bmatrix}$

$= \begin{bmatrix} 30 \\ 60 \end{bmatrix}$

6. $\begin{bmatrix} 1 & 1 & 90 \\ 10 & 5 & 800 \end{bmatrix} \Rightarrow \begin{bmatrix} 1 & 1 & 90 \\ 0 & 1 & 20 \end{bmatrix} \Rightarrow \begin{bmatrix} 1 & 0 & 70 \\ 0 & 1 & 20 \end{bmatrix} \Rightarrow \begin{bmatrix} x \\ y \end{bmatrix}$

$= \begin{bmatrix} 70 \\ 20 \end{bmatrix}$

7. $\begin{bmatrix} 4 & 1 & 180 \\ 10 & 5 & 800 \end{bmatrix} \Rightarrow \begin{bmatrix} 1 & \frac{1}{4} & 45 \\ 0 & 1 & 140 \end{bmatrix} \Rightarrow \begin{bmatrix} 1 & 0 & 10 \\ 0 & 1 & 140 \end{bmatrix} \Rightarrow$

$\begin{bmatrix} x \\ y \end{bmatrix} = \begin{bmatrix} 10 \\ 140 \end{bmatrix}$

8. $\begin{bmatrix} 1 & 1 & 6 \\ 8 & 2 & 24 \end{bmatrix} \Rightarrow \begin{bmatrix} 1 & 1 & 6 \\ 0 & 1 & 4 \end{bmatrix} \Rightarrow \begin{bmatrix} 1 & 0 & 2 \\ 0 & 1 & 4 \end{bmatrix} \Rightarrow \begin{bmatrix} x \\ y \end{bmatrix} = \begin{bmatrix} 2 \\ 4 \end{bmatrix}$

9. $\begin{bmatrix} 1 & 1 & 6 \\ 2 & 8 & 30 \end{bmatrix} \Rightarrow \begin{bmatrix} 1 & 1 & 6 \\ 0 & 1 & 3 \end{bmatrix} \Rightarrow \begin{bmatrix} 1 & 0 & 3 \\ 0 & 1 & 3 \end{bmatrix} \Rightarrow \begin{bmatrix} x \\ y \end{bmatrix} = \begin{bmatrix} 3 \\ 3 \end{bmatrix}$

10. Use substitution: $2x + 3x^2 = 4$, $3x^2 + 2x - 4 = 0$,

$x = \dfrac{-2 \pm \sqrt{4 - 4(3)(-4)}}{6}$,

$(x, y) \approx (-1.54, 2.36)$ or $(0.87, 0.75)$

Section 7.5 Exercises

1. Graph (c); boundary included

2. Graph (f); boundary excluded

3. Graph (b); boundary included

4. Graph (d); boundary excluded

5. Graph (e); boundary included

6. Graph (a); boundary excluded

7.

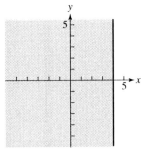

boundary line $x = 4$ included

8.

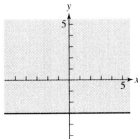

boundary line $y = -3$ included

9.

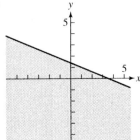

boundary line $2x + 5y = 7$ included

10.

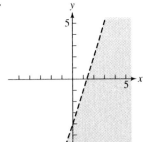

boundary line $3x - y = 4$ excluded

11.

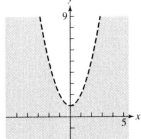

boundary curve $y = x^2 + 1$ excluded

12.

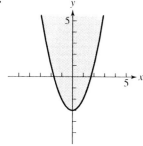

boundary curve $y = x^2 - 3$ included

13.

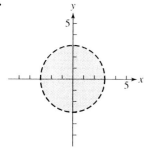

boundary circle $x^2 + y^2 = 9$ excluded

14.

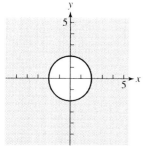

boundary circle $x^2 + y^2 = 4$ included

15.

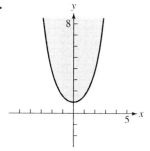

boundary curve $y = \dfrac{e^x + e^{-x}}{2}$ included

16.

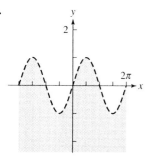

boundary curve $y = \sin x$ excluded

17.

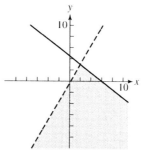

Corner at $(2, 3)$. Left boundary is excluded, the other is included.

18.

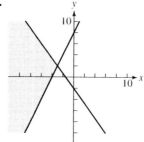

Corner at $(-3, 2)$. Boundaries included.

19.

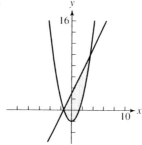

Corners at about $(-1.45, 0.10)$ and $(3.45, 9.90)$. Boundaries included.

20.

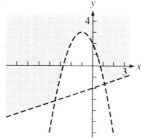

Corners at about $(-3.48, -3.16)$ and $(1.15, -1.62)$. Boundaries excluded.

21.

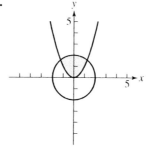

Corners at about $(\pm 1.25, 1.56)$ Boundaries included.

22.

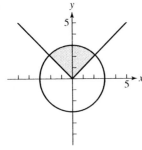

Corners at about $(\pm 2.12, 2.12)$

23.

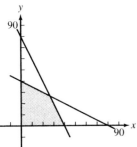

Corners at $(0, 40)$, $(26.7, 26.7)$, $(0, 0)$, and $(40, 0)$.
Boundaries included.

24.

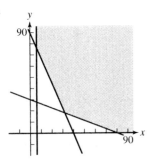

Corners at $(6, 76.5)$, $(32, 18)$, and $(80, 0)$. Boundaries
included.

25.

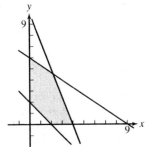

Corners at $(0, 2)$, $(0, 6)$, $(2.18, 4.55)$, $(4, 0)$, and $(2, 0)$.
Boundaries included.

26.

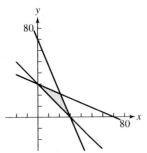

Corners at $(0, 30)$, $(21, 21)$, and $(30, 0)$. Boundaries
included.

27. $x^2 + y^2 \le 4$
$\qquad y \ge -x^2 + 1$

28. $x^2 + y^2 \le 4$
$\qquad y \ge 0$

For #29–30, first we must find the equations of the lines—then
the inequalities.

29. line 1: $m = \dfrac{\Delta y}{\Delta x} = \dfrac{(5 - 3)}{(0 - 4)} = \dfrac{2}{-4} = \dfrac{-1}{2}$, $y = \dfrac{-1}{2}x + 5$

line 2: $m = \dfrac{\Delta y}{\Delta x} = \dfrac{(0 - 3)}{(6 - 4)} = \dfrac{-3}{2}$,

$(y - 0) = \dfrac{-3}{2}(x - 6)$, $y = \dfrac{-3}{2}x + 9$

line 3: $x = 0$
line 4: $y = 0$

$y \le \dfrac{-1}{2}x + 5$

$y \le \dfrac{-3}{2}x + 9$

$x \ge 0$

$y \ge 0$

30. line 1: $\dfrac{\Delta y}{\Delta x} = \dfrac{(1 - 6)}{(2 - 0)} = \dfrac{-5}{2}$, $y = \dfrac{-5}{2}x + 6$

line 2: $\dfrac{\Delta y}{\Delta x} = \dfrac{(1 - 0)}{(2 - 5)} = \dfrac{1}{-3}$, $= \dfrac{-1}{3}$,

$(y - 0) = \dfrac{-1}{3}(x - 5)$, $y = \dfrac{-1}{3}x + \dfrac{5}{3}$

line 3: $x = 0$
line 4: $y = 0$

$y \ge \dfrac{-5}{2}x + 6$

$y \ge \dfrac{-1}{3}x + \dfrac{5}{3}$

$x \ge 0$

$y \ge 0$

For #31–36, the feasible area, use your grapher to determine
the feasible area, and then solve for the corner points graphically or algebraically. Evaluate $f(x)$ at the corner points to
determine maximum and minimum values.

31.

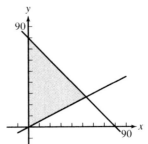

Corner points: $(0, 0)$
$\qquad\qquad\quad (0, 80)$, the y-intercept of $x + y = 80$
$\qquad\qquad\quad \left(\dfrac{160}{3}, \dfrac{80}{3}\right)$, the intersection of $x + y = 80$
$\qquad\qquad\quad$ and $x - 2y = 0$

(x, y)	$(0, 0)$	$(0, 80)$	$\left(\dfrac{160}{3}, \dfrac{80}{3}\right)$
f	0	240	$\dfrac{880}{3} \approx 293.33$

$f_{\min} = 0$ [at $(0, 0)$]; $f_{\max} \approx 293.33 \left[\text{at } \left(\dfrac{160}{3}, \dfrac{80}{3}\right)\right]$

32.

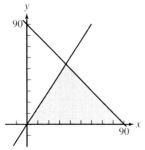

Corner points: $(0, 0)$

$(90, 0)$, the x-intercept of $x + y = 90$

$\left(\dfrac{45}{2}, \dfrac{135}{2}\right)$, the intersection of $x + y = 90$

and $3x - y = 0$

(x, y)	$(0, 0)$	$(90, 0)$	$\left(\dfrac{45}{2}, \dfrac{135}{2}\right)$
f	0	900	967.5

$f_{\min} = 0$ [at $(0, 0)$]; $f_{\max} = 967.5\left[\text{at }\left(\dfrac{45}{2}, \dfrac{135}{2}\right)\right]$

33.

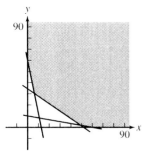

Corner points: $(0, 60)$ y-intercept of $5x + y = 60$

$(6, 30)$ intersection of $5x + y = 60$ and

$4x + 6y = 204$

$(48, 2)$ intersection of $4x + 6y = 204$ and

$x + 6y = 60$

$(60, 0)$ x-intercept of $x + 6y = 60$

(x, y)	$(0, 60)$	$(6, 30)$	$(48, 2)$	$(60, 0)$
f	240	162	344	420

$f_{\min} = 162$ [at $(6, 30)$]; $f_{\max} = $ none (region is unbounded)

34.

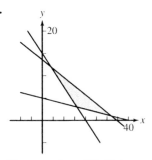

Corner points: $(16, 3)$ intersection of $3x + 4y = 60$ and

$x + 8y = 40$

$(4, 12)$ intersection of $3x + 4y = 60$ and

$11x + 28y = 380$

$(32, 1)$ intersection of $x + 8y = 40$ and

$11x + 28y = 380$

(x, y)	$(4, 12)$	$(16, 3)$	$(32, 1)$
f	360	315	505

$f_{\min} = 315$ [at $(16, 3)$]; $f_{\max} = 505$ [at $(32, 1)$]

35.

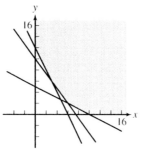

Corner points: $(0, 12)$ y-intercept of $2x + y = 12$

$(3, 6)$ intersection of $2x + y = 12$ and

$4x + 3y = 30$

$(6, 2)$ intersection of $4x + 3y = 30$ and

$x + 2y = 10$

$(10, 0)$ x-intercept of $x + 2y = 10$

(x, y)	$(0, 12)$	$(3, 6)$	$(6, 2)$	$(10, 0)$
f	24	27	34	50

$f_{\min} = 24$ [at $(0, 12)$]; $f_{\max} = $ none (region is unbounded)

36.

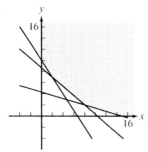

Corner points: $(0, 10)$ y-intercept of $3x + 2y = 20$

$(2, 7)$ intersection of $3x + 2y = 20$ and

$5x + 6y = 52$

$(8, 2)$ intersection of $5x + 6y = 52$ and

$2x + 7y = 30$

$(15, 0)$ x-intercept of $2x + 7y = 30$

(x, y)	$(0, 10)$	$(2, 7)$	$(8, 2)$	$(15, 0)$
f	50	41	34	45

$f_{\min} = 34$ [at $(8, 2)$]; $f_{\max} = $ none (region is unbounded)

For #37–40, first set up the equations; then solve.

37. Let $x = $ number of tons of ore R

$y = $ number of tons of ore S

$C = $ total cost $= 50x + 60y$, the objective function

$80x + 140y \geq 4000$ At least 4000 lb of mineral A

$160x + 50y \geq 3200$ At least 3200 lb of mineral B

$x \geq 0, y \geq 0$

The region of feasible points is the intersection of

$80x + 140y \geq 4000$ and $160x + 50y \geq 3200$ in the first

quadrant. The region has three corner points: $(0, 64)$,

$(13.48, 20.87)$, and $(50, 0)$. $C_{\min} = \$1,926.20$ when 13.48

tons of ore R and 20.87 tons of ore S are processed.

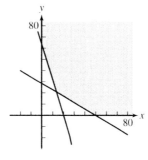

38. Let x = number of units of food substance A
y = number of units of food substance B
C = total cost = $1.40x + 0.90y$, the objective function
$3x + 2y \geq 24$ At least 24 units of carbohydrates
$4x + y \geq 16$ At least 16 units of protein
$x \geq 0, y \geq 0$
The region of feasible points is the intersection of
$3x + 2y \geq 24$ and $4x + y \geq 16$ in the first quadrant.
The corner points are $(0, 16), (1.6, 9.6)$, and $(8, 0)$.
$C_{\min}$ = $10.88 when 1.6 units of food substance A and
9.6 units of food substance B are purchased.

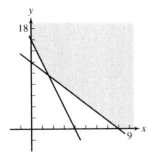

39. Let x = number of operations performed by Refinery 1
y = number of operations performed by Refinery 2
C = total cost = $300x + 600y$, the objective function
$x + y \geq 100$ At least 100 units of grade A
$2x + 4y \geq 320$ At least 320 units of grade B
$x + 4y \geq 200$ At least 200 units of grade C
$x \geq 0, y \geq 0$
The region of feasible points is the intersection of
$x + y \geq 100, 2x + 4y \geq 320$, and $x + 4y \geq 200$ in the
first quadrant. The corners are $(0, 100), (40, 60), (120, 20)$,
and $(200, 0)$. $C_{\min}$ = $48,000, which can be obtained by
using Refinery 1 to perform 40 operations and Refinery 2
to perform 60 operations, or using Refinery 1 to perform
120 operations and Refinery 2 to perform 20 operations, or
any other combination of x and y such that $2x + 4y = 320$
with $40 \leq x \leq 120$.

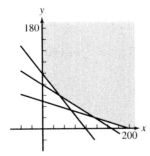

40. Let x = units produced of product A
y = units produced of product B
P = total profit = $2.25x + 2.00y$
$x + y \leq 3000$ No more than 3000 units produced
$y \geq \dfrac{1}{2}x$
$x \geq 0, y \geq 0$

The region of feasible points is the intersection of
$x + y \leq 3000$ and $\dfrac{1}{2}x - y \leq 0$ in the first quadrant. The
corners are $(0, 3000), (2000, 1000)$ and $(0, 0)$.
$P_{\max}$ = $6,500 when 2000 units of product A and
1000 units of product B are produced.

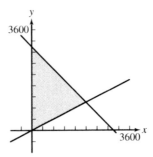

41. False. The graph is a half-plane.

42. True. The half-plane determined by the inequality
$2x - 3y < 5$ is bounded by the graph of the equation
$2x - 3y = 5$, or equivalently, $3y = 2x - 5$.

43. The graph of $3x + 4y \geq 5$ is Regions I and II plus the
boundary. The graph of $2x - 3y \leq 4$ is Regions I and IV
plus the boundary. And the intersection of the regions is
the graph of the system. The answer is A.

44. The graph of $3x + 4y < 5$ is Regions III and IV without the
boundary. The graph of $2x - 3y > 4$ is Regions II and III
without the boundary. And the intersection of the regions is
the graph of the system. The answer is C.

45. $(3, 4)$ fails to satisfy $x + 3y \leq 12$. The answer is D.

46. At $(3.6, 2.8), f = 46$. The answer is D.

47. (a) One possible answer: Two lines are parallel if they have
exactly the same slope. Let l_1 be $5x + 8y = a$
and l_2 be $5x + 8y = b$. Then l_1 becomes $y = \dfrac{-5}{8} + \dfrac{a}{8}$
and l_2 becomes $y = \dfrac{-5}{8}x + \dfrac{b}{8}$. Since $M_{l_1} = \dfrac{-5}{8}$
$= M_{l_2}$, the lines are parallel.

(b) One possible answer: If two lines are parallel, then a
line l_2 going through the point $(0, 10)$ will be further
away from the origin then a line l_1 going through the
point $(0, 5)$. In this case f_1 could be expressed as
$mx + 5$ and f_2 could be expressed as $mx + 10$. Thus,
l is moving further away from the origin as f increases.

(c) One possible answer: The region is bounded and
includes all its boundary points.

48. Two parabolas can intersect at no points, exactly one point,
two points, or infinitely many points.
None: $y_1 = x^2$ and $y_2 = x^2 + 1$
One point: $y_1 = x^2$ and $y_2 = -x^2$
Two points: $y_1 = x^2$ and $y_2 = \dfrac{1}{4}x^2 + 4$

49. $4x^2 + 9y^2 = 36$

$$9y^2 = 36 - 4x^2$$

$$y^2 = 4 - \frac{4}{9}x^2$$

$$y_1 = \sqrt{4 - \frac{4}{9}x^2} = 2\sqrt{1 - \frac{x^2}{9}}$$

$$y_2 = -\sqrt{4 - \frac{4}{9}x^2} = -2\sqrt{1 - \frac{x^2}{9}}$$

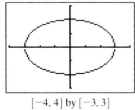

$[-4, 4]$ by $[-3, 3]$

50. $y^2 = x^2 - 4$

$$y_1 = \sqrt{x^2 - 4}$$

$$y_2 = -\sqrt{x^2 - 4}$$

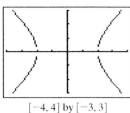

$[-4, 4]$ by $[-3, 3]$

51. $4x^2 + 9y^2 \le 36$

$$9y^2 \le 36 - 4x^2$$

$$y^2 \le \frac{36 - 4x^2}{9}$$

$$y_1 \le \sqrt{\frac{36 - 4x^2}{9}}$$

$$y_2 \ge -\sqrt{\frac{36 - 4x^2}{9}}$$

$$y_3 \ge x^2 - 1$$

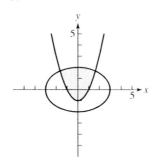

52.

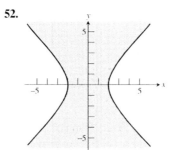

■ Chapter 7 Review

1. (a) $\begin{bmatrix} 1 & 2 \\ 8 & 3 \end{bmatrix}$ **(b)** $\begin{bmatrix} -3 & 4 \\ 0 & -3 \end{bmatrix}$ **(c)** $\begin{bmatrix} 2 & -6 \\ -8 & 0 \end{bmatrix}$ **(d)** $\begin{bmatrix} -7 & 11 \\ 4 & -6 \end{bmatrix}$

2. (a) $\begin{bmatrix} 1 & 5 & -1 & 6 \\ 3 & 3 & 1 & 0 \\ -2 & 1 & 3 & 4 \end{bmatrix}$ **(b)** $\begin{bmatrix} 3 & 1 & -1 & -2 \\ -1 & 5 & -5 & -6 \\ 2 & -7 & 1 & -2 \end{bmatrix}$ **(c)** $\begin{bmatrix} -4 & -6 & 2 & -4 \\ -2 & -8 & 4 & 6 \\ 0 & 6 & -4 & -2 \end{bmatrix}$ **(d)** $\begin{bmatrix} 8 & 5 & -3 & -2 \\ -1 & 14 & -12 & -15 \\ 4 & -17 & 4 & -3 \end{bmatrix}$

3. $AB = \begin{bmatrix} (-1)(3) + (4)(0) & (-1)(-1) + (4)(-2) & (-1)(5) + (4)(4) \\ (0)(3) + (6)(0) & (0)(-1) + (6)(-2) & (0)(5) + (6)(4) \end{bmatrix} = \begin{bmatrix} -3 & -7 & 11 \\ 0 & -12 & 24 \end{bmatrix}$; BA is not possible.

4. AB is not possible; $BA = \begin{bmatrix} (-2)(-1) + (3)(3) + (1)(4) & (-2)(2) + (3)(-1) + (1)(3) \\ (2)(-1) + (1)(3) + (0)(4) & (2)(2) + (1)(-1) + (0)(3) \\ (-1)(-1) + (2)(3) + (-3)(4) & (-1)(2) + (2)(-1) + (-3)(3) \end{bmatrix} = \begin{bmatrix} 15 & -4 \\ 1 & 3 \\ -5 & -13 \end{bmatrix}$.

5. $AB = [(-1)(5) + (4)(2) \quad (-1)(-3) + (4)(1)] = [3 \ 7]$; BA is not possible.

6. AB is not possible; $BA = \begin{bmatrix} (3)(-1) + (-4)(0) & (3)(1) + (-4)(1) \\ (1)(-1) + (2)(0) & (1)(1) + (2)(1) \\ (3)(-1) + (1)(0) & (3)(1) + (1)(1) \\ (1)(-1) + (1)(0) & (1)(1) + (1)(1) \end{bmatrix} = \begin{bmatrix} -3 & -1 \\ -1 & 3 \\ -3 & 4 \\ -1 & 2 \end{bmatrix}$.

7. $AB = \begin{bmatrix} (0)(2) + (1)(1) + (0)(-2) & (0)(-3) + (1)(2) + (0)(1) & (0)(4) + (1)(-3) + (0)(-1) \\ (1)(2) + (0)(1) + (0)(-2) & (1)(-3) + (0)(2) + (0)(1) & (1)(4) + (0)(-3) + (0)(-1) \\ (0)(2) + (0)(1) + (1)(-2) & (0)(-3) + (0)(2) + (1)(1) & (0)(4) + (0)(-3) + (1)(-1) \end{bmatrix} = \begin{bmatrix} 1 & 2 & -3 \\ 2 & -3 & 4 \\ -2 & 1 & -1 \end{bmatrix}$

$BA = \begin{bmatrix} (2)(0) + (-3)(1) + (4)(0) & (2)(1) + (-3)(0) + (4)(0) & (2)(0) + (-3)(0) + (4)(1) \\ (1)(0) + (2)(1) + (-3)(0) & (1)(1) + (2)(0) + (-3)(0) & (1)(0) + (2)(0) + (-3)(1) \\ (-2)(0) + (1)(1) + (-1)(0) & (-2)(1) + (1)(0) + (-1)(0) & (-2)(0) + (1)(0) + (-1)(1) \end{bmatrix} = \begin{bmatrix} -3 & 2 & 4 \\ 2 & 1 & -3 \\ 1 & -2 & -1 \end{bmatrix}$

8. As in #7, the multiplication steps take up a lot of space to write, but are easy to carry out, since A contains only 0s and 1s. The intermediate steps are not shown here, but note that the rows of AB are a rearrangement of the rows of B (specifically, rows 1 and 2, and rows 3 and 4, are swapped), while the columns of BA are a rearrangement of the columns of B (we swap columns 1 and 2, and columns 3 and 4). The nature of the rearrangement can be determined by noting the locations of the 1s in A.

$$AB = \begin{bmatrix} 3 & 0 & 2 & 1 \\ -2 & 1 & 0 & 1 \\ 3 & -2 & 1 & 0 \\ -1 & 1 & 2 & -1 \end{bmatrix};$$

$$BA = \begin{bmatrix} 1 & -2 & 1 & 0 \\ 0 & 3 & 1 & 2 \\ 1 & -1 & -1 & 2 \\ -2 & 3 & 0 & 1 \end{bmatrix}$$

9. Carry out the multiplication of AB and BA and confirm that both products equal I_4.

10. Carry out the multiplication of AB and BA and confirm that both products equal I_3.

11. Using a calculator:

$$\begin{bmatrix} 1 & 2 & 0 & -1 \\ 2 & -1 & 1 & 2 \\ 2 & 0 & 1 & 2 \\ -1 & 1 & 1 & 4 \end{bmatrix}^{-1} = \begin{bmatrix} -2 & -5 & 6 & -1 \\ 0 & -1 & 1 & 0 \\ 10 & 24 & -27 & 4 \\ -3 & -7 & 8 & -1 \end{bmatrix}$$

12. Using a calculator:

$$\begin{bmatrix} -1 & 0 & 1 \\ 2 & -1 & 1 \\ 1 & 1 & 1 \end{bmatrix}^{-1} = \begin{bmatrix} -0.4 & 0.2 & 0.2 \\ -0.2 & -0.4 & 0.6 \\ 0.6 & 0.2 & 0.2 \end{bmatrix}$$

13. $\det = \begin{vmatrix} 1 & -3 & 2 \\ 2 & 4 & -1 \\ -2 & 0 & 1 \end{vmatrix}$

$= (-2)(-1)^4 \begin{vmatrix} -3 & 2 \\ 4 & -1 \end{vmatrix} + 0 + (1)(-1)^6 \begin{vmatrix} 1 & -3 \\ 2 & 4 \end{vmatrix}$

$= -2(3 - 8) + (4 - (-6))$

$= 10 + 10$

$= 20$

14. $\det = \begin{vmatrix} -2 & 3 & 0 & 1 \\ 3 & 0 & 2 & 0 \\ 5 & 2 & -3 & 4 \\ 1 & -1 & 2 & 3 \end{vmatrix} = (3)(-1)^3 \begin{vmatrix} 3 & 0 & 1 \\ 2 & -3 & 4 \\ -1 & 2 & 3 \end{vmatrix} + 0 + 2(-1)^5 \begin{vmatrix} -2 & 3 & 1 \\ 5 & 2 & 4 \\ 1 & -1 & 3 \end{vmatrix} + 0$

$= -3 \left[3(-1)^2 \begin{vmatrix} -3 & 4 \\ 2 & 3 \end{vmatrix} + 0 + (1)(-1)^4 \begin{vmatrix} 2 & -3 \\ -1 & 2 \end{vmatrix} \right] - 2 \left[-2(-1)^2 \begin{vmatrix} 2 & 4 \\ -1 & 3 \end{vmatrix} + (3)(-1)^3 \begin{vmatrix} 5 & 4 \\ 1 & 3 \end{vmatrix} + (1)(-1)^4 \begin{vmatrix} 5 & 2 \\ 1 & -1 \end{vmatrix} \right]$

$= (-3)(3)(-9 - 8) + (-3)(1)(4 - 3) + (-2)(-2)(6 + 4) + (-2)(-3)(15 - 4) + (-2)(1)(-5 - 2)$

$= 153 - 3 + 40 + 66 + 14 = 270$

For #15–18, one possible sequence of row operations is shown.

15. $\begin{bmatrix} 1 & 0 & 2 \\ 3 & 1 & 5 \\ 1 & -1 & 3 \end{bmatrix} \xrightarrow[(-1)R_1 + R_3]{(-3)R_1 + R_2} \begin{bmatrix} 1 & 0 & 2 \\ 0 & 1 & -1 \\ 0 & -1 & 1 \end{bmatrix} \xrightarrow{(1)R_2 + R_3} \begin{bmatrix} 1 & 0 & 2 \\ 0 & 1 & -1 \\ 0 & 0 & 0 \end{bmatrix}$

16. $\begin{bmatrix} 2 & 1 & 1 & 1 \\ -3 & -1 & -2 & 1 \\ 5 & 2 & 2 & 3 \end{bmatrix} \xrightarrow{(1/2)R_1} \begin{bmatrix} 1 & 0.5 & 0.5 & 0.5 \\ -3 & -1 & -2 & 1 \\ 5 & 2 & 2 & 3 \end{bmatrix} \xrightarrow[(-5)R_1 + R_3]{(3)R_1 + R_2} \begin{bmatrix} 1 & 0.5 & 0.5 & 0.5 \\ 0 & 0.5 & -0.5 & 2.5 \\ 0 & -0.5 & -0.5 & 0.5 \end{bmatrix} \xrightarrow[(1)R_2 + R_3]{(1)R_3 + R_1}$

$\begin{bmatrix} 1 & 0 & 0 & 1 \\ 0 & 0.5 & -0.5 & 2.5 \\ 0 & 0 & -1 & 3 \end{bmatrix} \xrightarrow[(-1)R_3]{(2)R_2} \begin{bmatrix} 1 & 0 & 0 & 1 \\ 0 & 1 & -1 & 5 \\ 0 & 0 & 1 & -3 \end{bmatrix} \xrightarrow{(1)R_3 + R_2} \begin{bmatrix} 1 & 0 & 0 & 1 \\ 0 & 1 & 0 & 2 \\ 0 & 0 & 1 & -3 \end{bmatrix}$

17. $\begin{bmatrix} 1 & 2 & 3 & 1 \\ 2 & 3 & 3 & -2 \\ 1 & 2 & 4 & 6 \end{bmatrix} \xrightarrow[(-1)R_1 + R_3]{(-2)R_1 + R_2} \begin{bmatrix} 1 & 2 & 3 & 1 \\ 0 & -1 & -3 & -4 \\ 0 & 0 & 1 & 5 \end{bmatrix} \xrightarrow[(3)R_3 + R_2]{(2)R_2 + R_1} \begin{bmatrix} 1 & 0 & -3 & -7 \\ 0 & -1 & 0 & 11 \\ 0 & 0 & 1 & 5 \end{bmatrix} \xrightarrow[(3)R_3 + R_1]{(-1)R_2} \begin{bmatrix} 1 & 0 & 0 & 8 \\ 0 & 1 & 0 & -11 \\ 0 & 0 & 1 & 5 \end{bmatrix}$

18. $\begin{bmatrix} 1 & -2 & 0 & 4 \\ -2 & 5 & 3 & -6 \\ 2 & 4 & 1 & 9 \end{bmatrix} \xrightarrow[(-2)R_1 + R_3]{(2)R_1 + R_2} \begin{bmatrix} 1 & -2 & 0 & 4 \\ 0 & 1 & 3 & 2 \\ 0 & 0 & 1 & 1 \end{bmatrix} \xrightarrow[(-3)R_3 + R_2]{(2)R_2 + R_1} \begin{bmatrix} 1 & 0 & 6 & 8 \\ 0 & 1 & 0 & -1 \\ 0 & 0 & 1 & 1 \end{bmatrix} \xrightarrow{(-6)R_3 + R_1} \begin{bmatrix} 1 & 0 & 0 & 2 \\ 0 & 1 & 0 & -1 \\ 0 & 0 & 1 & 1 \end{bmatrix}$

For #19–22, use any of the methods of this chapter. Solving for x (or y) and substituting is probably easiest for these systems.

19. $(x, y) = (1, 2)$: From $\mathbf{E}_1$, $y = 3x - 1$; substituting in $\mathbf{E}_2$ gives $x + 2(3x - 1) = 5$. Then $7x = 7$, so $x = 1$. Finally, $y = 2$.

20. $(x, y) = (-3, -1)$: From $\mathbf{E}_1$, $x = 2y - 1$; substituting in $\mathbf{E}_2$ gives $-2(2y - 1) + y = 5$. Then $-3y = 3$, so $y = -1$. Finally, $x = -3$.

21. No solution: From $\mathbf{E}_1$, $x = 1 - 2y$; substituting in $\mathbf{E}_2$ gives $4y - 4 = -2(1 - 2y)$, or $4y - 4 = 4y - 2$ — which is impossible.

22. No solution: From $\mathbf{E}_1$, $x = 2y + 9$; substituting in $\mathbf{E}_2$

gives $3y - \dfrac{3}{2}(2y + 9) = -9$, or $-\dfrac{27}{2} = -9$ — which is not true.

23. $(x, y, z, w) = (2 - z - w, w + 1, z, w)$: Note that the last equation in the triangular system is not useful. z and w can be anything, then $y = w + 1$ and $x = 2 - z - w$.

$$
\begin{aligned}
x + z + w &= 2 \\
x + y + z &= 3 \Rightarrow \mathbf{E}_2 - \mathbf{E}_1 \Rightarrow \\
3x + 2y + 3z + w &= 8 \Rightarrow \mathbf{E}_3 - 3\mathbf{E}_1 \Rightarrow
\end{aligned}
\qquad
\begin{aligned}
x + z + w &= 2 \\
y - w &= 1 \\
2y - 2w &= 2 \Rightarrow \mathbf{E}_3 - 2\mathbf{E}_2 \Rightarrow
\end{aligned}
\qquad
\begin{aligned}
x \quad + z + w &= 2 \\
y - w &= 1 \\
0 &= 0
\end{aligned}
$$

24. $(x, y, z, w) = (-w - 2, -z - w, z, w)$: Note that the last equation in the triangular system is not useful. z and w can be anything, then $y = -z - w$ and $x = -w - 2$.

$$
\begin{aligned}
x + w &= -2 \\
x + y + z + 2w &= -2 \Rightarrow \mathbf{E}_2 - \mathbf{E}_1 \Rightarrow \\
-x - 2y - 2z - 3w &= 2 \quad \Rightarrow \mathbf{E}_3 + 2\mathbf{E}_2 \Rightarrow
\end{aligned}
\qquad
\begin{aligned}
x + w &= -2 \\
y + z + w &= 0 \\
x + w &= -2 \Rightarrow \mathbf{E}_3 - \mathbf{E}_1 \Rightarrow
\end{aligned}
\qquad
\begin{aligned}
x + w &= -2 \\
y + z + w &= 0 \\
0 &= 0
\end{aligned}
$$

25. No solution: $\mathbf{E}_1$ and $\mathbf{E}_3$ are inconsistent.

$$
\begin{aligned}
x + y - 2z &= 2 \\
3x - y + z &= 4 \\
-2x - 2y + 4z &= 6 \Rightarrow \mathbf{E}_3 + 2\mathbf{E}_1 \Rightarrow
\end{aligned}
\qquad
\begin{aligned}
x + y - 2z &= 2 \\
3x - y + z &= 4 \\
0 &= 10
\end{aligned}
$$

26. $(x, y, z) = \left(\dfrac{1}{4}z + \dfrac{3}{4}, \dfrac{7}{4}z + \dfrac{5}{4}, z\right)$: Note that the last equation in the triangular system is not useful. z can be anything,

then $y = \dfrac{7}{4}z + \dfrac{5}{4}$ and $x = 2 + 2z - \left(\dfrac{7}{4}z + \dfrac{5}{4}\right) = \dfrac{1}{4}z + \dfrac{3}{4}$.

$$
\begin{aligned}
x + y - 2z &= 2 \\
3x - y + z &= 1 \quad \Rightarrow \mathbf{E}_2 - 3\mathbf{E}_1 \Rightarrow \\
-2x - 2y + 4z &= -4 \Rightarrow \mathbf{E}_3 + 2\mathbf{E}_1 \Rightarrow
\end{aligned}
\qquad
\begin{aligned}
x + y - 2z &= 2 \\
-4y + 7z &= -5 \\
0 &= 0
\end{aligned}
$$

27. $(x, y, z, w) = (1 - 2z + w, 2 + z - w, z, w)$: Note that the last two equations in the triangular system give no additional information. z and w can be anything, then $y = 2 + z - w$ and $x = 13 - 6(2 + z - w) + 4z - 5w = 1 - 2z + w$.

$$
\begin{aligned}
-x - 6y + 4z - 5w &= -13 \\
2x + y + 3z - w &= 4 \quad \Rightarrow \mathbf{E}_2 + 2\mathbf{E}_1 \Rightarrow \\
2x + 2y + 2z &= 6 \quad \Rightarrow \mathbf{E}_3 + 2\mathbf{E}_1 \Rightarrow \\
-x - 3y + z - 2w &= -7 \Rightarrow \mathbf{E}_4 - \mathbf{E}_1 \Rightarrow
\end{aligned}
\qquad
\begin{aligned}
-x - 6y + 4z - 5w &= -13 \\
-11y + 11z - 11w &= -22 \Rightarrow -\dfrac{1}{11}\mathbf{E}_2 \Rightarrow \\
-10y + 10z - 10w &= -20 \Rightarrow -\dfrac{1}{10}\mathbf{E}_3 \Rightarrow \\
3y - 3z + 3w &= 6 \quad \Rightarrow \dfrac{1}{3}\mathbf{E}_4 \Rightarrow
\end{aligned}
\qquad
\begin{aligned}
-x - 6y + 4z - 5w &= -13 \\
y - z + w &= 2 \\
y - z + w &= 2 \\
y - z + w &= 2
\end{aligned}
$$

28. $(x, y, z, w) = (-w + 2, -z - 1, z, w)$: Note that the last two equations in the triangular system give no additional information. z and w can be anything, then $y = -z - 1$ and $x = 4 + 2(-z - 1) + 2z - w = 2 - w$.

$$
\begin{aligned}
-x + 2y + 2z - w &= -4 \\
y + z &= -1 \\
-2x + 2y + 2z - 2w &= -6 \Rightarrow \mathbf{E}_3 - 2\mathbf{E}_1 \Rightarrow \\
-x + 3y + 3z - w &= -5 \Rightarrow \mathbf{E}_4 - \mathbf{E}_1 \Rightarrow
\end{aligned}
\qquad
\begin{aligned}
-x + 2y + 2z - w &= -4 \\
y + z &= -1 \\
-2y - 2z &= 2 \quad \Rightarrow -\dfrac{1}{2}\mathbf{E}_3 \Rightarrow \\
y + z &= -1
\end{aligned}
\qquad
\begin{aligned}
-x + 2y + 2z - w &= -4 \\
y + z &= -1 \\
y + z &= -1 \\
y + z &= -1
\end{aligned}
$$

29. $(x, y, z) = \left(\dfrac{9}{4}, -\dfrac{3}{4}, -\dfrac{7}{4}\right)$:
$\begin{bmatrix} x \\ y \\ z \end{bmatrix} = \begin{bmatrix} 1 & 2 & 1 \\ 1 & -3 & 2 \\ 2 & -3 & 1 \end{bmatrix}^{-1} \begin{bmatrix} -1 \\ 1 \\ 5 \end{bmatrix} = \dfrac{1}{12}\begin{bmatrix} 3 & -5 & 7 \\ 3 & -1 & -1 \\ 3 & 7 & -5 \end{bmatrix}\begin{bmatrix} -1 \\ 1 \\ 5 \end{bmatrix}.$

30. $(x, y, z) = \left(\dfrac{1}{2}, -\dfrac{5}{2}, -\dfrac{5}{2}\right)$:
$\begin{bmatrix} x \\ y \\ z \end{bmatrix} = \begin{bmatrix} 1 & 2 & -1 \\ 2 & -1 & 1 \\ 1 & 1 & -2 \end{bmatrix}^{-1} \begin{bmatrix} -2 \\ 1 \\ 3 \end{bmatrix} = \dfrac{1}{8}\begin{bmatrix} 1 & 3 & 1 \\ 5 & -1 & -3 \\ 3 & 1 & -5 \end{bmatrix}\begin{bmatrix} -2 \\ 1 \\ 3 \end{bmatrix}.$

31. There is no inverse, since the coefficient matrix, shown on the right, has determinant 0 (found with a calculator). Note that this does not necessarily mean there is no solution — there may be infinitely many solutions. However, by other means one can determine that there is no solution in this case.

$\begin{bmatrix} 2 & 1 & 1 & -1 \\ 2 & -1 & 1 & -1 \\ -1 & 1 & -1 & 1 \\ 1 & -2 & 1 & -1 \end{bmatrix}$

32. $(x, y, z, w) = \left(\dfrac{13}{3}, -\dfrac{8}{3}, -\dfrac{1}{3}, \dfrac{22}{3}\right)$:
$\begin{bmatrix} x \\ y \\ z \\ w \end{bmatrix} = \begin{bmatrix} 1 & -2 & 1 & -1 \\ 2 & 1 & -1 & -1 \\ 1 & -1 & 2 & -1 \\ 1 & 3 & -1 & 1 \end{bmatrix}^{-1} \begin{bmatrix} 2 \\ -1 \\ -1 \\ 4 \end{bmatrix} = \dfrac{1}{9}\begin{bmatrix} 8 & -1 & -2 & 5 \\ -7 & 2 & 4 & -1 \\ -2 & -2 & 5 & 1 \\ 11 & -7 & -5 & 8 \end{bmatrix}\begin{bmatrix} 2 \\ -1 \\ -1 \\ 4 \end{bmatrix}.$

33. $(x, y, z, w) = (2 - w, z + 3, z, w)$ — z and w can be anything:

$$\begin{bmatrix} 1 & 2 & -2 & 1 & 8 \\ 2 & 3 & -3 & 2 & 13 \end{bmatrix} \xrightarrow{(-2)R_1 + R_2} \begin{bmatrix} 1 & 2 & -2 & 1 & 8 \\ 0 & -1 & 1 & 0 & -3 \end{bmatrix} \xrightarrow[\;(-1)R_2\;]{(2)R_2 + R_1} \begin{bmatrix} 1 & 0 & 0 & 1 & 2 \\ 0 & 1 & -1 & 0 & 3 \end{bmatrix}$$

34. $(x, y, z, w) = (2 - w, z + 3, z, w)$ — z and w can be anything. The final step, $(-1)R_2 + R_3$, is not shown:

$$\begin{bmatrix} 1 & 2 & -2 & 1 & 8 \\ 2 & 7 & -7 & 2 & 25 \\ 1 & 3 & -3 & 1 & 11 \end{bmatrix} \xrightarrow[\;(-1)R_1 + R_3\;]{(-2)R_1 + R_2} \begin{bmatrix} 1 & 2 & -2 & 1 & 8 \\ 0 & 3 & -3 & 0 & 9 \\ 0 & 1 & -1 & 0 & 3 \end{bmatrix} \xrightarrow[\;(-2)R_3 + R_1\;]{(1/3)R_2} \begin{bmatrix} 1 & 0 & 0 & 1 & 2 \\ 0 & 1 & -1 & 0 & 3 \\ 0 & 1 & -1 & 0 & 3 \end{bmatrix}$$

35. $(x, y, z, w) = (-2, 1, 3, -1)$:

$$\begin{bmatrix} 1 & 2 & 4 & 6 & 6 \\ 3 & 4 & 8 & 11 & 11 \\ 2 & 4 & 7 & 11 & 10 \\ 3 & 5 & 10 & 14 & 15 \end{bmatrix} \xrightarrow[\;R_{24}\;]{(-2)R_1 + R_3} \begin{bmatrix} 1 & 2 & 4 & 6 & 6 \\ 3 & 5 & 10 & 14 & 15 \\ 0 & 0 & -1 & -1 & -2 \\ 3 & 4 & 8 & 11 & 11 \end{bmatrix} \xrightarrow[\;(-1)R_3\;]{(-1)R_4 + R_2}$$

$$\begin{bmatrix} 1 & 2 & 4 & 6 & 6 \\ 0 & 1 & 2 & 3 & 4 \\ 0 & 0 & 1 & 1 & 2 \\ 3 & 4 & 8 & 11 & 11 \end{bmatrix} \xrightarrow[\;(-4)R_2 + R_4\;]{(-2)R_2 + R_1} \begin{bmatrix} 1 & 0 & 0 & 0 & -2 \\ 0 & 1 & 2 & 3 & 4 \\ 0 & 0 & 1 & 1 & 2 \\ 3 & 0 & 0 & -1 & -5 \end{bmatrix} \xrightarrow[\;(-2)R_3 + R_2\;]{(-3)R_1 + R_4} \begin{bmatrix} 1 & 0 & 0 & 0 & -2 \\ 0 & 1 & 0 & 1 & 0 \\ 0 & 0 & 1 & 1 & 2 \\ 0 & 0 & 0 & -1 & 1 \end{bmatrix}$$

$$\xrightarrow[\;(1)R_4 + R_3\;]{(1)R_4 + R_2} \begin{bmatrix} 1 & 0 & 0 & 0 & -2 \\ 0 & 1 & 0 & 0 & 1 \\ 0 & 0 & 1 & 0 & 3 \\ 0 & 0 & 0 & -1 & 1 \end{bmatrix} \xrightarrow{(-1)R_4} \begin{bmatrix} 1 & 0 & 0 & 0 & -2 \\ 0 & 1 & 0 & 0 & 1 \\ 0 & 0 & 1 & 0 & 3 \\ 0 & 0 & 0 & 1 & -1 \end{bmatrix}$$

36. $(x, y, z, w) = (1, -w - 3, w + 2, w)$:

$$\begin{bmatrix} 1 & 0 & 2 & -2 & 5 \\ 2 & 1 & 4 & -3 & 7 \\ 4 & 1 & 7 & -6 & 15 \\ 2 & 1 & 5 & -4 & 9 \end{bmatrix} \xrightarrow[\;(-1)R_2 + R_4\;]{(-4)R_1 + R_3} \begin{bmatrix} 1 & 0 & 2 & -2 & 5 \\ 2 & 1 & 4 & -3 & 7 \\ 0 & 1 & -1 & 2 & -5 \\ 0 & 0 & 1 & -1 & 2 \end{bmatrix}$$

$$\xrightarrow[\;(-2)R_4 + R_1\;]{(-2)R_1 + R_2} \begin{bmatrix} 1 & 0 & 0 & 0 & 1 \\ 0 & 1 & 0 & 1 & -3 \\ 0 & 1 & -1 & 2 & -5 \\ 0 & 0 & 1 & -1 & 2 \end{bmatrix} \xrightarrow{(-1)R_2 + R_3} \begin{bmatrix} 1 & 0 & 0 & 0 & 1 \\ 0 & 1 & 0 & 1 & -3 \\ 0 & 0 & -1 & 1 & -2 \\ 0 & 0 & 1 & -1 & 2 \end{bmatrix} \xrightarrow[\;(-1)R_3\;]{(1)R_3 + R_4}$$

$$\begin{bmatrix} 1 & 0 & 0 & 0 & 1 \\ 0 & 1 & 0 & 1 & -3 \\ 0 & 0 & 1 & -1 & 2 \\ 0 & 0 & 0 & 0 & 0 \end{bmatrix}$$

37. $(x, p) \approx (7.57, 42.71)$: Solve $100 - x^2 = 20 + 3x$ to give $x \approx 7.57$ (the other solution, $x \approx -10.57$, makes no sense in this problem). Then $p = 20 + 3x \approx 42.71$.

38. $(x, p) \approx (13.91, 60.65)$: Solve $80 - \frac{1}{10}x^2 = 5 + 4x$ to give $x \approx 13.91$ (the other solution, $x \approx -53.91$, makes no sense in this problem). Then $p = 5 + 4x \approx 60.65$.

39. $(x, y) \approx (0.14, -2.29)$

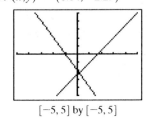

$[-5, 5]$ by $[-5, 5]$

40. $(x, y) = (-1, -2.5)$ or $(x, y) = (3, 1.5)$

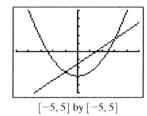

$[-5, 5]$ by $[-5, 5]$

41. $(x, y) = (-2, 1)$ or $(x, y) = (2, 1)$

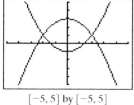

[−5, 5] by [−5, 5]

42. $(x, y) \approx (-1.47, 1.35)$ or $(x, y) \approx (1.47, 1.35)$ or
$(x, y) \approx (0.76, -1.85)$ or $(x, y) \approx (-0.76, -1.85)$

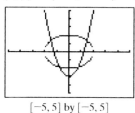

[−5, 5] by [−5, 5]

43. $(x, y) \approx (2.27, 1.53)$

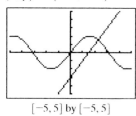

[−5, 5] by [−5, 5]

44. $(x, y) \approx (4.62, 2.22)$ or $(x, y) \approx (1.56, 1.14)$

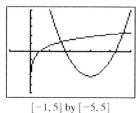

[−1, 5] by [−5, 5]

45. $(a, b, c, d) = \left(\dfrac{17}{840}, -\dfrac{33}{280}, -\dfrac{571}{420}, \dfrac{386}{35} \right)$
$= (0.020..., -0.117..., -1.359..., 11.028...)$. In matrix
form, the system is as shown below. Use a calculator to
find the inverse matrix and multiply.

$$\begin{bmatrix} 8 & 4 & 2 & 1 \\ 64 & 16 & 4 & 1 \\ 216 & 36 & 6 & 1 \\ 729 & 81 & 9 & 1 \end{bmatrix} \begin{bmatrix} a \\ b \\ c \\ d \end{bmatrix} = \begin{bmatrix} 8 \\ 5 \\ 3 \\ 4 \end{bmatrix}$$

46. $(a, b, c, d, e) = \left(\dfrac{19}{108}, -\dfrac{29}{18}, \dfrac{59}{36}, \dfrac{505}{54}, -\dfrac{68}{9} \right)$
$= (0.17\overline{592}, -1.6\overline{1}, 1.63\overline{8}, 9.3\overline{518}, -7.\overline{5})$. In matrix form,
the system is as shown below. Use a calculator to find the
inverse matrix and multiply.

$$\begin{bmatrix} 16 & -8 & 4 & -2 & 1 \\ 1 & 1 & 1 & 1 & 1 \\ 81 & 27 & 9 & 3 & 1 \\ 256 & 64 & 16 & 4 & 1 \\ 2401 & 343 & 49 & 7 & 1 \end{bmatrix} \begin{bmatrix} a \\ b \\ c \\ d \\ e \end{bmatrix} = \begin{bmatrix} -4 \\ 2 \\ 6 \\ -2 \\ 8 \end{bmatrix}$$

47. $\dfrac{3x - 2}{x^2 - 3x - 4} = \dfrac{A_1}{x + 1} + \dfrac{A_2}{x - 4}$, so $3x - 2$
$= A_1(x - 4) + A_2(x + 1)$. With $x = -1$, we see that
$-5 = -5A_1$, so $A_1 = 1$; with $x = 4$ we have $10 = 5A_2$,
so $A_2 = 2$: $\dfrac{1}{x + 1} + \dfrac{2}{x - 4}$.

48. $\dfrac{x - 16}{x^2 + x - 2} = \dfrac{A_1}{x + 2} + \dfrac{A_2}{x - 1}$, so $x - 16$
$= A_1(x - 1) + A_2(x + 2)$. With $x = -2$, we see that
$-18 = -3A_1$, so $A_1 = 6$; with $x = 1$ we have
$-15 = 3A_2$, so $A_2 = -5$: $\dfrac{6}{x + 2} - \dfrac{5}{x - 1}$.

49. The denominator factors into $(x + 2)(x + 1)^2$, so
$\dfrac{3x + 5}{x^3 + 4x^2 + 5x + 2} = \dfrac{A_1}{x + 2} + \dfrac{A_2}{x + 1} + \dfrac{A_3}{(x + 1)^2}$.
Then $3x + 5 = A_1(x + 1)^2 + A_2(x + 2)(x + 1)$
$+ A_3(x + 2)$. With $x = -2$, we have $-1 = A_1$; with
$x = -1$, we have $2 = A_3$; with $x = 0$, we have 5
$= A_1 + 2A_2 + 2A_3 = -1 + 2A_2 + 4$, so that $A_2 = 1$:
$-\dfrac{1}{x + 2} + \dfrac{1}{x + 1} + \dfrac{2}{(x + 1)^2}$.

50. The denominator factors into $(x - 1)(x + 2)^2$, so
$\dfrac{3(3 + 2x + x^2)}{x^3 + 3x^2 - 4} = \dfrac{A_1}{x - 1} + \dfrac{A_2}{x + 2} + \dfrac{A_3}{(x + 2)^2}$.
Then $3x^2 + 6x + 9 = A_1(x + 2)^2 + A_2(x - 1)(x + 2)$
$+ A_3(x - 1)$. With $x = 1$, we have $18 = 9A_1$, so $A_1 = 2$;
with $x = -2$, we have $9 = -3A_3$, so $A_3 = -3$; with $x = 0$,
we have $9 = 4A_1 - 2A_2 - A_3 = 8 - 2A_2 + 3$,
so that $A_2 = 1$: $\dfrac{2}{x - 1} + \dfrac{1}{x + 2} - \dfrac{3}{(x + 2)^2}$.

51. The denominator factors into $(x + 1)(x^2 + 1)$, so
$\dfrac{5x^2 - x - 2}{x^3 + x^2 + x + 1} = \dfrac{A}{x + 1} + \dfrac{Bx + C}{x^2 + 1}$. Then
$5x^2 - x - 2 = A(x^2 + 1) + (Bx + C)(x + 1)$.
With $x = -1$, we have $4 = 2A_1$, so $A = 2$; with $x = 0$,
$-2 = A + C$, so $C = -4$. Finally, with $x = 1$ we have
$2 = 2A + (B + C)(2) = 4 + 2B - 8$, so that $B = 3$:
$\dfrac{2}{x + 1} + \dfrac{3x - 4}{x^2 + 1}$

52. The denominator factors into $(x + 2)(x^2 + 4)$, so
$\dfrac{-x^2 - 5x + 2}{x^3 + 2x^2 + 4x + 8} = \dfrac{A}{x + 2} + \dfrac{Bx + C}{x^2 + 4}$. Then
$-x^2 - 5x + 2 = A(x^2 + 4) + (Bx + C)(x + 2)$.
With $x = -2$, we have $8 = 8A_1$, so $A = 1$, with $x = 0$,
$2 = 4A + 2C$, so $C = -1$. Finally, with $x = 1$ we have
$-4 = 5A + (B + C)(3) = 5 + 3B - 3$, so that
$B = -2$: $\dfrac{1}{x + 2} - \dfrac{2x + 1}{x^2 + 4}$

53. (c)

54. (d)

55. (b)

56. (a)

57.

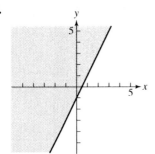

58.

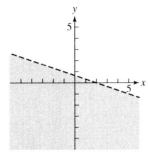

59. Corner points: $(0, 90)$, $(90, 0)$, $\left(\dfrac{360}{13}, \dfrac{360}{13}\right)$. Boundaries included.

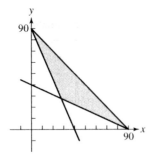

60. Corner points: $(0, 3)$, $(0, 7)$, $\left(\dfrac{30}{13}, \dfrac{70}{13}\right)$, $(3, 0)$, $(5, 0)$. Boundaries included.

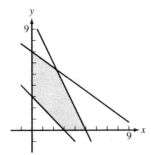

61. Corner points: approx. $(0.92, 2.31)$ and $(5.41, 3.80)$. Boundaries excluded.

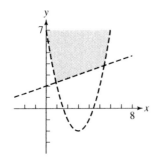

62. Corner points: approx. $(-2.41, 3.20)$ and $(2.91, 0.55)$. Boundaries included.

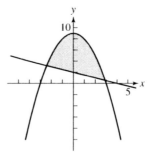

63. Corner points: approx. $(-1.25, 1.56)$ and $(1.25, 1.56)$. Boundaries included.

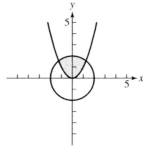

64. No corner points. Boundaries included.

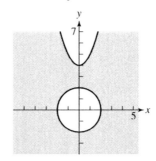

65. Corner points: $(0, 20)$, $(25, 0)$, and $(10, 6)$.

(x, y)	$(0, 20)$	$(10, 6)$	$(25, 0)$
f	120	106	175

$f_{\min} = 106$ [at $(10, 6)$]; $f_{\max} = $ none (unbounded)

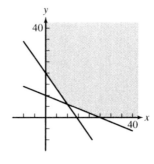

66. Corner points: $(0, 30)$, $(8, 10)$, and $(24, 0)$.

(x, y)	$(0, 30)$	$(8, 10)$	$(24, 0)$
f	150	138	264

$f_{min} = 138$ [at $(8, 10)$]; $f_{max} =$ none (unbounded)

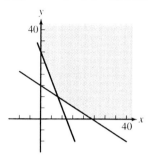

67. Corner points: $(4, 40)$, $(10, 25)$, and $(70, 10)$.

(x, y)	$(4, 40)$	$(10, 25)$	$(70, 10)$
f	292	205	280

$f_{min} = 205$ [at $(10, 25)$]; $f_{max} = 292$ [at $(4, 40)$]

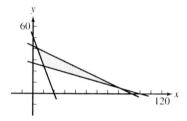

68. Corner points: $(0, 120)$, $(120, 0)$, and $(20, 30)$.

(x, y)	$(0, 120)$	$(120, 0)$	$(20, 30)$
f	1680	1080	600

$f_{min} = 600$ [at $(20, 30)$]; $f_{max} = 1680$ [at $(0, 120)$]

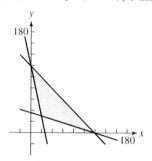

69. (a) $[1 \quad 2] \begin{bmatrix} \cos 45° & -\sin 45° \\ \sin 45° & \cos 45° \end{bmatrix} \approx \begin{bmatrix} 2.12 \\ 0.71 \end{bmatrix}$

(b) $[1 \quad 2] \begin{bmatrix} \cos 45° & \sin 45° \\ -\sin 45° & \cos 45° \end{bmatrix} \approx \begin{bmatrix} -0.71 \\ 2.12 \end{bmatrix}$

70. In this problem, the graphs are representative of the total Medicare Disbursements (in billions of dollars) for several years, where x is the number of years past 1990.

(a) The following is a scatter plot of the data with the linear regression equation $y = 11.4428x + 116.681$ superimposed on it.

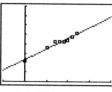

[−5, 20] by [0, 400]

(b) The following is a scatter plot of the data with the logistic regression equation $y = \dfrac{294.846}{1 + 1.6278e^{-0.1784x}}$ superimposed on it.

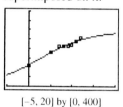

[−5, 20] by [0, 400]

(c) *Graphical solution:* The two regression models will predict the same disbursement amounts when the graph of their difference is 0. That will occur when the graph crosses the x-axis. This difference function is

$y = 11.4428x + 116.681 - \left(\dfrac{294.846}{1 + 1.6278e^{-0.1784x}} \right)$

and it crosses the x-axis when $x \approx 3.03$ and $x \approx 10.15$.

The disbursement amount of the two models will be the same sometime in the years 1993 and 2000.

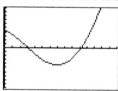

[0, 15] by [−10, 10]

Another graphical solution would be to find where the graphs of the two curves intersect.

Algebraic solution: The algebraic solution of the problem is not feasible.

(d) Both models appear to fit the data fairly well. The logistic model should be used to make predictions beyond 2000. The disbursements stabilize using the logistic model but continue to rise according to the linear model.

71. In this problem, the graphs are representative of the population (in thousands) of the states of Hawaii and Idaho for several years, where x is the number of years past 1980.

    (a) The following is a scatter plot of the Hawaii data with the linear regression equation
$y = 12.2614x + 979.5909$ superimposed on it.

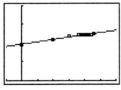

        [−5, 30] by [0, 2000]

    (b) The following is a scatter plot of the Idaho data with the linear regression equation
$y = 19.8270x + 893.9566$ superimposed on it.

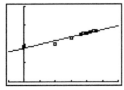

        [−5, 30] by [0, 2000]

    (c) *Graphical solution:* Graph the two linear equations
$y = 12.2614x + 979.5909$ and
$y = 19.8270x + 893.9566$ on the same axis and find their point of intersection. The two curves intersect at $x \approx 11.3$.
The population of the two states will be the same sometime in the year 1991.

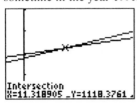

        [−5, 30] by [0, 2000]

    Another graphical solution would be to find where the graph of the difference of the two curves is equal to 0.

    Algebraic solution:
Solve $12.2614x + 979.5909 = 19.8270x + 893.9566$ for x.

$$12.2614x + 979.5909 = 19.8270x + 893.9566$$
$$7.5656x = 85.6343$$
$$x = \frac{85.6343}{7.5656} \approx 11.3$$

The population of the two states will be the same sometime in the year 1991.

72. **(a)** According to data from the U. S. Census Bureau, there were 143.0 million males and 147.8 million females in 2003. The ratio of males to the total population is

$\dfrac{143}{290.8} \approx 0.4917$ and the ratio of females to the total

population is $\dfrac{147.8}{290.8} \approx 0.5083$. If we define Matrix A

as the population matrix for the states of California,

Florida, and Rhode Island, we have $A = \begin{matrix} \text{CA} \\ \text{FL} \\ \text{RI} \end{matrix}\begin{bmatrix} 35.5 \\ 17.0 \\ 1.1 \end{bmatrix}$.

If we define Matrix B as the ratio of males and females to the total population in 2003, we have

$$\begin{matrix} \text{M} & \text{F} \end{matrix}$$
$$B = [0.4917 \ \ 0.5083].$$

The product AB gives the estimate of males and females in each of the three states in 2003.

$$C = \begin{bmatrix} 35.5 \\ 17.0 \\ 1.1 \end{bmatrix}[0.4917 \ \ 0.5083] = \begin{matrix} \\ \text{CA} \\ \text{FL} \\ \text{RI} \end{matrix}\begin{bmatrix} \text{M} & \text{F} \\ 17.5 & 18.0 \\ 8.4 & 8.6 \\ 0.54 & 0.56 \end{bmatrix}$$

(b) The matrix for the percentages of the populations of California, Florida, and Rhode Island under the age of 18 and age 65 or older is given as:

$$\begin{matrix} & <18 & \geq 65 \\ \text{CA} & \\ \text{FL} & \\ \text{RI} & \end{matrix}\begin{bmatrix} 26.5 & 10.6 \\ 23.1 & 17.0 \\ 22.8 & 14.0 \end{bmatrix}$$

(c) To change the matrix in (b) from percentages to decimals, multiply by the scalar 0.01 as follows:

$$0.01 \times \begin{bmatrix} 26.5 & 10.6 \\ 23.1 & 17.0 \\ 22.8 & 14.0 \end{bmatrix} = \begin{matrix} \\ \text{CA} \\ \text{FL} \\ \text{RI} \end{matrix}\begin{bmatrix} <18 & \geq 65 \\ 0.265 & 0.106 \\ 0.231 & 0.170 \\ 0.228 & 0.140 \end{bmatrix}$$

(d) The transpose of the matrix in (c) is

$$\begin{bmatrix} 0.265 & 0.231 & 0.228 \\ 0.106 & 0.170 & 0.140 \end{bmatrix}.$$

Multiplying the transpose of the matrix in (c) by the matrix in (a) gives the total number of males and females who are under the age of 18 or are 65 or older in all three states.

$$\begin{bmatrix} 0.265 & 0.231 & 0.228 \\ 0.106 & 0.170 & 0.140 \end{bmatrix}\begin{bmatrix} 17.5 & 18.0 \\ 8.4 & 8.6 \\ 0.54 & 0.56 \end{bmatrix} =$$

$$\begin{matrix} & \text{M} & \text{F} \\ <18 & \\ \geq 65 & \end{matrix}\begin{bmatrix} 6.7 & 6.9 \\ 3.4 & 3.4 \end{bmatrix}$$

(e) In 2003, there were about 6.7 million males under age 18 and about 3.4 million females 65 or older living in the three states.

73. **(a)** $N = [200 \quad 400 \quad 600 \quad 250]$

    (b) $P = [\$80 \quad \$120 \quad \$200 \quad \$300]$

    (c) $NP^T = [200 \quad 400 \quad 600 \quad 250]\begin{bmatrix} \$80 \\ \$120 \\ \$200 \\ \$300 \end{bmatrix} = \$259{,}000$

74. $(x, y) = (380, 72)$, where x is the number of students and y is the number of nonstudents.

$$x + y = 452$$
$$0.75x + 2.00y = 429$$

One method to solve the system is to solve by elimination as follows:

$$2x + 2y = 904$$
$$\underline{0.75x + 2y = 429}$$
$$1.25x = 475$$
$$x = 380$$

Substitute $x = 380$ into $x + y = 452$ to solve for y.

75. Let x be the number of vans, y be the number of small trucks, and z be the number of large trucks needed. The requirements of the problem are summarized above

$$8x + 15y + 22 \geq 115$$
$$3x + 10y + 20z \geq 85$$
$$2x + 6y + 5z \geq 35$$

(along with the requirements that each of x, y, and z must be a non-negative integer).
The methods of this chapter do not allow complete solution of this problem. Solving this system of *inequalities* as if it were a system of *equations* gives (x, y, z) $= (1.77, 3.30, 2.34)$, which suggests the answer $(x, y, z) = (2, 4, 3)$; one can easily check that (x, y, z) $= (2, 4, 2)$ actually works, as does $(1, 3, 3)$. The first of these solutions requires 8 vehicles, while the second requires only 7. There are a number of other seven-vehicle answers (these can be found by trial and error): Use no vans, anywhere from 0 to 5 small trucks, and the rest should be large trucks — that is, (x, y, z) should be one of $(0, 0, 7)$, $(0, 1, 6)$, $(0, 2, 5)$, $(0, 3, 4)$, $(0, 4, 3)$, or $(0, 5, 2)$.

76. $(x, y) = (21,333.33, 16,666.67)$, where x is the amount invested at 7.5% and y is the amount invested at 6%.

$$x + y = 38,000$$
$$0.075x + 0.06y = 2,600$$

One method to solve the system is to solve by substitution as follows:

$$x + y = 38,000 \Rightarrow x = 38,000 - y$$
$$0.075(38,000 - y) + 0.06y = 2600$$
$$2850 - 0.075y + 0.06y = 2600$$
$$-0.015y = -250$$
$$y = 16,666.67$$

Substitute $y = 16,666.67$ into $x + y = 38,000$ to solve for x.

77. $(x, y, z) = (160000, 170000, 320000)$, where x is the amount borrowed at 4%, y is the amount borrowed at 6.5%, and z is the amount borrowed at 9%. Solve the system below.

$$x + y + z = 650,000$$
$$0.04x + 0.065y + 0.09z = 46,250$$
$$2x - z = 0$$

One method to solve the system is to solve using Gaussian elimination:
Multiply equation 1 by -0.065 and add the result to equation 2, replacing equation 2:

$$x + y + z = 650,000$$
$$-0.025x + 0.025z = 4000$$
$$2x - z = 0$$

Divide equation 2 by 0.025 to simplify:

$$x + y + z = 650,000$$
$$-x + z = 160,000$$
$$2x - z = 0$$

Now add equation 2 to equation 3, replacing equation 3:

$$x + y + z = 650,000$$
$$-x + z = 160,000$$
$$x = 160,000$$

Substitute $x = 160,000$ into equation 2 to solve for z: $z = 320,000$. Substitute these values into equation 1 to solve for y: $y = 170,000$.

78. Sue: 9.3 hours (9 hours and 20 minutes), Esther: 12 hours, Murphy: 16.8 hours (16 hours 48 minutes). If x is the portion of the room Sue completes in one hour, y is the portion that Esther completes in one hour, and z is the portion that Murphy completes in one hour, then solving the system above gives (x, y, z)

$$x + y + z = 1/4$$
$$x + + z = 1/6$$
$$y + z = 1/7$$

$$= \left(\frac{3}{28}, \frac{1}{12}, \frac{5}{84}\right) = \left(\frac{1}{9.333}, \frac{1}{12}, \frac{1}{16.8}\right).$$

One method to solve the system is to find the row echelon form of the augmented matrix:

$$\begin{bmatrix} 1 & 1 & 1 & 1/4 \\ 1 & 0 & 1 & 1/6 \\ 0 & 1 & 1 & 1/7 \end{bmatrix} \xrightarrow{R_1 - R_2} \begin{bmatrix} 1 & 1 & 1 & 1/4 \\ 0 & 1 & 0 & 1/12 \\ 0 & 1 & 1 & 1/7 \end{bmatrix}$$

$$\xrightarrow{R_1 - R_3} \begin{bmatrix} 1 & 0 & 0 & 3/28 \\ 0 & 1 & 0 & 1/12 \\ 0 & 1 & 1 & 1/7 \end{bmatrix} \xrightarrow{R_3 - R_2}$$

$$\begin{bmatrix} 1 & 0 & 0 & 3/28 \\ 0 & 1 & 0 & 1/12 \\ 0 & 0 & 1 & 5/84 \end{bmatrix}$$

79. Pipe A: 15 hours. Pipe B: $\dfrac{60}{11} \approx 5.45$ hours (about 5 hours 27.3 minutes). Pipe C: 12 hours. If x is the portion of the pool that A can fill in one hour, y is the portion that B fills in one hour, and z is the portion that C fills in one hour, then solving the system above gives

$$x + y + z = 1/3$$
$$x + y = 1/4$$
$$y + z = 1/3.75$$

$$(x, y, z) = \left(\frac{1}{15}, \frac{11}{60}, \frac{1}{12}\right)$$

One method to solve the system is to use elimination:
Subtract equation 2 from equation 1:

$$x + y + z = 1/3$$
$$z = 1/12$$
$$y + z = 4/15 \quad \text{(convert 1/3.75 to simpler form)}$$

Subtract equation 2 from equation 3:

$$x + y + z = 1/3$$
$$z = 1/12$$
$$y = 11/60$$

Substitute the values for y and z into equation 1 to solve for x: $x = 1/15$.

80. B must be an $n \times n$ matrix. (There are n rows in B because AB is defined, and n columns in B since BA is defined.)

81. $n = p$ — the number of columns in A is the same as the number of rows in B.

Chapter 7 Project

1. The graphs are representative of the male and female population in the United States from 1990 to 2004, where x is the number of years after 1990.

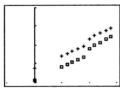

[−5, 15] by [120, 160]

The linear regression equation for the male population is $y \approx 1.7585x + 119.5765$.

The linear regression equation for the female population is $y \approx 1.6173x + 126.4138$.

2. The slope is the rate of change of people (in millions) per year. The y-intercept is the number of people (either males or females) in 1990.

3. Yes, the male population is predicted to eventually surpass the female population, because the males' regression line has a greater slope. But since 2000, the female population has always been greater. Since a span of only 15 years is represented, the data are most likely not enough to create a model for 100 or more years.

4.

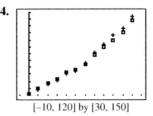

[−10, 120] by [30, 150]

5. Males: $y \approx \dfrac{412.574}{1 + 10.956e^{(-0.01539x)}}$

Females: $y \approx \dfrac{315.829}{1 + 9.031e^{(-0.01831x)}}$

The curves intersect at approximately (45, 64); this represents the time when the female population became greater than the male population.

The curves intersect at approximately (159, 212); this represents the time when the male population will again become greater the female population.

7. Approximately $\dfrac{138.1}{281.5} \approx 0.491 = 49.1\%$ male and 50.9% female

Chapter 8
Analytic Geometry in Two and Three Dimensions

■ Section 8.1 Conic Sections and Parabolas

Exploration 1

1. From Figure 8.4, we see that the axis of the parabola is $x = 0$. Thus, we want to find the point along $x = 0$ that is equidistant from both $(0, 1)$ and the line $y = -1$. Since the axis is perpendicular to the directrix, the point on the directrix closest to the parabola is $(0, 1)$ and $(0, -1)$, it must be located at $(0, 0)$.

2. Choose any point on the parabola (x, y). From figures 8.3 and 8.4, we see that the distance from (x, y) to the focus is $d_1 = \sqrt{(x - 0)^2 + (y - 1)^2} = \sqrt{x^2 + (y - 1)^2}$ and the distance from (x, y) to the directrix is $d_2 = \sqrt{(x - x)^2 + (y - (-1))^2} = \sqrt{(y + 1)^2}$. Since d_1 must equal d_2, we have

$$d_1 = \sqrt{x^2 + (y - 1)^2} = \sqrt{(y + 1)^2} = d_2$$
$$x^2 + (y - 1)^2 = (y + 1)^2$$
$$x^2 + y^2 - 2y + 1 = y^2 + 2y + 1$$
$$x^2 = 4y$$
$$\frac{x^2}{4} = y \text{ or } x^2 = 4y$$

3. From the figure, we see that the first dashed line above $y = 0$ is $y = 1$, and we assume that each subsequent dashed line increases by $y = 1$. Using the equation above, we solve $\left\{ 1 = \dfrac{x^2}{4}, 2 = \dfrac{x^2}{4}, 3 = \dfrac{x^2}{4}, 4 = \dfrac{x^2}{4}, 5 = \dfrac{x^2}{4}, 6 = \dfrac{x^2}{4} \right\}$ to find:

$\{(-2\sqrt{6}, 6), (-2\sqrt{5}, 5), (-4, 4), (-2\sqrt{3}, 3),$
$(-2\sqrt{2}, 2), (-2, 1), (0, 0), (2, 1), (2\sqrt{2}, 2), (2\sqrt{3}, 3),$
$(4, 4), (2\sqrt{5}, 5), (2\sqrt{6}, 6)\}$

Exploration 2

1.

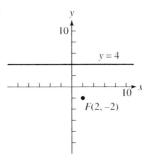

2.

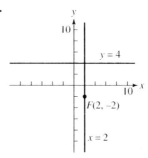

The equation of the axis is $x = 2$.

3.

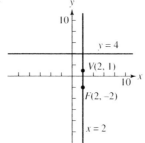

4. Since the focus $(h, k + p) = (2, -2)$ and the directrix $y = k - p = 4$, we have $k + p = -2$ and $k - p = 4$. Thus, $k = 1$, $p = -3$. As a result, the focal length p is -3 and the focal width $|4p|$ is 12.

5. Since the focal width is 12, each endpoint of the chord is 6 units away from the focus $(2, -2)$ along the line $y = -2$. The endpoints of the chord, then, are $(2 - 6, -2)$ and $(2 + 6, -2)$, or $(-4, -2)$ and $(8, -2)$.

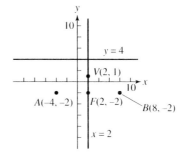

6.

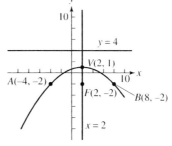

7. Downward

8. $h = 2, p = -3, k = 1,$ so $(x - 2)^2 = -12(y - 1)$

Quick Review 8.1

1. $\sqrt{(2 - (-1))^2 + (5 - 3)^2} = \sqrt{9 + 4} = \sqrt{13}$

2. $\sqrt{(a - 2)^2 + (b + 3)^2}$

3. $y^2 = 4x, y = \pm 2\sqrt{x}$

4. $y^2 = 5x, y = \pm \sqrt{5x}$

5. $y + 7 = -(x^2 - 2x), y + 7 - 1 = -(x - 1)^2,$
$y + 6 = -(x - 1)^2$

6. $y + 5 = 2(x^2 + 3x), y + 5 + \dfrac{9}{2} = 2\left(x + \dfrac{3}{2}\right)^2$
$y + \dfrac{19}{2} = 2\left(x + \dfrac{3}{2}\right)^2$

7. Vertex: $(1, 5)$. $f(x)$ can be obtained from $g(x)$ by stretching x^2 by 3, shifting up 5 units, and shifting right 1 unit.

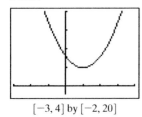

[-3, 4] by [-2, 20]

8. Vertex: $(3, 19)$. $f(x) = -2(x - 3)^2 + 19$. $f(x)$ can be obtained from $g(x)$ by stretching x^2 by 2, reflecting across the x-axis, shifting up 19 units and shifting right 3 units.

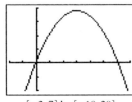

[-2, 7] by [-10, 20]

9. $f(x) = a(x + 1)^2 + 3,$ so $1 = a + 3, a = -2,$
$f(x) = -2(x + 1)^2 + 3.$

10. $f(x) = a(x - 2)^2 - 5,$ so $13 = 9a - 5, a = 2,$
$f(x) = 2(x - 2)^2 - 5$

Section 8.1 Exercises

1. $k = 0, h = 0, p = \dfrac{6}{4} = \dfrac{3}{2}$. Vertex: $(0, 0)$, Focus: $\left(0, \dfrac{3}{2}\right)$,
Directrix: $y = -\dfrac{3}{2}$, Focal width: $|4p| = \left|4 \cdot \dfrac{3}{2}\right| = 6$

2. $k = 0, h = 0, p = \dfrac{-8}{4} = -2$. Vertex: $(0, 0)$,
Focus: $(-2, 0)$, Directrix: $x = 2$,
Focal width: $|4p| = |4(-2)| = 8$

3. $k = 2, h = -3, p = \dfrac{4}{4} = 1$. Vertex: $(-3, 2)$,
Focus: $(-2, 2)$, Directrix: $x = -3 - 1 = -4$,
Focal width: $|4p| = |4(1)| = 4$.

4. $k = -1, h = -4, p = \dfrac{-6}{4} = \dfrac{-3}{2}$. Vertex: $(-4, -1)$,
Focus: $\left(-4, \dfrac{-5}{2}\right)$, Directrix: $y = -1 - \left(\dfrac{-3}{2}\right) = \dfrac{1}{2}$,
Focal width: $|4p| = \left|4\left(\dfrac{-3}{2}\right)\right| = 6$

5. $k = 0, h = 0, 4p = \dfrac{-4}{3}$, so $p = -\dfrac{1}{3}$. Vertex: $(0, 0)$,
Focus: $\left(0, -\dfrac{1}{3}\right)$, Directrix: $y = \dfrac{1}{3}$, Focal width:
$|4p| = \left|\left(\dfrac{-4}{3}\right)\right| = \dfrac{4}{3}$

6. $k = 0, h = 0, 4p = \dfrac{16}{5}$, so $p = \dfrac{4}{5}$. Vertex: $(0, 0)$,
Focus: $\left(\dfrac{4}{5}, 0\right)$, Directrix: $x = -\dfrac{4}{5}$,
Focal width: $|4p| = \left|4\left(\dfrac{4}{5}\right)\right| = \dfrac{16}{5}$

7. (c)

8. (b)

9. (a)

10. (d)

For #11–30, recall that the standard form of the parabola is dependent on the vertex (h, k), the focal length p, the focal width $|4p|$, and the direction that the parabola opens.

11. $p = -3$ and the parabola opens to the left, so
$y^2 = -12x.$

12. $p = 2$ and the parabola opens upward, so $x^2 = 8y.$

13. $-p = 4$ (so $p = -4$) and the parabola opens downward,
so $x^2 = -16y.$

14. $-p = -2$ (so $p = 2$) and the parabola opens to the right,
so $y^2 = 8x.$

15. $p = 5$ and the parabola opens upward, so $x^2 = 20y.$

16. $p = -4$ and the parabola opens to the left, so $y^2 = -16x.$

17. $h = 0, k = 0, |4p| = 8 \Rightarrow p = 2$ (since it opens to the
right): $(y - 0)^2 = 8(x - 0); y^2 = 8x.$

18. $h = 0, k = 0, |4p| = 12 \Rightarrow p = -3$ (since it opens to
the left): $(y - 0)^2 = -12(x - 0); y^2 = -12x$

19. $h = 0, k = 0, |4p| = 6 \Rightarrow p = -\dfrac{3}{2}$ (since it opens
downward): $(x - 0)^2 = -6(y - 0); x^2 = -6y$

20. $h = 0, k = 0, |4p| = 3 \Rightarrow p = \dfrac{3}{4}$ (since it opens upward):
$(x - 0)^2 = 3(y - 0); x^2 = 3y$

21. $h = -4, k = -4, -2 = -4 + p,$ so $p = 2$ and the
parabola opens to the right; $(y + 4)^2 = 8(x + 4)$

22. $h = -5, k = 6, 6 + p = 3,$ so $p = -3$ and the parabola
opens downward; $(x + 5)^2 = -12(y - 6)$

23. Parabola opens upward and vertex is halfway between focus and directrix on $x = h$ axis, so $h = 3$ and

$$k = \frac{4 + 1}{2} = \frac{5}{2}; 1 = \frac{5}{2} - p, \text{so } p = \frac{3}{2}.$$

$$(x - 3)^2 = 6\left(y - \frac{5}{2}\right)$$

24. Parabola opens to the left and vertex is halfway between focus and directrix on $y = k$ axis, so $k = -3$ and

$$h = \frac{2 + 5}{2} = \frac{7}{2}; 5 = \frac{7}{2} - p, \text{so } p = -\frac{3}{2}.$$

$$(y + 3)^2 = -6\left(x - \frac{7}{2}\right)$$

25. $h = 4, k = 3; 6 = 4 - p$, so $p = -2$ and parabola opens to the left. $(y - 3)^2 = -8(x - 4)$

26. $h = 3, k = 5; 7 = 5 - p$, so $p = -2$ and the parabola opens downward. $(x - 3)^2 = -8(y - 5)$

27. $h = 2, k = -1; |4p| = 16 \Rightarrow p = 4$ (since it opens upward): $(x - 2)^2 = 16(y + 1)$

28. $h = -3, k = 3; |4p| = 20 \Rightarrow p = -5$ (since it opens downward): $(x + 3)^2 = -20(y - 3)$

29. $h = -1, k = -4; |4p| = 10 \Rightarrow p = -\frac{5}{2}$ (since it opens to the left): $(y + 4)^2 = -10(x + 1)$

30. $h = 2, k = 3; |4p| = 5 \Rightarrow p = \frac{5}{4}$ (since it opens to the right): $(y - 3)^2 = 5(x - 2)$

31.
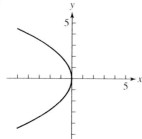

32.
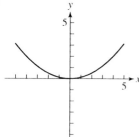

33.
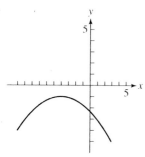

34.
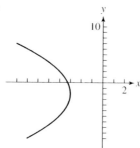

35.
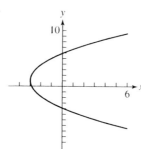

36.
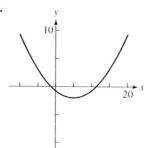

37.
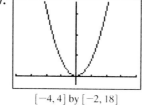

$[-4, 4]$ by $[-2, 18]$

38.
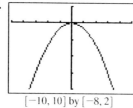

$[-10, 10]$ by $[-8, 2]$

39.
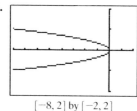

$[-8, 2]$ by $[-2, 2]$

40.

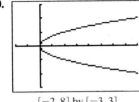

$[-2, 8]$ by $[-3, 3]$

41.

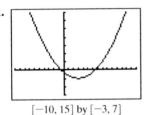

$[-10, 15]$ by $[-3, 7]$

42.

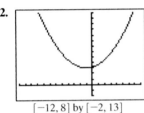

$[-12, 8]$ by $[-2, 13]$

43.

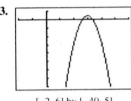

$[-2, 6]$ by $[-40, 5]$

44.

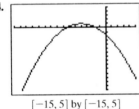

$[-15, 5]$ by $[-15, 5]$

45.

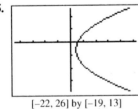

$[-22, 26]$ by $[-19, 13]$

46.

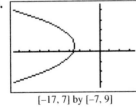

$[-17, 7]$ by $[-7, 9]$

47.

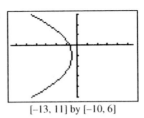

$[-13, 11]$ by $[-10, 6]$

48.

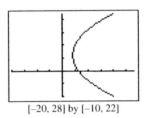

$[-20, 28]$ by $[-10, 22]$

49. Completing the square produces $y - 2 = (x + 1)^2$. The vertex is $(h, k) = (-1, 2)$, so the focus is

$$(h, k + p) = \left(-1, 2 + \frac{1}{4}\right) = \left(-1, \frac{9}{4}\right), \text{ and the}$$

directrix is $y = k - p = 2 - \frac{1}{4} = \frac{7}{4}$

50. Completing the square produces $2\left(y - \frac{7}{6}\right) = (x - 1)^2$.

The vertex is $(h, k) = \left(1, \frac{7}{6}\right)$, so the focus is

$$(h, k + p) = \left(1, \frac{7}{6} + \frac{1}{2}\right) = \left(1, \frac{5}{3}\right), \text{ and the directrix is}$$

$$y = k - p = \frac{7}{6} - \frac{1}{2} = \frac{2}{3}.$$

51. Completing the square produces $8(x - 2) = (y - 2)^2$.
The vertex is $(h, k) = (2, 2)$ so the focus is
$(h + p, k) = (2 + 2, 2) = (4, 2)$, and the directrix is
$x = h - p = 2 - 2 = 0$.

52. Completing the square produces

$$-4\left(x - \frac{13}{4}\right) = (y - 1)^2. \text{ The vertex is}$$

$$(h, k) = \left(\frac{13}{4}, 1\right) \text{ so the focus is}$$

$$(h + p, k) = \left(\frac{13}{4} - 1, 1\right) = \left(\frac{9}{4}, 1\right), \text{ and}$$

the directrix is $x = h - p = \frac{13}{4} + 1 = \frac{17}{4}$.

53. $h = 0, k = 2$, and the parabola opens to the left, so
$(y - 2)^2 = 4p(x)$. Using $(-6, -4)$, we find

$$(-4 - 2)^2 = 4p(-6) \Rightarrow 4p = -\frac{36}{6} = -6. \text{ The equation}$$

for the parabola is: $(y - 2)^2 = -6x$.

54. $h = 1, k = -3$, and the parabola opens to the right, so

$$(y + 3)^2 = 4p(x - 1). \text{ Using } \left(\frac{11}{2}, 0\right), \text{ we find}$$

$$(0 - 3)^2 = 4p\left(\frac{11}{2} - 1\right) \Rightarrow 4p = 9 \cdot \frac{2}{9} = 2. \text{ The equation}$$

for the parabola is: $(y + 3)^2 = 2(x - 1)$.

55. $h = 2, k = -1$ and the parabola opens down so
$(x - 2)^2 = 4p(y + 1)$. Using $(0, -2)$, we find that
$(0 - 2)^2 = 4p(-2 + 1)$, so $4 = -4p$ and $p = -1$.
The equation for the parabola is: $(x - 2)^2 = -4(y + 1)$.

56. $h = -1$, $k = 3$ and the parabola opens up so $(x + 1)^2 = 4p(y - 3)$. Using $(3, 5)$, we find that $(3 + 1)^2 = 4p(5 - 3)$, so $16 = 8p$ and $p = 2$. The equation for the parabola is $(x + 1)^2 = 8(y - 3)$

57. One possible answer:

If p is replaced by $-p$ in the proof, then the result is $x^2 = -4py$, which is the correct result.

58. One possible answer:

Let $P(x, y)$ be a point on the parabola with focus $(p, 0)$ and directrix $x = -p$. Then $\sqrt{(x - p)^2 + (y - 0)^2} = $ distance from (x, y) to $(p, 0)$ and $\sqrt{(x - (-p))^2 + (y - y)^2} = $ distance from (x, y) to line $x = -p$. Because a point on a parabola is equidistant from the focus and the directrix, we can equate these distances. After squaring both sides, we obtain

$$(x - p)^2 + (y - 0)^2 = (x - (-p))^2 + (y - y)^2$$
$$x^2 - 2px + p^2 + y^2 = x^2 + 2px + p^2$$
$$y^2 = 4px.$$

59. For the beam to run parallel to the axis of the mirror, the filament should be placed at the focus. As with Example 6, we must find p by using the fact that the points $(\pm 3, 2)$ must lie on the parabola. Then,

$$(\pm 3)^2 = 4p(2)$$
$$9 = 8p$$
$$p = \frac{9}{8} = 1.125 \text{ cm}$$

Because $p = 1.125$ cm, the filament should be placed 1.125 cm from the vertex along the axis of the mirror.

60. For maximum efficiency, the receiving antenna should be placed at the focus of the reflector. As with Example 6, we know that the points $(\pm 2.5, 2)$ lie on the parabola. Solving for p, we find

$$(\pm 2.5)^2 = 4p(2)$$
$$8p = 6.25$$
$$p = 0.78125 \text{ ft}$$

The receiving antenna should be placed 0.78125 ft, or 9.375 inches, from the vertex along the axis of the reflector.

61. $4p = 10$, so $p = \dfrac{5}{2}$ and the focus is at $(0, p) = (0, 2.5)$.

The electronic receiver is located 2.5 units from the vertex along the axis of the parabolic microphone.

62. $4p = 12$, so $p = 3$ and the focus is at $(0, p) = (0, 3)$. The light bulb should be placed 3 units from the vertex along the axis of the headlight.

63. Consider the roadway to be the axis. Then, the vertex of the parabola is $(300, 10)$ and the points $(0, 110)$ and $(600, 110)$ both lie on it. Using the standard formula, $(x - 300)^2 = 4p(y - 10)$. Solving for $4p$, we have $(600 - 300)^2 = 4p(110 - 10)$, or $4p = 900$, so the formula for the parabola is $(x - 300)^2 = 900(y - 10)$. The length of each cable is the distance from the parabola to the line $y = 0$. After solving the equation of the parabola for y ($y = \dfrac{1}{900}x^2 - \dfrac{2}{3}x + 110$), we determine that the length of each cable is

$$\sqrt{(x - x)^2 + \left(\frac{1}{900}x^2 - \frac{2}{3}x + 110 - 0\right)^2} =$$
$$\frac{1}{900}x^2 - \frac{2}{3}x + 110. \text{ Starting at the leftmost tower, the}$$

lengths of the cables are: $\approx \{79.44, 54.44, 35, 21.11, 12.78, 10, 12.78, 21.11, 35, 54.44, 79.44\}$.

64. Consider the x-axis as a line along the width of the road and the y-axis as the line from the middle stripe of the road to the middle of the bridge — the vertex of the parabola. Since we want a minimum clearance of 16 feet at each side of the road, we know that the points $(\pm 15, 16)$ lie on the parabola. We also know that the points $(\pm 30, 0)$ lie on the parabola and that the vertex occurs at some height k along the line $x = 0$, or $(0, k)$. From the standard formula, $(x - 0)^2 = 4p(y - k)$, or $x^2 = 4p(y - k)$. Using the points $(15, 16)$, and $(30, 0)$, we have:

$$30^2 = 4p(0 - k)$$
$$15^2 = 4p(16 - k)$$

Solving these two equations gives $4p = -42.1875$ and $k \approx 21.33$. The maximum clearance must be at least 21.33 feet.

65. False. Every point on a parabola is the same distance from its focus and its directrix.

66. False. The directrix of a parabola is perpendicular to the parabola's axis.

67. The word "oval" does not denote a mathematically precise concept. The answer is D.

68. $(0)^2 = 4p(0)$ is true no matter what p is. The answer is D.

69. The focus of $y^2 = 4px$ is $(p, 0)$. Here $p = 3$, so the answer is B.

70. The vertex of a parabola with equation $(y - k)^2 = 4p(x - h)$ is (h, k). Here, $k = 3$ and $h = -2$. The answer is D.

71. (a)–(c)

(d) As A moves, P traces out the curve of a parabola.

(e) With labels as shown, we can express the coordinates of P using the point-slope equation of the line PM:

$$y - \frac{\ell + c}{2} = \frac{x - b}{c - \ell}\left(x - \frac{x + b}{2}\right)$$
$$y - \frac{\ell + c}{2} = \frac{(x - b)^2}{2(c - \ell)}$$
$$2(c - \ell)\left(y - \frac{\ell + c}{2}\right) = (x - b)^2$$

This is the equation of a parabola with vertex at $\left(b, \dfrac{\ell + c}{2}\right)$ and focus at $\left(b, \dfrac{\ell + c}{2} + p\right)$ where $p = \dfrac{c - \ell}{2}$.

72. (a)–(d)

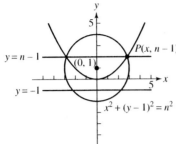

(e) A parabola with directrix $y = -1$ and focus at $(0, 1)$ has equation $x^2 = 4y$. Since P is on the circle $x^2 + (y - 1)^2 = n^2$ and on the line $y = n - 1$, its x-coordinate of P must be

$$x = \sqrt{n^2 - ((n - 1) - 1)^2} = \sqrt{n^2 - (n - 2)^2}.$$

Substituting $(\sqrt{n^2 - (n - 2)^2}, n - 1)$ into $x^2 = 4y$ shows that $(\sqrt{n^2 - (n - 2)^2})^2 = 4(n - 1)$ so P lies on the parabola $x^2 = 4y$.

73. (a)

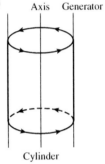

Cylinder

(b)

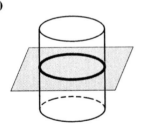

Circle   Single line

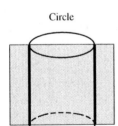

Two parallel lines

(c)

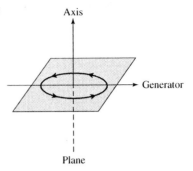

(d)

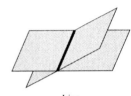

Plane   Line

74. The point (a, b) is on the parabola $y = \dfrac{1}{4p}x^2$ if and only if $b = \dfrac{a^2}{4p}$. The parabola $y = \dfrac{1}{4p}x^2$ and the line $y = m(x - a) + \dfrac{a^2}{4p}$ intersect in exactly one point (namely the point $\left(a, \dfrac{a^2}{4p}\right)$) if and only if the quadratic equation $\dfrac{1}{4p}x^2 - mx + am - \dfrac{a^2}{4p} = 0$ has exactly one solution. This happens if and only if the discriminant of the quadratic formula is zero.

$$(-m)^2 - 4\left(\frac{1}{4p}\right)\left(am - \frac{a^2}{4p}\right) = m^2 - \frac{am}{p} + \frac{a^2}{4p^2}$$

$$= \left(m - \frac{a}{2p}\right)^2 = 0 \text{ if and only if } m = \frac{a}{2p}.$$

Substituting $m = \dfrac{a}{2p}$ and $x = 0$ into the equation of the line gives the y-intercept

$$y = \frac{a}{2p}(0 - a) + \frac{a^2}{4p} = -\frac{a^2}{2p} + \frac{a^2}{4p} = -\frac{a^2}{4p} = -b.$$

75. (a) The focus of the parabola $y = \dfrac{1}{4p}x^2$ is at $(0, p)$ so any line with slope m that passes through the focus must have equation $y = mx + p$.

The endpoints of a focal chord are the intersection points of the parabola $y = \dfrac{1}{4p}x^2$ and the line $y = mx + p$.

Solving the equation $\dfrac{1}{4p}x^2 - mx - p = 0$ using the quadratic formula, we have

$$x = \frac{m \pm \sqrt{m^2 - 4\left(\frac{1}{4p}\right)(-p)}}{2\left(\frac{1}{4p}\right)}$$

$$= \frac{m \pm \sqrt{m^2 + 1}}{\frac{1}{2p}} = 2p(m \pm \sqrt{m^2 + 1}).$$

(b) The y-coordinates of the endpoints of a focal chord are

$$y = \frac{1}{4p}\left(2p(m + \sqrt{m^2 + 1})\right)^2 \text{ and}$$

$$y = \frac{1}{4p}\left(2p(m - \sqrt{m^2 + 1})\right)^2$$

$$\frac{1}{4p}(4p^2)(m^2 + 2m\sqrt{m^2 + 1} + (m^2 + 1))$$

$$= \frac{1}{4p}(4p^2)(m^2 - 2m\sqrt{m^2 + 1} + (m^2 + 1))$$

$$= p(2m^2 + 2m\sqrt{m^2 + 1} + 1)$$

$$= p(2m^2 - 2m\sqrt{m^2 + 1} + 1)$$

Using the distance formula for
$(2p(m - \sqrt{m^2 + 1}), p(2m^2 - 2m\sqrt{m^2 + 1} + 1))$
and $(2p(m + \sqrt{m^2 + 1}),$
$p(2m^2 + 2m\sqrt{m^2 + 1} + 1))$, we know that the
length of any focal chord is $\sqrt{(x_2 - x_1)^2 + (y_2 - y_1)^2}$

$$= \sqrt{(4p\sqrt{m^2 + 1})^2 + (4mp\sqrt{m^2 + 1})^2}$$

$$= \sqrt{(16m^2 p^2 + 16p^2) + (16m^4 p^2 + 16m^2 p^2)}$$

$$= \sqrt{16m^4 p^2 + 32m^2 p^2 + 16p^2}$$

The quantity under the radical sign is smallest when
$m = 0$. Thus the smallest focal chord has length
$\sqrt{16p^2} = |4p|$.

76. (a) For the parabola $x^2 = 4py$, the axis and directrix
intersect at the point $(0, -p)$. since the latus rectum is
perpendicular to the axis of symmetry, its slope is 0,
and from Exercise 65 we know the endpoints are
$(-2p, p)$ and $(2p, p)$. These points are symmetric
about the y-axis, so the distance from $(-2p, p)$ to
$(0, -p)$ equals the distance from $(2p, p)$ to $(0, -p)$.
The slope of the line joining $(0, -p)$ and $(2p, p)$ is

$$\frac{-p - p}{0 - (-2p)} = -1 \text{ and the slope of the line joining}$$

$(0, -p)$ and $(2p, p)$ is $\dfrac{-p - p}{0 - 2p} = 1$. So the lines are
perpendicular, and we know that the three points
form a right triangle.

(b) By Exercise 64, the line passing through $(2p, p)$ and
$(0, -p)$ must be tangent to the parabola; similarly for
$(-2p, p)$ and $(0, -p)$.

■ Section 8.2 Ellipses

Exploration 1

1. The equations $x = -2 + 3\cos t$ and $y = 5 + 7\sin t$ can be
rewritten as $\cos t = \dfrac{x + 2}{3}$ and $\sin t = \dfrac{y - 5}{7}$.
Substituting these into the identity $\cos^2 t + \sin^2 t = 1$
yields the equation $\dfrac{(x + 2)^2}{9} + \dfrac{(y - 5)^2}{49} = 1$.

2.

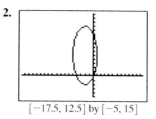

$[-17.5, 12.5]$ by $[-5, 15]$

3. Example 1: Since $\dfrac{x^2}{9} + \dfrac{y^2}{4} = 1$, a parametric solution is
$x = 3\cos t$ and $y = 2\sin t$.

Example 2: Since $\dfrac{y^2}{13} + \dfrac{x^2}{4} = 1$, a parametric solution is
$y = \sqrt{13}\sin t$ and $x = 2\cos t$.

Example 3: Since $\dfrac{(x - 3)^2}{25} + \dfrac{(y + 1)^2}{16} = 1$, a parametric
solution is $x = 5\cos t + 3$ and $y = 4\sin t - 1$.

4.

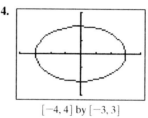

$[-4, 4]$ by $[-3, 3]$

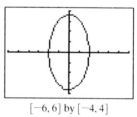

$[-6, 6]$ by $[-4, 4]$

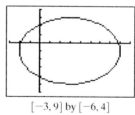

$[-3, 9]$ by $[-6, 4]$

Answers may vary. In general, students should find that
the eccentricity is equal to the ratio of the distance
between foci over distance between vertices.

5. Example 1: The equations $x = 3\cos t$, $y = 2\sin t$ can be
rewritten as $\cos t = \dfrac{x}{3}$, $\sin t = \dfrac{y}{2}$, which using

$\cos^2 t + \sin^2 t = 1$ yield $\dfrac{x^2}{9} + \dfrac{y^2}{4} = 1$ or $4x^2 + 9y^2 = 36$.

Example 2: The equations $x = 2\cos t$, $y = \sqrt{13}\sin t$ can
be rewritten as $\cos t = \dfrac{x}{2}$, $\sin t = \dfrac{y}{\sqrt{13}}$, which using

$\sin^2 t + \cos^2 t = 1$ yield $\dfrac{y^2}{13} + \dfrac{x^2}{4} = 1$.

Example 3: By rewriting $x = 3 + 5\cos t$,
$y = -1 + 4\sin t$ as $\cos t = \dfrac{x - 3}{5}$, $\sin t = \dfrac{y + 1}{4}$ and

using $\cos^2 t + \sin^2 t = 1$, we obtain

$$\frac{(x - 3)^2}{25} + \frac{(y + 1)^2}{16} = 1.$$

Exploration 2

Answers will vary due to experimental error. The theoretical answers are as follows.

2. $a = 9\,\text{cm}, b = \sqrt{80} \approx 8.94\,\text{cm}, c = 1\,\text{cm}, e = 1/9 \approx 0.11$, $b/a \approx 0.99$.

3. $a = 8\,\text{cm}, b = \sqrt{60} \approx 7.75\,\text{cm}, c = 2\,\text{cm}, e = 1/4 = 0.25$, $b/a \approx 0.97$;
$a = 7\,\text{cm}, b = \sqrt{40} \approx 6.32\,\text{cm}, c = 3\,\text{cm}, e = 3/7 \approx 0.43$, $b/a \approx 0.90$;
$a = 6\,\text{cm}, b = \sqrt{20} \approx 4.47\,\text{cm}, c = 4\,\text{cm}, e = 2/3 \approx 0.67$, $b/a \approx 0.75$.

4. The ratio b/a decreases slowly as $e = c/a$ increases rapidly. The ratio b/a is the height-to-width ratio, which measures the shape of the ellipse—when b/a is close to 1, the ellipse is nearly circular; when b/a is close to 0, the ellipse is elongated. The eccentricity ratio $e = c/a$ measures how off-center the foci are—when e is close to 0, the foci are near the center of the ellipse; when e is close to 1, the foci are far from the center and near the vertices of the ellipse. The foci must be extremely off-center for the ellipse to be significantly elongated.

5.

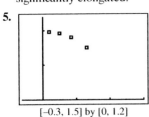

[–0.3, 1.5] by [0, 1.2]

$$\frac{b}{a} = \frac{\sqrt{a^2 - c^2}}{a}$$

$$= \sqrt{1 - \frac{c^2}{a^2}}$$

$$= \sqrt{1 - e^2}$$

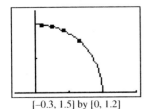

[–0.3, 1.5] by [0, 1.2]

Quick Review 8.2

1. $\sqrt{(2 - (-3))^2 + (4 - (-2))^2} = \sqrt{5^2 + 6^2} = \sqrt{61}$

2. $\sqrt{(a - (-3))^2 + (b - (-4))^2}$
$= \sqrt{(a + 3)^2 + (b + 4)^2}$

3. $4y^2 + 9x^2 = 36, 4y^2 = 36 - 9x^2$,
$y = \pm\sqrt{\dfrac{36 - 9x^2}{4}} = \pm\dfrac{3}{2}\sqrt{4 - x^2}$

4. $25x^2 + 36y^2 = 900, 36y^2 = 900 - 25x^2$,
$y = \pm\sqrt{\dfrac{900 - 25x^2}{36}} = \pm\dfrac{5}{6}\sqrt{36 - x^2}$

5. $3x + 12 = (10 - \sqrt{3x - 8})^2$
$3x + 12 = 100 - 20\sqrt{3x - 8} + 3x - 8$
$-80 = -20\sqrt{3x - 8}$
$4 = \sqrt{3x - 8}$
$16 = 3x - 8$
$3x = 24$
$x = 8$

6. $\qquad 6x + 12 = (1 + \sqrt{4x + 9})^2$
$\qquad 6x + 12 = (1 + 2\sqrt{4x + 9} + 4x + 9)$
$\qquad 2x + 2 = 2\sqrt{4x + 9}$
$\qquad x + 1 = \sqrt{4x + 9}$
$\qquad x^2 + 2x + 1 = 4x + 9$
$\qquad x^2 - 2x - 8 = 0$
$\qquad (x - 4)(x + 2) = 0$
$\qquad x = 4$

7. $6x^2 + 12 = (11 - \sqrt{6x^2 + 1})^2$
$6x^2 + 12 = 121 - 22\sqrt{6x^2 + 1} + 6x^2 + 1$
$-110 = -22\sqrt{6x^2 + 1}$
$6x^2 + 1 = 25$
$6x^2 - 24 = 0$
$x^2 - 4 = 0$
$x = 2, x = -2$

8. $\qquad 2x^2 + 8 = (8 - \sqrt{3x^2 + 4})^2$
$\qquad 2x^2 + 8 = 64 - 16\sqrt{3x^2 + 4} + 3x^2 + 4$
$\qquad 0 = x^2 - 16\sqrt{3x^2 + 4} + 60$
$\qquad x^2 + 60 = (16\sqrt{3x^2 + 4})^2$
$x^4 + 120x^2 + 3600 = 256(3x^2 + 4)$
$x^4 - 648x^2 + 2576 = 0$
$\qquad x = 2, x = -2$

9. $2\left(x - \dfrac{3}{2}\right)^2 - \dfrac{15}{2} = 0$, so $x = \dfrac{3 \pm \sqrt{15}}{2}$

10. $2(x + 1)^2 - 7 = 0$, so $x = -1 \pm \sqrt{\dfrac{7}{2}}$

Section 8.2 Exercises

1. $h = 0, k = 0, a = 4, b = \sqrt{7}$, so $c = \sqrt{16 - 7} = 3$
Vertices: $(4, 0), (-4, 0)$; Foci: $(3, 0), (-3, 0)$

2. $h = 0, k = 0, a = 5, b = \sqrt{21}$, so $c = \sqrt{25 - 21} = 2$
Vertices: $(0, 5), (0, -5)$; Foci: $(0, 2), (0, -2)$

3. $h = 0, k = 0, a = 6, b = 3\sqrt{3}$, so $c = \sqrt{36 - 27} = 3$
Vertices: $(0, 6), (0, -6)$; Foci: $(0, 3), (0, -3)$

4. $h = 0, k = 0, a = \sqrt{11}, b = \sqrt{7}$, so $c = \sqrt{11 - 7} = 2$
Vertices: $(\sqrt{11}, 0), (-\sqrt{11}, 0)$; Foci: $(2, 0), (-2, 0)$

5. $\dfrac{x^2}{4} + \dfrac{y^2}{3} = 1. h = 0, k = 0, a = 2, b = \sqrt{3}$, so
$c = \sqrt{4 - 3} = 1$
Vertices: $(2, 0), (-2, 0)$; Foci: $(1, 0), (-1, 0)$

6. $\dfrac{y^2}{9} + \dfrac{x^2}{4} = 1. h = 0, k = 0, a = 3, b = 2$, so
$c = \sqrt{9 - 4} = \sqrt{5}$.
Vertices: $(0, 3), (0, -3)$; Foci: $(0, \sqrt{5}), (0, -\sqrt{5})$

7. (d)

8. (c)

9. (a)

10. (b)

11.

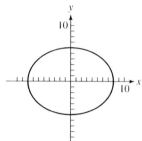

12.

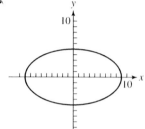

13.

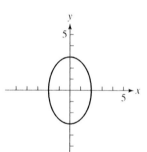

14.

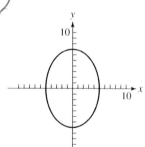

15.

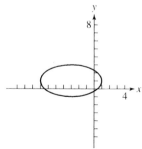

16.

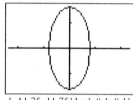

17.

$[-9.4, 9.4]$ by $[-6.2, 6.2]$

$$y = \pm\frac{2}{3}\sqrt{-x^2 + 36}$$

18.

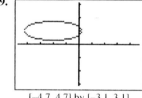

$[-11.75, 11.75]$ by $[-8.1, 8.1]$

$$y = \pm 2\sqrt{-x^2 + 16}$$

19.

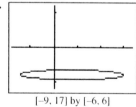

$[-4.7, 4.7]$ by $[-3.1, 3.1]$

$$y = 1 \pm \sqrt{-\frac{(x+2)^2}{10} + \frac{1}{2}}$$

20.

$[-9, 17]$ by $[-6, 6]$

$$y = -4 \pm \frac{1}{16}\sqrt{-x^2 + 8x + 112}$$

21. $\dfrac{x^2}{4} + \dfrac{y^2}{9} = 1$

22. $\dfrac{x^2}{49} + \dfrac{y^2}{25} = 1$

23. $c = 2$ and $a = \dfrac{10}{2} = 5$, so $b = \sqrt{a^2 - c^2} = \sqrt{21}$:

$$\dfrac{x^2}{25} + \dfrac{y^2}{21} = 1$$

24. $c = 3$ and $b = \dfrac{10}{2} = 5$, so $a = \sqrt{b^2 - c^2} = \sqrt{16} = 4$:

$$\dfrac{x^2}{16} + \dfrac{y^2}{25} = 1$$

25. $\dfrac{x^2}{16} + \dfrac{y^2}{25} = 1$

26. $\dfrac{x^2}{49} + \dfrac{y^2}{16} = 1$

27. $b = 4$; $\dfrac{x^2}{16} + \dfrac{y^2}{36} = 1$

28. $b = 2$; $\dfrac{x^2}{25} + \dfrac{y^2}{4} = 1$

29. $a = 5$; $\dfrac{x^2}{25} + \dfrac{y^2}{16} = 1$

30. $a = 13$; $\dfrac{x^2}{144} + \dfrac{y^2}{169} = 1$

31. The center (h, k) is $(1, 2)$ (the midpoint of the axes); a and b are half the lengths of the axes (4 and 6, respectively): $\dfrac{(x - 1)^2}{16} + \dfrac{(y - 2)^2}{36} = 1$

32. The center (h, k) is $(-2, 2)$ (the midpoint of the axes); a and b are half the lengths of the axes (2 and 5, respectively): $\dfrac{(x + 2)^2}{4} + \dfrac{(y - 2)^2}{25} = 1$

33. The center (h, k) is $(3, -4)$ (the midpoint of the major axis); $a = 3$, half the lengths of the major axis. Since $c = 2$ (half the distance between the foci), $b = \sqrt{a^2 - c^2} = \sqrt{5}$: $\dfrac{(x - 3)^2}{9} + \dfrac{(y + 4)^2}{5} = 1$

34. The center (h, k) is $(-2, 3)$ (the midpoint of the major axis); $b = 4$, half the lengths of the major axis. Since $c = 2$ (half the distance between the foci), $a = \sqrt{b^2 - c^2} = \sqrt{12}$: $\dfrac{(x + 2)^2}{12} + \dfrac{(y - 3)^2}{16} = 1$

35. The center (h, k) is $(3, -2)$ (the midpoint of the major axis); a and b are half the lengths of the axes (3 and 5, respectively): $\dfrac{(x - 3)^2}{9} + \dfrac{(y + 2)^2}{25} = 1$

36. The center (h, k) is $(-1, 2)$ (the midpoint of the major axis); a and b are half the lengths of the axes (4 and 3, respectively): $\dfrac{(x + 1)^2}{16} + \dfrac{(y - 2)^2}{9} = 1$

For #37–40, an ellipse with equation $\dfrac{(x - h)^2}{a^2} + \dfrac{(y - k)^2}{b^2} = 1$ has center (h, k), vertices $(h \pm a, k)$, and foci $(h \pm c, k)$ where $c = \sqrt{a^2 - b^2}$.

37. Center $(-1, 2)$; Vertices: $(-1 \pm 5, 2) = (-6, 2), (4, 2)$; Foci $(-1 \pm 3, 2) = (-4, 2), (2, 2)$

38. Center $(3, 5)$; Vertices: $(3 \pm \sqrt{11}, 5) \approx (6.32, 5), (-0.32, 5)$; Foci $= (3 \pm 2, 5) = (5, 5), (1, 5)$

39. Center $(7, -3)$; Vertices: $(7, -3 \pm 9) = (7, 6), (7, -12)$; Foci: $(7, -3 \pm \sqrt{17}) \approx (7, 1.12), (7, -7.12)$

40. Center $(-2, 1)$; Vertices: $(-2, 1 \pm 5) = (-2, -4), (-2, 6)$; Foci: $(-2, 1 \pm 3) = (-2, -2), (-2, 4)$

41.

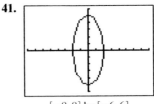

$[-8, 8]$ by $[-6, 6]$

$x = 2 \cos t$, $y = 5 \sin t$

42.

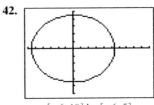

$[-6, 10]$ by $[-6, 5]$

$x = \sqrt{30} \cos t$, $y = 2\sqrt{5} \sin t$

43.

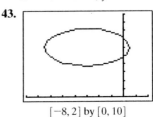

$[-8, 2]$ by $[0, 10]$

$x = 2\sqrt{3} \cos t - 3$, $y = \sqrt{5} \sin t + 6$

44.

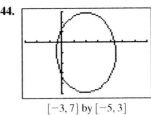

$[-3, 7]$ by $[-5, 3]$

$x = \sqrt{6} \cos(t) + 2$, $y = \sqrt{15} \sin(t) - 1$

For #45–48, complete the squares in x and y, then put in standard form. (The first one is done in detail; the others just show the final form.)

45. $9x^2 + 4y^2 - 18x + 8y - 23 = 0$ can be rewritten as $9(x^2 - 2x) + 4(y^2 + 2y) = 23$. This is equivalent to $9(x^2 - 2x + 1) + 4(y^2 + 2y + 1) = 23 + 9 + 4$, or $9(x - 1)^2 + 4(y + 1)^2 = 36$. Divide both sides by 36 to obtain $\dfrac{(x - 1)^2}{4} + \dfrac{(y + 1)^2}{9} = 1$. Vertices: $(1, -4)$ and $(1, 2)$ Foci: $(1, -1 \pm \sqrt{5})$. Eccentricity: $\dfrac{\sqrt{5}}{3}$.

46. $\dfrac{(x - 2)^2}{5} + \dfrac{(y + 3)^2}{3} = 1$. Vertices: $(2 \pm \sqrt{5}, -3)$. Foci: $(2 \pm \sqrt{2}, -3)$. Eccentricity: $\dfrac{\sqrt{2}}{\sqrt{5}} = \sqrt{\dfrac{2}{5}}$

47. $\dfrac{(x + 3)^2}{16} + \dfrac{(y - 1)^2}{9} = 1$. Vertices: $(-7, 1)$ and $(1, 1)$. Foci: $(-3 \pm \sqrt{7}, 1)$. Eccentricity: $\dfrac{\sqrt{7}}{4}$

48. $(x - 4)^2 + \dfrac{(y + 8)^2}{4} = 1$. Vertices: $(4, -10)$ and $(4, -6)$.

Foci: $(4, -8 \pm \sqrt{3})$. Eccentricity: $\dfrac{\sqrt{3}}{2}$

49. The center (h, k) is $(2, 3)$ (given); a and b are half the lengths of the axes (4 and 3, respectively):

$$\dfrac{(x - 2)^2}{16} + \dfrac{(y - 3)^2}{9} = 1$$

50. The center (h, k) is $(-4, 2)$ (given); a and b are half the lengths of the axes (4 and 3, respectively):

$$\dfrac{(x + 4)^2}{16} + \dfrac{(y - 2)^2}{9} = 1$$

51. Consider Figure 8.15(b); call the point $(0, c)$ F_1, and the point $(0, -c)$ F_2. By the definition of an ellipse, any point P (located at (x, y)) satisfies the equation $\overrightarrow{PF} + \overrightarrow{PF_2} = 2a$ thus, $\sqrt{(x - 0)^2 + (y - c)^2}$

$+ \sqrt{(x - 0)^2 + (y + c)^2} = \sqrt{x^2 + (y - c)^2}$

$+ \sqrt{x^2 + (y + c)^2} = 2a$

then $\sqrt{x^2 + (y - c)^2} = 2a - \sqrt{x^2 + (y + c)^2}$

$x^2 + (y - c)^2 = 4a^2 - 4a\sqrt{x^2 + (y + c)^2}$
$\qquad + x^2 + (y + c)^2$

$y^2 - 2cy + c^2 = 4a^2 - 4a\sqrt{x^2 + (y + c)^2}$
$\qquad + y^2 + 2cy + c^2$

$4a\sqrt{x^2 + (y + c)^2} = 4a^2 + 4cy$

$a\sqrt{x^2 + (y + c)^2} = a^2 + cy$

$a^2(x^2 + (y + c)^2) = a^4 + 2a^2cy + c^2y^2$

$a^2x^2 + (a^2 - c^2)y^2 = a^2(a^2 - c^2)$

$a^2x^2 + b^2y^2 = a^2b^2$

$\dfrac{x^2}{b^2} + \dfrac{y^2}{a^2} = 1$

52. Recall that $e = \dfrac{c}{a}$ means that $c = ea, b = \sqrt{a^2 - c^2}$ and a celestial object's perihelion occurs at $a - c$ for Pluto, $c = ea = (0.2484)(5900) \approx 1456.56$, so its perihelion is $5900 - 1456.56 = 4,434.44$ Gm. For Neptune, $c = ea = (0.0050)(4497) \approx 22.49$, so its perihelion is $4497 - 22.49 = 4,474.51$ Gm. As a result of its high by eccentric orbit, Pluto comes over 40 Gm closer to the Sun than Neptune.

53. Since the Moon is furthest from the Earth at 252,710 miles and closest at 221,463, we know that $2a = 252,710 + 221,463$, or $a = 237,086.5$. Since $c + 221,463 = a$, we know $c = 15,623.5$ and $b = \sqrt{a^2 - c^2} = \sqrt{(237,086.5)^2 - (15,623.5)^2}$ $\approx 236,571$.

From these, we calculate $e = \dfrac{c}{a} = \dfrac{15,623.5}{237,086.5} \approx 0.066$.

The orbit of the Moon is very close to a circle, but still takes the shape of an ellipse.

54. For Mercury, $c = ea = (0.2056)(57.9) \approx 11.90$ Gm and its perihelion $a - c = 57.9 - 11.90 \approx 46$ Gm. Since the diameter of the sin is 1.392 Gm. Mercury gets within $46 - \dfrac{1.392}{2} \approx 45.3$ Gm of the Sun's surface.

55. For Saturn, $c = ea = (0.0560)(1,427) \approx 79.9$ Gm. Saturn's perihelion is $a - c = 1427 - 79.9 \approx 1347$ Gm and its aphelion is $a + c = 1427 + 72.21 \approx 1507$ Gm.

56. Venus: $c = ea = (0.0068)(108.2) \approx 0.74$, so $b = \sqrt{(108.2)^2 - (0.74)^2} \approx 108.2$.

$$\dfrac{x^2}{11,707.24} + \dfrac{y^2}{11,706.70} = 1$$

Mars: $c = ea = (0.0934)(227.9) \approx 21.29$, so $b = \sqrt{(227.91)^2 - (21.29)^2} \approx 226.91$

$$\dfrac{x^2}{51,938} + \dfrac{y^2}{51,485} = 1$$

57. For sungrazers, $a - c < 1.5(1.392) = 2.088$. The eccentricity of their ellipses is very close to 1.

58. $a = \dfrac{36.18}{2}, b = \dfrac{9.12}{2}, c = \sqrt{a^2 - b^2}$

$= \sqrt{\left(\dfrac{36.18}{2}\right)^2 - \left(\dfrac{9.12}{2}\right)^2} \approx 17.51$ Au

thus, $e = \dfrac{17.51}{18.09} \approx 0.97$

59. $a = 8$ and $b = 3.5$, so $c = \sqrt{a^2 - b^2} = \sqrt{51.75}$. Foci at $(\pm\sqrt{51.75}, 0) \approx (\pm 7.19, 0)$.

60. $a = 13$ and $b = 5$, so $c = \sqrt{a^2 - b^2} = 12$ Place the source and the patient at opposite foci — 12 inches from the center along the major axis.

61. Substitute $y^2 = 4 - x^2$ into the first equation:

$$\dfrac{x^2}{4} + \dfrac{4 - x^2}{9} = 1$$
$$9x^2 + 4(4 - x^2) = 36$$
$$5x^2 = 20$$
$$x^2 = 4$$
$$x = \pm 2, y = 0$$

Solution: $(-2, 0)$, $(2, 0)$

62. Substitute $x = 3y - 3$ into the first equation:

$$\dfrac{(3y - 3)^2}{9} + y^2 = 1$$
$$y^2 - 2y + 1 + y^2 = 1$$
$$2y2 - 2y = 0$$
$$2y(y - 1) = 0$$
$$y = 0 \text{ or } y = 1$$
$$x = -3 \quad x = 0$$

Solution: $(-3, 0)$, $(0, 1)$

63. (a)

Intersection
X=1.0354863 Y=-.8555361

$[-4.7, 4.7]$ by $[-3.1, 3.1]$

Approximate solutions:
$(\pm 1.04, -0.86)$, $(\pm 1.37, 0.73)$

(b) $\left(\dfrac{\pm\sqrt{94 - 2\sqrt{161}}}{8}, \dfrac{1 + \sqrt{161}}{16}\right)$,

$\left(\dfrac{\pm\sqrt{94 + 2\sqrt{161}}}{8}, \dfrac{-1 + \sqrt{161}}{16}\right)$

64. One possibility: a circle is perfectly "centric": it is an ellipse with both foci at the center. As the foci move off the center and toward the vertices, the ellipse becomes more eccentric as measured by the ratio $= e = c/a$. In everyday life, we say a person is eccentric if he or she deviates from the norm or central tendencies of behavior.

65. False. The distance is $a - c = a(1 - c/a) = a(1 - e)$.

66. True, because $a^2 = b^2 + c^2$ in any ellipse.

67. $\dfrac{x^2}{4} + \dfrac{y^2}{1} = 1$, so $c = \sqrt{a^2 - b^2} = \sqrt{2^2 - 1^2} = \sqrt{3}$. The answer is C.

68. The focal axis runs horizontally through $(2, 3)$. The answer is C.

69. Completing the square produces
$\dfrac{(x - 4)^2}{4} + \dfrac{(y - 3)^2}{9} = 1$. The answer is B.

70. The two foci are a distance $2c$ apart, and the sum of the distances from each of the foci to a point on the ellipse is $2a$. The answer is C.

71. **(a)** When $a = b = r$, $A = \pi ab = \pi rr = \pi r^2$ and
$$P \approx \pi(2r)\left(3 - \frac{\sqrt{(3r + r)(r + 3r)}}{r + r}\right)$$
$$= 2\pi r\left(3 - \frac{\sqrt{16r^2}}{2r}\right) = 2\pi r\left(3 - \frac{4r}{2r}\right)$$
$$= 2\pi r\,(3 - 2) = 2\pi r.$$

(b) One possibility: $\dfrac{x^2}{16} + \dfrac{y^2}{9} = 1$ with $A = 12\pi$ and $P \approx (21 - \sqrt{195})\pi \approx 22.10$, and $\dfrac{x^2}{100} + y^2 = 1$ with $A = 10\pi$ and $P \approx (33 - \sqrt{403})\pi \approx 40.61$.

72. **(a)** Answers will vary. See Chapter III: The Harmony of Worlds in *Cosmos* by Carl Sagan, Random House, 1980.

(b) Drawings will vary. Kepler's Second Law states that as a planet moves in its orbit around the sun, the line segment from the sun to the planet sweeps out equal areas in equal times.

73. **(a)** Graphing in parametric mode with Tstep $= \dfrac{\pi}{24}$.

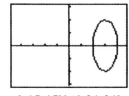

[−4.7, 4.7] by [−3.1, 3.1]

(b) The equations $x(t) = 3 + \cos(2t - 5)$ and $y(t) = -2\sin(2t - 5)$ can be rewritten as $\cos(2t - 5) = x - 3$ and $\sin(2t - 5) = -y/2$. Substituting these into the identity $\cos^2(2t - 5) + \sin^2(2t - 5) = 1$ yields the equation $y^2/4 + (x - 3)^2 = 1$. This is the equation of an ellipse with $x = 3$ as the focal axis. The center of the ellipse is $(3, 0)$ and the vertices are $(3, 2)$ and $(3, -2)$. The length of the major axis is 4 and the length of the minor axis is 2.

74. **(a)** The equations $x(t) = 5 + 3\sin\left(\pi t + \dfrac{\pi}{2}\right)$ and
$y(t) = 3\pi\cos\left(\pi t + \dfrac{\pi}{2}\right)$ can be rewritten as
$\sin\left(\pi t + \dfrac{\pi}{2}\right) = \dfrac{x - 5}{3}$ and $\cos\left(\pi t + \dfrac{\pi}{2}\right) = \dfrac{y}{3\pi}$.
Substituting these into the identity $\cos^2\left(\pi t + \dfrac{\pi}{2}\right) + \sin^2\left(\pi t + \dfrac{\pi}{2}\right) = 1$ yields the equation
$\dfrac{y^2}{9\pi^2} + \dfrac{(x - 5)^2}{9} = 1$. This is the equation of an ellipse.

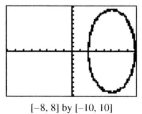

[−8, 8] by [−10, 10]

(b) The pendulum begins its swing at $t = 0$ so
$x(0) = 5 + 3\sin\left(\dfrac{\pi}{2}\right) = 8$ ft, which is the maximum distance away from the detector. When $t = 1$,
$x(1) = 5 + 3\sin\left(\pi + \dfrac{\pi}{2}\right) = 2$ ft, which is the minimum distance from the detector. When $t = 3$, the pendulum is back to the 8-ft position.

As indicated in the table, the maximum velocity (≈ 9.4 ft/sec) happens when the pendulum is at the halfway position of 5 ft from the detector.

T	X1T	Y1T
5.3	3.2366	7.6248
5.4	4.0729	8.9635
5.5	5	9.4248
5.6	5.9271	8.9635
5.7	6.7634	7.6248
5.8	7.4271	5.5397
5.9	7.8532	2.9124

T=5.5

75. Write the equation in standard form by completing the squares and then dividing by the constant on the right-hand side.
$$Ax^2 + Dx + \frac{D^2}{4A} + Cy^2 + Ey + \frac{E^2}{4C} = \frac{D^2}{4A} + \frac{E^2}{4C} - F$$
$$\frac{x^2 + \dfrac{D}{A}x + \dfrac{D^2}{4A^2}}{C} + \frac{y^2 + \dfrac{E}{C}y + \dfrac{E^2}{4C^2}}{A}$$
$$= \frac{1}{AC}\left(\frac{D^2}{4A} + \frac{E^2}{4C} - F\right)$$
$$\frac{\left(x + \dfrac{D}{2A}\right)^2}{C} + \frac{\left(y + \dfrac{E}{2C}\right)^2}{A} = \frac{CD^2 + AE^2 - 4ACF}{4A^2C^2}$$
$$\left(\frac{4A^2C^2}{CD^2 + AE^2 - 4ACF}\right) \times$$
$$\left[\frac{\left(x + \dfrac{D}{2A}\right)^2}{C} + \frac{\left(y + \dfrac{E}{2C}\right)^2}{A}\right] = 1$$

$$\frac{4A^2C\left(x + \frac{D}{2A}\right)^2}{CD^2 + AE^2 - 4ACF} + \frac{4AC^2\left(y + \frac{E}{2C}\right)^2}{CD^2 + AE^2 - 4ACF} = 1$$

Since $AC > 0$, $A \neq 0$ and $C \neq 0$ (we are not dividing by zero). Further, $AC > 0 \Rightarrow 4A^2C > 0$ and $4AC^2 > 0$ (either $A > 0$ and $C > 0$, or $A < 0$ and $C < 0$), so the equation represents an ellipse.

76. Rewrite the equation to $\left(\dfrac{x - h}{a}\right)^2 + \left(\dfrac{y - k}{b}\right)^2 = 0$

Since that $a \neq 0$ and $b \neq 0$ (otherwise the equation is not defined) we see that the only values of x, y that satisfy the equation are $(x, y) = (h, k)$. In this case, the degenerate ellipse is simply a single point (h, k). The semimajor and semiminor axes both equal 0. See Figure 8.2.

■ Section 8.3 Hyperbolas

Exploration 1

1. The equations $x = -1 + 3/\cos t = -1 + 3\sec t$ and $y = 1 + 2\tan t$ can be rewritten as

$\sec t = \dfrac{x + 1}{3}$ and $\tan t = \dfrac{y - 1}{2}$. Substituting these into the identity $\sec^2 t - \tan^2 t = 1$ yields the equation $\dfrac{(x + 1)^2}{9} - \dfrac{(y - 1)^2}{4} = 1$.

2.
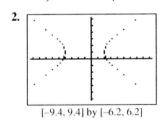 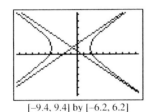
[-9.4, 9.4] by [-6.2, 6.2]   [-9.4, 9.4] by [-6.2, 6.2]

In Connected graphing mode, pseudo-asymptotes appear because the grapher connects computed points by line segments regardless of whether this makes sense. Using Dot mode with a small Tstep will produce the best graphs.

3. Example 1: $x = 3/\cos(t)$, $y = 2\tan(t)$
Example 2: $x = 2\tan(t)$, $y = \sqrt{5}/\cos(t)$
Example 3: $x = 3 + 5/\cos(t)$, $y = -1 + 4\tan(t)$
Example 4: $x = -2 + 3/\cos(t)$, $y = 5 + 7\tan(t)$

4. $4x^2 - 9y^2 = 36$
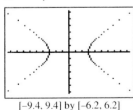
[-9.4, 9.4] by [-6.2, 6.2]
$\dfrac{y^2}{5} - \dfrac{x^2}{4} = 1$
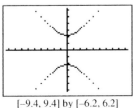
[-9.4, 9.4] by [-6.2, 6.2]

$\dfrac{(x - 3)^2}{25} - \dfrac{(y + 1)^2}{16} = 1$
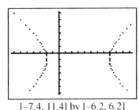
[-7.4, 11.4] by [-6.2, 6.2]
$\dfrac{(x + 2)^2}{9} - \dfrac{(y - 5)^2}{49} = 1$
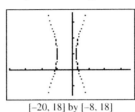
[-20, 18] by [-8, 18]

5. Example 1: The equations $x = 3/\cos t = 3\sec t$, $y = 2\tan t$ can be rewritten as $\sec t = \dfrac{x}{3}$, $\tan t = \dfrac{y}{2}$, which using the identity $\sec^2 t - \tan^2 t = 1$ yield $\dfrac{x^2}{9} - \dfrac{y^2}{4} = 1$.

Example 2: The equations $x = 2\tan t$, $y = \sqrt{5}/\cos t = \sqrt{5}\sec t$ can be rewritten as $\tan t = \dfrac{x}{2}$, $\sec t = \dfrac{y}{\sqrt{5}}$, which using $\sec^2 t - \tan^2 t = 1$ yield $\dfrac{y^2}{5} - \dfrac{x^2}{4} = 1$.

Example 3: By rewriting $x = 3 + 5/\cos t$, $y = -1 + 4\tan t$ as $\sec t = \dfrac{x - 3}{5}$, $\tan t = \dfrac{y + 1}{4}$ and using $\sec^2 t - \tan^2 t = 1$, we obtain $\dfrac{(x - 3)^2}{25} - \dfrac{(y + 1)^2}{16} = 1$.

Example 4: By rewriting $x = -2 + 3/\cos t$, $y = 5 + 7\tan t$ as $\sec t = \dfrac{x + 2}{3}$, $\tan t = \dfrac{y - 5}{7}$ and using $\sec^2 t - \tan^2 t = 1$, we obtain $\dfrac{(x + 2)^2}{9} - \dfrac{(y - 5)^2}{49} = 1$.

Quick Review 8.3

1. $\sqrt{(-7 - 4)^2 + (-8 - (-3))^2}$
$= \sqrt{(-11)^2 + (-5)^2} = \sqrt{146}$

2. $\sqrt{(b - a)^2 + (c - (-3))^2}$
$= \sqrt{(b - a)^2 + (c + 3)^2}$

3. $9y^2 - 16x^2 = 144$
$9y^2 = 144 + 16x^2$
$y = \pm\dfrac{4}{3}\sqrt{9 + x^2}$

4. $4x^2 - 36y^2 = 144$
$36y^2 = 4x^2 - 144$
$y = \pm\dfrac{2}{6}\sqrt{x^2 - 36}$
$y = \pm\dfrac{1}{3}\sqrt{x^2 - 36}$

5. $\sqrt{3x + 12} = 10 + \sqrt{3x - 8}$
$3x + 12 = 100 + 20\sqrt{3x - 8} + 3x - 8$
$-80 = 20\sqrt{3x - 8}$
$-4 = \sqrt{3x - 8}$ no solution

6. $\sqrt{4x + 12} = 1 + \sqrt{x + 8}$
$4x + 12 = 1 + 2\sqrt{x + 8} + x + 8$
$3x + 3 = 2\sqrt{x + 8}$
$9x^2 + 18x + 9 = 4x + 32$
$9x^2 + 14x - 23 = 0$
$$x = \frac{-14 + \sqrt{196 - 4(9)(-23)}}{18}$$
$$x = \frac{-14 \pm 32}{18}$$
$x = 1$ or $x = -\dfrac{23}{9}$. When $x = -\dfrac{23}{9}$,
$\sqrt{4x + 12} - \sqrt{x + 8}$
$= \sqrt{\dfrac{16}{9}} - \sqrt{\dfrac{49}{9}} = \dfrac{4}{3} - \dfrac{7}{3} = -1$
The only solution is $x = 1$.

7. $\sqrt{6x^2 + 12} = 1 + \sqrt{6x^2 + 1}$
$6x^2 + 12 = 1 + 2\sqrt{6x^2 + 1} + 6x^2 + 1$
$10 = 2\sqrt{6x^2 + 1}$
$25 = 6x^2 + 1$
$6x^2 - 24 = 0$
$x^2 - 4 = 0$
$x = 2, x = -2$

8. $\sqrt{2x^2 + 12} = -8 + \sqrt{3x^2 + 4}$
$2x^2 + 12 = 64 - 16\sqrt{3x^2 + 4} + 3x^2 + 4$
$x^2 + 56 = 16\sqrt{3x^2 + 4}$
$x^4 + 112x^2 + 3136 = 768x^2 + 1024$
$x^4 - 656x^2 + 2112 = 0$
$x = \{25.55, -25.55\}$ (the other solutions are extraneous)

9. $c = a + 2, (a + 2)^2 - a^2 = \dfrac{16a}{3}$,
$a^2 + 4a + 4 - a^2 = \dfrac{16a}{3}, 4a = 12: a = 3, c = 5$

10. $c = a + 1, (a + 1)^2 - a^2 = \dfrac{25a}{12}$,
$a^2 + 2a + 1 - a^2 = \dfrac{25a}{12}: a = 12, c = 13$

Section 8.3 Exercises

For #1–6, recall the Pythagorean relation that $c^2 = a^2 + b^2$.

1. $a = 4, b = \sqrt{7}, c = \sqrt{16 + 7} = \sqrt{23}$;
Vertices: $(\pm 4, 0)$; Foci: $(\pm\sqrt{23}, 0)$

2. $a = 5, b = \sqrt{21}, c = \sqrt{25 + 21} = \sqrt{46}$;
Vertices: $(0, \pm 5)$; Foci: $(0, \pm\sqrt{46})$

3. $a = 6, b = \sqrt{13}, c = \sqrt{36 + 13} = 7$;
Vertices: $(0, \pm 6)$; Foci: $(0, \pm 7)$

4. $a = 3, b = 4, c = \sqrt{9 + 16} = 5$;
Vertices: $(\pm 3, 0)$; Foci: $(\pm 5, 0)$

5. $\dfrac{x^2}{4} - \dfrac{y^2}{3} = 1; a = 2, b = \sqrt{3}, c = \sqrt{7}$;
Vertices: $(\pm 2, 0)$; Foci: $(\pm\sqrt{7}, 0)$

6. $\dfrac{x^2}{4} - \dfrac{y^2}{9} = 1; a = 2, b = 3, c = \sqrt{13}$;
Vertices: $(\pm 2, 0)$; Foci: $(\pm\sqrt{13}, 0)$

7. (c)

8. (b)

9. (a)

10. (d)

11. Transverse axis from $(-7, 0)$ to $(7, 0)$; asymptotes:
$y = \pm\dfrac{5}{7}x$,
$y = \pm\dfrac{5}{7}\sqrt{x^2 - 49}$

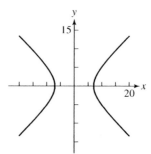

12. Transverse axis from $(0, -8)$ to $(0, 8)$; asymptotes:
$y = \pm\dfrac{8}{5}x$,
$y = \pm\dfrac{8}{5}\sqrt{x^2 + 25}$

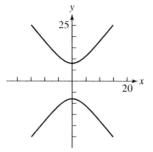

13. Transverse axis from $(0, -5)$ to $(0, 5)$; asymptotes:
$y = \pm\dfrac{5}{4}x$,
$y = \pm\dfrac{5}{4}\sqrt{x^2 + 16}$

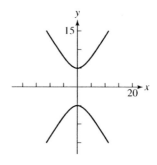

14. Transverse axis from $(-13, 0)$ to $(13, 0)$; asymptotes:
$$y = \pm\frac{12}{13}x,$$
$$y = \pm\frac{12}{13}\sqrt{x^2 - 169}$$

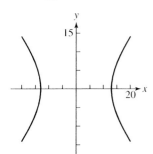

15. The center (h, k) is $(-3, 1)$. Since $a^2 = 16$ and $b^2 = 4$, we have $a = 4$ and $b = 2$. The vertices are at $(-3 \pm 4, 1)$ or $(-7, 1)$ and $(1, 1)$.

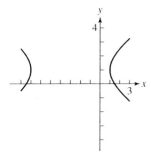

16. The center (h, k) is $(1, -3)$. Since $a^2 = 2$ and $b^2 = 4$, we have $a = \sqrt{2}$ and $b = 2$. The vertices are at $(1\pm\sqrt{2}, -3)$.

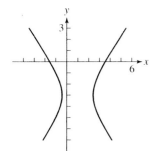

17.

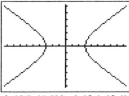

$[-18.8, 18.8]$ by $[-12.4, 12.4]$
$$y = \pm\frac{2}{3}\sqrt{x^2 - 36}$$

18.

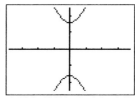

$[-18.8, 18.8]$ by $[-12.4, 12.4]$
$$y = \pm 2\sqrt{x^2 + 16}$$

19.

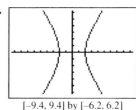

$[-9.4, 9.4]$ by $[-6.2, 6.2]$
$$y = \pm\frac{3}{2}\sqrt{x^2 - 4}$$

20.

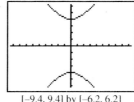

$[-9.4, 9.4]$ by $[-6.2, 6.2]$
$$y = \pm\frac{4}{3}\sqrt{x^2 + 9}$$

21.

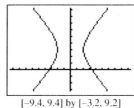

$[-9.4, 9.4]$ by $[-3.2, 9.2]$
$$y = 3 \pm\frac{1}{2}\sqrt{5x^2 - 20}$$

22.

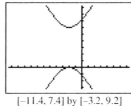

$[-11.4, 7.4]$ by $[-3.2, 9.2]$
$$y = 3 \pm\frac{3}{2}\sqrt{x^2 + 4x + 8}$$

23. $c = 3$ and $a = 2$, so $b = \sqrt{c^2 - a^2} = \sqrt{5}$: $\dfrac{x^2}{4} - \dfrac{y^2}{5} = 1$

24. $c = 3$ and $b = 2$, so $a = \sqrt{c^2 - b^2} = \sqrt{5}$: $\dfrac{y^2}{4} - \dfrac{x^2}{5} = 1$

25. $c = 15$ and $b = 4$, so $a = \sqrt{c^2 - b^2} = \sqrt{209}$:
$$\dfrac{y^2}{16} - \dfrac{x^2}{209} = 1$$

26. $c = 5$ and $a = 3/2$, so $b = \sqrt{c^2 - a^2} = \frac{1}{2}\sqrt{91}$:

$$\frac{x^2}{2.25} - \frac{y^2}{22.75} = 1 \text{ or } \frac{x^2}{9/4} - \frac{y^2}{91/4} = 1$$

27. $a = 5$ and $c = ea = 10$, so $b = \sqrt{100 - 25} = 5\sqrt{5}$:

$$\frac{x^2}{25} - \frac{y^2}{75} = 1$$

28. $a = 4$ and $c = ea = 6$, so $b = \sqrt{36 - 16} = 2\sqrt{5}$:

$$\frac{y^2}{16} - \frac{x^2}{20} = 1$$

29. $b = 5$, $a = \sqrt{c^2 - b^2} = \sqrt{169 - 25} = 12$:

$$\frac{y^2}{144} - \frac{x^2}{25} = 1$$

30. $c = 6$, $a = \frac{c}{e} = 3$, $b = \sqrt{c^2 - a^2} = \sqrt{36 - 9} = 3\sqrt{3}$:

$$\frac{x^2}{9} - \frac{y^2}{27} = 1$$

31. The center (h, k) is $(2, 1)$ (the midpoint of the transverse axis endpoints); $a = 2$, half the length of the transverse axis. And $b = 3$, half the length of the conjugate axis.

$$\frac{(y - 1)^2}{4} - \frac{(x - 2)^2}{9} = 1$$

32. The center (h, k) is $(-1, 3)$ (the midpoint of the transverse axis endpoints); $a = 6$, half the length of the transverse axis. And $b = 5$, half the length of the conjugate axis.

$$\frac{(x + 1)^2}{36} - \frac{(y - 3)^2}{25} = 1$$

33. The center (h, k) is $(2, 3)$ (the midpoint of the transverse axis); $a = 3$, half the length of the transverse axis.

Since $|b/a| = \frac{4}{3}$, $b = 4$: $\dfrac{(x - 2)^2}{9} - \dfrac{(y - 3)^2}{16} = 1$

34. The center (h, k) is $\left(-2, \dfrac{5}{2}\right)$, the midpoint of the transverse axis); $a = \dfrac{9}{2}$, half the length of the transverse axis. Since $|a/b| = \dfrac{4}{3}$, $b = \dfrac{27}{8}$:

$$\frac{(y - 5/2)^2}{81/4} - \frac{(x + 2)^2}{729/64} = 1$$

35. The center (h, k) is $(-1, 2)$, the midpoint of the transverse axis. $a = 2$, half the length of the transverse axis. The center-to-focus distance is $c = 3$, so $b = \sqrt{c^2 - a^2}$

$$= \sqrt{5}: \frac{(x + 1)^2}{4} - \frac{(y - 2)^2}{5} = 1$$

36. The center (h, k) is $\left(-3, -\dfrac{11}{2}\right)$, the midpoint of the transverse axis. $b = \dfrac{7}{2}$, half the length of the transverse axis. The center-to-focus distance is $c = \dfrac{11}{2}$, so

$$a = \sqrt{c^2 - b^2} = \sqrt{18}: \frac{(y + 5.5)^2}{49/4} - \frac{(x + 3)^2}{18} = 1$$

37. The center (h, k) is $(-3, 6)$, the midpoint of the transverse axis. $a = 5$, half the length of the transverse axis. The center-to-focus distance $c = ea$

$$= 2 \cdot 5 = 10, \text{ so } b = \sqrt{c^2 - a^2} = \sqrt{100 - 25} = 5\sqrt{5}$$

$$\frac{(y - 6)^2}{25} - \frac{(x + 3)^2}{75} = 1$$

38. The center (h, k) is $(1, -4)$, the midpoint of the transverse axis. $c = 6$, the center-to-focus distance

$$a = \frac{c}{e} = \frac{6}{2} = 3, b = \sqrt{c^2 - a^2} = \sqrt{36 - 9} = \sqrt{27}$$

$$\frac{(x - 1)^2}{9} - \frac{(y + 4)^2}{27} = 1$$

For #39–42, a hyperbola with equation $\dfrac{(x - h)^2}{a^2} - \dfrac{(y - k)^2}{b^2} = 1$ has center (h, k) vertices $(h \pm a, k)$, and foci $(h \pm c, k)$ where $c = \sqrt{a^2 + b^2}$.

A hyperbola with equation $\dfrac{(y - k)^2}{a^2} - \dfrac{(x - h)^2}{b^2} = 1$ has center (h, k), vertices $(h, k \pm a)$, and foci $(h, k \pm c)$ where again $c = \sqrt{a^2 + b^2}$.

39. Center $(-1, 2)$; Vertices: $(-1 \pm 12, 2) = (11, 2), (-13, 2)$; Foci: $(-1 \pm 13, 2) = (12, 2), (-14, 2)$

40. Center $(-4, -6)$; Vertices: $(-4 \pm \sqrt{12}, -6)$; Foci: $(-4 \pm 5, -6) = (1, -6), (-9, -6)$

41. Center $(2, -3)$; Vertices: $(2, -3 \pm 8) = (2, 5), (2, -11)$; Foci: $(2, -3 \pm \sqrt{145})$

42. Center $(-5, 1)$; Vertices: $(-5, 1 \pm 5) = (-5, -4), (-5, 6)$; Foci: $(-5, 1 \pm 6) = (-5, -5), (-5, 7)$

43.

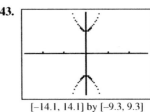

[−14.1, 14.1] by [−9.3, 9.3]

$y = 5/\cos t, x = 2 \tan t$

44.

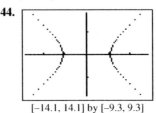

[−14.1, 14.1] by [−9.3, 9.3]

$x = \sqrt{30}/\cos t, y = 2\sqrt{5} \tan t$

45.

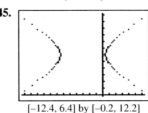

[−12.4, 6.4] by [−0.2, 12.2]

$x = -3 + 2\sqrt{3}/\cos t, y = 6 + \sqrt{5} \tan t$

46.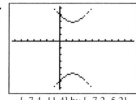

[−7.4, 11.4] by [−7.2, 5.2]

$y = -1 + \sqrt{15}/\cos t,\; x = 2 + \sqrt{6}\tan t$

47.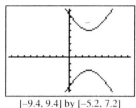

[−9.4, 9.4] by [−5.2, 7.2]

Divide the entire equation by 36. Vertices: (3, −2) and (3, 4), Foci: $(3, 1\pm\sqrt{13})$, $e = \dfrac{\sqrt{13}}{3}$.

48.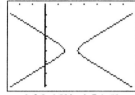

[−2.8, 6.8] by [−7.1, 0]

Vertices: $\left(\dfrac{3}{2}, -4\right)$ and $\left(\dfrac{5}{2}, -4\right)$, Foci: $\left(2 \pm \dfrac{\sqrt{13}}{6}, -4\right)$

$e = \dfrac{\sqrt{(1/4)+(1/9)}}{1/2} = 2\sqrt{\dfrac{9+4}{36}} = \dfrac{\sqrt{13}}{3}$.

For #49–50, complete the squares in x and y, then write the equation in standard form. (The first one is done in detail; the other shows just the final form.) As in the previous problems, the values of $h, k, a,$ and b can be "read" from the equation $\pm\dfrac{(x-h)^2}{a^2} \mp \dfrac{(y-k)^2}{b^2} = 1$. The asymptotes are $y - k = \pm\dfrac{b}{a}(x - h)$. If the x term is positive, the transverse axis endpoints are $(h \pm a, k)$; otherwise the endpoints are $(h, k \pm b)$.

49.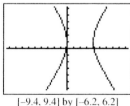

[−9.4, 9.4] by [−6.2, 6.2]

$9x^2 - 4y^2 - 36x + 8y - 4 = 0$ can be rewritten as $9(x^2 - 4x) - 4(y^2 - 2y) = 4$. This is equivalent to $9(x^2 - 4x + 4) - 4(y^2 - 2y + 1) = 4 + 36 - 4$, or $9(x - 2)^2 - 4(y - 1)^2 = 36$. Divide both sides by 36 to obtain $\dfrac{(x-2)^2}{4} - \dfrac{(y-1)^2}{9} = 1$. Vertices: (0, 1) and (4, 1). Foci: $(2\pm\sqrt{13}, 1)$, $e = \dfrac{\sqrt{13}}{2}$

50.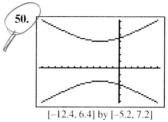

[−12.4, 6.4] by [−5.2, 7.2]

$\dfrac{(y-1)^2}{9} - \dfrac{(x+3)^2}{25} = 1$. Vertices: (−3, −2) and (−3, 4). Foci: $(-3, 1\pm\sqrt{34})$, $e = \dfrac{\sqrt{34}}{3}$

51. $a = 2, (h, k) = (0, 0)$ and the hyperbola opens to the left and right, so $\dfrac{x^2}{4} - \dfrac{y^2}{b^2} = 1$. Using (3, 2): $\dfrac{9}{4} - \dfrac{4}{b^2} = 1$, $9b^2 - 16 = 4b^2, 5b^2 = 16, b^2 = \dfrac{16}{5}; \dfrac{x^2}{4} - \dfrac{5y^2}{16} = 1$

52. $a = \sqrt{2}, (h, k) = (0, 0)$ and the hyperbola opens upward and downward, so $\dfrac{y^2}{2} - \dfrac{x^2}{b^2} = 1$. Using (2, −2): $\dfrac{4}{2} - \dfrac{4}{b^2} = 1, \dfrac{4}{b^2} = 1, b^2 = 4; \dfrac{y^2}{2} - \dfrac{x^2}{4} = 1$

53. Consider Figure 8.24(b). Label (0, c) as point F_1, label (0, −c) as point F_2 and consider any point $P(x, y)$ along the hyperbola. By definition, $PF_1 - PF_2 = \pm 2a$, with $c > a \geq 0$

$\sqrt{(x-0)^2 + (y-(-c))^2} - \sqrt{(x-0)^2 + (y-c)^2} = \pm 2a$
$\sqrt{x^2 + (y+c)^2} = \pm 2a + \sqrt{x^2 + (y-c)^2}$
$x^2 + y^2 + 2cy + c^2 = 4a^2 \pm 4a\sqrt{x^2 + (y-c)^2} + x^2 + y^2 - 2cy + c^2$
$\pm a\sqrt{x^2 + (y-c)^2} = a^2 - cy$
$a^2(x^2 + y^2 - 2cy + c^2) = a^4 - 2a^2cy + c^2y^2$
$-a^2x^2 + (c^2 - a^2)y^2 = a^2(c^2 - a^2)$
$b^2y^2 - a^2x^2 = a^2b^2$
$\dfrac{y^2}{a^2} - \dfrac{x^2}{b^2} = 1$

54. (a) $\dfrac{x^2}{4} - y^2 = 0$

$y^2 = \dfrac{x^2}{4}$

$y = \pm\dfrac{x}{2}$

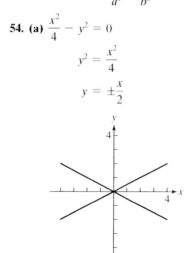

(b) $\dfrac{y^2}{9} - \dfrac{x^2}{16} = 0$

$$y^2 = \dfrac{9x^2}{16}$$

$$y = \pm\dfrac{3x}{4}$$

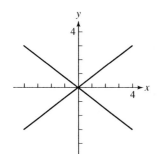

55.
$$c - a = 120, \ b^2 = 250a$$
$$c^2 - a^2 = b^2$$
$$(a + 120)^2 - a^2 = 250a$$
$$a^2 + 240a + 14{,}400 - a^2 = 250a$$
$$10a = 14{,}400$$
$$a = 1440 \text{ Gm}$$

$a = 1440 \text{ Gm}, b = 600 \text{ Gm}, c = 1560, e = \dfrac{1560}{1440} = \dfrac{13}{12}$.

The Sun is centered at focus $(c, 0) = (1560, 0)$.

56.
$$c - a = 140, \ b^2 = 405a$$
$$c^2 - a^2 = b^2$$
$$(a + 140)^2 - a^2 = 405a$$
$$a^2 + 280a + 19{,}600 - a^2 = 405a$$
$$125a = 19{,}600$$
$$a = 156.8$$

$a = 156.8 \text{ Gm}, b = 252 \text{ Gm}, c = 296.8 \text{ Gm}, e = \dfrac{53}{28}$.

The Sun is centered at focus $(c, 0) = (297, 0)$.

57. The *Princess Ann* is located at the intersection of two hyperbolas: one with foci O and R, and the other with foci O and Q. For the first of these, the center is $(0, 40)$, so the center-to-focus distance is $c = 40$ mi. The transverse axis length is $2b = (323.27 \ \mu\text{sec})(980 \text{ ft}/\mu\text{sec}) = 316{,}804.6 \text{ ft} \approx 60$ mi. Then $a \approx \sqrt{40^2 - 30^2} = \sqrt{700}$ mi. For the other hyperbola, $c = 100$ mi, $2a = (646.53 \ \mu\text{sec})(980 \text{ ft}/\mu\text{sec}) = 633599.4 \text{ ft} \approx 120$ mi, and $b \approx \sqrt{100^2 - 60^2} = 80$ mi. The two equations are therefore
$$\dfrac{(y - 40)^2}{900} - \dfrac{x^2}{700} = 1 \text{ and } \dfrac{(x - 100)^2}{3600} - \dfrac{y^2}{6400} = 1.$$
The intersection of the upper branch of the first hyperbola and the right branch of the second hyperbola (found graphically) is approximately $(886.67, 1045.83)$. The ship is located about 887 miles east and 1046 miles north of point O – a bearing and distance of about $40.29°$ and 1371.11 miles, respectively.

58. The gun is located at the intersection of two hyperbolas: one with foci A and B, and the other with foci B and C. For the first of these, the center is $(0, 2000)$, so the center-to-focus distance is $c = 2000$ mi. The transverse axis length is $2b = (2 \text{ sec})(1100 \text{ ft/sec}) = 2200$ ft. Then $a \approx \sqrt{2000^2 - 1100^2} = 100\sqrt{279}$ ft. For the other

hyperbola, $c = 3500$ ft, $2a = (4 \text{ sec})(1100 \text{ ft/sec}) = 4400$ ft, and $b \approx \sqrt{3500^2 - 2200^2} = 100\sqrt{741}$ ft. The two equations are therefore
$$\dfrac{(y - 2000)^2}{1100^2} - \dfrac{x^2}{2{,}790{,}000} = 1 \text{ and}$$
$$\dfrac{(x - 3500)^2}{2200^2} - \dfrac{y^2}{7{,}410{,}000} = 1.$$
The intersection of the upper branch of the first hyperbola and the right branch of the second hyperbola (found graphically) is approximately $(11{,}714.3, 9792.5)$. The gun is located about $11{,}714$ ft $(2.22$ mi$)$ east and 9793 ft $(1.85$ mi$)$ north of point B – a bearing and distance of about $50.11°$ and $15{,}628.2$ ft $(2.89$ mi$)$, respectively.

59.
$$\dfrac{x^2}{4} - \dfrac{y^2}{9} = 1$$
$$x - \dfrac{2\sqrt{3}}{3}y = -2$$

Solve the second equation for x and substitute into the first equation.

$$x = \dfrac{2\sqrt{3}}{3}y - 2$$

$$\dfrac{1}{4}\left(\dfrac{2\sqrt{3}}{3}y - 2\right)^2 - \dfrac{y^2}{9} = 1$$

$$\dfrac{1}{4}\left(\dfrac{4}{3}y^2 - \dfrac{8\sqrt{3}}{3}y + 4\right) - \dfrac{y^2}{9} = 1$$

$$\dfrac{2}{9}y^2 - \dfrac{2\sqrt{3}}{3}y = 0$$

$$\dfrac{2}{9}y(y - 3\sqrt{3}) = 0$$

$y = 0$ or $y = 3\sqrt{3}$

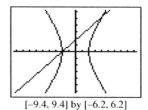

[–9.4, 9.4] by [–6.2, 6.2]

Solutions: $(-2, 0), (4, 3\sqrt{3})$

60. Add:
$$\dfrac{x^2}{4} - y^2 = 1$$
$$x^2 + y^2 = 9$$
$$\dfrac{5x^2}{4} = 10$$
$$x^2 = 8$$
$$x = \pm 2\sqrt{2}$$
$$x^2 + y^2 = 9$$
$$8 + y^2 = 9$$
$$y = \pm 1$$

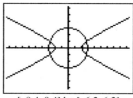

[–9.4, 9.4] by [–6.2, 6.2]

There are four solutions: $(\pm 2\sqrt{2}, \pm 1)$

61. (a)

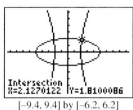

[-9.4, 9.4] by [-6.2, 6.2]

There are four solutions: $(\pm 2.13, \pm 1.81)$

(b) The exact solutions are $\left(\pm 10\sqrt{\dfrac{29}{641}}, \pm 10\sqrt{\dfrac{21}{641}} \right)$.

62. One possibility: Escape speed is the minimum speed one object needs to achieve in order to break away from the gravity of another object. For example, for a NASA space probe to break away from the Earth's gravity is must meet or exceed the escape speed for Earth $v_E = \sqrt{2GM/r} \approx 11{,}200$ m/s. If this escape speed is exceeded, the probe will follow a hyperbolic path.

63. True. The distance is $c - a = a(c/a - 1) = a(e - 1)$.

64. True. For an ellipse, $b^2 + c^2 = a^2$.

65. $\dfrac{x^2}{4} - \dfrac{y^2}{1} = 1$, so $c = \sqrt{4 + 1}$ and the foci are each $\sqrt{5}$ units away horizontally from $(0, 0)$. The answer is B.

66. The focal axis passes horizontally through the center, $(-5, 6)$. The answer is E.

67. Completing the square twice, and dividing to obtain 1 on the right, turns the equation into $\dfrac{(y + 3)^2}{4} - \dfrac{(x - 2)^2}{12} = 1$. The answer is B.

68. $a = 2, b = \sqrt{3}$, and the slopes are $\pm b/a$. The answer is C.

69. (a–d)

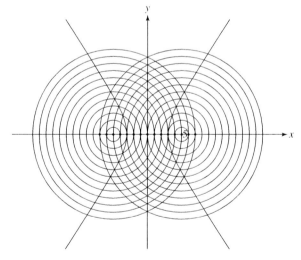

(e) $a = 3, c = 5, b = 4$; $x^2/9 - y^2/16 = 1$

70. Assume that the focus for the primary parabolic mirror occurs at F_P and the foci for the hyperbolic mirror occur at F_H and F_H. Assume also that the x-axis extends from the eye piece to the right most F_H, and that the y-axis is perpendicular through the x-axis 60 cm from the eye piece. Then, the center (h, k) of the hyperbolic mirror is $(0, 0)$, the foci $(\pm c, 0) = (\pm 60, 0)$ and the vertices $(\pm a, 0) = (\pm 40, 0)$.

Since $a = 40$, $c = 60$, $b^2 = c^2 - a^2 = 2000$. The equation for the hyperbolic mirror is $\dfrac{x^2}{1600} - \dfrac{y^2}{2000} = 1$.

71. From Section 8.2, Question #75, we have $Ax^2 + Cy^2 + Dx + Ey + F = 0$ becomes

$$\frac{4A^2C\left(x + \dfrac{D}{2A}\right)^2}{CD^2 + AE^2 - 4ACF} + \frac{4AC^2\left(y + \dfrac{F}{2C}\right)^2}{CD^2 + AE^2 - 4ACF} = 1$$

Since $AC < 0$ means that either $(A < 0$ and $C > 0)$ or $(A > 0$ and $C < 0)$, either $(4A^2C < 0$ and $4AC^2 > 0)$, or $(4A^2C > 0$ and $4AC^2 < 0)$. In the equation above, that means that the $+$ sign will become a $(-)$ sign once all the values A, B, C, D, E, and F are determined, which is exactly the equation of the hyperbola. Note that if $A > 0$ and $C < 0$, the equation becomes:

$$\frac{4AC^2\left(y + \dfrac{E}{2C}\right)^2}{CD^2 + AE^2 - 4ACF} - \frac{\left|4A^2C\right|\left(x + \dfrac{D}{2A}\right)^2}{CD^2 + AE^2 - 4ACF} = 1$$

If $A < 0$ and $C > 0$, the equation becomes:

$$\frac{4A^2C\left(x + \dfrac{D}{2A}\right)^2}{CD^2 + AE^2 - 4ACF} - \frac{\left|4AC^2\right|\left(y + \dfrac{E}{2C}\right)^2}{CD^2 + AE^2 - 4ACF} = 1$$

72. With $a \neq 0$ and $b \neq 0$, we have $\left(\dfrac{x - h}{a}\right)^2 = \left(\dfrac{y - k}{b}\right)^2$.

Then $\left(\dfrac{x - h}{a}\right) = \left(\dfrac{y - k}{b}\right)$ or $\left(\dfrac{x - h}{a}\right) = -\left(\dfrac{y - k}{b}\right)$. Solving these two equations, we find that $y = \pm\dfrac{b}{a}(x - h) + k$. The graph consists of two intersecting slanted lines through (h, k). Its symmetry is like that of a hyperbola. Figure 8.2 shows the relationship between an ordinary hyperbola and two intersecting lines.

73. The asymptotes of the first hyperbola are $y = \pm\dfrac{b}{a}(x - h) + k$ and the asymptotes of the second hyperbola are $y = \pm\dfrac{b}{a}(x - h) + k$; they are the same. [Note that in the second equation, the standard usage of $a + b$ has been revised.] The conjugate axis for hyperbola 1 is $2b$, which is the same as the transverse axis for hyperbola 2. The conjugate axis for hyperbola 2 is $2a$, which is the same as the transverse axis of hyperbola 1.

74. When $x = c$, $\dfrac{c^2}{a^2} - \dfrac{y^2}{b^2} = 1$

$$c^2 b^2 - a^2 y^2 = a^2 b^2$$
$$a^2 y^2 = b^2 (c^2 - a^2)$$
$$b^2 = c^2 - a^2$$
$$y^2 = \dfrac{b^4}{a^2}$$
$$y = \pm \dfrac{b^2}{a}$$

One possible answer: Draw the points $\left(c, \dfrac{b^2}{a}\right)$ and $\left(c, \dfrac{-b^2}{a}\right)$ on a copy of figure 8.24(a). Clearly the points $\left(c, \pm\dfrac{b^2}{a}\right)$ on the hyperbola are the endpoints of a segment perpendicular to the x-axis through the focus $(c, 0)$. Since this is the definition of the focal width used in the construction of a parabola, applying it to the hyperbola also makes sense.

75. The standard forms involved multiples of x, x^2, y, and y^2, as well as constants; therefore they can be rewritten in the general form $Ax^2 + Cy^2 + Dx + Ey + F = 0$ (none of the standard forms we have seen require a Bxy term). For example, rewrite $y = ax^2$ as $ax^2 - y = 0$; this is the general form with $A = a$ and $E = -1$, and all others 0.

Similarly, the hyperbola $\dfrac{y^2}{b^2} - \dfrac{x^2}{a^2} = 1$ can be put in standard form with $A = -\dfrac{1}{a^2}$, $C = \dfrac{1}{b^2}$, $F = -1$, and $B = D = E = 0$.

■ Section 8.4 Translation and Rotation of Axes

Quick Review 8.4

1. $\cos 2\alpha = \dfrac{5}{13}$

2. $\cos 2\alpha = \dfrac{8}{17}$

3. $\cos 2\alpha = \dfrac{1}{2}$

4. $\cos 2\alpha = \dfrac{2}{3}$

5. $2\alpha = \dfrac{\pi}{2}$, so $\alpha = \dfrac{\pi}{4}$

6. $2\alpha = \sin^{-1}\left(\dfrac{1}{2}\right) = \dfrac{\pi}{6}$, so $\alpha = \dfrac{\pi}{12}$

7. $\cos 2\alpha = 2\cos^2 \alpha - 1 = \dfrac{3}{5}$, $2\cos^2 \alpha = \dfrac{8}{5}$, $\cos^2 \alpha = \dfrac{4}{5}$,

$\cos \alpha = \dfrac{2}{\sqrt{5}}$

8. $\cos 2\alpha = 2\cos^2 \alpha - 1 = \dfrac{3}{4}$, $2\cos^2 \alpha = \dfrac{7}{4}$, $\cos^2 \alpha = \dfrac{7}{8}$,

$\cos \alpha = \sqrt{\dfrac{7}{8}} = \dfrac{\sqrt{7}}{2\sqrt{2}} = \dfrac{\sqrt{7}}{2\sqrt{2}} \cdot \dfrac{\sqrt{2}}{\sqrt{2}}$

$= \dfrac{\sqrt{14}}{4}$

9. $\cos 2\alpha = 1 - 2\sin^2 \alpha = \dfrac{5}{6}$, $-2\sin^2 \alpha = -\dfrac{1}{6} \Rightarrow$

$\sin^2 \alpha = \dfrac{1}{12} \Rightarrow \sin \alpha = \sqrt{\dfrac{1}{12}} \Rightarrow \sin \alpha = \dfrac{1}{\sqrt{12}}$

10. $\cos 2\alpha = 1 - 2\sin^2 \alpha = \dfrac{45}{53}$, $2\sin^2 \alpha = \dfrac{8}{53} \Rightarrow \sin^2 \alpha = \dfrac{8}{106} \Rightarrow$

$\sin \alpha = \dfrac{2}{\sqrt{53}}$

Section 8.4 Exercises

1. Use the quadratic formula with $a = 1$, $b = 10$, and $c = x^2 - 6x + 18$. Then $b^2 - 4ac = (10)^2 - 4(x^2 - 6x + 18) = -4x^2 + 24x + 28 = 4(-x^2 + 6x + 7)$, and

$$y = \dfrac{-10 \pm \sqrt{4(-x^2 + 6x + 7)}}{2}$$
$$= -5 \pm \sqrt{-x^2 + 6x + 7}$$

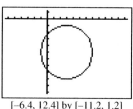

[−6.4, 12.4] by [−11.2, 1.2]

2. Use the quadratic formula with $a = 1$, $b = -2$, and $c = 4x^2 + 24x + 21$. Then $b^2 - 4ac = (-2)^2 - 4(4x^2 + 24x + 21) = -16x^2 - 96x - 80 = 16(-x^2 - 6x - 5)$, and

$$y = \dfrac{2 \pm \sqrt{16(-x^2 - 6x - 5)}}{2}$$
$$= 1 \pm 2\sqrt{-x^2 - 6x - 5}$$

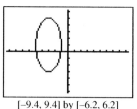

[−9.4, 9.4] by [−6.2, 6.2]

3. Use the quadratic formula with $a = 1$, $b = -8$, and $c = -8x + 8$. Then $b^2 - 4ac = (-8)^2 - 4(-8x + 8) = 32x + 32 = 32(x + 1)$, and

$$y = \dfrac{8 \pm \sqrt{32(x + 1)}}{2} = 4 \pm 2\sqrt{2x + 2}$$

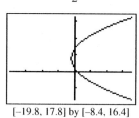

[−19.8, 17.8] by [−8.4, 16.4]

4. Use the quadratic formula with $a = -4$, $b = -40$, and
$c = x^2 + 6x + 91$. Then $b^2 - 4ac =$
$(-40)^2 - 4(-4)(x^2 + 6x + 91) = 16x^2 + 96x + 3056$
$= 16(x^2 + 6x + 191)$, and

$$y = \frac{40 \pm \sqrt{16(x^2 + 6x + 191)}}{-8}$$

$$= -5 \pm \frac{1}{2}\sqrt{x^2 + 6x + 191}$$

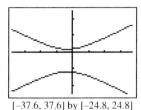

[−37.6, 37.6] by [−24.8, 24.8]

5. $-4xy + 16 = 0 \Rightarrow -4xy = -16 \Rightarrow y = 4/x$

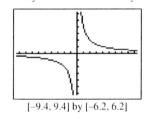

[−9.4, 9.4] by [−6.2, 6.2]

6. $2xy + 6 \Rightarrow 2xy = -6 \Rightarrow y = -3/x$

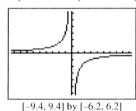

[−9.4, 9.4] by [−6.2, 6.2]

7. $xy - y - 8 = 0 \Rightarrow y(x - 1) = 8 \Rightarrow y = 8/(x - 1)$

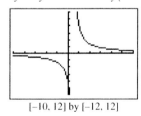

[−10, 12] by [−12, 12]

8. $2x^2 - 5xy + y = 0 \Rightarrow y(1 - 5x) = -2x^2 \Rightarrow$
$y = 2x^2/(5x - 1)$

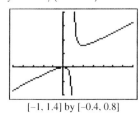

[−1, 1.4] by [−0.4, 0.8]

9. Use the quadratic formula with $a = 3$, $b = 4 - x$, and
$c = 2x^2 - 3x - 6$. Then $b^2 - 4ac$
$= (4 - x)^2 - 12(2x^2 - 3x - 6) = -23x^2 + 28x + 88$,
and $y = \dfrac{x - 4 \pm \sqrt{-23x^2 + 28x + 88}}{6}$

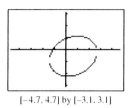

[−4.7, 4.7] by [−3.1, 3.1]

10. Use the quadratic formula with $a = 4$, $b = 3x - 10$, and
$c = -x^2 - 5x - 20$. Then $b^2 - 4ac = (3x - 10)^2$
$-16(-x^2 - 5x - 20) = 25x^2 + 20x + 420$, and

$$y = \frac{1}{8}[10 - 3x \pm \sqrt{25x^2 + 20x + 420}].$$

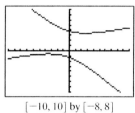

[−10, 10] by [−8, 8]

11. Use the quadratic formula with $a = 8$, $b = 4 - 4x$, and
$c = 2x^2 - 10x - 13$.
Then $b^2 - 4ac = (4 - 4x)^2 - 32(2x^2 - 10x - 13)$
$= -48x^2 + 288x + 432 = 48(-x^2 + 6x + 9)$, and

$$y = \frac{4x - 4 \pm \sqrt{48(-x^2 + 6x + 9)}}{16}$$

$$= \frac{1}{4}x - \frac{1}{4} \pm \frac{1}{4}\sqrt{3(-x^2 + 6x + 9)}.$$

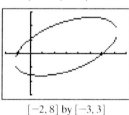

[−2, 8] by [−3, 3]

12. Use the quadratic formula with $a = 2$, $b = 6 - 4x$, and
$c = 2x^2 - 5x - 15$. Then $b^2 - 4ac = (6 - 4x)^2$
$-8(2x^2 - 5x - 15) = 156 - 8x = 4(39 - 2x)$, and

$$y = \frac{4x - 6 \pm \sqrt{4(39 - 2x)}}{4}$$

$$= x - \frac{3}{2} \pm \frac{1}{2}\sqrt{39 - 2x}.$$

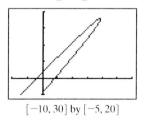

[−10, 30] by [−5, 20]

13. $h = 0$, $k = 0$ and the parabola opens downward, so
$4py = x^2$). Using $(2, -1)$: $-4p = 4$, $p = -1$.
The standard form is $x^2 = -4y$.

14. $h = 0$, $k = 0$ and the parabola opens to the right, so
$4px = y^2$ ($p > 0$). Using $(2, 4)$: $8p = 16$, $p = 2$.
The standard form is $y^2 = 8x$.

15. $h = 0$, $k = 0$ and the hyperbola opens to the right and left, so $a = 3$, and $b = 4$. The standard form is
$$\frac{x^2}{9} - \frac{y^2}{16} = 1.$$

16. $h = 0$, $k = 0$, and the x-axis is the focal axis, so $a = 4$ and $b = 3$. The standard form is $\dfrac{x^2}{16} + \dfrac{y^2}{9} = 1$.

For #17–20, recall that $x' = x - h$ and $y' = y - k$.

17. $(x', y') = (4, -1)$

18. $(x', y') = (2, 12)$

19. $(x', y') = (5, -3 - \sqrt{5})$

20. $(x', y') = (-5 - \sqrt{2}, -1)$

21. $4(y^2 - 2y) - 9(x^2 + 2x) = 41$, so
$4(y - 1)^2 - 9(x + 1)^2 = 41 + 4 - 9 = 36$. Then
$\dfrac{(y - 1)^2}{9} - \dfrac{(x + 1)^2}{4} = 1$. This is a hyperbola, with
$a = 3$, $b = 2$, and $c = \sqrt{13}$.
$\dfrac{(y')^2}{9} - \dfrac{(x')^2}{4} = 1$.

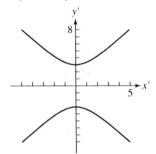

22. $2(x^2 + 6x) + 3(y^2 - 8y) = -60$, so
$2(x + 3)^2 + 3(y - 4^2) = -60 + 18 + 48 = 6$. Then
$\dfrac{(x + 3)^2}{3} + \dfrac{(y - 4)^2}{2} = 1$. This is an ellipse with
$a = \sqrt{3}$, $b = \sqrt{2}$, and $c = 1$. $\dfrac{(x')^2}{3} + \dfrac{(y')^2}{2} = 1$.

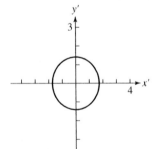

23. $y - 2 = (x + 1)^2$, a parabola. The vertex is
$(h, k) = (-1, 2)$, so $y' = (x')^2$.

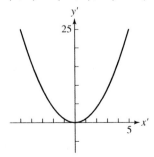

24. $2\left(y - \dfrac{7}{6}\right) = (x - 1)^2$, a parabola. The vertex is
$(h, k) = \left(1, \dfrac{7}{6}\right)$, so $2y' = (x')^2$.

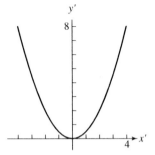

25. $9(x^2 - 2x) + 4(y^2 + 4y) = 11$, so
$9(x - 1)^2 + 4(y + 2)^2 = 11 + 9 + 16 = 36$. Then
$\dfrac{(x - 1)^2}{4} + \dfrac{(y + 2)^2}{9} = 1$.
This is an ellipse, with $a = 2$, $b = 3$, and $c = \sqrt{5}$.
Foci: $(1, -2 \pm \sqrt{5})$. Center $(1, -2)$, so
$\dfrac{(x')^2}{4} + \dfrac{(y')^2}{9} = 1$.

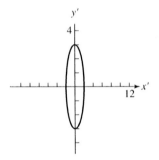

26. $16(x^2 - 2x) - (y^2 + 6y) = 57$, so $16(x - 1)^2 - (y + 3)^2 = 57 + 16 - 9 = 64$.
Then $\dfrac{(x - 1)^2}{4} - \dfrac{(y + 3)^2}{64} = 1$. This is a hyperbola, with
$a = 2$, $b = 8$, and $c = \sqrt{68} = 2\sqrt{17}$. Foci:
$(1 \pm 2\sqrt{17}, -3)$. Center $(1, -3)$, so $\dfrac{(x')^2}{4} - \dfrac{(y')^2}{64} = 1$.

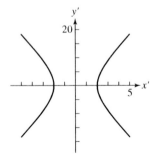

27. $8(x - 2) = (y - 2)^2$, a parabola. The vertex is $(h, k) = (2, 2)$, so $8x' = (y')^2$.

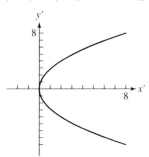

28. $2(x^2 - 2x) + (y^2 - 6y) = 9$, so $2(x - 1)^2 + (y - 3)^2$
$= 9 + 2 + 9 = 20$. Then $\dfrac{(x - 1)^2}{10} + \dfrac{(y - 3)^2}{20} = 1$.

This is an ellipse, with
$a = \sqrt{10}, b = \sqrt{20} = 2\sqrt{5}$, and $c = \sqrt{10}$.
Foci: $(1, 3 \pm \sqrt{10})$. Center $(1, 3)$, so $\dfrac{(x')^2}{10} + \dfrac{(y')^2}{20} = 1$

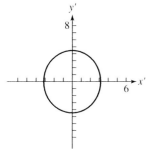

29. $2(x^2 + 2x) - y^2 = -6$, so $2(x + 1)^2 - y^2 = -6 + 2$
$= -4$. Then $\dfrac{y^2}{4} - \dfrac{(x + 1)^2}{2} = 1$. This is a hyperbola,
with $a = \sqrt{2}, b = 2$, and $c = \sqrt{6}$. Foci:
$(-1, \pm\sqrt{6})$. Center $(-1, 0)$, so $\dfrac{(y')^2}{4} - \dfrac{(x')^2}{2} = 1$.

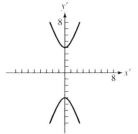

30. $-4(x - 3.25) = (y - 1)^2$, a parabola. The vertex is $(h, k) = (3.25, 1)$, so $-4x' = (y')^2$

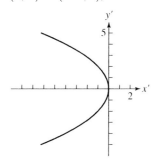

31. The horizontal distance from O to P is
$x = h + x' = x' + h$, and the vertical distance from O to P is $y = k + y' = y' + k$.

32. Given $x = x' + h$, subtract h from both sides: $x - h = x'$ or $x' = x - h$. And given $y = y' + k$, subtract k from both sides: $y - k = y'$ or $y' = y - k$.

For #33–36, recall that $x' = x \cos \alpha + y \sin \alpha$ and $y' = -x \sin \alpha + y \cos \alpha$.

33. $(x', y') = \left(-2 \cos \dfrac{\pi}{4} + 5 \sin \dfrac{\pi}{4}, 2 \sin \dfrac{\pi}{4} + 5 \cos \dfrac{\pi}{4} \right)$
$= \left(\dfrac{3\sqrt{2}}{2}, \dfrac{7\sqrt{2}}{2} \right)$

34. $(x', y') = \left(6 \cos \dfrac{\pi}{3} - 3 \sin \dfrac{\pi}{3}, -6 \sin \dfrac{\pi}{3} - 3 \cos \dfrac{\pi}{3} \right)$
$= \left(\dfrac{6}{2} - \dfrac{3\sqrt{3}}{2}, \dfrac{-6\sqrt{3}}{2} - \dfrac{3}{2} \right)$
$= \left(\dfrac{6 - 3\sqrt{3}}{2}, \dfrac{-6\sqrt{3} - 3}{2} \right) \approx (0.40, -6.70)$

35. $\alpha \approx 1.06$, $(x', y') = (-5 \cos (1.06) - 4 \sin (1.06),$
$5 \sin (1.06) - 4 \cos (1.06)) \approx (-5.94, 2.38)$

36. $\alpha \approx \dfrac{\pi}{4}$, (x', y')
$= \left(2 \cos \dfrac{\pi}{4} + 3 \sin \dfrac{\pi}{4}, -2 \sin \dfrac{\pi}{4} + 3 \cos \dfrac{\pi}{4} \right)$
$= \left(\dfrac{5\sqrt{2}}{2}, \dfrac{\sqrt{2}}{2} \right)$

For #37–40, use the discriminant $B^2 - 4AC$ to determine the type of conic. Then use the relationship of $\cot 2\alpha = \dfrac{A - C}{B}$ to determine the angle of rotation.

37. $B^2 - 4AC = 1 > 0$, hyperbola; $\cot 2\alpha = 0$, so $\alpha = \dfrac{\pi}{4}$.
Translating, $\left(\dfrac{x' - y'}{\sqrt{2}} \right)\left(\dfrac{x' + y'}{\sqrt{2}} \right) = 8$,
$\dfrac{(x')^2}{16} - \dfrac{(y')^2}{16} = 1, y' = \pm\sqrt{(x')^2 - 16}$

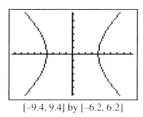

[–9.4, 9.4] by [–6.2, 6.2]

38. $B^2 - 4AC = 9 > 0$, hyperbola; $\cot 2\alpha = 0$, so $\alpha = \dfrac{\pi}{4}$.
Translating, $3\left(\dfrac{x' - y'}{\sqrt{2}} \right)\left(\dfrac{x' + y'}{\sqrt{2}} \right) + 15 = 0$,
$\dfrac{(y')^2}{10} - \dfrac{(x')^2}{10} = 1, y' = \pm\sqrt{(x')^2 + 10}$

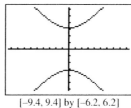

[–9.4, 9.4] by [–6.2, 6.2]

39. $B^2 - 4AC = 3 - 4(2)(1) = -5 < 0$, ellipse;

$\cot 2\alpha = \dfrac{1}{\sqrt{3}}, \alpha = \dfrac{\pi}{6}$. Translating,

$x = x' \cos \dfrac{\pi}{6} - y' \sin \dfrac{\pi}{6}, y = x' \sin \dfrac{\pi}{6} + y' \cos \dfrac{\pi}{6}$, so the

equation becomes $\dfrac{5(x')^2}{2} + \dfrac{(y')^2}{2} = 10$,

$\dfrac{(x')^2}{4} + \dfrac{(y')^2}{20} = 1$

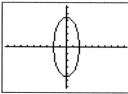

[–9.4, 9.4] by [–6.2, 6.2]

40. $B^2 - 4AC = 12 - 4(3)(1) = 0$, parabola; $\cot 2\alpha = \dfrac{1}{\sqrt{3}}$,

$\alpha = \dfrac{\pi}{6}$. Translating, $x = x' \cos \dfrac{\pi}{6} - y' \sin \dfrac{\pi}{6}$,

$y = x' \sin \dfrac{\pi}{6} + y' \cos \dfrac{\pi}{6}$, so $4(x')^2 = 14, x' = \pm\dfrac{\sqrt{14}}{2}$.

This is a degenerate form consisting of only two parallel lines.

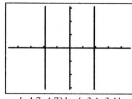

[–4.7, 4.7] by [–3.1, 3.1]

41. $B^2 - 4AC = -176 < 0$, ellipse. Use the quadratic formula with $a = 9, b = -20x$, and $c = 16x^2 - 40$. Then

$b^2 - 4ac = (-20x)^2 - 4(9)(16x^2 - 40)$

$= -176x^2 + 1440 = 16(-11x^2 + 90)$, and

$y = \dfrac{20x \pm \sqrt{16(-11x^2 + 90)}}{18}$

$= \dfrac{10x \pm 2\sqrt{90 - 11x^2}}{9}$

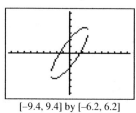

[–9.4, 9.4] by [–6.2, 6.2]

$\cot 2\alpha = -\dfrac{7}{20}, \alpha \approx 0.954 \approx 54.65°$

42. $B^2 - 4AC = 4 > 0$, hyperbola. Use the quadratic formula with $a = 2, b = -6x + 10$, and $c = 4x^2 - 3x - 6$. Then

$b^2 - 4ac = (-6x + 10)^2 - 4(2)(4x^2 - 3x - 6)$

$= 4x^2 - 96x + 148 = 4(x^2 - 24x + 37)$, and

$y = \dfrac{(6x - 10) \pm \sqrt{4(x^2 - 24x + 37)}}{4}$

$= \dfrac{(3x - 5) \pm \sqrt{x^2 - 24x + 37}}{2}$

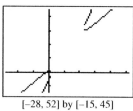

[–28, 52] by [–15, 45]

$\cot 2\alpha = -\dfrac{1}{3}, \alpha \approx 0.946 \approx 54.22°$

43. $B^2 - 4AC = 16 - 4(1)(10) = -24 < 0$; ellipse

44. $B^2 - 4AC = 16 - 4(1)(0) = 16 > 0$; hyperbola

45. $B^2 - 4AC = 36 - 4(9)(1) = 0$; parabola

46. $B^2 - 4AC = 1 - 4(0)(3) = 1 > 0$; hyperbola

47. $B^2 - 4AC = 16 - 4(8)(2) = -48 < 0$; ellipse

48. $B^2 - 4AC = 144 - 4(3)(4) = 96 > 0$; hyperbola

49. $B^2 - 4AC = 0 - 4(1)(-3) = 12 > 0$; hyperbola

50. $B^2 - 4AC = 16 - 4(5)(3) = -44 < 0$; ellipse

51. $B^2 - 4AC = 4 - 4(4)(1) = -12 < 0$; ellipse

52. $B^2 - 4AC = 16 - 4(6)(9) = -200 < 0$; ellipse

53. In the new coordinate system, the center $(x', y') = (0, 0)$, the vertices occur at $(\pm3, 0)$ and the foci are located at $(\pm3\sqrt{2}, 0)$. We use $x = x' \cos \dfrac{\pi}{4} - y' \sin \dfrac{\pi}{4}$,

$y = x' \sin \dfrac{\pi}{4} + y' \cos \dfrac{\pi}{4}$ to translate "back." Under the "old" coordinate system, the center $(x, y) = (0, 0)$, the

vertices occured at $\left(\dfrac{3\sqrt{2}}{2}, \dfrac{3\sqrt{2}}{2}\right)$ and $\left(-\dfrac{3\sqrt{2}}{2}, -\dfrac{3\sqrt{2}}{2}\right)$.

and the foci are located at $(3, 3)$ and $(-3, -3)$.

54. (a) Reversing the translation and rotation of the parabola, we see that the vertex in the (x'', y'')

coordinate system is $V(0, 0)$, with $h = \dfrac{21}{\sqrt{15}}$ and

$k = \dfrac{3\sqrt{5}}{10}$. This means that the vertex of the

parabola in the (x', y') coordinate system is

$(x'' + h, y'' + k) = \left(0 + \dfrac{21}{\sqrt{15}}, 0 + \dfrac{3\sqrt{5}}{10}\right)$. Since

$\cos \alpha = \dfrac{1}{\sqrt{5}}$ and $\sin \alpha = \dfrac{2}{\sqrt{5}}$, rotating "back" into the

(x, y) coordinate system gives

$(x, y) = (x' \cos \alpha - y' \sin \alpha, x' \sin \alpha + y' \cos \alpha)$

$\left(\dfrac{21}{\sqrt{5}} \cdot \dfrac{1}{\sqrt{5}} - \dfrac{3\sqrt{5}}{10} \cdot \dfrac{2}{\sqrt{15}}, \dfrac{21}{\sqrt{5}} \cdot \dfrac{2}{\sqrt{5}} + \dfrac{3\sqrt{5}}{10} \cdot \dfrac{1}{\sqrt{5}}\right)$

$= (3.6, 8.7)$.

(b) See (a).

55. Answers will vary. One possible answer: Using the geometric relationships illustrated, it is clear that

$x = x' \cos \alpha - y' \cos\left(\dfrac{\pi}{2} - \alpha\right) = x' \cos \alpha - y' \sin \alpha$

and that $y = x' \cos\left(\dfrac{\pi}{2} - \alpha\right) + y' \cos \alpha$

$= x' \sin \alpha + y' \cos \alpha$.

56. $x' = x \cos \alpha + y \sin \alpha$ $y' = -x \sin \alpha + y \cos \alpha$
$x' \cos \alpha = x \cos^2 \alpha + y \sin \alpha \cos \alpha$
$y' \sin \alpha = -x \sin^2 \alpha + y \cos \alpha \sin \alpha$
$x' \cos \alpha - y' \sin \alpha = x \cos^2 \alpha + y \sin \alpha \cos \alpha +$
$\qquad\qquad\qquad x \sin^2 \alpha - y \sin \alpha \cos \alpha$
$x' \cos \alpha - y' \sin \alpha = x \cos^2 \alpha + x \sin^2 \alpha$
$x' \cos \alpha - y' \sin \alpha = x$
Similarly,
$x' = \cos \alpha + y \sin \alpha$ $y' = -x \sin \alpha + y \cos \alpha$
$x' \sin \alpha = x \cos \alpha \sin \alpha + y \sin^2 \alpha$
$y' \cos \alpha = -x \sin \alpha \cos \alpha + y \cos^2 \alpha$
$x' \sin \alpha + y' \cos \alpha = x \cos \alpha \sin \alpha + y \sin^2 \alpha$
$\qquad\qquad\qquad - x \sin \alpha \cos \alpha + y \cos^2 \alpha$
$x' \sin \alpha + y' \cos \alpha = y(\sin^2 \alpha + \cos^2 \alpha)$
$x' \sin \alpha + y' \cos \alpha = y$

57. True. The Bxy term is missing and so the rotation angle α is zero.

58. True. Because the x^2 and y^2 terms have the same coefficient (namely 1), completing the square to put the equation in standard form will produce the same denominator under $(y - k)^2$ as under $(x - h)^2$.

59. Eliminating the cross-product term requires rotation, not translation. The answer is B.

60. Moving the center or vertex to the origin is done through translation, not rotation. The answer is C.

61. Completing the square twice, and dividing to obtain 1 on the right, turns the equation into
$$\frac{(x-1)^2}{16} + \frac{(y+2)^2}{9} = 1$$
The vertices lie 4 units to the left and right of center $(1, -2)$. The answer is A.

62. The equation is equivalent to $y = 4/x$. The answer is E.

63. (a) The rotated axes pass through the old origin with slopes of ± 1, so the equations are $y = \pm x$.

(b) The location of $(x'', y'') = (0, 0)$ in the xy system can be found by reversing the transformations. In the $x'y'$ system, $(x'', y'') = (0, 0)$ has coordinates
$(h, k) = \left(\dfrac{21}{\sqrt{5}}, \dfrac{3\sqrt{5}}{10} \right)$. The coordinates of this point in the xy system are then given by the second set of rotation formulas; with $\cos \alpha = \dfrac{1}{\sqrt{5}}$, $\sin \alpha = \dfrac{2}{\sqrt{5}}$:
$$x = \frac{21}{\sqrt{5}}\left(\frac{1}{\sqrt{5}}\right) - \frac{3\sqrt{5}}{10}\left(\frac{2}{\sqrt{5}}\right) = \frac{18}{5}$$
$$y = \frac{21}{\sqrt{5}}\left(\frac{2}{\sqrt{5}}\right) + \frac{3\sqrt{5}}{10}\left(\frac{1}{\sqrt{5}}\right) = \frac{87}{10}$$
The $x''y''$ axes pass through the point (x, y)
$= \left(\dfrac{18}{5}, \dfrac{87}{10} \right)$ with slopes of $\dfrac{2/\sqrt{5}}{1/\sqrt{5}} = 2$
and its negative reciprocal, $-\dfrac{1}{z}$. Using this information to write linear equations in point-slope form, and then converting to slope-intercept form, we obtain
$$y = 2x + \frac{3}{2}$$
$$y = -\frac{1}{2}x + \frac{21}{2}$$

64. (a) If the translation on $x' = x - h$ and $y' = y - k$ is applied to the equation, we have:
$A(x')^2 + Bx'y' + C(y')^2 + Dx' + Ey' + F = 0$,
so $A(x - h)^2 + B(x - h)(y - k) + C(y - k)^2 + D(x - h) + E(y - k) + F = 0$, which becomes
$Ax^2 + Bxy + Cy^2 + (D - Bk - 2Ah)x + (E - 2ck - Bh)y + (Ah^2 + Ck^2 - Ek - Dh) + Bhk + F = 0$
The discriminants are exactly the same; the coefficients of the x^2, xy, and y^2 terms do not change (no sign change).

(b) If the equation is multiplied by some constant k, we have $kAx^2 + kBxy + kCy^2 + kD + kE + kF = 0$, so the discriminant of the new equation becomes $(kB)^2 - 4(kA)(kC) = k^2B^2 - 4k^2AC = k^2(B^2 - 4AC)$. Since $k^2 > 0$ for $k \neq 0$, no sign change occurs.

65. First, consider the linear terms:
$$\begin{aligned} Dx + Ey &= D(x'\cos \alpha - y'\sin \alpha) \\ &\quad + E(x'\sin \alpha + y'\cos \alpha) \\ &= (D \cos \alpha + E \sin \alpha)x' \\ &\quad + (E \cos \alpha - D \sin \alpha)y' \end{aligned}$$
This shows that $Dx + Ey = D'x' + E'y'$, where $D' = D \cos \alpha + E \sin \alpha$ and $E' = E \cos \alpha - D \sin \alpha$.
Now, consider the quadratic terms:
$Ax^2 + Bxy + Cy^2 = A(x'\cos \alpha - y'\sin \alpha)^2 + B(x'\cos \alpha - y'\sin \alpha)(x'\sin \alpha + y'\cos \alpha) + C(x'\sin \alpha + y'\cos \alpha)^2$
$= A(x'^2 \cos^2 \alpha - 2x'y'\cos \alpha \sin \alpha + y'^2 \sin^2 \alpha) + B(x'^2 \cos \alpha \sin \alpha + x'y'\cos^2 \alpha - x'y'\sin^2 \alpha - y'^2 \sin \alpha \cos \alpha) + C(x'^2 \sin^2 \alpha + 2x'y'\sin \alpha \cos \alpha + y'^2 \cos^2 \alpha)$
$= (A \cos^2\alpha + B \cos \alpha \sin \alpha + C \sin^2 \alpha)x'^2 + [B(\cos^2 \alpha - \sin^2 \alpha) + 2(C - A)(\sin \alpha \cos \alpha)]x'y' + (C \cos^2 \alpha - B \cos \alpha \sin \alpha + A \sin^2 \alpha)y'^2$
$= (A \cos^2 \alpha + B \cos \alpha \sin \alpha + C \sin^2 \alpha)x'^2 + [B \cos 2\alpha + (C - A) \sin 2\alpha]x'y' + (C \cos^2\alpha - B \cos \alpha \sin \alpha + A \sin^2 \alpha)y'^2$
This shows that
$Ax^2 + Bxy + Cy^2 = A'x'^2 + B'x'y' + C'y'^2$, where
$A' = A \cos^2 \alpha + B \cos \alpha \sin \alpha + C \sin^2 \alpha$,
$B' = B \cos 2\alpha + (C - A) \sin 2\alpha$, and $C' = C \cos^2\alpha - B \cos \alpha \sin \alpha + A \sin^2 \alpha$.
The results above imply that if the formulas for A', B', C', D', and F' are applied, then $A'x'^2 + B'x'y' + C'y'^2 + D'x' + E'y' + F' = 0$ is equivalent to $Ax^2 + Bxy + Cy^2 + Dx + Ey + F = 0$. Therefore, the formulas are correct.

66. This equation is simply a special case of the equation we have used throughout the chapter, where $B = 0$. The discriminant $B^2 - 4AC$, then, reduces simply to $-4AC$. If $-4AC > 0$, we have a hyperbola; $-4AC = 0$, we have a parabola; $-4AC < 0$, we have a ellipse. More simply: a hyperbola if $AC < 0$; a parabola if $AC = 0$; an ellipse if $AC > 0$.

67. Making the substitutions $x = x'\cos\alpha - y'\sin\alpha$ and $y = x'\sin\alpha + y'\cos\alpha$, we find that:

$$B'x'y' = (B\cos^2\alpha - B\sin^2\alpha + 2C\sin\alpha\cos\alpha$$
$$- 2A\sin\alpha\cos\alpha)x'y'$$
$$Ax'^2 = (A\cos^2\alpha + B\sin\alpha\cos\alpha + C\sin^2\alpha)(x')^2$$
$$Cy'^2 = (A\sin^2\alpha + C\cos^2\alpha - B\cos\alpha\sin\alpha)(y')^2$$
$$B'^2 - 4A'C' = (B\cos(2\alpha) - (A - C)\sin(2\alpha))^2$$
$$- 4(A\cos^2\alpha + B\sin\alpha\cos\alpha + C\sin^2\alpha)$$
$$(A\sin^2\alpha - B\sin\alpha\cos\alpha + C\cos^2\alpha)$$

$$= \frac{1}{2}B^2\cos(4\alpha) + \frac{1}{2}B^2 + BC\sin(4\alpha) - BA\sin(4\alpha)$$

$$+ \frac{1}{2}C^2 - \frac{1}{2}C^2\cos(4\alpha) - CA + CA\cos(4\alpha)$$

$$+ \frac{1}{2}A^2 - \frac{1}{2}A^2\cos(4\alpha) - 4\left(\frac{1}{2}A\cos(2\alpha) + \frac{1}{2}A\right.$$

$$+ \frac{1}{2}B\sin(2\alpha) + \frac{1}{2}C - \frac{1}{2}C\cos(2\alpha)\right)$$

$$\left(\frac{1}{2}A - \frac{1}{2}A\cos(2\alpha) + \frac{1}{2}C\cos(2\alpha) + \frac{1}{2}C\right.$$

$$\left. - \frac{1}{2}B\sin(2\alpha)\right)$$

$$= \frac{1}{2}B^2\cos(4\alpha) + \frac{1}{2}B^2 + BC\sin(4\alpha) - BA\sin(4\alpha)$$

$$+ \frac{1}{2}C^2 - \frac{1}{2}C^2\cos(4\alpha) - CA + CA\cos(4\alpha) + \frac{1}{2}A^2$$

$$- \frac{1}{2}A^2\cos(4\alpha) - BC\sin(4\alpha) + BA\sin(4\alpha) - 3AC$$

$$- \frac{1}{2}C^2 - \frac{1}{2}A^2 + \frac{1}{2}A^2\cos(4\alpha) + \frac{1}{2}B^2 - \frac{1}{2}B^2\cos(4\alpha)$$

$$+ \frac{1}{2}C^2\cos(4\alpha) - AC\cos(4\alpha)$$

$$= B^2 - 4AC.$$

68. When the rotation is made to the (x', y') coordinate system, the coefficients A', B', C', D', E', and F' become:

$$A' = \frac{A}{2}(1 + \cos(2\alpha)) + \frac{B}{2}\sin(2\alpha)$$
$$+ \frac{C}{2}(1 - \cos(2\alpha))$$
$$B' = B\cos(2\alpha) - (A - C)\sin(2\alpha)$$
$$C' = \frac{A}{2}(1 - \cos(2\alpha)) - \frac{B}{2}\sin(2\alpha)$$
$$+ \frac{C}{2}(\cos(2\alpha) + 1)$$
$$D' = D\cos\alpha + E\sin\alpha$$
$$E' = -D\sin\alpha + E\cos\alpha$$
$$F' = F$$

(a) Since $F' = F$, F is invariant under rotation.

(b) Since $A' + C' = \frac{A}{2}[1 + \cos(2\alpha) + 1 - \cos(2\alpha)]$

$$+ \frac{B}{2}[\sin(2\alpha) - \sin(2\alpha)] + \frac{C}{2}[1 - \cos(2\alpha)$$

$$+ \cos(2\alpha) + 1] = A + C, A + C \text{ is invariant under rotation.}$$

(c) Since $D'^2 + E'^2 = (D\cos\alpha + E\sin\alpha)^2$
$$+ (-D\sin\alpha + E\cos\alpha)^2$$
$$= D^2\cos^2\alpha + 2DE\cos\alpha\sin\alpha + E^2\sin^2\alpha$$
$$+ D^2\sin^2\alpha - 2DE\cos\alpha\sin\alpha + E^2\cos^2\alpha$$
$$= D^2(\cos^2\alpha + \sin^2\alpha) + E^2(\sin^2\alpha + \cos^2\alpha)$$
$$= D^2 + E^2, D^2 + E^2 \text{ is invariant under rotation.}$$

69. Intersecting lines: $x^2 + xy = 0$ can be rewritten as $x = 0$ (the y-axis) and $y = -x$

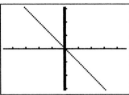

[−4.7, 4.7] by [−3.1, 3.1]

A plane containing the axis of a cone intersects the cone.

Parallel lines: $x^2 = 4$ can be rewritten as $x = \pm 2$ (a pair of vertical lines)

[−4.7, 4.7] by [−3.1, 3.1]

A degenerate cone is created by a generator that is parallel to the axis, producing a cylinder. A plane parallel to a generator of the cylinder intersects the cylinder and its interior.

One line: $y^2 = 0$ can be rewritten as $y = 0$ (the x-axis).

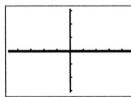

[−4.7, 4.7] by [−3.1, 3.1]

A plane containing a generator of a cone intersects the cone.

No graph: $x^2 = -1$

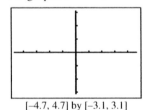

[−4.7, 4.7] by [−3.1, 3.1]

A plane parallel to a generator of a cylinder fails to intersect the cylinder.

Circle: $x^2 + y^2 = 9$

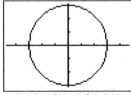

[−4.7, 4.7] by [−3.1, 3.1]

A plane perpendicular to the axis of a cone intersects the cone but not its vertex.

Point: $x^2 + y^2 = 0$, the point $(0, 0)$.

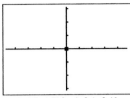

[−4.7, 4.7] by [−3.1, 3.1]

A plane perpendicular to the axis of a cone intersects the vertex of the cone.

No graph: $x^2 + y^2 = -1$

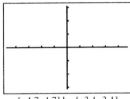

[−4.7, 4.7] by [−3.1, 3.1]

A degenerate cone is created by a generator that is perpendicular to the axis, producing a plane. A second plane perpendicular to the axis of this degenerate cone fails to intersect it.

■ Section 8.5 Polar Equations of Conics

Exploration 1

For $e = 0.7$ and $e = 0.8$, an ellipse; for $e = 1$, a parabola; for $e = 1.5$ and $e = 3$, a hyperbola.

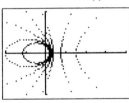

[−12, 24] by [−12, 12]

The five graphs all have a common focus, the pole $(0, 0)$, and a common directrix, the line $x = 3$. As the eccentricity e increases, the graphs move away from the focus and toward the directrix.

Quick Review 8.5

1. $r = -3$

2. $r = 2$

3. $\theta = \dfrac{7\pi}{6}$ or $-\dfrac{5\pi}{6}$

4. $\theta = -\dfrac{5\pi}{3}$ or $\dfrac{\pi}{3}$

5. $h = 0, k = 0, 4p = 16$, so $p = 4$
   The focus is $(0, 4)$ and the directrix is $y = -4$.

6. $h = 0, k = 0, 4p = -12$, so $p = -3$
   The focus is $(-3, 0)$ and the directrix is $x = 3$.

7. $a = 3, b = 2, c = \sqrt{5}$; Foci: $(\pm\sqrt{5}, 0)$; Vertices: $(\pm 3, 0)$

8. $a = 5, b = 3, c = 4$; Foci: $(0, \pm 4)$; Vertices: $(0, \pm 5)$

9. $a = 4, b = 3, c = 5$; Foci: $(\pm 5, 0)$; Vertices: $(\pm 4, 0)$

10. $a = 6, b = 2, c = 4\sqrt{2}$; Foci: $(0, \pm 4\sqrt{2})$;
   Vertices: $(0, \pm 6)$

Section 8.5 Exercises

1. $r = \dfrac{2}{1 - \cos\theta}$ — a parabola.

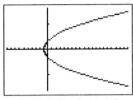

[−10, 20] by [−10, 10]

2. $r = \dfrac{5}{1 + \left(\dfrac{5}{4}\right)\cos\theta} = \dfrac{20}{4 + 5\cos\theta}$ — a hyperbola.

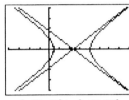

[−20, 40] by [−20, 20]

3. $r = \dfrac{\dfrac{12}{5}}{1 + \left(\dfrac{3}{5}\right)\sin\theta} = \dfrac{12}{5 + 3\sin\theta}$ — an ellipse.

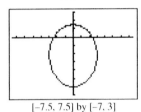

[−7.5, 7.5] by [−7, 3]

4. $r = \dfrac{2}{1 + \sin\theta}$ — a parabola.

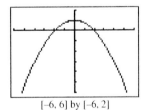

[−6, 6] by [−6, 2]

5. $r = \dfrac{\dfrac{7}{3}}{1 - \left(\dfrac{7}{3}\right)\sin\theta} = \dfrac{7}{3 - 7\sin\theta}$ — a hyperbola.

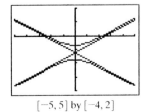

[−5, 5] by [−4, 2]

6. $r = \dfrac{\dfrac{10}{3}}{1 - \left(\dfrac{2}{3}\right)\cos\theta} = \dfrac{10}{3 - 2\cos\theta}$ — an ellipse.

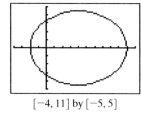

[−4, 11] by [−5, 5]

7. Parabola with $e = 1$ and directrix $x = 2$.

8. Hyperbola with $e = 2$ and directrix $x = 3$.

9. Divide numerator and denominator by 2.

Parabola with $e = 1$ and directrix $y = -\dfrac{5}{2} = -2.5$.

10. Divide numerator and denominator by 4.

Ellipse with $e = \dfrac{1}{4} = 0.25$ and directrix $x = -2$.

11. Divide numerator and denominator by 6.

Ellipse with $e = \dfrac{5}{6}$ and directrix $y = 4$.

12. Divide numerator and denominator by 2.

Hyperbola with $e = \dfrac{7}{2} = 3.5$ and directrix $y = -6$.

13. Divide numerator and denominator by 5.

Ellipse with $e = \dfrac{2}{5} = 0.4$ and directrix $x = 3$.

14. Divide numerator and denominator by 2.

Hyperbola with $e = \dfrac{5}{2} = 2.5$ and directrix $y = 4$.

15. (b) $[-15, 5]$ by $[-10, 10]$

16. (d) $[-5, 5]$ by $[-3, 3]$

17. (f) $[-5, 5]$ by $[-3, 3]$

18. (e) $[-5, 5]$ by $[-3, 5]$

19. (c) $[-10, 10]$ by $[-5, 10]$

20. (a) $[-3, 3]$ by $[-6, 6]$

For #21–28, one must solve two equations $a = \dfrac{ep}{1 + e}$ and $b = \dfrac{ep}{1 - e}$ for e and p (given two constants a and b). The general solution to this is $e = \dfrac{b - a}{b + a}$ and $p = \dfrac{2ab}{b - a}$.

21. The directrix must be $x = p > 0$, since the right major-axis endpoint is closer to $(0, 0)$ than the left one, so the equation has the form $r = \dfrac{ep}{1 + e\cos\theta}$. Then

$1.5 = \dfrac{ep}{1 + e\cos 0} = \dfrac{ep}{1 + e}$ and $6 = \dfrac{ep}{1 + e\cos\pi}$

$= \dfrac{ep}{1 - e}$ (so $a = 1.5$ and $b = 6$). Therefore $e = \dfrac{3}{5} = 0.6$

and $p = 4$, so $r = \dfrac{2.4}{1 + (3/5)\cos\theta} = \dfrac{12}{5 + 3\cos\theta}$.

22. The directrix must be $x = -p < 0$, since the left major-axis endpoint is closer to $(0, 0)$ than the right one, so the equation has the form $r = \dfrac{ep}{1 - e\cos\theta}$. Then

$1.5 = \dfrac{ep}{1 - e\cos 0} = \dfrac{ep}{1 - e}$ and $1 = \dfrac{ep}{1 - e\cos\pi}$

$= \dfrac{ep}{1 + e}$ (so $a = 1$ and $b = 1.5$). Therefore $e = \dfrac{1}{5} = 0.2$

and $p = 6$ (the directrix is $x = -6$) , so

$r = \dfrac{1.2}{1 - (1/5)\cos\theta} = \dfrac{6}{5 - \cos\theta}$.

23. The directrix must be $y = p > 0$, since the upper major-axis endpoint is closer to $(0, 0)$ than the lower one, so the equation has the form $r = \dfrac{ep}{1 + e\cos\theta}$. Then

$1 = \dfrac{ep}{1 + e\sin(\pi/2)} = \dfrac{ep}{1 + e}$ and $3 = \dfrac{ep}{1 + e\sin(3\pi/2)}$

$= \dfrac{ep}{1 - e}$ (so $a = 1$ and $b = 3$). Therefore $e = \dfrac{1}{2} = 0.5$

and $p = 3$, so $r = \dfrac{1.5}{1 + (1/2)\sin\theta} = \dfrac{3}{2 + \sin\theta}$.

24. The directrix must be $y = -p < 0$, since the lower major-axis endpoint is closer to $(0, 0)$ than the upper one, so the equation has the form $r = \dfrac{ep}{1 - e\cos\theta}$. Then

$3 = \dfrac{ep}{1 - e\sin(\pi/2)} = \dfrac{ep}{1 - e}$ and $\dfrac{3}{4} = \dfrac{ep}{1 - e\sin(3\pi/2)}$

$= \dfrac{ep}{1 + e}$ (so $a = \dfrac{3}{4}$ and $b = 3$). Therefore $e = \dfrac{3}{5} = 0.6$

and $p = 2$ (the directrix is $y = -2$) , so

$r = \dfrac{1.2}{1 - (3/5)\sin\theta} = \dfrac{6}{5 - 3\sin\theta}$.

25. The directrix must be $x = p > 0$, since both transverse-axis endpoints have positive x coordinates, so the equation has the form $r = \dfrac{ep}{1 + e\cos\theta}$. Then

$3 = \dfrac{ep}{1 + e\cos 0} = \dfrac{ep}{1 + e}$ and $-15 = \dfrac{ep}{1 + e\cos\pi}$

$= \dfrac{ep}{1 - e}$ (so $a = 3$ and $b = -15$). Therefore $e = \dfrac{3}{2}$

$= 1.5$ and $p = 5$, so $r = \dfrac{7.5}{1 + (3/2)\cos\theta} = \dfrac{15}{2 + 3\cos\theta}$.

26. The directrix must be $x = -p < 0$, since both transverse-axis endpoints have negative x coordinates, so the equation has the form $r = \dfrac{ep}{1 - e\cos\theta}$. Then

$-3 = \dfrac{ep}{1 - e\cos 0} = \dfrac{ep}{1 - e}$ and $1.5 = \dfrac{ep}{1 - e\cos\pi}$

$= \dfrac{ep}{1 + e}$ (so $a = 1.5$ and $b = -3$). Therefore $e = 3$

and $p = 2$ (the directrix is $x = -2$), so $r = \dfrac{6}{1 - 3\cos\theta}$.

27. The directrix must be $y = p > 0$, since both transverse-axis endpoints have positive y coordinates, so the equation has the form $r = \dfrac{ep}{1 + e \cos \theta}$. Then 2.4

$$= \frac{ep}{1 + e \sin(\pi/2)} = \frac{ep}{1 + e} \text{ and } -12 = \frac{ep}{1 + e \sin(3\pi/2)}$$

$$= \frac{ep}{1 - e} \text{ (so } a = 2.4 \text{ and } b = -12). \text{ Therefore } e = \frac{3}{2}$$

$= 1.5$ and $p = 4$, so $r = \dfrac{6}{1 + (3/2) \sin \theta} = \dfrac{12}{2 + 3 \sin \theta}$.

28. The directrix must be $y = -p < 0$, since both transverse-axis endpoints have negative y coordinates, so the equation has the form $r = \dfrac{ep}{1 - e \cos \theta}$. Then

$$-6 = \frac{ep}{1 - e \sin(\pi/2)} = \frac{ep}{1 - e} \text{ and } 2 = \frac{ep}{1 - e \sin(3\pi/2)}$$

$$= \frac{ep}{1 + e} \text{ (so } a = 2 \text{ and } b = -6). \text{ Therefore } e = 2$$

and $p = 3$ (the directrix is $y = -3$), so $r = \dfrac{6}{1 - 2 \sin \theta}$.

29. The directrix must be $x = p > 0$, so the equation has the form $r = \dfrac{ep}{1 + e \cos \theta}$. Then $0.75 = \dfrac{ep}{1 + e \cos 0} = \dfrac{ep}{1 + e}$

and $3 = \dfrac{ep}{1 + e \cos \pi} = \dfrac{ep}{1 - e}$ (so $a = 0.75$ and $b = 3$).

Therefore $e = \dfrac{3}{5} = 0.6$ and $p = 2$, so

$r = \dfrac{1.2}{1 + (3/5) \cos \theta} = \dfrac{6}{5 + 3 \cos \theta}$.

30. Since this is a parabola, $e = 1$, and with $y = p > 0$ as the directrix, the equation has the form $r = \dfrac{p}{1 + \sin \theta}$. Then

$1 = \dfrac{p}{1 + \sin(\pi/2)} = \dfrac{p}{1 + 1}$, $p = 2$, and therefore

$r = \dfrac{2}{1 + \sin \theta}$. Alternatively, for a parabola, the distance from the focus to the vertex is the same as the distance from the vertex to the directrix (the same is true for *all* points on the parabola). This distance is 1 unit, so we again conclude that the directrix is $y = 2$.

31. $r = \dfrac{21}{5 - 2 \cos \theta} = \dfrac{4.2}{1 - 0.4 \cos \theta}$, so $e = 0.4$. The vertices are $(7, 0)$ and $(3, \pi)$, so $2a = 10$, $a = 5$, $c = ae$
$= (0.4)(5) = 2$, so $b = \sqrt{a^2 - c^2} = \sqrt{25 - 4} = \sqrt{21}$.

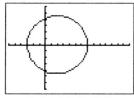

$[-6, 14]$ by $[-7, 6]$

$e = 0.4$, $a = 5$, $b = \sqrt{21}$, $c = 2$

32. $r = \dfrac{11}{6 - 5 \sin \theta} = \dfrac{11/6}{1 - (5/6) \sin \theta}$, so $e = \dfrac{5}{6}$. The vertices

are $\left(11, \dfrac{\pi}{2}\right)$ and $\left(1, \dfrac{3\pi}{2}\right)$, so $2a = 12$, $a = 6$.

$c = ae = \dfrac{5}{6} \cdot 6 = 5$, so

$b = \sqrt{a^2 - c^2} = \sqrt{36 - 25} = \sqrt{11}$.

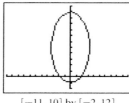

$[-11, 10]$ by $[-2, 12]$

$e = \dfrac{5}{6}$, $a = 6$, $b = \sqrt{11}$, $c = 5$

33. $r = \dfrac{24}{4 + 2 \sin \theta} = \dfrac{6}{1 + (1/2) \sin \theta}$, so $e = \dfrac{1}{2}$. The vertices

are $\left(4, \dfrac{\pi}{2}\right)$ and $\left(12, \dfrac{3\pi}{2}\right)$, so $2a = 16$, $a = 8$. $c = ae$

$= \dfrac{1}{2} \cdot 8 = 4$, so $b = \sqrt{a^2 - c^2} = \sqrt{64 - 16} = 4\sqrt{3}$.

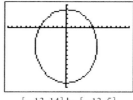

$[-13, 14]$ by $[-13, 5]$

$e = \dfrac{1}{2}$, $a = 8$, $b = 4\sqrt{3}$, $c = 4$

34. $r = \dfrac{16}{5 + 3 \cos \theta} = \dfrac{16/5}{1 + (3/5) \cos \theta}$, so $e = \dfrac{3}{5}$. The

vertices are $(2, 0)$ and $(8, \pi)$, so $2a = 10$, $a = 5$, $c = ae$

$= 5\left(\dfrac{3}{5}\right) = 3$, so $b = \sqrt{a^2 - c^2} = \sqrt{25 - 9} = 4$.

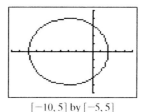

$[-10, 5]$ by $[-5, 5]$

$e = 0.6$, $a = 5$, $b = 4$, $c = 3$

35. $r = \dfrac{16}{3 + 5 \cos \theta} = \dfrac{16/3}{1 + (5/3) \cos \theta}$, so $e = \dfrac{5}{3}$. The

vertices are $(2, 0)$ and $(-8, \pi)$, so $2a = 6$, $a = 3$, $c = ae$

$= \dfrac{5}{3} \cdot 3 = 5$ and $b = \sqrt{c^2 - a^2} = \sqrt{25 - 9} = 4$.

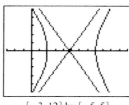

$[-3, 12]$ by $[-5, 5]$

$e = \dfrac{5}{3}$, $a = 3$, $b = 4$, $c = 5$

36. $r = \dfrac{12}{1 - 5\sin\theta}$, so $e = 5$. The vertices are $\left(-3, \dfrac{\pi}{2}\right)$ and $\left(2, \dfrac{3\pi}{2}\right)$, so $2a = 1$, $a = \dfrac{1}{2}$. $c = ae = 5\cdot\dfrac{1}{2} = \dfrac{5}{2}$ and $b = \sqrt{c^2 - a^2} = \sqrt{\dfrac{25}{4} - \dfrac{1}{4}} = \dfrac{2\sqrt6}{2} = \sqrt6.$

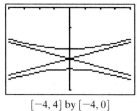

[−4, 4] by [−4, 0]

$e = 5$, $a = \dfrac{1}{2}$, $b = \sqrt6$, $c = \dfrac{5}{2}$

37. $r = \dfrac{4}{2 - \sin\theta} = \dfrac{2}{1 - (1/2)\sin\theta}$ so $e = \dfrac{1}{2}$ (an ellipse). The vertices are $\left(4, \dfrac{\pi}{2}\right)$ and $\left(\dfrac{4}{3}, \dfrac{3\pi}{2}\right)$ and the conic is symmetric around $x = 0$, so $x = 0$ is the semi-major axis and $2a = \dfrac{16}{3}$, so $a = \dfrac{8}{3}$. $c = ea = \dfrac{1}{2}\cdot\dfrac{8}{3} = \dfrac{4}{3}$ and $b = \sqrt{a^2 - c^2} = \sqrt{\left(\dfrac{8}{3}\right)^2 - \left(\dfrac{4}{3}\right)^2} = \dfrac{4\sqrt3}{3}$. The center $(h, k) = \left(0, \dfrac{12}{3} - \dfrac{8}{3}\right) = \left(0, \dfrac{4}{3}\right)$. The equation for the ellipse is

$$\dfrac{\left(y - \dfrac{4}{3}\right)^2}{\left(\dfrac{8}{3}\right)^2} + \dfrac{(x - 0)^2}{\left(\dfrac{4\sqrt3}{3}\right)^2} = \dfrac{9\left(y - \dfrac{4}{3}\right)^2}{64} + \dfrac{3x^2}{16} = 1$$

38. $r = \dfrac{6}{1 + 2\cos\theta}$, so $e = 2$ (a hyperbola). The vertices are $(2, 0)$ and $(-6, \pi)$ and the function is symmetric about the x-axis, so the semi-major axis runs along $x = 0$. $2a = 4$, $a = 2$, so $c = ea = 2(2) = 4$ and $b = \sqrt{c^2 - a^2} = \sqrt{16 - 4} = 2\sqrt3$. The vertex $(h, k) = (4, 0)$. The equation of the hyperbola is $\dfrac{(x - 4)^2}{2^2} - \dfrac{(y - 0)^2}{(2\sqrt3)^2} = \dfrac{(x - 4)^2}{4} - \dfrac{y^2}{12} = 1$

39. $r = \dfrac{4}{2 - 2\cos\theta} = \dfrac{2}{1 - \cos\theta}$, so $e = 1$ and $k = \dfrac{2}{e} = 2$. Since $k = 2p$, $p = 1$ and $4p = 4$, the vertex $(h, k) = (-1, 0)$ and the parabola opens to the right, so the equation is $y^2 = 4(x + 1)$.

40. $r = \dfrac{12}{3 + 3\cos\theta} = \dfrac{4}{1 + \cos\theta}$, so $e = 1$ and $k = \dfrac{4}{e} = 4$. Since $k = 2p$, $p = 2$ and $4p = 8$, the vertex $(h, k) = (2, 0)$ and the parabola opens to the left, so the equation is $y^2 = -8(x - 2)$.

41. Setting $e = 0.97$ and $a = 18.09$ AU, $r = \dfrac{18.09\,(1 - 0.97^2)}{1 + 0.97\cos\theta}$ The perihelion of Halley's Comet is $r = \dfrac{18.09\,(1 - 0.97^2)}{1 + 0.97} \approx 0.54$ AU

The aphelion of Halley's Comet is $r = \dfrac{18.09\,(1 - 0.97^2)}{1 - 0.97} \approx 35.64$ AU

42. Setting $e = 0.0461$ and $a = 19.18$, $r = \dfrac{19.18\,(1 - 0.0461^2)}{1 + 0.0461\cos\theta}$ Uranus' perihelion is $\dfrac{19.18\,(1 - 0.0461^2)}{1 + 0.0461} \approx 18.30$ AU Uranus' aphelion is $\dfrac{19.18\,(1 - 0.0461^2)}{1 - 0.0461} \approx 20.06$ AU

43. **(a)** The total radius of the orbit is $r = 250 + 1740 = 1990$ km $= 1{,}990{,}000$ m. Then $v \approx \sqrt{2{,}406{,}030} \approx 1551$ m/sec $= 1.551$ km/sec.

(b) The circumference of one orbit is $2\pi r \approx 12503.5$ km; one orbit therefore takes about 8061 seconds, or about 2 hr 14 min.

44. The total radius of the orbit is $r = 1000 + 2100 = 3100$ miles. One mile is about 1.61 km, so $r \approx 4991$ km $= 4{,}991{,}000$ m. Then $v \approx \sqrt{8{,}793{,}800} \approx 2965$ m/sec $= 2.965$ km/sec ≈ 1.843 mi/sec.

45. True. For a circle, $e = 0$. But when $e = 0$, the equation degenerates to $r = 0$, which yields a single point, the pole.

46. True. For a parabola, $e = 1$. But when $e = 1$, the equation degenerates to $r = 0$, which yields a single point, the pole.

47. Conics are defined in terms of the ratio distance to focus : distance to directrix. The answer is D.

48. As the eccentricity increases beginning from zero, the sequence of conics is circle ($e = 0$), ellipse ($e < 1$), parabola ($e = 1$), hyperbola ($e > 1$). The answer is C.

49. Conics written in polar form always have one focus at the pole. The answer is B.

50. $r = 1 + 2\cos\theta$ is a limaçon curve. (See Section 6.5). The answer is A.

51. **(a)** When $\theta = 0$, $\cos\theta = 1$, so $1 + e\cos\theta = 1 + e$. Then $\dfrac{a(1 - e^2)}{1 + e\cos\theta} = \dfrac{a(1 - e^2)}{1 + e} = a(1 - e)$ Similarly, when $\theta = \pi$, $\cos\theta = -1$, so $1 + e\cos\theta = 1 - e$. Then $\dfrac{a(1 - e^2)}{1 + e\cos\theta} = \dfrac{a(1 - e^2)}{1 - e} = a(1 + e)$

(b) $a(1 - e) = a\left(1 - \dfrac{c}{a}\right) = a - a\cdot\dfrac{c}{a} = a - c$

$a(1 + e) = a\left(1 + \dfrac{c}{a}\right) = a + a\cdot\dfrac{c}{a} = a + c$

(c)

Planet	Perihelion (in Au)	Aphelion
Mercury	0.307	0.467
Venus	0.718	0.728
Earth	0.983	1.017
Mars	1.382	1.665
Jupiter	4.953	5.452
Saturn	9.020	10.090

(d) The difference is greatest for Saturn.

52. $e = 0$ yields a circle (degenerate ellipse); $e = 0.3$ and $e = 0.7$ yield ellipses; $e = 1.5$ and $e = 3$ yield hyperbolas. When $e = 1$, we expect to obtain a parabola. But a has no meaning for a parabola, because a is the center-to-vertex distance and a parabola has no center. The equation

$$r = \frac{a(1 - e^2)}{1 + e \cos \theta}$$ yields no parabolas. When $e = 1, r = 0$.

53. If $r < 0$, then the point P can be expressed as the point $(r, \theta + \pi)$ then $PF = r$ and $PD = k - r \cos \theta$.

$$PF = ePD$$
$$r = e(k - r \cos \theta)$$
$$r = \frac{ke}{1 + e \cos \theta}$$

Recall that $P(r, \theta)$ can also be expressed as $(-r, \theta - \pi)$ then $PD = -r$ and $PF = -r \cos(\theta - \pi) - k$

$$PD = ePF$$
$$-r = e[-r \cos(\theta - \pi) - k]$$
$$-r = -er \cos(\theta - \pi) - ek$$
$$-r = er \cos \theta - ek$$
$$-r - er \cos \theta = -ek$$
$$r = \frac{ke}{1 + e \cos \theta}$$

54. (a)

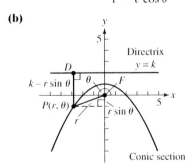

$PF = r$ and $PD = k + r \cos \theta$, so $PF = e PD$
becomes
$$r = e(k + r \cos \theta)$$
$$r - er \cos \theta = ek$$
$$r = \frac{ke}{1 - e \cos \theta}$$

(b)

$PF = r$ and $PD = k - r \sin \theta$, so $PF = e PD$
becomes
$$r = e(k - r \sin \theta)$$
$$r + er \sin \theta = ke$$
$$r = \frac{ke}{1 + e \sin \theta}$$

(c)

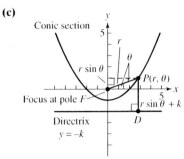

$PF = r$ and $PD = k + r \sin \theta$, so $PF = e PD$
becomes
$$r = e(k + r \sin \theta)$$
$$r - er \sin \theta = ek$$
$$r = \frac{ke}{1 - e \sin \theta}$$

55. Consider the polar equation $r = \dfrac{16}{5 - 3 \cos \theta}$. To transform this to a Cartesian equation, rewrite the equation as $5r - 3r \cos \theta = 16$. Then use the substitutions $r = \sqrt{x^2 + y^2}$ and $x = r \cos \theta$ to obtain
$5 \sqrt{x^2 + y^2} - 3x = 16$.
$5 \sqrt{x^2 + y^2} = 3x + 16$; $25(x^2 + y^2) = 9x^2 + 96x + 256$
$25x^2 + 25y^2 = 9x^2 + 96x + 256$
$16x^2 - 96x + 25y^2 = 256$;
Completing the square on the x term gives
$16(x^2 - 6x + 9) + 25y^2 = 256 + 144$
$16(x - 3)^2 + 25y^2 = 400$;
The Cartesian equation is $\dfrac{(x - 3)^2}{25} + \dfrac{y^2}{16} = 1$.

56. The focal width of a conic is the length of a chord through a focus and perpendicular to the focal axis. If the conic is given by $r = \dfrac{ke}{1 + e \cos \theta}$, the endpoints of the chord occur when $\theta = \dfrac{\pi}{2}$ and $\theta = \dfrac{3\pi}{2}$. Thus, the points are $\left(ke, \dfrac{\pi}{2} \right)$ and $\left(ke, \dfrac{3\pi}{2} \right)$ and the length of the chord is $ke + ke = 2ke$.
The focal width of a conic is $2ke$.

57. Apply the formula $e \cdot PD = PF$ to a hyperbola with one focus at the pole and directrix $x = -k$, letting P be the vertex closest to the pole. Then $a + k = c + PD$ and $PF = c - a$. Using $e = \dfrac{c}{a}$, we have:

$$e \cdot PD = PF$$
$$e(a + k - c) = c - a$$
$$e(a + k - ae) = ae - a$$
$$ae + ke - ae^2 = ae - a$$
$$ke - ae^2 = -a$$
$$ke = ae^2 - a$$
$$ke = a(e^2 - 1)$$

Thus, the equation $r = \dfrac{ke}{1 - e \cos \theta}$ becomes $r = \dfrac{a(e^2 - 1)}{1 - e \cos \theta}$.

58. (a) Let $P(x, y)$ be a point on the ellipse. The horizontal distance from P to the point $Q(a^2/c, y)$ on line L is $PQ = a^2/c - x$. The distance to the focus $(c, 0)$ is $PF = \sqrt{(x - c)^2 + y^2} = \sqrt{x^2 - 2cx + c^2 + y^2}$. To confirm that $PF/PQ = c/a$, cross-multiply to get $a\,PF = c\,PQ$; we need to confirm that $a\sqrt{x^2 - 2cx + c^2 + y^2} = a^2 - cx$. Square both sides: $a^2(x^2 - 2cx + c^2 + y^2) = a^4 - 2a^2cx + c^2x^2$. Substitute $a^2 - b^2$ for c^2, multiply out both sides, and cancel out terms, leaving $a^2y^2 - a^2b^2 = -b^2x^2$. Since P is on the ellipse, $x^2/a^2 + y^2/b^2 = 1$, or equivalent $b^2x^2 + a^2y^2 = a^2b^2$; this confirms the equality.

(b) According to the polar definition, the eccentricity is the ratio PF/PQ, which we found to be c/a in (a).

(c) Since $e = c/a$, $a/e = \dfrac{a}{c/a} = a^2/c$ and $ae = c$; the distance from F to L is $a^2/c - c = a/e - ea$ as desired.

59. (a) Let $P(x, y)$ be a point on the hyperbola. The horizontal distance from P to the point $Q(a^2/c, y)$ on line L is $PQ = |a^2/c - x|$. The distance to the focus $(c, 0)$ is $PF = \sqrt{(x - c)^2 + y^2} = \sqrt{x^2 - 2cx + c^2 + y^2}$. To confirm that $PF/PQ = c/a$, cross-multiply to get $a\,PF = c\,PQ$; we need to confirm that $a\sqrt{x^2 - 2cx + c^2 + y^2} = |a^2 - cx|$. Square both sides: $a^2(x^2 - 2cx + c^2 + y^2) = a^4 - 2a^2cx + c^2x^2$. Substitute $a^2 + b^2$ for c^2, multiply out both sides, and cancel out terms, leaving $a^2y^2 + a^2b^2 = b^2x^2$. Since P is on the hyperbola, $x^2/a^2 - y^2/b^2 = 1$, or equivalent $b^2x^2 - a^2y^2 = a^2b^2$; this confirms the equality.

(b) According to the polar definition, the eccentricity is the ratio PF/PQ, which we found to be c/a in (a).

(c) Since $e = c/a$, $a/e = \dfrac{a}{c/a} = a^2/c$ and $ae = c$; the distance from F to L is $c - \dfrac{a^2}{c} = ea - \dfrac{a}{e}$ as desired.

■ Section 8.6 Three-Dimensional Cartesian Coordinates

Quick Review 8.6

1. $\sqrt{(x - 2)^2 + (y + 3)^2}$

2. $\left(\dfrac{x + 2}{2}, \dfrac{y - 3}{2}\right)$

3. P lies on the circle of radius 5 centered at $(2, -3)$

4. $|\mathbf{v}| = \sqrt{(-4)^2 + (5)^2} = \sqrt{41}$

5. $\dfrac{\mathbf{v}}{|\mathbf{v}|} = \dfrac{\langle -4, 5 \rangle}{\sqrt{41}} = \left\langle \dfrac{-4}{\sqrt{41}}, \dfrac{5}{\sqrt{41}} \right\rangle$

6. $\dfrac{-7 \cdot \mathbf{v}}{|\mathbf{v}|} = \dfrac{\langle 28, -35 \rangle}{\sqrt{41}} = \left\langle \dfrac{28}{\sqrt{41}}, \dfrac{-35}{\sqrt{41}} \right\rangle$

7. Circle of radius 5 centered at $(-1, 5)$

8. A line of slope -2, passing through $(2, -4)$

9. $(x + 1)^2 + (y - 3)^2 = 4$. Center: $(-1, 3)$, radius: 2

10. $\langle -1 - 2, -4 - 5 \rangle, = \langle -3, -9 \rangle$

Section 8.6 Exercises

1.

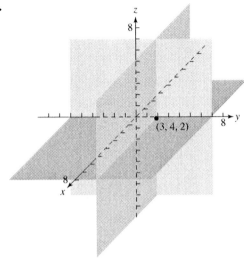

2.

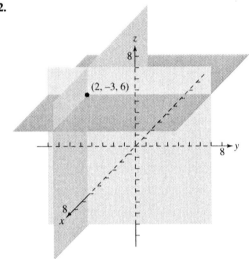

3.

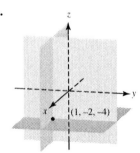

4.

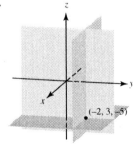

5. $\sqrt{(3 - (-1))^2 + (-4 - 2)^2 + (6 - 5)^2} = \sqrt{53}$

6. $\sqrt{(6 - 2)^2 + (-3 - (-1))^2 + (4 - (-8))^2} = 2\sqrt{41}$

7. $\sqrt{(a - 1)^2 + (b - (-3))^2 + (c - 2)^2}$
$= \sqrt{(a - 1)^2 + (b + 3)^2 + (c - 2)^2}$

8. $\sqrt{(x - p)^2 + (y - q)^2 + (z - r)^2}$

9. $\left(\dfrac{3 - 1}{2}, \dfrac{-4 + 2}{2}, \dfrac{6 + 5}{2}\right) = \left(1, -1, \dfrac{11}{2}\right)$

10. $\left(\dfrac{2 + 6}{2}, \dfrac{-1 - 3}{2}, \dfrac{-8 + 4}{2}\right) = (4, -2, -2)$

11. $\left(\dfrac{2x - 2}{2}, \dfrac{2y + 8}{2}, \dfrac{2z + 6}{2}\right) = (x - 1, y + 4, z + 3)$

12. $\left(\dfrac{3a - a}{2}, \dfrac{3b - b}{2}, \dfrac{3c - c}{2}\right) = (a, b, c)$

13. $(x - 5)^2 + (y + 1)^2 + (z + 2)^2 = 64$

14. $(x + 1)^2 + (y - 5)^2 + (z - 8)^2 = 5$

15. $(x - 1)^2 + (y + 3)^2 + (z - 2)^2 = a$

16. $(x - p)^2 + (y - q)^2 + (z - r)^2 = 36$

17.

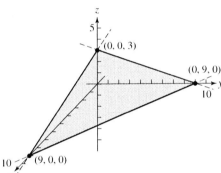

18.

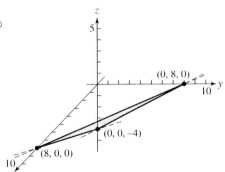

19.

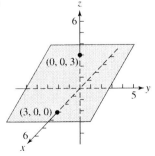

20.

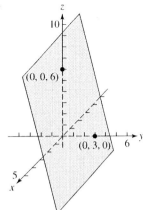

21.

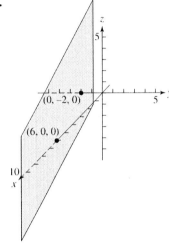

22.

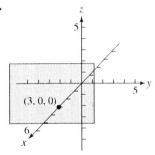

23. $\mathbf{r} + \mathbf{v} = \langle 1, 0, -3\rangle + \langle -3, 4, -5\rangle = \langle -2, 4, -8\rangle$

24. $\mathbf{r} - \mathbf{w} = \langle 1, 0, -3\rangle - \langle 4, -3, 12\rangle = \langle -3, 3, -15\rangle$

25. $\mathbf{v} \cdot \mathbf{w} = -12 - 12 - 60 = -84$

26. $|\mathbf{w}| = \sqrt{4^2 + (-3)^2 + 12^2} = 13$

27. $\mathbf{r} \cdot (\mathbf{v} + \mathbf{w}) = \mathbf{r} \cdot (\langle -3, 4, -5\rangle + \langle 4, -3, 12\rangle)$
$= \langle 1, 0, -3\rangle \cdot \langle 1, 1, 7\rangle = 1 + 0 - 21 = -20$

28. $\mathbf{r} \cdot \mathbf{v} + \mathbf{r} \cdot \mathbf{w} = (-3 + 0 + 15) + (4 + 0 - 36) = -20$

29. $\dfrac{\mathbf{w}}{|\mathbf{w}|} = \dfrac{\langle 4, -3, 12\rangle}{\sqrt{4^2 + (-3)^2 + 12^2}} = \left\langle \dfrac{4}{13}, -\dfrac{3}{13}, \dfrac{12}{13}\right\rangle$

30. $\mathbf{i} \cdot \mathbf{r} = \langle 1, 0, 0\rangle \cdot \langle 1, 0, -3\rangle = 1$

31. $\langle \mathbf{i} \cdot \mathbf{v}, \mathbf{j} \cdot \mathbf{v}, \mathbf{k} \cdot \mathbf{v}\rangle = \langle -3, 4, -5\rangle$

32. $(\mathbf{r} \cdot \mathbf{v})\mathbf{w} = (\langle 1, 0, -3\rangle \cdot \langle -3, 4, -5\rangle)\langle 4, -3, 12\rangle$
$= (-3 + 0 + 15)\langle 4, -3, 12\rangle = \langle 48, -36, 144\rangle$

33. The plane's velocity relative to the air is
$\mathbf{v}_1 = -200 \cos 20° \, \mathbf{i} + 200 \sin 20° \, \mathbf{k}$

The air's velocity relative to the ground is
$\mathbf{v}_2 = -10 \cos 45° \, \mathbf{i} - 10 \sin 45° \, \mathbf{j}$

Adding these two vectors and converting to decimal values rounded to two places produces the plane's velocity relative to the ground:
$\mathbf{v} = -195.01 \, \mathbf{i} - 7.07 \, \mathbf{j} + 68.40 \, \mathbf{k}$

34. The rocket's velocity relative to the air is
$\mathbf{v}_1 = 12{,}000 \cos 80° \, \mathbf{i} + 12{,}000 \sin 80° \, \mathbf{k}$

The air's velocity relative to the ground is
$\mathbf{v}_2 = 8 \cos 45° \, \mathbf{i} + 8 \sin 45° \, \mathbf{j}$

Adding these two vectors and converting to decimal values rounded to two places produces the rocket's velocity relative to the ground:
$\mathbf{v} = 2089.43 \, \mathbf{i} + 5.66 \, \mathbf{j} + 11{,}817.69 \, \mathbf{k}$

For #35–38, the vector form is $\mathbf{r}_0 + t\mathbf{v}$ with $\mathbf{r}_0\langle x_0, y_0, z_0 \rangle$, and the parametric form is $x = x_0 + ta$, $y = y_0 + tb$, $z = z_0 + tc$ where $\mathbf{v} = \langle a, b, c \rangle$.

35. Vector form: $\mathbf{r} = \langle 2, -1, 5 \rangle + t\langle 3, 2, -7 \rangle$; parametric form: $x = 2 + 3t$, $y = -1 + 2t$, $z = 5 - 7t$

36. Vector form: $\mathbf{r} = \langle -3, 8, -1 \rangle + t\langle -3, 5, 2 \rangle$; parametric form: $x = -3 - 3t$, $y = 8 + 5t$, $t = -1 + 2t$

37. Vector form: $\mathbf{r} = \langle 6, -9, 0 \rangle + t\langle 1, 0, -4 \rangle$; parametric form: $x = 6 + t$, $y = -9$, $z = -4t$

38. Vector form: $\mathbf{r} = \langle 0, -1, 4 \rangle + t\langle 0, 0, 1 \rangle$; parametric form: $x = 0$, $y = -1$, $z = 4 + t$

39. Midpoint of $\overline{BC}$: $\langle 1, 1, -1 \rangle$. Distance from A to midpoint of $\overline{BC}$:
$$\sqrt{(-1 - 1)^2 + (2 - 1)^2 + (4 - (-1))^2} = \sqrt{30}$$

40. $\langle 1 - (-1), 1 - 2, -1 - 4 \rangle = \langle 2, -1, -5 \rangle$

41. Direction vector: $\langle 0 - (-1), 6 - 2, -3 - 4 \rangle$
$= \langle 1, 4, -7 \rangle$, $\overrightarrow{OA} = \langle -1, 2, 4 \rangle$,
$\mathbf{r} = \langle -1, 2, 4 \rangle + t\langle 1, 4, -7 \rangle$

42. Direction vector: $\langle 2, -1, -5 \rangle$ (from #34). The vector equation of the line is $\mathbf{r} = \langle -1, 2, 4 \rangle + t\langle 2, -1, -5 \rangle$.

43. Direction vector: $\langle 2 - (-1), -4 - 2, 1 - 4 \rangle$
$= \langle 3, -6, -3 \rangle$, $\overrightarrow{OA} = \langle -1, 2, 4 \rangle$, so a vector equation of the line is $\mathbf{r} = \langle -1, 2, 4 \rangle + t\langle 3, -6, -3 \rangle$
$= \langle -1 + 3t, 2 - 6t, 4 - 3t \rangle$. This can be expressed in parametric form: $x = -1 + 3t$, $y = 2 - 6t$, $z = 4 - 3t$.

44. Direction vector: $\langle 2 - 0, -4 - 6, 1 - (-3) \rangle$
$= \langle 2, -10, 4 \rangle$, $\overrightarrow{OB} = \langle 0, 6, -3 \rangle$ so a vector equation of the line is $\mathbf{r} = \langle 0, 6, -3 \rangle + t\langle 2, -10, 4 \rangle$
$= \langle 2t, 6 - 10t, -3 + 4t \rangle$. This can be expressed in parametric form: $x = 2t$, $y = 6 - 10t$, $z = -3 + 4t$.

45. Midpoint of $\overline{AC}$: $\left(\dfrac{1}{2}, -1, \dfrac{5}{2} \right)$. Direction vector:

$\left\langle \dfrac{1}{2} - 0, -1 - 6, \dfrac{5}{2} - (-3) \right\rangle = \left\langle \dfrac{1}{2}, -7, \dfrac{11}{2} \right\rangle$,

$\overrightarrow{OB} = \langle 0, 6, -3 \rangle$, so a vector equation of the line is

$\mathbf{r} = \langle 0, 6, -3 \rangle + t\left\langle \dfrac{1}{2}, -7, \dfrac{11}{2} \right\rangle$

$= \left\langle \dfrac{1}{2} t, 6 - 7t, -3 + \dfrac{11}{2} t \right\rangle$. This can be expressed in

parametric form: $x = \dfrac{1}{2} t$, $y = 6 - 7t$, $z = -3 + \dfrac{11}{2} t$.

46. Midpoint of $\overline{AB}$: $\left(-\dfrac{1}{2}, 4, \dfrac{1}{2} \right)$. Direction vector:

$\left\langle -\dfrac{1}{2} - 2, 4 - (-4), \dfrac{1}{2} - 1 \right\rangle = \left\langle -\dfrac{5}{2}, 8, -\dfrac{1}{2} \right\rangle$,

$\overrightarrow{OC} = \langle 2, -4, 1 \rangle$, so a vector equation of the line is

$\mathbf{r} = \langle 2, -4, 1 \rangle + t\left\langle -\dfrac{5}{2}, 8, -\dfrac{1}{2} \right\rangle$

$= \left\langle 2 - \dfrac{5}{2} t, -4 + 8t, 1 - \dfrac{1}{2} t \right\rangle$. This can be expressed in

parametric form: $x = 2 - \dfrac{5}{2} t$, $y = -4 + 8t$, $z = 1 - \dfrac{1}{2} t$.

47. The length of $\overline{AB} =$
$\sqrt{(0 - (-1))^2 + (6 - 2)^2 + (-3 - 4)^2} = \sqrt{66}$; the
length of $\overline{BC} =$
$\sqrt{(2 - 0)^2 + (-4 - 6)^2 + (1 - (-3))^2} = 2\sqrt{30}$; the
length of $\overline{AC} =$
$\sqrt{(2 - (-1))^2 + (-4 - 2)^2 + (1 - 4)^2} = \sqrt{54}$. The
triangle ABC is scalene.

48. $M = (1, 1, -1)$ (from #33). The midpoint of
$\overline{AM} = \left(0, \dfrac{3}{2}, \dfrac{3}{2} \right)$

49. (a)

(b) the z-axis; a line through the origin in the direction $\mathbf{k}$.

50. (a)

(b) the intersection of the yz plane (at $x = 0$) and xy plane (at $z = 2$); a line parallel to the y-axis through $(0, 0, 2)$

51. (a)

(b) the intersection of the xz plane (at $y = 0$) and yz plane (at $x = -3$); a line parallel to the z-axis through $(-3, 0, 0)$

52. (a)

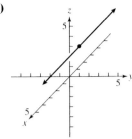

(b) the intersection of the xz plane (at $y = 1$) and xy plane (at $z = 3$); a line through $(0, 1, 3)$ parallel to the x-axis

53. Direction vector: $\langle x_2 - x_1, y_2 - y_1, z_2 - z_1 \rangle$,
$\overrightarrow{OP} = \langle x_1, y_2, z_3 \rangle$, so a vector equation of the line is
$\mathbf{r} = \langle x_1 + (x_2 - x_1)t, y_1 + (y_2 - y_1)t, z_1 + (z_2 - z_1)t \rangle$.

54. Using the result from Exercise 49, the parametric equations are $x = x_1 + (x_2 - x_1)t$, $y = y_1 + (y_2 - y_1)t$, $z = z_1 + (z_2 - z_1)t$.

55.

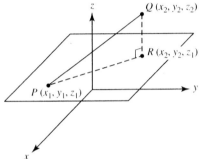

By the Pythagorean Theorem,
$d(P, Q) = \sqrt{(d(P, R))^2 + (d(R, Q))^2}$

$= \sqrt{(\sqrt{(x_1 - x_2)^2 + (y_1 - y_2)^2})^2 + (|z_1 - z_2|)^2}$

$= \sqrt{(x_1 - x_2)^2 + (y_1 - y_2)^2 + (z_1 - z_2)^2}$

56. Let $\mathbf{u} = \langle x_1, y_1, z_1 \rangle$. Then
$\mathbf{u} \cdot \mathbf{u} = x_1^2 + y_1^2 + z_1^2$
$= (\sqrt{x_1^2 + y_1^2 + z_1^2})^2$
$= |\mathbf{u}|^2$

57. True. This is the equation of a vertical elliptic cylinder. The equation can be viewed as an equation in three variables, where the coefficient of z is zero.

58. False. Because the coefficient of t is always 0, the equations simplify to $x = 1$, $y = 2$, $z = -5$; these represent the point $(1, 2, -5)$.

59. The general form for a first-degree equation in three variables is $Ax + By + Cz + D = 0$. The answer is B.

60. The equation for a plane is first-degree, or linear; there are no squared terms. The answer is A.

61. The dot product of two vectors is a scalar. The answer is C.

62. The conversion to parametric form begins with $x = 2 + 1t$, $y = -3 + 0t$, $z = 0 - 1t$. The answer is E.

63. (a) Each cross-section is its own ellipse.

$x = 0$: $\dfrac{y^2}{4} + \dfrac{z^2}{16} = 1$, an ellipse centered at $(0, 0)$

(in the yz plane) of "width" 4 and "height" 8.

$y = 0$: $\dfrac{x^2}{9} + \dfrac{z^2}{16} = 1$, an ellipse centered at $(0, 0)$

(in the xz plane) of "width" 6 and "height" 8.

$z = 0$: $\dfrac{x^2}{9} + \dfrac{y^2}{4} = 1$, an ellipse centered at $(0, 0)$

(in the xy plane) of "width" 6 and "height" 4.

(b) Algebraically, $z = \sqrt{1 - x^2 - y^2}$ has only positive values; $0 \le z \le 1$ and the "bottom" half of the sphere is never formed. The equation of the whole sphere is $x^2 + y^2 + z^2 = 1$.

(c)

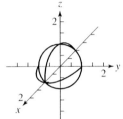

(d) A sphere is an ellipsoid in which all of the $x = 0$, $y = 0$, and $z = 0$ "slices" (i.e., the cross-sections of the coordinate planes) are circles. Since a circle is a degenerate ellipse, it follows that a sphere is a degenerate ellipsoid.

64. (a) Since $\mathbf{i}$ points east and $\mathbf{j}$ points north, we determine that the compass bearing θ is

$0 = 90° - \tan^{-1}\left(\dfrac{22.63}{193.88}\right) \approx 90 - 6.66 = 83.34°$.

(Recall that $\tan \theta$ refers to the x-axis (east) being located at $0°$; if the y-axis (north) is $0°$, we must adjust our calculations accordingly.)

(b) The speed along the ground is
$\sqrt{(193.88)^2 + (22.63)^2} \approx 195.2$ mph

(c) The tangent of the climb angle is the vertical speed divided by the horizontal speed, so
$\theta \approx \tan^{-1} \dfrac{125}{195.2}$

$\approx 32.63°$

(d) The overall speed is
$\sqrt{(193.88)^2 + (22.63)^2 + (125)^2} \approx 231.8$ mph

65. $\langle 2 - 3, -6 + 1, 1 - 4 \rangle = \langle -1, -5, -3 \rangle$

66. $\langle -2 + 6, 2 - 8, -12 + 1 \rangle = \langle 4, -6, -11 \rangle$

67. $\mathbf{i} \times \mathbf{j} = \langle 1, 0, 0 \rangle \times \langle 0, 1, 0 \rangle = \langle 0 - 0, 0 - 0, 1 - 0 \rangle = \langle 0, 0, 1 \rangle = \mathbf{k}$

68. $\mathbf{u} \cdot (\mathbf{u} \times \mathbf{v}) =$

$\langle u_1, u_2, u_3 \rangle \cdot \langle u_2 v_3 - u_3 v_2, u_3 v_1 - u_1 v_3, u_1 v_2 - u_2 v_1 \rangle$

$= (u_1 u_2 v_3 - u_1 u_3 v_2) + (u_2 u_3 v_1 - u_1 u_2 v_3)$
$\quad + (u_1 u_3 v_2 - u_2 u_3 v_1)$

$= 0$

$\mathbf{v} \cdot (\mathbf{u} \times \mathbf{v}) =$

$\langle v_1, v_2, v_3 \rangle \cdot \langle u_2 v_3 - u_3 v_2, u_3 v_1 - u_1 v_3, u_1 v_2 - u_2 v_1 \rangle$

$= (u_2 v_1 v_3 - u_3 v_1 v_2) + (u_3 v_1 v_2 - u_1 v_2 v_3)$
$\quad + (u_1 v_2 v_3 - u_2 v_1 v_3)$

$= 0$

So the angles between $\mathbf{u}$ and $\mathbf{u} \times \mathbf{v}$, and $\mathbf{v}$ and $\mathbf{u} \times \mathbf{v}$, both have a cosine of zero by the theorem in Section 6.2. It follows that the angles both measure $90°$.

■ Chapter 8 Review

1. $h = 0, k = 0, 4p = 12$, so $p = 3$.
Vertex: $(0, 0)$, focus: $(3, 0)$, directrix: $x = -3$,
focal width: 12

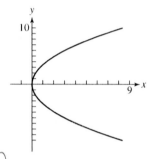

2. $h = 0, k = 0, 4p = -8$, so $p = -2$.
Vertex: $(0, 0)$, focus: $(0, -2)$, directrix: $y = 2$,
focal width: 8

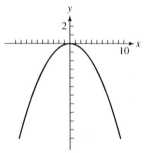

3. $h = -2, k = 1, 4p = -4$, so $p = -1$.
Vertex: $(-2, 1)$, focus: $(-2, 0)$, directrix: $y = 2$,
focal width: 4

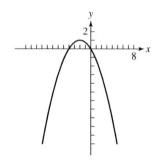

4. $h = 0, k = -2, 4p = 16$, so $p = 4$.
Vertex: $(0, -2)$, focus: $(4, -2)$, directrix: $x = -4$,
focal width: 16

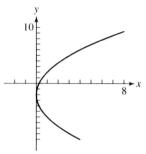

5. Ellipse. Center $(0, 0)$. Vertices: $(0, \pm 2\sqrt{2})$. Foci: $(0, \pm \sqrt{3})$ since $c = \sqrt{8 - 5} = \sqrt{3}$.

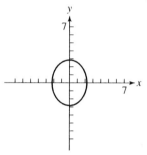

6. Hyperbola. Center: $(0, 0)$. Vertices: $(0, \pm 4)$.
Foci: $(0, \pm \sqrt{65})$ since $c = \sqrt{16 + 49} = \sqrt{65}$.

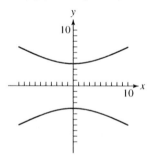

7. Hyperbola. Center: $(0, 0)$. Vertices: $(\pm 5, 0)$,
$c = \sqrt{a^2 + b^2} = \sqrt{25 + 36} = \sqrt{61}$, so the foci are:
$(\pm \sqrt{61}, 0)$

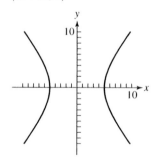

8. Hyperbola. Center: $(0, 0)$. Vertices: $(\pm 7, 0)$, $c = \sqrt{a^2 + 6^2} = \sqrt{49 + 9} = \sqrt{58}$, so the foci are: $(\pm\sqrt{58}, 0)$

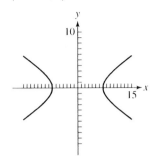

9. Hyperbola. Center: $(-3, 5)$. Vertices: $(-3 \pm 3\sqrt{2}, 5)$, $c = \sqrt{a^2 + b^2} = \sqrt{18 + 28} = \sqrt{46}$, so the foci are: $(-3 \pm \sqrt{46}, 5)$

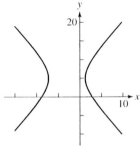

10. Hyperbola. Center: $(7, 3)$. Vertices: $(7, 3 \pm 3) = (7, 0)$ and $(7, 6)$, $c = \sqrt{a^2 + b^2} = \sqrt{9 + 12} = \sqrt{21}$, so the foci are: $(7, 3 \pm \sqrt{21})$

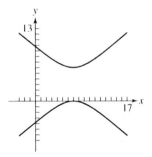

11. Ellipse. Center: $(2, -1)$. Vertices: $(2 \pm 4, -1) = (6, -1)$ and $(-2, -1)$, $c = \sqrt{a^2 - b^2} = \sqrt{16 - 7} = 3$, so the foci are: $(2 \pm 3, -1) = (5, -1)$ and $(-1, -1)$

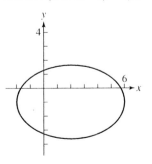

12. Ellipse. Center: $(-6, 0)$. Vertices: $(-6, \pm 6)$ $c = \sqrt{a^2 - b^2} = \sqrt{36 - 20} = 4$, so the foci are: $(-6, \pm 4)$

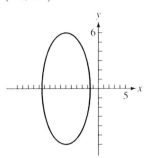

13. (b)

14. (g)

15. (h)

16. (e)

17. (f)

18. (d)

19. (c)

20. (a)

21. $B^2 - 4AC = 0 - 4(1)(0) = 0$, parabola $(x^2 - 6x + 9) = y + 3 + 9$, so $(x - 3)^2 = y + 12$

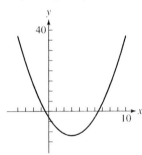

22. $B^2 - 4AC = 0 - 4(1)(3) = -12 < 0$, ellipse $(x^2 + 4x + 4) + 3y^2 = 5 + 4$, so $\dfrac{(x + 2)^2}{9} + \dfrac{y^2}{3} = 1$

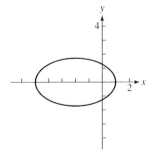

23. $B^2 - 4AC = 0 - 4(1)(-1) = 4 > 0$,
hyperbola $(x^2 - 2x + 1) - (y^2 - 4y + 4)$
$= 1 - 4 + 6$
$$\frac{(x - 1)^2}{3} - \frac{(y - 2)^2}{3} = 1$$

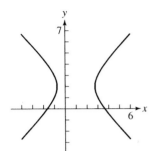

24. $B^2 - 4AC = 0 - 4(1)(0) = 0$,
parabola $(x^2 + 2x + 1) = -4y + 7 + 1$,
so $(x + 1)^2 = -4(y - 2)$

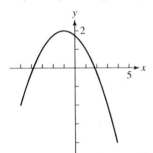

25. $B^2 - 4AC = 0 - 4(1)(0) = 0$,
parabola $(y^2 - 4y + 4) = 6x + 13 + 4$,
so $(y - 2)^2 = 6\left(x + \frac{17}{6}\right)$

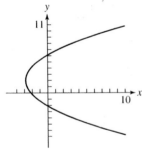

26. $B^2 - 4AC = 0 - 4(3)(0) = 0$,
parabola $3(x^2 - 2x + 1) = 4y + 9 + 3$,
so $(x - 1)^2 = \frac{4}{3}(y + 3)$

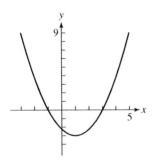

27. $B^2 - 4AC = 0 - 4(2)(-3) = 24 > 0$,
hyperbola $2(x^2 - 6x + 9) - 3(y^2 + 8y + 16)$
$= 18 - 48 - 60$, so
$$\frac{(y + 4)^2}{30} - \frac{(x - 3)^2}{45} = 1$$

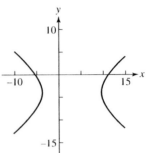

28. $B^2 - 4AC = 0 - 4(12)(-4) = 192 > 0$,
hyperbola $12(x^2 - 6x + 9) - 4(y^2 + 4y + 4)$
$= 108 - 16 - 44$, so
$$\frac{(x - 3)^2}{4} - \frac{(y + 2)^2}{12} = 1$$

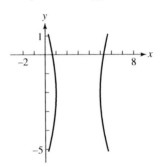

29. By definition, every point $P(x, y)$ that lies on the parabola is equidistant from the focus to the directrix. The distance between the focus and point P is:
$\sqrt{(x - 0)^2 + (y - p)^2} = \sqrt{x^2 + (y - p)^2}$, while the distance between the point P and the line $y = -p$ is:
$\sqrt{(x - x)^2 + (y + p)^2} = \sqrt{(y + p)^2}$. Setting these equal:
$$\sqrt{x^2 + (y - p)^2} = y + p$$
$$x^2 + (y - p)^2 = (y + p)^2$$
$$x^2 + y^2 - 2py + p^2 = y^2 + 2py + p^2$$
$$x^2 = 4py$$

30. Let the point $P(x, y)$ satisfy $y^2 = 4px$. Then we have
$$y^2 = 4px$$
$$x^2 - 2px + p^2 + y^2 = x^2 + 2px + p^2$$
$$(x - p)^2 + y^2 = (x + p)^2 + 0$$
$$(x - p)^2 + (y - 0)^2 = (x - (-p))^2 + (y - y)^2$$
$$\sqrt{(x - p)^2 + (y - 0)^2} = \sqrt{(x - (-p))^2 + (y - y)^2}$$
distance from $P(x, y)$ to $(p, 0)$ = distance from $P(x, y)$ to $x = -p$
Because $P(x, y)$ is equidistant from the point $(p, 0)$ and the line $x = -p$, by the definition of a parabola, $y^2 = 4px$ is the equation of a parabola with focus $(p, 0)$ and directrix $x = -p$.

31. Use the quadratic formula with $a = 6$, $b = -8x - 5$, and $c = 3x^2 - 5x + 20$. Then $b^2 - 4ac = (-8x - 5)^2 - 24(3x^2 - 5x + 20) = -8x^2 + 200x - 455$, and
$$y = \frac{1}{12}\left[8x + 5 \pm \sqrt{-8x^2 + 200x - 455}\right] - \text{an ellipse}$$

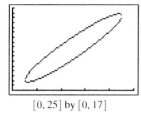

$[0, 25]$ by $[0, 17]$

32. Use the quadratic formula with $a = 6$, $b = -8x - 5$, and $c = 10x^2 + 8x - 30$. Then $b^2 - 4ac = (-8x - 5)^2 - 24(10x^2 + 8x - 30) = -176x^2 - 112x + 745$, and
$$y = \frac{1}{12}\left[8x + 5 \pm \sqrt{-176x^2 - 112x + 745}\right] \text{ an ellipse}$$

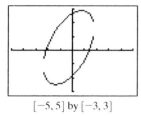

$[-5, 5]$ by $[-3, 3]$

33. This is a *linear* equation in y:
$(6 - 2x)y + (3x^2 - 5x - 10) = 0$. Subtract $3x^2 - 5x - 10$ and divide by $6 - 2x$, and we have
$$y = \frac{3x^2 - 5x - 10}{2x - 6} - \text{a hyperbola.}$$

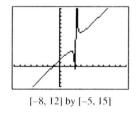

$[-8, 12]$ by $[-5, 15]$

34. Use the quadratic formula with $a = -6$, $b = 5x - 17$, and $c = 10x + 20$. Then $b^2 - 4ac = (5x - 17)^2 + 24(10x + 20) = 25x^2 + 70x + 769$, and
$$y = \frac{1}{12}\left[5x - 17 \pm \sqrt{25x^2 + 70x + 769}\right] \text{ a hyperbola.}$$

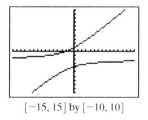

$[-15, 15]$ by $[-10, 10]$

35. Use the quadratic formula with $a = -2$, $b = 7x + 20$, and $c = -3x^2 - x - 15$. Then $b^2 - 4ac = (7x + 20)^2 + 8(-3x^2 - x - 15) = 25x^2 + 272x + 280$, and
$$y = \frac{1}{4}\left[7x + 20 \pm \sqrt{25x^2 + 272x + 280}\right] \text{ a hyperbola.}$$

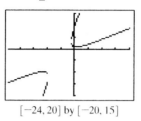

$[-24, 20]$ by $[-20, 15]$

36. Use the quadratic formula with $a = -2$, $b = 7x + 3$, and $c = -3x^2 - 2x - 10$. Then $b^2 - 4ac = (7x + 3)^2 + 8(-3x^2 - 2x - 10) = 25x^2 + 26x - 71$, and
$$y = \frac{1}{4}\left[7x + 3 \pm \sqrt{25x^2 + 26x - 71}\right] \text{ a hyperbola.}$$

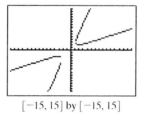

$[-15, 15]$ by $[-15, 15]$

37. $h = 0$, $k = 0$, $p = 2$, and the parabola opens to the right as $y^2 = 8x$.

38. $h = 0$, $k = 0$, $|4p| = 12$, and the parabola opens downward, so $x^2 = -12y$ ($p = -3$).

39. $h = -3$, $k = 3$, $p = k - y = 3 - 0 = 3$ (since $y = 0$ is the directrix) the parabola opens upward, so $(x + 3)^2 = 12(y - 3)$.

40. $h = 1$, $k = -2$, $p = 2$ (since the focal length is 2), and the parabola opens to the left, so $(y + 2)^2 = -8(x - 1)$.

41. $h = 0$, $k = 0$, $c = 12$ and $a = 13$, so $b = \sqrt{a^2 - c^2}$
$$= \sqrt{169 - 144} = 5. \frac{x^2}{169} + \frac{y^2}{25} = 1$$

42. $h = 0$, $k = 0$, $c = 2$ and $a = 6$, so $b = \sqrt{a^2 - c^2}$
$$= \sqrt{36 - 4} = 4\sqrt{2}. \frac{y^2}{36} + \frac{x^2}{32} = 1$$

43. $h = 0$, $k = 2$, $a = 3$, $c = 2 - h$ (so $c = 2$) and $b = \sqrt{a^2 - c^2} = \sqrt{9 - 4} = \sqrt{5}$
$$\frac{x^2}{9} + \frac{(y - 2)^2}{5} = 1$$

44. $h = -3$, $k = -4$, $a = 4$, $0 = -3 \pm c$, $c = 3$, $b = \sqrt{a^2 - c^2} = \sqrt{16 - 9} = \sqrt{7}$, so
$$\frac{(x + 3)^2}{16} + \frac{(y + 4)^2}{7} = 1$$

45. $h = 0$, $k = 0$, $c = 6$, $a = 5$, $b = \sqrt{c^2 - a^2} = \sqrt{36 - 25} = \sqrt{11}$, so
$$\frac{y^2}{25} - \frac{x^2}{11} = 1$$

46. $h = 0$, $k = 0$, $a = 2$, $\frac{b}{a} = 2$ ($b = 4$), so $\frac{x^2}{4} - \frac{y^2}{16} = 1$

47. $h = 2, k = 1, a = 3, \dfrac{b}{a} = \dfrac{4}{3}$ $(b = \dfrac{4}{3} \cdot 3 = 4)$, so

$$\frac{(x-2)^2}{9} - \frac{(y-1)^2}{16} = 1$$

48. $h = -5, k = 0, c - k = 3 \,(c = 3), a - k = 2 \,(a = 2),$
$b = \sqrt{c^2 - a^2} = \sqrt{9 - 4} = \sqrt{5}$, so

$$\frac{y^2}{4} - \frac{(x+5)^2}{5} = 1$$

49. $\dfrac{x}{5} = \cos t$ and $\dfrac{y}{2} = \sin t$, so $\dfrac{x^2}{25} + \dfrac{y^2}{4} = 1$ — an ellipse.

50. $\dfrac{x}{4} = \sin t$ and $\dfrac{y}{6} = \cos t$, so $\dfrac{x^2}{16} + \dfrac{y^2}{36} = 1$ — an ellipse.

51. $x + 2 = \cos t$ and $y - 4 = \sin t$, so
$(x + 2)^2 + (y - 4)^2 = 1$ — an ellipse (a circle).

52. $\dfrac{x - 5}{3} = \cos t$ and $\dfrac{y + 3}{3} = \sin t$, so
$\dfrac{(x-5)^2}{9} + \dfrac{(y+3)^2}{9} = 1$, or $(x - 5)^2 + (y + 3)^2 = 9$
— an ellipse (a circle).

53. $\dfrac{x}{3} = \sec t$ and $\dfrac{y}{5} = \tan t$, so $\dfrac{x^2}{9} - \dfrac{y^2}{25} = 1$ — a hyperbola.

54. $\dfrac{x}{4} = \sec t$ and $\dfrac{y}{3} = \tan t$, so $\dfrac{x^2}{16} - \dfrac{y^2}{9} = 1$ — a hyperbola.

55.

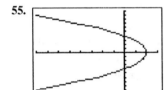

$[-8, 3]$ by $[-10, 10]$

Parabola with vertex at $(2, 0)$, so $h = 2, k = 0, e = 1$.

The graph crosses the y-axis, so $\left(4, \dfrac{\pi}{2}\right) = (0, 4)$ lies on the

parabola. Substituting $(0, 4)$ into $y^2 = 4p(x - 2)$ we have
$16 = 4p(-2)$, $p = -2$. $y^2 = -8(x - 2)$.

56.

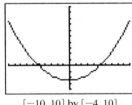

$[-10, 10]$ by $[-4, 10]$

$e = 1$, so a parabola. The vertex is $(h, k) = \left(0, -\dfrac{5}{2}\right)$ and

the point $(5, 0)$ lies on the curve. Substituting $(5, 0)$ into

$x^2 = 4p\left(y + \dfrac{5}{2}\right)$, we have $25 = 4p\left(\dfrac{5}{2}\right)$, $p = \dfrac{5}{2}$.

$x^2 = 10\left(y + \dfrac{5}{2}\right)$

57.

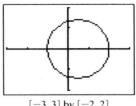

$[-3, 3]$ by $[-2, 2]$

$e = \dfrac{1}{3}$, so an ellipse. In polar coordinates the vertices are

$(2, 0)$ and $(1, \pi)$. Converting to Cartesian we have $(2, 0)$

and $(-1, 0)$, so $2a = 3, a = \dfrac{3}{2}, c = ea = \dfrac{1}{3} \cdot \dfrac{3}{2} = \dfrac{1}{2}$ and

the center $(h, k) = \left(2 - \dfrac{3}{2}, 0\right) = \left(\dfrac{1}{2}, 0\right)$ (since it's

symmetric about the polar x-axis). Solving for

$b = \sqrt{a^2 - c^2} = \sqrt{\left(\dfrac{3}{2}\right)^2 - \left(\dfrac{1}{2}\right)^2} = \sqrt{\dfrac{8}{4}} = \sqrt{2}$

$$\frac{4\left(x - \dfrac{1}{2}\right)^2}{9} + \frac{y^2}{2} = 1$$

58.

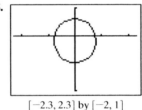

$[-2.3, 2.3]$ by $[-2, 1]$

$e = \dfrac{1}{4}$, so an ellipse. In polar coordinates the vertices are

$\left(\dfrac{3}{5}, \dfrac{\pi}{2}\right)$ and $\left(1, \dfrac{3\pi}{2}\right)$. Converting to Cartesian we have

$\left(0, \dfrac{3}{5}\right)$ and $(0, -1)$, so $2a = \dfrac{8}{5}, a = \dfrac{4}{5}, c = ea = \dfrac{1}{4} \cdot \dfrac{4}{5} = \dfrac{1}{5}$,

the center $(h, k) = \left(0, \dfrac{3}{5} - \dfrac{4}{5}\right) = \left(0, \dfrac{-1}{5}\right)$ (since it's

symmetric on the y-axis). Solving for

$b^2 = a^2 - c^2 = \left(\dfrac{4}{5}\right)^2 - \left(\dfrac{1}{5}\right)^2 = \dfrac{15}{25} = \dfrac{3}{5}$.

$$\frac{25\left(y + \dfrac{1}{5}\right)^2}{16} + \frac{5x^2}{3} = 1$$

59.

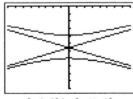

$[-8, 8]$ by $[-11, 0]$

$e = \dfrac{7}{2}$, so a hyperbola. In polar coordinates the vertices

are $\left(-7, \dfrac{\pi}{2}\right)$ and $\left(\dfrac{35}{9}, \dfrac{3\pi}{2}\right)$. Converting to Cartesian we

have $(0, -7)$ and $\left(0, \dfrac{-35}{9}\right)$, so $2a = \dfrac{28}{9}, a = \dfrac{14}{9}$,

$c = ea = \dfrac{7}{2} \cdot \dfrac{14}{9} = \dfrac{49}{9}$ the center (h, k)

$= \left(0, \dfrac{-35}{9} - \dfrac{14}{9}\right) = \left(0, \dfrac{-49}{9}\right)$ (since it's symmetric

on the y-axis). Solving for

$b = \sqrt{c^2 - a^2} = \sqrt{\left(\dfrac{49}{9}\right)^2 - \left(\dfrac{14}{9}\right)^2} = \dfrac{21\sqrt{5}}{9} = \dfrac{7\sqrt{5}}{3}$

$\dfrac{81\left(y + \dfrac{49}{9}\right)^2}{196} - \dfrac{9x^2}{245} = 1$

60.

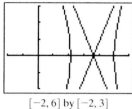

$[-2, 6]$ by $[-2, 3]$

$e = \dfrac{5}{2}$, so a hyperbola. In polar coordinates the vertices

are $\left(\dfrac{15}{7}, 0\right)$ and $(-5, \pi)$. Converting to Cartesian we

have $\left(\dfrac{15}{7}, 0\right)$ and $(5, 0)$, so $2a = \dfrac{20}{7}, a = \dfrac{10}{7}$,

$c = ea = \dfrac{5}{2} \cdot \dfrac{10}{7} = \dfrac{25}{7}$ the center (h, k)

$= \left(\dfrac{5 + 15/7}{2}, 0\right) = \left(\dfrac{25}{7}, 0\right)$ (since it's symmetric on

the y-axis). Solving for $b^2 = a^2 - c^2$

$= \left(\dfrac{25}{7}\right)^2 - \left(\dfrac{10}{7}\right)^2 = \dfrac{525}{49} = \dfrac{75}{7}$

$\dfrac{49\left(x - \dfrac{25}{7}\right)^2}{100} - \dfrac{7y^2}{75} = 1$

61.

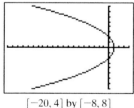

$[-20, 4]$ by $[-8, 8]$

$e = 1$, so a parabola. In polar coordinates, the vertex is

$(1, 0)$ and the parabola crosses the y-axis at $\left(2, \dfrac{\pi}{2}\right)$.

Converting to Cartesian form, we have the vertex
$(h, k) = (1, 0)$ and a point on the parabola is $(0, 2)$. Since
the parabola opens to the left, $y^2 = 4p(x - 1)$.
Substituting $(0, 2)$, we have $4 = -4p, p = -1$
$y^2 = -4(x - 1)$

62.

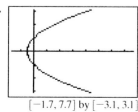

$[-1.7, 7.7]$ by $[-3.1, 3.1]$

$e = 1$, so this is a parabola. In polar coordinates, the vertex is $\left(\dfrac{1}{2}, \pi\right)$ and the parabola crosses the y-axis at

$\left(1, \dfrac{\pi}{2}\right)$. Converting to Cartesian form, we have the

vertex $(h, k) = \left(-\dfrac{1}{2}, 0\right)$ and a point on the parabola is

$(0, 1)$. Since the parabola opens to the right,

$y^2 = 4p\left(x + \dfrac{1}{2}\right)$. Substituting $(0, 1)$, we have $1 = 2p$,

$p = \dfrac{1}{2}. \; y^2 = 2\left(x + \dfrac{1}{2}\right)$

63. $\sqrt{(3 - (-1))^2 + (-2 - 0)^2 + (-4 - 3)^2}$
$= \sqrt{16 + 4 + 49} = \sqrt{69}$

64. $\left(\dfrac{3 - 1}{2}, \dfrac{-2 + 0}{2}, \dfrac{-4 + 3}{2}\right) = \left(1, -1, -\dfrac{1}{2}\right)$

65. $\mathbf{v} + \mathbf{w} = \langle -3, 1, -2 \rangle + \langle 3, -4, 0 \rangle = \langle 0, -3, -2 \rangle$

66. $\mathbf{v} - \mathbf{w} = \langle -3, 1, -2 \rangle - \langle 3, -4, 0 \rangle = \langle -6, 5, -2 \rangle$

67. $\mathbf{v} \cdot \mathbf{w} = \langle -3, 1, -2 \rangle \cdot \langle 3, -4, 0 \rangle = -9 - 4 + 0 = -13$

68. $|\mathbf{v}| = \sqrt{(-3)^2 + 1^2 + (-2)^2} = \sqrt{9 + 1 + 4} = \sqrt{14}$

69. $\dfrac{\mathbf{w}}{|\mathbf{w}|} = \dfrac{\langle 3, -4, 0 \rangle}{\sqrt{3^2 + (-4)^2 + 0^2}} = \left\langle \dfrac{3}{5}, -\dfrac{4}{5}, 0 \right\rangle$

70. $(\mathbf{v} \cdot \mathbf{w})(\mathbf{v} + \mathbf{w}) = -13 \langle 0, -3, -2 \rangle = \langle 0, 39, 26 \rangle$

71. $(x + 1)^2 + y^2 + (z - 3)^2 = 16$

72. The direction vector $\overrightarrow{PQ}$ is $\langle 3 - (-1), -2 - 0,$
$-4 - 3 \rangle = \langle 4, -2, -7 \rangle$. Since the line l through P in the
direction of $\overrightarrow{PQ}$ is $l = (-1, 0, 3) + t \,(4, -2, -7)$, the
parametric equations are: $x = -1 + 4t, y = -2t,$
$z = 3 - 7t$.

73. The direction vector is $\langle -3, 1, -2 \rangle$ so the vector equation
of a line in the direction of $\mathbf{v}$ through P is
$\mathbf{r} = \langle -1, 0, 3 \rangle + t \langle -3, 1 -2 \rangle$

74. The mid-point M of $\overrightarrow{PQ}$ is: $\left(1, -1, -\dfrac{1}{2}\right)$ (from Exercise

#64) so $\overrightarrow{OM} = \left\langle 1, -1, -\dfrac{1}{2} \right\rangle$. The direction vector is

$\mathbf{w} = \langle 3, -4, 0 \rangle$, so a vector equation of the line is

$\mathbf{v} = \left\langle 1 + 3t, -1 - 4t, -\dfrac{1}{2} \right\rangle$. This can be expresses in

parametric form: $x = 1 + 3t, y = -1 - 4t, z = -\dfrac{1}{2}$.

75. $4p = 18$, so $p = 4.5$; the focus is at $(0, 4.5)$.

76. $4p = 15$, so $p = 3.75$; the focus is at $(3.75, 0)$.

77. (a) The "shark" should aim for the other spot on the
table, since a ball that passes through one focus will
end up passing through the other focus if nothing gets
in the way.

(b) Let $a = 3, b = 2,$ and $c = \sqrt{5}$. Then the foci are at
$(-\sqrt{5}, 0)$ and $(\sqrt{5}, 0)$. These are the points at which
to aim.

78. The total radius of the orbit is $r = 0.500 + 6380 = 6380.5$ km, or 6,380,500 m.

    (a) $v = 7908$ m/sec $= 7.908$ km/sec

    (b) The circumference of the one orbit is $2\pi r \approx 40,090$ km; one orbit therefore takes about 5070 seconds, or about 1 hr 25 min.

79. The major axis length is 18,000 km, plus 170 km, plus the diameter of the earth, so $a \approx 15,465$ km $= 15,465,000$ m. At apogee, $r = 18,000 + 6380 = 24,380$ km, so $v \approx 2633$ m/sec. At perigee, $r = 6380 + 170 = 6550$ km, so $v \approx 9800$ m/sec.

80. Kepler's third law: $T^2 = a^3$, T is in Earth years and a is in AU.

$$a = T^{2/3} = \left(\frac{409 \text{ days}}{365.2 \text{ days/year}} \right)^{2/3} \approx 1.08 \text{ AU} = 161 \text{ Gm}$$

$c = ae = (161 \text{ Gm})(0.83) \approx 134$ Gm
perihelion: $a - c = 161$ Gm $- 134$ Gm $= 27$ Gm
aphelion: $a + c = 161$ Gm $+ 134$ Gm $= 295$ Gm

Chapter 8 Project

Answers are based on the sample data provided in the table.

1.
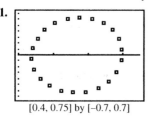

[0.4, 0.75] by [−0.7, 0.7]

2. The endpoints of the major and minor axes lie at approximately $(0.438, 0)$, $(0.700, 0)$, $(0.569, 0.640)$ and $(0.569, -0.640)$. The ellipse is taller than it is wide, even though the reverse appears to be true on the graphing calculator screen. The semimajor axis length is 0.640, and the semiminor axis length is $(0.700 - 0.438)/2 = 0.131$. The equation is

$$\frac{(y - 0)^2}{(0.640)^2} + \frac{(x - 0.569)^2}{(0.131)^2} = 1$$

3. With respect to the graph of the ellipse, the point (h, k) represents the center of the ellipse. The value a is the length of the semimajor axis, and b is the length of the semiminor axis.

4. Physically, $h = 0.569$ m is the pendulum's average distance from the CBR, and $k = 0$ m/sec is the pendulum's average velocity. The value $a = 0.64$ m/sec is the maximum velocity, and $b = 0.131$ m is the maximum displacement of the pendulum from its average position.

5. The parametric equations for the sample data set (using sinusoidal regression) are
$x_{1T} \approx 0.131 \sin(4.80T + 2.10) + 0.569$ and
$y_{1T} \approx 0.639 \sin(4.80T - 2.65)$.

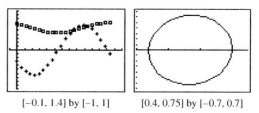

[−0.1, 1.4] by [−1, 1]   [0.4, 0.75] by [−0.7, 0.7]

Chapter 9
Discrete Mathematics

■ Section 9.1 Basic Combinatorics

Exploration 1

1. Six: ABC, ACB, BAC, BCA, CAB, CBA.

2. Approximately 1 person out of 6, which would mean 10 people out of 60.

3. No. If they all looked the same, we would expect approximately 10 people to get the order right simply by chance. The fact that this did not happen leads us to reject the "look-alike" conclusion.

4. It is likely that the salesman rigged the test to mislead the office workers. He might have put the copy from the more expensive machine on high-quality bond paper to make it look more like an original, or he might have put a tiny ink smudge on the original to make it look like a copy. You can offer your own alternate scenarios.

Quick Review 9.1

1. 52
2. 13
3. 6
4. 11
5. 10
6. 4
7. 11
8. 4
9. 64
10. 13

Section 9.1 Exercises

1. There are three possibilities for who stands on the left, and then two remaining possibilities for who stands in the middle, and then one remaining possibility for who stands on the right: $3 \cdot 2 \cdot 1 = 6$.

2. Any of the four jobs could be ranked most important, and then any of the remaining three jobs could be ranked second, and so on: $4 \cdot 3 \cdot 2 \cdot 1 = 24$.

3. Any of the five books could be placed on the left, and then any of the four remaining books could be placed next to it, and so on: $5 \cdot 4 \cdot 3 \cdot 2 \cdot 1 = 120$.

4. Any of the five dogs could be awarded 1st place, and then any of the remaining four dogs could be awarded 2nd place, and so on: $5 \cdot 4 \cdot 3 \cdot 2 \cdot 1 = 120$.

5. There are $3 \cdot 4 = 12$ possible pairs: K_1Q_1, K_1Q_2, K_1Q_3, K_1Q_4, K_2Q_1, K_2Q_2, K_2Q_3, K_2Q_4, K_3Q_1, K_3Q_2, K_3Q_3, and K_3Q_4.

6. There are $3 \cdot 4 = 12$ possible routes. In the tree diagram, B_1 represents the first road from town A to town B, etc.

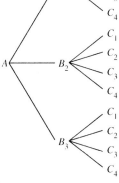

7. $9! = 362,880$ (ALGORITHM)

8. $22 \cdot 21 \cdot 20 = 9240$

9. There are 11 letters, where S and I each appear 4 times and P appears 2 times. The number of distinguishable permutations is
$$\frac{11!}{4!4!2!} = 34,650.$$

10. There are 11 letters, where A appears 3 times and O and T each appear 2 times. The number of distinguishable permutations is
$$\frac{11!}{3!2!2!} = 1,663,200.$$

11. The number of ways to fill 3 distinguishable offices from a pool of 13 candidates is $_{13}P_3 = \dfrac{13!}{10!} = 1716$.

12. The number of ways to select and prioritize 6 out of 12 projects is $_{12}P_6 = \dfrac{12!}{6!} = 665,280$.

13. $4 \cdot 3 \cdot 2 \cdot 1 = 24$

14. $(3 \cdot 2 \cdot 1)(1) = 6$

15. $\dfrac{6!}{(6-2)!} = \dfrac{6 \cdot 5 \cdot 4!}{4!} = 30$

16. $\dfrac{9!}{(9-2)!} = \dfrac{9 \cdot 8 \cdot 7!}{7!} = 72$

17. $\dfrac{10!}{7!(10-7)!} = \dfrac{10 \cdot 9 \cdot 8 \cdot 7!}{7! \cdot 3 \cdot 2 \cdot 1} = 120$

18. $\dfrac{10!}{3!(10-3)!} = \dfrac{10 \cdot 9 \cdot 8 \cdot 7!}{3! \cdot 7!} = \dfrac{10 \cdot 9 \cdot 8}{3 \cdot 2 \cdot 1} = 120$

19. combinations

20. permutations

21. combinations

22. permutations (different roles)

23. There are 10 choices for the first character, 9 for the second, 26 for the third, then 25, then 8, then 7, then 6: $10 \cdot 9 \cdot 26 \cdot 25 \cdot 8 \cdot 7 \cdot 6 = 19,656,000$.

24. There are 36 choices for each character: $36^5 = 60,466,176$.

25. There are 6 possibilities for the red die, and 6 for the green die: $6 \cdot 6 = 36$.

26. There are 2 possibilities for each flip: $2^{10} = 1024$.

27. $_{25}C_3 = \dfrac{25!}{3!(25-3)!} = \dfrac{25!}{3!22!} = 2300$

28. $_{52}C_5 = \dfrac{52!}{5!(52-5)!} = \dfrac{52!}{5!47!} = 2{,}598{,}960$

29. $_{48}C_3 = \dfrac{48!}{3!(48-3)!} = \dfrac{48!}{3!45!} = 17{,}296$

30. Choose 7 positions from the 20:

$_{20}C_7 = \dfrac{20!}{7!(20-7)!} = \dfrac{20!}{7!13!} = 77{,}520$

31. Choose A♠ and K♠, and 11 cards from the other 50:

$_2C_2 \cdot {}_{50}C_{11} = 1 \cdot {}_{50}C_{11} = \dfrac{50!}{11!(50-11)!} = \dfrac{50!}{11!39!}$

$\qquad = 37{,}353{,}738{,}800$

32. $_8C_3 = \dfrac{8!}{3!(8-3)!} = \dfrac{8!}{3!5!} = 56$

33. We either have 3, 2, or 1 student(s) nominated:
$_6C_3 + {}_6C_2 + {}_6C_1 = 20 + 15 + 6 = 41$

34. We either have 3, 2, or 1 appetizer(s) represented:
$_5C_3 + {}_5C_2 + {}_5C_1 = 10 + 10 + 5 = 25$

35. Each of the 5 dice have 6 possible outcomes: $6^5 = 7776$

36. $_{20}C_8 = \dfrac{20!}{8!(20-8)!} = \dfrac{20!}{8!12!} = 125{,}970$

37. $2^9 - 1 = 511$

38. $3 \times 4 \times 3 \times 2^6 = 2304$

39. Since each topping can be included or left off, the total number of possibilities with n toppings is 2^n. Since $2^{11} = 2048$ is less than 4000 but $2^{12} = 4096$ is greater than 4000, Luigi offers at least 12 toppings.

40. There are 2^n subsets, of which $2^n - 2$ are proper subsets.

41. $2^{10} = 1024$

42. $5^{10} = 9{,}765{,}625$

43. True. $\dbinom{n}{a} = \dfrac{n!}{a!(n-a)!} = \dfrac{n!}{a!b!} = \dfrac{n!}{(n-b)!b!} = \dbinom{n}{b}$

44. False. For example, $\dbinom{5}{2} = 10$ is greater than $\dbinom{5}{4} = 5$.

45. There are $\dbinom{6}{2} = 15$ different combinations of vegetables. The total number of entreé-vegetable-dessert variations is $4 \cdot 15 \cdot 6 = 360$. The answer is D.

46. $_{10}P_5 = 30{,}240$. The answer is D.

47. $_nP_n = \dfrac{n!}{(n-n)!} = n!$ The answer is B.

48. There are as many ways to vote as there are subsets of a set with 5 members. That is, there are 2^5 ways to fill out the ballot. The answer is C.

49. Answers will vary. Here are some possible answers:

(a) Number of 3-card hands that can be dealt from a deck of 52 cards

(b) Number of ways to choose 3 chocolates from a box of 12 chocolates

(c) Number of ways to choose a starting soccer team from a roster of 25 players (where position matters)

(d) Number of 5-digit numbers that can be formed using only the digits 1 and 2

(e) Number of possible pizzas that can be ordered at a place that offers 3 different sizes and up to 10 different toppings.

50. Counting the number of ways to choose the 2 eggs you are going to have for breakfast is equivalent to counting the number of ways to choose the ten eggs you are *not* going to have for breakfast.

51. (a) Twelve

(b) Every 0 represents a factor of 10, or a factor of 5 multiplied by a factor of 2. In the product $50 \cdot 49 \cdot 48 \cdot \ldots \cdot 2 \cdot 1$, the factors 5, 10, 15, 20, 30, 35, 40, and 45 each contain 5 as a factor once, and 25 and 50 each contain 5 twice, for a total of twelve occurrences. Since there are 47 factors of 2 to pair up with the twelve factors of 5, 10 is a factor of 50! twelve times.

52. (a) Each combination of the n vertices taken 2 at a time determines a segment that is either an edge or a diagonal. There are $_nC_2$ such combinations.

(b) Subtracting the n edges from the answers in (a),

we find that $_nC_2 - n = \dfrac{n!}{2!(n-2)!} - n$

$\qquad\qquad\qquad = \dfrac{n(n-1)}{2} - \dfrac{2n}{2} = \dfrac{n^2 - 3n}{2}.$

53. In the nth week, 5^n copies of the letter are sent. In the last week of the year, that's $5^{52} \approx 2.22 \times 10^{36}$ copies of the letter. This exceeds the population of the world, which is about 6×10^9, so someone (several people, actually) has had to receive a second copy of the letter.

54. Six. No matter where the first person sits, there are the $3! = 6$ ways to sit the others in different positions relative to the first person.

55. Three. This is equivalent to the round table problem (Exercise 42), except that the necklace can be *turned upside-down*. Thus, each different necklace accounts for two of the six different orderings.

56. The chart on the left is more reasonable. Each pair of actresses will require about the same amount of time to interview. If we make a chart showing n (the number of actresses) and $_nC_2$ (the number of pairings), we can see that chart 1 allows approximately 3 minutes per pair throughout, while chart 2 allows less and less time per pair as n gets larger.

Number n	Number of pairs $_nC_2$	Time per Pair Chart 1	Time per Pair Chart 2
3	3	3.33	3.33
6	15	3	2
9	36	3.06	1.67
12	66	3.03	1.52
15	105	3.05	1.43

57. There are $_{52}C_{13} = 635{,}013{,}559{,}600$ distinct bridge hands. Every day has $60 \cdot 60 \cdot 24 = 86{,}400$ seconds; a year has 365.24 days, which is $31{,}556{,}736$ seconds. Therefore it will take about $\dfrac{635{,}013{,}559{,}600}{31{,}556{,}736} \approx 20{,}123$ years. (Using 365 days per year, the computation gives about 20,136 years.)

58. Each team can choose 5 players in $_{12}C_5 = 792$ ways, so there are $792^2 = 627{,}264$ ways total.

■ Section 9.2 The Binomial Theorem

Exploration 1

1. $_3C_0 = \dfrac{3!}{0!3!} = 1$, $_3C_1 = \dfrac{3!}{1!2!} = 3$,

$_3C_2 = \dfrac{3!}{2!1!} = 3$, $_3C_3 = \dfrac{3!}{3!0!} = 1$. These are (in order) the coefficients in the expansion of $(a + b)^3$.

2. $\{1\ 4\ 6\ 4\ 1\}$. These are (in order) the coefficients in the expansion of $(a + b)^4$.

3. $\{1\ 5\ 10\ 10\ 5\ 1\}$. These are (in order) the coefficients in the expansion of $(a + b)^5$.

Quick Review 9.2

1. $x^2 + 2xy + y^2$

2. $a^2 + 2ab + b^2$

3. $25x^2 - 10xy + y^2$

4. $a^2 - 6ab + 9b^2$

5. $9s^2 + 12st + 4t^2$

6. $9p^2 - 24pq + 16q^2$

7. $u^3 + 3u^2v + 3uv^2 + v^3$

8. $b^3 - 3b^2c + 3bc^2 - c^3$

9. $8x^3 - 36x^2y + 54xy^2 - 27y^3$

10. $64m^3 + 144m^2n + 108mn^2 + 27n^3$

Section 9.2 Exercises

1. $(a + b)^4 = \dbinom{4}{0}a^4b^0 + \dbinom{4}{1}a^3b^1 + \dbinom{4}{2}a^2b^2 + \dbinom{4}{3}a^1b^3$
$+ \dbinom{4}{4}a^0b^4$
$= a^4 + 4a^3b + 6a^2b^2 + 4ab^3 + b^4$

2. $(a + b)^6 = \dbinom{6}{0}a^6b^0 + \dbinom{6}{1}a^5b^1 + \dbinom{6}{2}a^4b^2 + \dbinom{6}{3}a^3b^3$
$+ \dbinom{6}{4}a^2b^4 + \dbinom{6}{5}a^1b^5 + \dbinom{6}{6}a^0b^6$
$= a^6 + 6a^5b + 15a^4b^2 + 20a^3b^3 + 15a^2b^4$
$+ 6ab^5 + b^6$

3. $(x + y)^7 = \dbinom{7}{0}x^7y^0 + \dbinom{7}{1}x^6y^1 + \dbinom{7}{2}x^5y^2 + \dbinom{7}{3}x^4y^3$
$+ \dbinom{7}{4}x^3y^4 + \dbinom{7}{5}x^2y^5$
$+ \dbinom{7}{6}x^1y^6 + \dbinom{7}{7}x^0y^7$
$= x^7 + 7x^6y + 21x^5y^2 + 35x^4y^3 + 35x^3y^4$
$+ 21x^2y^5 + 7xy^6 + y^7$

4. $(x + y)^{10} = \dbinom{10}{0}x^{10}y^0 + \dbinom{10}{1}x^9y^1 + \dbinom{10}{2}x^8y^2$
$+ \dbinom{10}{3}x^7y^3 + \dbinom{10}{4}x^6y^4$
$+ \dbinom{10}{5}x^5y^5 + \dbinom{10}{6}x^4y^6$
$+ \dbinom{10}{7}x^3y^7 + \dbinom{10}{8}x^2y^8$
$+ \dbinom{10}{9}x^1y^9 + \dbinom{10}{10}x^0y^{10}$
$= x^{10} + 10x^9y + 45x^8y^2 + 120x^7y^3 + 210x^6y^4$
$+ 252x^5y^5 + 210x^4y^6 + 120x^3y^7$
$+ 45x^2y^8 + 10xy^9 + y^{10}$

5. Use the entries in row 3 as coefficients:
$(x + y)^3 = x^3 + 3x^2y + 3xy^2 + y^3$

6. Use the entries in row 5 as coefficients:
$(x + y)^5 = x^5 + 5x^4y + 10x^3y^2 + 10x^2y^3$
$+ 5xy^4 + y^5$

7. Use the entries in row 8 as coefficients:
$(p + q)^8 = p^8 + 8p^7q + 28p^6q^2 + 56p^5q^3 + 70p^4q^4$
$+ 56p^3q^5 + 28p^2q^6 + 8pq^7 + q^8$

8. Use the entries in row 9 as coefficients:
$(p + q)^9 = p^9 + 9p^8q + 36p^7q^2 + 84p^6q^3 + 126p^5q^4$
$+ 126p^4q^5 + 84p^3q^6 + 36p^2q^7 + 9pq^8 + q^9$

9. $\dbinom{9}{2} = \dfrac{9!}{2!7!} = \dfrac{9 \cdot 8}{2 \cdot 1} = 36$

10. $\dbinom{15}{11} = \dfrac{15!}{11!4!} = \dfrac{15 \cdot 14 \cdot 13 \cdot 12}{4 \cdot 3 \cdot 2 \cdot 1} = 1365$

11. $\dbinom{166}{166} = \dfrac{166!}{166!0!} = 1$

12. $\dbinom{166}{0} = \dfrac{166!}{0!166!} = 1$

13. $\dbinom{14}{3} = \dbinom{14}{11} = 364$

14. $\dbinom{13}{8} = \dbinom{13}{5} = 1287$

15. $(-2)^8\dbinom{12}{8} = (-2)^8\dbinom{12}{4} = 126{,}720$

16. $(-3)^4\dbinom{11}{4} = (-3)^4\dbinom{11}{7} = 26{,}730$

17. $f(x) = (x - 2)^5$
$= x^5 + 5x^4(-2) + 10x^3(-2)^2 + 10x^2(-2)^3$
$+ 5x(-2)^4 + (-2)^5$
$= x^5 - 10x^4 + 40x^3 - 80x^2 + 80x - 32$

18. $g(x) = (x + 3)^6$
$= x^6 + 6x^5 \cdot 3 + 15x^4 \cdot 3^2 + 20x^3 \cdot 3^3$
$+ 15x^2 \cdot 3^4 + 6x \cdot 3^5 + 3^6$
$= x^6 + 18x^5 + 135x^4 + 540x^3 + 1215x^2 + 1458x$
$+ 729$

19. $h(x) = (2x - 1)^7$
$= (2x)^7 + 7(2x)^6(-1) + 21(2x)^5(-1)^2$
$+ 35(2x)^4(-1)^3 + 35(2x)^3(-1)^4$
$+ 21(2x)^2(-1)^5 + 7(2x)(-1)^6 + (-1)^7$
$= 128x^7 - 448x^6 + 672x^5 - 560x^4 + 280x^3$
$- 84x^2 + 14x - 1$

20. $f(x) = (3x + 4)^5$
$$= (3x)^5 + 5(3x)^4 \cdot 4 + 10(3x)^3 \cdot 4^2$$
$$+ 10(3x)^2 \cdot 4^3 + 5(3x) \cdot 4^4 + 4^5$$
$$= 243x^5 + 1620x^4 + 4320x^3 + 5760x^2 + 3840x$$
$$+ 1024$$

21. $(2x + y)^4 = (2x)^4 + 4(2x)^3y + 6(2x)^2y^2 + 4(2x)y^3 + y^4$
$$= 16x^4 + 32x^3y + 24x^2y^2 + 8xy^3 + y^4$$

22. $(2y - 3x)^5 = (2y)^5 + 5(2y)^4(-3x) + 10(2y)^3(-3x)^2$
$$+ 10(2y)^2(-3x)^3 + 5(2y)(-3x)^4$$
$$+ (-3x)^5$$
$$= 32y^5 - 240y^4x + 720y^3x^2 - 1080y^2x^3$$
$$+ 810yx^4 - 243x^5$$

23. $(\sqrt{x} - \sqrt{y})^6 = (\sqrt{x})^6 + 6(\sqrt{x})^5(-\sqrt{y}) + 15(\sqrt{x})^4$
$$\cdot (-\sqrt{y})^2 + 20(\sqrt{x})^3(-\sqrt{y})^3$$
$$+ 15(\sqrt{x})^2(-\sqrt{y})^4$$
$$+ 6(\sqrt{x})(-\sqrt{y})^5 + (-\sqrt{y})^6$$
$$= x^3 - 6x^{5/2}y^{1/2} + 15x^2y - 20x^{3/2}y^{3/2}$$
$$+ 15xy^2 - 6x^{1/2}y^{5/2} + y^3$$

24. $(\sqrt{x} + \sqrt{3})^4 = (\sqrt{x})^4 + 4(\sqrt{x})^3(\sqrt{3}) + 6(\sqrt{x})^2$
$$\cdot (\sqrt{3})^2 + 4(\sqrt{x})(\sqrt{3})^3 + (\sqrt{3})^4$$
$$= x^2 + 4x\sqrt{3x} + 18x + 12\sqrt{3x} + 9$$

25. $(x^{-2} + 3)^5 = (x^{-2})^5 + 5(x^{-2})^4 \cdot 3 + 10(x^{-2})^3 \cdot 3^2$
$$+ 10(x^{-2})^2 \cdot 3^3 + 5(x^{-2}) \cdot 3^4 + 3^5$$
$$= x^{-10} + 15x^{-8} + 90x^{-6} + 270x^{-4} + 405x^{-2}$$
$$+ 243$$

26. $(a - b^{-3})^7 = a^7 + 7a^6(-b^{-3}) + 21a^5(-b^{-3})^2$
$$+ 35a^4(-b^{-3})^3 + 35a^3(-b^{-3})^4$$
$$+ 21a^2(-b^{-3})^5 + 7a(-b^{-3})^6 + (-b^{-3})^7$$
$$= a^7 - 7a^6b^{-3} + 21a^5b^{-6} - 35a^4b^{-9}$$
$$+ 35a^3b^{-12} - 21a^2b^{-15} + 7ab^{-18} - b^{-21}$$

27. Answers will vary.

28. Answers will vary.

29. $\dbinom{n}{1} = \dfrac{n!}{1!(n-1)!} = n = \dfrac{n!}{(n-1)!1!}$
$$= \dfrac{n!}{(n-1)![n-(n-1)]!} = \dbinom{n}{n-1}$$

30. $\dbinom{n}{r} = \dfrac{n!}{r!(n-r)!} = \dfrac{n!}{(n-r)!r!}$
$$= \dfrac{n!}{(n-r)![n-(n-r)]!} = \dbinom{n}{n-r}$$

31. $\dbinom{n-1}{r-1} + \dbinom{n-1}{r}$
$$= \dfrac{(n-1)!}{(r-1)![(n-1)-(r-1)]!} + \dfrac{(n-1)!}{r!(n-1-r)!}$$
$$= \dfrac{r(n-1)!}{r(r-1)!(n-r)!} + \dfrac{(n-1)!(n-r)}{r!(n-r)(n-r-1)!}$$
$$= \dfrac{r(n-1)!}{r!(n-r)!} + \dfrac{(n-r)(n-1)!}{r!(n-r)!}$$
$$= \dfrac{(r+n-r)(n-1)!}{r!(n-r)!}$$
$$= \dfrac{n!}{r!(n-r)!}$$
$$= \dbinom{n}{r}$$

32. **(a)** Any pair (n, m) of nonnegative integers — except for $(1, 1)$ — provides a counterexample. For example, $n = 2$ and $m = 3$: $(2 + 3)! = 5! = 120$, but $2! + 3! = 2 + 6 = 8$.

(b) Any pair (n, m) of nonnegative integers — except for $(0, 0)$ or any pair $(1, m)$ or $(n, 1)$ — provides a counterexample. For example, $n = 2$ and $m = 3$: $(2 \cdot 3)! = 6! = 720$, but, $2! \cdot 3! = 2 \cdot 6 = 12$.

33. $\dbinom{n}{2} + \dbinom{n+1}{2} = \dfrac{n!}{2!(n-2)!} + \dfrac{(n+1)!}{2!(n-1)!}$
$$= \dfrac{n(n-1)}{2} + \dfrac{(n+1)(n)}{2}$$
$$= \dfrac{n^2 - n + n^2 + n}{2} = n^2$$

34. $\dbinom{n}{n-2} + \dbinom{n+1}{n-1} = \dfrac{n!}{(n-2)![n-(n-2)]!}$
$$+ \dfrac{(n+1)!}{(n-1)![(n+1)-(n-1)]!}$$
$$= \dfrac{n!}{(n-2)!2!} + \dfrac{(n+1)!}{(n-1)!2!}$$
$$= \dfrac{n(n-1)}{2} + \dfrac{(n+1)n}{2}$$
$$= \dfrac{n^2 - n + n^2 + n}{2} = n^2$$

35. True. The signs of the coefficients are determined by the powers of the $(-y)$ terms, which alternate between odd and even.

36. True. In fact, the sum of every row is a power of 2.

37. The fifth term of the expansion is
$$\dbinom{8}{4}(2x)^4(1)^4 = 1120x^4.$$ The answer is C.

38. The two smallest numbers in row 10 are 1 and 10. The answer is B.

39. The sum of the coefficients of $(3x - 2y)^{10}$ is the same as the value of $(3x - 2y)^{10}$ when $x = 1$ and $y = 1$.
The answer is A.

40. The even-numbered terms in the two expressions are opposite-signed and cancel out, while the odd-numbered terms are identical and add together. The answer is D.

41. **(a)** 1, 3, 6, 10, 15, 21, 28, 36, 45, 55.

(b) They appear diagonally down the triangle, starting with either of the 1's in row 2.

(c) Since n and $n + 1$ represent the sides of the given rectangle, then $n(n + 1)$ represents its area. The triangular number is 1/2 of the given area. Therefore, the triangular number is $\dfrac{n(n+1)}{2}$.

(d) From part (c), we observe that the nth triangular number can be written as $\dfrac{n(n+1)}{2}$. We know that binomial coefficients are the values of $\dbinom{n}{r}$ for $r = 0, 1, 2, 3, \ldots, n$. We can show that $\dfrac{n(n+1)}{2} = \dbinom{n+1}{2}$ as follows:

$$\frac{n(n+1)}{2} = \frac{(n+1)n(n-1)!}{2(n-1)!}$$

$$= \frac{(n+1)!}{2!(n-1)!}$$

$$= \frac{(n+1)!}{2!((n+1)-2)!}$$

$$= \binom{n+1}{2}$$

So, to find the fourth triangular number, for example, compute $\dbinom{4+1}{2} = \dbinom{5}{2} = \dfrac{5!}{2!(5-2)!} = \dfrac{5 \cdot 4 \cdot 3!}{2!3!}$

$$= \frac{5 \cdot 4}{2} = 10.$$

42. (a) 2. (Every other number appears at least twice.)

(b) 1

(c) No. (They all appear in order down the second diagonal.)

(d) 0. (See Exercise 44 for a proof.)

(e) All are divisible by p.

(f) Rows that are powers of 2: 2, 4, 8, 16, etc.

(g) Rows that are 1 less than a power of 2: 1, 3, 7, 15, etc.

(h) For any prime numbered row, or row where the first element is a prime number, all the numbers in that row (excluding the 1's) are divisible by the prime. For example, in the seventh row (1   7   21   35   35   21   7   1) 7, 21, and 35 are all divisible by 7.

43. The sum of the entries in the nth row equals the sum of the coefficients in the expansion of $(x + y)^n$. But this sum, in turn, is equal to the value of $(x + y)^n$ when $x = 1$ and $y = 1$:

$$2^n = (1 + 1)^n$$

$$= \binom{n}{0}1^n 1^0 + \binom{n}{1}1^{n-1}1^1 + \binom{n}{2}1^{n-2}1^2$$

$$\quad + \cdots + \binom{n}{n}1^0 1^n$$

$$= \binom{n}{0} + \binom{n}{1} + \binom{n}{2} + \cdots + \binom{n}{n}$$

44. $0 = (1 - 1)^n$

$$= \binom{n}{0}1^n + \binom{n}{1}1^{n-1}(-1) + \binom{n}{2}1^{n-2}(-1)^2$$

$$\quad + \cdots + \binom{n}{n}(-1)^n$$

$$= \binom{n}{0} - \binom{n}{1} + \binom{n}{2} + \cdots + (-1)^n\binom{n}{n}$$

45. $3^n = (1 + 2)^n$

$$= \binom{n}{0}1^n + \binom{n}{1}1^{n-1}2 + \binom{n}{2}1^{n-2}2^2 + \cdots + \binom{n}{n}2^n$$

$$= \binom{n}{0} + 2\binom{n}{1} + 4\binom{n}{2} + \cdots + 2^n\binom{n}{n}$$

■ Section 9.3   Probability

Exploration 1

1.

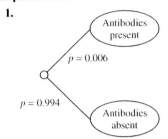

2.

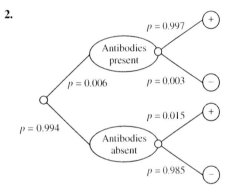

3.

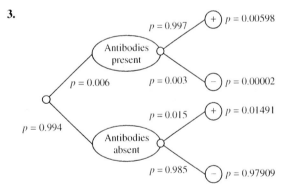

4. $P(+) = 0.00598 + 0.01491 = 0.02089$

5. $P(\text{antibody present} \mid +) = \dfrac{P(\text{antibody present and} +)}{P(+)}$

$\dfrac{0.00598}{0.02089} \approx 0.286$ (A little more than 1 chance in 4.)

Quick Review 9.3

1. 2

2. 6

3. $2^3 = 8$

4. $6^3 = 216$

5. $_{52}C_5 = 2{,}598{,}960$

6. $_{10}C_2 = 45$

7. $5! = 120$

8. $_5P_3 = 60$

9. $\dfrac{_5C_3}{_{10}C_3} = \dfrac{\frac{5!}{3!2!}}{\frac{10!}{3!7!}} = \dfrac{1}{12}$

10. $\dfrac{_5C_2}{_{10}C_2} = \dfrac{\frac{5!}{2!3!}}{\frac{10!}{2!8!}} = \dfrac{2}{9}$

Section 9.3 Exercises

For #1–8, consider ordered pairs (a, b) where a is the value of the red die and b is the value of the green die.

1. $E = \{(3, 6), (4, 5), (5, 4), (6, 3)\}$: $P(E) = \dfrac{4}{36} = \dfrac{1}{9}$

2. $E = \{\text{both dice even}\}, \{\text{both dice odd}\}$:
$$P(E) = \dfrac{3 \cdot 3 + 3 \cdot 3}{36} = \dfrac{18}{36} = \dfrac{1}{2}$$

3. $E = \{(2, 1), (3, 1), (3, 2), (4, 1), (4, 2), (4, 3), (5, 1), (5, 2),$
$(5, 3), (5, 4), (6, 1), (6, 2), (6, 3), (6, 4), (6, 5)\}$:
$$P(E) = \dfrac{15}{36} = \dfrac{5}{12}$$

4. $E = \{(1, 1), (1, 2), \ldots, (6, 2), (6, 3)\}$
$$P(E) = \dfrac{30}{36} = \dfrac{5}{6}$$

5. $P(E) = \dfrac{3 \cdot 3}{36} = \dfrac{1}{4}$

6. $P(E) = \dfrac{3 \cdot 3}{36} = \dfrac{1}{4}$

7. $E = \{(1, 1), (1, 2), (1, 4), (1, 6), (2, 1), (2, 3), (2, 5), (3, 2),$
$(3, 4), (4, 1), (4, 3), (5, 2), (5, 6), (6, 1), (6, 5)\}$
$$P(E) = \dfrac{15}{36} = \dfrac{5}{12}$$

8. $E = \{(1, 6), (2, 5), (3, 4), (4, 3), (5, 2), (5, 6), (6, 1), (6, 5)\}$:
$$P(E) = \dfrac{8}{36} = \dfrac{2}{9}$$

9. (a) No. $0.25 + 0.20 + 0.35 + 0.30 = 1.1$. The numbers do not add up to 1.

(b) There is a problem with Alrik's reasoning. Since the gerbil must always be in exactly one of the four rooms, the proportions must add up to 1, just like a probability function.

10. Since $4 + 3 + 2 + 1 = 10$, we can divide each number in the ratio by 10 and get the proportions relative to the whole. The table then becomes

Compartment	A	B	C	D
Proportion	0.4	0.3	0.2	0.1

Yes, this is a valid probability function.

11. $P(B \text{ or } T) = P(B) + P(T) = 0.3 + 0.1 = 0.4$

12. $P(R \text{ or } G \text{ or } O) = P(R) + P(G) + P(O)$
$= 0.2 + 0.1 + 0.1 = 0.4$

13. $P(R) = 0.2$

14. $P(\text{not } R) = 1 - P(R) = 1 - 0.2 = 0.8$

15. $P[\text{not } (O \text{ or } Y)] = 1 - P(O \text{ or } Y)$
$= 1 - (0.2 + 0.1) = 0.7$

16. $P[\text{not } (B \text{ or } T)] = 1 - P(B \text{ or } T) = 1 - (0.3 + 0.1)$
$= 0.6$

17. $P(B_1 \text{ and } B_2) = P(B_1) \cdot P(B_2) = (0.3)(0.3) = 0.09$

18. $P(O_1 \text{ and } O_2) = P(O_1) \cdot P(O_2) = (0.1)(0.1) = 0.01$

19. $P[(R_1 \text{ and } G_2) \text{ or } (G_1 \text{ and } R_2)] = P(R_1) \cdot P(G_2)$
$+ P(G_1) \cdot P(R_2) = (0.2)(0.2) + (0.2)(0.2) = 0.08$

20. $P(B_1 \text{ and } Y_2) = P(B_1) \cdot P(Y_2) = (0.3)(0.2) = 0.06$

21. $P(\text{neither is yellow}) = P(\text{not } Y_1 \text{ and not } Y_2)$
$= P(\text{not } Y_1) \cdot P(\text{not } Y_2) = (0.8)(0.8) = 0.64$

22. $P(\text{not } R_1 \text{ and not } O_2) = P(\text{not } R_1) \cdot P(\text{not } O_2)$
$= (0.8)(0.9) = 0.72$

23. There are $_{24}C_6 = 134{,}596$ possible hands; of these, only 1 consists of all spades, so the probability is $\dfrac{1}{134{,}596}$.

24. Of the $_{24}C_6 = 134{,}596$ possible hands, one consists of all spades, one consists of all clubs, one consists of all hearts, and one consists of all diamonds, so the probability is
$$\dfrac{4}{134{,}596} = \dfrac{1}{33{,}649}.$$

25. Of the $_{24}C_6 = 134{,}596$ possible hands, there are $_4C_4 \cdot _{20}C_2 = 190$ hands with all the aces, so the probability is $\dfrac{190}{134{,}596} = \dfrac{5}{3542}$.

26. There are $_2C_2 \cdot _{22}C_4 = 7315$ ways to get both black jacks and 4 "other" cards. Similarly, there are 7315 ways to get both red jacks. These two numbers together count twice the $_2C_2 \cdot _2C_2 \cdot _{20}C_2 = 190$ ways to get all four jacks. Therefore, altogether we have $2 \cdot 7315 - 190 = 14{,}440$ distinct ways to have both bowers, so the probability is $\dfrac{14{,}440}{134{,}596} = \dfrac{190}{1771}$.

27. (a)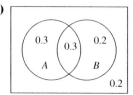

(b) 0.3

(c) 0.2

(d) 0.2

(e) Yes. $P(A \mid B) = \dfrac{P(A \text{ and } B)}{P(B)} = \dfrac{0.3}{0.5} = 0.6 = P(A)$

28. (a)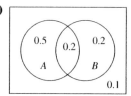

(b) 0.5

(c) 0.2

(d) 0.1

(e) No. $P(A \mid B) = \dfrac{P(A \text{ and } B)}{P(B)} = \dfrac{0.2}{0.4} = 0.5 \neq P(A)$

29. $P(\text{John will practice}) = (0.6)(0.8) + (0.4)(0.4) = 0.64$

30. **(a)** $P(\text{meatloaf is served}) = \dfrac{1}{5} = 0.20$

(b) $P(\text{meatloaf and peas are served}) = (0.20)(0.70)$
$= 0.14$

(c) $P(\text{peas are served}) = (0.20)(0.70) + (0.80)(0.30)$
$= 0.38$

31. If all precalculus students were put on a single list and a name then randomly chosen, the probability $P(\text{from Mr. Abel's class} \mid \text{girl})$ would be $12 \mid 22 = 6 \mid 11$. But when one of the two classes is selected at random, and then a student from this class is selected,
$P(\text{from Mr. Abel's class} \mid \text{girl})$
$$= \frac{P(\text{girl from Mr. Abel's class})}{P(\text{girl})}$$
$$= \frac{\left(\dfrac{1}{2}\right)\left(\dfrac{12}{20}\right)}{\left(\dfrac{1}{2}\right)\left(\dfrac{12}{20}\right) + \left(\dfrac{1}{2}\right)\left(\dfrac{10}{25}\right)}$$
$$= \frac{3}{5}$$

32. Within each box, any of the coins is equally likely to be chosen and either side is equally likely to be shown. But a head in the 2-coin box is more likely to be displayed than a head in the 3-coin box.
$P(\text{from 2-coin box} \mid H) = \dfrac{P(\text{H from 2-coin box})}{P(\text{H})}$
$$= \frac{\left(\dfrac{1}{2}\right)\left(\dfrac{3}{4}\right)}{\left(\dfrac{1}{2}\right)\left(\dfrac{3}{4}\right) + \left(\dfrac{1}{2}\right)\left(\dfrac{3}{6}\right)}$$
$$= \frac{3}{5}$$

33. $\dfrac{{}_{20}C_2}{{}_{25}C_2} = \dfrac{190}{300} = \dfrac{19}{30}$

34. $P(\text{none are defective}) = {}_4C_0 \cdot (0.037)^0 (0.963)^4$
$= (0.963)^4 \approx 0.860$

35. **(a)** $P(\text{cardiovascular disease or cancer}) = 0.45 + 0.22$
$= 0.67$

(b) $P(\text{other cause of death}) = 1 - 0.67 = 0.33$

36. $P(\text{Yahtzee}) = 6 \cdot \left(\dfrac{1}{6}\right)^5 = \dfrac{1}{1296}$

37. The sum of the probabilities is greater than 1 – an impossibility, since the events are mutually exclusive.

38. $P(\text{at least one false positive})$
$= 1 - P(\text{no false positives}) = 1 - (0.993)^{60} \approx 0.344.$

39. **(a)** $P(\text{a woman}) = \dfrac{172}{254} = \dfrac{86}{127}$

(b) $P(\text{went to graduate school}) = \dfrac{124 + 58}{254} = \dfrac{91}{127}$

(c) $P(\text{a woman who went to graduate school})$
$= \dfrac{124}{254} = \dfrac{62}{127}$

40. **(a)** $\dfrac{{}_{14}C_8}{{}_{20}C_8} = \dfrac{3003}{125{,}970} = \dfrac{77}{3230}$

(b) $\dfrac{{}_{14}C_5 \cdot {}_6C_3}{{}_{20}C_8} = \dfrac{40{,}040}{125{,}970} = \dfrac{308}{969}$

(c) $\dfrac{{}_{14}C_6 \cdot {}_6C_2 + {}_{14}C_7 \cdot {}_6C_1 + {}_{14}C_8 \cdot {}_6C_0}{{}_{20}C_8}$

$= \dfrac{45{,}045 + 20{,}592 + 3003}{125{,}970} = \dfrac{68{,}640}{125{,}970} = \dfrac{176}{323}$

41. $\dfrac{1}{{}_9C_2} = \dfrac{1}{36}$

42. This cannot be true. Let A be the event that it is cloudy all day, B be the event that there is at least 1 hour of sunshine, and C be the event that there is some sunshine, but less than 1 hour. Then A, B, and C are mutually exclusive events, so $P(A \text{ or } B \text{ or } C) = P(A) + P(B) + P(C)$ $= 0.22 + 0.78 + P(C) = 1 + P(C)$. Then it must be the case that $P(C) = 0$. This is absurd; there must be some probability of having more than 0 but less than 1 hour of sunshine.

43. $P(\text{HTTTTTTTTT}) = \left(\dfrac{1}{2}\right)^{10} = \dfrac{1}{2^{10}} = \dfrac{1}{1024}$

44. $P(\text{THTTTTHTTT}) = \left(\dfrac{1}{2}\right)^{10} = \dfrac{1}{1024}$

45. $P(\text{HHHHHHHHHH}) = \left(\dfrac{1}{2}\right)^{10} = \dfrac{1}{1024}$

46. $P(9 \text{ H and } 1 \text{ T}) = {}_{10}C_1 \cdot \left(\dfrac{1}{2}\right)^{10} = \dfrac{10}{1024} = \dfrac{5}{512}$

47. $P(2 \text{ H and } 8 \text{ T}) = {}_{10}C_2 \cdot \left(\dfrac{1}{2}\right)^{10} = \dfrac{45}{1024}$

48. $P(3 \text{ H and } 7 \text{ T}) = {}_{10}C_3 \cdot \left(\dfrac{1}{2}\right)^{10} = \dfrac{120}{1024} = \dfrac{15}{128}$

49. $P(\text{at least one H}) = 1 - P(0 \text{ H}) = 1 - {}_{10}C_0 \cdot \left(\dfrac{1}{2}\right)^{10}$
$= 1 - \dfrac{1}{1024} = \dfrac{1023}{1024}$

50. $P(\text{at least two H}) = 1 - P(0 \text{ H}) - P(1 \text{ H}) =$
$1 - {}_{10}C_0 \cdot \left(\dfrac{1}{2}\right)^{10} - {}_{10}C_1 \cdot \left(\dfrac{1}{2}\right)^{10} = 1 - \dfrac{11}{1024} = \dfrac{1013}{1024}$

51. False. A sample space consists of outcomes, which are not necessarily equally likely.

52. False. All probabilities are between 0 and 1, inclusive.

53. Of the 36 different, equally-likely ways the dice can land, 4 ways have a total of 5. So the probability is $4/36 = 1/9$. The answer is D.

54. A probability must always be between 0 and 1, inclusive. The answer is E.

55. $P(B \text{ and } A) = P(B)\,P(A|B)$, and for independent events, $P(B \text{ and } A) = P(B)P(A)$. It follows that the answer is A.

56. A specific sequence of one "heads" and two "tails" has probability $(1/2)^3 = 1/8$. There are three such sequences. The answer is C.

57. (a)

Type of Bagel	Probability
Plain	0.37
Onion	0.12
Rye	0.11
Cinnamon Raisin	0.25
Sourdough	0.15

(b) $(0.37)(0.37)(0.37) \approx 0.051$

(c) No. They are more apt to share bagel preferences if they arrive at the store together.

58. (a) $P(\text{at least one king}) = 1 - P(\text{no kings})$

$= 1 - \dfrac{{}_{48}C_5}{{}_{52}C_5} = \dfrac{18{,}472}{54{,}145} \approx 0.34$

(b) The number of ways to choose, e.g., 3 fives and 2 jacks is ${}_4C_3 \cdot {}_4C_2$. There are ${}_{13}P_2 = 13 \cdot 12$ different combinations of cards that can make up the full house, so

$P(\text{full house}) = \dfrac{13 \cdot 12 \cdot {}_4C_3 \cdot {}_4C_2}{{}_{52}C_5} = \dfrac{6}{4165} \approx 0.0014$

59. (a) We expect $(8)(0.23) = 1.84$ (about 2) to be married.

(b) Yes, this would be an unusual sample.

(c) $P(5 \text{ or more are married}) = {}_8C_5 \cdot (0.23)^5(0.77)^3$
$+ {}_8C_6 \cdot (0.23)^6(0.77)^2 + {}_8C_7 \cdot (0.23)^7(0.77)^1$
$+ {}_8C_8 \cdot (0.23)^8(0.77)^0 \approx 0.01913 = 1.913\%.$

60. (a) ${}_{32}C_{17} \cdot (0.75)^{17}(0.25)^{15} \approx 0.00396 = 0.396\%$

(b) $\displaystyle\sum_{k=0}^{17} {}_{32}C_k \cdot (0.75)^k(0.25)^{15-k} \approx 0.00596 = 0.596\%$

(c) The university's graduation rate seems to be exaggerated; at least, this particular class did not fare as well as the university claims.

61. (a) \$1.50

(b) $3 \cdot \dfrac{2}{6} + (-1) \cdot \dfrac{4}{6} = \dfrac{6}{6} - \dfrac{4}{6} = \dfrac{1}{3}$

62. (a) $\dfrac{10}{9{,}366{,}819} \approx 0.0000010676$

(b)

Value	Probability
-10	$\dfrac{9{,}366{,}809}{9{,}366{,}819}$
$+3{,}999{,}990$	$\dfrac{10}{9{,}366{,}819}$

(c) $3{,}999{,}990 \cdot \dfrac{10}{9{,}366{,}819} + (-10)$

$\cdot \left(1 - \dfrac{10}{9{,}366{,}819}\right) \approx -5.73$

(d) In the long run, Gladys is losing \$5.73 every time she buys the ten tickets. Given the low probability of a positive payoff, she stands to lose a lot of money if she does this often.

■ Section 9.4 Sequences

Quick Review 9.4

1. $3 + (5 - 1)4 = 3 + 16 = 19$

2. $\dfrac{5}{2}[(6 + (5 - 1)4] = \dfrac{5}{2}(22) = 55$

3. $5 \cdot 4^2 = 80$

4. $\dfrac{5(1 - 4^3)}{(1 - 4)} = \dfrac{-315}{-3} = 105$

5. $a_{10} = \dfrac{10}{11}$

6. $a_{10} = 5 + (10 - 1)3 = 32$

7. $a_{10} = 5 \cdot 2^9 = 2560$

8. $a_{10} = \left(\dfrac{4}{3}\right)\left(\dfrac{1}{2}\right)^9 = \left(\dfrac{4}{3}\right)\left(\dfrac{1}{512}\right) = \dfrac{1}{384}$

9. $a_{10} = 32 - 17 = 15$

10. $a_{10} = \dfrac{10^2}{2^{10}} = \dfrac{100}{1024} = \dfrac{25}{256}$

Section 9.4 Exercises

For #1–4, substitute $n = 1$, $n = 2, \ldots, n = 6$, and $n = 100$.

1. $2, \dfrac{3}{2}, \dfrac{4}{3}, \dfrac{5}{4}, \dfrac{6}{5}, \dfrac{7}{6}; \dfrac{101}{100}$

2. $\dfrac{4}{3}, 1, \dfrac{4}{5}, \dfrac{2}{3}, \dfrac{4}{7}, \dfrac{1}{2}; \dfrac{2}{51}$

3. $0, 6, 24, 60, 120, 210; 999{,}900$

4. $-4, -6, -6, -4, 0, 6; 9500$

For #5–10, use previously computed values of the sequence to find the next term in the sequence.

5. $8, 4, 0, -4; -20$

6. $-3, 7, 17, 27; 67$

7. $2, 6, 18, 54; 4374$

8. $0.75, -1.5, 3, -6; -96$

9. $2, -1, 1, 0; 3$

10. $-2, 3, 1, 4; 23$

11. $\displaystyle\lim_{n\to\infty} n^2 = \infty$, so the sequence diverges.

12. $\displaystyle\lim_{n\to\infty} \dfrac{1}{2^n} = 0$, so the sequence converges to 0.

13. $\dfrac{1}{1}, \dfrac{1}{4}, \dfrac{1}{9}, \dfrac{1}{16}, \ldots, \dfrac{1}{n^2}, \ldots$

$\displaystyle\lim_{n\to\infty} \dfrac{1}{n^2} = 0$, so the sequence converges to 0.

14. $\displaystyle\lim_{n\to\infty} (3n - 1) = \infty$, so the sequence diverges.

15. Since the degree of the numerator is the same as the degree of the denominator, the limit is the ratio of the leading coefficients. Thus $\displaystyle\lim_{n\to\infty} \dfrac{3n - 1}{2 - 3n} = -1$. The sequence converges to -1.

16. Since the degree of the numerator is the same as the degree of the denominator, the limit is the ratio of the leading coefficients. Thus $\displaystyle\lim_{n\to\infty} \dfrac{2n - 1}{n + 1} = 2$. The sequence converges to 2.

17. $\displaystyle\lim_{n\to\infty} (0.5)^n = \lim_{n\to\infty} \left(\dfrac{1}{2}\right)^n = 0$, so the sequence converges to 0.

18. $\displaystyle\lim_{n\to\infty} (1.5)^n = \lim_{n\to\infty} \left(\dfrac{3}{2}\right)^n = \infty$, so the sequence diverges.

19. $a_1 = 1$ and $a_{n+1} = a_n + 3$ for $n \geq 1$ yields $1, 4, 7,$
$\ldots, (3n - 2), \ldots$

$\lim_{n \to \infty} (3n - 2) = \infty$, so the sequence diverges.

20. $u_1 = 1$ and $u_{n+1} = \dfrac{u_n}{3}$ for $n \geq 1$ yields $1, \dfrac{1}{3}, \dfrac{1}{9}, \ldots, \dfrac{1}{3^{n-1}}, \ldots$

$\lim_{n \to \infty} \dfrac{1}{3^{n-1}} = 0$, so the sequence converges to 0.

For #21–24, subtract the first term from the second to find the common difference d. Use the formula $a_n = a_1 + (n - 1)d$ with $n = 10$ to find the tenth term. The recursive rule for the nth term is $a_n = a_{n-1} + d$, and the explicit rule is the one given above.

21. **(a)** $d = 4$

(b) $a_{10} = 6 + 9(4) = 42$

(c) Recursive rule: $a_1 = 6$; $a_n = a_{n-1} + 4$ for $n \geq 2$

(d) Explicit rule: $a_n = 6 + 4(n - 1)$

22. **(a)** $d = 5$

(b) $a_{10} = -4 + 9(5) = 41$

(c) Recursive rule: $a_1 = -4$; $a_n = a_{n-1} + 5$ for $n \geq 2$

(d) Explicit rule: $a_n = -4 + 5(n - 1)$

23. **(a)** $d = 3$

(b) $a_{10} = -5 + 9(3) = 22$

(c) Recursive rule: $a_1 = -5$; $a_n = a_{n-1} + 3$ for $n \geq 2$

(d) Explicit rule: $a_n = -5 + 3(n - 1)$

24. **(a)** $d = 11$

(b) $a_{10} = -7 + 9(11) = 92$

(c) Recursive rule: $a_1 = -7$; $a_n = a_{n-1} + 11$ for $n \geq 2$

(d) Explicit rule: $a_n = -7 + 11(n - 1)$

For #25–28, divide the second term by the first to find the common ratio r. Use the formula $a_n = a_1 \cdot r^{n-1}$ with $n = 8$ to find the eighth term. The recursive rule for the nth term is $a_n = a_{n-1} \cdot r$, and the explicit rule is the one given above.

25. **(a)** $r = 3$

(b) $a_8 = 2 \cdot 3^7 = 4374$

(c) Recursive rule: $a_1 = 2$; $a_n = 3a_{n-1}$ for $n \geq 2$

(d) Explicit rule: $a_n = 2 \cdot 3^{n-1}$

26. **(a)** $r = 2$

(b) $a_8 = 3 \cdot 2^7 = 384$

(c) Recursive rule: $a_1 = 3$; $a_n = 2a_{n-1}$ for $n \geq 2$

(d) Explicit rule: $a_n = 3 \cdot 2^{n-1}$

27. **(a)** $r = -2$

(b) $a_8 = (-2)^7 = -128$

(c) Recursive rule: $a_1 = 1$; $a_n = -2a_{n-1}$ for $n \geq 2$

(d) Explicit rule: $a_n = (-2)^{n-1}$

28. **(a)** $r = -1$

(b) $a_8 = -2 \cdot (-1)^7 = 2$

(c) Recursive rule: $a_1 = -2$; $a_n = -1a_{n-1} = -a_{n-1}$ for $n \geq 2$

(d) Explicit rule: $a_n = -2 \cdot (-1)^{n-1} = 2 \cdot (-1)^n$

29. $a_4 = -8 = a_1 + 3d$ and $a_7 = 4 = a_1 + 6d$, so
$a_7 - a_4 = 12 = 3d$. Therefore $d = 4$, so
$a_1 = -8 - 3d = -20$ and $a_n = a_{n-1} + 4$ for $n \geq 2$.

30. $a_5 = -5 = a_1 + 4d$ and $a_9 = -17 = a_1 + 8d$, so
$a_9 - a_5 = -12 = 4d$. Therefore $d = -3$, so
$a_1 = -5 - 4d = 7$ and $a_n = a_{n-1} - 3$ for $n \geq 2$.

31. $a_2 = 3 = a_1 \cdot r^1$ and $a_8 = 192 = a_1 \cdot r^7$, so
$a_8/a_2 = 64 = r^6$. Therefore $r = \pm 2$, so $a_1 = 3/(\pm 2)$
$= \pm \dfrac{3}{2}$ and $a_n = -\dfrac{3}{2} \cdot (-2)^{n-1} = 3 \cdot (-2)^{n-2}$ or
$a_n = \dfrac{3}{2} \cdot 2^{n-1} = 3 \cdot 2^{n-2}$.

32. $a_3 = -75 = a_1 \cdot r^2$ and $a_6 = -9375 = a_1 \cdot r^5$, so
$a_6/a_3 = 125 = r^3$. Therefore $r = 5$, so $a_1 = -75/5^2 = -3$
and $a_n = -3 \cdot 5^{n-1}$.

33.

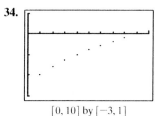

$[0, 5]$ by $[-2, 5]$

34.

$[0, 10]$ by $[-3, 1]$

35.

$[0, 10]$ by $[-10, 100]$

36.

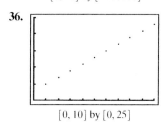

$[0, 10]$ by $[0, 25]$

37. The height (in cm) will be an arithmetic sequence with common difference $d = 2.3$ cm, so the height in week n is $700 + 2.3(n - 1)$: $700, 702.3, 704.6, 706.9, \ldots, 815, 817.3$.

38. The first column is an arithmetic sequence with common difference $d = 14$. The second column is a geometric sequence with common ratio $r = \dfrac{1}{2}$.

Time (billions of years)	Mass (g)
0	16
14	8
28	4
42	2
56	1

39. The numbers of seats in each row form a finite arithmetic sequence with $a_1 = 7, d = 2,$ and $n = 25$. The total number of seats is
$$\frac{25}{2}[2(7) + (25 - 1)(2)] = 775.$$

40. The numbers of tiles in each row form a finite arithmetic sequence with $a_1 = 15, a_n = 30,$ and $n = 16$. The total number of tiles is
$$16\left(\frac{15 + 30}{2}\right) = 360.$$

41. The ten-digit numbers will vary; thus the sequences will vary. The end result will, however, be the same. Each limit will be 9. One example is:

Five random digits: $1, 4, 6, 8, 9$
Five random digits: $2, 3, 4, 5, 6$
List: $1, 2, 3, 4, 4, 5, 6, 6, 8, 9$
Ten-digit number: $2, 416, 345, 689$
Ten-digit number: $9, 643, 128, 564$
a_1 = positive difference of the ten-digit numbers
    $= 7, 226, 782, 875$
a_{n+1} = sum of the digits of a_n, so
a_2 = sum of the digits of $a_1 = 54$
a_3 = sum of the digits of $a_2 = 9$
All successive sums of digits will be 9, so the sequence converges and the limit is 9.

42. Everyone should end up at the word "all".

43. True. Since two successive terms are negative, the common ratio r must be positive, and so the sign of the first term determines the sign of every number in the sequence.

44. False. For example, consider the sequence $5, 1, -3, -7, \ldots$.

45. $a_1 = 2$ and $a_2 = 8$ implies $d = 8 - 2 = 6$
$c = a_1 - d$ so $c = 2 - 6 = -4$
$a_4 = 6 \cdot 4 + (-4) = 20$
The answer is A.

46. $\lim_{n \to \infty} \sqrt{n} = \lim_{n \to \infty} n^{1/2} = \infty$, so the sequence diverges.
The answer is B.

47. $r = \dfrac{a_2}{a_1} = \dfrac{6}{2} = 3$
$a_6 = a_1 r^5 = 2 \cdot 3^5 = 486$ and $a_2 = 6$, so
$\dfrac{a_6}{a_2} = \dfrac{486}{6} = 81.$
The answer is E.

48. The geometric sequence will be defined by $a_{n+1} = a_n \div 3$ for $n \geq 1$ and $a_1 \neq 0$.
$a_2 = \dfrac{a_1}{3}$
$a_3 = \dfrac{a_2}{3} = \dfrac{a_1/3}{3} = \dfrac{a_1}{9}$
$a_4 = \dfrac{a_3}{3} = \dfrac{a_1/9}{3} = \dfrac{a_1}{27}$
$a_n = \dfrac{a_1}{3^{n-1}}$, which represents a geometric sequence.
The answer is C.

49. (a) $a_1 = 1$ because there is initially one male-female pair (this is the number of pairs after 0 months). $a_2 = 1$ because after one month, the original pair has only just become fertile. $a_3 = 2$ because after two months, the original pair produces a new male-female pair.

(b) Notice that after $n - 2$ months, there are a_{n-1} pairs, of which a_{n-2} (the number of pairs present one month earlier) are fertile. Therefore, after $n - 1$ months, the number of pairs will be $a_n = a_{n-1} + a_{n-2}$: to last month's total, we add the number of new pairs born. Thus $a_4 = 3, a_5 = 5, a_6 = 8, a_7 = 13, a_8 = 21, a_9 = 34, a_{10} = 55, a_{11} = 89, a_{12} = 144, a_{13} = 233.$

(c) Since a_1 is the initial number of pairs, and a_2 is the number of pairs after one month, we see that a_{13} is the number of pairs after 12 months.

50. Use a calculator: $a_1 = 1, a_2 = 1, a_3 = 2, a_4 = 3, a_5 = 5, a_6 = 8, a_7 = 13$. These are the first seven terms of the Fibonacci sequence.

51. (a) For a polygon with n sides, let A be the vertex in quadrant I at the top of the vertical segment, and let B be the point on the x-axis directly below A. Together with $(0, 0)$, these two points form a right triangle; the acute angle at the origin has measure
$\theta = \dfrac{2\pi}{2n} = \dfrac{\pi}{n}$, since there are $2n$ such triangles making up the polygon. The length of the side opposite this angle is
$\sin \theta = \sin \dfrac{\pi}{n}$, and there are $2n$ such sides making up the perimeter of the polygon, so $\sin \dfrac{\pi}{n} = \dfrac{a_n}{2n}$, or
$a_n = 2n \sin(\pi/n).$

(b) $a_{10} \approx 6.1803, a_{100} \approx 6.2822, a_{1000} \approx 6.2832, a_{10,000} \approx 6.2832 \approx 2\pi$. It appears that $a_n \to 2\pi$ as $n \to \infty$, which makes sense since the perimeter of the polygon should approach the circumference of the circle.

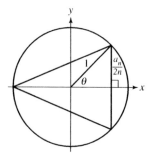

52. $P_1 = 525,000; P_n = 1.0175P_{n-1}, n \geq 2$

53. The difference of successive terms in $\{\log(a_n)\}$ will be of the form $\log(a_{n+1}) - \log(a_n) = \log\left(\dfrac{a_{n+1}}{a_n}\right)$. Since $\{a_n\}$ is geometric, $\dfrac{a_{n+1}}{a_n}$ is constant. This makes $\log\left(\dfrac{a_{n+1}}{a_n}\right)$ constant, so $\{\log(a_n)\}$ is a sequence with a constant difference (arithmetic).

54. The ratios of successive terms in $\{10^{b_n}\}$ will be of the form $10^{b_{n+1}} \div 10^{b_n} = 10^{b_{n+1} - b_n}$. Since $\{b_n\}$ is arithmetic, $b_{n+1} - b_n$ is constant. This makes $10^{b_{n+1} - b_n}$ constant, so $\{10^{b_n}\}$ is a sequence with a common ratio (geometric).

55. $a_1 = [1 \ \ 1], a_2 = [1 \ \ 2], a_3 = [2 \ \ 3], a_4 = [3 \ \ 5],$
$a_5 = [5 \ \ 8], a_6 = [8 \ \ 13], a_7 = [13 \ \ 21].$ The entries in
the terms of this sequence are successive pairs of terms
from the Fibonacci sequence.

56. $a_1 = [1 \ \ a] \quad r = \begin{bmatrix} 1 & d \\ 0 & 1 \end{bmatrix}$

$a_2 = a_1 \cdot r = [1 \ \ a + d]$
$a_3 = a_2 \cdot r = [1 \ \ d + a + d] = [1 \ \ a + 2d]$
$a_4 = a_3 \cdot r = [1 \ \ d + a + 2d] = [1 \ \ a + 3d]$
$a_n = [1 \ \ a + (n - 1)d].$

So, the second entries of this geometric sequence of
matrices form an arithmetic sequence with the first term a
and common difference d.

■ Section 9.5 Series

Exploration 1

1. $3 + 6 + 9 + 12 + 15 = 45$

2. $5^2 + 6^2 + 7^2 + 8^2 = 25 + 36 + 49 + 64 = 174$

3. $\cos(0) + \cos(\pi) + \cdots + \cos(11\pi) + \cos(12\pi)$
$= 1 - 1 + 1 + \cdots - 1 + 1 = 1$

4. $\sin(0) + \sin(\pi) + \cdots + \sin(k\pi)$
$+ \cdots = 0 + 0 + \cdots + 0 + \cdots = 0$

5. $\dfrac{3}{10} + \dfrac{3}{100} + \dfrac{3}{1,000} + \cdots + \dfrac{3}{1,000,000} + \cdots = \dfrac{1}{3}$

Exploration 2

1. $1 + \ \ 2 + \ \ 3 + \cdots + 99 + 100$

2. $100 + \ \ 99 + \ \ 98 + \cdots + \ \ 2 + \ \ 1$

3. $101 + 101 + 101 + \cdots + 101 + 101$

4. $100(101) = 10,100$

5. The sum in 4 involves two copies of the same progression,
so it doubles the sum of the progression. The answer that
Gauss gave was 5050.

Quick Review 9.5

1. $a_1 = 4; \ d = 2$ so $a_{10} = a_1 + (n - 1)d$
$a_{10} = 4 + (10 - 1)2 = 4 + 18 = 22$
$a_{10} = 22$

2. $a_1 = 3; \ a_2 = 1$ so $d = 1 - 3 = -2$
$a_{10} = a_1 + (n - 1)d$
$a_{10} = 3 + (10 - 1)(-2) = 3 - 18 = -15$
$a_{10} = -15$

3. $a_3 = 6$ and $a_8 = 21$
$a_3 = a_1 + 2d$ and $a_8 = a_1 + 7d$
$(a_1 + 7d) - (a_1 + 2d) = 21 - 6$ so $5d = 15 \Rightarrow d = 3.$
$6 = a_1 + 2(3)$ so $a_1 = 0$
$a_{10} = 0 + 9(3) = 27$
$a_{10} = 27$

4. $a_5 = 3$, and $a_{n+1} = a_n + 5$ for $n \geq 1 \Rightarrow$
$a_6 = 3 + 5 = 8$
$a_5 = 3$ and $a_6 = 8 \Rightarrow d = 5$
$a_5 = a_1 + 4d$ so $3 = a_1 + 4(5) \Rightarrow a_1 = -17$
$a_{10} = -17 + 9(5) = 28$
$a_{10} = 28$

5. $a_1 = 1$ and $a_2 = 2$ yields $r = \dfrac{2}{1} = 2$

$a_{10} = 1 \cdot 2^9 = 512$
$a_{10} = 512$

6. $a_4 = 1$ and $a_4 = a_1 \cdot r^3;$ $a_6 = 2$ and $a_6 = a_1 \cdot r^5$

$\dfrac{a_1 \cdot r^5}{a_1 \cdot r^3} = \dfrac{2}{1}$

$r^2 = 2 \Rightarrow r = \sqrt{2}$

$1 = a_1(\sqrt{2})^3; \quad a_1 = \dfrac{1}{(\sqrt{2})^3} = \dfrac{1}{2\sqrt{2}}$

$a_{10} = \dfrac{1}{2\sqrt{2}}(\sqrt{2})^9 = \dfrac{16\sqrt{2}}{2\sqrt{2}} = 8$

$a_{10} = 8$

7. $a_7 = 5$ and $r = -2 \Rightarrow 5 = a_1(-2)^6$

$a_1 = \dfrac{5}{64}; \quad a_{10} = \dfrac{5}{24}(-2)^9 = \dfrac{-2560}{24} = -40$

$a_{10} = -40$

8. $a_8 = 10$ and $a_8 = a_1 \cdot r^7;$ $a_{12} = 40 \Rightarrow a_{12} = a_1 \cdot r^{11}$

$\dfrac{a_1 \cdot r^{11}}{a_1 \cdot r^7} = \dfrac{40}{10}$

$r^4 = 4;$ so $r = (4)^{1/4}$

$10 = a_1((4)^{1/4})^7; \quad a_1 = \dfrac{10}{4^{7/4}}$

$a_{10} = \dfrac{10}{4^{7/4}}(4^{1/4})^9 = \dfrac{10(4^{9/4})}{4^{7/4}} = 10(4^{2/4}) = 10 \cdot 2 = 20$

$a_{10} = 20$

9. $\displaystyle\sum_{n=1}^{5} n^2 = 1 + 4 + 9 + 16 + 25 = 55$

10. $\displaystyle\sum_{n=1}^{5} (2n - 1) = 1 + 3 + 5 + 7 + 9 = 25$

Section 9.5 Exercises

1. $\displaystyle\sum_{k=1}^{11} (6k - 13)$

2. $\displaystyle\sum_{k=1}^{10} (3k - 1)$

3. $\displaystyle\sum_{k=1}^{n+1} k^2$

4. $\displaystyle\sum_{k=1}^{n+1} k^3$

5. $\displaystyle\sum_{k=0}^{\infty} 6(-2)^k$

6. $\displaystyle\sum_{k=0}^{\infty} 5(-3)^k$

For #7–12, use one of the formulas $S_n = n\left(\dfrac{a_1 + a_n}{2}\right)$ or

$S_n = \dfrac{n}{2}[2a_1 + (n - 1)d].$ In most cases, the first of these is
easier (since the last term a_n is given); note that
$n = \dfrac{a_n - a_1}{d} + 1.$

7. $6 \cdot \left(\dfrac{-7 + 13}{2}\right) = 6 \cdot 3 = 18$

8. $6 \cdot \left(\dfrac{-8 + 27}{2} \right) = 3 \cdot 19 = 57$

9. $80 \cdot \left(\dfrac{1 + 80}{2} \right) = 40 \cdot 81 = 3240$

10. $35 \cdot \left(\dfrac{2 + 70}{2} \right) = 35 \cdot 36 = 1260$

11. $13 \cdot \left(\dfrac{117 + 33}{2} \right) = 13 \cdot 75 = 975$

12. $\left(\dfrac{111 + 27}{2} \right) = 29 \cdot 69 = 2001$

For #13–16, use the formula $S_n = \dfrac{a_1(1 - r^n)}{1 - r}$. Note that $n = 1 + \log_{|r|} \left| \dfrac{a_n}{a_1} \right| = 1 + \dfrac{\ln |a_n/a_1|}{\ln |r|}$.

13. $\dfrac{3(1 - 2^{13})}{1 - 2} = 24{,}573$

14. $\dfrac{5(1 - 3^{10})}{1 - 3} = 147{,}620$

15. $\dfrac{42[1 - (1/6)^9]}{1 - (1/6)} = 50.4(1 - 6^{-9}) \approx 50.4$

16. $\dfrac{42[1 - (-1/6)^{10}]}{1 - (-1/6)} = 36(1 - 6^{-10}) = 36 - 6^{-8} \approx 36$

For #17–22, use one of the formulas $S_n = \dfrac{n}{2}[2a_1 + (n - 1)d]$ or $S_n = \dfrac{a_1(1 - r^n)}{1 - r}$.

17. Arithmetic with $d = 3$: $\dfrac{10}{2}[2 \cdot 3 + (10 - 1)(3)]$

$= 5 \cdot 31 = 155$

18. Arithmetic with $d = -6$: $\dfrac{9}{2}[2 \cdot 14 + (9 - 1)(-6)]$

$= 9 \cdot (-10) = -90$

19. Geometric with $r = -\dfrac{1}{2}$: $\dfrac{4[1 - (-1/2)^{12}]}{1 - (-1/2)}$

$= \dfrac{8}{3} \cdot (1 - 2^{-12}) \approx 2.666$

20. Geometric with $r = -\dfrac{1}{2}$: $\dfrac{6[1 - (-1/2)^{11}]}{1 - (-1/2)}$

$= 4 \cdot (1 + 2^{-11}) \approx 4.002$

21. Geometric with $r = -11$: $\dfrac{-1[1 - (-11)^9]}{1 - (-11)}$

$= -\dfrac{1}{12} \cdot (1 + 11^9) = -196{,}495{,}641$

22. Geometric with $r = -12$: $\dfrac{-2[1 - (-12)^8]}{1 - (-12)}$

$= -\dfrac{2}{13} \cdot (1 - 12^8) = 66{,}151{,}030$

23. (a) The first six partial sums are $\{0.3, 0.33, 0.333, 0.3333, 0.33333, 0.333333\}$. The numbers appear to be approaching a limit of $0.\overline{3} = 1/3$. The series is convergent.

(b) The first six partial sums are $\{1, -1, 2, -2, 3, -3\}$. The numbers approach no limit. The series is divergent.

24. (a) The first six partial sums are $\{-2, 0, -2, 0, -2, 0\}$. The numbers approach no limit. The series is divergent.

(b) The first six partial sums are $\{1, 0.3, 0.23, 0.223, 0.2223, 0.22223\}$. The numbers appear to be approaching a limit of $0.\overline{2} = 2/9$. The series is convergent.

25. $r = \dfrac{1}{2}$, so it converges to $S = \dfrac{6}{1 - (1/2)} = 12$.

26. $r = \dfrac{1}{3}$, so it converges to $S = \dfrac{4}{1 - (1/3)} = 6$.

27. $r = 2$, so it diverges.

28. $r = 3$, so it diverges.

29. $r = \dfrac{1}{4}$, so it converges to $S = \dfrac{3/4}{1 - (1/4)} = 1$.

30. $r = \dfrac{2}{3}$, so it converges to $S = \dfrac{10/3}{1 - (2/3)} = 10$.

31. $7 + \dfrac{14}{99} = \dfrac{693}{99} + \dfrac{14}{99} = \dfrac{707}{99}$

32. $5 + \dfrac{93}{99} = 5 + \dfrac{31}{33} = \dfrac{196}{33}$

33. $-17 - \dfrac{268}{999} = -\dfrac{17{,}251}{999}$

34. $-12 - \dfrac{876}{999} = -12 - \dfrac{292}{333} = -\dfrac{4288}{333}$

35. (a) The ratio of any two successive account balances is $r = 1.1$. That is,
$$\dfrac{\$22{,}000}{\$20{,}000} = \dfrac{\$24{,}200}{\$22{,}000} = \dfrac{\$26{,}620}{\$24{,}200} = \dfrac{\$29{,}282}{\$26{,}620} = 1.1.$$

(b) Each year, the balance is 1.1 times as large as the year before. So, n years after the balance is $\$20{,}000$, it will be $\$20{,}000 (1.1)^n$.

(c) The sum of the eleven terms of the geometric sequence is $\dfrac{\$20{,}000(1 - 1.1^{11})}{1 - 1.1} = \$370{,}623.34$

36. (a) The difference of any two successive account balances is $d = \$2016$. That is $\$20{,}016 - \$18{,}000 = \$22{,}032 - \$20{,}016 = \$24{,}048 - \$22{,}032 = \$26{,}064 - \$24{,}048 = \$2016$.

(b) Each year, the balance is $\$2016$ more than the year before. So, n years after the balance is $\$18{,}000$, it will be $\$18{,}000 + \$2016n$.

(c) The sum of the eleven terms of the arithmetic sequence is
$$\dfrac{11}{2}[2(\$18{,}000) + (10)(\$2016)] = \$308{,}880$$

37. (a) The first term, $120(1 + 0.07/12)^0$, simplifies to 120. The common ratio of terms, r, equals $1 + 0.07/12$.

(b) The sum of the 120 terms is
$$\dfrac{120[1 - (1 + 0.07/12)^{120}]}{1 - (1 + 0.07/12)} = \$20{,}770.18$$

38. (a) The first term, $100(1 + 0.08/12)^0$, simplifies to 100. The common ratio of terms, r, equals $1 + 0.08/12$.

(b) The sum of the 120 terms is
$$\dfrac{100[1 - (1 + 0.08/12)^{120}]}{1 - (1 + 0.08/12)} = \$18{,}294.60.$$

39. $2 + 2 \cdot [2(0.9) + (2(0.9)^2 + 2(0.9)^3 + \ldots + 2(0.9)^9]$

$= 2 + \sum_{k=1}^{9} 4(0.9)^k = 2 + \dfrac{3.6(1 - 0.9^9)}{1 - 0.9} =$

$38 - 36(0.9^9) \approx 24.05$ m: The ball travels down 2 m. Between the first and second bounces, it travels $2(0.9)$ m up, then the same distance back down. Between the second and third bounces, it travels $2(0.9)^2$ m up, then the same distance back down, etc.

40. $f(x)$ does have a horizontal asymptote to the left (since as $x \to -\infty$, $f(x) \to -40$), but as $x \to \infty$, $f(x) \to \infty$. The given series is geometric with $r = 1.05$; the sum of the first n terms in the series is $f(n)$. Observing that $f(x) \to \infty$ as $x \to \infty$ is confirmation that the geometric series diverges.

41. False. The series might diverge. For example, examine the series $1 + 2 + 3 + 4 + 5$ where all of the terms are positive. Consider the limit of the sequence of partial sums. The first five partial sums are $\{1, 3, 6, 10, 15\}$. These numbers increase without bound and do not approach a limit. Therefore, the series diverges and has no sum.

42. False. Justifications will vary. One example is to examine

$\sum_{n=1}^{\infty} n$ and $\sum_{n=1}^{\infty} (-n)$.

Both of these diverge, but $\sum_{n=1}^{\infty} (n + (-n)) = \sum_{n=1}^{\infty} 0 = 0$.

So the sum of the two divergent series converges.

43. $3^{-1} + 3^{-2} + 3^{-3} + \cdots + 3^{-n} + \cdots =$

$\dfrac{1}{3} + \dfrac{1}{9} + \dfrac{1}{27} + \dfrac{1}{81} + \dfrac{1}{243} + \cdots + \dfrac{1}{3^n} + \cdots$

The first five partial sums are $\left\{ \dfrac{1}{3}, \dfrac{4}{9}, \dfrac{13}{27}, \dfrac{40}{81}, \dfrac{121}{243} \right\}$. These appear to be approaching a limit of $1/2$, which would suggest that the series converges to $1/2$. The answer is A.

44. If $\sum_{n=1}^{\infty} x^n = 4$, then $x = 0.8$.

$\sum_{n=1}^{\infty} 0.8^n = 0.8 + 0.64 + 0.512 + 0.4096 + 0.32768$

$\qquad\qquad + 0.262144 + \cdots$

The first six partial sums are $\{0.8, 1.44, 1.952, 2.3616,$ $2.68928, 2.951424\}$. It appears from this sequence of partial sums that the series is converging. If the sequence of partial sums were extended to the 40th partial sum, you would see that the series converges to 4. The answer is D.

45. The common ratio is $0.75/3 = 0.25$, so the sum of the infinite series is $3/(1 - 0.25) = 4$. The answer is C.

46. The sum is an infinite geometric series with $|r| = 5/3 > 1$. The answer is E.

47. (a) Heartland: 19,237,759 people.

Southeast: 42,614,977 people.

(b) Heartland: 517,825 mi^2.

Southeast: 348,999 mi^2.

(c) Heartland: $\dfrac{19,237,759}{517,825} \approx 37.15$ people/mi^2.

Southeast: $\dfrac{42,614,977}{348,999} \approx 122.11$ people/mi^2.

Heartland:		Southeast:	
Iowa	≈ 52.00	Alabama	≈ 86.01
Kansas	≈ 32.68	Arkansas	≈ 50.26
Minnesota	≈ 58.29	Florida	≈ 272.53
Missouri	≈ 80.28	Georgia	≈ 138.97
Nebraska	≈ 22.12	Louisiana	≈ 93.59
N. Dakota	≈ 9.08	Mississippi	≈ 59.65
S. Dakota	≈ 9.79	S.Carolina	≈ 128.95
Total	≈ 264.24	Total	≈ 829.96
Average	≈ 37.75	Average	≈ 118.57

(d) The table is shown on the right; the answer differs because the overall population density

$\dfrac{\sum \text{population}}{\sum \text{area}}$ is generally not the same as the average of the population densities, $\dfrac{1}{n} \sum \left(\dfrac{\text{population}}{\text{area}} \right)$. The larger states

within each group have a greater effect on the overall mean density. In a similar way, if a student's grades are based on a 100-point test and four 10-point quizzes, her overall average grade depends more on the test grade than on the four quiz grades.

48. $\displaystyle\sum_{k=1}^{8} (k^2 - 2)$

49. The table suggests that $S_n = \displaystyle\sum_{k=1}^{n} F_k = F_{n+2} - 1$.

n	F_n	S_n	$F_{n+2} - 1$
1	1	1	1
2	1	2	2
3	2	4	4
4	3	7	7
5	5	12	12
6	8	20	20
7	13	33	33
8	21	54	54
9	34	88	88

50. The nth triangular number is simply the sum of the first n consecutive positive integers:

$$1 + 2 + 3 + \cdots + n = n\left(\frac{1 + n}{2}\right) = \frac{n(n + 1)}{2}$$

51. Algebraically: $T_{n-1} + T_n = \dfrac{(n - 1)n}{2} + \dfrac{n(n + 1)}{2}$

$$= \frac{n^2 - n + n^2 + n}{2} = n^2.$$

Geometrically: the array of black dots in the figure represents $T_n = 1 + 2 + 3 + \cdots + n$ (that is, there are T_n dots in the array). The array of gray dots represents $T_{n-1} = 1 + 2 + 3 + \cdots + (n - 1)$. The two triangular arrays fit together to form an $n \times n$ square array, which has n^2 dots.

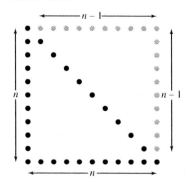

52. If $\displaystyle\sum_{k=1}^{n} \frac{1}{k} \geq \ln n$ for all n, then the sum diverges since as $n \to \infty$, $\ln n \to \infty$.

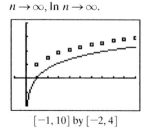

$[-1, 10]$ by $[-2, 4]$

■ Section 9.6 Mathematical Induction

Exploration 1

1. Start with the rightmost peg if n is odd and the middle peg if n is even. From that point on, the first move for moving any smaller stack to a destination peg should be directly to the destination peg if the smaller stack's size n is odd and to the other available peg if n is even. The fact that the winning strategy follows such predictable rules is what makes it so interesting to students of computer programming.

Exploration 2

1. 43, 47, 53, 61, 71, 83, 97, 113, 131, 151. Yes.

2. 173, 197, 223, 251, 281, 313, 347, 383, 421, 461. Yes.

3. 503, 547, 593, 641, 691, 743, 797, 853, 911, 971. Yes. Inductive thinking might lead to the conjecture that $n^2 + n + 41$ is prime for all n, but we have no proof as yet!

4. The next 9 numbers are all prime, but $40^2 + 40 + 41$ is not. Quite obviously, neither is the number $41^2 + 41 + 41$.

Quick Review 9.6

1. $n^2 + 5n$

2. $n^2 - n - 6$

3. $k^3 + 3k^2 + 2k$

4. $(n + 3)(n - 1)$

5. $(k + 1)^3$

6. $(n - 1)^3$

7. $f(1) = 1 + 4 = 5, f(t) = t + 4,$
$f(t + 1) = t + 1 + 4 = t + 5$

8. $f(1) = \dfrac{1}{1 + 1} = \dfrac{1}{2}, f(k) = \dfrac{k}{k + 1},$
$f(k + 1) = \dfrac{k + 1}{k + 1 + 1} = \dfrac{k + 1}{k + 2}$

9. $P(1) = \dfrac{2 \cdot 1}{3 \cdot 1 + 1} = \dfrac{1}{2},$
$P(k) = \dfrac{2k}{3k + 1} = \dfrac{2(k + 1)}{3(k + 1) + 1} = \dfrac{2k + 2}{3k + 4}$

10. $P(1) = 2(1)^2 - 1 - 3 = -2, P(k) = 2k^2 - k - 3,$
$P(k + 1) = 2(k + 1)^2 - (k + 1) - 3 = 2k^2 + 3k - 2$

Section 9.6 Exercises

1. P_n: $2 + 4 + 6 + \cdots + 2n = n^2 + n$.
P_1 is true: $2(1) = 1^2 + 1$.
Now assume P_k is true: $2 + 4 + 6 + \cdots + 2k$
$= k^2 + k$. Add $2(k + 1)$ to both sides:
$2 + 4 + 6 + \cdots + 2k + 2(k + 1)$
$= k^2 + k + 2(k + 1) = k^2 + 3k + 2$
$= k^2 + 2k + 1 + k + 1 = (k + 1)^2 + (k + 1)$, so
P_{k+1} is true. Therefore, P_n is true for all $n \geq 1$.

2. P_n: $8 + 10 + 12 + \cdots + (2n + 6) = n^2 + 7n$.
P_1 is true: $2(1) + 6 = 1^2 + 7 \cdot 1$.
Now assume P_k is true:
$8 + 10 + 12 + \cdots + (2k + 6) = k^2 + 7k$.
Add $2(k + 1) + 6 = 2k + 8$ to both sides:
$8 + 10 + 12 + \cdots + (2k + 6) + [2(k + 1) + 6]$
$= k^2 + 7k + 2k + 8 = (k^2 + 2k + 1) + 7k + 7$
$= (k + 1)^2 + 7(k + 1)$, so P_{k+1} is true.
Therefore, P_n is true for all $n \geq 1$.

3. P_n: $6 + 10 + 14 + \cdots + (4n + 2) = n(2n + 4)$.
P_1 is true: $4(1) + 2 = 1(2 + 4)$.
Now assume P_k is true:
$6 + 10 + 14 + \cdots + (4k + 2) = k(2k + 4)$.
Add $4(k + 1) + 2 = 4k + 6$ to both sides:
$6 + 10 + 14 + \cdots + (4k + 2) + [4(k + 1) + 2]$
$= k(2k + 4) + 4k + 6 = 2k^2 + 8k + 6$
$= (k + 1)(2k + 6) = (k + 1)[2(k + 1) + 4]$, so P_{k+1}
is true. Therefore, P_n is true for all $n \geq 1$.

4. P_n: $14 + 18 + 22 + \cdots + (4n + 10) = 2n(n + 6)$.
P_1 is true: $4(1) + 10 = 2 \cdot 1(1 + 6)$. Now assume P_k is
true:
$14 + 18 + 22 + \cdots + (4k + 10) = 2k(k + 6)$. Add
$4(k + 1) + 10 = 4k + 14$ to both sides:
$14 + 18 + 22 + \cdots + (4k + 10) + [4(k + 1) + 10]$
$= 2k(k + 6) + (4k + 14)$
$= 2(k^2 + 8k + 7) = 2(k + 1)(k + 7)$
$= 2(k + 1)(k + 1 + 6)$, so P_{k+1} is true. Therefore, P_n
is true for all $n \geq 1$.

5. P_n: $5n - 2$. P_1 is true: $a_1 = 5 \cdot 1 - 2 = 3$.
Now assume P_k is true: $a_k = 5k - 2$.
To get a_{k+1}, add 5 to a_k; that is,
$a_{k+1} = (5k - 2) + 5 = 5(k + 1) - 2$ This shows that
P_{k+1} is true. Therefore, P_n is true for all $n \geq 1$.

6. P_n: $a_n = 2n + 5$. P_1 is true: $a_1 = 2 \cdot 1 + 5 = 7$.
Now assume P_k is true: $a_k = 2k + 5$.
To get a_{k+1}, add 2 to a_k; that is,
$a_{k+1} = (2k + 5) + 2 = 2(k + 1) + 5$ This shows that
P_{k+1} is true. Therefore, P_n is true for all $n \geq 1$.

7. P_n: $a_n = 2 \cdot 3^{n-1}$.
P_1 is true: $a_1 = 2 \cdot 3^{1-1} = 2 \cdot 3^0 = 2$.
Now assume P_k is true: $a_k = 2 \cdot 3^{k-1}$.
To get a_{k+1}, multiply a_k by 3; that is,
$a_{k+1} = 3 \cdot 2 \cdot 3^{k-1} = 2 \cdot 3k = 2 \cdot 3^{(k+1)-1}$. This shows that
P_{k+1} is true. Therefore, P_n is true for all $n \geq 1$.

8. P_n: $a_n = 3 \cdot 5^{n-1}$.
P_1 is true: $a_1 = 3 \cdot 5^{1-1} = 3 \cdot 5^0 = 3$.
Now assume P_k is true: $a_k = 3 \cdot 5^{k-1}$.
To get a_{k+1}, multiply a_k by 5; that is,
$a_{k+1} = 5 \cdot 3 \cdot 5^{k-1} = 3 \cdot 5^k = 3 \cdot 5^{(k+1)-1}$. This shows that
P_{k+1} is true. Therefore, P_n is true for all $n \geq 1$.

9. P_1: $1 = \dfrac{1(1 + 1)}{2}$.

P_k: $1 + 2 + \cdots + k = \dfrac{k(k + 1)}{2}$

P_{k+1}: $1 + 2 + \cdots + k + (k + 1) = \dfrac{(k + 1)(k + 2)}{2}$.

10. P_1: $(2(1) - 1)^2 = \dfrac{1(2 - 1)(2 + 1)}{3}$.

P_k: $1^2 + 3^2 + \cdots + (2k - 1)^2 = \dfrac{k(2k - 1)(2k + 1)}{3}$.

P_{k+1}: $1^2 + 3^2 + \cdots + (2k - 1)^2 + (2k + 1)^2$
$= \dfrac{(k + 1)(2k + 1)(2k + 3)}{3}$.

11. P_1: $\dfrac{1}{1 \cdot 2} = \dfrac{1}{1 + 1}$.

P_k: $\dfrac{1}{1 \cdot 2} + \dfrac{1}{2 \cdot 3} + \cdots + \dfrac{1}{k(k + 1)} = \dfrac{k}{k + 1}$.

P_{k+1}: $\dfrac{1}{1 \cdot 2} + \dfrac{1}{2 \cdot 3} + \cdots + \dfrac{1}{k(k + 1)}$

$+ \dfrac{1}{(k + 1)(k + 2)} = \dfrac{k + 1}{k + 2}$.

12. P_1: $1^4 = \dfrac{1(1 + 1)(2 + 1)(3 + 3 - 1)}{30}$.

P_k: $1^4 + 2^4 + \cdots + k^4$
$= \dfrac{k(k + 1)(2k + 1)(3k^2 + 3k - 1)}{30}$.

P_{k+1}: $1^4 + 2^4 + \cdots + k^4 + (k + 1)^4$
$= \dfrac{(k + 1)(k + 2)(2k + 3)(3k^2 + 9k + 5)}{30}$.

13. P_n: $1 + 5 + 9 + \cdots + (4n - 3) = n(2n - 1)$.
P_1 is true: $4(1) - 3 = 1 \cdot (2 \cdot 1 - 1)$.
Now assume P_k is true:
$1 + 5 + 9 + \cdots + (4k - 3) = k(2k - 1)$.
Add $4(k + 1) - 3 = 4k + 1$ to both sides:
$1 + 5 + 9 + \cdots + (4k - 3) + [4(k + 1) - 3]$
$= k(2k - 1) = 4k + 1 = 2k^2 + 3k + 1$
$= (k + 1)(2k + 1) = (k + 1)[2(k + 1) - 1]$,
so P_{k+1} is true.
Therefore, P_n is true for all $n \geq 1$.

14. P_n: $1 + 2 + 2^2 + \cdots + 2^{n-1} = 2^n - 1$.
P_1 is true: $2^{1-1} = 2^1 - 1$.
Now assume P_k is true:
$1 + 2 + 2^2 + \cdots + 2^{k-1} = 2^k - 1$.
Add 2^k to both sides,
$1 + 2 + 2^2 + \cdots + 2^{k-1} + 2^k$
$= 2^k - 1 + 2^k = 2 \cdot 2^k - 1 = 2^{k+1} - 1$, so
P_{k+1} is true.
Therefore, P_n is true for all $n \geq 1$.

15. P_n: $\dfrac{1}{1 \cdot 2} + \dfrac{1}{2 \cdot 3} + \cdots + \dfrac{1}{n(n + 1)} = \dfrac{n}{n + 1}$.

P_1 is true: $\dfrac{1}{1 \cdot 2} = \dfrac{1}{1 + 1}$.

Now assume P_k is true:

$\dfrac{1}{1 \cdot 2} + \dfrac{1}{2 \cdot 3} + \cdots + \dfrac{1}{k(k + 1)}$.

Add $\dfrac{1}{(k + 1)(k + 2)}$ to both sides:

$\dfrac{1}{1 \cdot 2} + \dfrac{1}{2 \cdot 3} + \cdots + \dfrac{1}{k(k + 1)} + \dfrac{1}{(k + 1)(k + 2)}$

$= \dfrac{k}{k + 1} + \dfrac{1}{(k + 1)(k + 2)} = \dfrac{k(k + 2) + 1}{(k + 1)(k + 2)}$

$= \dfrac{(k + 1)(k + 1)}{(k + 1)(k + 2)} = \dfrac{k + 1}{k + 2} = \dfrac{k + 1}{(k + 1) + 1}$,

so P_{k+1} is true.
Therefore, P_n is true for all $n \geq 1$.

16. P_n: $\dfrac{1}{1\cdot 3} + \dfrac{1}{3\cdot 5} + \cdots + \dfrac{1}{(2n-1)(2n+1)} = \dfrac{n}{2n+1}$.

P_1 is true: it says that $\dfrac{1}{1\cdot 3} = \dfrac{1}{2\cdot 1 + 1}$.

Now assume P_k is true:

$\dfrac{1}{1\cdot 3} + \dfrac{1}{3\cdot 5} + \cdots + \dfrac{1}{(2k-1)(2k+1)} = \dfrac{k}{2k+1}$.

Add $\dfrac{1}{[2(k+1)-1][2(k+1)+1]}$

$= \dfrac{1}{(2k+1)(2k+3)}$ to both sides, and we have

$\dfrac{1}{1\cdot 3} + \dfrac{1}{3\cdot 5} + \cdots + \dfrac{1}{(2k-1)(2k+1)}$

$\qquad + \dfrac{1}{[2(k+1)-1][2(k+1)+1]}$

$= \dfrac{k}{2k+1} + \dfrac{1}{(2k+1)(2k+3)} = \dfrac{k(2k+3)+1}{(2k+1)(2k+3)}\cdots$

$= \dfrac{(2k+1)(k+1)}{(2k+1)(2k+3)} = \dfrac{k+1}{2(k+1)+1}$,

so P_{k+1} is true.

Therefore, P_n is true for all $n \geq 1$.

17. P_n: $2^n \geq 2n$.

P_1 is true: $2^1 \geq 2\cdot 1$ (in fact, they are equal). Now assume P_k is true: $2^k \geq 2k$.

Then $2^{k+1} = 2\cdot 2^k \geq 2\cdot 2k$

$= 2\cdot(k+k) \geq 2(k+1)$, so P_{k+1} is true. Therefore, P_n is true for all $n \geq 1$.

18. P_n: $3^n \geq 3n$.

P_1 is true: $3^1 \geq 3\cdot 1$ (in fact, they are equal). Now assume P_k is true: $3^k \geq 3k$.

Then $3^{k+1} = 3\cdot 3^k \geq 3\cdot 3k$

$= 3\cdot(k+2k) \geq 3(k+1)$, so P_{k+1} is true. Therefore, P_n is true for all $n \geq 1$.

19. P_n: 3 is a factor of $n^3 + 2n$.

P_1 is true: 3 is a factor of $1^3 + 2\cdot 1 = 3$.

Now assume P_k is true: 3 is a factor of $k^3 + 2k$.

Then $(k+1)^3 + 2(k+1)$

$= (k^3 + 3k^2 + 3k + 1) + (2k + 2)$

$= (k^3 + 2k) + 3(k^2 + k + 1)$.

Since 3 is a factor of both terms, it is a factor of the sum, so P_{k+1} is true. Therefore, P_n is true for all $n \geq 1$.

20. P_n: 6 is a factor of $7^n - 1$.

P_1 is true: 6 is a factor of $7^1 - 1 = 6$.

Now assume P_k is true, so that 6 is a factor of $7^k - 1 = 6$.

Then $7^{k+1} - 1 = 7\cdot 7^k - 1 = 7(7^k - 1) + 6$. Since 6 is a factor of both terms of this sum, it is a factor of the sum, so P_{k+1} is true.

Therefore, P_n is true for all positive integers n.

21. P_n: The sum of the first n terms of a geometric sequence

with first term a_1 and common ratio $r \neq 1$ is $\dfrac{a_1(1-r^n)}{1-r}$.

P_1 is true: $a_1 = \dfrac{a_1(1-r^1)}{1-r}$.

Now assume P_k is true so that

$a_1 + a_1 r + \cdots = a_1 r^{k-1} = \dfrac{a_1(1-r^k)}{(1-r)}$.

Add $a_1 r^k$ to both sides: $a_1 + a_1 r + \cdots = a_1 r^{k-1}$

$+ a_1 r^k = \dfrac{a_1(1-r^k)}{(1-r)} + a_1 r^k$

$= \dfrac{a_1(1-r^k) + ar^k(1-r)}{1-r}$

$= \dfrac{a_1 - a_1 r^k - a_1 r^{k+1}}{1-r} = \dfrac{a_1 - a_1 r^{k+1}}{1-r}$,

so P_{k+1} is true. Therefore, P_n is true for all positive integers n.

22. P_n: $S_n = \dfrac{n}{2}[2a_1 + (n-1)d]$.

First note that $a_n = a_1 + (n-1)d$. P_1 is true:

$S_1 = \dfrac{1}{2}[2a_1 + (1-1)d] = \dfrac{1}{2}(2a_1) = a_1$.

Now assume P_k is true: $S_k = \dfrac{k}{2}[2a_1 + (k-1)d]$.

Add $a_{k+1} = a_1 + kd$ to both sides, and observe that $S_k + a_{k+1} = S_{k+1}$.

Then we have

$S_{k+1} = \dfrac{k}{2}[2a_1 + (k-1)d] + a_1 + kd$

$= ka_1 + \dfrac{1}{2}k(k-1)d + a_1 + kd$

$= (k+1)a_1 + \dfrac{1}{2}k(k+1)d$

$= \dfrac{k+1}{2}[2a_1 + (k+1-1)d]$.

Therefore, P_{k+1} is true, so P_n is true for all $n \geq 1$.

23. P_n: $\displaystyle\sum_{k=1}^{n} k = \dfrac{n(n+1)}{2}$.

P_1 is true: $\displaystyle\sum_{k=1}^{1} k = 1 = \dfrac{1\cdot 2}{2}$.

Now assume P_k is true: $\displaystyle\sum_{i=1}^{k} i = \dfrac{k(k+1)}{2}$.

Add $(k+1)$ to both sides, and we have

$\displaystyle\sum_{i=1}^{k+1} i = \dfrac{k(k+1)}{2} + (k+1)$

$= \dfrac{k(k+1)}{2} + \dfrac{2(k+1)}{2} = \dfrac{(k+1)(k+2)}{2}$

$= \dfrac{(k+1)(k+1+1)}{2}$, so P_{k+1} is true.

Therefore, P_n is true for all $n \geq 1$.

24. P_n: $\displaystyle\sum_{k=1}^{n} k^3 = \dfrac{n^2(n+1)^2}{4}$. P_1 is true: $1^3 = \dfrac{1^2 2^2}{4}$.

Now assume P_k is true so that

$1^3 + 2^3 + \cdots + k^3 = \dfrac{k^2(k+1)^2}{4}$. Add $(k+1)^3$ to both

sides and we have

$1^3 + 2^3 + \cdots + k^3 + (k+1)^3$

$= \dfrac{k^2(k+1)^2}{4} + (k+1)^3 = \dfrac{k^2(k+1)^2 + 4(k+1)^3}{4}$

$= \dfrac{(k+1)^2(k^2 + 4k + 4)}{4} = \dfrac{(k+1)^2((k+1)+1)^2}{4}$

so P_{k+1} is true. Therefore, P_n is true for all positive integers.

25. Use the formula in 23: $\sum_{k=1}^{500} k = \dfrac{(500)(501)}{2} = 125,250$

26. Use the formula in Example 2: $\sum_{k=1}^{250} k^2 = \dfrac{(250)(251)(501)}{6}$

$= 5,239,625$

27. Use the formula in 23: $\sum_{k=4}^{n} k = \sum_{k=1}^{n} k - \sum_{k=1}^{3} k$

$= \dfrac{n(n+1)}{2} - \dfrac{3 \cdot 4}{2} = \dfrac{n^2 + n - 12}{2} = \dfrac{(n-3)(n+4)}{2}$

28. Use the formula in 24: $\sum_{k=1}^{75} k^3 = \dfrac{(75^2)(76^2)}{4}$

$= 8,122,500$

29. Use the formula in 14: $\sum_{k=1}^{35} 2^{k-1}$

$= 2^{35} - 1 \approx 3.44 \times 10^{10}$

30. Use the formula in 24: $\sum_{k=1}^{15} k^3 = \dfrac{(15^2)(16^2)}{4}$

$= 14,400$

31. $\sum_{k=1}^{n} (k^2 - 3k + 4) = \sum_{k=1}^{n} k^2 - \sum_{k=1}^{n} 3k + \sum_{k=1}^{n} 4$

$= \dfrac{n(n+1)(2n+1)}{6} - 3\left[\dfrac{n(n+1)}{2}\right] + 4n$

$= \dfrac{n(n^2 - 3n + 8)}{3}$

32. $\sum_{k=1}^{n} (2k^2 + 5k - 2) = \sum_{k=1}^{n} 2k^2 + \sum_{k=1}^{n} 5k - \sum_{k=1}^{n} 2 = 2$

$= 2\left[\dfrac{n(n+1)(2n+1)}{6}\right] + 5\left[\dfrac{n(n+1)}{2}\right] - 2n$

$= \dfrac{n(4n^2 + 21n + 5)}{6} = \dfrac{n(n+5)(4n+1)}{6}$

33. $\sum_{k=1}^{n} (k^3 - 1) = \sum_{k=1}^{n} k^3 - \sum_{k=1}^{n} 1 = \dfrac{n^2(n+1)^2}{4} - n$

$= \dfrac{n(n^3 + 2n^2 + n - 4)}{4} = \dfrac{n(n-1)(n^2 + 3n + 4)}{4}$

34. $\sum_{k=1}^{n} (k^3 + 4k - 5) = \sum_{k=1}^{n} k^3 + \sum_{k=1}^{n} 4k - \sum_{k=1}^{n} 5$

$= \dfrac{n^2(n+1)^2}{4} + 4\left[\dfrac{n(n+1)}{2}\right] - 5n$

$= \dfrac{n(n^3 + 2n^2 + 9n - 12)}{4} = \dfrac{n(n-1)(n^2 + 3n + 12)}{4}$

35. The inductive step does not work for 2 people. Sending them alternately out of the room leaves 1 person (and one blood type) each time, but we cannot conclude that their blood types will match *each other.*

36. The number k is a fixed number for which the statement P_k is known to be true. Once the anchor is established, we can assume that such a number k exists. We can not assume that P_n is true, because n is not fixed.

37. False. Mathematical induction is used to show that a statement P_n is true for all positive integers.

38. True. $(1+1)^2 = 4 = 4(1)$. P_n is false, however, for all other values of n.

39. The inductive step assumes that the statement is true for some positive integer k. The answer is E.

40. The anchor step, proving P_1, comes first. The answer is A.

41. Mathematical induction could be used, but the formula for a finite arithmetic sequence with $a_1 = 1, d = 2$ would also work. The answer is B.

42. The first two partial sums are 1 and 9. That eliminates all answers except C. Mathematical induction can be used to show directly that C is the correct answer.

43. P_n: 2 is a factor of $(n+1)(n+2)$. P_1 is true because 2 is a factor of $(2)(3)$. Now assume P_k is true so that 2 is a factor of $(k+1)(k+2)$. Then
$[(k+1) + 1][(k+2) + 2]$
$= (k+2)(k+3) = k^2 + 5k + 6$
$= k^2 + 3k + 2 + 2k + 4$
$= (k+1)(k+2) + 2(x+2)$. Since 2 is a factor of both terms of this sum, it is a factor of the sum, and so P_{k+1} is true. Therefore, P_n is true for all positive integers n.

44. P_n: 6 is a factor of $n(n+1)(n+2)$. P_1 is true because 6 is a factor of $(1)(2)(3)$. Now assume P_k is true so that 6 is a factor of $k(k+1)(k+2)$. Then
$(k+1)[(k+1) + 1][(k+1) + 2]$
$= k(k+1)(k+2) + 3(k+1)(k+2)$. Since 2 is a factor of $(k+1)(k+2)$, 6 is a factor of both terms of the sum and thus of the sum itself, and so P_{k+1} is true.

45. Given any two consecutive integers, one of them must be even. Therefore, their product is even. Since $n+1$ and $n+2$ are consecutive integers, their product is even. Therefore, 2 is a factor of $(n+1)(n+2)$.

46. Given any three consecutive integers, one of them must be a multiple of 3, and at least one of them must be even. Therefore, their product is a multiple of 6. Since $n, n+1$ and $n+2$ are three consecutive integers, 6 is a factor of $n(n+1)(n+2)$.

47. P_n: $F_{n+2} - 1 = \sum_{k=1}^{n} F_k$. P_1 is true since

$F_{1+2} = 1 = F_3 - 1 = 2 - 1 = 1$, which equals

$\sum_{k=1}^{1} F_k = 1$. Now assume that P_k is true:

$F_{k+2} - 1 = \sum_{i=1}^{k} F_i$. Then $F_{(k+1)+2} - 1$

$= F_{k+3} - 1 = F_{k+1} + F_{k+2} - 1$

$= (F_{k+2} - 1) + F_{k+1} = \left(\sum_{i=1}^{k} F_i\right) + F_{k+1}$

$= \sum_{i=1}^{k+1} F_i$, so P_{k+1} is true. Therefore, P_n is true

for all $n \geq 1$.

48. P_n: $a_n < 2$. P_1 is easy: $a_1 = \sqrt{2} < 2$. Now assume that P_k is true: $a_k < 2$. Note that
$a_{k+1} = \sqrt{2 + a_k}$, so that
$a^2_{k+1} < 2 + a_k < 2 + 2 = 4$; therefore $a_{k+1} < 2$, so P_{k+1} is true. Therefore, P_n is true for all $n \geq 1$.

49. P_n: $a - 1$ is a factor of $a^n - 1$. P_1 is true because $a - 1$ is a factor of $a - 1$. Now assume P_k is true so that $a - 1$ is a factor of $a^k - 1$. Then $a^{k+1} - 1 = a \cdot ak - 1$
$= a(a^k - 1) + (a - 1)$. Since $a - 1$ is a factor of both terms in the sum, it is a factor of the sum, and so P_{k+1} is true. Therefore, P_n is true for all positive integers n.

50. Let $P(a) = a^n - 1$. Since $P(1) = 1^n - 1 = 0$, the Factor Theorem for polynomials allows us to conclude that $a - 1$ is a factor of P.

51. P_n: $3n - 4 \geq n$ for $n \geq 2$. P_2 is true since $3 \cdot 2 - 4 \leq 2$. Now assume that P_k is true: $3k - 4 \geq 2$. Then $3(k + 1) - 4 = 3k + 3 - 4 = (3k - 4) + 3k \geq k + 3 \geq k + 1$, so P_{k+1} is true. Therefore, P_n is true for all $n \geq 2$.

52. P_n: $2^n \geq n^2$ for $n \geq 4$. P_4 is true since $2^4 \geq 4^2$. Now assume that P_k is true: $2^k \geq k^2$. Then $2^{k+1} = 2 \cdot 2^k \geq 2 \cdot k^2 \geq 2 \cdot k^2 \geq k^2 + 2k + 1 = (k + 1)^2$. The inequality $2k^2 \geq k^2 + 2k + 1$, or equivalently, $k^2 \geq 2k + 1$, is true for all $k \geq 4$ because $k^2 = k \cdot k \geq 4k = 2k + 2k > 2k + 1$.) Thus P_{k+1} is true, so P_n is true for all $n \geq 4$.

53. Use P_3 as the anchor and obtain the inductive step by representing any n-gon as the union of a triangle and an $(n - 1)$-gon.

■ Section 9.7 Statistics and Data (Graphical)

Exploration 1

1. We observe that the numbers seem to be centered a bit below 13. We would need to take into account the different state populations (not given in the table) in order to compute the national average exactly; but, just for the record, it was about 12.5 percent.

2. We observe in the stemplot that 3 states have percentages above 15.

3. We observe in the stemplot that the bottom five states are all below 10%. Returning to the table, we pick these out as Alaska, Colorado, Georgia, Texas, and Utah.

4. The low outlier is Alaska, where older people would be less willing or able to cope with the harsh winter conditions. The high outlier is Florida, where the mild weather and abundant retirement communities attract older residents.

Quick Review 9.7

1. $\approx 15.48\%$

2. $\approx 20.94\%$

3. $\approx 14.44\%$

4. $\approx 27.22\%$

5. ≈ 1723

6. 9200

7. 235 thousand

8. 238 million

9. 1 million

10. 1 billion

Section 9.7 Exercises

1.
```
0 | 5 8 9
1 | 3 4 6
2 | 3 6 8
3 | 3 9
4 |
5 |
6 | 1
```
61 is an outlier.

2.
```
 Maris        Aaron
 9 8 5 | 0 |
 6 4 3 | 1 | 0 2 3
 8 6 3 | 2 | 0 4 6 7 9
   9 3 | 3 | 0 2 4 4 8 9 9
       | 4 | 0 0 4 4 4 4 5 7
       | 5 |
     1 | 6 |
```
Except for Maris's one record-breaking year, his home run output falls well short of Aaron's.

3.
```
        Males
 6 | 0 3
 6 | 7 8 8 8
 7 | 1 2 2 3 3 3
 7 |
```
This stemplot shows the life expectancies of males in the nations of South America are clustered near 70, with two lower values clustered near 60.

4.
```
        Females
 6 | 5 8
 7 | 1 2
 7 | 5 6 7 7 9 9
 8 | 0 0
```
This stemplot shows the life expectancies of females in the nations of South America are clustered in the high 70's and at 80, with four lower values in the high 60's and low 70's.

5.
```
        Males           Females
       3 0 | 6 |
     8 8 8 7 | 6 | 5 8
 3 3 3 2 2 1 | 7 | 1 2
           | 7 | 5 6 7 7 9 9
           | 8 | 0 0
```
This stemplot shows that the life expectancies of the women in the nations of South America are about 5–6 years higher than that of the men in the nations of South America.

6. Female-Male Difference
```
 3 | 5
 4 | 7 8
 5 | 2 4 8
 6 | 3 5 7
 7 | 7 8
 8 | 1
```
This stemplot of differences shows that the women in the nations of South America have higher life expectancies than the men, by about 5–6 years.

7.

Life expectancy (years)	Frequency
60.0–64.9	2
65.0–69.9	4
70.0–74.9	6

8.

Life expectancy (years)	Frequency
60.0–64.9	1
65.0–69.9	1
70.0–74.9	2
75.0–79.9	8

9.

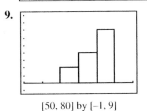

[50, 80] by [−1, 9]

10.

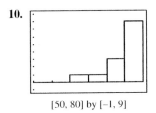

[50, 80] by [−1, 9]

11.

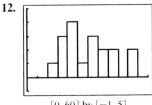

[0, 60] by [−1, 5]

12.

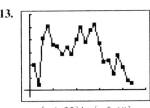

[0, 60] by [−1, 5]

13.

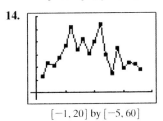

[−1, 25] by [−5, 60]

14.

[−1, 20] by [−5, 60]

15.

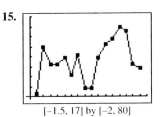

[−1.5, 17] by [−2, 80]

16.

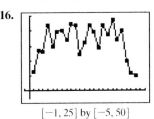

[−1, 25] by [−5, 50]

17.

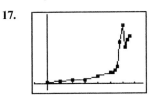

[1965, 2008] by [−1000, 11000]

The top male's earnings appear to be growing exponentially, with unusually high earnings in 1999 and 2000. Since the graph shows the earnings of only the top player (as opposed to a mean or median for all players), it can behave strangely if the top player has a very good year — as Tiger Woods did in 1999 and 2000.

18.

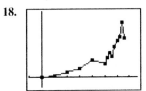

[1965, 2008] by [−500, 3400]

The top female's earnings appear to be growing faster than linearly, but with more fluctuation since 1990. Since the graph shows the earnings of only the top player (as opposed to a mean or median for all players), it is strongly affected by how well the top player does in a given year. The top player in 2002 and 2003, Annika Sorenstam, played in fewer tournaments in 2003 and hence won less money.

19.

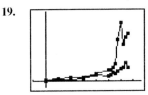

[1965, 2008] by [−1000, 11000]

After approaching parity in 1985, the top PGA player's earnings have grown much faster than the top LPGA player's earnings, even if the unusually good years for Tiger Woods (1999 and 2000) are not considered part of the trend.

20. The 1985 male total was unusually low in the context of the rest of the time plot. If it had been in line with the earlier and later data, the difference between the PGA and LPGA growth rates would not have been that large. (The unusual PGA point in 1985, oddly enough, belonged to Curtis Strange.)

21.

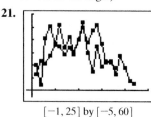

[−1, 25] by [−5, 60]

The two home run hitters enjoyed similar success, with Mays enjoying a bit of an edge in the earlier and later years of his career, and Mantle enjoying an edge in the middle years.

22.

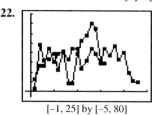

[–1, 25] by [−5, 80]

The two home run hitters were comparable for the first seven years of their careers.

23. (a)

Stem	Leaf
28	2
29	3 7
30	
31	6 7
32	7 8
33	5 5 5 8
34	2 8 8
35	3 3 4
36	3 7
37	
38	5

(b)

Interval	Frequency
25.0–29.9	3
30.0–34.9	11
35.0–39.9	6

(c)

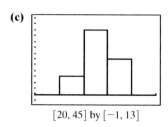

[20, 45] by [−1, 13]

(d) Time is not a variable in the data.

24. (a)

Stem	Leaf
6	2 3 9 9
7	7 9 9 9
8	0 2 3 7 7 8 9 9
9	0 0 0 1 1 2 3 3 3 4 5 6 7
10	2 3 3 6 6 6 7 9
11	0 2 4 6
12	0 5 9

(b)

Interval	Frequency
6.0–6.9	4
7.0–7.9	4
8.0–8.9	8
9.0–9.9	13
10.0–10.9	8
11.0–11.9	4
12.0–12.9	3

(c)

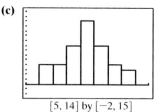

[5, 14] by [−2, 15]

(d) The data are not categorical.

25.

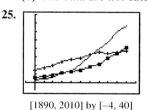

[1890, 2010] by [−4, 40]

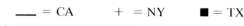

——— = CA   + = NY   ■ = TX

26.

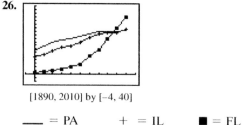

[1890, 2010] by [−4, 40]

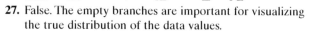

——— = PA   + = IL   ■ = FL

27. False. The empty branches are important for visualizing the true distribution of the data values.

28. False. They are outliers only if they are significantly higher or lower than the other numbers in the data set.

29. A time plot uses a continuous line. The answer is C.

30. Back-to-back stemplots are designed for comparing data sets. The answer is B.

31. The histogram suggests data values clustered near an upper limit — such as the maximum possible score on an easy test. The answer is A.

32. 45° is 1/8, or 12.5%, of 360°. The answer is B.

33. Answers will vary. Possible outliers could be the pulse rates of long-distance runners and swimmers, which are often unusually low. Students who have had to run to class from across campus might have pulse rates that are unusually high.

34. Answers will vary. Female heights typically have a distribution that is uniformly lower than male heights, but the difference might not be apparent from a stem plot, especially if the sample is small.

35.

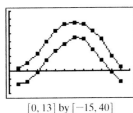

[0, 13] by [−15, 40]

36. Using the form $f(t) = k + a \sin[b(t - h)]$, we have $b = \pi/6$ for both graphs since the period is 12. a is half the difference between the extremes, and k is the average of the extremes. Finally, h is the offset to the first time this average occurs.

The maxima of both graphs occur in July ($t = 7$), while the minima occur in January ($t = 1$), so we should choose $b = 3.5$ or 4 (if the latter is halfway between the maximum and the minimum, but the former gives a better match for some values of t). Thus, for the high temperature, use $f(t) \approx 17 + 15 \sin\left[\dfrac{\pi}{6}(t - 3.5)\right]$ or $17 + 15 \sin\left[\dfrac{\pi}{6}(t - 4)\right]$, and for the low temperature, use

$$g(t) \approx 6.5 + 15.5 \sin\left[\dfrac{\pi}{6}(t - 3.5)\right] \text{ or}$$

$$6.5 + 15.5 \sin\left[\dfrac{\pi}{6}(t - 4)\right].$$

■ Section 9.8   Statistics and Data (Algebraic)

Exploration 1

1. In Figure 9.19 (a) the extreme values will cause the range to be big, but the compact distribution of the rest of the data indicate a small interquartile range. The data in Figure 9.19 (b) exhibit high variability.

2. Figure 9.20 (b) has a longer "tail" to the right (skewed right), so the values in the tail pull the mean to the right of the (resistant) median. Figure 9.20 (c) is skewed left, so the values in the tail pull the mean to the left of the median. Figure 9.20 (a) is symmetric about a vertical line, so the median and the mean are close together.

Quick Review 9.8

1. $\displaystyle\sum_{i=1}^{7} x_i = x_1 + x_2 + x_3 + x_4 + x_5 + x_6 + x_7$

2. $\displaystyle\sum_{i=1}^{5} (x_i - \overline{x}) = (x_1 - \overline{x}) + (x_2 - \overline{x}) + (x_3 - \overline{x}) + (x_4 - \overline{x}) + (x_5 - \overline{x}) = x_1 + x_2 + x_3 + x_4 + x_5 - 5\overline{x}.$

Note that, since $\overline{x} = \dfrac{1}{5}\displaystyle\sum_{i=1}^{5} x_i$, this simplifies to 0.

3. $\dfrac{1}{7}\displaystyle\sum_{i=1}^{7} x_i = \dfrac{1}{7}(x_1 + x_2 + x_3 + x_4 + x_5 + x_6 + x_7)$

4. $\dfrac{1}{5}\displaystyle\sum_{i=1}^{5} (x_i - \overline{x}) = \dfrac{1}{5}(x_1 + x_2 + x_3 + x_4 + x_5 - 5\overline{x}) = \dfrac{1}{5}(x_1 + x_2 + x_3 + x_4 + x_5) - \overline{x}.$ Note that, since $\overline{x} = \dfrac{1}{5}\displaystyle\sum_{i=1}^{5} x_i$, this simplifies to 0.

5. The expression at the end of the first line is a simple expansion of the sum (and is a reasonable answer to the given question). By expanding further, we can also arrive at the final expression below, which is somewhat simpler.

$$\dfrac{1}{5}\sum_{i=1}^{5} (x_i - \overline{x})^2 = \dfrac{1}{5}[(x_1 - \overline{x})^2 + (x_2 - \overline{x})^2 + \cdots + (x_5 - \overline{x})^2]$$

$$= \dfrac{1}{5}[(x_1^2 - 2x_1\overline{x} + \overline{x}^2) + (x_2^2 - 2x_2\overline{x} + \overline{x}^2) + \cdots + (x_5^2 - 2x_5\overline{x} + \overline{x}^2)]$$

$$= \dfrac{1}{5}[x_1^2 + x_2^2 + \cdots + x_5^2 - 2\overline{x}(x_1 + x_2 + \cdots + x_5)] + \overline{x}^2$$

$$= \dfrac{1}{5}(x_1^2 + x_2^2 + \cdots + x_5^2) - 2\overline{x}^2 + \overline{x}^2 = \dfrac{1}{5}(x_1^2 + x_2^2 + \cdots + x_5^2) - \overline{x}^2$$

6. The square root does not allow for further simplication. The final answer is the square root of the expression from #5: either

$$\sqrt{\dfrac{1}{5}[(x_1 - \overline{x})^2 + (x_2 - \overline{x})^2 + \cdots + (x_5 - \overline{x})^2]} \text{ or } \sqrt{\dfrac{1}{5}(x_1^2 + x_2^2 + \cdots + x_5^2) - \overline{x}^2}.$$

7. $\displaystyle\sum_{i=1}^{8} x_i f_i$

8. $\displaystyle\sum_{i=1}^{10} (x_i - \overline{x})^2$

9. $\dfrac{1}{50}\displaystyle\sum_{i=1}^{50} (x_i - \overline{x})^2$

10. $\sqrt{\dfrac{1}{7}\displaystyle\sum_{i=1}^{7} (x_i - \overline{x})^2}$

Section 9.8 Exercises

1. **(a)** Statistic. The number characterizes a set of known data values.

   (b) Parameter. The number describes an entire population, on the basis of some statistical inference.

   (c) Statistic. The number is calculated from information about all rats in a small, experimental population.

2. **(a)** Mode. No quantitative measure beyond what is "most common" is implied.

   (b) Mean. A pitcher's earned run average (ERA) is total earned runs divided by number of nine-inning blocks pitched.

   (c) Median. The middle height is considered average.

3. $\bar{x} = \frac{1}{5}(12 + 23 + 15 + 48 + 36) = \frac{134}{5} = 26.8$

4. $\bar{x} = \frac{1}{6}(4 + 8 + 11 + 6 + 21 + 7) = \frac{57}{6} = 9.5$

5. $\bar{x} = \frac{1}{6}(32.4 + 48.1 + 85.3 + 67.2 + 72.4 + 55.3) = \frac{360.7}{6} = \frac{3607}{60} \approx 60.12$

6. $\bar{x} = \frac{1}{7}(27.4 + 3.1 + 9.7 + 32.3 + 12.8 + 39.4 + 73.7) = \frac{198.4}{7} = \frac{992}{35} \approx 28.3$

7. $\bar{x} = \frac{1}{6}(1.5 + 0.5 + 4.8 + 7.3 + 6.3 + 3.0) = 3.9$ million, or 3,900,000

8. $\bar{x} = \frac{1}{6}(29.8 + 12.9 + 11.4 + 18.0 + 11.9 + 17.0) \approx 16.83$ million, or about 16,830,000

9. $\bar{x} = \frac{1}{9}(0 + 0 + 1 + 2 + 61 + 33 + 26 + 13 + 1) = \frac{137}{9} \approx 15.2$ satellites

10. $\bar{x} = \frac{1}{7}(30{,}065{,}000 + 13{,}209{,}000 + 44{,}579{,}000 + \cdots + 17{,}819{,}000) = \frac{1}{7}(148{,}196{,}000) = 21{,}171{,}000 \text{ km}^2$

11. There are 9 data values, which is an odd number, so the median is the middle data value when they are arranged in order. In order, the data values are {0, 0, 1, 1, 2, 8, 21, 28, 30}. The median is 2.

12. There are 7 data values, which is an odd number, so the median is the middle data value when they are arranged in order. In order, the data values are {7687, 9938, 13,209, 17,819, 24,256, 30,065, 44,579} in thousands of km². The median is 17,819,000 km².

13. Mays: $\frac{660}{22} = 30$ home runs/year. Mantle: $\frac{536}{18} \approx 29.8$ home runs/year. Mays had the greater production rate.

14. State College: $\frac{12}{5} = 2.4$ houses/day. College Station: $\frac{15}{7} \approx 2.14$ houses/day. The State College workers were faster.

15. No computations needed — Hip-Hop House: 1147 skirts in 4 weeks. What-Next Fashions: 1516 skirts in 4 weeks. What-Next Fashions had the greater production rate.

16. India: $\frac{311{,}000{,}000{,}000}{882{,}575{,}000} \approx \$352$.

    Mexico: $\frac{218{,}000{,}000{,}000}{87{,}715{,}000} \approx \$2485$. Mexico has the higher PCI.

17. For {79.5, 82.1, 82.3, 82.9, 84.0, 84.5, 84.8, 85.4, 85.7, 85.7, 86.0, 86.4, 87.0, 87.5, 87.7, 88.0, 88.0, 88.2, 88.2, 88.5, 89.2, 89.2, 89.8, 89.8, 91.1, 91.3, 91.6, 91.8, 94.1, 94.4}, the median is $\frac{87.7 + 88.0}{2} = 87.85$, and there is no mode.

18. $\bar{x} = \dfrac{5(18{,}522) + 4(27{,}102) + 3(31{,}286) + 2(20{,}732) + 1(18{,}875)}{18{,}522 + 27{,}102 + 31{,}286 + 20{,}732 + 18{,}875}$

    ≈ 3.05

19. $\bar{x} = \dfrac{5(9879) + 4(5119) + 3(6143) + 2(2616) + 1(3027)}{9879 + 5119 + 6143 + 2616 + 3027}$

    ≈ 3.61

20. **(a)** Non-weighted: $\bar{x} = \frac{1}{12}(2 + 5 + 12 + 20 + \cdots + 10 + 3) = \frac{221}{12} \approx 18.42°\text{C}$

    (b) Weighted: $\bar{x} = \dfrac{(2)(31) + (5)(28) + (12)(31) + (20)(30) + \cdots + (10)(30) + (3)(31)}{31 + 28 + 31 + 30 + \cdots + 30 + 31} = \dfrac{6748}{365} \approx 18.49°\text{C}$

    (c) The weighted average is the better indicator.

21. (a) Non-weighted: $\bar{x} = \dfrac{1}{12}(-9 - 7 - 1 + 7 + \cdots - 1 - 7) = \dfrac{77}{12} \approx 6.42°C$

(b) Weighted: $\bar{x} = \dfrac{(-9)(31) + (-7)(28) + (-1)(31) + (7)(30) + \cdots + (-1)(30) + (-7)(31)}{31 + 28 + 31 + 30 + \cdots + 30 + 31} = \dfrac{2370}{365} \approx 6.49°C$

(c) The weighted average is the better indicator.

22. The ordered data for Mark McGwire is $\{\underline{3}, 9, 9, \underline{22}, \underline{29}, 32,$
$32, \underline{33}, \underline{39}, 39, 42, \underline{49}, \underline{52}, 58, 65, \underline{70}\}$ so the median is
$\dfrac{33 + 39}{2} = 36,$

$Q_3 = \dfrac{49 + 52}{2} = 50.5, Q_1 = \dfrac{22 + 29}{2} = 25.5.$

Five-number summary: $\{3, 25.5, 36, 50.5, 70\}$
Range: $70 - 3 = 67$
IQR: $50.5 - 25.5 = 25$
No outliers
The ordered data for Barry Bonds is:
$\{\underline{16}, 19, 24, \underline{25}, \underline{25}, 33, 33, \underline{34}, \underline{34}, 37, 37, \underline{40}, \underline{42}, 46, 49, \underline{73}\}$ so
the median is $\dfrac{34 + 34}{2} = 34,$

$Q_3 = \dfrac{40 + 42}{2} = 41,$ and $Q_1 = \dfrac{25 + 25}{2} = 25$

Five-number summary: $\{16, 25, 34, 41, 73\}$
Range: $73 - 16 = 57$
IQR: $41 - 25 = 16$
Outlier: 73

23. The ordered data for Willie Mays is: $\{\underline{4}, 6, 8, 13, 18, \underline{20}, 22,$
$23, 28, 29, \underline{29}, \underline{34}, 35, 36, 37, 38, \underline{40}, 41, 47, 49, 51, \underline{52}\}$ so the
median is
$\dfrac{29 + 34}{2} = 31.5, Q_3 = 40,$ and $Q_1 = 20$

Five-number summary: $\{4, 20, 31.5, 40, 52\}$
Range: $52 - 4 = 48$
IQR: $40 - 20 = 20$
No outliers
The ordered data for Mickey Mantle is:
$\{\underline{13}, 15, 18, 19, \underline{21}, 22, 23, 23, \underline{27}, \underline{30}, 31, 34, 35, \underline{37}, 40, 42,$
$52, \underline{54}\}$ so the median is
$\dfrac{27 + 30}{2} = 28.5, Q_3 = 37,$ and $Q_1 = 21$

Five-number summary: $\{13, 21, 28.5, 37, 54\}$
Range: $54 - 13 = 41$
IQR: $37 - 21 = 16$
No outliers

24. While a stemplot is not needed to answer this question,
the sorted stemplot below is more compact than a sorted
list of the 44 numbers. The underlined numbers are the
ones used for the five-number summary, which is

Min	Q_1	Median	Q_3	Max
6.2	8.5	9.25	10.6	12.9
	$= \dfrac{8.3 + 8.7}{2}$	$= \dfrac{9.2 + 9.3}{2}$	$= \dfrac{10.6 + 10.6}{2}$	

The range is $12.9 - 6.2 = 6.7$ and
IQR $= 10.6 - 8.5 = 2.1$. There are no outliers, since
none of the numbers fall below $Q_1 - 1.5 \times$ IQR $= 5.35$
or above $Q_3 + 1.5 \times IQG = 13.75.$

Stem	Leaf
6	$\underline{2}$ 3 9 9
7	7 9 9 9
8	0 2 $\underline{3}$ 7 7 8 9 9
9	0 0 0 1 $\underline{1}$ $\underline{2}$ $\underline{3}$ 3 3 4 5 6 7
10	2 3 $\underline{3}$ $\underline{6}$ $\underline{6}$ 6 7 9
11	0 2 4 6
12	0 5 $\underline{9}$

25. The sorted list is $\{\underline{28.2}, 29.3, 29.7, 31.6, \underline{31.7}, 32.7, 32.8, 33.5,$
$33.5, \underline{33.5}, 33.8, 34.2, 34.8, 34.8, \underline{35.3}, 35.4, 36.7, 37.3, \underline{38.5}\}$. Since
there are 19 numbers, the median is the 10th, Q_1 is the
5th, and Q_3 is the 15th; no additional computations are
needed. All these numbers are underlined above, and are
summarized below:

Min	Q_1	Median	Q_3	Max
28.2	31.7	33.5	35.3	38.5

The range is $38.5 - 28.2 = 10.3,$ and
IQR $= 35.3 - 31.7 = 3.6.$ There are no outliers, since
none of the numbers fall below $Q_1 - 1.5 \times$ IQR $= 26.3$
or above $Q_3 + 1.5 \times$ IQR $= 40.7.$

Note that some computer software may return

$Q_1 = 32.2 = \dfrac{31.7 + 32.7}{2}$ and $Q_3 = 35.05 = \dfrac{34.8 + 35.3}{2}$

(The TI calculator which computes the five-number
summary produces the results shown in the table).

26. (a)

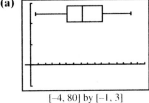

[−4, 80] by [−1, 3]

(b)

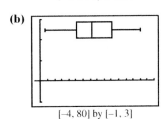

[−4, 80] by [−1, 3]

27. (a)

[−3, 80] by [−1, 2]

(b)

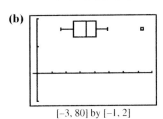

[−3, 80] by [−1, 2]

28. (a)

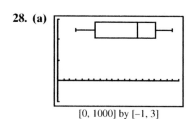

[0, 1000] by [−1, 3]

(b)

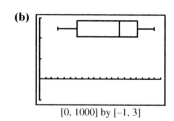

[0, 1000] by [−1, 3]

29. 12 of the 44 numbers are more than 10.5: $\dfrac{12}{44} = \dfrac{3}{11}$

30. All but 4 of the 44 numbers are more than 7.5: $\dfrac{40}{44} = \dfrac{10}{11}$

31. The five-number summaries are:
Mays: 4, 20, 31.5, 40, 52 (top of graph)
Mantle: 13, 21, 28.5, 37, 54
(bottom of graph)

(a) Mays's data set has the greater range.

(b) Mays's data set also has the greater *IQR*.

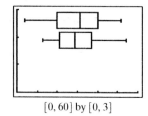

[0, 60] by [0, 3]

32. Although Mays' best year was not as good as Mantle's best year, Mays was in some ways a better home-run hitter: his median season was 31.5 home runs, compared to 28.5 for Mantle. However, Mays had three extremely bad years when he hit fewer than 10 home runs; these make him look worse by comparison.

For #33–38, the best way to do the computation is with the statistics features of a calcuator.

33. $\sigma \approx 9.08$, $\sigma^2 = 82.5$

34. $\sigma \approx 23.99$, $\sigma^2 = 575.64$

35. $\sigma \approx 186.36$; $\sigma^2 \approx 34{,}828.12$

36. $\sigma \approx 126.84$; $\sigma^2 \approx 16{,}088.08$

37. $\sigma \approx 1.53$, $\sigma^2 \approx 2.34$

38. $\sigma \approx 2.60$, $\sigma^2 \approx 6.77$

39. No. An outlier would need to be less than $25.5 - 1.5(25) = -12$ or greater than $50.5 + 1.5(25) = 88$.

40. The standard deviation of a set can never be negative, since it is the (positive) square root of the variance. It is possible for the standard deviation of a set to be zero, but all the numbers in the set would have to be the same.

41. (a) 68%

(b) 2.5%

(c) A parameter, since it applies to the entire population.

42. (a) 16%

(b) 32.7

(c) No. The mean would have to be *weighted* according to the number of people in each state who took the ACT.

43. False. The median is a resistant measure. The *mean* is strongly affected by outliers.

44. True. The box extends from the first quartile, Q_1, to the third quartile, Q_3, and $Q_3 - Q_1$ is the interquartile range.

45. The plot of an ideal normal distribution is a symmetric "bell curve." The answer is A.

46. $\bar{x} = \dfrac{10(3) + 9(3) + 8(5) + 7(6) + 6(4) + 5(3) + 4(1) + 3(0) + 2(0) + 1(0)}{25}$

$= 7.28$
The answer is B.

47. The total number of points from all 30 exams combined is $30 \times 81.3 = 2439$. Adding 9 more points and recalculating produces a new mean of $(2439 + 9)/30 = 81.6$. The median will be unaffected by an adjustment in the top score. The answer is B.

48. In a normal distribution, 95% of the data values lie within 2 standard deviations of the mean. The answer is C.

49. There are many possible answers; examples are given.
(a) {2, 2, 2, 3, 6, 8, 20} — mode = 2, median = 3, and $\bar{x} = \dfrac{43}{7} \approx 6.14$.

(b) {1, 2, 3, 4, 6, 48, 48} — median = 4, $\bar{x} = 16$, and mode = 48

(c) {−20, 1, 1, 1, 2, 3, 4, 5, 6} — $\bar{x} = \dfrac{1}{3}$, mode = 1, and median = 2.

50. There are many possible answers; examples are given.
(a) {2, 4, 6, 8} — $\sigma \approx 2.24$ and IQR = $7 - 3 = 4$.

(b) {1, 5, 5, 6, 6, 9} — IQR = $6 - 5 = 1$, and $\sigma \approx 2.36$.

(c) {3, 3, 3, 9, 9, 9} — IQR = $9 - 3 = 6$ and range = $9 - 3 = 6$.

51. No: $(x_i - \bar{x}) \le (\text{max} - \text{min})^2 = (\text{range})^2$, so that
$\sigma^2 = \dfrac{1}{n}\sum_{i=1}^{n}(x_i - \bar{x})^2 \le \dfrac{1}{n}\sum_{i=1}^{n}(\text{range})^2 = (\text{range})^2$. Then
$\sigma = \sqrt{\sigma^2} \le \sqrt{(\text{range})^2} = \text{range}$.

52. The mode does not have to be a numerical value because it is the data value that occurs most often; both the mean and the median are for numerical data only, since they both involve calculations of numerical data values.

53. There are many possible answers; example data sets are given.

   (a) $\{1, 1, 2, 6, 7\}$ — median = 2 and $\bar{x}$ = 3.4.

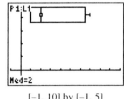

    [–1, 10] by [–1, 5]

   (b) $\{1, 6, 6, 6, 6, 10\}$ — $2 \times \text{IQR} = 2(6 - 6) = 0$ and range = $10 - 1 = 9$.

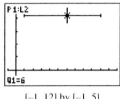

    [–1, 12] by [–1, 5]

   (c) $\{1, 1, 2, 6, 7\}$ — range = $7 - 1 = 6$ and $2 \times \text{IQR} = 2(6 - 1) = 10$.

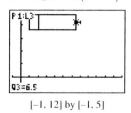

    [–1, 12] by [–1, 5]

54. One possible answer: $\{1, 2, 3, 4, 5, 6, 6, 6, 30\}$.

55. For women living in South American nations, the mean life expectancy is
$$\bar{x} = \frac{(79.7)(39.1) + (67.9)(8.7) + \cdots + (79.2)(3.4) + (77.3)(25.0)}{39.1 + 8.7 + \cdots + 3.4 + 25.0} = \frac{27{,}825.56}{366.4} \approx 75.9 \text{ years.}$$

56. For men living in South American nations, the mean life expectancy is
$$\bar{x} = \frac{(72.0)(39.1) + (62.5)(8.7) + \cdots + (72.7)(3.4) + (71.0)(25.0)}{39.1 + 8.7 + \cdots + 3.4 + 25.0} = \frac{25{,}160.64}{366.4} \approx 68.7 \text{ years.}$$

57. Since $\sigma = 0.05$ mm, we have $2\sigma = 0.1$ mm, so 95% of the ball bearings will be acceptable. Therefore, 5% will be rejected.

58. Use $\mu = 12.08$ and $\sigma = 0.04$.

Then $\mu - 2\sigma = 12.00$ and $\mu + 2\sigma = 12.16$, so 95% of the cans contain 12 to 12.16 oz of cola, 2.5% contain less than 12 oz, and 2.5% contain more than 12 oz. Therefore, 2.5% of the cans contain less than the advertised amount.

■ Chapter 9 Review

1. $\dbinom{12}{5} = \dfrac{12!}{5!(12-5)!} = \dfrac{12!}{5!7!} = 792$

2. $\dbinom{789}{787} = \dfrac{789!}{787!(789-787)!} = \dfrac{789!}{787!2!} = 310{,}866$

3. ${}_{18}C_{12} = \dfrac{18!}{12!(18-12)!} = \dfrac{18!}{12!6!} = 18{,}564$

4. ${}_{35}C_{28} = \dfrac{35!}{28!(35-28)!} = \dfrac{35!}{28!7!} = 6{,}724{,}520$

5. ${}_{12}P_7 = \dfrac{12!}{(12-7)!} = \dfrac{12!}{5!} = 3{,}991{,}680$

6. ${}_{15}P_8 = \dfrac{15!}{(15-8)!} = \dfrac{15!}{7!} = 259{,}459{,}200$

7. $26 \cdot 36^4 = 43{,}670{,}016$ code words

8. $3 + (3 \cdot 4) = 15$ trips

9. ${}_{26}P_2 \cdot {}_{10}P_4 + {}_{10}P_3 \cdot {}_{26}P_3 = 14{,}508{,}000$ license plates

10. ${}_{45}C_3 = 14{,}190$ committees

11. Choose 10 more cards from the other 49:
${}_3C_3 \cdot {}_{49}C_{10} = {}_{49}C_{10} = 8{,}217{,}822{,}536$ hands

12. Choose a king, then 8 more cards from the other 44:
${}_4C_4 \cdot {}_4C_1 \cdot {}_{44}C_8 = {}_4C_1 \cdot {}_{44}C_8 = 708{,}930{,}508$ hands

13. ${}_5C_2 + {}_5C_3 + {}_5C_4 + {}_5C_5 = 2^5 - {}_5C_0 - {}_5C_1 = 26$ outcomes

14. ${}_{21}C_2 \cdot {}_{14}C_2 = 19{,}110$ committees

15. ${}_5P_1 + {}_5P_2 + {}_5P_3 + {}_5P_4 + {}_5P_5 = 325$

16. $2^4 = 16$ (This includes the possibility that he has *no* coins in his pocket.)

17. (a) There are 7 letters, all different. The number of distinguishable permutations is $7! = 5040$. (GERMANY can be rearranged to spell MEG RYAN.)

   (b) There are 13 letters, where E, R, and S each appear twice. The number of distinguishable permutations is
$$\frac{13!}{2!2!2!} = 778{,}377{,}600$$

   (PRESBYTERIANS can be rearranged to spell BRITNEY SPEARS.)

18. (a) There are 7 letters, all different. The number of distinguishable permutations is $7! = 5040$.

   (b) There are 11 letters, where A appears 3 times and L, S, and E each appear 2 times. The number of distinguishable permutations is
$$\frac{11!}{3!2!2!2!} = 831{,}600$$

19. $\begin{aligned}(2x + y)^5 &= (2x)^5 + 5(2x)^4 y + 10(2x)^3 y^2 \\ &\quad + 10(2x)^2 y^3 + 5(2x)y^4 + y^5 \\ &= 32x^5 + 80x^4 y + 80x^3 y^2 + 40x^2 y^3 \\ &\quad + 10xy^4 + y^5\end{aligned}$

20. $(4a - 3b)^7 = (4a)^7 + 7(4a)^6(-3b) + 21(4a)^5(-3b)^2$
$+ 35(4a)^4(-3b)^3 + 35(4a)^3(-3b)^4$
$+ 21(4a)^2(-3b)5 + 7(4a)(-3b)^6$
$+ (-3b)^7$
$= 16{,}384a^7 - 86{,}016a^6b + 193{,}536a^5b^2$
$- 241{,}920a^4b^3 + 181{,}440a^3b^4$
$- 81{,}648a^2b^5 + 20{,}412ab^6 - 2187b^7$

21. $(3x^2 + y^3)^5 = (3x^2)^5 + 5(3x^2)^4(y^3)$
$+ 10(3x^2)^3(y^3)^2 + 10(3x^2)^2(y^3)^3$
$+ 5(3x^2)(y^3)^4 + (y^3)^5$
$= 243x^{10} + 405x^8y^3 + 270x^6y^6$
$+ 90x^4y^9 + 15x^2y^{12} + y^{15}$

22. $\left(1 + \dfrac{1}{x}\right)^6 = 1 + 6(x^{-1}) + 15(x^{-1})^2 + 20(x^{-1})^3$
$+ 15(x^{-1})^4 + 6(x^{-1})^5 + (x^{-1})^6$
$= 1 + 6x^{-1} + 15x^{-2} + 20x^{-3}$
$+ 15x^{-4} + 6x^{-5} + x^{-6}$

23. $(2a^3 - b^2)^9 = (2a^3)^9 + 9(2a^3)^8(-b^2) + 36(2a^3)^7(-b^2)^2$
$+ 84(2a^3)^6(-b^2)^3 + 126(2a^3)^5(-b^2)^4$
$+ 126(2a^3)^4(-b^2)^5 + 84(2a^3)^3(-b^2)^6$
$+ 36(2a^3)^2(-b^2)^7 + 9(2a^3)(-b^2)^8$
$+ (-b^2)^9$
$= 512a^{27} - 2304a^{24}b^2 + 4608a^{21}b^4$
$- 5376a^{18}b^6 + 4032a^{15}b^8$
$- 2016a^{12}b^{10} + 672a^9b^{12}$
$- 144a^6b^{14} + 18a^3b^{16} - b^{18}$

24. $(x^{-2} + y^{-1})^4 = (x^{-2})^4 + 4(x^{-2})^3(y^{-1})$
$+ 6(x^{-2})^2(y^{-1})^2 + 4(x^{-2})(y^{-1})^3$
$+ (y^{-1})^4$
$= x^{-8} + 4x^{-6}y^{-1} + 6x^{-4}y^{-2}$
$+ 4x^{-2}y^{-3} + y^{-4}$

25. $\dbinom{11}{8}(1)^8(-2)^3 = -\dfrac{11!8}{8!3!} = -\dfrac{11 \cdot 10 \cdot 9 \cdot 8}{3 \cdot 2 \cdot 1} = -1320$

26. $\dbinom{8}{2}(2)^2(1)^6 = \dfrac{8!4}{2!6!} = \dfrac{8 \cdot 7 \cdot 4}{2 \cdot 1} = 112$

27. $\{1, 2, 3, 4, 5, 6\}$

28. $\{(1, 1), (1, 2), (1, 3), (1, 4), (1, 5), (1, 6), (2, 1), (2, 2), \dots, (6, 6)\}$

29. $\{13, 16, 31, 36, 61, 63\}$

30. {Defective, Nondefective}

31. {HHH, HHT, HTH, HTT, THH, THT, TTH, TTT}

32. {HHT, HTH, THH, TTH, THT, HTT}

33. {HHH, TTT}

34. $P(\text{at least one head}) = 1 - P(\text{no heads}) = 1 - \left(\dfrac{1}{2}\right)^3$
$= \dfrac{7}{8}$

35. $P(\text{HHTHTT}) = \left(\dfrac{1}{2}\right)^6 = \dfrac{1}{2^6} = \dfrac{1}{64}$

36. $P(2\text{ H and }3\text{ T}) = {}_5C_2 \cdot \left(\dfrac{1}{2}\right)^5 = \dfrac{10}{2^5} = \dfrac{5}{16}$

37. $P(1\text{ H and }3\text{ T}) = {}_4C_1 \cdot \left(\dfrac{1}{2}\right)^4 = \dfrac{4}{2^4} = \dfrac{1}{4}$

38. $P(10\text{ nondefectives in a row}) = (0.997)^{10} \approx 0.97$

39. $P(3\text{ successes and }1\text{ failure}) = {}_4C_1 \cdot \left(\dfrac{1}{2}\right)^4 = \dfrac{4}{2^4} = \dfrac{1}{4} = 0.25$

40. We can redefine the words "success" and "failure" to mean the opposite of what they meant before. In this sense, the experiment is symmetrical, because $P(\text{S}) = P(\text{F})$.

41. $P(\text{SF}) = (0.4)(0.6) = 0.24$

42. $P(\text{SFS}) = (0.4)(0.6)(0.4) = 0.096$

43. $P(\text{at least 1 success}) = 1 - P(\text{no successes})$
$= 1 - (0.6)^2 = 0.64$

44. Successes are less likely than failures, so the two are not interchangeable.

45. (a) $P(\text{brand } A) = 0.5$

(b) $P(\text{cashews from brand } A) = (0.5)(0.3) = 0.15$

(c) $P(\text{cashew}) = (0.5)(0.3) + (0.5)(0.4) = 0.35$

(d) $P(\text{brand } A/\text{cashew}) = \dfrac{0.15}{0.35} \approx 0.43$

46. (a) $P(\text{track wet and Mudder Earth wins})$
$= (0.80)(0.70) = 0.56$

(b) $P(\text{track dry and Mudder Earth wins})$
$= (0.20)(0.40) = 0.08$

(c) $0.56 + 0.08 = 0.64$

(d) $P(\text{track wet/Mudder Earth wins}) = \dfrac{0.56}{0.64} = 0.875$

For #47–48, substitute $n = 1$, $n = 2$, ..., $n = 6$, and $n = 40$.

47. 0, 1, 2, 3, 4, 5; 39

48. $-1, \dfrac{4}{3}, -2, \dfrac{16}{5}, -\dfrac{16}{3}, \dfrac{64}{7}; \approx 2.68 \times 10^{10}$

For #49–54, use previously computed values of the sequence to find the next term in the sequence.

49. $-1, 2, 5, 8, 11, 14; 32$

50. $5, 10, 20, 40, 80, 160; 10{,}240$

51. $-5, -3.5, -2, -0.5, 1, 2.5; 11.5$

52. $3, 1, \dfrac{1}{3}, \dfrac{1}{9}, \dfrac{1}{27}, \dfrac{1}{81}; 3^{-10} = \dfrac{1}{59{,}049}$

53. $-3, 1, -2, -1, -3, -4; -76$

54. $-3, 2, -1, 1, 0, 1; 13$

For #55–62, check for common difference or ratios between successive terms.

55. Arithmetic with $d = -2.5$;
$a_n = 12 + (-2.5)(n - 1) = 14.5 - 2.5n$

56. Arithmetic with $d = 4$;
$a_n = -5 + 4(n - 1) = 4n - 9$

57. Geometric with $r = 1.2$;
$a_n = 10 \cdot (1.2)^{n-1}$

58. Geometric with $r = -2$;
$a_n = \dfrac{1}{8} \cdot (-2)^{n-1} = -\dfrac{1}{16}(-2)^n$

59. Arithmetic with $d = 4.5$;
$a_n = -11 + 4.5(n - 1) = 4.5n - 15.5$

60. Geometric with $r = \dfrac{1}{4}$;
$b_n = 7 \cdot \left(\dfrac{1}{4}\right)^{n-1} = 28 \cdot \left(\dfrac{1}{4}\right)^n$

61. $a_n = a_1 r^{n-1}$, so $-192 = a_1 r^3$ and $196{,}608 = a_1 r^8$. Then $r^5 = -1024$, so $r = -4$, and $a_1 = \dfrac{-192}{(-4)^3} = 3$; $a_n = 3(-4)^{n-1}$

62. $a_n = a_1 + (n-1)d$, so $14 = a_1 + 2d$, and $-3.5 = a_1 + 7d$. Then $5d = -17.5$, so $d = -3.5$, and $a_1 = 14 - 2(-3.5) = 21$; $a_n = 21 - 3.5(n-1) = 24.5 - 3.5n$.

For #63–66, use one of the formulas $S_n = n\left(\dfrac{a_1 + a_n}{2}\right)$ or $S_n = \dfrac{n}{2}[2a_1 + (n-1)d]$. In most cases, the first of these is easier (since the last term a_n is given); note that $n = \dfrac{a_n - a_1}{d} + 1$.

63. $8 \cdot \left(\dfrac{-11 + 10}{2}\right) = 4 \cdot (-1) = -4$

64. $7 \cdot \left(\dfrac{13 - 11}{2}\right) = 7$

65. $27 \cdot \left(\dfrac{2.5 - 75.5}{2}\right) = \dfrac{1}{2} \cdot 27 \cdot (-73) = -985.5$

66. $31 \cdot \left(\dfrac{-5 + 55}{2}\right) = 31 \cdot 25 = 775$

For #67–70, use the formula $S_n = \dfrac{a_1(1 - r^n)}{1 - r}$. Note that $n = 1 + \log_{|r|}\left|\dfrac{a_n}{a_1}\right| = 1 + \dfrac{\ln|a_n/a_1|}{\ln|r|}$.

67. $\dfrac{4(1 - (-1/2)^6)}{1 - (-1/2)} = \dfrac{21}{8}$

68. $\dfrac{-3(1 - (1/3)^5)}{1 - (1/3)} = -\dfrac{121}{27}$

69. $\dfrac{2(1 - 3^{10})}{1 - 3} = 59{,}048$

70. $\dfrac{1(1 - (-2)^{14})}{1 - (-2)} = -5461$

71. Geometric with $r = \dfrac{1}{3}$:
$$S_{10} = \dfrac{2187(1 - (1/3)^{10})}{1 - (1/3)} = \dfrac{29{,}524}{9} = 3280.\overline{4}$$

72. Arithmetic with $d = -3$:
$$S_{10} = \dfrac{10}{2}[2(94) + 9(-3)] = 5 \cdot 161 = 805$$

73.

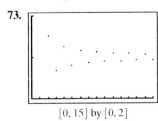

$[0, 15]$ by $[0, 2]$

74.

$[0, 16]$ by $[-10, 460]$

75. With $a_1 = \$150$, $r = 1 + 0.08/12$, and $n = 120$, the sum becomes
$$\dfrac{\$150\,[1 - (1 + 0.08/12)^{120}]}{1 - (1 + 0.08/12)} = \$27{,}441.91$$

76. The payment amount P must be such that
$$P\left(1 + \dfrac{0.08}{12}\right)^0 + P\left(1 + \dfrac{0.08}{12}\right)^1 + \cdots$$
$$+ P\left(1 + \dfrac{0.08}{12}\right)^{119} \geq \$30{,}000$$
Using the formula for the sum of a finite geometric series,
$$\dfrac{P\,[1 - (1 + 0.08/12)^{120}]}{1 - (1 + 0.08/12)} \geq \$30{,}000$$
or $P \geq \$30{,}000 \dfrac{-0.08/12}{1 - (1 + 0.08/12)^{120}}$
$$\approx \$163.983$$
$$\approx \$163.99 \text{ rounded up}$$

77. Converges: geometric with $a_1 = \dfrac{3}{2}$ and $r = \dfrac{3}{4}$, so
$$S = \dfrac{3/2}{1 - (3/4)} = \dfrac{3/2}{1/4} = 6$$

78. Converges: geometric with $a_1 = -\dfrac{2}{3}$ and $r = -\dfrac{1}{3}$, so
$$S = \dfrac{-2/3}{1 - (-1/3)} = \dfrac{-2/3}{4/3} = -\dfrac{1}{2}$$

79. Diverges: geometric with $r = -\dfrac{4}{3}$

80. Diverges: geometric with $r = \dfrac{6}{5}$

81. Converges: geometric with $a_1 = 1.5$ and $r = 0.5$, so
$$S = \dfrac{1.5}{1 - 0.5} = \dfrac{1.5}{0.5} = 3$$

82. Diverges; geometric with $r = 1.2$

83. $\displaystyle\sum_{k=1}^{21}[-8 + 5(k-1)] = \sum_{k=1}^{21}(5k - 13)$

84. $\displaystyle\sum_{k=1}^{10}4(-2)^{k-1} = \sum_{k=1}^{10}(-2)^{k+1}$

85. $\displaystyle\sum_{k=0}^{\infty}(2k + 1)^2$ or $\displaystyle\sum_{k=1}^{\infty}(2k - 1)^2$

86. $\displaystyle\sum_{k=0}^{\infty}\left(\dfrac{1}{2}\right)^k$ or $\displaystyle\sum_{k=1}^{\infty}\left(\dfrac{1}{2}\right)^{k-1}$

87. $\displaystyle\sum_{k=1}^{n}(3k + 1) = 3\sum_{k=1}^{n}k + \sum_{k=1}^{n}1$
$$= 3 \cdot \dfrac{n(n+1)}{2} + n = \dfrac{3n^2 + 5n}{2} = \dfrac{n(3n + 5)}{2}$$

88. $\displaystyle\sum_{k=1}^{n}3k^2 = 3\sum_{k=1}^{n}k^2 = 3 \cdot \dfrac{n(n+1)(2n+1)}{6}$
$$= \dfrac{n(n+1)(2n+1)}{2}$$

89. $\sum_{k=1}^{25}(k^2 - 3k + 4) = \dfrac{25 \cdot 26 \cdot 51}{6} - 3 \cdot \dfrac{25 \cdot 26}{2}$
$+ 4 \cdot 25 = 4650$

90. $\sum_{k=1}^{175}(3k^2 - 5k + 1) = 3 \cdot \dfrac{175 \cdot 176 \cdot 351}{6}$
$- 5 \cdot \dfrac{175 \cdot 176}{2} + 175 = 5{,}328{,}575$

91. $P_n: 1 + 3 + 6 + \cdots + \dfrac{n(n+1)}{2} = \dfrac{n(n+1)(n+2)}{6}.$

P_1 is true: $\dfrac{1(1+1)}{2} = \dfrac{1(1+1)(1+2)}{6}.$

Now assume P_k is true: $1 + 3 + 6 + \cdots + \dfrac{k(k+1)}{2}$

$= \dfrac{k(k+1)(k+2)}{6}.$ Add $\dfrac{(k+1)(k+2)}{2}$ to both sides:

$1 + 3 + 6 + \cdots + \dfrac{k(k+1)}{2} + \dfrac{(k+1)(k+2)}{2}$

$= \dfrac{k(k+1)(k+2)}{6} + \dfrac{(k+1)(k+2)}{2}$

$= (k+1)(k+2)\left(\dfrac{k}{6} + \dfrac{1}{2}\right)$

$= (k+1)(k+2)\left(\dfrac{k+3}{6}\right)$

$= \dfrac{(k+1)((k+1)+1)((k+1)+2)}{6},$

so P_{k+1} is true. Therefore, P_n is true for all $n \geq 1$.

92. $P_n: 1 \cdot 2 + 2 \cdot 3 + 3 \cdot 4 + \cdots + n(n+1)$

$= \dfrac{n(n+1)(n+2)}{3}.$ P_1 is true:

$1(1+1) = \dfrac{1(1+1)(1+2)}{3}.$

Now assume P_k is true: $1 \cdot 2 + 2 \cdot 3 + 3 \cdot 4 + \cdots + k(k+1)$

$= \dfrac{k(k+1)(k+2)}{3}.$

Add $(k+1)(k+2)$ to both sides:

$1 \cdot 2 + 2 \cdot 3 + \cdots + k(k+1) + (k+1)(k+2)$

$= \dfrac{k(k+1)(k+2)}{3} + (k+1)(k+2)$

$= (k+1)(k+2)\left(\dfrac{k}{3} + 1\right)$

$= (k+1)(k+2)\left(\dfrac{k+3}{3}\right)$

$= \dfrac{(k+1)((k+1)+1)((k+1)+2)}{3};$

so P_k is true. Therefore, P_n is true for all $n \geq 1$.

93. $P_n: 2^{n-1} \leq n!$. P_1 is true: it says that $2^{1-1} \leq 1!$ (they are equal). Now assume P_k is true: $2^{k-1} \leq k!$. Then $2^{k+1-1} = 2 \cdot 2^{k-1} \leq 2 \cdot k! \leq (k+1)k! = (k+1)!$, so P_{k+1} is true. Therefore, P_n is true for all $n \geq 1$.

94. $P_n: n^3 + 2n$ is divisible by 3. P_1 is true because $1^3 + 2 \cdot 1 = 3$ is divisible by 3. Now assume P_k is true: $k^3 + 2k$ is divisible by 3. Then note that $(k+1)^3 + 2(k+1) = (k^3 + 3k^2 + 3k + 1)$ $+ (2k + 2) = (k^3 + 2k) + 3(k^2 + k + 1).$

Since both terms are divisible by 3, so is the sum, so P_{k+1} is true. Therefore, P_n is true for all $n \geq 1$.

95. (a)
```
 9 | 1 2
10 | 6 7
11 | 4 5 5 7 7
12 | 0 2 4 6 7 7
13 | 5 6
14 | 1 6 7 7 8
15 | 4 8
16 | 1 4
17 | 0 6
18 |
19 |
20 |
21 | 9
22 |
23 | 4
```

(b)

Price	Frequency
90,000–99,999	2
100,000–109,999	2
110,000–119,999	5
120,000–129,999	6
130,000–139,999	2
140,000–149,999	5
150,000–159,999	2
160,000–169,999	2
170,000–179,999	2
210,000–219,999	1
230,000–239,999	1

(c)

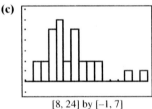

[8, 24] by [−1, 7]

96. (a)
```
1 | 1 1 1 1 1 2 2 3 3 4 4
1 | 5 9 9 9
2 | 0 0 0
2 | 6 8 9
3 | 3
4 |
4 |
5 |
5 | 8
6 | 1
6 |
7 | 1
```

(b)

Number of Visitors	Frequency
10,000,000–14,999,999	11
15,000,000–19,999,999	4
20,000,000–24,999,999	3
25,000,000–29,999,999	3
30,000,000–34,999,999	1
35,000,000–39,999,999	0
40,000,000–44,999,999	0
45,000,000–49,999,999	0
55,000,000–59,999,999	1
60,000,000–64,999,999	1
65,000,000–69,999,999	0
70,000,000–74,999,999	1

(c)

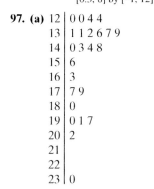

$[0.5, 8]$ by $[-1, 12]$

97. (a)

```
12 | 0 0 4 4
13 | 1 1 2 6 7 9
14 | 0 3 4 8
15 | 6
16 | 3
17 | 7 9
18 | 0
19 | 0 1 7
20 | 2
21 |
22 |
23 | 0
```

(b)

Length (in seconds)	Frequency
120—129	4
130—139	6
140—149	4
150—159	1
160—169	1
170—179	2
180—189	1
190—199	3
200—209	1
210—219	0
220—229	0
230—239	1

(c)

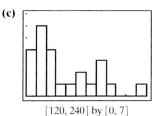

$[120, 240]$ by $[0, 7]$

98. (a) For the stemplot (but not for the other frequency table or histogram), round to nearest hundred yards first:

```
Stem  Leaf
  1 | 1
  2 | 3 4 5 7 8
  3 | 1 3 5 5 6
  4 | 0 2 3 7 7
  5 | 0 6
```

(b)

Yardage	Frequency
1000–1999	1
2000–2999	5
3000–3999	6
4000–4999	3
5000–5999	2

(c)

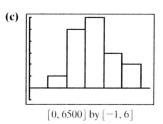

$[0, 6500]$ by $[-1, 6]$

99. The ordered data is $\{\underline{9.1}, 9.2, 10.6, 10.7, 11.4, 11.5, 11.5, \underline{11.7}, 11.7, 12, 12.2, 12.4, 12.6, 12.7, \underline{12.7}, \underline{13.5}, 13.6, 14.1, 14.6, 14.7, 14.7, 14.8, \underline{15.4}, 15.8, 16.1, 16.4, 17.0, 17.6, 21.9, \underline{23.4}\}$ so the

median is $\dfrac{12.7 + 13.5}{2} = 13.1$, $Q_3 = 15.4$, and $Q_1 = 11.7$.

Five-number summary: $\{9.1, 11.7, 13.1, 15.4, 23.4\}$
Range: $23.4 - 9.1 = 14.3$ ($\$143{,}000$)
IQR: $15.4 - 11.7 = 3.7$ ($\$37{,}000$)
$\sigma \approx 3.19$, $\sigma^2 \approx 10.14$
Outliers: 21.9 and 23.4 are greater than $15.4 + 1.5(3.7) = 20.95$.

100. The ordered data is $\{\underline{1.1}, 1.1, 1.1, 1.1, 1.1, \underline{1.2}, \underline{1.2}, 1.3, 1.3, 1.4, 1.4, 1.5, \underline{1.9}, 1.9, 1.9, 2.0, 2.0, 2.0, \underline{2.6}, \underline{2.8}, 2.9, 3.3, 5.8, 6.1, \underline{7.1}\}$ so the median is 1.9,

$Q_3 = \dfrac{2.6 + 2.8}{2} = 2.7$ and $Q_1 = 1.2$.

Five-number summary: $\{1.1, 1.2, 1.9, 2.7, 7.1\}$
Range: $7.1 - 1.1 = 6.0$ (6 million)
IQR: $2.7 - 1.2 = 1.5$ (1.5 million)
$\sigma \approx 1.63$, $\sigma^2 \approx 2.64$
Outliers: 5.8, 6.1, and 7.1 are greater than $2.7 + 1.5(1.5) = 4.95$.

101. The ordered data is $\{\underline{120}, 120, 124, 124, 131, \underline{131}, \underline{132}, 136, 137, 139, 140, \underline{143}, \underline{144}, 148, 156, 163, 177, \underline{179}, \underline{180}, 190, 191, 197, 202, \underline{230}\}$ so the median is

$\dfrac{143 + 144}{2} = 143.5$, $Q_3 = \dfrac{179 + 180}{2} = 179.5$, and

$Q_1 = \dfrac{131 + 132}{2} = 131.5$.

Five-number summary: $\{120, 131.5, 143.5, 179.5, 230\}$
Range: $230 - 120 = 110$
IQR: $179.5 - 131.5 = 48$
$\sigma = 29.9$, $\sigma^2 = 891.4$
No Outliers.

102. The ordered data is: $\{\underline{1112}, 2327, 2382, 2521, \underline{2709}, 2806, 3127, 3338, \underline{3485}, \underline{3489}, 3631, 3959, 4228, \underline{4264}, 4689, 4690, 5000, \underline{5648}\}$,

so the median is $\dfrac{3485 + 3489}{2} = 3487$,

$Q_3 = 4264$ and $Q_1 = 2709$.
Five-number summary: $\{1112, 2709, 3487, 4264, 5648\}$
Range: $5648 - 1112 = 4536$
IQR: $4264 - 2709 = 1555$
$\sigma \approx 1095$, $\sigma^2 \approx 1{,}199{,}223$
No Outliers.

103.(a)

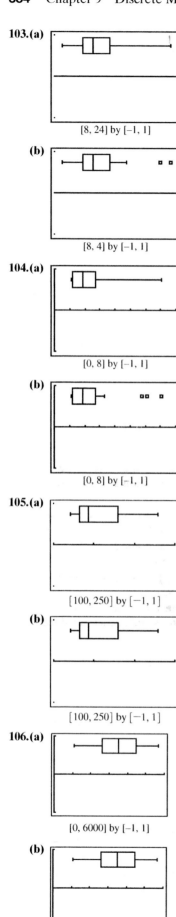

[8, 24] by [−1, 1]

(b)

[8, 4] by [−1, 1]

104.(a)

[0, 8] by [−1, 1]

(b)

[0, 8] by [−1, 1]

105.(a)

[100, 250] by [−1, 1]

(b)

[100, 250] by [−1, 1]

106.(a)

[0, 6000] by [−1, 1]

(b)

[0, 6000] by [−1, 1]

107.

```
4 0 0 | 12 | 4
9 2 1 | 13 | 1 6 7
8 4 3 0 | 14 |
      | 15 | 6
    3 | 16 |
    7 | 17 | 9
      | 18 | 0
      | 19 | 0 1 7
      | 20 | 2
      | 21 |
      | 22 |
      | 23 | 0
```

The songs released in the earlier years tended to be shorter.

108. Earlier years are in the upper box plot. The range and interquartile range are both greater in the lower graph, which shows the times for later years.

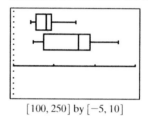

[100, 250] by [−5, 10]

109.

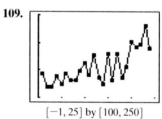

[−1, 25] by [100, 250]

Again, the data demonstrates that songs appearing later tended to be longer in length.

110.

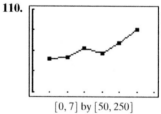

[0, 7] by [50, 250]

The average times are {130.5, 132.75, 157, 142.5, 168.75, 202} The trend is clearly increasing overall, with less fluctuation than the time plot for Exercise 105.

111. 1 9 36 84 126 84 36 9 1

112. $_nP_k \times _{n-k}P_j = \dfrac{n!}{(n-k)!} \dfrac{(n-k)!}{[(n-k)-j]!}$

$$= \dfrac{n!}{(n-k-j)!}$$

$$= \dfrac{n!}{[n-(k+j)]!} = _nP_{k+j}$$

113. (a) $P(\text{no defective bats}) = (0.98)^4 \approx 0.922$

(b) $P(\text{one defective bat}) = _4C_1 \cdot (0.98)^3(0.02)$
$= 4(0.98)^3(0.02) \approx 0.075$

114. (a) $P(\text{no defective light bulbs}) = (0.9996)^{10} \approx 0.996$

(b) $P(\text{two defective light bulbs}) = _{10}C_2 \cdot$
$(0.9996)^8(0.0004)^2 \approx 7.18 \times 10^{-6}$

Chapter 9 Project

Answers are based on the sample data shown in the table.

1. Stem   Leaf

   5 |
   5 | 9
   6 | 1 1 2 3 3 3 4 4 4 4
   6 | 5 6 6 6 7 8 8 9 9
   7 | 0 0 1 1 1 2 2 3
   7 | 5

   The average is about 66 or 67 inches.

2. A large number of students are between 63 and 64 inches and also between 69 and 72 inches.

Height	Frequency
59–60	1
61–62	3
63–64	7
65–66	4
67–68	3
69–70	5
71–72	5
73–74	1
75–76	1

3.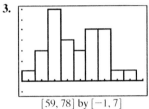

   [59, 78] by [−1, 7]

   Again, the average appears to be about 66 or 67 inches. Since the data are not broken out by gender, one can only speculate about average heights for males and females separately. Possibly the two peaks within the distribution represent an average height of 63–64 inches for females and 70–71 inches for males.

4. Mean = 66.9 in.; median = 66.5 in.; mode = 64 in. The mean and median both appear to be good measures of the average, but the mode is too low. Still, the mode might well be similar in other classes.

5. The data set is well distributed and probably does not have outliers.

6. The stem and leaf plot puts the data in order.
   Minimum value: 59
   Maximum value: 75
   Median: $\frac{66 + 67}{2} = 66.5$

   Q_1: 64
   Q_3: 70
   The five-number summary is {59, 64, 66.5, 70, 75}.

7.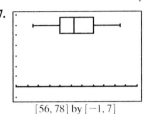

   [56, 78] by [−1, 7]

   The boxplot visually represents the five-number summary. The whisker-to-whisker size of the boxplot represents the range of the data, while the width of the box represents the interquartile range.

8. Mean = 67.5; median = 67; The new five-number summary is {59, 64, 67, 71, 86}.

   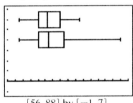

   [56, 88] by [−1, 7]

   The minimum and first quartile are unaffected, but the median, third quartile, and maximum are shifted upon to varying degrees.

9. The new student's height, 86 inches, lies 15 inches away from Q_3, and that is more than $1.5(Q_3 − Q_1) = 10.5$. The height of the new student should probably be tossed out during prediction calculations.

10. Mean = 68.9; median = 68; The new five-number summary is {59, 64, 68, 71, 86}.
    All three of the new students are outliers by the $1.5 \times IQR$ test. Their heights should be left out during prediction-making.

Chapter 10
An Introduction to Calculus: Limits, Derivatives, and Integrals

■ Section 10.1 Limits and Motion: The Tangent Problem

Exploration 1

1. $m = \dfrac{4 - 1}{2 - 1} = \dfrac{3}{1} = 3$

2. $v_{ave} = \dfrac{\Delta s}{\Delta t} = \dfrac{3 \text{ ft}}{1 \text{ sec}} = 3 \text{ ft/sec}$

3. They are the same.

4. As the slope of the line joining $(a, s(a))$ and $(b, s(b))$

Quick Review 10.1

1. $m = \dfrac{-1 - 3}{5 - (-2)} = \dfrac{-4}{7} = -\dfrac{4}{7}$

2. $m = \dfrac{3 - (-1)}{3 - (-3)} = \dfrac{4}{6} = \dfrac{2}{3}$

3. $y - 3 = \dfrac{3}{2}(x + 2)$ or $y = \dfrac{3}{2}x + 6$

4. $m = \dfrac{-1 - 6}{4 - 1} = \dfrac{-7}{3} = -\dfrac{7}{3}, \ y - 6 = -\dfrac{7}{3}(x - 1)$

5. $y - 4 = \dfrac{3}{4}(x - 1)$

6. $y - 4 = -\dfrac{4}{3}(x - 1)$

7. $\dfrac{4 + 4h + h^2 - 4}{h} = \dfrac{4h + h^2}{h} = h + 4$

8. $\dfrac{9 + 6h + h^2 + 3 + h - 12}{h} = \dfrac{h^2 + 7h}{h} = h + 7$

9. $\dfrac{\dfrac{1}{2 + h} - \dfrac{1}{2}}{h} = \dfrac{2 - (2 + h)}{2(2 + h)} \cdot \dfrac{1}{h}$

$= \dfrac{-h}{h} \cdot \dfrac{1}{2(2 + h)} = -\dfrac{1}{2(h + 2)}$

10. $\dfrac{\dfrac{1}{x + h} - \dfrac{1}{x}}{h} = \dfrac{x - (x + h)}{x(x + h)} \cdot \dfrac{1}{h}$

$= \dfrac{-h}{h} \cdot \dfrac{1}{x(x + h)} = -\dfrac{1}{x(x + h)}$

Section 10.1 Exercises

1. $v_{ave} = \dfrac{\Delta s}{\Delta t} = \dfrac{21 \text{ miles}}{1.75 \text{ hours}} = 12 \text{ mi per hour}$

2. $v_{ave} = \dfrac{\Delta s}{\Delta t} = \dfrac{540 \text{ km}}{4.5 \text{ hours}} = 120 \text{ km per hour}$

3. $s'(4) = \lim\limits_{h \to 0} \dfrac{s(4 + h) - s(4)}{h}$

$= \lim\limits_{h \to 0} \dfrac{3(h + 4) - 5 - 7}{h}$

$= \lim\limits_{h \to 0} 3 = 3$

4. $s'(2) = \lim\limits_{h \to 0} \dfrac{s(2 + h) - s(2)}{h}$

$= \lim\limits_{h \to 0} \dfrac{\dfrac{2}{h + 2 + 1} - \dfrac{2}{3}}{h}$

$= \lim\limits_{h \to 0} \dfrac{6 - 2(h + 3)}{3(h + 3)} \cdot \dfrac{1}{h}$

$= \lim\limits_{h \to 0} \dfrac{-2h}{h} \cdot \dfrac{1}{3(h + 3)}$

$= \lim\limits_{h \to 0} \dfrac{-2}{3(h + 3)} = -\dfrac{2}{9}$

5. $s'(2) = \lim\limits_{h \to 0} \dfrac{s(2 + h) - s(2)}{h}$

$= \lim\limits_{h \to 0} \dfrac{a(h + 2)^2 + 5 - (4a + 5)}{h}$

$= \lim\limits_{h \to 0} \dfrac{ah^2 + 4ah}{h}$

$= \lim\limits_{h \to 0} (ah + 4a) = 4a$

6. $s'(1) = \lim\limits_{h \to 0} \dfrac{s(1 + h) - s(1)}{h}$

$= \lim\limits_{h \to 0} \dfrac{\sqrt{h + 2} - \sqrt{2}}{h}$

$= \lim\limits_{h \to 0} \dfrac{\sqrt{h + 2} - \sqrt{2}}{h} \cdot \dfrac{\sqrt{h + 2} + \sqrt{2}}{\sqrt{h + 2} + \sqrt{2}}$

$= \lim\limits_{h \to 0} \dfrac{h + 2 - 2}{h(\sqrt{h + 2} + \sqrt{2})}$

$= \lim\limits_{h \to 0} \dfrac{h}{h} \cdot \dfrac{1}{\sqrt{h + 2} + \sqrt{2}} = \lim\limits_{h \to 0} \dfrac{1}{\sqrt{h + 2} + \sqrt{2}}$

$= \dfrac{1}{2\sqrt{2}}$

7. Try $\dfrac{f(1) - f(0)}{1 - 0} = \dfrac{3 - 2}{1} = 1$

8. Try $\dfrac{f(2) - f(1)}{2 - 1} = \dfrac{1 - 2}{1} = -1$

9. No tangent

10. No tangent

11.

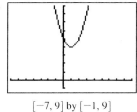

$[-7, 9]$ by $[-1, 9]$

$m = 4$

12.

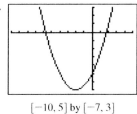

$[-10, 5]$ by $[-7, 3]$

$m = 4$

13.

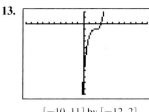

$[-10, 11]$ by $[-12, 2]$

$m = 12$

14.

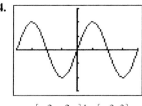

$[-2\pi, 2\pi]$ by $[-3, 3]$

$m = -2$

15. (a) $f'(0) = \lim\limits_{h \to 0} \dfrac{f(0 + h) - f(0)}{h}$

$= \lim\limits_{h \to 0} \dfrac{3 + 48(0 + h) - 16(0 + h)^2 - 3}{h}$

$= \lim\limits_{h \to 0} \dfrac{48h - 16h^2}{h} = 48$

(b) The initial velocity of the rock is $f'(0) = 48$ ft/sec.

16. (a) $f'(0) = \lim\limits_{h \to 0} \dfrac{f(0 + h) - f(0)}{h}$

$= \lim\limits_{h \to 0} \dfrac{170(0 + h) - 16(0 + h)^2 - 0}{h}$

$= \lim\limits_{h \to 0} (170 - 16h) = 170$

(b) The initial velocity of the rock is $f'(0) = 170$ ft/sec.

17. (a) $m = \lim\limits_{h \to 0} \dfrac{f(-1 + h) - f(-1)}{h}$

$= \lim\limits_{h \to 0} \dfrac{2(h - 1)^2 - 2}{h} = \lim\limits_{h \to 0} \dfrac{2h^2 - 4h + 2 - 2}{h}$

$= \lim\limits_{h \to 0} (2h - 4) = -4$

(b) Since $(-1, f(-1)) = (-1, 2)$ the equation of the tangent line is $y - 2 = -4(x + 1)$.

(c)

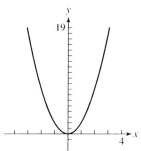

18. (a) $m = \lim\limits_{h \to 0} \dfrac{f(2 + h) - f(2)}{h}$

$= \lim\limits_{h \to 0} \dfrac{2(h + 2) - (h + 2)^2 - 0}{h}$

$= \lim\limits_{h \to 0} \dfrac{2h + 4 - h^2 - 4h - 4}{h} = \lim\limits_{h \to 0} (-h - 2)$

$= -2$

(b) Since $(2, f(2)) = (2, 0)$ the equation of the tangent line is $y = -2(x - 2)$.

(c)

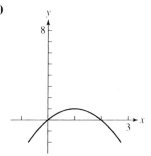

19. (a) $m = \lim\limits_{h \to 0} \dfrac{f(2 + h) - f(2)}{h}$

$= \lim\limits_{h \to 0} \dfrac{2(h + 2)^2 - 7(h + 2) + 3 - (-3)}{h}$

$= \lim\limits_{h \to 0} \dfrac{2h^2 + 8h + 8 - 7h - 14 + 6}{h}$

$= \lim\limits_{h \to 0} (2h + 1) = 1$

(b) Since $(2, f(2)) = (2, -3)$ the equation of the tangent line is $y + 3 = 1(x - 2)$, or $y = x - 5$.

(c)

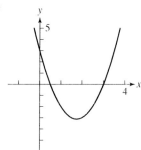

20. (a) $m = \lim\limits_{h \to 0} \dfrac{f(1 + h) - f(1)}{h}$

$= \lim\limits_{h \to 0} \dfrac{\dfrac{1}{h + 1 + 2} - \dfrac{1}{3}}{h} = \lim\limits_{h \to 0} \dfrac{3 - (h + 3)}{3(h + 3)} \cdot \dfrac{1}{h}$

$= \lim\limits_{h \to 0} \dfrac{-h}{h} \cdot \dfrac{1}{3(h + 3)} = \lim\limits_{h \to 0} \dfrac{-1}{3(h + 3)} = -\dfrac{1}{9}$

(b) Since $(1, f(1)) = \left(1, \dfrac{1}{3}\right)$ the equation of the tangent

line is $y - \dfrac{1}{3} = -\dfrac{1}{9}(x - 1)$.

(c)

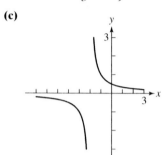

21.

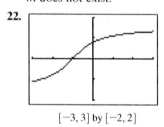

$[-5, 5]$ by $[-1, 5]$

At $x = -2$: $m = -1$, at $x = 2$: $m = 1$, at $x = 0$, m does not exist.

22.

$[-3, 3]$ by $[-2, 2]$

At $x = -2$: $m = 0.5$, at $x = 2$: $m = 0.1$, at $x = 0$, $m = 0.5$.

23. $\lim\limits_{h \to 0} \dfrac{f(2 + h) - f(2)}{h} = \lim\limits_{h \to 0} \dfrac{1 - (2 + h)^2 - (1 - 4)}{h}$

$= \lim\limits_{h \to 0} \dfrac{-h^2 - 4h - 4 + 4}{h} = \lim\limits_{h \to 0} (-h - 4) = -4$

24. $\lim\limits_{h \to 0} \dfrac{f(2 + h) - f(2)}{h}$

$= \lim\limits_{h \to 0} \dfrac{2(2 + h) + \dfrac{1}{2}(2 + h)^2 - 4 - 2}{h}$

$= \lim\limits_{h \to 0} \dfrac{4 + 2h + \dfrac{1}{2}h^2 + 2h + 2 - 6}{h}$

$= \lim\limits_{h \to 0} \left(\dfrac{1}{2}h + 4\right) = 4$

25. $\lim\limits_{h \to 0} \dfrac{f(-2 + h) - f(-2)}{h}$

$= \lim\limits_{h \to 0} \dfrac{3(h - 2)^2 + 2 - (14)}{h}$

$= \lim\limits_{h \to 0} \dfrac{3h^2 - 12h + 12 - 12}{h} = \lim\limits_{h \to 0} (3h - 12) = -12$

26. $\lim\limits_{h \to 0} \dfrac{f(1 + h) - f(1)}{h}$

$= \lim\limits_{h \to 0} \dfrac{(h + 1)^2 - 3(h + 1) + 1 - (-1)}{h}$

$= \lim\limits_{h \to 0} \dfrac{h^2 + 2h + 1 - 3h - 3 + 2}{h} = \lim\limits_{h \to 0} (h - 1)$

$= -1$

27. $\lim\limits_{h \to 0} \dfrac{f(-2 + h) - f(-2)}{h} = \lim\limits_{h \to 0} \dfrac{|h - 2 + 2| - 0}{h}$

$= \lim\limits_{h \to 0} \dfrac{|h|}{h}$. When $h > 0$, $\dfrac{|h|}{h} = 1$ while when $h < 0$,

$\dfrac{|h|}{h} = -1$. The limit does not exist. The derivative does

not exist.

28. $\lim\limits_{h \to 0} \dfrac{f(-1 + h) - f(-1)}{h} = \lim\limits_{h \to 0} \dfrac{\dfrac{1}{h - 1 + 2} - \dfrac{1}{1}}{h}$

$= \lim\limits_{h \to 0} \dfrac{1 - (h + 1)}{h + 1} \cdot \dfrac{1}{h} = \lim\limits_{h \to 0} \dfrac{-h}{h} \cdot \dfrac{1}{h + 1}$

$= \lim\limits_{h \to 0} -\dfrac{1}{h + 1} = -1$

29. $f'(x) = \lim\limits_{h \to 0} \dfrac{2 - 3(x + h) - (2 - 3x)}{h}$

$= \lim\limits_{h \to 0} \dfrac{2 - 3x - 3h - 2 + 3x}{h} = \lim\limits_{h \to 0} \dfrac{-3h}{h} = -3$

30. $f'(x) = \lim\limits_{h \to 0} \dfrac{(2 - 3(x + h)^2) - (2 - 3x^2)}{h}$

$= \lim\limits_{h \to 0} \dfrac{2 - 3x^2 - 6xh - 3h^2 - 2 + 3x^2}{h}$

$= \lim\limits_{h \to 0} \dfrac{-6xh - 3h^2}{h} = \lim\limits_{h \to 0} (-6x - 3h) = -6x$

31. $f'(x)$

$= \lim\limits_{h \to 0} \dfrac{3(x + h)^2 + 2(x + h) - 1 - (3x^2 + 2x - 1)}{h}$

$= \lim\limits_{h \to 0} \dfrac{3x^2 + 6xh + 3h^2 + 2x + 2h - 1 - 3x^2 - 2x + 1}{h}$

$= \lim\limits_{h \to 0} \dfrac{6xh + 3h^2 + 2h}{h} = \lim\limits_{h \to 0} (6x + 3h + 2) = 6x + 2$

32. $f'(x) = \lim\limits_{h \to 0} \dfrac{\dfrac{1}{(x + h) - 2} - \dfrac{1}{x - 2}}{h}$

$= \lim\limits_{h \to 0} \dfrac{(x - 2) - (x + h - 2)}{(x + h - 2)(x - 2)} \cdot \dfrac{1}{h}$

$= \lim\limits_{h \to 0} \dfrac{-h}{h} \cdot \dfrac{1}{(x + h - 2)(x - 2)}$

$= \lim\limits_{h \to 0} \dfrac{1}{(x + h - 2)(x - 2)} = -\dfrac{1}{(x - 2)^2}$

33. (a) Between 0.5 and 0.6 seconds: $\dfrac{3.2 - 2.3}{0.6 - 0.5} = 9$ ft/sec

Between 0.8 and 0.9 seconds: $\dfrac{7.3 - 5.8}{0.9 - 0.8} = 15$ ft/sec

(b) $f(x) = 8.94x^2 + 0.05x + 0.01,\ x = $ time in seconds

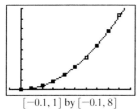

$[-0.1, 1]$ by $[-0.1, 8]$

(c) $f(2) \approx 35.9$ ft

34. (a) $\dfrac{15.76 - 21.24}{1.0 - 0.8} = -27.4$ ft/sec

(b) $s(t) = -16.01t^2 + 1.43t + 30.35$

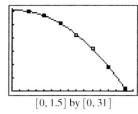

$[0, 1.5]$ by $[0, 31]$

(c) $s'(t) = \displaystyle\lim_{h \to 0} \dfrac{s(t + h) - s(t)}{h}$

$= \displaystyle\lim_{h \to 0} \dfrac{[-16.015(t + h)^2 + 1.43(t + h) + 30.35] - (-16.015t^2 + 1.43t + 30.35)}{h}$

$= \displaystyle\lim_{h \to 0} \dfrac{-32.03th - 16.015h^2 + 1.43h}{h}$

$= \displaystyle\lim_{h \to 0}(-32.03t - 16.015h + 16.015)$

$= -32.03t + 1.43;$

$s'(1) = -32.03(1) + 1.43 = -30.6$

At $t = 1$, the velocity is about -30.60 ft/sec.

35. (a)

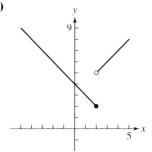

(b) Since the graph of the function does not have a definable slope at $x = 2$, the derivative of f does not exist at $x = 2$. The function is not continuous at $x = 2$.

(c) Derivatives do not exist at points where functions have discontinuities.

36. (a)

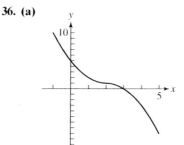

(b) From the graph of the function, it appears that the derivative may exist at $x = 2$. Using the first definition of the derivative and taking secant lines on the left of $x = 2$ (so that $f(x) = 1 + (x - 2)^2$), we have

$\displaystyle\lim_{x \to 2} \dfrac{f(x) - f(2)}{x - 2} = \lim_{x \to 2} \dfrac{1 + (x - 2)^2 - 1}{x - 2}$

$= \displaystyle\lim_{x \to 2} \dfrac{(x - 2)^2}{x - 2} = \lim_{x \to 2} (-|x - 2|) = 0.$

Now, taking secant lines on the right of $x = 2$ (so that $f(x) = 1 - (x - 2)^2$), we have

$$\lim_{x \to 2} \frac{f(x) - f(2)}{x - 2} = \lim_{x \to 2} \frac{1 - (x - 2)^2 - 1}{x - 2}$$

$$= \lim_{x \to 2} \frac{-(x - 2)^2}{x - 2} = \lim_{x \to 2} (-|x - 2|) = 0.$$

Since the limits are the same, $f'(x)$ exists at $x = 2$ and $f'(2) = 0$.

37. (a)

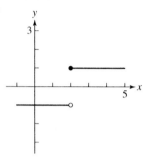

(b) Since the graph of the function does not have a definable slope at $x = 2$, the derivative of f does not exist at $x = 2$. The function is not continuous at $x = 2$.

(c) Derivatives do not exist at points where functions have discontinuities.

38. (a)

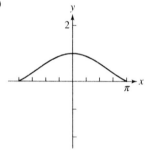

(b) From the graph of the function, it appears that the derivative may exist at $x = 0$.

$$f'(0) = \lim_{h \to 0} \frac{f(0 + h) - f(0)}{h} = \lim_{h \to 0} \frac{\dfrac{\sin h}{h} - 1}{h}$$

$$= \lim_{h \to 0} \frac{\sin h - h}{h^2}$$

This limit cannot be found using algebraic techniques. The table of values below suggests that this limit equals 0.

x	$\dfrac{\sin x - x}{x^2}$
-0.1	0.01666
-0.01	0.00167
-0.001	0.00017
0.001	-0.00017
0.01	-0.00167
0.1	-0.01666

The graph supports this since it appears that there is a horizontal tangent line at $x = 0$. Thus, $f'(0) = 0$.

39. Answers will vary. One possibility:

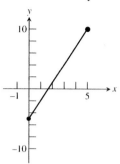

40. Answers will vary. One possibility:

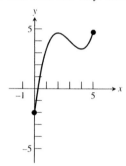

41. Answers will vary. One possibility:

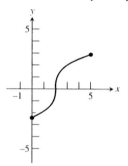

42. Answers will vary. One possibility:

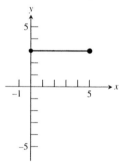

43. Since $f(x) = ax + b$ is a linear function, the rate of change for any x is exactly the slope of the line. No calculations are necessary since it is known that the slope $a = f'(x)$.

44. $f'(0) = \lim_{x \to 0} \dfrac{f(x) - f(0)}{x - 0} = \lim_{x \to 0} \dfrac{|x| - |0|}{x}$

$= \lim_{x \to 0} \dfrac{|x|}{x}$. Looking at secant lines, we see that this limit does not exist. If the secant line is to the left of $x = 0$, it will have slope $m = -1$, while if it is to the right of $x = 0$, it will have slope $m = 1$. At $x = 0$, the graph of the function does not have a definable slope.

45. False. The instantaneous velocity is a limit of average velocities. It is nonzero when the ball is moving.

46. True. Both the derivative and the slope equal
$$\lim_{x \to a} \frac{f(x) - f(a)}{x - a}.$$

47. For $Y_1 = x^2 + 3x - 4$, at $x = 0$ the calculator shows $dy/dx = 3$. The answer is D.

48. For $Y_1 = 5x - 3x^2$, at $x = 2$ the calculator shows $dy/dx = -7$. The answer is A.

49. For $Y_1 = x^3$, at $x = 2$ the calculator shows $dy/dx = 12$. The answer is C.

50. For $Y_1 = \dfrac{1}{x - 3}$, at $x = 1$ the calculator shows $dy/dx = -0.25$. The answer is A.

51. (a)

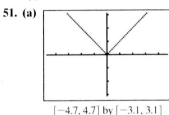

$[-4.7, 4.7]$ by $[-3.1, 3.1]$

No, there is no derivative because the graph has a corner at $x = 0$.

(b) No

52. (a)

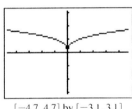

$[-4.7, 4.7]$ by $[-3.1, 3.1]$

No, there is no derivative because the graph has a cusp ("spike") at $x = 0$.

(b) Yes, the tangent line is $x = 0$.

53. (a)

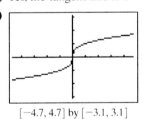

$[-4.7, 4.7]$ by $[-3.1, 3.1]$

No, there is no derivative because the graph has a vertical tangent (no slope) at $x = 0$.

(b) Yes, the tangent line is $x = 0$.

54. (a)

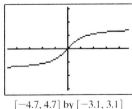

$[-4.7, 4.7]$ by $[-3.1, 3.1]$

Yes, there is a derivative because the graph has a nonvertical tangent line at $x = 0$.

(b) Yes, the tangent line is $y = x$.

55. (a) The average velocity is
$$\frac{\triangle s}{\triangle t} = \frac{16(3)^2 - 16(0)^2}{3 - 0} = 48 \text{ ft/sec}.$$

(b) The instantaneous velocity is
$$\lim_{h \to 0} \frac{16(3 + h)^2 - 144}{h} = \lim_{h \to 0} \frac{96h + h^2}{h}$$
$$= \lim_{h \to 0} (96 + h) = 96 \text{ ft/sec}$$

56. (a) $g = \dfrac{y}{t^2} = \dfrac{125}{25} = 5 \text{ m/sec}^2$

(b) Average speed: $\dfrac{\triangle x}{\triangle t} = \dfrac{125}{5} = 25 \text{ m/sec}$

(c) Since $y = 5t^2$, the instantaneous speed at $t = 5$ is
$$\lim_{h \to 0} \frac{5(5 + h)^2 - 5(5)^2}{h} = \lim_{h \to 0} \frac{50h + 5h^2}{h}$$
$$= \lim_{h \to 0} (50 + 5h)$$
$$= 50 \text{ m/sec}$$

57.

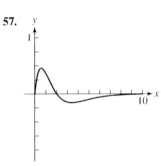

58.

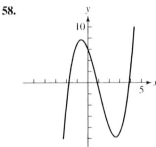

■ Section 10.2 Limits and Motion: The Area Problem

Exploration 1

1. The total amount of water remains 1 gallon. Each of the 10 teacups holds $\dfrac{1 \text{ gal}}{10} = 0.1$ gallon of water.

2. The total amount of water remains 1 gallon. Each of the 100 teacups holds $\dfrac{1 \text{ gal}}{100} = 0.01$ gallon of water.

3. The total amount of water remains 1 gallon. Each of the 1,000,000,000 teacups holds $\dfrac{1 \text{ gal}}{1,000,000,000} = 0.000\ 000\ 001$ gallon of water.

4. The total amount of water remains 1 gallon. Each of the teacups holds an amount of water that is less than what was in each of the 1 billion teacups in step 3. Thus each teacup holds about 0 gallons of water.

Quick Review 10.2

1. $\dfrac{1}{8}, \dfrac{1}{2}, \dfrac{9}{8}, 2, \dfrac{25}{8}, \dfrac{9}{2}, \dfrac{49}{8}, 8, \dfrac{81}{8}, \dfrac{25}{2}$

2. $\dfrac{81}{64}, \dfrac{25}{16}, \dfrac{121}{64}, \dfrac{9}{4}, \dfrac{169}{64}, \dfrac{49}{16}, \dfrac{225}{64}, 4, \dfrac{289}{64}, \dfrac{81}{16}$

3. $\dfrac{1}{2}[2 + 3 + 4 + 5 + 6 + 7 + 8 + 9 + 10 + 11] = \dfrac{65}{2}$

4.
$$\begin{array}{cccccccc} & 2 & + 3 & & + & 4 & + \ldots + & n & & + (n+1) \\ + & (n+1) & + (n) & & + & (n-1) & + \ldots + & 3 & & + 2 \\ \hline (n+3) & + (n+3) & + (n+3) & + & \ldots & + (n+3) & + (n+3) \end{array}$$

Thus $2\displaystyle\sum_{k=1}^{n}(k+1) = n(n+3)$, and

$$\sum_{k=1}^{n}(k+1) = \frac{1}{2}n(n+3).$$

5. $\dfrac{1}{2}[4 + 9 + \ldots + 121] = \dfrac{505}{2}$

6. $\dfrac{1}{2}[1 + 4 + 9 + \ldots + (n-1)^2 + n^2]$

$= \dfrac{1}{2}\left[\dfrac{n(n+1)(2n+1)}{6}\right] = \dfrac{n(n+1)(2n+1)}{12}$

7. $(57 \text{ mph})(4 \text{ hours}) = 228 \text{ miles}$

8. $\left(\dfrac{5 \text{ gal}}{\text{min}}\right)(120 \text{ min}) = 600 \text{ gallons}$

9. $\left(\dfrac{200 \text{ ft}^3}{\text{sec}}\right)(6 \text{ hours})\left(\dfrac{60 \text{ minutes}}{\text{hour}}\right)\left(\dfrac{60 \text{ seconds}}{\text{minute}}\right)$
$= 4{,}320{,}000 \text{ ft}^3$

10. $\left(\dfrac{560 \text{ people}}{\text{mi}^2}\right)(35{,}000 \text{ mi}^2) = 19{,}600{,}000 \text{ people}$

Section 10.2 Exercises

1. Let the line $y = 65$ represent the situation. The area under the line is the distance traveled, a rectangle, $(65)(3) = 195$ miles.

2. Let the line $y = 15$ represent the situation. The area under the line is the number of gallons pumped, a rectangle, $(15)(30) = 450$ gallons.

3. Let the line $y = 150$ represent the situation. The area under the line is the total number of cubic feet of water pumped, a rectangle, $(150)(3600) = 540{,}000 \text{ ft}^3$.

4. Let the line $y = 650$ represent the situation. The area under the line is the total population, a rectangle, $(650)(20) = 13{,}000$ people.

5. $\Delta s = \dfrac{\Delta s}{\Delta t} \cdot \Delta t = (640 \text{ km/h})(3.4 \text{ h}) = 2176 \text{ km}$

6. $\Delta s = \dfrac{\Delta s}{\Delta t} \cdot \Delta t = (24 \text{ mi/h})\left(4\dfrac{5}{6} \text{ h}\right) = 116 \text{ mi}$

7. $\displaystyle\sum_{k=1}^{5} 1 \cdot f(k) = f(1) + f(2) + f(3) + f(4) + f(5)$

$= 3\dfrac{1}{2} + 4\dfrac{1}{4} + 3\dfrac{1}{2} + 1\dfrac{3}{4} + 0 = 13$ (answers will vary)

8. $\displaystyle\sum_{k=1}^{5} 1 \cdot f(k) = f(1) + f(2) + f(3) + f(4) + f(5)$

$= 1 + 3 + 4\dfrac{1}{2} + 4 + 0 = 12\dfrac{1}{2}$ (answers will vary)

9. $\displaystyle\sum_{k=1}^{5} 1 \cdot f(k) = f(0.5) + f(1.5) + f(2.5) + f(3.5) + f(4.5)$

$= 3.5 + 5.25 + 2.75 + 0.25 + 1.25 = 13$ (answers will vary)

10. $\displaystyle\sum_{k=1}^{5} 1 \cdot f(k) = f(0.5) + f(1.5) + f(2.5) + f(3.5) + f(4.5)$

$= 3 + 1.5 + 1.75 + 3.25 + 5 = 14.5$ (answers will vary)

11. $\displaystyle\sum_{i=1}^{8}(10 - x_i^2)\Delta x_i$

$= (9 + 9.75 + 10 + 9.75 + 9 + 7.75 + 6 + 3.75)(0.5)$
$= 32.5$ square units

12. $\displaystyle\sum_{i=1}^{8}(10 - x_i^2)\Delta x_i$

$= (9.75 + 10 + 9.75 + 9 + 7.75 + 6 + 3.75 + 1)(0.5)$
$= 28.5$ square units

13. $\left[0, \dfrac{1}{2}\right], \left[\dfrac{1}{2}, 1\right], \left[1, \dfrac{3}{2}\right], \left[\dfrac{3}{2}, 2\right]$

14. $\left[0, \dfrac{1}{4}\right], \left[\dfrac{1}{4}, \dfrac{1}{2}\right], \left[\dfrac{1}{2}, \dfrac{3}{4}\right], \left[\dfrac{3}{4}, 1\right], \left[1, \dfrac{5}{4}\right], \left[\dfrac{5}{4}, \dfrac{3}{2}\right], \left[\dfrac{3}{2}, \dfrac{7}{4}\right], \left[\dfrac{7}{4}, 2\right]$

15. $\left[1, \dfrac{3}{2}\right], \left[\dfrac{3}{2}, 2\right], \left[2, \dfrac{5}{2}\right], \left[\dfrac{5}{2}, 3\right], \left[3, \dfrac{7}{2}\right], \left[\dfrac{7}{2}, 4\right]$

16. $\left[1, \dfrac{3}{2}\right], \left[\dfrac{3}{2}, 2\right], \left[2, \dfrac{5}{2}\right], \left[\dfrac{5}{2}, 3\right], \left[3, \dfrac{7}{2}\right], \left[\dfrac{7}{2}, 4\right], \left[4, \dfrac{9}{2}\right], \left[\dfrac{9}{2}, 5\right]$

For #17–20, the intervals are of width 1, so the area of each rectangle is $1 \cdot f(k) = f(k)$.

17. (a)
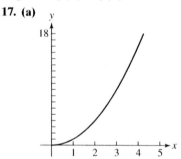

(b)
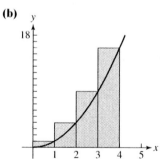

RRAM: $f(1) + f(2) + f(3) + f(4)$
$= 1 + 4 + 9 + 16 = 30$

(c)

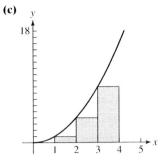

LRAM: $f(0) + f(1) + f(2) + f(3)$
$= 0 + 1 + 4 + 9 = 14$

(d) Average: $\dfrac{14 + 30}{2} = 22$

18. (a)

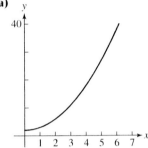

(b)

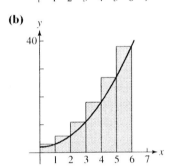

RRAM: $f(1) + f(2) + \ldots + f(6)$
$= 3 + 6 + 11 + 18 + 27 + 38 = 103$

(c)

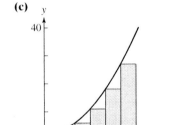

LRAM: $f(0) + f(1) + \ldots + f(5)$
$= 2 + 3 + 6 + 11 + 18 + 27 = 67$

(d) Average: $\dfrac{67 + 103}{2} = 85$

19. (a)

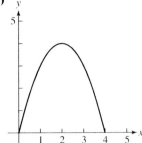

(b)

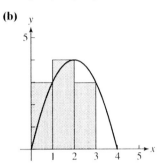

RRAM: $f(1) + f(2) + f(3) + f(4)$
$= 3 + 4 + 3 + 0 = 10$

(c)

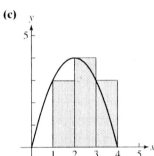

LRAM: $f(0) + f(1) + f(2) + f(3)$
$= 0 + 3 + 4 + 3 = 10$

(d) Average: $\dfrac{10 + 10}{2} = 10$

20. (a)

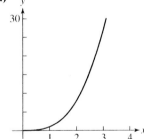

(b)

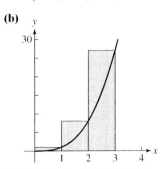

RRAM: $f(1) + f(2) + f(3) = 1 + 8 + 27 = 36$

(c)

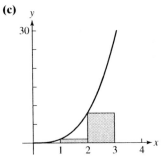

LRAM: $f(0) + f(1) + f(2) = 0 + 1 + 8 = 9$

(d) Average: $\dfrac{9 + 36}{2} = \dfrac{45}{2}$

21. $\displaystyle\int_3^7 5\, dx = 20$ (Rectangle with base 4 and height 5)

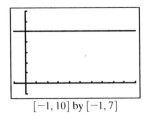

$[-1, 10]$ by $[-1, 7]$

22. $\displaystyle\int_{-1}^4 6\, dx = 30$ (Rectangle with base 5 and height 6)

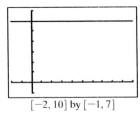

$[-2, 10]$ by $[-1, 7]$

23. $\displaystyle\int_0^5 3x\, dx = 37.5$ (Triangle with base 5 and altitude 15)

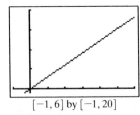

$[-1, 6]$ by $[-1, 20]$

24. $\displaystyle\int_1^7 0.5x\, dx = 12$ (Trapezoid with bases of 0.5 and 3.5 and height 6)

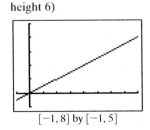

$[-1, 8]$ by $[-1, 5]$

25. $\displaystyle\int_1^4 (x + 3)\, dx = 16.5$ (Trapezoid with bases 4 and 7 and altitude 3)

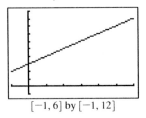

$[-1, 6]$ by $[-1, 12]$

26. $\displaystyle\int_1^4 (3x - 2)\, dx = 16.5$ (Trapezoid with bases 1 and 10 and altitude 3)

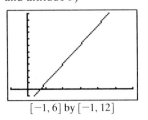

$[-1, 6]$ by $[-1, 12]$

27. $\displaystyle\int_{-2}^2 \sqrt{4 - x^2}\, dx = 2\pi$ (Semicircle with radius 2)

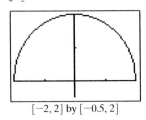

$[-2, 2]$ by $[-0.5, 2]$

28. $\displaystyle\int_0^6 \sqrt{36 - x^2}\, dx = 9\pi$ (Quarter circle with radius 6)

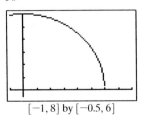

$[-1, 8]$ by $[-0.5, 6]$

29. $\displaystyle\int_0^\pi \sin x\, dx = 2$ (One arch of sine curve)

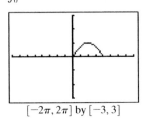

$[-2\pi, 2\pi]$ by $[-3, 3]$

30. $\int_0^\pi (\sin x + 2)\, dx = 2 + 2\pi$ (Arch of sine curve plus rectangle with base π and height 2)

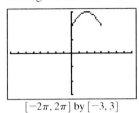

$[-2\pi, 2\pi]$ by $[-3, 3]$

31. $\int_2^{2+\pi} \sin (x - 2)\, dx = 2$ (One arch of sine curve translated 2 units right)

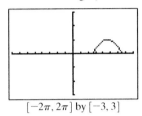

$[-2\pi, 2\pi]$ by $[-3, 3]$

32. $\int_{-\pi/2}^{\pi/2} \cos x\, dx = 2$ (One arch of cosine curve, which is sine curve translated $\pi/2$ units)

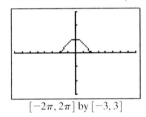

$[-2\pi, 2\pi]$ by $[-3, 3]$

33. $\int_0^{\pi/2} \sin x\, dx = 1$ (Half-arch of sine curve)

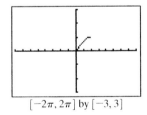

$[-2\pi, 2\pi]$ by $[-3, 3]$

34. $\int_0^{\pi/2} \cos x\, dx = 1$ (Half-arch of cosine curve, congruent to half-arch of sine curve)

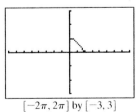

$[-2\pi, 2\pi]$ by $[-3, 3]$

35. $\int_0^\pi 2 \sin x\, dx = 4$ (Rectangles in sum are twice as tall, yielding twice the sum)

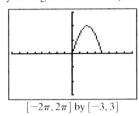

$[-2\pi, 2\pi]$ by $[-3, 3]$

36. $\int_0^{2\pi} \sin\left(\frac{x}{2}\right) dx = 4$ (Rectangles in sum are twice as wide, yielding twice the sum)

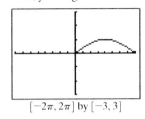

$[-2\pi, 2\pi]$ by $[-3, 3]$

37. $\int_0^{2\pi} |\sin x|\, dx = 4$ (Two arches of the sine curve)

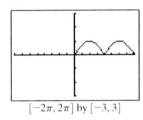

$[-2\pi, 2\pi]$ by $[-3, 3]$

38. $\int_{-\pi}^{3\pi/2} |\cos x|\, dx = 5$ (Two-and-a-half arches of the cosine curve)

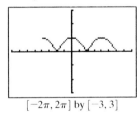

$[-2\pi, 2\pi]$ by $[-3, 3]$

39. The graph of $f(x) = kx + 3$ is a line. If k is a number between 0 and 4, the integral is the area of a trapezoid with bases of $0k + 3 = 3$ and $4k + 3$ and height of $4 - 0 = 4$. The area is $\frac{1}{2}(4)(3 + 4k + 3) = 2(4k + 6)$ $= 8k + 12$, so $\int_0^4 (kx + 3)dx = 8k + 12$.

40. The graph of $f(x) = 4x + 3$ is a line. The integral is the area of a trapezoid with bases of $4 \cdot 0 + 3 = 3$ and $4k + 3$ and height of $k - 0 = k$. The area is $\frac{1}{2}k(3 + 4k + 3) = \frac{1}{2}k(4k + 6) = 2k^2 + 3k$, so $\int_0^k (4x + 3)dx = 2k^2 + 3k.$

41. The graph of $f(x) = 3x + k$ is a line. The integral is the area of a trapezoid with bases of $3 \cdot 0 + k = k$ and $3 \cdot 4 + k = 12 + k$ and height of $4 - 0 = 4$. The area is $\frac{1}{2}(4)(k + 12 + k) = 2(12 + 2k) = 24 + 4k$, so
$$\int_0^4 (3x + k)dx = 24 + 4k.$$

42. The graph of $f(x) = 4x + 3$ is a line. The integral is the area of a trapezoid with bases of $4k + 3$ and $4 \cdot 4 + 3 = 19$ and height of $4 - k$. The area is
$$\frac{1}{2}(4 - k)(4k + 3 + 19) = \frac{1}{2}(4 - k)(22 + 4k)$$
$$= (4 - k)(11 + 2k) = 44 - 2k^2 - 3k$$

43. Since $g(x) = -f(x)$, we consider g to be symmetric with f about the x-axis. For every value of x in the interval, $|f(x)|$ is the distance to the x-axis and similarly, $|g(x)|$ is the distance to the x-axis; $f(x)$ and $g(x)$ are equidistant from the x-axis. As a result, the area under $f(x)$ must be exactly equal to the area above $g(x)$.

44. The graph of $f(x) = \sqrt{16 - x^2}$ is the top half of a circle of radius 4. The area of the graph from $x = 0$ to $x = 4$ is the area of $\frac{1}{4}$ of the entire circle. Thus the desired area is
$$\frac{1}{4}(\pi \cdot 4^2) = \frac{1}{4}(16\pi) = 4\pi.$$

45. The distance traveled will be the same as the area under the velocity graph, $v(t) = 32t$, over the interval $[0, 2]$. That triangular region has an area of $A = (1/2)(2)(64) = 64$. The ball falls 64 feet during the first 2 seconds.

46. The distance traveled will be the same as the area under the velocity graph, $v(t) = 6t$, over the interval $[0, 7]$. That triangular region has an area of $A = (1/2)(7)(42) = 147$. The car travels 147 feet in the first 7 seconds.

47. (a)

[0, 3] by [0, 50]

(b) The ball reaches its maximum height when the velocity function is zero; this is the point where the ball changes direction and starts its descent. Solving for t when $48 - 32t = 0$, we find $t = 1.5$ sec.

(c) The distance the ball has traveled is the area under the curve, a triangle with base 1.5 and height 48 thus, $d = 0.5(1.5)(48) = 36$ units.

48. (a)

[0, 8] by [0, 180]

(b) The rocket reaches its maximum height when the velocity function is zero; this is the point where the rocket changes direction and starts its descent. Solving for t when $170 - 32t = 0$, $t \approx 5.31$ sec.

(c) The distance the rocket has traveled is the area under the curve, a triangle with base 5.3125 and height 170 thus, $d = \frac{1}{2}(170)(5.3125) \approx 451.6$ ft.

49. (a)

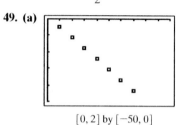

[0, 2] by [−50, 0]

(b) Each RRAM rectangle will have width 0.2. The heights (using the absolute value of the velocity) are 5.05, 11.43, 17.46, 24.21, 30.62, 37.06, and 43.47. The height of the building is approximately $0.2[5.05 + 11.43 + 17.46 + 24.21 + 30.62 + 37.06 + 43.47] = 33.86$ feet.

50. Work is defined as force times distance. The work done in moving the barrel 35 feet is the area under the curve created by the given data points, assuming the barrel weighs approximately 550 lbs after being moved 35 feet. In this case, the area under the curve is the sum of a rectangle of width 35 and height 550 and a triangle of base 35 and height $(1250 - 550) = 700$. The total work performed is
$$(35)(550) + \frac{1}{2}(35)(700) = 31{,}500 \text{ ft-pounds.}$$

51. True. The exact area under a curve is given by the limit as n approaches infinity. This is true whether LRAM or RRAM is used.

52. False. The statement $\lim_{x \to \infty} f(x) = L$ means that $f(x)$ gets arbitrarily close to L as x gets arbitrarily large.

53. Since $y = 2\sqrt{x}$ represents a vertical stretch, by a factor of 2, of $y = \sqrt{x}$, the area under the curve between $x = 0$ and $x = 9$ is doubled. The answer is A.

54. Since $y = \sqrt{x} + 5$ represents a vertical shift, by 5 units upward, of $y = \sqrt{x}$, the area is increased by the contribution of a 9-by-5 rectangle—an area of 45 square units. The answer is E.

55. $y = \sqrt{x - 5}$ is shifted right 5 units compared to $y = \sqrt{x}$, but the limits of integration are shifted right 5 units also, so the area is unchanged. The answer is C.

56. $y = \sqrt{3x}$ represents a horizontal compression, by a factor of 1/3, and the interval of integration is shrunk in the same way. So the new area is 1/3 of the old area. The answer is D.

57. In the definition of the definate integral, if $f(x)$ is negative, then $\sum_{i=1}^{n} f(x_i)\Delta x$ is negative, so the definite integral is negative. For $f(x) = \sin x$ on $[0, 2\pi]$, the "positive area" (from 0 to π) cancels the "negative area" (from π to 1), so the definite integral is 0.

Since $g(x) = x - 1$ forms a triangle with area $\dfrac{1}{2}$ below the x-axis on $[0, 1]$, $\displaystyle\int_{0}^{1} (x - 1)dx = -\dfrac{1}{2}$.

58. (a)

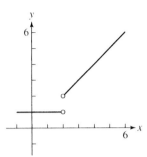

Domain: $(-\infty, 2) \cup (2, \infty)$
Range: $\{1\} \cup (2, \infty)$

(b) The area under f from $x = 0$ to $x = 4$ is a rectangle of width 4 and height 1 and a trapezoid with bases of 1 and 3 and height 2. It does not really make any difference that the function has no value at $x = 2$.

59. True
$$\int_{a}^{b} f(x)dx + \int_{a}^{b} g(x)dx$$
$$= \left[\lim_{n\to\infty} \sum_{i=1}^{n} f(x_i)\Delta x\right] + \left[\lim_{n\to\infty} \sum_{i=1}^{n} g(x_i)\Delta x\right]$$
$$= \lim_{n\to\infty}\left[\sum_{i=1}^{n} f(x_i)\Delta x + \sum_{i=1}^{n} g(x_i)\Delta x\right]$$
$$= \lim_{n\to\infty} \sum_{i=1}^{n} [f(x_i) + g(x_i)]\Delta x$$
$$= \int_{a}^{b} (f(x) + g(x))dx$$

Note: There are some subtleties here, because the x_i that are chosen for $f(x)$ may be different from the x_i that are chosen for $g(x)$; however, the result is true, provided the limits exist.

60. True, because multiplying the function by 8 will multiply the area by 8.

61. False. Counterexample: Let $f(x) = 1$, $g(x) = 1$. Then $\displaystyle\int_{0}^{2} f(x)g(x)dx = 2$ but $\displaystyle\int_{0}^{2} f(x)dx \cdot \int_{0}^{2} g(x)dx = 4$.

62. True, because (area from a to c) + (area from c to b) = (area from a to b)

63. False. Interchanging a and b reverses the sign of $\Delta x = \dfrac{b - a}{n}$, which reverses the sign of the integral.

64. True. For any value of n, $\Delta x = \dfrac{a - a}{n} = 0$.
$$\int_{a}^{a} f(x)dx = \lim_{n\to\infty} \sum_{i=1}^{n} f(x_i)\Delta x = \lim_{n\to\infty} \sum_{i=1}^{n} f(a) \cdot 0$$
$$= \lim_{n\to\infty} 0 = 0$$

■ Section 10.3   More on Limits

Exploration 1

1. Answers will vary. Possible answers include:
Solving graphically or algebraically shows that $7x = 14$ when $x = 2$, so we know that 14 is the limit.

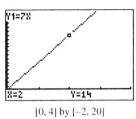

[0, 4] by [−2, 20]

A table of values also shows that the value of the function approaches 14 as x approaches 2 from either direction.

X	Y1
1.997	13.979
1.998	13.986
1.999	13.993
2	**14**
2.001	14.007
2.002	14.014
2.003	14.021

X=2

2. Answers will vary. Possible answers include:
The graphs suggest that the limit exists and is 2. Because the graph is a line with a discontinuity at $x = 0$, there is no asymptote at $x = 0$.

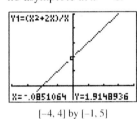   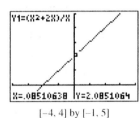

[−4, 4] by [−1, 5]   [−4, 4] by [−1, 5]

A table of values also suggests that the limit is 2.

X	Y1
−.003	1.997
−.002	1.998
−.001	1.999
0	**ERROR**
.001	2.001
.002	2.002
.003	2.003

X=0

To show that 2 is the limit and $1.999\overline{9}$ is not, we can solve algebraically.
$$\lim_{x\to 0} \frac{x^2 + 2x}{x} = \lim_{x\to 0} \frac{x(x + 2)}{x}$$
$$= \lim_{x\to 0} (x + 2)$$
$$= 2$$

Exploration 2

1.

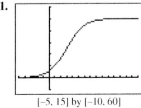

[−5, 15] by [−10, 60]

$\lim_{x\to\infty} f(x) = 50$, $\lim_{x\to -\infty} f(x) = 0$

2. The two horizontal asymptotes are $y = 50$ and $y = 0$.

3. As $x \to \infty$, $2^{3-x} \to 0$ and $1 + 2^{3-x} \to 1$.
As $x \to -\infty$, $2^{3-x} \to \infty$ and $1 + 2^{3-x} \to \infty$.

Quick Review 10.3

1. (a) $f(-2) = \dfrac{-4 + 1}{(-4 - 4)^2} = -\dfrac{3}{64}$,

(b) $f(0) = \dfrac{0 + 1}{(0 - 4)^2} = \dfrac{1}{16}$,

(c) $f(2) = \dfrac{4 + 1}{(4 - 4)^2}$ is undefined.

2. (a) $f(-2) = \dfrac{\sin (-2)}{-2} = \dfrac{\sin 2}{2} \approx 0.45$,

(b) $f(0) = \dfrac{\sin 0}{0}$ is undefined.

(c) $f(2) = \dfrac{\sin 2}{2} \approx 0.45$

3. (a) Since $x^2 - 4 = 0$ and $x = \pm 2$, the graph of f has vertical asymptotes at $x = -2$ and $x = 2$.

(b) Since $\lim\limits_{x \to -\infty} f(x) = 2$ and $\lim\limits_{x \to \infty} f(x) = 2$, the graph of f has a horizontal asymptote of $y = 2$.

4. (a) Since $x^2 + x - 2 = 0$ when $x = -2$ and $x = 1$, the graph of f has vertical asymptotes at $x = -2$ and $x = 1$.

(b) Since $\lim\limits_{x \to -\infty} f(x) = \infty$ and $\lim\limits_{x \to \infty} f(x) = -\infty$, the graph of f has no horizontal asymptotes.

5. Since $\dfrac{2x^3}{-x} = -2x^2$, the end behavior asymptote is

(b) $y = -2x^2$.

6. Since $\dfrac{x^4}{x} = x^3$, the end behavior asymptote is (c) $y = x^3$.

7. (a) $[-2, \infty)$

(b) None

8. (a) $(-\infty, -2) \cup (-2, 2) \cup (2, \infty)$

(b) $x = -2$, $x = 2$

9.

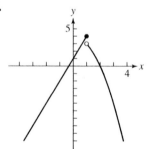

10. Continuous on $(-\infty, 1) \cup (1, \infty)$; discontinuous at $x = 1$

Section 10.3 Exercises

1. $(-1)(-2)^2 = -4$

2. $(2)^{12} = 4096$

3. $8 - 4 + 3 = 7$

4. $-8 + 2 + 5 = -1$

5. $\sqrt{7}$

6. $(-6)^{2/3} \approx 3.30$

7. $\lim\limits_{x \to 0} (e^x \sin(x)) = \lim\limits_{x \to 0} e^x \lim\limits_{x \to 0} \sin(x) = 1 \cdot 0 = 0$

8. $\lim\limits_{x \to \pi} \ln\left(\sin \dfrac{x}{2}\right) = \ln(1) = 0 = 0$

9. $a^2 - 2$

10. $\dfrac{a^2 - 1}{a^2 + 1}$ (Since $a^2 + 1 > 0$ for all a, we don't have to worry about division by zero.)

11. (a) division by zero

(b) $\lim\limits_{x \to -3} \dfrac{x^2 + 7x + 12}{x^2 - 9} = \lim\limits_{x \to -3} \dfrac{(x + 4)(x + 3)}{(x + 3)(x - 3)}$

$= \lim\limits_{x \to -3} \dfrac{x + 4}{x - 3} = -\dfrac{1}{6}$

12. (a) division by zero

(b) $\lim\limits_{x \to 3} \dfrac{(x + 3)(x - 3)}{(x + 5)(x - 3)} = \lim\limits_{x \to 3} \dfrac{x + 3}{x + 5} = \dfrac{6}{8} = \dfrac{3}{4}$

13. (a) division by zero

(b) $\lim\limits_{x \to -1} \dfrac{(x + 1)(x^2 - x + 1)}{x + 1} = \lim\limits_{x \to -1} (x^2 - x + 1) = 3$

14. (a) division by zero

(b) $\lim\limits_{x \to 2} \dfrac{(x - 2)(x^2 + 1)}{x - 2} = \lim\limits_{x \to 2} (x^2 + 1) = 5$

15. (a) division by zero

(b) $\lim\limits_{x \to -2} \dfrac{(x + 2)(x - 2)}{x + 2} = \lim\limits_{x \to -2} (x - 2) = -4$

16. (a) division by zero

(b) $\lim\limits_{x \to -2} \dfrac{|(x + 2)(x - 2)|}{x + 2}$. Check left- and right-hand limits.

Right: $\lim\limits_{x \to -2^+} \dfrac{(-1)(x + 2)(x - 2)}{x + 2} = \lim\limits_{x \to -2^+} (-x + 2) = 4$

Left: $\lim\limits_{x \to -2^-} \dfrac{(x + 2)(x - 2)}{x + 2} = \lim\limits_{x \to -2^-} (x - 2) = -4$

Since $4 \neq -4$, the limit does not exist.

17. (a) The square root of negative numbers is not defined in the real plane.

(b) The limit does not exist.

18. (a) division by zero

(b) The limit does not exist.

19. $\lim\limits_{x \to 0} \dfrac{\sin x}{2x^2 - x} = \lim\limits_{x \to 0} \dfrac{\sin x}{x(2x - 1)} = \lim\limits_{x \to 0} \dfrac{\sin x}{x} \cdot \lim\limits_{x \to 0} \dfrac{1}{2x - 1}$
$= 1 \cdot -1 = -1$ (Recall example 11 and the product rule)

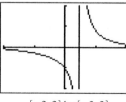

$[-2, 2]$ by $[-2, 2]$

20. $\lim\limits_{x\to 0} \dfrac{\sin 3x}{x} = \lim\limits_{x\to 0} \dfrac{3\sin(3x)}{(3x)} = \lim\limits_{x\to 0} 3\cdot\lim\limits_{x\to 0} \dfrac{\sin(3x)}{(3x)}$

$= 3\cdot 1 = 3$

(Recall example 11 and the product rule).

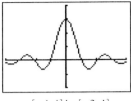

$[-4, 4]$ by $[-2, 4]$

21. $\lim\limits_{x\to 0} \dfrac{\sin^2 x}{x} = \lim\limits_{x\to 0} \dfrac{\sin x}{x}\cdot\sin x = \lim\limits_{x\to 0}\sin x\cdot\lim\limits_{x\to 0}\dfrac{\sin x}{x}$

$= 0\cdot 1 = 0$

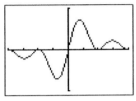

$[-2\pi, 2\pi]$ by $[-1, 1]$

22. $\lim\limits_{x\to 0} \dfrac{x+\sin x}{2x} = \dfrac{1}{2}\lim\limits_{x\to 0}\dfrac{x}{x} + \dfrac{1}{2}\lim\limits_{x\to 0}\dfrac{\sin x}{x}$

$= \dfrac{1}{2}\cdot 1 + \dfrac{1}{2}\cdot 1 = 1$

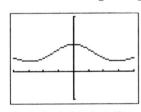

$[-2\pi, 2\pi]$ by $[-1, 2]$

In Exercises #23–26, the function is defined and continuous at the value approached by x, and so the limit is simply the function evaluated at that value.

23. $\lim\limits_{x\to 0} \dfrac{e^x - \sqrt{x}}{\log_4(x+2)} = \dfrac{e^0 - \sqrt{0}}{\log_4(0+2)} = \dfrac{1}{1/2} = 2$

24. $\lim\limits_{x\to 0} \dfrac{3\sin x - 4\cos x}{5\sin x + \cos x} = \dfrac{3\sin 0 - 4\cos 0}{5\sin 0 + \cos 0} = \dfrac{-4}{1} = -4$

25. $\lim\limits_{x\to \pi/2} \dfrac{\ln(2x)}{\sin^2 x} = \dfrac{\ln\pi}{\sin^2(\pi/2)} = \dfrac{\ln\pi}{1} = \ln\pi$

26. $\lim\limits_{x\to 27} \dfrac{\sqrt{x+9}}{\log_3 x} = \dfrac{\sqrt{36}}{\log_3 27} = \dfrac{6}{3} = 2$

27. (a) $\lim\limits_{x\to 2^-} f(x) = 3$

(b) $\lim\limits_{x\to 2^+} f(x) = 1$

(c) $3\neq 1$, so the limit does not exist.

28. (a) $\lim\limits_{x\to 3^-} f(x) = 2$

(b) $\lim\limits_{x\to 3^+} f(x) = 4$

(c) $2\neq 4$, so the limit does not exist.

29. (a) $\lim\limits_{x\to 3^-} f(x) = 4$

(b) $\lim\limits_{x\to 3^+} f(x) = 4$

(c) $\lim\limits_{x\to 3} f(x) = 4$

30. (a) $\lim\limits_{x\to 1^-} f(x) = 1$

(b) $\lim\limits_{x\to 1^+} f(x) = 3$

(c) $1\neq 3$, so the limit does not exist.

31. (a) True

(b) True

(c) False

(d) False

(e) False

(f) False

(g) False

(h) True

(i) False

(j) True

32. (a) True

(b) False

(c) False

(d) True

(e) False

(f) False

(g) False

(h) False (The limit does not exist at $x = 0$.)

(i) True

33.

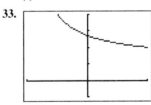

$[-1, 1]$ by $[-1, 4]$

(a) $\lim\limits_{x\to 0^-} f(x) \approx 2.72$

(b) $\lim\limits_{x\to 0^+} f(x) \approx 2.72$

(c) $\lim\limits_{x\to 0} f(x) \approx 2.72$

34.

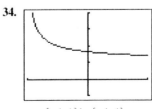

$[-1, 1]$ by $[-1, 4]$

(a) $\lim\limits_{x\to 0^-} f(x) \approx 1.65$

(b) $\lim\limits_{x\to 0^+} f(x) \approx 1.65$

(c) $\lim\limits_{x\to 0} f(x) \approx 1.65$

35. (a) $\lim\limits_{x \to 4} (g(x) + 2) = 4 + 2 = 6$ (sum rule)

(b) $\lim\limits_{x \to 4} x \cdot f(x) = \lim\limits_{x \to 4} x \cdot \lim\limits_{x \to 4} f(x) = 4(-1) = -4$
(product rule)

(c) $\lim\limits_{x \to 4} g^2(x) = \lim\limits_{x \to 4} g(x) \cdot \lim\limits_{x \to 4} g(x) = 4 \cdot 4 = 16$
(product rule)

(d) $\lim\limits_{x \to 4} \dfrac{g(x)}{f(x) - 1} = \dfrac{\lim\limits_{x \to 4} g(x)}{\lim\limits_{x \to 4} f(x) - \lim\limits_{x \to 4} 1} = \dfrac{4}{-1 - 1} = -2$
(quotient rule)

36. (a) $\lim\limits_{x \to a} (f(x) + g(x)) = \lim\limits_{x \to a} f(x) + \lim\limits_{x \to a} g(x)$
$= 2 - 3 = -1$ (sum rule)

(b) $\lim\limits_{x \to a} (f(x) \cdot g(x)) = \lim\limits_{x \to a} f(x) \cdot \lim\limits_{x \to a} g(x)$
$(2)(-3) = -6$ (product rule)

(c) $\lim\limits_{x \to a} (3g(x) + 1) = 3 \lim\limits_{x \to a} g(x) + \lim\limits_{x \to a} 1$
$= 3(-3) + 1 = -8$
(constant multiple and sum rules)

(d) $\lim\limits_{x \to a} \dfrac{f(x)}{g(x)} = \dfrac{\lim\limits_{x \to a} f(x)}{\lim\limits_{x \to a} g(x)} = \dfrac{2}{-3} = -\dfrac{2}{3}$ (quotient rule)

37. (a)

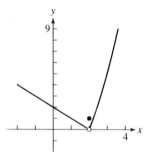

(b) $\lim\limits_{x \to 2^+} f(x) = 0$, $\lim\limits_{x \to 2^-} f(x) = 0$

(c) $\lim\limits_{x \to 2} f(x) = 0$

38. (a)

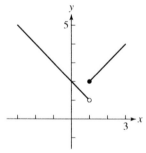

(b) $\lim\limits_{x \to 1^+} f(x) = 2$, $\lim\limits_{x \to 1^-} f(x) = 1$

(c) Limit does not exist because $\lim\limits_{x \to 1^+} f(x) \neq \lim\limits_{x \to 1^-} f(x)$.

39. (a)

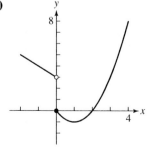

(b) $\lim\limits_{x \to 0^+} f(x) = 0$, $\lim\limits_{x \to 0^-} f(x) = 3$

(c) Limit does not exist because $\lim\limits_{x \to 0^+} f(x) \neq \lim\limits_{x \to 0^-} f(x)$.

40. (a)

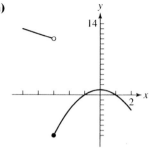

(b) $\lim\limits_{x \to -3^+} f(x) = -8$, $\lim\limits_{x \to -3^-} f(x) = 11$

(c) Limit does not exist because $\lim\limits_{x \to -3^+} f(x) \neq \lim\limits_{x \to -3^-} f(x)$.

For Exercises #41–43, use Figure 10.14.

41. $\lim\limits_{x \to 2^+} \text{int } x = 2$

42. $\lim\limits_{x \to 2^-} \text{int } x = 1$

43. $\lim\limits_{x \to 0.0001} \text{int } x = 0$

44. $\lim\limits_{x \to 5/2^-} \text{int } (2x) = 4$

45. $\lim\limits_{x \to -3^+} \dfrac{x + 3}{|x + 3|} = \lim\limits_{x \to -3^+} \dfrac{x + 3}{x + 3} = 1$

46. $\lim\limits_{x \to 0^-} \dfrac{5x}{|2x|} = \lim\limits_{x \to 0^-} \dfrac{5x}{-2x} = -\dfrac{5}{2}$

47. (a) $\lim\limits_{x \to \infty} \dfrac{\cos x}{1 + x} = 0$

(b) $\lim\limits_{x \to -\infty} \dfrac{\cos x}{x} = 0$

48. (a) $\lim\limits_{x \to \infty} \dfrac{x + \sin x}{x} = \lim\limits_{x \to \infty} \dfrac{x}{x} + \lim\limits_{x \to \infty} \dfrac{\sin x}{x} = 1 + 0 = 1$

(b) $\lim\limits_{x \to -\infty} \dfrac{x + \sin x}{x} = \lim\limits_{x \to -\infty} \dfrac{x}{x} + \lim\limits_{x \to -\infty} \dfrac{\sin x}{x}$
$= 1 + 0 = 1$

49. (a) $\lim\limits_{x \to \infty} (1 + 2^x) = \infty$

(b) $\lim\limits_{x \to -\infty} (1 + 2^x) = 1$

50. (a) $\lim\limits_{x \to \infty} \dfrac{x}{1 + 2^x} = 0$

(b) $\lim\limits_{x \to -\infty} \dfrac{x}{1 + 2^x} = -\infty$

51. (a) $\lim\limits_{x \to \infty} (x + \sin x) = \infty$

(b) $\lim\limits_{x \to -\infty} (x + \sin x) = -\infty$

52. (a) $\lim\limits_{x \to \infty} (e^{-x} + \sin x)$ is undefined, because e^{-x} goes to zero but $\sin x$ oscillates.

(b) $\lim\limits_{x \to -\infty} (e^{-x} + \sin x) = \infty$

53. (a) $\lim\limits_{x \to \infty} (-e^x \sin x)$ is undefined, because $\sin x$ oscillates between positive and negative values.

(b) $\lim\limits_{x \to -\infty} (-e^x \sin x) = 0$

54. (a) $\lim\limits_{x \to \infty} e^{-x} \cos x = 0$

(b) $\lim\limits_{x \to -\infty} e^{-x} \cos x$ is undefined, because $\cos x$ oscillates between positive and negative values.

55. $\lim\limits_{x \to 3^-} \dfrac{1}{x - 3} = -\infty; \; x = 3$

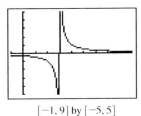

$[-1, 9]$ by $[-5, 5]$

56. $\lim\limits_{x \to 3^+} \dfrac{1}{x - 3} = \infty; \; x = 3$

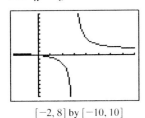

$[-2, 8]$ by $[-10, 10]$

57. $\lim\limits_{x \to -2^+} \dfrac{1}{x + 2} = \infty; \; x = -2$

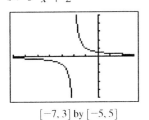

$[-7, 3]$ by $[-5, 5]$

58. $\lim\limits_{x \to -2^-} \dfrac{x}{x - 2} = \infty; \; x = -2$

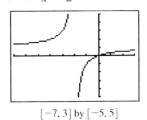

$[-7, 3]$ by $[-5, 5]$

59. $\lim\limits_{x \to 2} \dfrac{1}{(x - 5)^5} = \infty; \; x = 5$

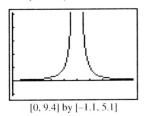

$[0, 9.4]$ by $[-1.1, 5.1]$

60. $\lim\limits_{x \to 2} \dfrac{1}{x^2 - 4}$ is undefined; $x = 2$ and $x = -2$

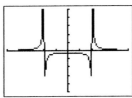

$[-5, 5]$ by $[-5, 5]$

61. $\lim\limits_{x \to 0} \dfrac{(1 + x)^3 - 1}{x} = \lim\limits_{x \to 0} \dfrac{x^3 + 3x^2 + 3x + 1 - 1}{x}$

$= \lim\limits_{x \to 0} \dfrac{x(x^2 + 3x + 3)}{x}$

$= \lim\limits_{x \to 0} (x^2 + 3x + 3) = 3$

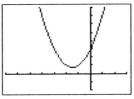

$[-7, 3]$ by $[-2, 8]$

62. $\lim\limits_{x \to 0} \dfrac{\dfrac{1}{3 + x} - \dfrac{1}{3}}{x}$

$= \lim\limits_{x \to 0} \dfrac{3 - (3 + x)}{3(3 + x)} \cdot \dfrac{1}{x} = \dfrac{1}{3} \lim\limits_{x \to 0} -\dfrac{x}{x} \cdot \dfrac{1}{x + 3}$

$\dfrac{1}{3} \lim\limits_{x \to 0} \left(-\dfrac{1}{x + 3} \right) = -\dfrac{1}{9}$

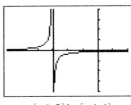

$[-6, 2]$ by $[-4, 4]$

63. $\lim\limits_{x \to 0} \dfrac{\tan x}{x} = \lim\limits_{x \to 0} \dfrac{\sin x}{x \cos x} = \lim\limits_{x \to 0} \dfrac{\sin x}{x} \cdot \lim\limits_{x \to 0} \dfrac{1}{\cos x}$

$= 1 \cdot 1 = 1$

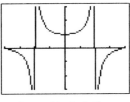

$[-\pi, \pi]$ by $[-3, 3]$

64. $\lim\limits_{x\to 2}\dfrac{x-4}{x^2-4}$ is undefined.

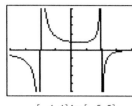

$[-4,4]$ by $[-5,5]$

65. $\lim\limits_{x\to 0}\dfrac{|x|}{x^2}=\lim\limits_{x\to 0}\left|\dfrac{x}{x^2}\right|=\lim\limits_{x\to 0}\left|\dfrac{1}{x}\right|=\infty$

66. $\lim\limits_{x\to 0}\dfrac{x^2}{|x|}=\lim\limits_{x\to 0}\left|\dfrac{x^2}{x}\right|=\lim\limits_{x\to 0}|x|=0$

67. $\lim\limits_{x\to 0}\left[x\sin\left(\dfrac{1}{x}\right)\right]=0$ because $x\to 0$

and $-1\le\sin\left(\dfrac{1}{x}\right)\le 1$.

68. $\lim\limits_{x\to 27}\cos\left(\dfrac{1}{x}\right)=\cos\left(\dfrac{1}{27}\right)\approx 0.9993$

69. $\lim\limits_{x\to 1}\dfrac{x^2+1}{x-1}$ is undefined, since $\lim\limits_{x\to 1^-}\dfrac{x^2+1}{x-1}=-\infty$

and $\lim\limits_{x\to 1^+}\dfrac{x^2+1}{x-1}=\infty$

70. $\lim\limits_{x\to\infty}\dfrac{\ln x^2}{\ln x}=\lim\limits_{x\to\infty}\dfrac{2\ln x}{\ln x}=2$

71. $\lim\limits_{x\to\infty}\dfrac{\ln x}{\ln x^2}=\lim\limits_{x\to\infty}\dfrac{\ln x}{2\ln x}=\dfrac{1}{2}$

72. $\lim\limits_{x\to\infty}3^{-x}=\lim\limits_{x\to\infty}\dfrac{1}{3^x}=0$

73. False. $\lim\limits_{x\to 3}f(x)=\lim\limits_{x\to 3^-}f(x)=\lim\limits_{x\to 3^+}f(x)=5$

74. False. For example, if $f(x)=\sin(1/x)$ and $g(x)=x$, then $\lim\limits_{x\to 0}f(x)$ does not exist but $\lim\limits_{x\to 0}[f(x)\cdot g(x)]=0$.

75. $\lim\limits_{x\to 3}\dfrac{x^2-2x-3}{x-3}=\lim\limits_{x\to 3}\dfrac{(x+1)(x-3)}{x-3}$
$=\lim\limits_{x\to 3}(x+1)=4$. The answer is B.

76. $\lim\limits_{x\to 3^-}\dfrac{x^2+2x+3}{x-3}=-\infty,\ \lim\limits_{x\to 3^+}\dfrac{x^2+2x+3}{x-3}=\infty.$
The answer is A.

77. $\lim\limits_{x\to 3^-}\dfrac{x^2-2x-9}{x-3}=\infty,\ \lim\limits_{x\to 3^+}\dfrac{x^2-2x-9}{x-3}=-\infty.$
The answer is C.

78. $\lim\limits_{x\to 3}\dfrac{x^3-27}{x-3}=\lim\limits_{x\to 3}\dfrac{(x-3)(x^2+3x+9)}{x-3}$
$=\lim\limits_{x\to 3}(x^2+3x+9)=27.$ The answer is D.

79. (a)

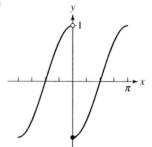

(b) $(-\pi,0)\cup(0,\pi)$

(c) $x=\pi$

(d) $x=-\pi$

80. (a)

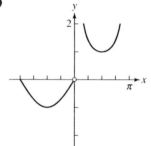

(b) $(-\pi,0)\cup(0,\pi)$

(c) $x=0$

(d) $x=-\pi$

81. (a)

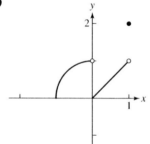

(b) $(-1,0)\cup(0,1)$

(c) $x=1$

(d) $x=-1$

82. (a)

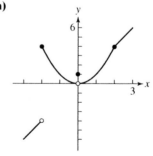

(b) $(-\infty,-2)\cup(-2,\infty)$

(c) None

(d) None

83. (a)

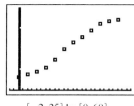

$[-2, 25]$ by $[0, 60]$

(b) $f(x) \approx \dfrac{57.71}{1 + 6.39e^{-0.19x}}$, where $x =$ the number of months $\displaystyle\lim_{x\to\infty} f(x) \approx 57.71$

(c) The rabbit population will stabilize at a little less than 58,000.

(d) One possible answer: As populations burgeon, resources such as food, water, and safe havens from predators become more scarce and the population tends to stabilize based on the resources available to it—this is what is often call a maximum sustainable population.

84.

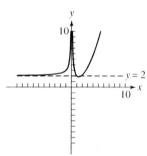

85.

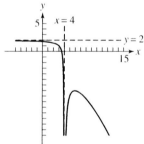

86.

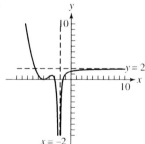

87.

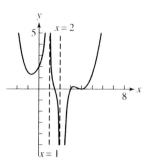

88. (a) $\displaystyle\lim_{x\to 0}\frac{2}{x^2} = \infty;\ \lim_{x\to 0} x^2 = 0;\ \lim_{x\to 0}\frac{2}{x^2}\cdot x^2 = \lim_{x\to 0} 2 = 2$

(b) $\displaystyle\lim_{x\to 0}\left|\frac{1}{x}\right| = \infty;\ \lim_{x\to 0}\sqrt[3]{x} = 0;\ \lim_{x\to 0}\frac{\sqrt[3]{x}}{|x|}$ is not defined

(c) $\displaystyle\lim_{x\to 1}\left|\frac{3}{x-1}\right| = \infty;\ \lim_{x\to 1}(x-1)^2 = 0;$

$\displaystyle\lim_{x\to 1^+}\frac{3(x-1)^2}{|x-1|} = \lim_{x\to 1^+}\frac{3(x-1)^2}{x-1}$
$= \lim_{x\to 1^+} 3(x-1) = 0$

$\displaystyle\lim_{x\to 1^-}\frac{3(x-1)^2}{|x-1|} = \lim_{x\to 1^-}\frac{3(x-1)^2}{-(x-1)}$
$= \lim_{x\to 1^-} -3(x-1) = 0$

Thus, $\displaystyle\lim_{x\to 1} fg = 0$

(d) $\displaystyle\lim_{x\to 1}\frac{1}{(x-1)^4} = \infty;\ \lim_{x\to 1}(x-1)^2 = 0;$

$\displaystyle\lim_{x\to 1}\frac{(x-1)^2}{(x-1)^4} = \lim_{x\to 1}\frac{1}{(x-1)^2} = \infty$

(e) One possible answer: Nothing can really be said—the limit may be undefined, ∞, or a number.

89. (a) For an 8-sided polygon, we have 8 isosceles triangles of area $\frac{1}{2}bh$. Thus, $A = 8\cdot\frac{1}{2}bh = 4bh$. Similarly, for an n-sided polygon, we have n triangles of area $\frac{1}{2}bh$. Thus $A = n\cdot\frac{1}{2}\cdot bh = \frac{1}{2}nhb$.

(b) Consider an n-sided polygon inscribed in a circle of radius r. Since a circle always is $360°$, we see that each angle extending from the center of the circle to two consecutive vertices is an angle of $\dfrac{360°}{n}$. Dropping a perpendicular from the center of the circle to the midpoint of the base of the triangle (which is also one of the n sides) results in an angle of $\dfrac{360°}{2n}$. Since $\tan\left(\dfrac{360°}{2n}\right) = \dfrac{(b/2)}{h}$, we have $\dfrac{b}{2} = h\tan\left(\dfrac{360°}{2n}\right)$ and finally $b = 2h\tan\left(\dfrac{360°}{2n}\right)$.

(c) Since $A = \frac{1}{2}nhb$ and $b = 2h\tan\left(\dfrac{360°}{2n}\right)$, we have

$A = \frac{1}{2}nh\left(2h\tan\left(\dfrac{360°}{2n}\right)\right) = nh^2\tan\left(\dfrac{360°}{2n}\right)$.

(d)

n	A
4	4
8	3.3137
16	3.1826
100	3.1426
500	3.1416
1,000	3.1416
5,000	3.1416
10,000	3.1416
100,000	3.1416

Yes, $A \to \pi$ as $n \to \infty$.

(e)

n	A
4	36
8	29.823
16	28.643
100	28.284
500	28.275
1,000	28.274
5,000	28.274
10,000	28.274
100,000	28.274

Yes, $n \to \infty$, $A \to 9\pi$.

(f) One possible answer:

$$\lim_{n \to \infty} A = \lim_{n \to \infty} nh^2 \tan\left(\frac{180°}{n}\right) = h^2 \lim_{n \to \infty} n \tan\left(\frac{180°}{n}\right)$$
$$= h^2\pi = \pi h^2$$

As the number of sides of the polygon increases, the distance between h and the edge of the circle becomes progressively smaller. As $n \to \infty$, $h \to$ radius of the circle.

90. (a)

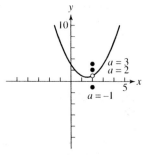

(b) Since $(2)^2 - 3(2) + 3 = 4 - 6 + 3 = 1$, $a = 1$.

91. (a)

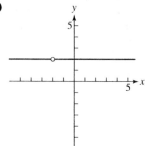

(b) $f(x) = \dfrac{2x + 4}{x + 2} = \dfrac{2(x + 2)}{x + 2} = 2$

(c) $g(x) = 2$

92. (a)

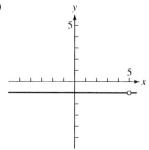

(b) $\dfrac{x - 5}{5 - x} = -\dfrac{(x - 5)}{(x - 5)} = -1$

(c) $g(x) = -1$

93. (a)

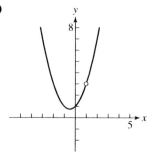

(b) $\dfrac{x^3 - 1}{x - 1} = \dfrac{(x - 1)(x^2 + x + 1)}{x - 1} = x^2 + x + 1$

(c) $g(x) = x^2 + x + 1$

■ Section 10.4 Numerical Derivatives and Integrals

Exploration 1

1. RRAM value ≈ 1.364075504 and the NINT value ≈ 1.386294361.

2. The new command is
   sum(seq($1/(1 + K \cdot 3/100) \cdot 3/100, K, 1, 100$)). The calculated value ≈ 1.3751, which is a better approximation than for 50 rectangles.

3. The integral is $\displaystyle\int_0^\pi \sin x\, dx$. The RRAM value is ≈ 1.999342 and the NINT value is 2.

4. The command is
   sum(seq($\sqrt{(4 + K \cdot 5/50)} \cdot 5/50, K, 1, 50$)). The calculated value ≈ 12.7166 and the NINT value is 12.666667.

Quick Review 10.4

1. $\dfrac{\Delta y}{\Delta x} = \dfrac{4^2 - 1^2}{4 - 1} = \dfrac{15}{3} = 5$

2. $\dfrac{\Delta y}{\Delta x} = \dfrac{\sqrt{4} - \sqrt{1}}{4 - 1} = \dfrac{2 - 1}{3} = \dfrac{1}{3}$

3. $\dfrac{\Delta y}{\Delta x} = \dfrac{\log_2 4 - \log_2 1}{4 - 1} = \dfrac{2 - 0}{3} = \dfrac{2}{3}$

4. $\dfrac{\Delta y}{\Delta x} = \dfrac{3^4 - 3^1}{4 - 1} = \dfrac{81 - 3}{3} = 26$

5. $\dfrac{\Delta y}{\Delta x} = \dfrac{11 - 2}{4 - 1} = \dfrac{9}{3} = 3$

6. $\dfrac{\Delta y}{\Delta x} = \dfrac{10 - (-2)}{4 - 1} = \dfrac{12}{3} = 4$

7. $\dfrac{\sin(1.01) - \sin(0.99)}{2(0.01)} \approx 0.5403$

8. $\dfrac{1.001^4 - 0.999^4}{2(0.001)} \approx 4.000$

9. $\dfrac{\ln 1.001 - \ln 0.999}{2(0.001)} \approx 1.000$

10. $\dfrac{e^{1.0001} - e^{0.9999}}{2(0.0001)} \approx 2.7183$

Exercises 10.4

In #1–10, use NDER on a calculator to find the numerical derivative of the function at the specific point.

1. -4

2. 4

3. -12

4. -1

5. 0

6. ≈ -1.0000

7. ≈ 1.0000

8. ≈ 2.0000

9. ≈ -3.0000

10. ≈ -3.0000

In #11–22, use NINT on a calculator to find the numerical integral of the function over the specified interval.

11. $\dfrac{64}{3}$

12. $\dfrac{64}{3}$

13. 2

14. -2

15. ≈ 0

16. 2

17. 1

18. ≈ 0.69315

19. ≈ 3.1416

20. 10

21. ≈ 106.61 mi

22. ≈ 16.95 mi

23. (a) $v_{ave} = \dfrac{435 - 485}{2 - 1} = \dfrac{-50}{1} = -50$ ft/sec

(b)

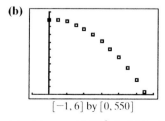

$[-1, 6]$ by $[0, 550]$

(c) $s(t) \approx -16.08t^2 + 0.36t + 499.77$

(d) $v(1.5\,\mathrm{sec}) \approx -47.88$ ft/sec

(e) Set $s(t)$ equal to zero and solve for t using the quadratic equation.
$$t = \dfrac{-0.36 - \sqrt{0.36^2 - 4(-16.08)(499.77)}}{2(-16.08)}$$
≈ 5.586 sec (The minus sign was chosen to give $t \geq 0$.) Using NDER at $t = 5.586$ sec gives $v \approx -179.28$ ft/sec.

24. (a) The average rate of change between two data points is found by examining $\dfrac{\Delta y}{\Delta x}$. The average rate of change of the gross domestic product from 1997–1998 is $\dfrac{8747.0 - 8304.3}{1998 - 1997} = \$442.7$ billion per year. The average rate of change of the gross domestic product from 2001–2002 is $\dfrac{10{,}480.8 - 10{,}100.8}{2002 - 2001} = \$380.0$ billion per year.

(b) The quadratic regression model for the data is $y = 6.2337x^2 + 325.3225x + 5757.0867$.

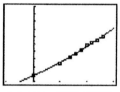

$[-5, 15]$ by $[5000, 15000]$

(c) To estimate the rate of change of the gross domestic product in 1997, we will use the calculator NDER computation and evaluate that when $x = 7$ to obtain $\$412.6$ billion per year.

To estimate the rate of change of the gross domestic product in 2001, we will use the calculator NDER computation and evaluate that when $x = 11$ to obtain $\$462.5$ billion per year.

(d) Using the quadratic regression model $y = 6.2337x^2 + 325.3225x + 5757.0867$ to predict the gross domestic product in 2007 where $x = 17$ yields $6.2337(17)^2 + 325.3225(17) + 5757.0867 = \$13{,}089.1$ billion or $\$13.1$ trillion.
This answer is reasonable because the gross domestic product will probably continue to increase.

25. (a) The midpoints of the subintervals will be 0.25, 0.75, 1.25, etc. The average velocities will be the successive height differences divided by 0.5—that is, times 2.

Midpoint	$\Delta s/\Delta t$
0.25	-10 ft/sec
0.75	-20
1.25	-40
1.75	-60
2.25	-70
2.75	-90
3.25	-100
3.75	-120
4.25	-140
4.75	-150
5.25	-170

(b)

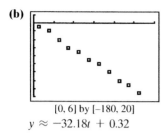

[0, 6] by [−180, 20]

$y \approx -32.18t + 0.32$

(c) Substituting $t = 1.5$ leads to $y \approx -47.95$ ft/sec. This is close to the value of -47.88 ft/sec found in Exercise 23d.

26. (a) Let 1990 be $x = 0$. The first subinterval has a midpoint of $\dfrac{0 + 5}{2} = 2.5$. On that interval, the average rate of change is $\dfrac{\Delta y}{\Delta x} = \dfrac{7397.7 - 5803.1}{5 - 0} = \dfrac{1594.6}{5} = 318.9$.

The rest of the midpoints and values of $\Delta y/\Delta x$ are computed similarly and are shown in the following table.

Midpoint	$\Delta y/\Delta x$
2.5	318.9
6.0	453.3
7.5	442.7
8.5	521.4
9.5	548.6
10.5	283.8
11.5	380.0
12.5	507.1

(b)

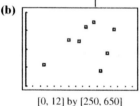

[0, 12] by [250, 650]

(c) The linear regression model for the data is $y = 7.911x + 364.234$. Using this regression model to approximate the rate of change in 1997 yields $y = 7.911(7) + 364.234 = 419.6$. Using the same model to approximate the rate of change in 2001 yields $y = 7.911(11) + 364.234 = 451.3$. These values are reasonably close to the results of NDER from Exercise 24c.

27. The average velocities, $\Delta s/\Delta t$, for the successive 0.5-second intervals are 8, 24, 40, 56, and 72 ft/sec. Multiplying each by 0.5 sec and then summing them gives the estimated distance: 100 ft.

28. The average velocities, $\Delta s/\Delta t$, for the successive 0.2-second intervals are as given:

Interval	$\Delta s/\Delta t$
1	1.09 m/sec
2	0.85
3	0.61
4	0.42
5	0.32
6	0.37
7	0.615
8	1.095

Multiplying each $\Delta s/\Delta t$ by 0.2 sec and then summing

them gives the estimated distance: 1.074 m.

29. The program accepts inputs which determine the width and number of approximating rectangles. These rectangles are summed and the result is output to the screen.

30. The program accepts inputs which determine the width and number of approximating rectangles. These rectangles are summed and the result is output to the screen.

For #31–42, verify the function is non-negative by graphing it over the interval.

31. (b)

N	LRAM	RRAM	Average
10	15.04	19.84	17.44
20	16.16	18.56	17.36
50	16.86	17.82	17.34
100	17.09	17.57	17.33

(c) fnInt gives 17.33; at N_{100}, the average is 17.3344.

32. (b)

N	LRAM	RRAM	Average
10	96.72	132.72	114.72
20	105.18	123.18	114.18
50	110.43	117.63	114.03
100	112.21	115.81	114.01

(c) fnInt gives 114; N_{100} is very close at 114.01.

33. (b)

N	LRAM	RRAM	Average
10	7.84	11.04	9.44
20	8.56	10.16	9.36
50	9.02	9.66	9.34
100	9.17	9.49	9.33

(c) fnInt gives 9.33; at N_{100}, the average is 9.3344.

34. (b)

N	LRAM	RRAM	Average
10	107.76	132.96	120.36
20	113.79	126.39	120.09
50	117.49	122.53	120.01
100	118.74	121.26	120

(c) fnInt gives 120; N_{100} has the same result.

35. (b)

N	LRAM	RRAM	Average
10	98.24	112.64	105.44
20	101.76	108.96	105.36
50	103.90	106.78	105.34
100	104.61	106.05	105.33

(c) fnInt gives 105.33; at N_{100}, the average is 105.3344.

36. (b)

N	LRAM	RRAM	Average
10	136.16	185.76	160.96
20	147.84	172.64	160.24
50	155.08	165.00	160.04
100	157.53	162.49	160.01

(c) fnInt gives 160, very close to N_{100} of 160.01.

37. (b)

N	LRAM	RRAM	Average
10	7.70	8.12	7.91
20	7.81	8.02	7.91
50	7.87	7.95	7.91
100	7.89	7.93	7.91

(c) fnInt gives 7.91, the same result as N_{100}.

38. (b)

N	LRAM	RRAM	Average
10	4.51	4.81	4.66
20	4.59	4.74	4.67
50	4.64	4.70	4.67
100	4.65	4.68	4.67

(c) fnInt gives 4.67, the same result as N_{100}.

39. (b)

N	LRAM	RRAM	Average
10	1.08	0.92	1.00
20	1.04	0.96	1.00
50	1.02	0.98	1.00
100	1.01	0.99	1.00

(c) fnInt gives 1, the same result as N_{100}.

40. (b)

N	LRAM	RRAM	Average
10	0.57	0.57	0.57
20	0.57	0.57	0.57
50	0.57	0.57	0.57
100	0.57	0.57	0.57

(c) fnInt = 0.57, the same result as N_{100}.

41. (b)

N	LRAM	RRAM	Average
10	0.56	0.62	0.59
20	0.58	0.61	0.593
50	0.59	0.60	0.594
100	0.59	0.60	0.594

(c) fnInt = 0.594, the same result as N_{100}.

42. (b)

N	LRAM	RRAM	Average
10	1.17	1.03	1.10
20	1.13	1.07	1.10
50	1.11	1.09	1.10
100	1.11	1.09	1.10

(c) fnInt gives 1.10, which is the same result as N_{100}.

43. True. The notation NDER refers to a symmetric difference quotient using $\Delta x = h = 0.001$.

44. False. NINT will vary the value of Δx until the numerical integral gets close to a limiting value.

45. NINT will use as many rectangles as are needed to obtain an accurate estimate. The answer is B. (Note: NDER estimates the derivative, not the integral.)

46. The most accurate estimate is a symmetric difference quotient with a small h (and of course with $2h$, not h, in the denominator). The answer is E.

47. Instantaneous velocity is the derivative, not an integral, of the position function. The answer is C.

48. Area under a curve that represents $f(x)$ is an integral, not the derivative, of $f(x)$. The answer is D.

49. (a) $f'(x)$

$$= \frac{2(x + h)^2 + 3(x + h) + 1 - 2x^2 - 3x - 1}{h}$$

$$= \lim_{h \to 0} \frac{2(x^2 + 2xh + h^2) + 3x + 3h - 2x^2 - 3x}{h}$$

$$= \lim_{h \to 0} \frac{4xh + 2h^2 + 3h}{h} = \lim_{h \to 0} 4x + 2h + 3$$

$$= 4x + 3$$

(b) $g'(x) = \lim\limits_{h \to 0} \dfrac{(x + h)^3 + 1 - x^3 - 1}{h}$

$$= \lim_{h \to 0} \frac{3x^2 h + 3xh^2 + h^3}{h}$$

$$= \lim_{h \to 0} 3x^2 + 3xh + h^2 = 3x^2$$

(c) Standard: $\dfrac{f(2.001) - f(2)}{0.001} = \dfrac{15.011002 - 15}{0.001} = 11.002$

Symmetric: $\dfrac{f(2.001) - f(1.999)}{0.002}$

$$= \frac{15.011002 - 14.989002}{0.002} = 11$$

(d) The symmetric method provides a closer approximation to $f'(2) = 11$.

(e) Standard: $\dfrac{g(2.001) - g(2)}{0.001} \approx \dfrac{9.012006 - 9}{0.001}$

$$= 12.006001$$

Symmetric: $\dfrac{g(2.001) - g(1.999)}{2(0.001)} \approx 12.000001$

The symmetric method provides a closer approximation to $g'(2) = 12$.

50. (a)

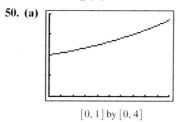

[0, 1] by [0, 4]

(b) ≈ 2.72

(c) ≈ 2.72

(d) Answers will vary but the true answer is $e \approx 2.72$.

51. $f'(0) = \lim\limits_{h \to 0} \dfrac{f(0 + h) - f(0)}{h} = \lim\limits_{h \to 0} \dfrac{|h| - 0}{h}$

$$= \lim_{h \to 0} \frac{|h|}{h} = 1$$

if 0 is approached from the right, and -1 if 0 is approached from the left. This occurs because calculators tend to take average values for derivatives instead of applying the definition. For example, a calculator may calculate the derivative of $f(0)$ by taking

$$\frac{f(0.0001) - f(-0.0001)}{0.0001 - (-0.0001)} = 0.$$

52.

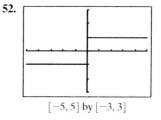

[−5, 5] by [−3, 3]

$f'(0)$ does not exist because $f(x)$ is discontinuous at $x = 0$. The calculator gives an incorrect answer, NDER $f(0) = 1000$, because it divides by $2h = 0.002$ instead of letting $h \to 0$.

53. (a) Let $y_1 = $ abs$(\sin(x))$, which is $|f(x)|$. Then NINT $(Y_1, X, 0, 2\pi)$ gives 4.

(b) Let $y_1 = $ abs$(x^2 - 2x - 3)$, which is $|f(x)|$. Then NINT $(Y_1, X, 0, 5)$ gives ≈ 19.67.

54. Some functions, such as $\dfrac{1}{x-2}$ have a singularity, they

cease to exist at that point and the $\lim\limits_{x \to 2} \dfrac{1}{x-2} = \infty$. Using

our rectangular approximations, however, we can find the area under the curve with successively smaller widths. Since each of these widths are finite, we simply determine "how close" our approximation must be to determine the finite area under the curve. Eventually the rectangle "next" to $x = 2$ becomes so thin as to render its area "close enough" to zero to be ignored.

55. Since $f(x) \geq g(x)$ for all values of x on the interval,

$$A = \lim_{N \to \infty} \sum_{k=1}^{n} \left\{ \left[\left(\frac{b-a}{N} \right) f\left(a + \frac{k(b-a)}{N} \right) \right] \right.$$
$$\left. - \left[\left(\frac{b-a}{N} \right) g\left(a + \frac{k(b-a)}{N} \right) \right] \right\}$$
$$= \lim_{N \to \infty} \sum_{k=1}^{n} \left(\frac{b-a}{N} \right) \left[f\left(a + \frac{k(b-a)}{N} \right) \right.$$
$$\left. - g\left(a + \frac{k(b-a)}{N} \right) \right].$$

If the area of both curves is already known and $f(x) \geq g(x)$ for all values of x, the area between the curves is simply the area under f minus the area under g.

56. (b)

x	$A(x)$
0.25	0.0625
0.5	0.25
1	1
1.5	2.25
2	4
2.5	6.25
3	9

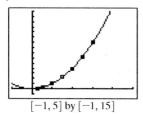

[0, 5] by [−1, 10]

(c) $y = x^2$

[−1, 5] by [−1, 15]

(d) The data seem to support a curve of $A(x) = x^2$.

(e) $A'(x) = \lim\limits_{h \to 0} \dfrac{f(x+h) - f(h)}{h} = \lim\limits_{h \to 0} \dfrac{(x+h)^2 - x^2}{h}$
$$= \lim_{h \to 0} \frac{2xh + h^2}{h} = 2x.$$

The two functions are exactly the same.

57. (b)

x	$A(x)$
0.25	0.0156
0.5	0.125
1	1
1.5	3.375
2	8
2.5	15.625
3	27

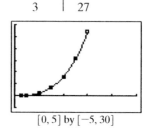

[0, 5] by [−5, 30]

(c) $f(x) \approx x^3$

[−2, 5] by [−5, 30]

(d) The exact value of $A(x)$ for any x greater than zero appears to be x^3.

(e) $A'(x) = \lim\limits_{h \to 0} \dfrac{f(x+h) - f(x)}{h} = \lim\limits_{h \to 0} \dfrac{(x+h)^3 - x^3}{h}$
$$= \lim_{h \to 0} \frac{3x^2 h + 3xh^2}{h} = 3x^2.$$

The functions are exactly the same.

58. Answers may vary.

■ Chapter 10 Review

1. **(a)** 2

  (b) Does not exist.

2. **(a)** -1

  (b) Does not exist.

3. **(a)** 2

  (b) 2

4. **(a)** 2

  (b) 2

5. $\displaystyle\lim_{x \to -1} \frac{x - 1}{x^2 + 1} = \frac{-1 - 1}{2} = -1$

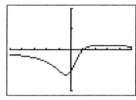

$[-5, 5]$ by $[-2, 2]$

6. $\displaystyle\lim_{x \to 0} \frac{\sin 5x}{x} = \lim_{x \to 0} \frac{\sin(2x)\cos(3x) + \cos(2x)\sin(3x)}{x}$

$\displaystyle = \lim_{x \to 0} \frac{(2\sin x \cos x)(4\cos^3 x - 3\cos x) + (2\cos^2 x - 1)(3\sin x - 4\sin^3 x)}{x}$

$\displaystyle = \lim_{x \to 0} \left(\frac{\sin x}{x}\right) [8\cos^4 x - 6\cos^2 x + (2\cos^2 x - 1)(3 - 4\sin^2 x)]$

$= 1 \cdot [8 - 6 + (2 - 1)(3 - 0)] = 5$

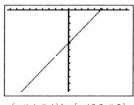

$[-2\pi, 2\pi]$ by $[-2, 5]$

7. $\displaystyle\lim_{x \to -2} \frac{(x - 5)(x + 2)}{x + 2} = \lim_{x \to -2} x - 5 = -7$

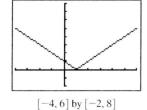

$[-9.4, 9.4]$ by $[-12.2, 0.2]$

8. $\displaystyle\lim_{x \to 1} |x - 1|$

$= \left. \begin{cases} \displaystyle\lim_{x \to 1^+} |x - 1| = \lim_{x \to 1^+} (x - 1) = 0 \\ \displaystyle\lim_{x \to 1^-} |x - 1| = \lim_{x \to 1} (-x + 1) = 0 \end{cases} \right\}$

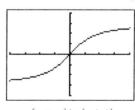

$[-4, 6]$ by $[-2, 8]$

9. $\displaystyle\lim_{x \to 0} 2\tan^{-1}(x) = \lim_{x \to 0} 2\frac{\sin^{-1}(x)}{\cos^{-1}(x)} = \frac{2 \cdot 0}{1} = 0$

$[-\pi, \pi]$ by $[-4, 4]$

10. $\displaystyle\lim_{x \to 0} \frac{2}{1 - 2^x} = \begin{cases} \displaystyle\lim_{x \to 0^+} \frac{2}{1 - 2^x} = -\infty \\ \displaystyle\lim_{x \to 0^-} \frac{2}{1 - 2^x} = \infty \end{cases} \Rightarrow$ undefined

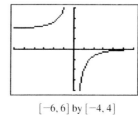

$[-6, 6]$ by $[-4, 4]$

11.

x	$x(f)$
-3	-1
-10	$-\dfrac{1}{64}$
-100	$-\dfrac{1}{9604}$
-1000	$-\dfrac{1}{996{,}004}$

$\Rightarrow \lim\limits_{x \to -\infty} f(x) = 0$

12.

x	$f(x)$
4	9
8	$\dfrac{13}{5}$
16	$\dfrac{21}{13}$
32	$\dfrac{37}{29}$
128	$\dfrac{133}{125}$
1024	$\dfrac{1029}{1021}$

$\Rightarrow \lim\limits_{x \to \infty} f(x) = 1$

13.

x	$f(x)$
1	2
2	-1
5	-4.6
10	-9.8
100	-99.98
1000	-999.998

$\Rightarrow \lim\limits_{x \to \infty} f(x) = -\infty$

14.

x	$f(x)$
0	0
-1	$-\dfrac{1}{3}$
-5	$-\dfrac{25}{7}$
-10	$-\dfrac{25}{3}$
-100	$-\dfrac{5000}{51}$
-1000	$-\dfrac{500{,}000}{501}$

$\Rightarrow \lim\limits_{x \to -\infty} f(x) = -\infty$

15. $\lim\limits_{x \to 2^+} \dfrac{1}{x-2} = \infty$

16. $\lim\limits_{x \to 2^-} \dfrac{1}{x^2-4} = -\infty$

17. $\lim\limits_{x \to 0} \dfrac{\dfrac{1}{2+x} - \dfrac{1}{2}}{x} = \lim\limits_{x \to 0} \dfrac{2-(2+x)}{2(2+x)} \cdot \dfrac{1}{x}$

$= \lim\limits_{x \to 0} \dfrac{-x}{x} \cdot \dfrac{1}{2(2+x)} = -\dfrac{1}{4}$

18. $\lim\limits_{x \to 0} \dfrac{(x+2)^3 - 8}{x} = \lim\limits_{x \to 0} \dfrac{x^3 + 6x^2 + 12x}{x}$

$= \lim\limits_{x \to 0} x^2 + 6x + 12 = 12$

19. $f(x) = \dfrac{x-5}{(x+5)(x+1)}$, so f has vertical asymptotes at $x = -1$ and $x = -5$. Since $\lim\limits_{x \to \infty} f(x) = 0$ and $\lim\limits_{x \to -\infty} f(x) = 0$, f also has a horizontal asymptote at $y = 0$.

20. $f(x) = \dfrac{x^2+1}{2(x-2)}$, so f has a vertical asymptote at $x = 2$. Since $\lim\limits_{x \to \infty} f(x) = \infty$ and $\lim\limits_{x \to -\infty} f(x) = -\infty$, f has no horizontal asymptotes.

21. $\lim\limits_{x \to 3} \dfrac{(x+5)(x-3)}{3-x} = \lim\limits_{x \to 3} -x - 5 = -8$.

22. $\lim\limits_{x \to 1} \dfrac{(x-3)(x-1)}{x-1} = \lim\limits_{x \to 1} x - 3 = -2$

23. $\lim\limits_{x \to 0} \dfrac{\dfrac{1}{x-3} + \dfrac{1}{3}}{x} = \lim\limits_{x \to 0} \dfrac{3 + (x-3)}{3(x-3)} \cdot \dfrac{1}{x}$

$= \lim\limits_{x \to 0} \dfrac{x}{x} \cdot \dfrac{1}{3(x-3)} = -\dfrac{1}{9}$

24. $\lim\limits_{x \to 2} \dfrac{\sin(3x-6)}{\cos(3x-6)} \cdot \dfrac{1}{x-2}$

$= \lim\limits_{x \to 2} \dfrac{\sin(3(x-2))}{\cos(3x-6)} \cdot \dfrac{1}{(x-2)} =$

$= \lim\limits_{x \to 2} \dfrac{(3\sin(x-2) - 4\sin^3(x-2))}{(x-2)} \cdot \dfrac{1}{\cos(3x-6)}$

$= \lim\limits_{x \to 2} \left(3\dfrac{\sin(x-2)}{x-2} - 4\dfrac{\sin^2(x-2)\sin(x-2)}{x-2} \right)$

$\dfrac{1}{\cos(3x-6)} = (3 - 0 \cdot 1)\left(\dfrac{1}{1}\right) = 3$

25. $\lim\limits_{x \to 2} \dfrac{(x-2)(x-3)}{(x-2)(x-1)} = \lim\limits_{x \to 2} \dfrac{x-3}{x-1} = -\dfrac{1}{1} = -1$

26. $\lim\limits_{x \to 3} (x-3) = 0$

27. $\lim\limits_{x \to 1} \dfrac{(x-1)(x^2+x+1)}{x-1} = \lim\limits_{x \to 1} (x^2 + x + 1) = 3$

$F(x) = \begin{cases} \dfrac{x^3 - 1}{x - 1} & x \neq 1 \\ 3 & x = 1 \end{cases}$

28. $\lim\limits_{x \to 5} \dfrac{(x-5)(x-1)}{(x-5)} = \lim\limits_{x \to 5} x - 1 = 4$

$F(x) = \begin{cases} \dfrac{x^2 - 6x + 5}{x - 5} & x \neq 5 \\ 4 & x = 5 \end{cases}$

29. $f'(x) = \lim\limits_{h \to 0} \dfrac{f(2+h) - f(2)}{h}$

$= \lim\limits_{h \to 0} \dfrac{1 - (h+2) - 2(h+2)^2 - (-9)}{h}$

$= \lim\limits_{h \to 0} \dfrac{-2h^2 - 8h - 8 - h + 8}{h} = \lim\limits_{h \to 0} \dfrac{-2h^2 - 9h}{h}$

$= \lim\limits_{h \to 0} (-2h - 9) = -9$

30. $f'(x) = \lim\limits_{h \to 0} \dfrac{f(2+h) - f(2)}{h}$

$= \lim\limits_{h \to 0} \dfrac{(2+h+3)^2 - 25}{h} = \lim\limits_{h \to 0} \dfrac{h^2 + 10h}{h}$

$= \lim\limits_{h \to 0} h + 10 = 10$

31. (a) $\dfrac{f(3.01) - f(3)}{3.01 - 3} = \dfrac{12.0801 - 12}{0.01} = 8.01$

(b) $\lim\limits_{h \to 0} \dfrac{f(3+h) - f(3)}{h}$

$= \lim\limits_{h \to 0} \dfrac{(h+3)^2 + 2(h+3) - 3 - 12}{h}$

$= \lim\limits_{h \to 0} \dfrac{h^2 + 6h + 9 + 2h + 6 - 15}{h}$

$= \lim\limits_{h \to 0} \dfrac{h^2 + 8h}{h} = 8$

32. (a) $\dfrac{f(3.01) - f(3)}{3.01 - 3} = \dfrac{\dfrac{3}{5.01} - 0.6}{0.01} = -\dfrac{20}{167} \approx -0.12$

(b) $\lim\limits_{h \to 0} \dfrac{f(3+h) - f(3)}{h} = \lim\limits_{h \to 0} \dfrac{\dfrac{3}{h+3+2} - \dfrac{3}{5}}{h}$

$= \lim\limits_{h \to 0} \dfrac{15 - 3(h+5)}{5(h+5)} \cdot \dfrac{1}{h}$

$= \lim\limits_{h \to 0} \dfrac{-3h}{h} \cdot \dfrac{1}{5(h+5)} = -\dfrac{3}{25}$

33. (a) $m = \lim\limits_{h \to 0} \dfrac{f(h+1) - f(1)}{h}$

$= \lim\limits_{h \to 0} \dfrac{(h+1)^3 - 2(h+1) + 1 - 0}{h}$

$= \lim\limits_{h \to 0} \dfrac{h^3 + 3h^2 + h}{h} = \lim\limits_{h \to 0} h^2 + 3h + 1 = 1$

(b) $(1, f(1)) = (1, 0)$ so the equation of the tangent line at $x = 1$ is $y = x - 1$.

34. (a) $m = \lim\limits_{h \to 0} \dfrac{f(h+7) - h(7)}{h} = \lim\limits_{h \to 0} \dfrac{\sqrt{h+3} - \sqrt{3}}{h}$

$= \lim\limits_{h \to 0} \dfrac{h + 3 - 3}{h(\sqrt{h+3} + \sqrt{3})}$

$= \lim\limits_{h \to 0} \dfrac{1}{\sqrt{h+3} + \sqrt{3}} = \dfrac{\sqrt{3}}{6}$

(b) $(7, f(7)) = (7, \sqrt{3})$ so the equation of the tangent line at $x = 7$ is $y = \dfrac{\sqrt{3}}{6} x - \dfrac{\sqrt{3}}{6}$.

35. $\lim\limits_{h \to 0} \dfrac{f(x+h) - f(x)}{h}$

$= \lim\limits_{h \to 0} \dfrac{5(x+h)^2 + 7(x+h) - 1 - 5x^2 - 7x + 1}{h}$

$= \lim\limits_{h \to 0} \dfrac{5x^2 + 10xh + 5h^2 + 7x + 7h - 5x^2 - 7x}{h}$

$= \lim\limits_{h \to 0} \dfrac{10xh + 5h^2 + 7h}{h} = 10x + 7$

36. $\lim\limits_{h \to 0} \dfrac{f(x+h) - f(x)}{h}$

$= \lim\limits_{h \to 0} \dfrac{3(x+h)^2 - 8(x+h) + 2 - 3x^2 + 8x - 2}{h}$

$= \lim\limits_{h \to 0} \dfrac{6xh + 3h^2 - 8h}{h} = \lim\limits_{h \to 0} 6x + 3h - 8$

$= 6x - 8$

For #37–38, verify the function is non-negative through graphical or numerical analysis.

37. (b) LRAM: 42.2976
RRAM: 40.3776
Average: $\dfrac{42.2976 + 40.3776}{2} = 41.3376$

38. (b) LRAM: 49.2352
RRAM: 52.1152
Average: $\dfrac{49.2352 + 52.1152}{2} = 50.6752$

39. (a) Using $x = 0$ for 1990, the scatter plot of the data is:

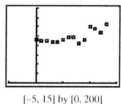

[–5, 15] by [0, 200]

(b) The average rate of change for 1990 to 1991 is found by examining $\dfrac{\Delta x}{\Delta y}$.

$\dfrac{\Delta y}{\Delta x} = \dfrac{114.0 - 116.4}{1 - 0} = -2.4$ cents per year.

The average rate of change for 1997 to 1998 is found by examining $\dfrac{\Delta x}{\Delta y}$.

$\dfrac{\Delta y}{\Delta x} = \dfrac{105.9 - 123.4}{1 - 0} = -17.5$ cents per year.

(c) The average rate exhibits the greatest increase from one year to the next consecutive year in the interval from 1999–2000.

(d) The average rate exhibits the greatest decrease from one year to the next consecutive year in the interval from 1997–1998.

(e) The linear regression model for the data is:
$y = 3.0270x + 104.6600.$

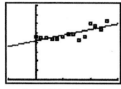

[-5, 15] by [0, 200]

(f) The cubic regression model for the data is:
$y = 0.0048x^3 + 0.3659x^2 - 2.4795x + 116.2006.$

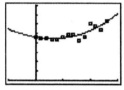

[-5, 15] by [0, 200]

Most of the data points touch the regression curve, which would suggest that this is a fairly good model. One possible answer: The cubic regression model is the best. It shows a larger rate of increase in fuel prices, which is what is happening in today's market.

(g) The cubic regression model for the data is:
$y = 0.0048x^3 + 0.3659x^2 - 2.4795x + 116.2006.$
Using NDER with this regression model yields the following instantaneous rates of change for:

1997	3.4 cents per gallon
1998	4.3 cents per gallon
1999	5.3 cents per gallon
2000	6.3 cents per gallon

The cubic regression model is showing a rate of increase. The true rate of change, however, may be higher than what the model indicates.

(h) If we use the given cubic regression model, the average price of a gallon of regular gas in 2007 will be 203.4 cents per gallon. Based on what is happening with the current fuel prices, this prediction may not be high enough.

40. (a)

x	$A(x)$
0	0
0.4	0.38942
0.8	0.71736
1.2	0.93204
1.6	0.99957
2.0	0.90930
2.4	0.67546
2.8	0.33499
3.2	−0.05837
3.6	−0.44252
4.0	−0.75680
4.4	−0.95160
4.8	−0.99616
5.2	−0.88345
5.6	−0.63127
6.0	−0.27942
6.4	0.11655

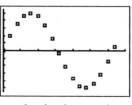

[0, 7] by [−1.1, 1.1]

(b) $f(x) = \sin x$

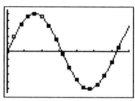

[0, 7] by [−1.1, 1.1]

(c) $f'(x) = \cos x$, the function being integrated.

(d) The derivative of $\text{NINT}(f(t), t, 0, x)$ gives $f(t)$.

Chapter 10 Project

1. The scatter plot of the population data for Clark County, NV, is as follows. The year 1970 is represented by $t = 0$.

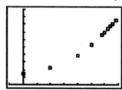

[−5, 35] by [0, 2000000]

2. The average population growth rate from 1970–2004 is
$$\frac{1,715,337 - 277,230}{2004 - 1970} = \frac{1,438,107}{34} = 42,297 \text{ people/year.}$$

The average population growth rate from 1980–2004 is
$$\frac{1,715,337 - 463,087}{2004 - 1980} = \frac{1,252,250}{24} = 52,177 \text{ people/year.}$$

The average population growth rate from 1990–2004 is
$$\frac{1,715,337 - 770,280}{2004 - 1990} = \frac{945,057}{14} = 67,504 \text{ people/year.}$$

The average population growth rate from 1995–2004 is
$$\frac{1,715,337 - 1,055,435}{2004 - 1995} = \frac{659,902}{9} = 73,322 \text{ people/year.}$$

3. The exponential regression model for the population data is $y = 271,661.8371 \cdot 1.0557797^t$.

4. If we use NDER with the given exponential regression model, the instantaneous population growth rate in 2004 is 93,359 people/year. The average growth rate from 1995–2004 most closely matches the instantaneous growth rate of 2004.

5. Using the exponential regression model
$y = 271,661.8371 \cdot 1.0557797^t$ to predict the population of Clark County for the years 2010, 2020, and 2030 yields:
$y = 271,661.8371 \cdot 1.0557797^{40} = 2,382,105$ people
$y = 271,661.8371 \cdot 1.0557797^{50} = 4,099,152$ people
$y = 271,661.8371 \cdot 1.0557797^{60} = 7,053,864$ people

The web site predictions are probably more reasonable, since the given data and scatter plot suggest that growth in recent years has been fairly linear.

Appendix A

■ Section 1 Radicals and Rational Exponents

Section 1 Exercises

For Exercises 1–6, recall that there are two real nth roots if n is even, and only one if n is odd.

1. $\sqrt{81} = 9$ or -9, since $81 = (\pm 9)^2$

2. $\sqrt[4]{81} = 3$ or -3, since $81 = (\pm 3)^4$

3. $\sqrt[3]{64} = 4$, since $64 = 4^3$

4. $\sqrt[5]{243} = 3$, since $243 = 3^5$

5. $\sqrt{\dfrac{16}{9}} = \dfrac{\sqrt{16}}{\sqrt{9}} = \dfrac{4}{3}$ or $-\dfrac{4}{3}$, since $\dfrac{16}{9} = \left(\pm\dfrac{4}{3}\right)^2$

6. $\sqrt[3]{-\dfrac{27}{8}} = -\dfrac{\sqrt[3]{27}}{\sqrt[3]{8}} = -\dfrac{3}{2}$

7. $\sqrt{144} = 12$ since $12 \cdot 12 = 144$

8. No real answer — no real number multiplied by itself gives -16.

9. $\sqrt[3]{-216} = -6$, since $(-6)^3 = -216$

10. $\sqrt[3]{216} = 6$, since $6^3 = 216$

11. $\sqrt[3]{-\dfrac{64}{27}} = -\dfrac{4}{3}$, since $\left(-\dfrac{4}{3}\right)^3 = -\dfrac{64}{27}$

12. $\sqrt{\dfrac{64}{25}} = \dfrac{8}{5}$, since $8^2 = 64$ and $5^2 = 25$

13. 4

14. 5

15. $\dfrac{5}{2}$ or 2.5

16. $\dfrac{7}{2}$ or 3.5

17. 729

18. 32

19. $\dfrac{1}{4}$ or 0.25

20. $\dfrac{1}{81}$ or 0.012345679

21. -2

22. $-\dfrac{4}{5}$ or -0.8

23. $\sqrt{1.69} = 1.3$ since $1.3^2 = 1.69$

24. $\sqrt{19.4481} = 4.41$ since $4.41 = 19.4481$

25. $\sqrt[4]{19.4481} = 2.1$ since $2.1^4 = 19.4481$

26. $\sqrt[3]{3.375} = 1.5$ since $1.5^3 = 3.375$

27. $\sqrt{288} = \sqrt{12^2 \cdot 2} = \sqrt{12^2} \cdot \sqrt{2} = 12\sqrt{2}$

28. $\sqrt[3]{500} = \sqrt[3]{5^3 \cdot 4} = \sqrt[3]{5^3} \cdot \sqrt[3]{4} = 5\sqrt[3]{4}$

29. $\sqrt[3]{-250} = \sqrt[3]{(-5)^3 \cdot 2} = \sqrt[3]{(-5)^3} \cdot \sqrt[3]{2} = -5\sqrt[3]{2}$

30. $\sqrt[4]{192} = \sqrt[4]{2^4 \cdot 12} = \sqrt[4]{2^4} \cdot \sqrt[4]{12} = 2\sqrt[4]{12}$

31. $\sqrt{2x^3y^4} = \sqrt{(xy^2)^2 \cdot 2x}$
$= \sqrt{(xy^2)^2} \cdot \sqrt{2x} = |x|y^2\sqrt{2x}$

32. $\sqrt[3]{-27x^3y^6} = \sqrt[3]{(-3xy^2)^3} = -3xy^2$

33. $\sqrt[4]{3x^8y^6} = \sqrt[4]{(x^2y)^4 \cdot 3y^2}$
$= \sqrt[4]{(x^2y)^4} \cdot \sqrt[4]{3y^2} = |x^2y|\sqrt[4]{3y^2} = x^2|y|\sqrt[4]{3y^2}$

34. $\sqrt[3]{8x^6y^4} = \sqrt[3]{(2x^2y)^3 \cdot y}$
$= \sqrt[3]{(2x^2y)^3} \cdot \sqrt[3]{y} = 2x^2y\sqrt[3]{y}$

35. $\sqrt[5]{96x^{10}} = \sqrt[5]{(2x^2)^5 \cdot 3} = \sqrt[5]{(2x^2)^5} \cdot \sqrt[5]{3} = 2x^2\sqrt[5]{3}$

36. $\sqrt{108x^4y^9} = \sqrt{(6x^2y^4)^2 \cdot 3y}$
$= \sqrt{(6x^2y^4)^2} \cdot \sqrt{3y} = 6x^2y^4\sqrt{3y}$

37. $\dfrac{4}{\sqrt[3]{2}} \cdot \dfrac{\sqrt[3]{4}}{\sqrt[3]{4}} = \dfrac{4\sqrt[3]{4}}{\sqrt[3]{8}} = \dfrac{4\sqrt[3]{4}}{2} = 2\sqrt[3]{4}$

38. $\dfrac{1}{\sqrt{5}} \cdot \dfrac{\sqrt{5}}{\sqrt{5}} = \dfrac{\sqrt{5}}{\sqrt{25}} = \dfrac{\sqrt{5}}{5}$

39. $\dfrac{1}{\sqrt[5]{x^2}} \cdot \dfrac{\sqrt[5]{x^3}}{\sqrt[5]{x^3}} = \dfrac{\sqrt[5]{x^3}}{\sqrt[5]{x^5}} = \dfrac{\sqrt[5]{x^3}}{x}$

40. $\dfrac{2}{\sqrt[4]{y}} \cdot \dfrac{\sqrt[4]{y^3}}{\sqrt[4]{y^3}} = \dfrac{2\sqrt[4]{y^3}}{\sqrt[4]{y^4}} = \dfrac{2\sqrt[4]{y^3}}{y}$

41. $\sqrt[3]{\dfrac{x^2}{y}} = \dfrac{\sqrt[3]{x^2}}{\sqrt[3]{y}} \cdot \dfrac{\sqrt[3]{y^2}}{\sqrt[3]{y^2}} = \dfrac{\sqrt[3]{x^2y^2}}{\sqrt[3]{y^3}} = \dfrac{\sqrt[3]{x^2y^2}}{y}$

42. $\sqrt[5]{\dfrac{a^3}{b^2}} = \dfrac{\sqrt[5]{a^3}}{\sqrt[5]{b^2}} \cdot \dfrac{\sqrt[5]{b^3}}{\sqrt[5]{b^3}} = \dfrac{\sqrt[5]{a^3b^3}}{\sqrt[5]{b^5}} = \dfrac{\sqrt[5]{a^3b^3}}{b}$

43. $[(a + 2b)^2]^{1/3} = (a + 2b)^{2/3}$

44. $(x^2y^3)^{1/5} = (x^2)^{1/5}(y^3)^{1/5} = x^{2/5}y^{3/5}$

45. $2x(x^2y)^{1/3} = 2x(x^2)^{1/3}y^{1/3} = 2x^{3/3}x^{2/3}y^{1/3} = 2x^{5/3}y^{1/3}$

46. $xy(xy^3)^{1/4} = xyx^{1/4}(y^3)^{1/4} = x^{4/4}y^{4/4}x^{1/4}y^{3/4} = x^{5/4}y^{7/4}$

47. $a^{3/4}b^{1/4} = \sqrt[4]{a^3} \cdot \sqrt[4]{b} = \sqrt[4]{a^3b}$

48. $x^{2/3}y^{1/3} = \sqrt[3]{x^2} \cdot \sqrt[3]{y} = \sqrt[3]{x^2y}$

49. $x^{-5/3} = \sqrt[3]{x^{-5}} = \dfrac{1}{\sqrt[3]{x^5}}$

50. $(xy)^{-3/4} = \sqrt[4]{x^{-3}y^{-3}} = \dfrac{1}{\sqrt[4]{x^3y^3}}$

51. $\sqrt{\sqrt{2x}} = [(2x)^{1/2}]^{1/2} = (2x)^{1/4} = \sqrt[4]{2x}$

52. $\sqrt{\sqrt[3]{3x^2}} = [(3x)^{1/3}]^{1/2} = (3x^2)^{1/6} = \sqrt[6]{3x^2}$

53. $\sqrt[4]{\sqrt{xy}} = [(xy)^{1/2}]^{1/4} = (xy)^{1/8} = \sqrt[8]{xy}$

54. $\sqrt[3]{\sqrt{ab}} = [(ab)^{1/2}]^{1/3} = (ab)^{1/6} = \sqrt[6]{ab}$

55. $\dfrac{\sqrt[5]{a^2}}{\sqrt[3]{a}} = \dfrac{a^{2/5}}{a^{1/3}} = a^{2/5 - 1/3} = a^{1/15} = \sqrt[15]{a}$

56. $\sqrt{a}\sqrt[3]{a^2} = a^{1/2}a^{2/3} = a^{1/2 + 2/3} = a^{7/6} = \sqrt[6]{a^7} = a\sqrt[6]{a}$

57. $a^{3/5}a^{1/3}a^{-3/2} = a^{3/5 + 1/3 - 3/2} = a^{-17/30} = \dfrac{1}{a^{17/30}}$

58. $\sqrt{x^2y^4} = \sqrt{(xy^2)^2} = |xy^2| = |x|y^2$

59. $(a^{5/3}b^{3/4})(3a^{1/3}b^{5/4}) = 3 \cdot a^{5/3}a^{1/3} \cdot b^{3/4}b^{5/4} = 3 \cdot a^{6/3} \cdot$
$b^{8/4} = 3a^2b^2 \ (b \geq 0)$

60. $\left(\dfrac{x^{1/2}}{y^{2/3}}\right)^6 = \dfrac{(x^{1/2})^6}{(y^{2/3})^6} = \dfrac{x^{6/2}}{y^{12/3}} = \dfrac{x^3}{y^4} \ (x \geq 0)$

61. $\left(\dfrac{-8x^6}{y^{-3}}\right)^{2/3} = (-8x^6y^3)^{2/3} = (-8)^{2/3}(x^6)^{2/3}(y^3)^{2/3}$
$= [(-8)^2]^{1/3} \, x^{12/3}y^{6/3} = 64^{1/3}x^4y^2 = 4x^4y^2$

62. $\dfrac{(p^2q^4)^{1/2}}{(27q^3p^6)^{1/3}} = \dfrac{\sqrt{p^2q^4}}{\sqrt[3]{27q^3p^6}} = \dfrac{\sqrt{(pq^2)^2}}{\sqrt[3]{(3qp^2)^3}} = \dfrac{|pq^2|}{3qp^2} = \dfrac{|p|q^2}{3qp^2}$
$= \dfrac{q}{3|p|}$

63. $\dfrac{(x^9y^6)^{-1/3}}{(x^6y^2)^{-1/2}} = \dfrac{(x^6y^2)^{1/2}}{(x^9y^6)^{1/3}} = \dfrac{\sqrt{x^6y^2}}{\sqrt[3]{x^9y^6}} = \dfrac{|x^3y|}{x^3y^2} = \dfrac{|x^3| \cdot |y|}{x^3y^2}$
$= \dfrac{1}{|y|} \cdot \dfrac{|x|}{x} = \dfrac{|x|}{x|y|}$

64. $\left(\dfrac{2x^{1/2}}{y^{2/3}}\right)\left(\dfrac{3x^{-2/3}}{y^{1/2}}\right) = \dfrac{6x^{1/2-2/3}}{y^{2/3+1/2}} = \dfrac{6x^{-1/6}}{y^{7/6}} = \dfrac{6}{x^{1/6}y^{7/6}}$

65. $\sqrt{9x^{-6}y^4} = |3x^{-3}y^2| = 3y^2|x^{-3}| = \dfrac{3y^2}{|x^3|}$

66. $\sqrt{16y^8z^{-2}} = |4y^4z^{-1}| = 4y^4|z^{-1}| = \dfrac{4y^4}{|z|}$

67. $\sqrt[4]{\dfrac{3x^8y^2}{8x^2}} = \sqrt[4]{\dfrac{2 \cdot 3x^8y^2}{2 \cdot 8x^2}} = \dfrac{\sqrt[4]{6x^6y^2}}{2} = \dfrac{\sqrt[4]{6x^4x^2y^2}}{2}$
$= \dfrac{|x|\sqrt[4]{6x^2y^2}}{2}$

68. $\sqrt[5]{\dfrac{4x^6y}{9x^3}} = \sqrt[5]{\dfrac{27 \cdot 4x^6y}{27 \cdot 9x^3}} = \sqrt[5]{\dfrac{108x^6y}{3^5x^3}} = \dfrac{\sqrt[5]{108x^3y}}{3}$

69. $\sqrt[3]{\dfrac{4x^2}{y^2}} \cdot \sqrt[3]{\dfrac{2x^2}{y}} = \sqrt[3]{\dfrac{(4x^2)(2x^2)}{(y^2)(y)}} = \sqrt[3]{\dfrac{8x^4}{y^3}} = \dfrac{2\sqrt[3]{x^4}}{y}$
$= \dfrac{2x\sqrt[3]{x}}{y}$

70. $\sqrt[5]{9ab^6} \cdot \sqrt[5]{27a^2b^{-1}} = \sqrt[5]{(9ab^6)(27a^2b^{-1})} = \sqrt[5]{243a^3b^5}$
$= 3b\sqrt[5]{a^3}$

71. $3\sqrt{4^2 \cdot 3} - 2\sqrt{6^2 \cdot 3} = 3 \cdot 4\sqrt{3} - 2 \cdot 6\sqrt{3}$
$= 12\sqrt{3} - 12\sqrt{3} = 0$

72. $2\sqrt{5^2 \cdot 7} - 4\sqrt{2^2 \cdot 7} = 2 \cdot 5\sqrt{7} - 4 \cdot 2\sqrt{7}$
$= 10\sqrt{7} - 8\sqrt{7} = 2\sqrt{7}$

73. $\sqrt{x^2 \cdot x} - \sqrt{(2y)^2 \cdot x} = |x|\sqrt{x} - 2|y| \cdot \sqrt{x}$
$= (|x| - 2|y|)\sqrt{x} = (x - 2|y|)\sqrt{x}$ (since the square
root is undefined when $x < 0$)

74. $\sqrt{(3x)^2 \cdot 2y} + \sqrt{y^2 \cdot 2y} = 3|x|\sqrt{2y} + |y| \cdot \sqrt{2y}$
$= (3|x| + |y|)\sqrt{2y} = (3|x| + y)\sqrt{2y}$ (since the square
root is undefined when $y < 0$)

For Exercises 75–82, evaluate each side using a calculator or
paper and pencil.

75. $\sqrt{2 + 6} < \sqrt{2} + \sqrt{6}$ (2.828... < 3.863...)

76. $\sqrt{4} + \sqrt{9} > \sqrt{4 + 9}$ (5 > 3.605...)

77. $(3^{-2})^{-1/2} = 3$

78. $(2^{-3})^{1/3} < 2 \left(\dfrac{1}{2} < 2\right)$

79. $\sqrt[4]{(-2)^4} > -2 \ (2 > -2)$

80. $\sqrt[3]{(-2)^3} = -2$

81. $2^{2/3} < 3^{3/4}$ (1.587... < 2.279...)

82. $4^{-2/3} < 3^{-3/4}$ (0.396... < 0.438...)

83. $t = 1.1\sqrt{10} \approx 3.48$ sec

84. $t = 0.45\sqrt{200} = 4.5\sqrt{2} \approx 6.36$ sec

85. If n is even, then there are two real nth roots of a (when
$a > 0$): $\sqrt[n]{a}$ and $-\sqrt[n]{a}$.

■ Section 2 Polynomials and Factoring

Section 2 Exercises

1. $3x^2 + 2x - 1$; degree 2

2. $-2x^3 + x^2 - 2x + 1$; degree 3

3. $-x^7 + 1$; degree 7

4. $-x^4 + x^2 + x - 3$; degree 4

5. No — cannot have a negative exponent like x^{-1}

6. No — cannot have a variable in the denominator

7. Yes

8. Yes

9. $(x^2 - 3x + 7) + (3x^2 + 5x - 3) = (x^2 + 3x^2)$
$+ (-3x + 5x) + (7 - 3) = 4x^2 + 2x + 4$

10. $(-3x^2 - 5) + (-x^2 - 7x - 12) = (-3x^2 - x^2)$
$-7x + (-5 - 12) = -4x^2 - 7x - 17$

11. $(4x^3 - x^2 + 3x) + (-x^3 - 12x + 3)$
$= (4x^3 - x^3) - x^2 + (3x - 12x) + 3$
$= 3x^3 - x^2 - 9x + 3$

12. $(-y^2 - 2y + 3) + (5y^2 + 3y + 4)$
$= (-y^2 + 5y^2) + (-2y + 3y) + (3 + 4)$
$= 4y^2 + y + 7$

13. $2x(x^2) - 2x(x) + 2x(3) = 2x^3 - 2x^2 + 6x$

14. $y^2(2y^2) + y^2(3y) - y^2(4) = 2y^4 + 3y^3 - 4y^2$

15. $(-3u)(4u) + (-3u)(-1) = -12u^2 + 3u$

16. $(-4v)(2) + (-4v)(-3v^3) = -8v + 12v^4 = 12v^4 - 8v$

17. $2(5x) - x(5x) - 3x^2(5x) = 10x - 5x^2 - 15x^3$
$= -15x^3 - 5x^2 + 10x$

18. $1(2x) - x^2(2x) + x^4(2x) = 2x - 2x^3 + 2x^5$
$= 2x^5 - 2x^3 + 2x$

19. $x(x + 5) - 2(x + 5) = (x)(x) + (x)(5) - (2)(x)$
$- (2)(5) = x^2 + 5x - 2x - 10 = x^2 + 3x - 10$

20. $2x(4x + 1) + 3(4x + 1) = (2x)(4x) + (2x)(1)$
$+ (3)(4x) + (3)(1) = 8x^2 + 2x + 12x + 3$
$= 8x^2 + 14x + 3$

21. $3x(x + 2) - 5(x + 2) = (3x)(x) + (3x)(2)$
$- (5)(x) - (5)(2) = 3x^2 + 6x - 5x - 10$
$= 3x^2 + x - 10$

22. $(2x)^2 - (3)^2 = 4x^2 - 9$

23. $(3x)^2 - (y)^2 = 9x^2 - y^2$

24. $(3)^2 - 2(3)(5x) + (5x)^2 = 9 - 30x + 25x^2$
$= 25x^2 - 30x + 9$

25. $(3x)^2 + 2(3x)(4y) + (4y)^2 = 9x^2 + 24xy + 16y^2$

26. $(x)^3 - 3(x)^2(1) + 3(x)(1)^2 - (1)^3$
$= x^3 - 3x^2 + 3x - 1$

27. $(2u)^3 - 3(2u)^2(v) + 3(2u)(v)^2 - (v)^3$
$= 8u^3 - 3v(4u^2) + 6uv^2 - v^3$
$= 8u^3 - 12u^2v + 6uv^2 - v^3$

28. $(u)^3 + 3(u)^2(3v) + 3(u)(3v)^2 + (3v)^3 = u^3 + 9u^2v$
$+ 3u(9v^2) + 27v^3 = u^3 + 9u^2v + 27uv^2 + 27v^3$

29. $(2x^3)^2 - (3y)^2 = 4x^6 - 9y^2$

30. $(5x^3)^2 - 2(5x^3)(1) + (1)^2 = 25x^6 - 10x^3 + 1$

31. $x^2(x + 4) - 2x(x + 4) + 3(x + 4)$
$= (x^2)(x) + (x^2)(4) - (2x)(x) - (2x)(4)$
$+ (3)(x) + (3)(4)$
$= x^3 + 4x^2 - 2x^2 - 8x + 3x + 12$
$= x^3 + 2x^2 - 5x + 12$

32. $x^2(x - 3) + 3x(x - 3) - 2(x - 3)$
$= (x^2)(x) + (x^2)(-3) + (3x)(x) + (3x)(-3)$
$- (2)(x) - (2)(-3)$
$= x^3 - 3x^2 + 3x^2 - 9x - 2x + 6 = x^3 - 11x + 6$

33. $x^2(x^2 + x + 1) + x(x^2 + x + 1) - 3(x^2 + x + 1)$
$= (x^2)(x^2) + (x^2)(x) + (x^2)(1) + (x)(x^2) + (x)(x)$
$+ (x)(1) - (3)(x^2) - (3)(x) - (3)(1)$
$= x^4 + x^3 + x^2 + x^3 + x^2 + x - 3x^2 - 3x - 3$
$= x^4 + 2x^3 - x^2 - 2x - 3$

34. $2x^2(x^2 - x + 2) - 3x(x^2 - x + 2) + 1(x^2 - x + 2)$
$= (2x^2)(x^2) + (2x^2)(-x) + (2x^2)(2) - (3x)(x^2)$
$- (3x)(-x) - (3x)(2) + (1)(x^2) + (1)(-x)$
$+ (1)(2)$
$= 2x^4 - 2x^3 + 4x^2 - 3x^3 + 3x^2 - 6x + x^2 - x + 2$
$= 2x^4 - 5x^3 + 8x^2 - 7x + 2$

35. $(x)^2 - (\sqrt{2})^2 = x^2 - 2$

36. $(x^{1/2})^2 - (y^{1/2})^2 = x - y, x \geq 0$ and $y \geq 0$

37. $(\sqrt{u})^2 - (\sqrt{v})^2 = u - v, u \geq 0$ and $v \geq 0$

38. $(x^2)^2 - (\sqrt{3})^2 = x^4 - 3$

39. $x(x^2 + 2x + 4) - 2(x^2 + 2x + 4) = (x)(x^2)$
$+ (x)(2x) + (x)(4) - (2)(x^2) - (2)(2x) - (2)(4)$
$= x^3 + 2x^2 + 4x - 2x^2 - 4x - 8 = x^3 - 8$

40. $x(x^2 - x + 1) + 1(x^2 - x + 1) = (x)(x^2) +$
$(x)(-x) + (x)(1) + (1)(x^2) + (1)(-x) + (1)(1)$
$= x^3 - x^2 + x + x^2 - x + 1 = x^3 + 1$

41. $5(x - 3)$

42. $5x(x^2 - 4)$

43. $yz(z^2 - 3z + 2)$

44. $(x + 3)(2x - 5)$

45. $z^2 - 7^2 = (z + 7)(z - 7)$

46. $(3y)^2 - 4^2 = (3y + 4)(3y - 4)$

47. $8^2 - (5y)^2 = (8 + 5y)(8 - 5y)$

48. $4^2 - (x + 2)^2 = [4 + (x + 2)]$
$[(4 - (x + 2)] = (6 + x)(2 - x)$

49. $y^2 + 2(y)(4) + 4^2 = (y + 4)^2$

50. $(6y)^2 + 2(6y)(1) + 1^2 = (6y + 1)^2$

51. $(2z)^2 - 2(2z)(1) + 1^2 = (2z - 1)^2$

52. $(3z)^2 - 2(3z)(4) + 4^2 = (3z - 4)^2$

53. $y^3 - 2^3 = (y - 2)[y^2 + (y)(2) + 2^2]$
$= (y - 2)(y^2 + 2y + 4)$

54. $z^3 + 4^3 = (z + 4)[z^2 - (z)(4) + 4^2]$
$= (z + 4)(z^2 - 4z + 16)$

55. $(3y)^3 - 2^3 = (3y - 2)[(3y)^2 + (3y)(2) + 2^2]$
$= (3y - 2)(9y^2 + 6y + 4)$

56. $(4z)^3 + 3^3 = (4z + 3)[(4z)^2 - (4z)(3) + 3^2]$
$= (4z + 3)(16z^2 - 12z + 9)$

57. $1^3 - x^3 = (1 - x)[1^2 + (1)(x) + x^2]$
$= (1 - x)(1 + x + x^2) = (1 - x)(1 + x + x^2)$

58. $3^3 - y^3 = (3 - y)[3^2 + (3)(y) + y^2]$
$= (3 - y)(9 + 3y + y^2) = (3 - y)(9 + 3y + y^2)$

59. $(x + 2)(x + 7)$

60. $(y - 5)(y - 6)$

61. $(z - 8)(z + 3)$

62. $(2t + 1)(3t + 1)$

63. $(2u - 5)(7u + 1)$

64. $(2v + 3)(5v + 4)$

65. $(3x + 5)(4x - 3)$

66. $(x - y)(2x - y)$

67. $(2x + 5y)(3x - 2y)$

68. $(3x + 7y)(5x - 2y)$

69. $(x^3 - 4x^2) + (5x - 20) = x^2(x - 4) + 5(x - 4)$
$= (x - 4)(x^2 + 5)$

70. $(2x^3 - 3x^2) + (2x - 3) = x^2(2x - 3) + 1(2x - 3)$
$= (2x - 3)(x^2 + 1)$

71. $(x^6 - 3x^4) + (x^2 - 3) = x^4(x^2 - 3) + 1(x^2 - 3)$
$= (x^2 - 3)(x^4 + 1)$

72. $(x^6 + 2x^4) + (x^2 + 2) = x^4(x^2 + 2) + 1(x^2 + 2)$
$= (x^2 + 2)(x^4 + 1)$

73. $(2ac + 6ad) - (bc + 3bd) = 2a(c + 3d) - b(c + 3d)$
$= (c + 3d)(2a - b)$

74. $(3uw + 12uz) - (2vw + 8vz) = 3u(w + 4z)$
$-2v(w + 4z) = (w + 4z)(3u - 2v)$

75. $x(x^2 + 1)$

76. $y(4y^2 - 20y + 25) = y[(2y)^2 - 2(2y)(5) + 5^2]$
$= y(2y - 5)^2$

77. $2y(9y^2 + 24y + 16) = 2y[(3y)^2 + 2(3y)(4)$
$+ 4^2] = 2y(3y + 4)^2$

78. $2x(x^2 - 8x + 7) = 2x(x - 1)(x - 7)$

79. $y(16 - y^2) = y(4^2 - y^2) = y(4 + y)(4 - y)$

80. $3x(x^3 + 8) = 3x(x^3 + 2^3)$
$= 3x(x + 2)[x^2 - (x)(2) + 2^2]$
$= 3x(x + 2)(x^2 - 2x + 4)$

81. $y(5 + 3y - 2y^2) = y(1 + y)(5 - 2y)$

82. $z(1 - 8z^3) = z[1^3 - (2z)^3]$
$= z(1 - 2z)[1^2 + (1)(2z) + (2z)^2]$
$= z(1 - 2z)(1 + 2z + 4z^2)$

83. $2[(5x + 1)^2 - 9] = 2[(5x + 1)^2 - 3^2]$
$= 2[(5x + 1) + 3][(5x + 1) - 3]$
$= 2(5x + 4)(5x - 2)$

84. $5[(2x - 3)^2 - 4] = 5[(2x - 3)^2 - 2^2]$
$= 5[(2x - 3) + 2][(2x - 3) - 2]$
$= 5(2x - 1)(2x - 5)$

85. $2(6x^2 + 11x - 10) = 2(2x + 5)(3x - 2)$

86. $(x + 5y)(3x - 2y)$

87. $(2ac + 4ad) - (2bd + bc) = 2a(c + 2d) - b(2d + c)$
$= (c + 2d)(2a - b) = (2a - b)(c + 2d)$

88. $(6ac + 4bc) - (2bd + 3ad)$
$= 2c(3a + 2b) - d(2b + 3a) = (3a + 2b)(2c - d)$

89. $(x^3 - 3x^2) - (4x - 12) = x^2(x - 3) - 4(x - 3)$
$= (x - 3)(x^2 - 4) = (x - 3)(x + 2)(x - 2)$

90. $x(x^3 - 4x^2 - x + 4)$
$= x(x - 1)(x^2 - 3x - 4)$
$= x(x - 1)(x + 1)(x - 4)$

91. $(2ac + bc) - (2ad + bd)$
$= c(2a + b) - d(2a + b) = (c - d)(2a + b)$
Neither of the groupings $(2ac - bd)$ and $(-2ad + bc)$ has a common factor to remove.

■ Section 3 Fractional Expressions

Section 3 Exercises

1. $\dfrac{5}{9} + \dfrac{10}{9} = \dfrac{5 + 10}{9} = \dfrac{15}{9} = \dfrac{5}{3}$

2. $\dfrac{17}{32} - \dfrac{9}{32} = \dfrac{17 - 9}{32} = \dfrac{8}{32} = \dfrac{1}{4}$

3. $\dfrac{20}{21} \cdot \dfrac{9}{22} = \dfrac{20 \cdot 9}{21 \cdot 22} = \dfrac{180}{462} = \dfrac{30}{77}$

4. $\dfrac{33}{25} \cdot \dfrac{20}{77} = \dfrac{33 \cdot 20}{25 \cdot 77} = \dfrac{660}{1925} = \dfrac{12}{35}$

5. $\dfrac{2}{3} \div \dfrac{4}{5} = \dfrac{2}{3} \cdot \dfrac{5}{4} = \dfrac{2 \cdot 5}{3 \cdot 4} = \dfrac{10}{12} = \dfrac{5}{6}$

6. $\dfrac{9}{4} \div \dfrac{15}{10} = \dfrac{9}{4} \div \dfrac{3}{2} = \dfrac{9}{4} \cdot \dfrac{2}{3} = \dfrac{9 \cdot 2}{4 \cdot 3} = \dfrac{18}{12} = \dfrac{3}{2}$

7. The LCD of the denominators is $2 \cdot 7 \cdot 3 \cdot 5 = 210$:
$\dfrac{1}{14} + \dfrac{4}{15} - \dfrac{5}{21} = \dfrac{15}{210} + \dfrac{56}{210} - \dfrac{50}{210}$
$= \dfrac{15 + 56 - 50}{210} = \dfrac{21}{210} = \dfrac{1}{10}$

8. The LCD of the denominators is $2 \cdot 3 \cdot 5 \cdot 7 = 210$:
$\dfrac{1}{6} + \dfrac{6}{35} - \dfrac{4}{15} = \dfrac{35}{210} + \dfrac{36}{210} - \dfrac{56}{210}$
$= \dfrac{35 + 36 - 56}{210} = \dfrac{15}{210} = \dfrac{1}{14}$

9. No values are restricted, so the domain is all real numbers.

10. No values are restricted, so the domain is all real numbers.

11. The value under the radical must be nonnegative, so $x - 4 \geq 0$: $x \geq 4$ or $[4, \infty)$.

12. The value under the radical must be positive, so $x + 3 > 0$: $x > -3$ or $(-3, \infty)$.

13. The denominator cannot be 0, so $x^2 + 3x \neq 0$ or $x(x + 3) \neq 0$. Then $x \neq 0$ and $x + 3 \neq 0$: $x \neq 0$ and $x \neq -3$.

14. The denominator cannot be 0, so $x^2 - 4 \neq 0$ or $(x + 2)(x - 2) \neq 0$. Then $x + 2 \neq 0$ and $x - 2 \neq 0$: $x \neq -2$ and $x \neq 2$.

15. The denominator cannot be 0, so $x - 1 \neq 0$, or $x \neq 1$. Then $x \neq 2$ and $x \neq 1$.

16. The denominator cannot be 0, so $x - 2 \neq 0$, or $x \neq 2$. Then $x \neq 2$ and $x \neq 0$.

17. $x^{-1} = \dfrac{1}{x}$ and the denominator cannot be 0, so $x \neq 0$.

18. $x(x + 1)^{-2} = \dfrac{x}{(x + 1)^2}$ and the denominator cannot be 0, so $(x + 1)^2 \neq 0$ or $x + 1 \neq 0$: $x \neq -1$.

19. The denominator is $12x^3 = (3x)(4x^2)$, so the new numerator is $2(4x^2) = 8x^2$.

20. The numerator is $15y = (5)(3y)$, so the new denominator is $(2y)(3y) = 6y^2$.

21. The numerator is $x^2 - 4x = (x - 4)(x)$, so the new denominator is $(x)(x) = x^2$.

22. The denominator is $x^2 - 4 = (x - 2)(x + 2)$, so the new numerator is $x(x - 2) = x^2 - 2x$.

23. The denominator is $x^2 + 2x - 8 = (x + 4)(x - 2)$, so the new numerator is $(x + 3)(x + 4) = x^2 + 7x + 12$.

24. The numerator is $x^2 - x - 12 = (x - 4)(x + 3)$, so the new denominator is $(x + 5)(x + 3) = x^2 + 8x + 15$.

25. The numerator is $x^2 - 3x = x(x - 3)$, so the new denominator is $x(x^2 + 2x)$ or $x^3 + 2x^2$.

26. The denominator is $x^2 - 9 = (x + 3)(x - 3)$, so the new numerator is
$(x + 3)(x^2 + x - 6) = x(x^2 + x - 6)$
$+ 3(x^2 + x - 6) = x^3 + x^2 - 6x + 3x^2$
$+ 3x - 18 = x^3 + 4x^2 - 3x - 18$.

27. $(x - 2)(x + 7)$ cancels out during simplification; the restriction indicates that the values 2 and -7 were not valid in the original expression.

28. $(x + 1)(x - 2)$ cancels out during simplification; the restriction indicates that the values -1 and 2 were not valid in the original expression.

29. No factors were removed from the expression; we can see by inspection that $\dfrac{2}{3}$ and 5 are not valid.

30. x cancels out during simplification; the restriction indicates that 0 was not valid in the original expression.

31. $(x - 3)$ ends up in the numerator of the simplified expression; the restriction reminds us that it began in the denominator so that 3 is not allowed.

32. When $a = b$ in the original, we get division by 0; this is not apparent in the simplified expression because we canceled a factor of $b - a$.

33. $\dfrac{3x(6x^2)}{3x(5)} = \dfrac{6x^2}{5}, x \neq 0$

34. $\dfrac{3y^2(25)}{3y^2(3y^2)} = \dfrac{25}{3y^2}$

35. $\dfrac{x(x^2)}{x(x - 2)} = \dfrac{x^2}{x - 2}, x \neq 0$

36. $\dfrac{2y(y + 3)}{4(y + 3)} = \dfrac{y}{2}, y \neq -3$

37. $\dfrac{z(z - 3)}{(3 - z)(3 + z)} = -\dfrac{z}{z + 3}, z \neq 3$

38. $\dfrac{(x + 3)^2}{(x + 3)(x - 4)} = \dfrac{x + 3}{x - 4}, x \neq -3$

39. $\dfrac{(y + 5)(y - 6)}{(y + 3)(y - 6)} = \dfrac{y + 5}{y + 3}, y \neq 6$

40. $\dfrac{y(y^2 + 4y - 21)}{(y + 7)(y - 7)} = \dfrac{y(y + 7)(y - 3)}{(y + 7)(y - 7)}$

$= \dfrac{y(y - 3)}{y - 7}, \; y \neq -7$

41. $\dfrac{(2z)^3 - 1^3}{(z + 3)(2z - 1)} = \dfrac{(2z - 1)[(2z)^2 + (2z)(1) + 1^2]}{(z + 3)(2z - 1)}$

$= \dfrac{4z^2 + 2z + 1}{z + 3}, \; z \neq \dfrac{1}{2}$

42. $\dfrac{2z(z^2 + 3z + 9)}{z^3 - 3^3} = \dfrac{2z(z^2 + 3z + 9)}{(z - 3)[z^2 + (z)(3) + 3^2]}$

$= \dfrac{2z(z^2 + 3z + 9)}{(z - 3)(z^2 + 3z + 9)} = \dfrac{2z}{z - 3}$

43. $\dfrac{(x^3 + 2x^2) - (3x + 6)}{x^2(x + 2)} = \dfrac{x^2(x + 2) - 3(x + 2)}{x^2(x + 2)}$

$= \dfrac{(x + 2)(x^2 - 3)}{x^2(x + 2)} = \dfrac{x^2 - 3}{x^2}, \; x \neq -2$

44. $\dfrac{y(y + 3)}{(y^3 + 3y^2) - (5y + 15)} = \dfrac{y(y + 3)}{y^2(y + 3) - 5(y + 3)}$

$= \dfrac{y(y + 3)}{(y + 3)(y^2 - 5)} = \dfrac{y}{y^2 - 5}, \; y \neq -3$

45. $\dfrac{1}{x - 1} \cdot \dfrac{(x + 1)(x - 1)}{3} = \dfrac{x + 1}{3}, \; x \neq 1$

46. $\dfrac{x + 3}{7} \cdot \dfrac{14}{2(x + 3)} = 1, \; x \neq -3$

47. $\dfrac{x + 3}{x - 1} \cdot \dfrac{-(x - 1)}{(x + 3)(x - 3)} = -\dfrac{1}{x - 3}, \; x \neq 1 \text{ and } x \neq -3$

48. $\dfrac{3x(6x - 1)}{3xy} \cdot \dfrac{12y^2}{6x - 1} = 12y, \; x \neq 0, \; y \neq 0 \text{ and } x \neq \dfrac{1}{6}$

49. $\dfrac{(x - 1)(x^2 + x + 1)}{2x^2} \cdot \dfrac{4x}{x^2 + x + 1} = \dfrac{2(x - 1)}{x}$

50. $\dfrac{y(y^2 + 2y + 4)}{y^2(y + 2)} \cdot \dfrac{(y + 2)(y - 2)}{(y - 2)(y^2 + 2y + 4)} = \dfrac{1}{y},$

$y \neq -2 \text{ and } y \neq 2$

51. $\dfrac{(y + 5)(2y - 1)}{(y + 5)(y - 5)} \cdot \dfrac{y - 5}{y(2y - 1)} = \dfrac{1}{y}, \; y \neq 5, \; y \neq -5 \text{ and }$

$y \neq \dfrac{1}{2}$

52. $\dfrac{(y + 4)^2}{(3y + 2)(y - 1)} \cdot \dfrac{y(3y + 2)}{y + 4} = \dfrac{y(y + 4)}{y - 1}, \; y \neq -4 \text{ and }$

$y \neq -\dfrac{2}{3}$

53. $\dfrac{1}{2x} \cdot \dfrac{4}{1} = \dfrac{2}{x}$

54. $\dfrac{4x}{y} \cdot \dfrac{x}{8y} = \dfrac{x^2}{2y^2}, \; x \neq 0$

55. $\dfrac{x(x - 3)}{14y} \cdot \dfrac{3y^2}{2xy} = \dfrac{3(x - 3)}{28}, \; x \neq 0 \text{ and } y \neq 0$

56. $\dfrac{7(x - y)}{14(x - y)} = \dfrac{3}{8}, \; x \neq y \text{ and } y \neq 0$

57. $\dfrac{2x^2y}{(x - 3)^2} \cdot \dfrac{x - 3}{8xy} = \dfrac{x}{4(x - 3)}, \; x \neq 0 \text{ and } y \neq 0$

58. $\dfrac{(x + y)(x - y)}{2xy} \cdot \dfrac{4x^2y}{(y + x)(y - x)} = -2x, \; x \neq 0, \; y \neq 0,$

$x \neq y \text{ and } x \neq -y$

59. $\dfrac{2x + 1 - 3}{x + 5} = \dfrac{2x - 2}{x + 5}$

60. $\dfrac{3 + x + 1}{x - 2} = \dfrac{x + 4}{x - 2}$

61. $\dfrac{3}{x(x + 3)} - \dfrac{1}{x} - \dfrac{6}{(x + 3)(x - 3)}$

$= \dfrac{3(x - 3)}{x(x + 3)(x - 3)} - \dfrac{1(x + 3)(x - 3)}{x(x + 3)(x - 3)}$

$- \dfrac{6x}{x(x + 3)(x - 3)}$

$= \dfrac{(3x - 9) - (x^2 - 9) - (6x)}{x(x + 3)(x - 3)}$

$= \dfrac{-x^2 - 3x}{x(x + 3)(x - 3)} = -\dfrac{x(x + 3)}{x(x + 3)(x - 3)}$

$= -\dfrac{1}{x - 3} = \dfrac{1}{3 - x}, \; x \neq 0 \text{ and } x \neq -3$

62. $\dfrac{5}{(x + 3)(x - 2)} - \dfrac{2}{x - 2} + \dfrac{4}{(x + 2)(x - 2)}$

$= \dfrac{5(x + 2)}{(x + 2)(x + 3)(x - 2)} - \dfrac{2(x + 2)(x + 3)}{(x + 2)(x + 3)(x - 2)}$

$+ \dfrac{4(x + 3)}{(x + 2)(x + 3)(x - 2)}$

$= \dfrac{(5x + 10) - (2x^2 + 10x + 12) + (4x + 12)}{(x + 2)(x + 3)(x - 2)}$

$= \dfrac{-2x^2 - x + 10}{(x + 2)(x + 3)(x - 2)}$

$= -\dfrac{(2x + 5)(x - 2)}{(x + 2)(x + 3)(x - 2)}$

$= -\dfrac{2x + 5}{(x + 2)(x + 3)} = -\dfrac{2x + 5}{x^2 + 5x + 6}, \; x \neq 2$

63. $\dfrac{\dfrac{x^3 - y^3}{x^2y^2}}{\dfrac{x^2 - y^2}{x^2y^2}} = \dfrac{x^3 - y^3}{x^2y^2} \cdot \dfrac{x^2y^2}{x^2 - y^2}$

$= \dfrac{(x - y)(x^2 + xy + y^2)}{(x - y)(x + y)} = \dfrac{x^2 + xy + y^2}{x + y},$

$x \neq y, \; x \neq 0, \text{ and } y \neq 0$

64. $\dfrac{\dfrac{y + x}{xy}}{\dfrac{y^2 - x^2}{x^2y^2}} = \dfrac{y + x}{xy} \cdot \dfrac{x^2y^2}{y^2 - x^2}$

$= \dfrac{xy(y + x)}{(y - x)(x + y)} = \dfrac{xy}{y - x},$

$x \neq -y, \; x \neq 0, \text{ and } y \neq 0$

65. $\dfrac{\dfrac{2x(x - 4) + 13x - 3}{x - 4}}{\dfrac{2x(x - 4) + x + 3}{x - 4}} = \dfrac{2x^2 + 5x - 3}{x - 4} \cdot \dfrac{x - 4}{2x^2 - 7x + 3}$

$= \dfrac{(2x - 1)(x + 3)}{(2x - 1)(x - 3)} = \dfrac{x + 3}{x - 3}, \; x \neq 4 \text{ and } x \neq \dfrac{1}{2}$

66. $\dfrac{\dfrac{2(x+5)-13}{x+5}}{\dfrac{2(x-3)+3}{x-3}} = \dfrac{2x-3}{x+5}\cdot\dfrac{x-3}{2x-3} = \dfrac{x-3}{x+5}$,

$x \neq 3$, and $x \neq \dfrac{3}{2}$

67. $\dfrac{\dfrac{x^2-(x+h)^2}{x^2(x+h)^2}}{h} = \dfrac{x^2-(x^2+2xh+h^2)}{x^2(x+h)^2}\cdot\dfrac{1}{h}$

$= \dfrac{-2xh-h^2}{hx^2(x+h)^2} = \dfrac{-h(2x+h)}{hx^2(x+h)^2}$

$= -\dfrac{2x+h}{x^2(x+h)^2}, h \neq 0$

68. $\dfrac{\dfrac{(x+h)(x+2)-x(x+h+2)}{(x+h+2)(x+2)}}{h}$

$= \dfrac{x^2+2x+hx+2h-x^2-hx-2x}{(x+h+2)(x+2)}\cdot\dfrac{1}{h}$

$= \dfrac{2h}{h(x+h+2)(x+2)}$

$= \dfrac{2}{(x+h+2)(x+2)}, h \neq 0$

69. $\dfrac{\dfrac{b^2-a^2}{ab}}{\dfrac{b-a}{ab}} = \dfrac{(b+a)(b-a)}{ab}\cdot\dfrac{ab}{b-a} = b+a$

$= a+b, a \neq 0, b \neq 0, \text{ and } a \neq b$

70. $\dfrac{\dfrac{b+a}{ab}}{\dfrac{b^2-a^2}{ab}} = \dfrac{b+a}{ab}\cdot\dfrac{ab}{(b+a)(b-a)} = \dfrac{1}{b-a}$

$a \neq 0, b \neq 0, \text{ and } a \neq -b$

71. $\left(\dfrac{x+y}{xy}\right)\left(\dfrac{1}{x+y}\right) = \dfrac{1}{xy}, x \neq -y$

72. $\dfrac{x-y}{x+y}, x \neq y$

73. $\dfrac{1}{x}+\dfrac{1}{y} = \dfrac{y}{xy}+\dfrac{x}{xy} = \dfrac{x+y}{xy}$

74. $\dfrac{1}{x^{-1}+y^{-1}} = \dfrac{1}{\dfrac{1}{x}+\dfrac{1}{y}} = \dfrac{1}{\dfrac{y+x}{xy}} = \dfrac{xy}{y+x}$,

$x \neq 0, \text{ and } y \neq 0$

Appendix C

Section 1 Logic: An Introduction

Section 1 Exercises

1. (a) $2 + 4 = 8$ is a false statement.

(b) "Shut the window" is an instruction, which is neither true nor false. It is not a statement.

(c) "Los Angeles is a state" is a false statement.

(d) "He is in town" is neither true nor false when "he" is unspecified. It is not a statement.

(e) "What time is it?" is a question, which is neither true nor false. Is it not a statement.

(f) $5x = 15$ is neither true nor false when x is unspecified. It is not a statement.

(g) $3 \cdot 2 = 6$ is a true statement.

(h) $2x^2 > x$ is neither true nor false when x is unspecified. It is not a statement.

(i) "This statement is false" is true if it is false, and false if it is true. So it fails to be either true or false but not both. It is not a statement.

(j) "Stay put!" is a command, which is neither true nor false. It is not a statement.

2. (a) The equation is true when $x = 3$: There exists a natural number x such that $x + 8 = 11$.

(b) Apply the Identity Property of Addition: For all natural numbers x, $x + 0 = x$.

(c) The equation is true when $x = 2$ or -2: There exists a natural number x such that $x^2 = 4$. (Read "a natural number" as "at least one natural number.")

(d) Subtracting x from both sides produces $1 = 2$, which is impossible. There is no natural number x such that $x + 1 = x + 2$.

3. In each case, negate the corresponding quantified statement from Exercise 2.

(a) There is no natural number x such that $x + 8 = 11$.

(b) It is not true that for all natural numbers x, $x + 0 = x$. That is: There exists a natural number x such that $x + 0 \neq x$.

(c) There is no natural number x such that $x^2 = 4$.

(d) There exists a natural number x such that $x + 1 = x + 2$.

4. (a)

p	$\sim p$	$\sim(\sim p)$
T	F	T
F	T	F

(b)

p	$\sim p$	$p \vee \sim p$	$p \wedge \sim p$
T	F	T	F
F	T	T	F

(c) Yes, p and $\sim(\sim p)$ are equivalent, because they always have the same truth value.

(d) No, $p \vee \sim p$ and $p \wedge \sim p$ are not equivalent, because they sometimes have different truth values. Indeed, they *always* have different truth values: $p \vee \sim p$ is always true and $p \wedge \sim p$ is always false.

5. (a) The book does not have 500 pages.

(b) Six is not less than eight.

(c) $3 \cdot 5 \neq 15$

(d) It is not true that some people have blond hair. In other words: No people have blond hair.

(e) Not all dogs have four legs. (Or, in other words: Some dogs do not have four legs.)

(f) It is not true that some cats do not have nine lives. In other words: All cats have nine lives.

(g) Not all squares are rectangles. (Or, in other words: Some squares are not rectangles.)

(h) All rectangles are squares.

(i) It is not true that for all natural numbers x, $x + 3 = 3 + x$. In other words: There exists a natural number x such that $x + 3 \neq 3 + x$.

(j) There does not exist a natural number x such that $3 \cdot (x + 2) = 12$. In other words: For all natural numbers x, $3 \cdot (x + 2) \neq 12$.

(k) Not every counting number is divisible by itself and 1. (Or, in other words: Some natural counting number is not divisible by itself and 1.)

(l) All natural numbers are divisible by 2.

(m) It is not true that for all natural numbers x, $5x + 4x = 9x$. In other words: For some natural number x, $5x + 4x \neq 9x$.

6. Use q: "This course is easy" and r: "Lazy students do not study."

(a) The conjunction of q and r is $q \wedge r$.

(b) The disjunction that joins r to the negation of q is $r \vee \sim q$.

(c) The negation of the statement in part (a) is $\sim(q \wedge r)$.

(d) The negation of q is $\sim q$.

7. Use the truth tables for the connectives.

(a) $p \wedge q$ is false because p is false (and a true conjunction requires both sides true).

(b) $p \vee q$ is true because q is true (and a true disjunction requires only one side true).

(c) $\sim p$ is true because p is false.

(d) $\sim q$ is false because q is true.

(e) $\sim(\sim p)$ is false because $\sim p$ is true [part (c)].

(f) $\sim p \vee q$ is true because $\sim p$ and q are both true. (Either one would suffice.)

(g) $p \wedge \sim q$ is false because p and $\sim q$ are both false. (Either one false would suffice to make the conjunction false.)

(h) $\sim(p \vee q)$ is false because $p \vee q$ is true [part (b)].

(i) $\sim(\sim p \wedge q)$ is false because $\sim p$ and q both true makes $\sim p \wedge q$ true.

(j) $\sim q \wedge \sim p$ is false because $\sim q$ is false [part (d)].

8. Use the truth tables for the connectives.

(a) $p \wedge q$ is false because p and q are both false. (Either one false would suffice to make the conjunction false.)

(b) $p \vee q$ is false because p and q are both false (and a true disjunction requires at least one side true).

(c) $\sim p$ is true because p is false.

(d) $\sim q$ is true because q is false.

(e) $\sim(\sim p)$ is false because $\sim p$ is true [part (c)].

(f) $\sim p \vee q$ is true because $\sim p$ is true.

(g) $p \wedge \sim q$ is false because p is false.

(h) $\sim(p \vee q)$ is true because $p \vee q$ is false [part (b)].

(i) $\sim(\sim p \wedge q)$ is true because q false makes $\sim p \wedge q$ false.

(j) $\sim q \wedge \sim p$ is true because $\sim q$ and $\sim p$ are both true.

9. (a) r, $\vee$, and s are analogous to R, $\cup$, and S, respectively, so $r \vee s$ corresponds to $R \cup S$.

(b) q, $\wedge$, and $\sim q$ are analogous to Q, $\cap$, and $\overline{Q}$, respectively, so $q \wedge \sim q$ corresponds to $Q \cap \overline{Q}$.

(c) r, $\vee$, and q are analogous to R, $\cup$, and Q, respectively, so $\sim(r \vee q)$ corresponds to $\overline{R \cup Q}$.

(d) p, $\wedge$, r, $\vee$, and s are analogous to P, $\cap$, R, $\cup$, and S, respectively, so $p \wedge (r \vee s)$ corresponds to $P \cap (R \cup S)$.

10. (a)

p	q	$p \vee q$	$\sim(p \vee q)$	$\sim p$	$\sim q$	$\sim p \vee \sim q$
T	T	T	F	F	F	F
T	F	T	F	F	T	T
F	T	T	F	T	F	T
F	F	F	T	T	T	T
			*			*

The statements $\sim(p \vee q)$ and $\sim p \vee \sim q$ are not equivalent, because their truth values can differ.

(b)

p	q	$p \vee q$	$\sim(p \vee q)$	$\sim p$	$\sim q$	$\sim p \wedge \sim q$
T	T	T	F	F	F	F
T	F	T	F	F	T	F
F	T	T	F	T	F	F
F	F	F	T	T	T	T
			*			*

The statements $\sim(p \vee q)$ and $\sim p \wedge \sim q$ are equivalent, because their truth values are always the same.

(c)

p	q	$p \wedge q$	$\sim(p \wedge q)$	$\sim p$	$\sim q$	$\sim p \wedge \sim q$
T	T	T	F	F	F	F
T	F	F	T	F	T	F
F	T	F	T	T	F	F
F	F	F	T	T	T	T
			*			*

The statements $\sim(p \wedge q)$ and $\sim p \wedge \sim q$ are not equivalent, because their truth values can differ.

(d)

p	q	$p \wedge q$	$\sim(p \wedge q)$	$\sim p$	$\sim q$	$\sim p \vee \sim q$
T	T	T	F	F	F	F
T	F	F	T	F	T	T
F	T	F	T	T	F	T
F	F	F	T	T	T	T
			*			*

The statements $\sim(p \wedge q)$ and $\sim p \vee \sim q$ are equivalent, because their truth values are always the same.

11. (a) The statements $\sim(p \vee q)$ and $\sim p \wedge \sim q$ are equivalent, and the statements $\sim(p \wedge q)$ and $\sim p \vee \sim q$ are equivalent.

(b) The corresponding De Morgan Laws for sets are $\overline{P \cup Q} = \overline{P} \cap \overline{Q}$ and $\overline{P \cap Q} = \overline{P} \cup \overline{Q}$. The analogy comes from letting p mean "x is a member of P" and letting q mean "x is a member of Q." Then, for the first law, $\sim(p \vee q)$ means "x is a member of $\overline{P \cup Q}$," which is equivalent to "x is a member of $\overline{P} \cap \overline{Q}$," which translates into $\sim p \wedge \sim q$. Similar reasoning holds for the second law.

12.

p	q	$\sim p$	$\sim q$	$\sim p \vee q$
T	T	F	F	T
T	F	F	T	F
F	T	T	F	T
F	F	T	T	T

Note that the column for $\sim q$ is not really necessary.

13. Restate using De Morgan's Laws.

(a) Today is not Wednesday or the month is not June.

(b) I did not eat breakfast yesterday, or I did not watch television yesterday.

(c) It is not true that both it is raining and it is July.

■ Section 2 Conditionals and Biconditionals

Section 2 Exercises

1. Use p: "It is raining" and q: "The grass is wet."

(a) The conditional "If p, then q" is $p \rightarrow q$.

(b) The conditional "If not-p, then q" is $\sim p \rightarrow q$.

(c) The conditional "If p, then not-q" is $p \rightarrow \sim q$.

(d) The conditional "q if p" is $p \rightarrow q$.

(e) The conditional "Not-q implies not-p" is $\sim q \rightarrow \sim p$.

(f) The biconditional "q if, and only if, p" is $q \leftrightarrow p$.

2. (a)

p	q	$p \vee q$	$p \rightarrow (p \vee q)$
T	T	T	T
T	F	T	T
F	T	T	T
F	F	F	T

(b)

p	q	$p \wedge q$	$(p \wedge q) \rightarrow q$
T	T	T	T
T	F	F	T
F	T	F	T
F	F	F	T

(c)

p	$\sim p$	$\sim(\sim p)$	$p \leftrightarrow \sim(\sim p)$
T	F	T	T
F	T	F	T

(d)

p	q	$p \to q$	$\sim(p \to q)$
T	T	T	F
T	F	F	T
F	T	T	F
F	F	T	F

3. If the implication is $p \to q$, then the converse is $q \to p$, the inverse is $\sim p \to \sim q$, and the contrapositive is $\sim q \to \sim p$.

(a) Converse: If you are good in sports, then you eat Meaties; Inverse: If you do not eat Meaties, then you are not good in sports; Contrapositive: If you are not good in sports, then you do not eat Meaties.

(b) Converse: If you do not like mathematics, then you do not like this book; Inverse: If like this book, then you like mathematics; Contrapositive: If you like mathematics, then you like this book.

(c) Converse: If you have cavities, then you do not use Ultra Brush toothpaste; Inverse: If you use Ultra Brush toothpaste, then you do not have cavities; Contrapositive: If you do not have cavities, then you use Ultra Brush toothpaste.

(d) Converse: If your grades are high, then you are good at logic; Inverse: If you are not good at logic, then your grades are not high; Contrapositive: If your grades are not high, then you are not good at logic.

4. No, an implication and its converse cannot both be false. For $p \to q$ to be false, p must be true and q must be false. But then $q \to p$ is true.

5. Use the truth tables for the connectives.

(a) $\sim p \to \sim q$ is true because $\sim p$ is false and $\sim q$ is true. (Either one would suffice to make the implication true.)

(b) $\sim(p \to q)$ is true because p true and q false makes $p \to q$ false.

(c) $(p \vee q) \to (p \wedge q)$ is false because p true and q false makes $p \vee q$ true and $p \wedge q$ false.

(d) $p \to \sim p$ is false because p is true and $\sim p$ is false.

(e) $(p \vee \sim p) \to p$ is true because p is true. ($p \vee \sim p$ is always true.)

(f) $(p \vee q) \leftrightarrow (p \wedge q)$ is false because $(p \vee q) \to (p \wedge q)$ is false [part (c)].

6. Use the truth tables for the connectives.

(a) $\sim p \to \sim q$ is true because $\sim q$ is true.

(b) $\sim(p \to q)$ is false because p false makes $p \to q$ true.

(c) $(p \vee q) \to (p \wedge q)$ is true because p and q both false makes $p \vee q$ false.

(d) $p \to \sim p$ is true because p is false and $\sim p$ is true. (Either one would suffice to make the implication true.)

(e) $(p \vee \sim p) \to p$ is false because p is false. ($p \vee \sim p$ is always true.)

(f) $(p \vee q) \leftrightarrow (p \wedge q)$ is true because p and q both false makes $p \vee q$ and $p \wedge q$ both false.

7. No. If it does not rain and Iris goes to the movies, then the first statement is true, but the second statement is false.

8. (a) This is the inverse, which is not logically equivalent to the original implication.

(b) This is the contrapositive, which *is* equivalent to the original implication.

(c) This is the converse, which is not logically equivalent to the original implication.

9. The contrapositive is logically equivalent: "If a number is not a multiple of 4, it is not a multiple of 8."

10. (a)

p	q	r	$p \to q$	$p \wedge r$	$(p \wedge r) \to q$	$(p \to q) \to [(p \wedge r) \to q]$
T	T	T	T	T	T	T
T	T	F	T	F	T	T
T	F	T	F	T	F	T
T	F	F	F	F	T	T
F	T	T	T	F	T	T
F	T	F	T	F	T	T
F	F	T	T	F	T	T
F	F	F	T	F	T	T

$(p \to q) \to [(p \wedge r) \to q]$ is always true.

(b)

p	q	$p \to q$	$(p \to q) \wedge p$	$[(p \to q) \wedge p] \to q$
T	T	T	T	T
T	F	F	F	T
F	T	T	F	T
F	F	T	F	T

$[(p \to q) \wedge p] \to q$ is always true.

(c)

p	q	$\sim p$	$\sim q$	$p \to q$	$(p \to q) \wedge \sim q$	$[(p \to q) \wedge \sim q] \to \sim p$
T	T	F	F	T	F	T
T	F	F	T	F	F	T
F	T	T	F	T	F	T
F	F	T	T	T	T	T

$[(p \to q) \wedge \sim q] \to \sim p$ is always true.

(d)

p	q	r	$p \to q$	$q \to r$	$p \to r$	$(p \to q) \land (q \to r)$	$[(p \to q) \land (q \to r)] \to (p \to r)$
T	T	T	T	T	T	T	T
T	T	F	T	F	F	F	T
T	F	T	F	T	T	F	T
T	F	F	F	T	F	F	T
F	T	T	T	T	T	T	T
F	T	F	T	F	T	F	T
F	F	T	T	T	T	T	T
F	F	F	T	T	T	T	T

$[(p \to q) \land (q \to r)] \to (p \to r)$ is always true.

11. (a) For $r \to s$ to be true when s is false, r must be false also. By the same reasoning, q must be false, and so must p.

(b) p must be false, because if p were true, $p \land q$ would be true, and then $(p \land q) \to r$ could not be true while r was false.

(c) Not only can q be true, but it has to be true, since q true and p false makes $p \to q$ true and is the only way for $q \to p$ to be false.

12. (a) Use p: "Mary's little lamb follows her to school," q: "The lamb's appearance at school will break the rules," and r: "Mary will be sent home." Then the statement translates as $p \to (q \land r)$.

(b) Use p: "Jack is nimble," q: "Jack is quick," and r: "Jack will make it over the candlestick." Then the statement translates as $\sim(p \land q) \to \sim r$.

(c) Use p: "The apple hit Newton on the head" and q: "The laws of gravity were discovered." Then the statement translates as $\sim p \to \sim q$.

13. (a) All college students are poor.
Helen is a college student.
Helen is poor.
(A Venn diagram will confirm that this is valid.)

(b) Some freshmen like mathematics.
All people who like mathematics are intelligent.
Some freshmen are intelligent.
(A Venn diagram will confirm that this is valid.)

(c) If I study for the final, then I will pass the final.
If I pass the final, then I will pass the course.
If I pass the course, then I will look for a teaching job.
If I study for the final, then I will look for a teaching job.
(This involves two successive applications of the chain rule.)

(d) Every equilateral triangle is isosceles.
There exist triangles that are equilateral.
There exist triangles that are isosceles.
(A Venn diagram will confirm that this is valid.)

14. (a) Draw a Venn diagram satisfying the hypotheses, and the conclusion is automatically satisfied.

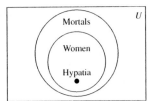

The argument is valid.

(b) Draw a Venn diagram satisfying the hypotheses, and the conclusion is automatically satisfied.

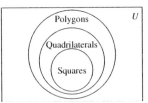

The argument is valid.

(c) Draw a Venn diagram satisfying the hypotheses, and the conclusion is automatically satisfied.

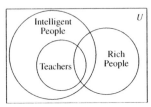

The argument is valid.

(d) It is possible to draw a Venn diagram that satisfies the hypotheses but not the conclusion.

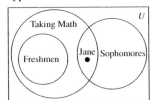

The argument is invalid.

15. (a) If a figure is a square, then it is a rectangle.

(b) If a number is an integer, then it is a rational number.

(c) If a figure has exactly three sides, then it may be a triangle.

(d) If it rains, it is cloudy.